ooter's Bible

No. 67 1976
Bicentennial Edition

EDITORIAL CONSULTANTS:
Vincent Pestilli
Jon Sundra

ART DIRECTOR
Caryn Seifer

ARTISTS:
Maria Barranco
Jeanne Lee McGlynn

COPY EDITOR:
Paula Ann Strus

EDITORIAL RESEARCHERS:
Irene Hinds
Debbie Maisano
Bonny Ryver

TECHNICAL CONSULTANTS:
Brian Brodhead
Frank Gologorsky
Hermann Koelling

MANAGING EDITOR:
George M. Horn

ASSISTANT MANAGING EDITOR:
John C. Rhodes

PRODUCTION EDITOR:
Bob Dana

ASSISTANT PRODUCTION EDITOR:
Jeff Arnold

PUBLISHER:
Robert F. Scott

Stoeger Publishing Company

Distributed to the book trade by Follett Publishing
Company and to the sporting goods trade by
Stoeger Industries.

In Canada, distributed to the book trade by Nelson,
Foster and Scott, Ltd., and to the sporting goods
trade by Stoeger Trading Company.

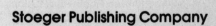

Copyright © 1975 by Stoeger Publishing Company

Published by Stoeger Publishing Company

Library of Congress Catalog Card No.: 63-6200

International Standard Book No.: 0-88317-055-8

Manufactured in the United States of America

Distributed to the book trade by Follett Publishing Company, 1010 West Washington Boulevard, Chicago, Illinois 60607 and to the sporting goods trade by Stoeger Industries, 55 Ruta Court, South Hackensack, New Jersey 07606

In Canada, distributed to the book trade by Nelson, Foster and Scott, Ltd., 299 Yorkland Boulevard, Willowdale, Ontario M2J 1S9 and to the sporting goods trade by Stoeger Trading Company, 900 Ontario Street East, Montreal, Quebec H2L 1P4

Contents

Foreword

This year's edition of the SHOOTER'S BIBLE celebrates the two-hundredth birthday of the United States and marks more than fifty years of Stoeger participation in publishing.

In this Bicentennial Edition, those of you who know the SHOOTER'S BIBLE of yore will find a familiar volume in more modern format, but still embodying the time-tested features that have made it a best seller year after year. To the host of new readers who discover the SHOOTER'S BIBLE each year, I can only say that I envy you the experience.

Feature articles have been expanded in number and in length. Among the new departments are a guide to the weapons museums of the United States and Canada, and a directory of the game animals to be found in the countries of the world outside the United States. (This will alternate yearly with a similar directory for the United States and Canada.)

Hunters play an important role in conservation, so a list of the endangered bird and mammal species of the world has been included that gives their scientific names and habitats. An informative list of federal, state and provincial agencies concerned with wildlife protection and exploitation has also been added.

The number of organizations and associations of interest to the hunter and shooter has been amplified enormously as has "The Shooter's Bookshelf," which lists every hunting, shooting and gun book in print. Magazines and periodicals for the hunter and shooter are given, as are the names and addresses of all firearms, ammunition and accessory manufacturers.

Last, but by no means least, are the sections detailing the specifications and descriptions of handguns, rifles, shotguns, black powder guns, air guns, sights, scopes and mounts, ammunition and reloading tools and components.

Continuing the practice begun in the ANGLER'S BIBLE, the companion volume to the SHOOTER'S BIBLE, we have included a number of hunting and shooting classics attesting to the fact that hunters and shooters have changed little over the years. Among the authors of these are names you will recognize instantly as well as some that will be unfamiliar to you.

Henry Clay Watson, who died in 1867 at the unripe young age of 36, selected our first classic (written in 1849 by Charles St. John) for his *Thrilling Adventures of Hunters in the Old World and the New* published in 1853. This delightful contribution shows that, as in the Appalachians, there were individuals in the Scottish Highlands who had reason to avoid the "Revenuers."

Next, Stanley Waterloo (1846-1913) offers a graphic picture of a mid-nineteenth century squirrel shoot in Michigan. And Maximilian Foster (1872-1943) was a master at giving subtle nature lessons to the reader as his dramatic *The Conqueror* of 1901 so ably demonstrates.

Kentucky-born Irvin S. Cobb gives us in *The Plural of Moose is Mise* a humorous account of a frenetic hunting trip in the company of Damon Runyon and other unforgettable characters. If nothing else, it will clear up a problem of grammar that has long bothered many. A humorist to the end, a few weeks before his death in 1944 Cobb suggested that his epitaph should read, "Anyhow he left here."

Undoubtedly many hunters have encountered the counterparts of Uncle Jeff Coongate and Zack Bourne, but few writers have captured them with as much realism as does Edmund Ware Smith in his *Two Eyes that Shone as One.*

Explorer Harold McCracken graphically describes what the collecting of an Alaskan grizzly was like some sixty years ago. Ed Zern, best known perhaps for his *To Hell with Hunting* and *To Hell with Fishing*, adds a gemlike miniature portrait of the almost legendary Frank King.

Combining hunting and the mystery story is not easy, but Rufus King succeeds admirably in *The Seven Good Hunters.* Finally, in *Mollie*, novelist and short-story writer Paul Hyde Bonner memorably describes a most remarkable Missouri mule.

What, then, do we celebrate in this Bicentennial Edition of the SHOOTER'S BIBLE? We celebrate the uncommon value of the common men of both sides. Soldiers of Great Britain and their associated German mercenaries fought and died thousands of miles from home in a strange land against an enemy who seemed not to be awed by the fact that they had challenged the professional armies of the most powerful nation on earth at that time. For their part, the Americans—poorly equipped, ill-fed and badly clothed—in their fight for independence paved the way for two documents of such classic splendor as to dazzle and change the course of much of the civilized world.

One misconception about the American Revolution should perhaps be laid to rest: the militia phenomenon. Much maligned by some historians, nevertheless it was Patriot militia who mauled the British in many battles. (Nor should we forget that the British employed Tory militia—called "Provincials"—and that many units attained the competence of regulars.) Time and again the militia of both sides demonstrated that if led by experienced officers who understood their strengths and weaknesses, the militia could give a good account of themselves.

A British Army historian summed up the performance of American militia this way: "There was always that incalculable factor, the American militia, a factor which could never be counted upon by its friends, but equally could never be ignored by its enemies."

At a time when the basic concept of a militia is under attack from some quarters, it is appropriate that the not inconsiderable contribution of an armed militia be acknowledged.

Outside the National Archives Building in Washington, which houses the Declaration of Independence and the Constitution, is a statue whose inscription is an eloquent reminder from Shakespeare of the uses of history. It says simply, "What's past is prologue."

—ROBERT F. SCOTT

Feature Articles

The Guns of

the Revolution

by George M. Horn

It shall be, as it was in the past,
  Not with dreams but with blood and with iron
Shall a nation be molded to last.
  —SWINBURNE, *A Word for the Country*

AS ANY STUDENT of the American Revolution quickly comes to realize, the key to an understanding of the tactics and even the strategy of that conflict in a large measure lies in a knowledge of the kinds of weapons employed.

The Continental soldier had a motley assortment of weapons: muskets, musketoons, rifles, carbines, fusils, pistols, wall guns and artillery, with a wide variety in each type. Standard issue was unheard of, and calibers themselves were subject to variation.

The separate states were responsible for equipping with arms the regiments they raised for the Continental line, while it was the fledgling Congress' task to arm the other Continental troops.

Guns came from every conceivable source — from American gun dealers and from gunsmiths at home and abroad. Some were received as outright gifts; others were captured from the enemy or confiscated from Tories still loyal to the British crown. A few troops even brought their own guns with them when they enlisted.

Nevertheless, a shortage of arms was chronic. Little more than a year after the outbreak of the war, one quarter of the Continental Army had no guns, although this was only shortly before the crucial battle of Long Island. Recruits frequently drilled without muskets. On retreating, militiamen often abandoned knapsacks and guns to facilitate their escape.

The arsenal at Springfield, Massachusetts, was so badly managed that the Board of War of the Continental Congress recommended in 1780 that it be closed. (Today's Springfield Arsenal dates from 1794.)

The shortage of weapons was aggravated by a shortage of powder, which resulted chiefly from a lack of saltpeter. Although American gunsmiths were undoubtedly the finest in the world, American gunpowder was definitely inferior.

Rifles. Of all the guns of the Revolution, popular tradition has clothed the rifle with an almost magical and glamorous quality, describing it sometimes as "the gun that made victory certain in the American Revolution." There can be no doubt as to the rifle's spectacular accuracy over astonishingly long ranges. The first companies of frontier riflemen to be raised, dressed as they were in buckskin hunting shirts, with awesome knives and tomahawks in their belts, created a sensation as they proceded from Pennsylvania and Virginia to join the military units and state militia laying siege to the British in the Massachusetts capital.

Their guns were basically civilian weapons made by individual gunsmiths. Calibers ranged between .55 and .60. The barrels were octagonal and of great length, with blade front sight and an open-V rear sight. Stocks, often of native curly maple, extended almost to the muzzle. Brass was the most common material for the mountings and for the patch box cover on the stock.

Despite the rifle's later-acquired reputation, riflemen were at a serious disadvantage in any battle. For one thing, their weapon was slow in loading and was further handicapped by the absence of a bayonet. As a weapon of infantry, it was virtually useless, although it was excellent for scouts, snipers and skirmishers and in engaging the Indians who were utilized along the frontier by the British.

The rifle had been known in Europe for many years as a hunting weapon, but was not considered to be an effective military arm because of the time required for reloading and because it was not equipped with a bayonet. During the campaigns against the Indians and in the Coloial Wars, sporting and military applications were combined — to the surprise of European observers. Not only could the American frontiersman deliver a high rate of accurate fire, but he could also reload on the run.

Even before appointing George Washington to command the Continental Army, the Continental Congress in 1775 passed a resolution calling for six companies of expert riflemen to be raised immediately in Pennsylvania, as well as two in Maryland and two in Virginia. Response from Pennsylvanians was so great that Congress raised that state's authorization to eight companies, organized as the Pennsylvania Rifle Battailion under the command of Col. William Thompson. One Virginia company of 96 men raised by Dan Morgan rode 600 miles to Boston in 21 days without losing a man. Washington, himself a Virginian, was so moved by this feat that he went along the company front shaking hands with each man as tears streamed down his cheeks. The frontiersmen were objects of curiosity at Boston but were useless except for picking off an occasional British regular who incautiously showed himself. Eventually the "shirtmen," as the buckskin-clad riflemen were called, became a nuisance and a disciplinary problem because of their rowdy, frontier ways.

The culmination came when the adjutant of Thompson's Rifle Battailion arrested and confined a sergeant. Because the "shirtmen" had threatened to break into

Washington crossing the Delaware.

the jail and release him, the prisoner was moved to the main American guardhouse in Cambridge.

Their anger aroused, some Pennsylvania riflemen marched toward the jail with weapons loaded. The guard detail was strengthened and several regiments nearby were alerted to stand by under arms. Fortunately, the mutineers were intercepted on Prospect Hill outside of Boston, only grounding their arms when ordered to by Generals Washington, Charles Lee and Greene.

Ironically, the spectacular triumph of American riflemen at King's Mountain in South Carolina in 1780 was at the expense of Major Patrick Ferguson, commander of the British forces in that battle and the inventor of the first breechloading rifle used in the British Army. This weapon, patented in 1776, was not only very accurate and had a high rate of fire but was dependable in rainy weather when flintlocks were not.

In 1777 Ferguson was in a position to have altered the entire course of the American Revolution. Leading his own ranger detachment in an advance on Brandywine Creek in Pennsylvania, he had an opportunity to pick off George Washington but did not, explaining, "It was not pleasant to fire at the back of an unoffending individual who was acquitting himself very cooly of his duty, so I let him alone."

Ferguson was wounded in the elbow at Brandywine, permanently crippling his arm. While he was convalescing, his corps was disbanded by General Howe, allegedly unhappy because a junior officer had quite obviously invented a superior weapon. Ferguson's rifles were put into storage, and no one knows what has become of them. (Interestingly, almost a century later Federal officers would still be resisting the introduction of breechloading rifles into the Union Army.)

References are sometimes encountered to the "Dechard rifle," which was supposedly carried by the "Over Mountain Men" who gave such a good account of themselves at King's Mountain. This was actually a long rifle made by Jacob Dickert of Lancaster, Pennsylvania. A Dickert rifle was used in the defense of the Alamo in 1836 and is on display in the Long Barracks Museum in San Antonio.

Another gun around which many misconceptions have sprung up is the double-barreled Golcher or Goulcher rifle, made by John Golcher of Easton, Pennsylvania. Tradition credits Timothy Murphy, perhaps the most famous marksman of the American Revolution, with the use of this gun at Bemis Heights in the battle of Saratoga on October 7, 1777. Firing from a perch in a tree, Murphy is said to have picked off Sir Francis Clerke, British General John Burgoyne, and General Simon Fraser at a range of over 300 yards.

Golcher became famous in the years after the Revolutionary War for his over-and-under revolving rifles but it is doubtful whether one was used by Murphy in performing his feat.

Muskets. It was the musket that bore the brunt of the fighting during the Revolution — in fact, the majority of troops in the Continental line were regular infantry, while riflemen and cavalry were used only in special operations or in support of the infantry.

The typical Revolutionary War musket was a smooth bore, single-shot, flintlock muzzleloader. Its length was somewhere between 54 and 60 inches; its caliber ranged between .69 and .80. As a consequence of its smooth bore, accuracy suffered considerably, for the bullet tended to fit somewhat loosely in the bore. The effective range was seldom more than 100 yards.

Because one of the chief sources of American muskets was the stores of British arms in the colonies dating from the Colonial Wars, it was almost inevitable that British guns would be selected as the model for the infant nation's military weapons when made by American gunsmiths.

A well-equipped gunsmith's shop would ideally include several barrel forges, a lock shop with forges and benches for filers, benches for gunstock makers, a brass foundry for mountings, forges for bayonets and ramrods, a mill for grinding and polishing them, a forge for fittings, and an assembly shop. Needless to say, most American-made weapons were manufactured under less-than-ideal conditions.

The Brown Bess. This was the soldiers' nickname for the "long land musket" adopted as a military weapon during the reign of George I (1714-1727) and not during that of Queen Elizabeth, as popular tradition has it. The name "Brown Bess" is reputed to have come from the color of the stock; earlier British weapons had black-painted stocks. However, some authorities maintain that its name came from the acid pickling process that gave the barrel a brown hue. The evidence seems to be that the word "Brown" predates the practice of browning the barrels of muskets and that "Bess" may be a feminine equivalent of the "Brownbill," the old weapon of the British infantry or a corruption of the "buss" from "Blunderbuss."

The musket came in another model — a so-called "short land musket" with barrel only 42 inches long, which had been introduced around 1740, eventually superseding the older and longer gun around 1765. Both guns had a caliber of .75.

British infantry muskets were marked on the locks to indicate their provenance. These markings included the letters *"GR"* (for *Georgius Rex*) to indicate the reign during which it was manufactured, and a broad

General Henry Knox arriving with artillery.

arrow to show that the weapon was crown property. Those muskets assembled at a royal arsenal bore the name of the specific arsenal ("TOWER," if from the infamous Tower of London or, less frequently, "DUBLIN CASTLE," for its Irish counterpart.

A gun stamped with a pair of crossed scepters and the letters "BGP" in the angles thus formed could not have been used in the American Revolution. This mark was first used by the Birmingham proof house in 1813.

Committee of Safety Muskets. This is a misnomer applied to many American-made muskets of the Revolution; it should be reserved only for those muskets made by private gunsmiths under contract to a local committee or council of safety and should not include domestic and foreign weapons purchased and issued by such bodies. The number of genuine extant examples of such guns is believed to be very small.

Imported Muskets. Foreign arms dealers were an important source for firearms in the American Revolution. Prussian, Dutch and even British dealers supplied some guns, but the major source of imported arms was France. Still smarting from their defeat at the hands of the British in the French and Indian Wars and the loss of Canada and their other possessions, the French government was not unwilling to help the colonies with arms. To this end a dummy company, Roderigue Hortalez et Cie., was set up. The managing director of this enterprise was Pierre Augustin de Caron, who assumed the name Beaumarchais and is perhaps today better known for his literary works, *The Barber of Seville* and *The Marriage of Figaro,* than for his efforts on behalf of the new nation. Beaumarchais was directly responsible to the French foreign minister, the Count of Vergennes.

In 1776 two secret committees of Congress sent a Connecticut merchant and former member of the Continental Congress, Silas Deane, to France to purchase guns and equipment for the Continental Army.

Deane sailed for Europe in April, with instructions from the Commercial Committee to buy American produce, ship it abroad and sell it, and bring back supplies needed by the colonies with the proceeds. The Secret Committee instructed Deane to buy clothing and equipment for 25,000 men and to purchase artillery and

The Battle of Lexington

munitions — all this on credit.

Historians have always viewed Deane as a dedicated patriot. However, later evidence has been uncovered which throws new light on his role. Upon his arrival in Paris, Deane looked up an old friend, Edward Bancroft, passing both American and French secrets to him. Deane's idea was to make a fortune by profiteering. What Deane did not know (and the world would not learn until nearly seventy years after Bancroft's death) was that Bancroft was actually a British agent.

As a consequence, details of the purchasing operations were immediately passed on to British representatives in Paris and thence to British authorities in Lon-

don. Because Deane and Bancroft craftily withheld specific information about shipments in which they had a personal stake, vital supplies continued to flow to America and only one ship was intercepted by the British.

During this period a number of firms unloaded many substandard arms on American agents. The guns of Pliarne, Penet et Cie. of France were notorious, as were those of James Gruel and Company, which bought its weapons in Liege, Belgium.

French Muskets. By the year 1778, the subterfuge of a dummy company and private shippers became unnecessary since France had entered the war openly.

From this time on, French muskets were shipped directly to America from French arsenals. Six models comprised the French contribution, making exact identification sometimes difficult; these bore the designations 1763, 1766, 1770-71, 1773, 1774, and 1777. (There may even have been a 1768 model, too.) All were of .69 caliber, with a barrel fastened to the stock by means of three iron bands. This was an important consideration, since it made for a lighter gun than the .75 caliber Brown Bess (which needed a forend stout enough to support the heavy barrel-fastening pins).

Another significant difference in the French muskets lay in the fact that they all had reinforced throat-hole cocks, in contrast to the weaker British gooseneck cocks. The French muskets were made at the royal arsenals at Charleville, St. Etienne and Maubeuge.

A word about tactics may be in order here. The popular myth that the Revolution was fought between American troops who fired rifles from behind trees and stone walls and British soldiers foolish enough to stand in rigid formations in the open needs debunking.

Thanks to a European tradition and the training program of German drillmaster General von Steuben, the Americans fought in the accepted European fashion, as a study of the tactics of the Revolution shows. (Lexington and Concord and King's Mountain were the only notable exceptions.)

Much is sometimes made of the musket's inherent lack of accuracy in comparison with the rifle; this is only because infantry tactics of the 18th century are not understood now. When firearms were developed, linear tactics were adopted (as opposed to phalanx tactics so successful when the principal weapons were the lance and the sword), in order to derive the most effective firepower from muskets. The line of battle consisted of two ranks standing shoulder to shoulder. Another rank of "file closers" often followed to replace those who fell. With bayonets fixed, the line of attackers would move forward confident in the knowledge that until they were about 100 yards from the enemy, they were comparatively safe. Officers strove to achieve enough discipline to make their men hold their fire until they were within 50 yards of the enemy. Israel Putnam's famous order at Bunker Hill, "Don't one of you fire until you see the whites of their eyes," was not intended to win him a place in books of quotations. It was an admonition that could only have been directed at men with muskets. When the commanders at the battle of Fontenoy in 1745 invited their opponents to fire first, they were not being gallant but clever. The French broke before the British did, and were systematically cut down with repeated volleys.

Volley firing from the line was a standard practice,

with all loading and firing being done on command (a modern soldier would call it "by the numbers"). Precision aiming as is done today was unknown. The volley was directed to the front or right or left oblique as commanded; rapidity of fire was more desirable than accuracy. Experienced soldiers could deliver a sustained rate of fire of four shots per minute, which would allow at least two shots at a line of charging enemy before they closed with you.

Twelve separate motions were required in the British manual of arms for the Brown Bess. (It is said that the troops of Frederick the Great could fire six shots per minute.) The first volley was always the most effective because it was properly loaded in leisurely fashion before the 16- or 17-inch bayonet was fixed.

British General George Hanger, who served in America during the Revolution, later wrote, *"A soldier's musket, if not exceedingly ill-bored (as many of them are), will strike the figure of a man at 80 yards; it may even at 100; but a soldier must be very unfortunate indeed who shall be wounded by a common musket at 150 yards, provided his antagonist aims at him; and as to firing at a man at 200 yards with a common musket, you may just as well fire at the moon and have the same hopes of hitting your object. I do maintain and will prove, whenever called on, that no man was ever killed at 200 yards by a common soldier's musket, by the person who aimed at him."*

After about two volleys had been exchanged, both sides clashed with bayonets – if they had them. Some American regiments were without bayonets; British soldiers often prayed for rain so they could mount a bayonet attack without fear of enemy fire or of facing cold steel. The American defeat at Bunker Hill has been attributed not only to a shortage of ammunition but also to a lack of bayonets.

In attacks at night the bayonet alone was usually employed; the advantage of surprise could not be sacrificed by a nervous soldier firing prematurely (and in the dark it was all too easy to fire upon friendly forces). The usual practice was to load the piece but not to prime it; the last step could always be completed if necessary. Another procedure was to put in the priming charge, close the firing pan and remove the flint. British Major General Charles "No-flint" Grey earned his nickname in two night attacks which were bloody but spectacularly successful.

In 1777, American General "Mad Anthony" Wayne had secretly occupied a position near Paoli, Pennsylvania, with the intention of harassing General Howe's advance northward from Philadelphia. Learning of Wayne's position and intentions, the British sent Grey to make a night attack. Major John André, who was later to be captured and hung as a spy, left an account of this attack: *"No soldier was suffered to load; those who could not unload their pieces took out the flints. We knew nearly the spot where the Rebel corps lay, but nothing of the disposition of their camp. It was represented to the men that firing discovered us to the enemy, hid them from us, killed our friends and produced a confusion favourable to the escape of the Rebels. On the other hand, by not firing we knew the foe to be wherever fire appeared and a charge ensured his destruction."*

Shortly after midnight, the British struck Wayne's camp. Four sentries fired and ran, while Wayne's men turned out to repel the attackers. In the ensuing action, the Americans lost 150 men. The British took 71 prisoners with them, leaving 40 of the most seriously wounded at houses along the way. Fifty-three "mangled dead" were reportedly found at the scene of what was immediately called the "Paoli Massacre" and used with good effect to drum up anti-British sentiment. The "Tappan Massacre" one year later in northern New Jersey was a repeat performance by "No-flint" Grey, and has been called "a textbook model of the surprise of a detachment."

No matter what the tactics employed, the simple truth is that the shooting by both sides was awful: the marksmanship of the Americans was poor and that of the British was practically nonexistent. In the first major exchange at Lexington and Concord, only one American bullet out of 300 found its mark, and only one man in 15 hit anybody. Six years later at the battle of Wetzell's Mill in North Carolina, 25 expert American riflemen, who had fought spectacularly at King's Mountain, fired from close range at British Lt. Col. James Webster as he led his troops on horseback across a ford they were covering. Although 33 or 34 shots were fired at him (some men were able to reload and fire twice), Webster was not hit once.

An even more embarassing example of the lack of marksmanship training occurred during the battle for Fort Ticonderoga in 1777. As the British advanced toward the American positions, an American officer ordered a sergeant to pick off a British skirmisher only 40 yards away. This touched off wholesale unauthorized firing and the enemy dropped back, leaving the original target on the ground. The "casualty" turned out to be a drunken Irishman from the 47th Regiment who was unhurt. In addition to eight cannons, the Americans had fired about 3,000 rounds from 1,000 muskets at less than 100 yards. A British lieutenant and two Indians were all they hit, with one fatality among the Indians.

If American marksmanship was poor, no attempt was made to teach the British soldier to aim at all. One of the Americans captured at Fort Washington at the northern end of Manhattan Island in 1776 said that no fewer than ten guns were fired at his group within a range of 40 to 50 yards — some within 20 yards — and he was alive to make this comment: "I observed that they took no aim and the movement of presenting and firing was the same." In wet weather only one shot out of four could be counted on to go off. And while an American flint was good for some 60 rounds without resharpening, a British flint could be used for only six.

Defective equipment was another bugaboo. At the indecisive skirmish at the Warren (or White Horse) Tavern in Pennsylvania in 1777, as the opposing forces were preparing for battle a heavy rain began. "I wish I could give a description of the downpour which began during the engagement and continued until the next morning," wrote a Hessian officer. "It came down so hard that in a few minutes we were drenched and stuck in mud up to our calves."

Because the tops of their cartridge boxes did not extend far enough to keep out the rain, the Americans lost tens of thousands of rounds of ammunition; many regiments were unable to fire a shot. As a result, the Americans were forced to retreat to replenish their supplies of ammunition. Thanks to obviously superior design of their cartridge boxes, the British lost comparatively little ammunition.

Musketoons and Carbines. As always, mounted soldiers needed shorter shoulder arms for the special situations encountered by cavalrymen. In the Continental Army these were provided by captured British weapons or from French sources. In most cases such guns resembled contemporary infantry muskets with the exception that calibers were .65 and a sliding ring had replaced the sling swivels.

Fusils. During the 17th century a light flintlock musket or fusil had been developed for artillery guards and for the light infantry (called "fusiliers"). These were similar to their bigger counterparts in every respect except size. Such guns were sometimes carried by infantry officers — more often in the British Army, however. George Washington thought that guns diverted an officer's attention and made him less able to capitalize on the swiftly changing fluid situations that developed during a battle.

Spontoons. In addition to swords, infantry officers carried a spontoon (sometimes called an espontoon or half pike), which was both a badge of rank and an efficient weapon that had evolved from the halberd. The spontoon was a spear between six and seven feet long, topped with a leaf-shaped iron point socketed to a sturdy pole about an inch and a quarter in diameter. Often a crossbar was added to prevent an enemy sword

Surrender of the Army of Lord Cornwallis.

or bayonet from sliding down the haft and injuring the hands of the spontoon wielder.

In the years before the American Revolution the spontoon was carried by infantry officers of every army until it was supplanted by the fusil. This change took place in the French Army in 1754 and in the British Army in 1786 (although British troops in America had started to abandon the spontoon earlier). General Edward Braddock, whose name is forever linked with the word "defeat," ordered his troops not to carry them on the expedition against the Indians that ended in disaster on July 9, 1755. His dying words were, "We shall better

British General Burgoyne surrenders at Saratoga to American militiamen. (Note the spontoon carried by officer at center of engraving.)

know how to deal with them another time."

Most British troops did not carry spontoons in the field during the American Revolution. Although Colonel Timothy Pickering and others had favored their abandonment, George Washington and Anthony Wayne, among others, were believers in the effectiveness of pole arms. Spontoons were carried in the battle of Trenton. And Anthony Wayne himself carried one in his famous morale-building capture of the British garrison at Stony Point, New York, in 1779. At the battle of the Cowpens in South Carolina, a certain Captain Anderson used his spontoon to pole vault ahead of a fellow American officer, Captain Ewing, and so capture a British cannon first.

Cavalry Pistols. These were omnipresent — either in the troopers' saddle holsters, pockets or boots. Some pistols were British, while others were of American manufacture and patterned after their British counterparts; still others were French. There were two models — heavy and light. In bore, the heavy dragoon pistol was identical with the carbine (.65 caliber) with a barrel 12 inches long.

The light dragoon pistol was the preferred sidearm during the Revolutionary War. Its length was only 9 inches (but the caliber had been enlarged to .69). Lacking sights, these guns were only useful at close range. When French pistols eventually made an appearance, they turned out to be longer, heavier — and less foolproof. With a straighter butt, the French pistol had a total length of almost 16 inches; the bore was also .69. Officers' pistols resembled those of enlisted men, with the exception that workmanship was finer and decoration more ornate. Of especial interest to collectors is the popular American-made box-lock pistol, whose lock was mounted at the center rather than at the side. No forestock was necessary, so these pistols were invariably lighter. Barrels could often be unscrewed, making it possible to load them at the breech, thus eliminating the ramrod.

Another characteristically American handgun was the "Kentucky pistol," a modern-day appellation because of their resemblance to the so-called "Kentucky rifle" (which was earlier called the "Pennsylvania rifle"). These pistols have stocks of curly maple or fruitwood, with octagonal barrels or round barrels octagonal at the breech. Because they are rifled and with front and rear sights, such guns pose a problem for collectors. Some experts maintain that many date from the War of 1812.

Wall Guns. So called because they were intended to be mounted on a swivel and fired from a fort (or a small boat), these "amusettes" threw a four-ounce ball; some were rifled, and all had an impressive range.

Artillery. No account of the guns of the American Revolution can fail to mention the artillery weapons employed. For the defense of and siege of forts, heavy guns had to be used. The Continental Army started the war in 1775 with only the cannon, ammunition and gunpowder the British had left in America in the hands of the colonial militia plus what could be captured from royal arsenals. The first British operations of the war — against Salem, Massachusetts, in February of 1775 and Lexington and Concord less than two months later — had as their objective the confiscation of weapons. The capture of Fort Ticonderoga by the Americans in May of that year gave them access to a vast store of heavy siege artillery whose lack was critical during the year-long siege of Boston. Getting them over the 300 miles of primitive roads to that city was quite another problem. It was solved by 25-year old Henry Knox (who had just been appointed Colonel of the virtually non-existent Continental Regiment of Artillery) in a daring plan that quickly won General Washington's approval.

Arriving on December 5th, Knox inspected the Ticonderoga guns, selected some 50 to 60 cannons, had 42 heavy sledges built, and rounded up 80 yoke of oxen. A month later, Knox's expedition had reached the southern end of Lake George and headed south through Saratoga and Albany and then eastward up the slopes of the Berkshires in the dead of winter. Knox's "Noble Train of Artillery" reached Framingham, Massachusetts, on January 24th. By emplacing the guns on Dorchester Heights, the Americans were able to force the British evacuation of Boston.

Some idea of the magnitude of Knox's feat may be gleaned from these statistics: about 59 weapons were successfully moved; three of the large mortars of 13-inch bore (including one dubbed "Old Sow") weighed a ton each. Total weight of the load was 60 tons, including a ton of lead and a barrel of much-needed flints.

In the linear tactics used in 18th-century warfare, there was little need for field artillery. Because of the wooded, unfavorable terrain in North America, when artillery was moved it often went by water. The British used water-borne artillery to good effect in the retaking of Fort Ticonderoga and at the battle of Freeman's Farm at Saratoga in 1777. At this time, the British Army in America had four times the number of expert gunners as did the Americans. Nevertheless, what the Continental Army lacked in numbers it made up eventually in proficiency.

Because of the shortage of artillery pieces, the Americans had originally begun casting cannons of bronze and iron and making gun carriages. As a consequence of the French Army's adoption of the Gribeauval system of artillery, some obsolete French field guns eventually reached America.

Usually of bronze, the mobile guns of the Continental Army ranged from 3- to 24-pounders and 5½- and 8-inch howitzers. A few 18-, 24- and 32-pound iron siege guns were also available. "Grasshoppers" was the soldiers' nickname for the small three-pounder guns which had legs instead of wheels. When fired, these weapons would jump, earning them their distinctive nickname.

Ammunition was round, grape or case shot; mortars (so named because of their resemblance to a pharmacist's grinding tool) fired bomb and carcasses, the latter a form of incendiary projectile. Side boxes on each side of the gun carriage held 21 rounds of ammunition. Horses or oxen (with civilian drivers) provided the transport. On the battlefield, matrosses dragged the guns into position and assisted the canoneers in loading, firing and swabbing the guns. Maximum effective range of artillery manned by skilled artillerymen firing solid shot was about 1,200 yards. For untrained gunners, this could be as little as 400 yards.

These, then, were the tools with which independence was forged. They served the fledgling country well and now stand mute in museums and gun collections — those, that is, that were not broken up for scrap or beaten into ploughshares.

No matter whether you stand among the silent field guns of the Revolution in the artillery park at West Point or view an 18th-century musket or rifle behind the glass of a display case, do not think of them as the cold and dusty exhibits of a museum. Know them instead as warm and vibrant products of man's ingenuity that enabled a nation to win its freedom. Although they never lived, they will paradoxically never die.

Competition Benchrest in the Mid-70's

by Skip Gordon

"This will be the first Record Match at 100 yards. You will have 7 minutes. Commence Fire!"

THE RANGEMASTER'S LITANY will be heard by a record number of competitors in 1976 as more and more shooters take the plunge into benchrest. Some will be varmint shooters with a background of accuracy shooting, looking to go one step further. Some will be hunters seeking off-season recreation that will benefit them next fall. Some will be wives who have discovered in benchrest an activity that allows them to share their husband's love of shooting, and to do it on an equal basis. Best of all, some will be youngsters, who bring to the sport a zestful enthusiasm and a complete lack of self-seriousness which is communicated to the older folks and contributes to everyone's enjoyment.

Although competitive benchrest became more or less organized in 1947 and reached new levels of participation in the 1960's, the history books will probably record the sport as having reached a state of *youthful* maturity in the 1970's.

Benchrest has, in effect, become the "field lab" for many segments of the firearms industry. In the last 25-plus years, the practitioners of precision riflery have been instrumental in the development of components and equipment which today are taken for granted.

For example, the super-accurate 52-grain .224 bullets, the 70-grain .243's, and the 168-grain .30's are offered in match grade by a number of manufacturers — the "match" refers to benchrest in which consistency is critical. Or take those new lightweight (as little as 17 oz.) scopes that can be had in powers up to 24X. Even the primer, once considered the most prosaic of components (if, indeed, it was considered at all), is available to all shooters in what at least one manufacturer labels "benchrest" quality.

Knowledgeable gunsmiths and manufacturers of rifles also pay homage to the benchresters' contributions to their fields. Few will argue, in the mid-1970's, the proven advantages of short, stiff barrels for medium-range accuracy. Bedding techniques now include the use of plastic compounds, and a number of experts swear by the glue-in method.

Bench shooters some time ago recognized the necessity for a stiff, non-bending receiver, and the sleeving practice became common. (It had the additional benefits of making it possible to keep the scope off the barrel.)

Finally, it was the stool shooters who accepted with open arms the fiberglass stock, which is absolutely unchanged to environmental conditions and their effect on bedding. The traditional rifleman with his love for fine wood has not yet accepted fiberglass for his field rifles — but many of us believe it is just a question of time before he does. There are simply too many advantages offered by fiberglass.

Benchrest is divided into essentially three classes. Of these, only Hunter is *accuracy* oriented; that is, the placing of shots into a specific area of a target. Originally the class was dreamed up as a means by which factory rifles — not custom equipment — could be fired in competition off of sandbags. The thinking was that it would create interest in this type of shooting, and that the participants would eventually graduate to the varmint classes.

Using that always reliable 20-20 hindsight, everyone realizes now that the idea had all the validity of teaching someone to ride a bicycle in order to matriculate into an unlimited-class hydroplane! When things didn't work out according to plan, the class was allowed to exist — but just barely. The governing associations have not seen fit to give it the attention it deserves, and growth has suffered because of a lack of leadership, rule definition and foresight. Potentially the phase of the sport with the broadest popular appeal, it survives today only because of the dedication of individual clubs and shooters.

The basic problem is the rule book, which allows too many modifications, including such goodies as stainless-steel barrels, bedding modifications, and non-factory triggers. Sam Shooter who goes to a match with his Model 70 in .308 is going to find himself competing with semi-custom equipment that may have a price tag in the neighborhood of $600. If Sam hasn't the money, or inclination to spend several hundred dollars, he says "nuts to it," and is never seen again.

But all is not lost, because those aforementioned aficionados *know* what the potential is for Hunter. The class is not merely surviving, but prospering in Texas, New Jersey, New York, Ohio and Pennsylvania. In 1974, the Trans-Continental Hunter Rifle League was established; since then a series of postal matches have been fired regularly.

Concerned shooters are working long and hard to affect changes that will benefit the class. Probably the most effective of proposed plans are those that would

The John Zink Range in Skiatook, Oklahoma, is one of the best. There are 50 firing positions. The only complaint the shooters have — those concrete benches are tough on elbows.

Barrel-maker Pat McMillan, like all benchresters, cleans a barrel after every match.

establish two classes — Factory and Modified. Shooter classification would be discontinued, in line with other benchrest classes so that everyone competes on an even footing. (Presently, shooters are classed as Marksman, Hunter or Master Hunter, depending on previous performance in registered competition.) Caliber, scope and weight restrictions will probably remain unchanged to assure that equipment is truly Hunter; case capacity must be equal to a .30-30, scopes are limited to 6X, and the rifle can weigh no more than ten pounds.

Finally, because Hunter is a stepchild of the sport, there is a strong sentiment in many areas that a separate organization is needed, if it is to realize its potential. In view of the eastern and western shooters coming under different governing associations' jurisdiction, *neither* of which has demonstrated any overwhelming interest, such a development would seem to be both logical, and desirable.

A Hunter tournament consists of one warm-up and five record matches at each distance to be fired. As many "sighters" as the shooter wishes can be fired to determine conditions. He can fire one shot on each of five record targets, trying to place each shot in a "10 ring." Each ring has a value, from 10 to 3. Ties are resolved by counting "X's." Maximum score for a match is 50-5X; for a tournament, 250-25X. (see photo)

Hunter class benchrest is a challenge; one that will appeal to all rifle shooters. The indications are that it's about to take its place in the sunshine of popularity — not as an offshoot, but as an exciting part of benchrest, deserving to grow and mature with group-shooter classes.

At the other end of the benchrest spectrum, we find the Benchrest and Experimental classes: the Big Guns, Rail Rigs, Iron Monsters, and so forth.

By whatever name, these "unlimiteds" — with no restriction governing weight, caliber, or barrel dimension — are something else. The rules state that guns must be manually fired (no hydraulic or electrical "trigger fingers") and that rests must be separate from the rifle. The rests can be return-to-battery mechanical devices, or they can be sandbags. The former are classified as "Experimental" under IBS rules, while a sandbag gun falls into "Heavy Benchrest." Under NBRSA, both fall under "Unrestricted."

Despite sophistication of design, many knowledgeable people in the sport consider these rifles ideal for the beginning competitor, especially an Experimental equipped with return-to-battery rests. Because he need not concern himself with holding the rifle, complete attention can be given to learning to read conditions — wind and mirage — and their effects. When a shot falls

Probably the best known of the custom actions, Shilen Rifle's DGA. What does it stand for? Why, "darn good action," of course.

out of a group he knows the fault is his, not something traceable to how he squeezed it off. And success in *all* benchrest is predicated on understanding the effects of conditions, and how to compensate for them.

While a big gun fired off of sandbags sacrifices some minute amount of stability, it most emphatically offers advantages that many shooters believe more than make up for the penalties. Foremost among these is the ability to make fast alterations in point of aim by manipulating the rear bag. (Adjustments on the Experimental rifles are accomplished by mechanical means.)

The heart of any rifle, the action. This is a Remington XP-100. The rifle is a .222 LV, stocked by Brown Precision, and smithed by Tom Seitz.

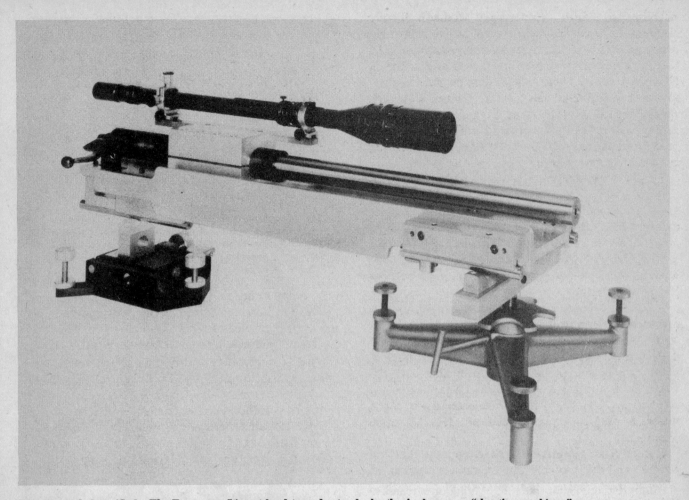

Experimental-class rifle by The Fergusons. It's not hard to understand why they're known as "shooting machines."

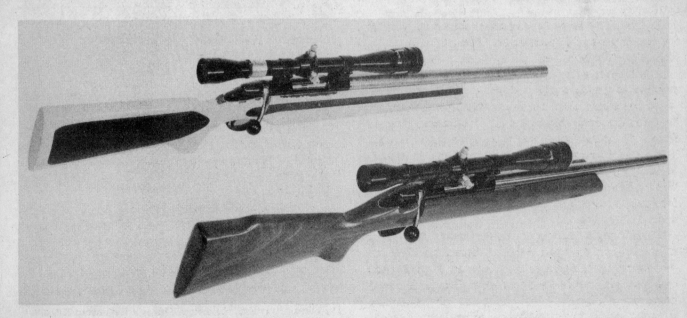

A pair of 10½ pounders built on prototype Franchi-FFV actions: (l) Fiberglass-stocked .222 by Bob White, with Shilen barrel; (r) 6X47 Sporter by R. W. Hart, with C. P. Hart barrel.

Author's son Conrad, practicing for 1974 Speer Matches in Austin, Texas. Rifle is a 12-year old Shilen. Rebarreled several times, it's still a winner.

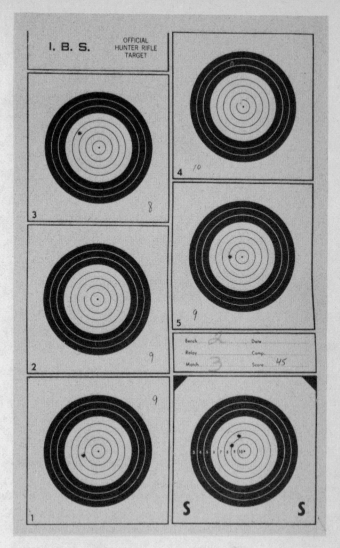

Hunter-class target. Sighter is at bottom right. Scores for each shot have been noted. It's NOT a very good target.

You may be surprised that sandbag rigs can hold their own with rail guns — and then some, on occasion. One of the most popular wins in benchrest history was the late Bob Hart's at the 1973 IBS Heavy Bench and Experimental Championships. Firing on the notoriously treacherous range of the Pine Tree Rifle Club in Johnstown, New York, Hart ended up in first place, with a .385 MOA (Minute of Angle). Not only did he beat the top Experimental rifle's .390, firing off of sandbags, but he did it with a 13½-pound Heavy Varmint rifle! Bob Hart was *some kind* of shooter, and, I might add, *some kind* of man. People are still talking about it.

The course of fire for the big guns consists of five 10-shot record targets at each distance. Tournaments normally combine 100- and 200-yard, or 200- and 300-yard stages. The time limit per match is 12 minutes.

Along with the Varmint classes, this is precision shooting. The group can be anywhere on the target, so long as it is within the target area. The sighting square— the heavy black figure in the top center part of the target —as well as the circles, is for reference only. In this most exacting type of competitive shooting, it is ironic that the shooter must be careful NOT to place his shots precisely where he aims, for to do so is to destroy his aiming point. The rank amateur who fired the two targets illustrated was holding on the center ring and adjusted his scope to move his point of impact to the left.

The Varmint classes, by far the most popular, consist of three rifles: Sporter, Light Varmint and Heavy Varmint.

The Sporter and LV's are both 10½ pounders, but the former must be of a caliber larger than .22. The

Heavy Varmints can be of any caliber and weight up to 13½ pounds. There are no limitations on scopes.

In order of popularity, the Heavy Varmint is in first place. After that, it could well be a toss-up; in the East the 6X47 Sporter would seem to have the edge, while in the West the lightweight .222's are somewhat more popular.

Although a more difficult rifle for many of us, the Sporter can be fired successfully in all three classes, which is a major advantage to the shooter who has to watch his wallet. How successfully? In 1973, Jack Deming won the 3-gun honors at the IBS Championships. What that means is that he fired the same 10½-pound rifle in all three classes, along with 100 or so other competitors (most of whom used at least a 13½-pound rig in the Heavy Varmint), and was "Top Gun"

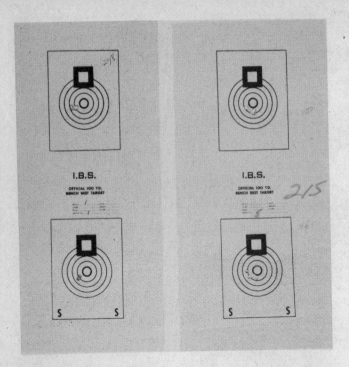

100-Yard Varmint-class targets. Each record (at top) target shows two distinct groups, indicating the shooter "missed" a condition.

after all 30 record targets were averaged! That took a heap of shootin'.

Another example of the 10½-pound rifle's prowess is the 5-shot, 100-yard group fired by M. P. McMillan in 1973 with a .222 LV (talk about a vintage year!). It measured a mind-bending .009 inch. It is the smallest group ever fired with *any* rifle—only nine thousandths of an inch from perfection.

(NOTE: Group size is determined by measuring outside-to-outside, and subtracting the diameter of the bullet. Mac's group, therefore, actually "spanned" .233 inch.)

The novice will find the Heavy Varmint the easiest rifle to start with—those extra three pounds will compensate for an occasional twitch, or less-than-perfect trigger squeeze. In caliber he will probably find the .222, .222½, or .222 Magnum most satisfying. There are a number of adherents to the "heavier-bullets-are-desirable-for-wind-bucking" school of thought, and they usually rely on 6X47's, or .308's. Incidentally, this is one of the classic arguments in bench; it's been going on for years apparently, and there doesn't seem to be any cut-and-dried answer. Like so many facets of the sport, if a man is convinced something gives him an advantage, it probably does, even if it's psychological. However, I can report the 1974 IBS 300-yard Championship was won by a .222.

Competition runs the gamut from events hosted by local clubs, through state and regional tournaments, to the Championships sponsored by each association. There are postal matches which take place between clubs in different states and between shooters representing various countries. There are tournaments sponsored by individual corporations, J-4, Inc.—the bullet-jacket people; and Speer, Inc., manufacturer of hunting and match bullets. Finally, there is the Super Shoot, sponsored by more than 60 firms representing the entire firearms industry, as well as by the popular magazines published for shooters and hunters.

There is competition 12 months a year, although the Arizona and New Mexico types lay low in the broiling summers. There is, however, no corresponding lull during eastern winters, when clubs maintain a full schedule. It's always cold, frequently raining or snowing, and without fail at least one club shoots at night.

Benchrest is essentially a trophy, patch and glory thing. The chief exception is the Super Shoot which annually affords a cash payout in excess of $10,000. There are, of course, many of us who enjoy side bets with friends, but these rarely exceed a quarter.

Anyone who has ever spent time at a major tournament as an onlooker becomes aware of the complete openness, the lack of secrecy between competitors. Quite simply, there are no secrets. Shooters are forever exchanging not merely information, but frequently components, tools and even rifles. Everyone wants to win, but never at the cost of sportsmanship or friendship. One of the things that any veteran will tell you he finds enjoyable is the feeling of mutual interest, of encouragement by everyone on the line. Of course, there are those who never quite learn what it's all about—those who are interested only in the winning—but they are very lonely people, and rarely last for more than a season or two. Most significantly, they don't even win very often. And if they do manage to cop the big trophy, it's a hollow kind of victory, because there's no one with whom to enjoy it.

In the few years I have been shooting, one example of this peer interest stands out in my mind. At the aforementioned 300-yard Championships, I was one shot away from a 300-yard record. Those first four shots looked like quite a respectable 100-yard group. (They later measured .258.) I sat waiting for my condition to return—a single shot away from glory. Most of the shooters had completed their firing, but, as always, whenever there's a "possible" going, most had stayed at the benches with their scopes on my target. Time was running out, however, and the 30-second warning was given. A quick shot into the sighter, eject the case, load and lock, estimate the conditions' influence ("15 sec-

Red Cornelison, Hall of Fame member, with his Heavy Varmint based on prototype Franchi-FFV action. He placed 2nd at NBRSA's 1974 Championship.

He shoots what he makes. Ray Speer, president of the bullet-making company, is an active competitor, and past president of N.B.R.S.A.

onds . . . 15 seconds") and squeeze it off. The group was now two groups, but there was no time to dwell on my disappointment. By the time I was on my feet there were a dozen competitors surrounding me—they were really upset that the group had gotten away. It was probably at that exact moment I realized that which every shooter must — I wasn't in Mainville, Pennsylvania, to break records — I was there to have fun.

How does one get started in benchrest?

I am assuming you have visited a match or two, talked to some of the shooters, and done some homework in the pages of the magazines devoted to the game; the time has come to buy a rifle.

For the sake of discussion, let's assume you've opted for a Heavy Varmint. The first possibility is to latch onto a used rifle. Unlike the family car, a benchrest rifle doesn't wear out, except for the barrel (about $75 to $100). But shooters *do* grow tired of a gun, or decide they want something different which they can't afford until they sell the old iron. Also, for one reason or another, people do get out of the sport—usually for something like water skiing or transcendental meditation. Whatever the reason, because of its availability, take a good look at any used equipment you come across.

Check that weight! A rifle exceeding the rule-book maximum will be disqualified.

Typical loading bench, this one was being used by at least three shooters. Competitor is using a Belding & Mull measure. The arbor press will be used to seat bullets.

Although ads in the magazines may turn something up, your best bet probably lies in writing the four or five gunsmiths who build the rifles and let them know what you have in mind. Frequently they will have one in the shop that was taken in trade or on deposit. You can be sure of an honest appraisal from any of them. If possible, a visit to one of these craftsmen should be made—Ed Shilen, Tom Seitz or Bob White can teach you more about the building of an accurate rifle in a few hours than you can learn on your own in years.

The alternative to a used rifle is, of course, a new one. The new shooter should consider the Remington 40XB-BR, at this writing still the only off-the-shelf bench rifle manufactured by a major firearms company. Introduced in 1968, the 40X's have earned a reputation for championship-caliber performance. A good rifle when it comes from the factory has super-good potential when "tuned" by a competent gunsmith. Not surprisingly, it is somewhat less expensive than a custom-built rifle. Finally, 40X's are available in a broad choice of calibers and configurations, which will allow the buyer to obtain practically anything he wants.

The other alternative is to have a rifle built. If the tyro has been following the sport or at least knows a number of active competitors, the custom rifle is a logical step. However, because of the myriad of options open, the beginner with limited exposure to benchrest may be better off starting with a used gun, or a less-expensive 40XB-BR. There is nothing sadder than a

man with a brand-new $600 rig, who discovers the Brown or McMillan fiberglass stocks at his first match, and for one reason or another, decides "glass is the only way to go." There he is with his brand-new rifle, already convinced he's at a disadvantage because of a laminated walnut stock.

The best advice I can give the new shooter is to move slowly, read everything he can get his hands on, and ask a lot of questions. Incidentally, the one must-read book for any bench shooter is Warren Page's *The Accurate Rifle*. Page, one of six members of the Benchrest Hall of Fame, covers the entire sport: history, gunsmithing, component development, reloading and firing techniques. Available from Winchester Press in a hardbound edition, and from Stoeger Publishing Company in a quality paperback, it conveys the excitement and challenge of benchrest as nothing else ever written.

The stool shooter, no matter what his previous experience, soon becomes a knowledgeable reloader. Unlike other riflemen who require only routine accuracy, the benchrester's interest is in controlling performance to hundredths of inches or better. He soon learns that a couple of thousandths' variation in seating depth or neck wall thickness is critical; that powder charges must be refined to a tenth of a grain; that primers seated at varying depths—again we're talking of one thousandths—can have a dramatically negative effect on a group.

Precise reloading is the heart of the sport. A $600 or $700 rifle is just like a computer — "garbage in, garbage out." Even experienced reloaders are sometimes taken aback by the care with which competition rounds are put together.

Powder measures are used by most shooters, though a few of the clan weigh every charge and arrive at a match with loads in small prescription vials. For the most part, the measures are conversions of stock instruments, engineered for absolute consistency by people like "Cat" Castleberry, Homer Culver and Seely Masker. Of the stock measures, the Belding and Mull, and the Bonanza units are the most popular.

Hand tools and knock-out dies are the rule, although there are people like world-record-holders Donalee and Jim Stekl who use essentially stock RCBS equipment. As noted earlier, primer seating depth is critical, and a number of fine tools are made to ensure consistent seating at the correct depth. Again, however, there is a production product — the Lee priming tool — which enjoys great popularity and costs less than $5.00.

Even though more and more shooters are making their own bullets today, the vast majority of us are still using commercially available projectiles. In the past few years, the major manufacturers have developed superbly uniform bullets. A visitor to any match in 1976 will notice boxes bearing the names of Hornady, Nosler, Remington, Sierra, Speer and Winchester, all of whom offer bullets in at least one caliber considered to be of benchrest quality.

Case care is a major concern, and the wise shooter watches overall length, wall thickness and flash hole concentricity closely. Primer pockets are cleaned after every firing, and necks are carefully wiped to remove any residue. (Some bench rifles are chambered so tight that the bolt cannot be closed on a round unless the entire case is cleaned.) As a result of this loving care, a dozen carefully prepared and maintained cases will usually outlast the barrel of the rifle in which they're being used.

Benchrest is finally outgrowing the unfortunate reputation with which it was once saddled; i.e., that it was something that only a select few could enjoy. Once the province of the greybeards, more and more women and

A pensive Mrs. Donna Hall of Ennis, Texas, before she learned she was Number One at the first Super Shoot.

Donalee and Jim Stekl, who have ten World Records between them. Daughter Debbie, 12, is already shooting.

young shooters are on the line—and winning consistently. Gals like Bobby Burns, Jay Knox, Becky Sinclair, Donalee Stekl, Olive Walker and Phyllis Wolfe are not just holding their own—they are making life absolutely "miserable" for their husbands. And the kids are doing well also. Seventeen-year old John Hollister's fourth-place finish at the first Super Shoot was extremely impressive; and Debbie Stekl's third place in the qualifying round of Super Shoot II even more so, for Debbie was 11 years old, and it was her *first* match.

Abroad, the sport is already firmly established in Australia and Canada. In Europe, Great Britain and Italy have undertaken active programs, and other nations are on the verge.

At home, major manufacturers are designing and marketing the components and equipment needed. Firearms magazines directed at the consumer are covering matches and devoting editorial space to benchrest. New clubs are being formed and ranges are being built to accommodate the growing number of shooters.

Those of us who are already into benchrest understand the need for new blood, for without it there can be no future. Consequently, the new shooter can be sure of a warm welcome at any benchrest tournament, for he is, quite literally, representative of the most important ingredient in our planning—tomorrow's competitor.

Readers who want more information on benchrest should write:

International Benchrest Shooters
RD 1
Robinson Rd.
Mohawk, New York 13047
    or
National Bench Rest Shooters Assn. (NBRSA)
607 West Line St.
Minerva, Ohio 44657

Benchrest Records

Single Groups	Heavy Varmint	Light Varmint	Sporter	Experimental Heavy Bench
5—100	.070"	.009"	.090"	.063"
5—200	.192"	.236"	.242"	.161"
5—300	.505"	.559"	.709"	.553"
10—100				.138"
10—200				.298"
10—300				.691"
Aggregates—MOA				
5—5—100	.2142	.2110	.2550	.1852
5—5—200	.2474	.2552	.3129	.2290
5—5—300	.4093	.4224	.4798	.3547
5—10—100				.2270
5—10—200				.2496
5—10—300				.4248
Grand Aggregates—MOA				
5—5 (100 plus 200)	.2491	.2579	.2954	.2275
5—5 (200 plus 300)	.4261	.4684	.4990	.3639
5—10 (100 plus 200)				.2563
5—10 (200 plus 300)				.4419

NOTE: MOA—Minute of Angle

Single group of 5—100 indicates five shots at 100 yards, etc.

Aggregate: MOA of 5—5—100 indicates five 5-shot groups at 100 yards, etc.

Grand Aggregate—MOA indicates the MOA average of five 5-shot groups at 100 yards, and five 5-shot groups at 200 yards.

THE HAWKEN—

America's First

Big Game Rifle

by Jim Brady

THE "KENTUCKY" muzzle-loading rifle, and the many legends and facts surrounding its use in the hands of the frontiersmen who roamed the hardwood forests east of the Mississippi River from the mid-1700's to the early 1800's, have captured the imiginations of generations of Americans.

In the hands of such specialized troops as Morgan's Pennsylvania Rifle Battalion and Cresap's Maryland Riflemen during the American Revolution, it proved to be one of the first instruments of what, in more modern times, would come to be known as "psychological warfare." Pity the poor British soldier opposed by these wraith-like American rifle units. Harassed by accurate sniper fire and sudden ambushes by an enemy with whom he could not come to grips in close combat—where his smoothbore Brown Bess musket was most effective and the type of warfare for which he had been trained—he came to look on this astonishing American weapon as "the world's greatest orphan and widow maker."

After independence had been won, the Pennsylvania-Kentucky rifle was carried back into the eastern forest which had given birth to it. It was the ideal weapon for the far-ranging hunters and trappers who traveled on foot through these trackless woodlands. Fairly light in weight, and usually of .36 to .44 caliber, it required its foot-traveling owner to carry no great weight of powder

and ball to keep it shooting for months at a time while far from civilization. With a full powder horn, 100 or so precast lead balls, and some extra flints (total weight about six pounds), the man armed with one of these rifles was pretty well fixed for ammunition. When game had been shot, the fired balls could usually be retrieved and cast into perfect bullets again in the light, single-cavity bullet mould carried in the hunting bag.

For a half-century, while the frontier remained in the dense forests that stretched from the Alleghenies to the Mississippi, the Pennsylvania-Kentucky rifle remained the choice of those who roamed the outlands. The largest game encountered would likely be deer and black bear, and these rifles were more than adequate for taking these animals. They were the perfect weapons for their time and place.

In the early 1800's, the restless frontiersmen, pushed by what seemed to them the onrush of civilization, broke out from under the forest canopy onto the plains and into the mountains west of the Mississippi River. In this new country, they found shooting conditions quite different from those they were accustomed to in the eastern woodlands. Game was larger and more dangerous, and ranges apt to be considerably longer. Travel on horseback became the rule, and travel afoot the exception.

These conditions changed the requirements for weaponry drastically. The woodland long rifle was still used

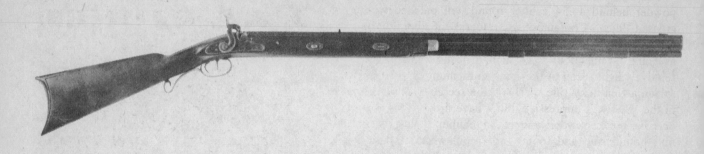

An original Hawken rifle from a private collection in Texas. (John D. Baird)

by many, but as the hunters, trappers, and traders gained experience and exchanged ideas around their campfires, the nature and specifications for a rifle more suitable for use on the plains and in the mountains began to take shape.

It is very probable that some of these hunters and trappers had handled or acquired specimens of the first regulation U.S. Rifle, the Model 1803 produced at Harper's Ferry Arsenal. It is known that some members of the Lewis and Clark expedition of 1803 carried these rifles and that they were found adequate for most of the larger game animals encountered. One notable exception was the grizzly bears that often weighed a thousand pounds and more. As Lewis wryly observed in his journal, "These bear being so hard to die rather intimidate us all; I must confess I do not like the gentlemen and had rather fight two Indians than one bear." This entry was made after a number of incidents in which multiple hits by rifle bullets failed to stop charging grizzlies. Nevertheless, the Model 1803 Rifle was well-liked by members of the Lewis and Clark party and by

those of the Zebulon Pike expedition into the Southwest in 1806-1807.

A brief description of this rifle is in order since it has a bearing on what finally emerged as the favorite and preferred weapon of the "Mountain Men," the title by which the hunters and trappers who roam this vast new frontier became known.

The Model 1803 rifle marked a radical departure from the usual American tradition of small caliber and long barrels for rifled long guns. The .54 caliber barrel of the Model 1803 was rifled with seven grooves and was 35 inches in length. It was round for most of its length and octagonal for the last 11 to 13 inches at the breech. Ignition was by flintlock. The half-stock—another departure from tradition—was fitted with brass trim throughout, including a large patch box with brass cover. The butt was curved to fit the shoulder. An iron rib extended under the barrel to within three inches of the muzzle. Two thimbles for holding the ramrod were attached to this rib. The trigger guard extended to the rear to form a half pistol grip. No provision was made

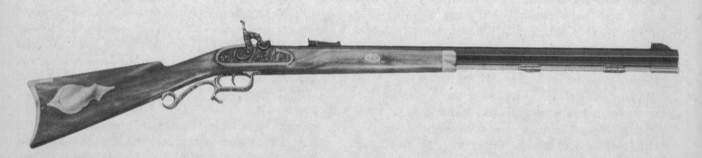

Modern reproduction of a .50 caliber Hawken rifle made by Thompson/Center Arms Company, Rochester, New Hampshire. (Thompson/Center Arms Company)

for attaching a bayonet—this arm was to be used strictly as a rifle.

The load for this rifle was 90 to 100 grains of black powder behind a .54 caliber round ball patched with greased linen. Contemporary remarks of the era in which the Model 1803 appeared describe the recoil as being "tremendous." To a man accustomed to the relatively light recoil of the small to medium-bore Pennsylvania-Kentucky rifle, perhaps the recoil of this load in the 1803 was impressive, but I have fired 102 grains of FFg black powder and a .54 caliber ball from a nine-pound rifle and found the recoil, while certainly authoritative, was not all that uncomfortable.

As happens so many times in recorded history, whenever a need arises, a man or men will appear to fill that need. Henry Hawkins was a gunsmith who worked successively at Lancaster, Pennsylvania, at the U.S. Arsenal at Harper's Ferry, Virginia, and at Hagerstown, Maryland. His two sons were born in Hagerstown: Jacob in 1786, and Samuel in 1792. Both boys learned the gunsmithing trade under their father's guidance and the family moved to St. Louis, Missouri in 1807. The two sons changed the family name to Hawken.

Jacob Hawken worked in St. Louis as a gunsmith and blacksmith. These two crafts were often practiced together in those times. In 1815, Jacob opened his own gunsmithing shop and the St. Louis directory for 1821 contains a listing for "Hawken, Jacob, gunsmith, 214 North Main Street." The business prospered, and Samuel, who had moved to Xenia, Ohio, returned to St. Louis and became Jacob's partner in 1822. Their shop became a popular stopping place for the trappers, traders, and plainsmen before setting off on their expeditions into the vast plains and mountains.

Known collectively as "The Mountain Men," they were the most unique and colorful group ever to appear on the American frontier. Described as being more Indian than the Indians themselves, they adopted many Indian ways and customs. Many of them wore their hair in the Indian fashion and dressed in beaded buckskin clothing and moccasins. Intermarriage with Indian women was fairly common, and many mountain men were full-fledged members of one of the tribes, most notably the Northern Shoshones.

As this extraordinary breed of men visited the Hawken brothers gunshop, the shape of the rifle that was to reign supreme on the plains and in the rugged Rockies for almost a half century began to materialize. Since the largest game animals were no longer the deer and black bear of the eastern forests that the small-bore woodland long rifle handled so well, the mountain men argued for a rifle of larger bore using a hefty charge of powder.

J. & S. HAWKEN,
MANUFACTURERS AND REPAIRERS OF

RIFLES AND SHOT GUNS,
No. 33 Washington Avenue, St. Louis, Mo.

J & S Hawken advertisement as it appeared in the St. Louis City Directory of 1842. (John D. Baird)

The large bore and heavier powder charges would take down large game such as elk, buffalo, and especially the fearsome grizzly bears that would sometimes attack for no apparent reason — and still do to this day. Contact with a grizzly bear — dubbed "Old Ephraim" by the mountain men — was a common occurrence as the trappers made the rounds of the beaver creeks and ponds while tending their traps. The trappers had a healthy respect for this animal, the world's largest carnivore. Under these conditions, the use of a small-bore rifle with light charges of powder was a guarantee of sudden departure from all worldly cares.

To a man on horseback, the long barrel of the woodland rifle was a pesty nuisance, so the barrel could well be considerably shortened so as to make it a more maneuverable piece. Larger bore, shorter barrel — what else was needed to make a rifle more suitable for use in the far reaches of the western wilderness? As the mountain men talked in their shop, the Hawken brothers listened attentively. The fairly heavy charges of powder needed to propel lead balls weighing between 190 to 240 grains with sufficient velocity and penetration to bring down a grizzly bear would generate quite a bit of recoil, and a rifle of sufficient weight to handle it would be needed. A half-stock like that on the U.S. Model 1803 would do, and the extension of the 1803's trigger guard to form a half pistol grip was a nice touch. I tend to believe that the Hawken brothers thought rather highly of the 1803 rifle. But, like anything else, it could be improved.

The brass or other bright metal furniture common to both the Pennsylvania-Kentucky rifle and the U.S. Model 1803 were of no practical use. The reflection of sunlight from polished metal might draw the attention of enemies or alert game being stalked. What these very practical men desired above all else was efficiency, and efficiency was the hallmark of the rifles turned out by Jake and Sam Hawken. The buttplate, trigger guard, barrel key escutcheons, nosecap and thimbles that held the ramrod were made of plain iron on most Hawken rifles.

Patch boxes were eliminated from most Hawken rifles, but where they were provided, they too were of plain iron. The Hawkens could and did make rifles as fancy as the customer desired, but most of the mountain men looked on their rifles as tools for survival in a harsh and often hostile environment. Fancy doodads were not of much use when a man was trying to keep his hair or bring down a charging grizzly bear.

At the time that the Hawken brothers were establishing their reputation as the best rifle makers on the new frontier, the percussion lock had just about supplanted the flintlock. The percussion ignition system, commonly called the caplock, was more reliable than the flintlock, especially in rainy or snowy weather, gave quicker ignition, and was slightly faster to reload. There were also fewer parts in the lock that might fail at some crucial moment and repairs by the user were easier to make. Some of the earlier Hawken rifles may have been made with the flintlock, but my research has not disclosed any existing specimens. It is possible that the Hawkens made some of their early rifles as flintlocks and that these were later converted to the percussion system. This was a common conversion that gunsmiths of the era were called upon to make.

The barrels of the Hawken rifles averaged from 34 to 38 inches in length, were octagonal in shape, and made of soft iron. Most of them were of .50 to .54 caliber and rifled with a slow twist. Barrels for the .50 caliber ball and greased patch were the most popular among the mountain men. The iron rear sight was set in a mortise cut in the top barrel flat and could be moved right or left. This rear sight was typically slanted slightly toward the breech in order to reduce reflections from its rear surface that might cause sighting errors. On most Hawkens, the front sight was, a silver blade set in a copper base.

Double-set triggers were provided on the Hawken rifles so that the user could extract all of the inherent accuracy of the finely rifled barrels when taking a deliberate shot. The front trigger also functioned as a single-stage trigger when a fast shot was necessary.

The half stock was typical of the Hawken rifle, although some were fitted with full stocks. Walnut or maple were the preferred woods, and a cheekpiece and butt curved to fit the shoulder were constant features. The wrist or grip of the stock was thicker than those

Model posed as a mountain man. (Thompson/Center Arms Company)

found on the Pennsylvania-Kentucky rifles. These heavier grips were much less likely to break if the rifle was dropped from horseback or slammed against an outcropping of rock.

The Hawken Gun Shop is at right in this old photograph taken near Ead's Bridge in St. Louis. (Missouri Historical Society)

It has been stated that the typical Hawken rifle was a heavy, cumbersome, clubby piece of cavernous caliber designed to digest huge charges of powder, and weighing around 15 pounds. Not so! The average weight of the Hawken was ten pounds or a little over, and the most popular boring was the .50 caliber. The usual charge was 80 to 100 grains of powder. A mountain man was often over a thousand miles from the nearest source of supplies. All ammunition had to be carried on his person with reserve supplies on pack animals that might become lost or stolen by Indians—a favorite pastime of the latter.

The large powder horn usually carried by these men held approximately 1½ pounds of powder. This was sufficient for about 100 shots when spillage in loading and such things is considered. One hundred .50 caliber lead balls weigh about 2½ pounds, making the total weight of ammunition carried about four pounds, exclusive of some extra balls carried in case of loss. It doesn't sound like much, but add to it the weight of the rifle, traps, beaver scent, and other equipment that was

carried on the person over rough country, and you come up with a sizeable load indeed. Horses could not always be used while tending traps, so much travel on the actual trapping grounds was on foot. The .50 caliber was the golden mean that met the requirements of ample bullet weight in front of a stiff charge of powder to provide power enough for all normal circumstances.

The Hawken rifles of .53 caliber and larger came along at a later period when sources of supply were nearer and ranges were longer. Meanwhile, if the mountain trapper knew he was likely to be bothered by a particularly truculent bear, he would often pour in a charge of 130 to 140 grains in his .50 caliber and when the confrontation occurred, let fly. That usually settled the matter.

The Hawken shop did turn out large caliber rifles that weighed in the neighborhood of 15 pounds, but these were special order guns intended for use on buffalo and to be used from fixed positions. Supply wagons in which the rifles could be carried along with the ammunition and other equipment of the buffalo hunter were usually

SAMUEL HAWKEN

BORN OCTOBER 26, 1792
DIED MAY 9, 1884
MEMORIAL AND TRIBUTE TO SAMUEL HAWKEN AND
HIS BROTHER, JACOB HAWKEN 1786 - 1849,
MAKERS OF THE FAMOUS "HAWKEN ROCKY MOUNTAIN
AND PLAINS RIFLE" WHICH FOR NEARLY HALF A
CENTURY PRECEDING THE CIVIL WAR WAS THE
OUTSTANDING CHOICE OF THE OLD MOUNTAIN MEN,
TRAPPERS, AND FUR TRADERS. GENERAL WILLIAM
ASHLEY, THE FAMOUS SCOUT KIT CARSON, AND
BUFFALO BILL CODY WERE AMONG THE MANY OF THESE
MEN WHO WOULD HAVE NO OTHER MAKE IF IT WAS
POSSIBLE TO GET A "HAWKEN."
DEDICATED TO HIS MEMORY
WITH LOVE BY HIS GRANDSONS
FRANK S. HAWKEN, Sr.
AND
OTIS R. HAWKEN, Jr.

Tombstone of Samuel Hawken. (John D. Baird)

close by. Many Hawken rifles found with bores larger than .50 to .53 caliber have been "freshed out"—that is, recut to larger bores when the original barrels became worn from much use and had lost their accuracy. The usual Hawken of from .50 to .54 caliber had a certain grace, good looks, and fine handling properties derived from the aura of efficiency that still clings to it. There is nothing remotely resembling clumsiness here.

If the Hawken rifles now in the hands of individual collectors and museums could tell their stories, much more would be known of the history of the early West. Contrary to the imaginings of some writers, armed conflict

with the Indians was not at all frequent and was usually the result of the mountain man's embroilment in the feuds and quarrels between various tribes, clans, and groups of Indians. The mountain man taking the side of "his" tribe.

The recent motion picture "Jeremiah Johnson" is, more or less, based on the story of the mountain man known as "Liver Eatin' Johnson" and his famous feud with the Crow tribe after some of them had killed his Indian wife and child. The picture of course does not delve into the practice from which Johnson's cognomen was derived. An earlier picture, "Man In The Wilderness," is based on the story of mountain man Hugh Glass and his spectacular and successful fight for survival after being left for dead and without weapons following an encounter with a grizzly bear. One thing the mountain men would not do was to fight with Indians against other mountain men. They have been described by some historians as being a sub-tribe in themselves.

Many of the encounters with Indians in which the Hawken rifles played a part were isolated engagements between one or two trappers and small bands of marauding Indians bent on stealing horses. That the mountain men usually came out on top in these affairs is a tribute to their marksmanship as well as to the fine and extremely accurate Hawken rifles. One large battle was fought in the valley of the Little Snake River near the present Colorado-Wyoming border in the summer of 1841.

A band of about 30 trappers and some Shoshone Indians, led by the elderly veteran mountain man Henry Frack, were attacked by a large war party of mixed Cheyennes, Arraphoes, and Sioux. The mountain men "forted up" behind dead horses and logs. The Indians mounted many charges throughout the day, often coming to within ten yards of the besieged trappers. Frack ordered his men to shoot in turn so that some of them always held loaded rifles. The mountain men maintained a steady and accurate fire from their powerful Hawken rifles.

At the end of the day, the Indians broke off the fight and departed but Frack had been killed. One of his men remarked later: "He was the ugliest dead man I ever saw, and I've seen a good many. His face was all covered with blood and he had rotten front teeth and a horrible grin. When he was killed he never fell, but sat braced against a stump, a sight to behold." The mountain men lost four of their number, but their accurate and deadly Hawken rifles had laid low a much greater number of Indians.

The battle is commemorated by the names the mountain men gave to various features of the terrain nearby such as Battle Creek, Battle Mountain, and Battle Lake. A mountain to the south is called Squaw Mountain, recalling that the mountain men and their Shoshone traveling companions had hidden their women there during the battle.

This was an unusual incident, and the reason for the Indian's attack on such a large party is hard to fathom. Perhaps they had a little horse stealing in mind or were displaying the usual dislike of other Indians for the Shoshones. It may very well be that they just had nothing else to do on that fine summer day in 1841. If so, it cost them dearly to exercise that bit of whimsy.

As the reputation of the Hawken rifles grew, the brothers employed as many as 15 workers in their shop in order to keep up with the demand for their products. Most of these men were fine gunsmiths in their own right, notably John P. Gemmer, Charles Siever, Christian Hoffman, and Tristram Campbell. Among the famous mountain men who carried and used Hawken rifles were Jim Bridger, Tom Fitzpatrick, Kit Carson, Tom Tobin, Mariano Modena, Jim Baker, and Jedediah Smith.

In 1849, tragedy struck the Hawken operation. Jacob, the founder and senior partner, died in the cholera epidemic that swept St. Louis. It is believed that his body was cremated along with other victims of the disease in an effort to halt its spread. No longer would the mountain men's favored rifle bear the familiar stamping "J & S Hawken." Hawken rifles made in 1850 and thereafter were simply stamped S. Hawken.

Samuel carried on the business of supplying the famous rifles to the new waves of adventurers, settlers, and sportsmen who swarmed into St. Louis. It is an interesting fact that more Hawken rifles were made after Jake's death than in all the years before. Even after the advent of the Spencer carbine and other breech-loading and repeating rifles, the muzzle-loading Hawken was still in demand for hunting large and dangerous game because of its superior power. None of the early breech loaders used as heavy a charge of powder as the Hawkens, and were therefore far below them in muzzle energy.

In 1859, Samuel turned the business over to his son, William S. Hawken. From William, the business passed to various other proprietors, and finally to John P. Gemmer, the trusted employee and friend of the Hawken brothers. Gemmer continued to turn out Hawken rifles that were faithful in design and workmanship. In 1884, Samuel died, but Gemmer continued the business until he closed the shop in 1915.

For almost a half-century the Hawken rifle reigned as king of the plains and mountains of America. It influenced rifle design for big-game hunting in this country, and a somewhat shorter and slightly lighter version migrated back East to become the muzzle-loading Adirondack-New England deer and bear rifle. The Hawken was truly America's first big-game rifle.

Muzzle-loading rifles influenced by the Hawken design, most notably those manufactured in the modern plant of the Thompson/Center Arms Company located in New Hampshire, are being used today to take big game as more and more states institute special primitive weapons seasons restricted to bows and muzzle-loading firearms. I'm sure old Jake and Sam would approve.

THE SPORT of little kings

by don lewis

A CHILL WIND whipped across the October pasture field announcing winter wouldn't be far behind. It was late in the year for a chuck hunter to be out, but my determination to nail the big clover eater denned at the base of a decaying stump made me forget the cold wind and late season.

The monstrous chuck and I were not strangers. It had deflated my shooting ego twice during the summer when I failed to connect on the 295-yard shot. Once it had been with a Mossberg 800CTV-22-250 heavy barrel, and again with a heavy-barrel Remington 700 chambered for the 6mm cartridge. There was nothing wrong with either rifle; it was just poor shooting on my part. For this hunt, I decided on a Ruger No. 1 single-shot 22-250 mated with its best accuracy load of 35½ grains of 4064 behind a 53-grain Hornady Match Hollow-Point bullet. My chronograph gave an instrumental velocity reading of 3,754 fps 15 feet from the muzzle, and this load would print ⅝-inch groups at 100 yards on a consistent basis.

I banked my hopes on this combination but had no way of knowing that wind would be a real factor. Ten minutes after getting into position. I started wishing I had a .243 or the sleek Ithaca LSA 65 25-06 I had just received for testing. Hoping was only a waste of time, and my best bet would be to shoot between wind gusts.

As the afternoon wore on, it looked as though my efforts would be in vain. The wind did diminish some, but a dark, foreboding eeriness filled the air. I snuggled close against a stake-and-rider fence hiding from the wind and hoped for the best. The clock was running out, and this would be the last time I would make the 20-mile drive to match wits with a chuck I believe would hit 15 pounds.

A look skyward told me shooting light was leaving at a fast clip, and I'd better call it a day. From force of habit, I glassed the stump again and noticed something different. Perhaps I might have overlooked this if the chuck would have remained motionless. When my binoculars told me for sure it was legal game, I slid into the prone position and realized the moment of truth had arrived.

The 12X-3200 Redfield target scope showed a clear outline of the chuck, but before I could squeeze off a shot, the wary critter holed. Frustration raced through my veins as I stared hard through the scope. This chuck was my nemesis and there was little I could do about it. My frustration was short-lived when the chuck's head came into view. Using the bottom rail for a rest, I squirmed into a cramped position and steadied the heavy-barrel single shot until the reticle was motionless.

Squeezing an even pressure against the light trigger shattered the evening air with a crescendo befitting only the varmint rifle. The chuck was gone, and I wondered whether I had missed.

Experience gleaned from nearly 40 years of chuck shooting had taught me to check after every shot, and I wasn't about to make an exception. Still entertaining the belief I connected on the long shot, my hopes sank when I failed to see one bit of proof the bullet had found its mark. It wasn't until I looked in the hole that sure signs of a hit were in evidence. A minute later, I extracted a large chuck that pulled my spring-type scale to an even 14 pounds. It was a perfect head shot, and a most appropriate way for a dedicated chuck hunter to end a season.

Over the years, I've matched my hunting and shooting skills against the wily woodchuck, and I suppose at one time or other I've fired every varmint cartridge of yesterday and today a dozen times over. I downed my first chuck along a creek bank shortly after President Roosevelt made his famous, "nothing to fear but fear itself" speech. The rifle that started me on a lifetime of chuck hunting was a single-shot Model 60 Winchester .22 rimfire, but it ignited a fire in my bloodstream that the years have not extinguished. Since then, I have run the gamut of varmint cartridges always searching for something better.

When my first chuck slid down the dusty creek bank, stalking was the only hunting method I knew. The mark of a good chuck hunter then was to get as close as possible. More than once, I slid, crawled and wriggled to within 40 yards of an unsuspecting chuck to make a perfect head shot. How things have changed! The modern varmint outfit is capable of making precise shots at ranges never dreamed of when I started to hunt. On the other hand, the entire philosophy of varmint hunting has completely changed. Today, it's speed and distance.

As late as 1946 when the hunting ranks were being swelled by thousands of returning service men and women, varmint hunting didn't rate a second glance from most hunters. I could hardly wait to get back to the pasture fields with a vintage .22 Hornet, but for the most part I hunted alone. In fact, it was sometimes difficult to persuade a hunting buddy to come along. Mostly, I roamed by myself. In fact, I seldom heard or saw another hunter; then things changed.

It could have been because the common .22 rimfire wasn't accepted as a true hunting rifle, or it might have been the failure of the .22 Hornet and .218 Bee to generate much enthusiasm in the hunting fraternity that kept varmint shooting at such a low ebb. Then, the advent of the Remington .222 added a new dimension and varmint shooting took on a different look. I have no idea whether the .222 made its appearance at just the right

Author Don Lewis chuck hunting. Note variety of equipment. Each rifle is sighted-in for a different range.

moment or if it was the totally new cartridge design that caught the fancy of hunters of all ages, but whatever it was, the .222 was an overnight success. Even today, with a multitude of faster and more powerful cartridges in the varmint field, the Remington .222 is still one of the most accurate and best balanced cartridges ever.

I'll go into the history of varmint hunting only to say that for years the .22 rimfire reigned as king of the varmint rifles. The 25-20 and 250-3000 Savage offered more in speed and killing power, yet only a minority of hunters pitted their skills against coyotes, prairie dogs, foxes, crows and woodchucks. Things began to look up when the .22 Hornet was introduced in 1930. With a velocity of 2,450 fps, it was a whale of an increase over the mild 1,175 boasted by the .22 rimfire.

The Hornet held the spotlight for years, with only the .218 Bee for a serious competitor. An argument between the Hornet and Bee factions over the merits of each cartridge can help pass the long winter evenings, but in all fairness, the .218 Bee was derived from a necked-down 32-20 case, which gave it a greater powder capacity. The end result was more speed than the Hornet but with the same weight bullet. I fired both on the range and in the field, and while the Bee had a slight edge in velocity, it was not dramatic enough to send me scrambling for a typewriter to tell the shooting world the good news.

Around 1935, Winchester introduced the controversial .220 Swift in its Model 54 bolt action, but instead of getting rave notices from the press, it was set upon with vengeance. Not that the .220 Swift deserved this unjust treatment for it's a top cartridge in the .224 caliber, but its critics were so successful that it began a long, deteriorating journey to an ignominious end. In 1964, Winchester phased it out and introduced the .225 cartridge, which also fell by the wayside. In 1973, Sturm, Ruger & Co., Inc. revived the Swift in their Model M-77 bolt action, and now Savage offers it in a sleek heavy-barrel bolt-action single-shot known as the Model 112-V.

I'm partial to the Swift and I do have a real affection for this great varmint cartridge. From its inception, a lot of wild claims labeled the Swift as cantankerous, pressure building and case consuming. Most of this was just pure speculation—something dramatic to write about. Actually, the Swift has a very strong case and never indicated to me any insatiable desire to eat its own cases. Early claims that the .220 had to be fired with maximum loads for accuracy were false, but it could have been the reason why pressure problems were encountered. My best loads stay under 3,850 fps; speeds above this will in time reduce barrel life and detract from accuracy.

Chuck shot at 125 yards with Remington 5mm Magnum.

Chuck shot at 245 yards with a Remington .222 in the 40XB-BR Model scoped with a 3200 Redfield 12X.

Some of the author's varmint equipment.

With the Swift on its way out, there was no question that a better cartridge was needed to replace the Hornet and Bee. When the classy .222 cartridge with its sizzling speed of better than 3,200 fps along with pin-point accuracy made the scene, varmint hunting got a shot in the arm and was no longer relegated to the ranks of an eccentric minority. Finally, it had become a genuine part of the hunting picture.

In the late 1950's, Winchester's Model 70 heavy barrel in the .243 caliber was probably the first factory product designed with the varmint hunter in mind. The thick, stiff barrel plus the extra weight were all advantages for the long-range shooter. I got excellent results with the 85-grain bullet in front of 47 grains of 4831. Instrumental velocity 15 feet from the muzzle was a surprising 3,275 fps. I developed much faster loads with

the 75-grain hollow point, but the 85 grain worked best over the longer ranges.

Soon after Winchester brought out the heavy-barrel varminter, other gun companies took notice of the varmint hunter's needs. Today, varmint rifles are available in a wide variety of models and cartridges. Also, new creations such as the Remington .17 caliber along with the standardization of a number of "Wildcats" such as the 22-250 and 25-06 have added to the problem of selecting the proper one. The new varmint hunter can become confused with the maze of models and chamberings and needs some criterion to use in selecting what will best fit his needs.

It's not always the fastest and most powerful, either. If this were the case, Remington's 7mm Magnum would be the answer. The best approach is to define one's

Expert chuck hunter Helen Lewis points out a target to gun-writer, Bob Bell. Bell is using Ruger M-77 heavy barrel .22-250 with Unertl 10 Ultra Varmint scope.

needs. For instance, in congested areas where shots are under 150 yards, the .22 Hornet with its low noise level would be ideal. This fine old cartridge went down the drain a few years ago, but is back in four superb models: the Ruger No. 3 single shot; Interarm's Walther KKJ; while Savage offers it in their 1432 Anschutz and 340 Model. I have no qualms about saying the little Hornet is a very potent short-range cartridge.

The tiny .17 caliber brought out by Remington in the 700 Model caused quite a stir with its blistering 4,000 fps velocity. There was some talk that the .17 caliber would outdo the .224's with ease. However, I used it in not only Remington's standard version but also in Harrington & Richardson's 317 Ultra Wildcat .17/.223. The H & R cartridge is truly a wildcat version since it's made from a .223 case which the Army called the 5.56mm. Making the .17/.223 is simple and requires only running a .223 case into a .17/.223 sizing die to reduce neck size. My best load for the H & R was 19 grains of 4895 behind a 25-grain Hornady HP bullet.

Remington's version is still based on the Remington .223 case except that Remington shoved the shoulder back .087 inch. This modification would make it dan-

gerous to fire a factory Remington .17 shell in the H & R outfit due to excessive headspace. I stuck exclusively with Remington 7½ primers and the 25-grain Power-Lokt bullet. Remington's version is more of a heavy-barrel type, but I fired a few ⅝-inch groups with both models.

The .17 caliber will never replace the .224's by any sense of the word. Its 25-grain bullet does have tremendous speed, but is highly susceptible to wind. I made a few nice shots around the 250-yard mark, but eventually reached the conclusion that the little .17 caliber is definitely a 200-yard cartridge and no more. It made clean kills, and I enjoyed the whiplike crack it produced.

I've already stated my feelings about the Remington .222, but it must be classed as a 250-yard outfit. This may raise the bloodpressure of avid .222 buffs, but it lacks the velocity to compete with the .220 Swift and 22-250. There's no question the .222 is a very versatile cartridge and is equally at home at the benchrest or in the field. All in all, it's a terrific cartridge.

I suppose the most popular varmint cartridge today is the Remington 22-250. Recently standardized by

Custom Dumoulin .22-250 scoped with 10X Unertl Target scope. Note thumbhole stock.

Remington, the 22-250 lived for more than 30 years as a true "wildcat," with its cartridges being made from necked-down Savage 250-3000 cases. Almost capable of duplicating the .220 Swift's velocity with the 45-grain bullet, the old-timer is a superb varmint cartridge up to 350 yards. It's very easy to handload and works best with powders such as 4064 and 4895.

The 22-250 is available in a host of makes and models, and I think I've tested most of them from Mossberg's 800CTV, Remington's 700 BDL, and Ithaca's LSA 55. All heavy barrels, and all shot inch or less groups at 100 yards once I found the proper load combination for each rifle. I am certain any one of them would have satisfied the most demanding varmint shooter.

Winchester's .243 and Remington's 6mm use the same .243 diameter bullet and are equal in nearly every respect. The 6mm has a little more case capacity, but like the Hornet and Bee controversy, it is not worth getting excited about. The heavier bullets such as the 85 and 90 grain offer more stability in wind than the lighter .224 bullets, but don't add a lot of extra yardage. Rumors have it these two 6mm cartridges are capable of 500-yard shots on a consistent basis, but this is

whistling past the graveyard. The advantage of the .243 caliber rests in the fact that its heavier bullets can be used for whitetail deer and antelope.

The old 25 Neidner finally came into its own in the form of the new Remington 25-06. Like the 22-250, the 25-06 has been around for years, but was not too successful until slow-burning powders such as 4831 and 4350 were developed. The 25-06 is really more of a combination cartridge than either of the 6mm's. A little on the heavy side for small varmints, the 25-06 is probably best suited for heavier game.

I had one 25-06 that gave top hunting results with the 75-grain hollow point in front of 58 grains of 4831. Instrumental velocity was just over 3,500 fps, and I could bank on 1¼-inch groups at 100 yards. A 60-grain bullet is available in the .257 caliber, but, if I may get a little technical, has a very poor sectional density which really means a high loss of velocity. I've always had mixed emotions about accuracy with the .257 bullet. Nevertheless, the 25-06 is here to stay, and for the hunter who fights a constant battle with wind, this cartridge could be his best choice.

The next step up the ladder brings us face to face with the .284 caliber which today means the Remington 7mm Magnum. I can't think of another cartridge with the exception of the Winchester .270 that caused as much clamor. Some hunters wouldn't touch it with a ten-foot pole while others literally revere it. Most of this is pure gossip that cannot be substantiated. During the last five years, more than a hundred 7mm Magnums have crossed my benchrest, and I have seen nothing to fear or revere. By all means, it is an excellent long-range cartridge with plenty of speed and kinetic energy. But it doesn't stand aloof from all the other fine cartridges.

I found it far too powerful for chuck hunting. Connecting on a eight-pound groundhog with a 140-grain bullet is similar to hitting a mouse with a golf driver. This doesn't detract from the fact the 7mm Magnum is one whale of a cartridge. I dropped a trotting ten-point buck at 235 yards as easily as the little .22 Winchester Rimfire Magnum would topple a crow at 100 yards.

Perhaps the most misunderstood aspect of the 7mm Magnum is recoil. Too many shooters believe this cartridge to be a shoulder breaker. While the recoil is not mild, it's not unbearable. I've seen my wife, Helen, shoot this cartridge a dozen times or more in one afternoon without complaining. Adding a recoil pad will cut down considerably on the stinging blow of any high-recoil cartridge.

The paramount requisite for a varmint rifle is to be able to place the first shot on the aiming point from an

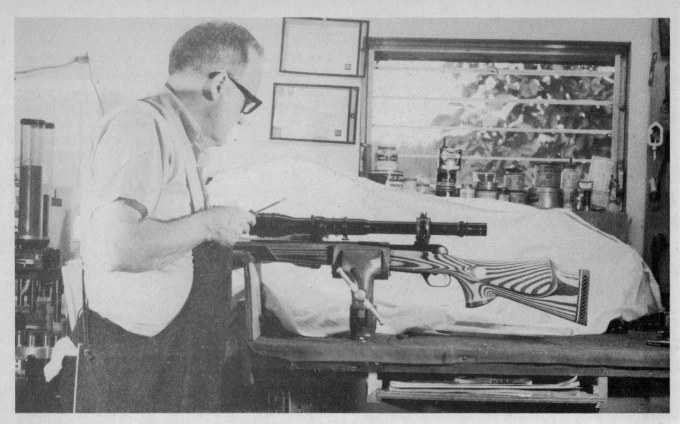

Putting finishing touches on custom .25-06 with thumbhole stock and 6x24 B & L Scope. Stock is laminated.

unwarmed barrel. There are many factors involved in this, but an important one is the bullet. I seem to be a voice crying in a wilderness when I advocate using benchrest bullets for hunting with the .224 caliber. To begin with, the benchrest slug is made from the same components but held to much closer tolerances. This is what makes the good bullet.

While much fuss is written over the concentricity of the bullet, the fact remains that being completely round is no guarantee of one-hole groups. It is important that the bullet be round, but it's just as important that it have a square base. The millionth of a second in which the bullet leaves the muzzle will determine largely how true the bullet will fly. If the base is rounded or uneven, gases will escape prematurely on that side, causing the bullet to tip or wobble. The square base makes a perfect seal, and starts the bullet in true alignment with the bore.

The use of a bullet spinner is necessary in determining if a bullet is concentric and has a square base. The spinner is really nothing more than a miniature lathe using a dial indicator instead of a cutting knife. While the bullet is turned with the thumb and index finger between two spindles, a reading in tenths of a thousandth shows on the indicator. Benchrest shooters won't settle for bullets that have a read-out of more than .0003

Four top varmint cartridges. L. to R. .22 Hornet — .218 Bee — .22-250 & .243 Winchester.

Chronographing .220 Swift loads — Rifle M77V/.220 Swift, Scope Redfield Widefield 1¾ x 5.

The results of what can be expected from a good varmint cartridge. Rifle: Ruger M77V/.220 Swift Scope: Redfield 3200 16X.

(three tenths of one thousandth of an inch) but the varmint shooter can add a tenth or two without problems. Normally, in a box of factory benchrest bullets more than half will stay under .0004. Regular hunting bullets come nowhere near this.

Another factor in precise shooting is the trigger, since it is the only communication the shooter has with the shot he is about to fire. Trigger play, excessive weight of pull and overtravel are demons on a varmint rifle. An adjustable type of trigger is a must. A poor trigger setup will never allow the shooter or the rifle to reach full potential.

The same can be said for the sighting arrangement. No varmint hunter can shoot any better than he can see. Still, he must use discretion when choosing the proper scope. In this era of power, the varmint hunter can defeat his purpose by going for too much power. From a good many years of field-testing scopes, I feel 12X should be the maximum. Possibly, the best power would be 10X, and on rifles having less than a 200-yard range, a 6X or 8X would be more than adequate. By all means, the scope should have a very fine crosswire (reticle).

Fortunately, the modern factory varmint rifle is accurate, but the modern shooter has become so "minute of angle" conscious that one-hole groups are expected from every rifle. Well, there's nothing like a varmint rifle that will put all its shots in less than an inch at 100 yards, and it's a fine standard to judge by, but cutting ½-inch groups on a consistent basis is no small matter; few rifles will do it even with carefully assembled handloads.

I think it is common knowledge that accuracy improves somewhat when velocities are lowered, but this is not always best for the long-range shooter. For myself, I develop a powder/bullet combination that is relatively fast and prints under 1¼ inch at 100 yards. With bigger calibers, I'll allow the groups to expand even more as long as the chronograph shows sufficient speed to cover the longer ranges.

Whether it's a 125-yard shot with the .22 Hornet or a shot covering four football field lengths with the 7mm Magnum, varmint hunting truly reflects a precision type of hunting. Normally, targets are small and there's no room for error. I might be overdoing it when I say varmint hunting requires the patience of a chess master, the skill of a surgeon, and the nerves of a fighter pilot—yet, is simplicity at best. It lacks the beauty of a ram high on a crag, and it's void of the face-to-face danger of a Cape Buffalo, but only a very few hunters participate in these exotic hunts. For the rest of us, we'll just have to settle for the insignificant varmint of our choice and enjoy to the fullest the sport of little kings.

TODAY'S CARTRIDGE-GUN REPLICAS

by George C. Nonte, Jr.

As ANY AWARE gun buff knows, an entire "Replica Industry" has grown up since the mid-1950's. It is largely devoted to supplying all manner of muzzle-loading guns and related items and accessories. In the main, those guns are copies or near-copies of percussion and flintlock arms of all types from the Brown Bess smoothbore musket up through the latest percussion revolvers and target rifles. Even cannon and mortars are included.

Yet few take cognizance of the fact that we now have replicas of many black-powder cartridge guns. By this, we mean guns originally designed around self-contained metallic cartridges, not the separately primed, transition types. Most of these replicas are chambered for centerfire calibers, but a few are made for the ubiquitous .22 rimfire. The latter is the only black-powder rimfire to survive while numerous center-fires are still with us.

In most instances, these cartridge replicas are line-for-line copies of designs that originated during the period 1855-1892. At most, they incorporate minor changes to adapt them to modern production methods, such as investment casting. In fact, without investment casting, it is doubtful that it would be economically feasible to produce some of today's complex designs. The hundreds of machining operations originally required would simply be too costly. The same applies, of course, to the muzzle-loading replicas.

In addition, modern cartridge replicas contain much improved and stronger materials. Frames, breech blocks, and receivers originally made from cast or wrought iron, or from soft steel, are today made from very strong steel alloys such as #4140. Today's Remington Rolling Block replica has a receiver several times stronger than originals made in the 1860's and 1870's. The same applies to Winchester M1873 copies, Martini actions, and, in fact, to all cartridge replicas except those intended only for low-power cartridges using brass or bronze for major structural components. The Navy Arms "Yellow Boy" replica of the Winchester M1866 is the most prominent example of the latter.

So, with the exceptions noted, modern cartridge replicas are far superior in strength to their antecedents. In fact, some replicas are factory-chambered for cartridges developing three times the chamber pressure intended for the originals. Some single-shot rifle replicas of black-powder designs are quite safe with magnum cartridges developing over 50,000 CUP (psi) chamber pressure. Most notable among these are the copies of the Winchester 1885 High Wall single shot and the Sharps Borchardt of 1878.

What we really have in modern cartridge replicas are guns far superior to the originals in strength and durability. We can have our cake and eat it too, in that we can shoot the "old" guns without being handicapped by their original weaknesses, and without the limitations of black-powder ammunition.

Although mechanically superior to the originals, cartridge replicas do suffer somewhat in one area of comparison. Octagon barrels and receivers of the 1880's were slowly and carefully polished by hand, then given a velvety-blue finish in the old way. The finish of today's guns is more black than blue, and the polishing is inferior. Much the same may be said of color-hardening,

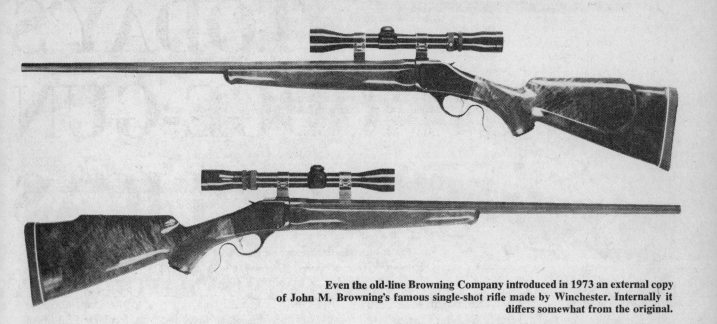

Even the old-line Browning Company introduced in 1973 an external copy of John M. Browning's famous single-shot rifle made by Winchester. Internally it differs somewhat from the original.

and also today's wood is generally of lower quality. There are other subtle differences such as visible casting marks and metal checkering cast-in instead of being hand-filed. We'd like these things done the old way, but costs don't allow it.

Such cartridge replicas are offered by several manufacturers and importers—the bulk of them being produced abroad and sold principally in this country. The largest supplier by far is Service Armament—Navy Arms Co., who offers more types and models than all other sources combined.

Pricewise the better cartridge replicas are bargains. Though across-counter prices range from around $150 to nearly $300, one cannot evaluate them except by comparison with the cost of the originals. For example, in the 1880's, a standard .45-70 Remington Rolling Block cost around $16 to $17, at a time when a prospective purchaser might be receiving 50 cents to a dollar for a long, hard day's work. Today's Rolling Block replica costs $165.

This means today's buyer has to work less than one-third as long as did his 1880 counterpart to earn the price of a new Rolling Block rifle. That makes it a bargain as far as I am concerned, and the same may be said of the other cartridge replicas.

Cartridge replicas originated for the same reasons as did muzzle loaders. Original guns in safe shooting condition became scarce and prohibitively costly as collectors removed them from circulation. Thirty years ago I paid $7.00 for a very clean, shootable .45-70 Remington Rolling Block carbine. No replica could have been

made to compete with that price, but today that old gun is worth far more than the $165 price of a new Navy Rolling Block. Thus today's replicas are not only a bargain, but highly desirable among shooters.

So much for background. The subject of most interest is the cartridge reproductions that are actually available, and what it will cost to own them. For this purpose, here are modest descriptions and photos, shown under the original name applied to the item.

BROWNING SINGLE SHOT: Before selling his design to Winchester which became the M1885 single shot, John Browning produced the same gun in Odgen, Utah. Browning of today is again producing a modified copy of this gun designated "Browning '78 Single-Shot Rifle." It differs somewhat internally, but the appearance is the same as the original, and functioning remains essentially unchanged. It is offered in classic style with 26-inch barrel of light, tapered, octagon; medium weight round; and heavy round form. The pistol-grip buttstock is checkered and the forend carries a traditional schnabel.

COLT SINGLE-ACTION ARMY: Made by Colt today more or less just as the original SAA was produced from 1873 to 1941. Although not considered by some to be a replica, it still falls into that category by our definition. It differs from other cartridge replicas only in that it is made by its original manufacturer. Offered by Colt in many short-run variations, it is basically available in .45 Colt, .357 Magnum, and .44-40 with 5½ and 7½-

Not precisely a replica or reproduction, this revolving rifle comes close enough to be included. It is a long-barrel variation of the M1875 Remington SA modified for a permanent shoulder stock, offered in .357 Magnum or .45 Colt with 20-inch barrel.

The British Martini-Henry, immortalized by Kipling, is copied today by Service Armament-Navy Arms in .444 Marlin and .45-70 with several barrel styles available.

inch barrels in blue or nickel finish; blued guns have color-hardening on the receiver. Standard grips are checkered, black plastic.

MARTINI RIFLE: An accurate British-made copy of the old Peabody/Martini-Henry action produced and marked for Navy Arms. Originally dimensioned for the .577 case, the action will accept the very largest cartridges and carries the long "monkey-tail" operating lever. This replica is stronger than the original, which had an enviable reputation for strength. Both Standard and Creedmoor models are available in .45-70 and .444 Marlin calibers. Receiver is color-hardened with cast-in ornamentation and bright-polished breech block; barrel is blued; walnut PG stock with checkered grip and schnabel forend.

Standard Rifle: 26″ or 24″, half-octagon or octagon barrel; .45-70 or .444 Marlin; open sights.

Creedmoor Rifle: 28″ or 30″ barrel; half-octagon or octagon bbl; .45-70 or .444 Marlin; Creedmoor-style tang sight.

REMINGTON "BABY" ROLLING BLOCK CARBINE: This is a copy of the small 1901 Remington action with a light 20-inch barrel and overall weight of 4¾ pounds. Offered by Navy Arms in calibers .22 LR, .22 Hornet, or .357 Magnum. Action is color-hardened; barrel is blued; butt plate and trigger guard are polished brass.

REMINGTON M1875 FRONTIER REVOLVER: This is an exceedingly good copy of the original Remington that was intended to compete with the SAA Colt

of 1873. The design was superior to the Colt, and still is. This copy has been modified by the internal addition of a hammer safety, a considerable improvement on the original that does not detract from its appearance or performance in the least. Manufactured exclusively for Navy Arms with smooth, walnut grips in calibers .357 Magnum, .45 Colt, and .44-40 Winchester. The first two calibers come with 7½-inch barrel, blue or full-nickel finish. Blued guns have color-hardened frame and polished brass trigger guard. Caliber .44-40 comes in 7¼-inch barrel, nickel finish only.

REMINGTON REVOLVING RIFLE: Not a genuine copy of an original model, this is a carbine adaptation of the Navy Arms M1875 Remington revolver, patterned after the old Remington percussion revolving carbine. It follows the pattern set in muzzle-loading replicas in which modern adaptations of one or more originals are made in traditional style and form. In short, it isn't really a replica, yet it falls more into the replica class than anywhere else. Navy Arms offers this model in .357 Magnum or .45 Colt caliber with a 20-inch barrel, sculptured trigger guard, and smooth walnut buttstock with polished brass crascent butt plate. Finish is blue with color-hardened frame.

REMINGTON ROLLING BLOCK PISTOL: An adaptation of the small rolling block action originally called "Baby" and made mainly for rimfire calibers. Marketed by Navy Arms with eight-inch barrel in calibers .22 RF, .22 Magnum, or .357 Magnum. Barrel is half-octagon, fitted with modern open sights; smooth, walnut grip and forend; color-hardened receiver, blued barrel.

Technically, the famous 1873 Colt SAA must be included.
Original manufacture continued until 1941, then was resumed in the mid-1950's with minor changes. The current guns differ from other reproductions only in being made by the original manufacturer. Several foreign companies also make copies.

Outstanding among handguns is this Uberti (Italy) copy of the 1875 Remington SA revolver made for and sold by Service Armament-Navy Arms. Offered in .44-40 caliber, with nickeled, 7¼" barrel; also in .45 Colt and .357 Magnum, 7½" barrel. In the 1870's, this design was superior to the SA Colt, and it still is.

A variation of the "Baby" Remington action is the basis for this Service Armament-Navy Arms rolling block pistol in .22 LR, .22 WRFM or .357 Magnum.

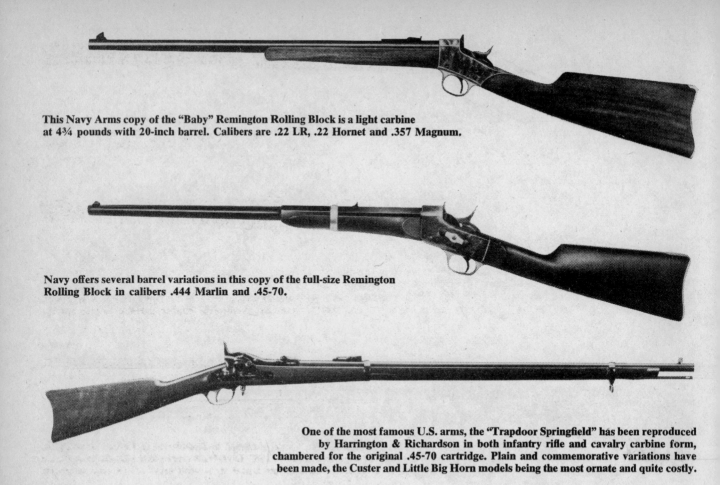

This Navy Arms copy of the "Baby" Remington Rolling Block is a light carbine at 4¾ pounds with 20-inch barrel. Calibers are .22 LR, .22 Hornet and .357 Magnum.

Navy offers several barrel variations in this copy of the full-size Remington Rolling Block in calibers .444 Marlin and .45-70.

One of the most famous U.S. arms, the "Trapdoor Springfield" has been reproduced by Harrington & Richardson in both infantry rifle and cavalry carbine form, chambered for the original .45-70 cartridge. Plain and commemorative variations have been made, the Custer and Little Big Horn models being the most ornate and quite costly.

REMINGTON ROLLING BLOCK RIFLE: Manufactured in Italy exclusively for Navy Arms and so marked. The action copies the basic, big-frame Remington of 1901 with a barrel shank and receiver large enough for cartridges up to .50 caliber. Two barrel styles, full-octagon and half-octagon are offered in calibers .45-70 and .444 Marlin. A few are being also chambered for the long RCBS .45 basic case (3⅛ inches long). Open sights of modern style are standard, and the upper tang is drilled and tapped for an accessory long-range tang sight. Actions are color-hardened and barrels are blued; trigger guard, butt plates, and stock bands are polished brass.

These guns have demonstrated exceptional accuracy with factory-loaded .45-70 cartridges, as well as with handloads. Blow-up tests prove them to be many times stronger than the original, and they accept magnum-class loads without any sign of trouble.

Standard Rifle: 22″ octagon barrel; 24″ or 26″ octagon or half-octagon barrel; .45-70 or .444 Marlin.

Creedmoor Rifle: 28″ or 30″ half-octagon barrel; .45-70 or .444 Marlin.

SPRINGFIELD TRAP DOOR M1873: Famous for being the first breech-loading rifle adopted by the U.S. Army and for the part it played in the Indian Wars, this rifle has been copied very accurately by Harrington & Richardson. Conceived originally as a commemorative item in carbine form, it has been continued in the H&R line as a plain, standard item in .45-70 caliber. The "Little Big Horn" and "Custer" commemorative carbines are the most ornate and costly commemorative guns yet produced in this country. The standard models are perfectly ordinary in appearance, almost indistinguishable from the originals.

Cavalry Carbine: 22″ barrel; .45-70; blue finish; sling ring and bridle.

Officers Model: 26″ barrel; .45-70; blue finish; engraved action; metal forend cap; checkered grip; vernier tang sight.

Infantry Rifle: 32″ barrel; .45-70; blue finish.

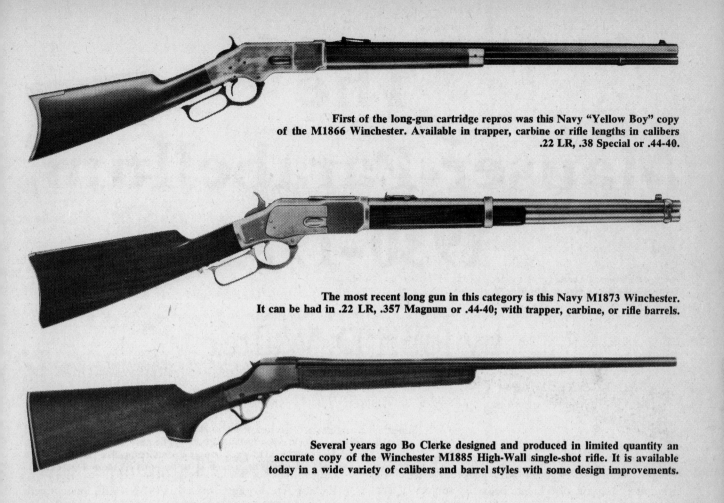

First of the long-gun cartridge repros was this Navy "Yellow Boy" copy of the M1866 Winchester. Available in trapper, carbine or rifle lengths in calibers .22 LR, .38 Special or .44-40.

The most recent long gun in this category is this Navy M1873 Winchester. It can be had in .22 LR, .357 Magnum or .44-40; with trapper, carbine, or rifle barrels.

Several years ago Bo Clerke designed and produced in limited quantity an accurate copy of the Winchester M1885 High-Wall single-shot rifle. It is available today in a wide variety of calibers and barrel styles with some design improvements.

WINCHESTER M1866 "YELLOW BOY": An Italian-made copy of the '66 Winchester with some minor modifications. Made with a brass frame, it does not have the greater strength of other cartridge replicas. Receiver, forend tip, and butt plate are polished brass, balance is blued. Offered by Navy Arms in several variations and calibers, including ornate engraving on special order.

Trapper Model: 16½" round barrel; open sights; calibers .22 LR, .38 Spl., .44-40.

Carbine Model: 19" round barrel; open sights; calibers .22 LR, .38 Spl., 44-40.

Rifle Model: 24" octagonal barrel; open sights; calibers .38 Spl., .44-40.

WINCHESTER M1873: A modern copy of the famous '73 Winchester for Navy Arms by Uberti of Italy. All-steel construction, dimensionally correct. Stronger than the original, but still somewhat limited in strength by the slender links locking the bolt. Offered by Navy Arms in several calibers and variations with smooth, walnut stocks.

Trapper Model: 16½" round barrel; blue finish; calibers .22 LR, .357 Mag., .44-40; open sights.

Carbine Model: 19" round barrel; blue finish; calibers .22 LR, .357 Mag., .44-40; open sights.

Rifle Model: 24" octagonal barrel; blued barrel, color-hardened receiver; calibers .357 Mag. .44-40; open sights.

WINCHESTER SINGLE-SHOT M1885: Manufactured domestically by Clerke Recreation Products, this replica is designated the "Clerke High Wall." It is a slightly modified copy of the original Winchester high-wall action. Modifications adapt it to modern production methods, but appearance and functioning remain unchanged. There are numerous variations of stocking, caliber, and barrel length and weight — ranging from a plain, classic style to modern. Stronger than the original Winchester, the Clerke High Wall action is regularly used with chamber pressures in the 50,000 CUP range.

The Mauser-Parabellum, 1930-1975

by John D. Walter

THE HISTORY OF the Parabellum, popularly called the "Luger" after the engineer who adapted it from the original Borchardt pistol, has been the subject of several books and innumerable articles — some good, some bad.

The first recognizable Borchardt-Luger appeared in the Swiss trials of late 1898, where it was known as the "Versuchsmodell III": the original Borchardt seems to have been the Model I and the so-called improved Borchardt (no specimen of which has survived) was the Model II. The (Luger-improved) improved Borchardt, which was a Borchardt with an internal cam-roller on the rear toggle-link, was submitted to the Swiss but never tested and was quickly replaced by the true Borchardt-Luger. The (Luger-improved) improved Borchardt is the pistol described in US patent 639,414 (granted on December 19, 1899) and in the comparable German patent (DRP 109,481) of September 1898. It is not a genuine Borchardt-Luger.

By 1899, the experimental Borchardt-Luger design foreshadowed that of the 1900's; it was marketed commercially and adopted by the Swiss army on May 4, 1900.

Production continued in Deutsche Waffen- und Munitions fabriken's factories, first in Berlin-Charlottenburg and then in Berlin-Wittenau, until 1930. Other companies and arsenals had also taken part, among them the Königliche Gewehrfabrik in Erfurt (1910–1918), Eidgenössische Waffenfabrik Bern (1919–c. 1947-8), Vickers-Armstrong Limited (1922–1926, assembled from old DWM parts?). Simson & Cie and Heinrich Krieghoff Waffenfabrik were both involved in the Weimar and Third Reich days. The Königliche Gewehrfabrik in Spandau never made complete Pistolen 08, although some could conceivably have been assembled from Erfurt-made parts; but some of the "Spandau" guns that now exist are undeniably fakes made of Erfurt guns and re-marked toggle-links!

In 1922 the management of DWM and Waffenfabrik Mauser underwent a change, and both were finally controlled by the same holding company. DWM's famous name disappeared, replaced by Berlin-Karlsruher Industrie-Werke (BKIW), and Waffenfabrik Mauser became Mauser-Werke AG. BKIW/DWN continued to make pistols, which still bore the well-known monogram on the toggle-links, until 1930. Contracts placed by Finland and the Netherlands were fulfilled in this period. The decision was taken in 1929–1930 to rationalize production and move Parabellum manufacture to Mauser's Oberndorf factory, where pistols were already being made. The move began on May 1, 1930, when tools and technicians left Berlin for Württemberg, and BKIW/DWM's interest in handguns ceased. Some 1.3 million Parabellums had been made in the DWM plants in the

The founders: Peter-Paul (1838–1914) and Wilhelm (1834–1882) Mauser from photographs taken c. 1880. (Courtesy of Mauser-Jagdwaffen GmbH.

period from 1898 to 1930.

In addition to the men and machines, Mauser-Werke also acquired large numbers of unassembled components and incomplete contracts for the Netherlands and Morocco ("Riff contract"). The first "Mauser" pistols were simply assembled from old DWM parts until full production finally began at serial number 413V[1]. The initial batch of new guns was acquired by Stoeger. Many pre-1936 guns bore the DWM monogram rather than the Mauser banner trademark.

Hitler's rise to power accelerated the rearmament program begun in Weimar days, and found Mauser-Werke and Simson & Cie making and reworking many pistols for the fast-growing armed forces (Wehrmacht) and the paramilitary branches of the NSDAP[2]. A coding system was quickly introduced to disguise who was making which guns in what quantities, and special offices were created to supervise their acceptance.

Mauser's production during the Third Reich fell into three classes: guns made under the rework program, standard Pistolen 08 made for the forces and occa-

sionally for commercial sale, and the various contract weapons. The last group contained 7.65mm pistols made for Portugal, Latvia, Sweden and some comparable commercial pieces.

The reworks do not bear Mauser's name or trademark, but have new nitro proofs that differ from those used by Simson. Some dating later than 1935 bear the marks of Waffenamt 66 — WaA 66 — in Oberndorf, responsible only for accepting reworks; a second bureau (WaA 63 prior to 1937, but later renumbered) took the new weapons.

New guns bear a curious selection of markings. In 1934 Mauser-Werke was allocated the code "S/42" to disguise its products, and the code letters K (1934) and G (1935) hid the production date[3]. In 1936 the use of date-letters was abandoned and the two-digit "36" date appeared instead, while the manufacturer's code changed to "42". Year dates thereafter appeared in full above the chamber. In 1941 the three-letter group "byf" was adopted and remained until the end of the war, although production of the Parabellum ceased in 1942[4].

New pistols were originally accepted by Waffenamt 63 (WaA 63), although some bearing "K"-date letters have the marks of the Wehrmachtswaffenamt, the predecessor of the army weapons office (Heerfeswaffenamt) that controlled the regional "WaA" bureau. The Oberndorf office became WaA 655 in 1937, and in 1942, it was renumbered WaA 135, remaining so until the end of the war.

Commercial guns, and some intended for Latavia and Sweden, bore the Mauser banner — although there were a few exceptions that bore military-style codes instead of or in addition to it. The total commercial production was tiny compared to the enormous quantity of guns made for the forces and the police.

All foreign orders for the Parabellum were fulfilled by Mauser-Werke; and their sizes, calibers, barrel lengths and markings make a confused list.

Holland

The Dutch weapons were in two classes. One was obtained by the air force of the Netherlands Indies army (Militaire Luchtvaart der Nederlanse Indien Leger) and consisted of 9mm caliber 1906-type guns fitted with grip safeties. All bore the DWM monogram; though,

the last few were supplied by Mauser-Werke. Acquisitions were:

September 1928 (DWM):
   3820 pieces, numbered 10182–14001

May 1933:
     2 pieces, numbered 14002 and 14003

December 1934:
     2 pieces, numbered 14004 and 14005

November 1935:
     10 pieces, numbered 14006–14015

January 1937:
     5 pieces, numbered 14016–14020

The Dutch navy (Koninlijke Marine) bought some standard 9mm, 1908 Parabellums. Those delivered prior to 1937, numbers 2129 and below, bore the DWM monogram on the toggle-link; those delivered afterwards bore the Mauser banner. The last consignment of 600, ordered and readied for delivery in 1940, was given to the German forces after the invasion of Holland.

July 1928   77 pieces, numbered 1–77
February 1929   492 pieces, numbered 78–569

Mauser-Werke's Oberndorf factory in the 1930's. (Courtesy of Mauser-Jagdwaffen GmbH.)

The first true Borchardt-Luger, renamed the "Parabellum" in 1901. The pistol shown — bearing the serial number 4 — is the only known "Borchardt-Luger-Selbstladepistole Modell 1898" and was submitted to the Swiss army trials of November 1898. Although the details are most distinctive, the basic construction and design are little different to the new Mauser-Parabellums. (Courtesy of Eidgenössische Waffenfabrik, Bern.)

July 1929	515 pieces, numbered 570–1084
January 1930	400 pieces, numbered 1085–1484
November 1930	302 pieces, numbered 1485–1786
June 1931	100 pieces, numbered 1787–1886
March 1932	125 pieces, numbered 1887–2011
November 1932	68 pieces, numbered 2012–2079
January 1936	50 pieces, numbered 2080–2129
1937	200 pieces, numbered 2130–2329
1938	100 pieces, numbered 2330v–2429v
1939	225 pieces, numbered 2430v–2654v
1940	600 pieces, numbered 2655v–3254v

A total of 7093 Parabellums was supplied to the Dutch in the period from 1928–1940; 5304 were made and marked by DWM, 664 were made by Mauser but marked with the DWM monogram, and 1125 were made and marked by Mauser.

Turkey

About 1000 standard 9mm Pistolen 08 were supplied to the Turkish general directorate of security affairs (security police) c. 1935, bearing Turkish inscriptions (not in the old Turkish script) on the extractor and the lever safety. The Mauser banner appears on the toggle-link.

Portugal

Several deliveries were made to Portugal, culminating in the last 4000+ Parabellums ever made.

September 1935	564 pieces, numbered 1921v–2484v
September 1935	70 pieces, numbers not known
June 1937	50 pieces, numbered 4301v–4350v
November 1940	1 piece, numbered 4988v

October 1941	30 pieces, numbers not known
1943	4000 pieces, numbered 1–4000(?)
1943–1945	1500 pieces, numbered 4001–5500(?)

The first September 1935 delivery, intended for the national guard, was of 7.65mm 12cm barreled, 1906-type guns made by Mauser but marked with DWM monogram. All the other guns were apparently 9mm caliber with 10cm barrels. The second 1935 and 1937 deliveries were probably 1906-pattern pistols, marked with the DWM monogram and with grip safeties. The single gun, 4988v, had the chamber date "1940" and the Mauser-Werke banner on the toggle-link; the 1941 batch can be assumed to have been similar. Both would thus have been standard Pistolen 08.

The total number of pistols acquired by the Portuguese is in some dispute because of differences of opinion over the 1943 delivery. The official figures compiled by the Heereswaffenamt[5] show that the 4000 assembled from parts in December 1942 were purchased by Portugal, where they were received in February 1943. It is popularly supposed that their numbers — in addition to the standard German serials — were 1 to 4000, but Kornmayer[6] (whose figures are generally reliable) records serial numbers in the range 685-5263 and suggests that the delivery was at least 4578. It is interesting that the lowest of his numbers, 685, would be the first of a continuation from the Guardia Nacional Republicana purchases if these were the contracts of 1935–1937.

Whatever the story, the Portuguese acquired more 9mm Pistolen 08 (known in Portugal as the M/943) than the original 4000 — perhaps the extra guns were received postwar, perhaps they were simply guns assembled by Mauser in excess of the HWa's "4000" estimate. The present political state of Portugal has made it impossible to obtain any confirmation.

The total acquired by Portugal, of all calibers and types, is consequently in excess of 4715, 4031 of which were made and marked by Mauser-Werke, and 684 of which were Mauser-made DWM-marked products. The extra guns would have been Mauser made and marked.

Latvia

The Latvian purchases are a confused collection. All were apparently Pistolen 08, but some were 7.65mm caliber with 118mm barrels instead of the standard 120mm. The records are most emphatic, but why this was necessary is no longer known.

February 1936	1 piece, number not known
June 1936	450 pieces, numbered 3001v–3450v
July 1936	6 pieces, numbered 1647v–1652v
December 1937	10 pieces, numbered 4537v–4546v

August 1938	151 pieces, numbered 4558–4708v
January 1939	1 piece, numbered 4889v–(?)
January 1939	14 pieces, numbered 5611v–5625v
April 1939*	1 piece, numbered 5638v
April 1939*	8 pieces, numbered 5652v–5659v
June 1939	201 pieces, numbered 5001v–5200v
June 1939*	1 piece, number not known
June 1939*	8 pieces, numbers not known

7.65mm 118mm-barrel guns are marked with an asterisk (*). The Latvians acquired 853 guns, 834 in 9mm and 19 in 7.65mm, and it seems that all were supplied from Mauser-Werke's commercial v-suffix production. They would consequently bear the banner mark; no distinctive Latvian proofing is known to exist.

Persia (Iran)

In 1936, Mauser fulfilled a contract placed by Persia for 2000 standard and 1000 long (i.e.: artillery-type) Pistolen 08. All bore the Persian crest and an arabic translation of Mauser's name. There is no direct evidence as Datig suggests[7], that the delivery was in two lots — 1936 and 1942.

Sweden

Sweden, like Latvia, purchased 7.65mm and 9mm's Parabellums. These were issued in the trials of 1938 to 1939 that which led to the adoption of the Finnish Lahti submachine gun; and the two calibers were required to maintain cartridge interchangeability with the two different calibers of submachine gun. Mauser supplied the pistols from the regular v-suffix commercial production: the 9mm 1908-type guns had 120mm barrels while the 7.65mm ones had "Latvian-length" 118mm barrels. A small number of 7.65mm pistols with 10cm barrels, bearing serial numbers in the range 7500w-7700w, were sent to Sweden in about 1940 for commercial sale.

September 1938	275 pieces, numbered 5701v–5975v
December 1938	10 pieces, numbered 5976v–5985v
February 1939*	14 pieces, numbers not known
August 1939	20 pieces, numbers not know

Batches marked (*) had 118mm barrels. Thus Mauser sent a mere 319 pistols to Sweden for military use, all of which bore the Mauser banner on the toggle-link; 285 chambered the 9mm round, the remainder the 7.65mm.

Others

Very little definite information has been uncovered about the so-called "Moroccan," or "Riff" contract,

A prototype — V21, the last of the series — of the Swiss Ordon-nanzpistole 06/29, differing from the later service issue solely in the design of the butt-heel. The first postwar Mauser pistols were adaptations of this Swiss design. (Courtesy of Eidgenössische Waffenfabrik, Bern.)

except that it was placed with DWM before the business was transferred to Mauser-Werke in 1930. The Spanish army had a long tradition of involvement in Morocco, where four provinces were more-or-less an integral part of Spain and where a protectorate had also been established. The Riff tribesmen, who gave the war its popular name, periodically rebelled against their overlords. A state of war had existed since about 1908; in 1921 the Spanish army was defeated at Anual, but the tables were turned in 1925 and the wars were finally concluded in 1927 with French help.

Apart from its pre-1930 origins, nobody knows who actually purchased the pistols — it is unlikely to have been either the Spanish or French armies — but it could have been the Riffs themselves or some wealthy backer prepared to help them out. Most of the guns were assembled by Mauser in 1930, which suggests that the contract was let after the wars had ended in the hope that they would begin again. The buyers must have defaulted, because the bulk of the consignment remained in Germany and was never delivered. The pistols were finally acquired by either the Reichswehr or the police and, except for their serial numbers, bore no distinguishing marks. The numbers seem to have been in the u-suffix block (one known example being 3623u), which dates them to the time between the transfer of business and the start of Mauser's own production. A distinctive acceptance mark, H 66, was applied to the pistols by their ultimate purchaser.

A theory has been advanced that these guns — how many there were is not known, although August Weiss recalls that the order was "large for its day" (2500?), were for the Spanish Foreign Legion or some of the irregular colonial troops, and that when the wars

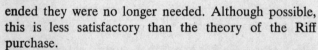

The Walther P38, which replaced the Parabellum as the German service pistol; Mauser-Werke made Pistolen 38 in Oberndorf from 1942 until May 1946. (Courtesy Carl Walther Sportwaffen-fabrik.)

The 45 ACP prototype Mauser-Parabellum. The large-diameter barrel and the design of the grip are most distinctive. (Courtesy of Dr. Rolf Gminder.)

ended they were no longer needed. Although possible, this is less satisfactory than the theory of the Riff purchase.

In addition to the "Riff" contract, a delivery was also made to the Austrians, distinguished by the "eagle BH" property stamp of the Bundesheer. It has been suggested that these were supplied in prewar days, but the standard of finish and the rounded edge to the front toggle-link on either side of the Mauser banner suggests that the guns postdate 1945. They were originally assembled at Oberndorf under the supervision of the French occupation authorities[8] and sold to Austria c. 1950–1952 after sufficient indigenous self-loading pistols had been obtained to permit the Pistolen 08 and 38 to be withdrawn from front-line service in the French army. Presumably the guns were acquired for the Austrian army, which explains the property stamp, but they were probably passed to the police when quantities of the Walther Pistole 38 were acquired c. 1958–1960; many were ultimately bought by a German weapons firm from the police and not from the army. It is not known how many guns were given to Austria, but the quantity may have been in the region of 1500 or 2000.

Mauser continued to supply Finland with pistols, mainly Pistolen 08 in 7.65mm and 9mm. How many were supplied – the deliveries may simply have been from commercial runs or as a continuation of the orders placed in DWM days – in the "Mauser" period is not yet known.

Production of the Parabellum continued until 1942, but it had been realized as early as 1934 that a new pistol was needed – particularly, one that was easier and cheaper to make. Datig[9] states that no fewer

than 778 separate operations (642 machine and 136 hand) were required to make one pistol, and that the time necessary to make each gun was approximately 2½ hours. The 1939 cost price of a parabellum was 11.50 Reichsmarks, and it sold for 40 Reichsmarks. This, however, included two magazines.

The army authorities (Oberkommando des Heeres), through their weapons office (Heereswaffenamt) undertook a final series of trials in 1937–1938. Among the entrants were the Walther Armee-Pistole, the Mauser HSv and the Sauer Heeres-Pistole; the Sauer and Mauser designs were both discarded, and the Walther AP was redesigned at the army's request. It was then adopted by the Germans as the 9mm Pistole 38.

The result was elegant and efficient, lacking the ideal grip angle of the Pistole 08 but much easier to make. The cost price of the Walther weapon, again according to Datig[10], was 5.60 Reichsmarks: a mere 49 per cent of the Parabellum price.

The Pistole 38 was originally manufactured by Carl Walther Waffenfabrik of Zella-Mehlis, but in July 1941 Mauser-Werke was ordered to start production. Spreewerke GmbH joined P38 production in 1943. Production of the Parabellum was discontinued in June 1942 but the parts on hand permitted continued assembly until December.

Deutsche Waffen- und Munitionsfabriken marked guns, made by Mauser-Werke AG prior to 1934-6

Dutch navy deliveries, 1930-6	645
Moroccan ("Riff") delivery, c. 1930, never fulfilled	2,500+

Dutch Indies army air service deliveries, 1933-6	19
Turkish security police contract, c. 1935	1,000
Portuguese deliveries (all to GNR?), 1935-7	684
Total	**4,848**

Mauser-marked guns

Dutch navy deliveries, 1937-40	1,125
Portuguese deliveries, 1940-3	4,031+
Latvian acquisitions, 1936-9	853
Persian contract, 1936 (1936 and 1942? See text)	3,000
Swedish acquisitions	319
All commercial weapons, 1934-45	36,000
Military acquisitions, 1934-42	930,600
Police and paramilitary acquisitions, 1934-42	30,000+?
Total	**1,005,928**

Simson-marked guns, new production

All types, mostly military, 1925-35	**16,000**

Krieghoff–marked guns

Commercial weapons, Krieghoff-made, 1935-7	1,500
Military pieces, assembled from parts (?), 1935-6	4,000
Military pieces, newly made, 1937-44/45	9,200
Total	**14,700**
Total, all manufacturers, 1934-45	**1,041,476**

Notes: many of these figures, especially Mauser's commercial production and the German military and police

One of the 9mm pocket Parabellums, this one with a Pistole 08-style swell-front grip and barrel/foresight assembly. (Courtesy of Dr. Rolf Gminder.)

acquisitions, must be considered as approximations supported only by serial number analysis. Others, notably the Moroccan "contract," are suspect. The serial numbers of the contract deliveries have been previously discussed; those of the commercial guns present a confused list.

According to Kornmayer and others, the Portuguese purchases exceeded 4580; and the figure of 4031 given above must consequently be regarded as a minimum, pending confirmation from Portugal.

The bulk of the guns in the table are 9mm Pistolen 08, but a small number (perhaps 1000) 7.65mm 08-pattern weapons are included. In addition, approximately 2000, 7.65mm 1906-pattern pistols (with grip safeties and short frames) were made; these, however, are not included in the table.

Quantities of Mauser-made commercial pistols, by type

DWM or Mauser marks with v-suffix serial numbers in the range 1v–6000v, omitting blocks for contracts	3300

(Portuguese GNR) and experimental or trials guns (Sweden, Latvia, etc.); 1935–1938? The range also contains some so-called "Swiss commercial" 7.65mm 1906-pattern long-frame pistols. Probably about 200 long-frame and 650 short-frame Parabellums are contained in the total.

Undated Mauser banner guns numbered in no-suffix and a-suffix blocks, 1934–1936.	14,000
Mauser banner pistols of the 7.65mm short-frame type, dated over the chamber (1937–1941) and without safety marks. Numbered in the block 1s-1000s.	1,000
S/42 marked commercial pistols, serialled in the block 5300v–5500v with a few gaps.	200?
Commercial pistols supplied to Sweden, dated 1940, numbered in the range 7500w–7700w, and marked "Kal. 7.65" on the barrels.	150+
Mauser banner commercial pieces, in 7.65mm (rare) and 9mm, dated 1936–1942. Pistole 08 type.	2,000+
42 to date byf code commercial weapons, 1942, numbered in a high w-suffix block.	2,000
42 to date Mauser banner commercial pistols, with numbers in no-suffix and a-suffix blocks, 1942.	13,350
Total production, 1930–1942	**36,000**
1908 pattern (7.65mm — rare — and 9mm)	34,150
1906 pattern (150–200 with long frames)	1,850

Some of the distinctive national markings applied to contract pistols. Top row: the "American Eagle" impressed on some guns sold to Stoeger, the DWM monogram continued on Mauser production until the mid-1930's, the Persian (Iranian) national crest of 1936. Bottom: the Portuguese Guardia Nacional Republicana and the Turkish "Türkiye Cümhuríyetí" monograms.

The closing portion of chapter 10 of Fred Datig's book *The Luger Pistol* — the first chapter of the 1958 additions — states, referring to the possibility of Mauser resuming Parabellum production:

While we were at Mauser, we discussed with Dr. Doerge the possibility of once again resuming production of Luger pistols. While the demand throughout the world is definitely in evidence and many countries and undoubtedly many more individuals would be prospective buyers of a new Luger pistol, the Doctor did not feel that the costs of retooling and producing a weapon which is, after all, relatively obsolete and which would have to compete on today's market with less

A partly cutaway Mauser-Parabellum bearing the marks of Interarms. (Courtesy Mauser-Jagdwaffen GmbH.)

𝔖/42

S/42

S/42

آیا بندول کار موزر

42

byf

Some of the toggle codes associated with Mauser-Werke. Top to bottom: "gothic S" of some 1934 guns, "large S" of 1934–5, 1936–9 standard, Iranian arabic, 1939–1942 "42," and 1942 "byf."

complicated and certainly less expensive pistols, would warrant more than consideration and immediate rejection of the plan . . . it is highly improbable that Luger pistols will ever again be produced in Germany.

So things were in 1958, but, about 1964, Samuel Cummings of the American International Armaments Company (Interarmco) approached both Mauser-Jagdwaffen and the Eidgenössische Waffenfabrik at Bern to obtain quotes for the resumption of producton. Both promptly undertook feasibility studies.

The Bern plant still had the machinery left over from the late 1940's, when production of the Ordonnanz-pistole 06/29 W + F had finally stopped, and work was begun on the design of a simplified version of the gun. The result was the so-called "Pistole 29/65 W + F," only a single prototype of which was ever made although blueprints and production plans were also readied. Mauser's price, however, was more competitve and so no further work was done in Switzerland.

With the contract negotiated, Mauser produced pilot models of the new Parabellum in 1968. The first prototypes were made in both 7.65mm Parabellum and 9mm Parabellum. The company adopted a serial prefix "10" for 7.65mm and "11" for 9mm guns. The initial prototypes were Swiss-type guns with straight front grip straps, Swiss-style foresights and plain unknurled toggle grips; the walnut grips were chequered in a narrow strip with broad plain borders. Production weapons, however, reverted to knurled toggle grips and completely chequered grips, although they retained the straight grip strap and the plain Swiss-pattern lever safety. Production began in November 1970 at numbers 10.001001 (7.65mm) and 11.001001 (9mm), and most of the first guns bore the marks of the Interarmco company —

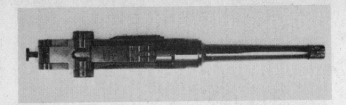

A longitudinal section of the action of the Mauser-Parabellum.

a sunburst and the two-line inscription "Interarms/ Alexandria, Virginia." The toggle-links were marked with the Mauser banner (transversely instead of longitudinally) and the word "original," while the left side of the frame bore "Mauser-Parabellum" over the caliber designation.

In November 1971, with production well under way, the design was altered to approximate more the Pistole 08 than the Swiss 06/29 design. The front grip strap was altered to a swell pattern from the straight, or Swiss, original, while the plain safety lever was replaced by one with a ribbed thumbpiece. The machined housing on the cover-plate was also reduced in height, approximating more to the standard German one (which only extended about two-thirds of the plate's height) rather than the original one that extended to the top of the cover-plate. A German style foresight also replaced the Swiss-pattern original.

By 1974, approximately 30,000 Mauser-Parabellums had been made. Guns in 7.65mm caliber are offered with barrels of 120mm (4.72 in) or 150mm (5.91 in), while the 9mm weapons are offered with barrels of 100mm (3.97 in) or 150mm (5.91 in).

During the time in which the standard guns have been mass-produced, Mauser has also developed a range of prototypes and pre-production Parabellums — some of which might well appear on the market in 1975. One experimental gun has been made in the US .45 M1911

(0.45 in ACP) caliber, built on a straight-strap Swiss-type frame with a 127mm (5.00 in) barrel and with a magazine containing seven rounds. Several prototype pocket pistols, very much like Georg Luger's personal seven-shot gun of c. 1907, have also been made; all are seven-shot types with barrels of 75mm (2.95 in), some are chambered for the 7.65mm and others for the 9mm cartridges.

A small quantity of a semi-experimental target pistol was also made, and it is possible that the gun will be introduced on a wider scale: it can already be obtained on special order. The weapon has a heavy 120mm (4.72 in) barrel that lacks the graceful taper — and hence some of the aesthetic appeal of the standard pistols of similar length — and a special frame that mates the German-style safety lever and cover-plate machining with a new parallel-side grip. This weapon has been produced to capitalize on the design's outstanding accuracy.

The lure of the Parabellum is such that, despite its high price, it will undoubtedly sell to the enthusiast for a number of years to come.

My grateful thanks are offered to the many friends and colleagues who have generously given their assistance, and ensured that this article is more comprehensive than it would otherwise have been — although any errors are ultimately my responsibility. Dr. Rolf Gminder, August Weiss and Mauser-Jagdwaffen GmbH have been especially helpful; and Dick Deibel, Eugen Heer, Eidgenössische Waffenfabrik Bern all kindly supplied material and knowledge. I must also acknowledge a great debt to Fred Datig and to his book, *The Luger Pistol,* which has done much to further the study of the Parabellum — and which has laid the groundwork for so many of us.

Adapted from LUGER: AN ILLUSTRATED HISTORY OF THE HANDGUNS OF HUGO BORCHARDT AND GEORG LUGER, 1875–1975. Copyright © 1975 by John D. Walter.

Footnotes

1. This, according to Mauser, was the start of commercial production; a small number of pre-production guns (which need not have borne serial numbers) were probably made before the go-ahead was finally given. The guns bore the DWM monogram on the toggle-links, and most had the "American Eagle" over their chambers: see Kenyon, *Lugers at Random,* pp 244-9.

2. The Waffen-SS occasionally used Pistolen 08, the police certainly did; but the majority of the paramilitary groups — the SA, the SS, the NSKK and others — favoured low-power double-action blowbacks such as the Walther PP, the Mauser HSc and the Sauer 38H.

3. Most writers — Kenyon, Datig, Whittington and Kornmayer among them — note unhesitatingly that the date letters were the ones given here. There is no reason to doubt them, and it seems that date letters were also allocated (probably in 1934) to the years 1936–1939; these were naturally superseded and never used.

4. Production stopped in June, but assembly of existing parts

continued until December. Pistolen 38 made in the Oberndorf plant retained the "byf" code until the beginning of 1945, when it changed to "SVW."

5. Given by Fred Datig, *The Luger Pistol,* pp 165-6.

6. Reinhard Kornmayer, *Die Parabellum-Pistole in Portugal,* in the *Deutsches Waffen Journal,* September 1969, pp 688-93.

7. Datig, *The Luger Pistol,* pp 158 and 162-3.

8. The French occupied and used the Oberndorf facilities until May 1946, but there is some dispute about the quantities of pistols made and assembled there: some have stated that as many as 75,000 Pistolen 08 (Parabellum) and 38 (Walther) were taken by the French, but other estimates place the totals at about 37,000 Pistolen 38 assembled and made anew and about 15,000 to 20,000 Pistolen 08 reworked. These, however, have yet to be confirmed.

9. Datig, *The Luger Pistol,* pp 305 and 309.

10. Datig, *The Luger Pistol,* p 309.

CAMERAS AND TECHNIQUE FOR THE HUNTER

by Allen Chester Russell

I SUPPOSE EVERY shooter going on a hunting trip wants to come back with a stunning set of pictures to reinforce his memories of the adventure. More often than not, the hunt is a success, but the pictures are a dismal disappointment.

On the other hand, a set of good pictures can actually make a rather undistinguished hunt into something less than a complete bust by refreshing and sharpening memories of other aspects of the trip which may have been dimmed by the failure to bag a good trophy or a satisfying number of birds.

Now let me say right off — getting good photo coverage of a hunting trip, be it for woodchucks or moose, is not easy. Good pictures just don't happen because something interesting is taking place. *Someone* has to take them; that means someone has to be in the right place at the right time with the appropriate camera and lens, and press the release button at the right moment.

Many people, so absorbed by the drama they see unfolding in the viewfinder, have forgotten to preserve that moment by tripping the shutter. This happened to me recently when I had a quail shooter with his pointing dog and the bird being hit as it headed toward me. It was the best composition of such action I've ever been blessed to see through my lens. What a pity, I was so astonished by my good luck that I, like the most inexperienced tyro, failed to snap the shutter! So don't swear at your wife, guide or companion if that happens on your hunting trip: it is one of the hazards of the game.

Aside from failing to take a picture at just the right second to freeze the moment of truth, you might be surprised, however, to learn just how many cameras go along on hunting trips without seeing any action at all. This happens because the matters relating directly to the hunt take all one's time, and the cameras are either forgotten or put aside as a damned nuisance. This too has happened to me. In the crunch, all too often one must decide whether one is a hunter or a photographer.

But even long before the pressure of the hunt precludes giving thought to the camera, many cameras are left unused in a big case or gadget bag packed deep in the station wagon instead of being near at hand, ready to record easily and quickly the highlights of the trip. If your camera stays in camp instead of going into the field with you, it can't record your hunt either — except possibly a posed shot of you and the dressed-out trophy back in camp.

Quite obviously, the hunter's camera should therefore be light and compact enough to be carried, handy for use when traveling in your car and to fit in your glove compartment, and carried with you when in the field hunting.

This really rules out all the large format cameras (even 2¼ x 2¼), and I would not consider anything larger than the 35mm SLR (single lens reflex) cameras. As it happens, the 35mm SLR has all the features one could ask for when seeking the ideal camera for a hunter's use (except that one might like it to be even smaller, but without giving up its basic features). Although it is the largest of any cameras to be considered for this use, it is also the most versatile and therefore capable of bringing back the best coverage of a hunt.

Because it is a "single lens reflex" camera, you are able to view, frame and focus the scene through the actual taking lens. Thus you see an image much more like your final print or slide than the image seen when looking through the conventional viewfinder of non-reflex cameras, where everything looks sharp from inches in front of the lens to the horizon.

However, this is not the case with the actual image formed by the taking lens. The ability to see the true image formed by the taking lens is especially important when photographing objects at very close range when focus is critical, and also when using the longer focal-length zoom or telephoto lenses. Also viewing the image through the actual taking lens completely eliminates the "parallax" factor which exists to some degree with most viewfinder cameras, because the viewfinder is above or off to one side of the taking lens and, therefore, doesn't see exactly what the lens sees. This is far more critical with long lenses than with short, the normal lenses usually fitted to such cameras.

I'll come back to the SLR cameras after taking a look at the other

Using one of the earliest single-lens reflex cameras, the famous Graflex. This 50-year old camera, now fitted with a modern lens, makes impressive 5x7 color shots.

types from which you can make your selection.

Next to the SLR's in capability are the more simple "compact" 35mm cameras in which the image is seen, not through the taking lens, but through a separate viewfinder; the focusing is accomplished by means of a coupled range-finder or footage scale on the lens mount. With the better cameras of this type, there is an automatic correction of viewfinder parallax as the lens is focused. But very few of these cameras are designed to use interchangeable lenses and are unsuitable for use with really long lenses. (This is one of the reasons the SLR camera was a natural development of the early forms of these 35mm viewfinder cameras.)

The basic virtue of these viewfinder cameras is their convenient size and light weight as compared with the 35mm SLR's, even though they produce an image of the same size and quality using identical film. They also cost much less. These cameras are virtually automatic. That is, the exposure is automatic-

ally determined and set by the built-in exposure meter. Some cameras of this type have a manual override that is especially useful if there is a failure of the delicate exposure-control mechanism. When everything works well, this automated exposure control can be a real boon for the hunter. You simply point the camera, focus and shoot. In most action shots, the focus will be set at infinity or close to it; one merely has to raise the camera, make sure that the subject is in the frame and press the release, confident that a good picture will result.

However, if absolute minimum size and weight are going to be the prime considerations, there are cameras even more convenient to carry in the field — those designated as using "110" or "Instamatic" film cartridges. These smaller cameras achieve their marvelously compact size (about 6x2x1 inches, eight ounces) by the use of a small-size film and image. Each frame or picture has less than half the area of the full-size 35mm cameras. Recent improvements in color films and

The relative size of a 35mm SLR camera and projector contrasted with a pair of "110" Kodak Instamatics and a "110" projector, was a time exposure made with a Kodak Instamatic 60. Note the size of the original negative superimposed in the right lower corner. The quality of the "110" slides, when projected with a proper "110" projector, is outstanding — sharp, crisp, brilliant and virtually grainless. Fully the equal of 35mm slides projected the same size and viewed from the same position. Color prints are satisfactory rather than exceptional. Black and white enlargements will vary accordingly with the standards of the lab doing the processing. Author got excellent 5x7 prints, hard to tell from enlargements made from 35mm negatives. Having overcome his initial distrust of these very small cameras, author now is completely sold on the possibilities of the "110" format and will be using it for professional work in appropriate circumstances.

print making have made such reduced image-size less of a handicap than might be anticipated.

But, as with the viewfinder 35's, these "110" cameras are unable to utilize interchangeable lenses of appreciably longer than normal focal length satisfactorily. Being limited to working with the relatively wide-angle normal lens of these cameras is like a hunter having to use a 2x scope all the time when there are many occasions when an 8x or even a 20x would be more effective.

We have all seen slides or prints in which the hunter-photographer has to point to an almost invisible speck and explain that this is the magnificent elk he almost bagged. Well, it is also the magnificent elk we almost saw — simply because the picture was made with a "normal" 50mm lens on a 35mm camera; what was needed was a lens nearer 500mm in focal length.

This brings me to the basic problem of selecting the hunter's camera and its use. The relatively compact and reasonably light 35mm SLR camera with a normal 50mm lens weighs only about two pounds and is a mere 3¼ inches from front to back. It is quite comfortable to use on a neck strap and small enough to fit in a largish jacket pocket. But fitted with a 500mm lens for a reasonably close-up picture of that mountain sheep or of an elk across the draw, it becomes a five-pound millstone around one's neck and measures almost two feet from front to back. It cannot fit into any pocket!

Therefore, I'd forget about such a long lens and consider an acceptable and practical compromise — something like a 75-250mm zoom lens, now weighing, with camera, only about three pounds and about 12 inches from front to back (with lens hood retracted). It is still too large to go into a pocket but, nevertheless, practical to carry on a strap over one's shoulder or, for short periods, on a neck strap. This is the best compromise with respect to bulk and performance; without having to change lenses, the hunter-photographer has, in effect, a quite "normal" lens with the zoom at 70 or 80mm and a very useful "telephoto" with it at 200 to 250mm that will produce useful size images of game at considerable distances. Even with proper equipment however, taking good pictures on a hunt is not easy, for a 250mm lens will not produce a sharp image unless carefully focused and held very steady as the shutter is tripped. Even at a 125 sec. shutter speed, the camera should be resting on something.

I do not recommend carrying a number of fixed focal-length lenses and changing them in the field when a telephoto or a wider-angle lens is required. There is simply no substitute for a zoom lens in the circumstances under which a hunter must function to take his pictures. Frankly, were I buying a new outfit, I would eliminate the "normal" lens and put that money toward the more useful zoom in the 70 to 250mm range.

Now there is still another way to go, especially if pictures of your hunt are really important to you. A 35mm SLR with either a long 250mm zoom lens or an even longer telephoto for getting pictures of game, plus a genuine "pocket" camera such as the most compact of the 35mm rangefinder cameras, or one of the "110" variety would be a good investment. Even the relatively wide angle of the

At work with a Nikon SLR with an 80-250mm Bushnell zoom lens photographing sea bird skeletons on the Paracas desert in Peru.

Your friends might not believe you when you repeat some of the tales you heard about the size of Arctic wolves seen on a Canadian hunting trip . . . but with a simple "still life" photograph you can make believers out of them, for it takes a magnificent animal to put down a 6-inch paw print! An SLR makes this sort of closeup photography easy and certain, especially with a close-focusing macro lens.

"normal" lenses of these cameras (and the small negative size of the 110's) will serve perfectly well for the closer shots of the hunter with the bagged trophy, dressing out the kill, carrying the horns back to camp, in-camp scenes, and even for most of the travel scenes. Some of these small cameras have the additional quality of a built-in or incredibly compact attachable flash unit which will ensure a shot under poor light conditions and even at night.

You think two cameras sound illogical? Lots of hunters carry a rifle and a handgun for different jobs on the hunt; why not two cameras for two different photographic situations?

As to specific recommendations for cameras, lenses and film, it has been said that the most difficult aspect of photography with 35mm cameras is trying to decide on the equipment. There must be at least 20 SLR's with hundreds of lenses, and an equal number of the compact rangefinder cameras from which to choose. The wide range of "110" size equipment is continually expanding.

As with almost everything else, you get what you pay for when buying a camera. The best has to cost more than the run-of-the-mill product be it cars, guns, hi-fi equipment or cameras. There simply isn't space here to deal with all the possibilities

or even cover all the superior cameras; so I'll discuss only what I, as a professional photographer, use or would buy if replacing or adding to my present equipment.

I started using 35mm cameras years ago with the first model Leica around 1930 and consider their present 35mm SLR one of the best, but perhaps too expensive for a hunter's use. I have used a Nikon F single-lens reflex (expensive) ever since they first came on the market about 15 years ago. Although two have been stolen, I've never had a mechanical failure with any of the three, despite hard use all over the world. However, like the Canon

The great moment of the hunt which every hunter hopes his camera will capture to reinforce his fleeting memory of this split second climax of the trip. This highlight of a wild buffalo hunt in the Arctic near Great Slave Lake was recorded with a 50mm lens on a 35mm SLR but could equally well have been shot with a 35mm viewfinder camera or even a "110" Instamatic.

If you take a picture of a party of hunters, don't have them lined up grinning at the camera — pose them as naturally as possible as has been done here.

An unsuccessful picture — a perfect example of the need for tripping the shutter at the split second the action is just right. This shot fails because the bird the hunter is shooting at is lost to sight behind his head. A second later and the bird would have been in the clear to the right of the shooter, and the nearest bird on the left still in view. A motor drive on this SLR would have produced a series of six or eight pictures within a two-second period and almost certainly have captured a fine action picture.

SLR, the Nikon is heavier and bulkier than some of the newer designs. Speaking as a hunting photographer, I would give serious consideration to the new Olympus OM1 which is exceptionally light and somewhat smaller. It also has a remarkably compact motor drive.

If you want a SLR with automatic exposure control (with manual override) the Konica T3 is a good choice, for a wide variety of automatic lenses are available including an 80-200mm zoom and a 300mm telephoto.

Whatever SLR camera you acquire, I urge you to pass up the f.1.4 or f.1.8 high-speed 50mm lens which is usually fitted to these cameras. Instead, get one of the 55mm "Macro" lenses which are appreciably sharper and far more useful in their capability for doing extreme close-ups without the use of extension tubes. The speed of f.3.5 or 2.8 is no real handicap. Most high-speed lenses are sucker bait for gullible amateurs or, at best, specialized tools for photographers hooked on available light work.

I think I would forego the phony wood-trim package on my next station wagon and even the tinted glass, and spend the money I saved on a motor drive for my SLR. The ability to snap off up to five exposures per second can be very useful indeed, especially when trying to capture events which happen so quickly that it is almost impossible to judge just when to press the shutter release to nail the vital moment with a single frame.

I might also get a smaller engine with a manual gearbox on that new station wagon and invest in a true "pocket" camera as a back-up unit for use when the SLR with zoom lens is too much size or weight, or when a flash might be needed. The pocket camera I'd choose would definitely be the new Konica C35EF, which is a scale focusing 35mm

That self-timed Nikon SLR and a hard 25-yard sprint to the driver's seat made possible what appears to be an action shot of the Wagoneer and Airstream passing through some impressive country on the way to a hunting area.

Never pass up the opportunity of shooting "atmosphere" scenes that relate to a hunting trip. This shot on the way to a blind says more about a duck shoot than being posed with a string of dead birds.

viewfinder camera with a tiny built-in electronic flash unit. The flash unit alone is smaller than most small flash units and really no larger than its less-versatile competitors in this class. Because this camera uses the same film cartridges as my SLR, it simplifies the film supply problem. The Konica is of the automatic-exposure-control type but, unfortunately, without manual override. However, its built-in flash and automatic compensation, for the well-balanced filling in of shadows with flash in back-lighted scenes in bright sunlight, made me select it over the rest in the field.

I find it difficult to make up my mind as to the value of the "110" or "Instamatic" cameras (or the subminiatures like the Minox), convenient as they are for carrying. They do lend themselves to quick use and their shape is most suitable for carrying in a pocket. I suppose my problem with them is that I'm so used to the shape and feel, and the through-the-lens image of the SLR's that I'm just not at home with the little cameras. This would not be the case with someone with less years of experience and conditioning. My suggestion is to arrange to try one of these cameras for a few days and satisfy yourself on the matter. I know the quality of the prints and slides will please most people, for it is surprisingly good, especially when the slides are projected by a projector such as the excellent Kodak pocket Carousel.

But remember, even with the best possible selection of a camera or cameras for the job, there can be no record of the hunter connecting with a sharptail grouse or dropping a pronghorn antelope dead in its tracks if he has to shoot both gun and camera.

In order to record the climax of any hunt, the hunter must have help; he must turn the camera over to someone else. This had better be planned for and rehearsed in advance while still in camp. You only ask for trouble if, just before raising your rifle, the camera is unexpectedly thrust into the hands of a startled guide or companion with a whispered admonition to the effect: "Be sure to get me and the moose both in the frame."

There are just too many factors involved in organizing the photographing of the highlight of your hunt for me to give any valid specific advice. All I can say is, "plan ahead and be lucky."

However, one good piece of advice is to shoot lots of film of *all* aspects of the trip and hunt. It is easy to put aside the extra or less-interesting shots, but it is impossible to take the ones you failed to shoot while on the trip once you get home.

A son or daughter too young to shoot a gun can often do some useful shooting with a camera, if the photographic coverage and problems are discussed and sorted out as thoroughly as possible before hand. With automated cameras, it is best to put in fresh batteries and shoot a roll of film as a test before leaving home for Wyoming or Quebec; only a non-functioning gun can be more aggravating than a camera which fails when wanted most.

As I said earlier, with equipment, you get what you pay for, and as for the pictures of your hunt, you get what you *plan* for. Of course, both good and bad luck enters into the results, but a lot of the bad luck can be eliminated by good planning, which goes for the hunt as well.

Just as most hunters think about equipment matters primarily in terms of gun and scope (leaving the question of ammunition a poor last) I have done the same with film. Because of the need to provide both black and white, and color pictures (or a choice of them) for magazine reproduction, I am often forced to carry two cameras so as to be able to

The built-in self timer on the Nikon made possible this effective, memory-evoking shot of two hunters having a dawn cup of coffee.

shoot with the proper film as circumstances dictate. I happen to like large 16x20 prints of my best pictures, so I really prefer black and white. But I freely admit that color slides are most impressive and unquestionably the best way to record the events of a hunting trip. Therefore, the film you want to use for this purpose is Kodachrome, the type which produces a positive color transparency. Reversal-type color prints can also be made from this film, although if you are mainly interested in color prints it is best to use a color negative film to start with, such as Kodacolor.

There are other color films on the market such as GAF and Fuji, both of which are excellent and may have some special qualities that appeal to some photographers. Kodak's color films and Kodak's processing are so dependable that I find no reason to use any other. Kodachrome X has recently been improved and its extra speed makes it the ideal choice for a hunter's use. High-speed Ektachrome has some value in making possible the use of higher shutter speeds with telephoto lenses to reduce the possibility of a blurred image as a result

of camera movement. However, the very fast films have more grain and do not produce as sharp an image as the slower ones, and their color values are often inferior.

With the reversal films, such as Kodachrome for color slides, slight underexposure is preferable to overexposure. Bear this in mind when in doubt.

Equally important as making technically excellent photographs is to be sure that the pictures say something: your pictures should convey part of the story of the trip to the hunting area and the hunt itself. There should always be a reason for pressing the shutter release. Don't always expect the action to naturally unfold before your waiting lens. If it doesn't do so, you may have to arrange for it to happen. Events may have to be restaged for the camera if they were missed when they first took place. Of course, you can't kill your moose again just for the camera, but many other events of a hunting trip can be repeated for the camera. Remember the more pictures you shoot, the greater the chances of coming home with a few good ones!

HUNTING HANDGUNS

by Hal Swiggett

WHAT IS A hunting handgun?

Ask three handgun hunters and you will get at least three different answers.

I tend to think of a hunting handgun as one that a man carries in the field in search of game. It can be almost anything.

Normally a High Standard .22 Derringer wouldn't be thought of as a "hunting handgun" but, to prove a point, some years back mine put three cottontails on the table.

One time while doing an article on an imported MKE .32 autoloading pistol, I was so impressed by its accuracy that rather than state, "it ought to be good for small-game hunting," I used it several times and bagged as many cottontails as would have been possible with any handgun in my battery.

Can any of us say those aren't "hunting handguns" based on my experience?

Regardless of the size hole in the barrel or how cartridges are stuffed in, there are certain things the gun should offer to allow maximum proficiency. Handguns limit a shooter, at best, so make use of every plus possible.

Does it feel good?

By this I mean the way it balances in the hand and how the grips fit. Handgun stocks, like a rifle and shotgun, are made for that mythical "average man." Most of us can adapt to any piece of wood that might be installed, but to shoot our best it has to fit.

Next, look at the sights. To be a practical hunting handgun it must wear an adjustable rear sight. As a rule, hunters shoot many loads, but even if they don't, the point of impact must be precise — for "Kentucky windage" will more often than not make a shooter a great conservationist. In others words, he'll miss a lot.

Every shooter has a different idea about sights, but I like mine to be a good ramp front with the rear notch a little wider than normal. A bit of extra daylight seen on each side makes it much easier to find when light is bad, which can mean most of the time when hunting.

I'm very fond of S&W's great red ramp available on their big Magnums and also their fine white-outlined rear sight.

What about scopes?

Some are "for 'em" and some are "again 'em." I belong to the "for 'em" school. Most riflemen wouldn't think of going hunting without a glass sight. And a rifle is umpteen times easier to shoot than a handgun. Yet some yell loud and long because they feel such a sight on a handgun is out of order.

Why should it be?

The object of shooting is to hit a target. If a man can hit better with glass sights, why shouldn't he use them? Personally, I feel most people can shoot better with a scope sight.

A beginning shooter can do a lot better right from the start. I've had new shooters hitting cans with their first shots simply because all they had to do was put the crosshair on the target and squeeze the trigger. No trying to hold a sight picture and squeeze a trigger at the same time. With a scope all effort is on trigger control.

In the field a scope allows much more precise bullet placement; the same applies when one is mounted on a rifle. Since clean killing is the name of the game, why not take every advantage possible!

The same goes for holding a handgun. One-handed shooting is for targets and smart alecks. Anytime I see a man in the field holding a gun with a single hand, he has already told me all I need to know about his handgun-hunting ability. God gave us two hands so use both of them. Grip the gun firmly with the shooting hand; then set it in the palm of the off hand, so the forefinger of the support hand reaches to about the third finger of the gun-holding hand, just under the trigger guard.

As the trigger is squeezed push gently forward with the gun hand. This automatically causes the support hand to pull back against that slight pressure. This little gimmick gives the sturdiest off-hand hold I know.

Whenever possible use a rest — a stump or log, the side of a tree, or the top of a fence post. The hood of a pickup serves well in the southwest. Whatever support you use don't let the gun touch it. Keep your hand between it and the gun — however, don't put your hand under the stock when shooting off a hard object. A handgun rotates in recoil. As the muzzle goes up the butt comes down hard. Should you forget, it will only happen once when shooting the bigger Magnums. In this case use your forearms to raise the gun above your support.

If no other rest is available try a sitting position. Some like a reclining position with the gun held alongside the leg. This one never works for me because I burn myself with the blast from the cylinder. Nor am I great on prone shooting. I seldom get into country where it can be used.

A kneeling position comes in handy on occasion. Frankly, I cannot successfully pull off either a sitting or kneeling position because it brings the gun too near my eyes.

If I can't find a stump, log, tree, fence post or the like, my stance is the age-old two-handed, off-hand position.

If the shot is a long one I've been known to tuck my chin into the bicep of my right arm, still using the two-

When Swiggett shoots .45 autoloaders, it is one of these two. The Colt Mark IV, left, or his Llama. Both have taken a good deal of game using handloads and Remington's new 185-grain factory load.

handed, off-hand hold for a stock I guess you could say. It does add a degree of steadiness.

I find it best when shooting over a rest to put my forearms over the support, leaving my hands and the gun out in front.

Trigger pull is your personal preference, but to me pounds involved are not nearly as important as a crisp, clean, let-off. I don't like less than three pounds and don't want over five, with most of mine running from three and a half to four and a half.

Barrel length, too, is a personal thing. Autoloader shooters have little choice, but revolver and single-shot guns can be had in many lengths. For several reasons I'd suggest you not go shorter than six inches, unless you have some experience. First, longer-barreled guns are easier to hold. Second, that longer distance between the front and rear sight really does mean something. And third, at least for beginners, they don't bark as loud.

Just as with dogs, the bark is often worse than the bite. Handguns with short barrels are definitely louder and sharper in report than lengthier tubes. An inch makes a big difference.

Every handgunner will shoot better if he wears good ear protection. Even big Magnums don't seem to kick so hard when they can't be heard.

The choice between semiautomatic, revolver or single shot is totally optional up to a point. We'll cover these different choices as we go along.

For the moment, let's talk about center-fire medium calibers. For the smaller varmints and game over cottontail size, I feel the 9mm Luger should be at the bottom. The .38 Super is a bit more potent. As you know, both are caliber 9mm. There are some .38 Spl loadings which bring that caliber within reach of the two 9mm's and, for all practical purposes, make them comparable.

By all means stick to hollow-point or soft-point ammo. Jacketed, of course. No round-nosed lead slugs or military full-metal-jacket bullets.

Here the great .45 ACP gets trapped in the middle. It's not potent enough for really big game but somewhat oversized as a small-game load. The .45 ACP is great on varmints and will do anything a .357 Magnum will do, and in most cases with modern factory loads it can do the job a bit better. Otherwise it is worthless as a game killer. Round-nosed full-metal-jacket bullet do little damage in flesh.

The various barrel lengths suitable as hunting handguns. Starting at the top: Thompson/Center Contender 10-inch (this one is in .30-30 and topped with Leupold's M8 2X scope and Conetrol mounts); Colt .45 with 7½-inch barrel; Colt .357 Magnum Python with 6-inch barrel, and Llama .357 Magnum with 4-inch barrel.

The .357 Auto Mag with 8½-inch barrel. Truly a hunting handgun. Shown with it is Bianchi's shoulder holster — the only practical way to carry a big gun.

Remington loads an excellent 185-grain hollow point. Before this load came into being I took a lot of game with my Colt and Llama .45's, and my Model 1950 S&W revolver shooting that same cartridge, using much too hot handloads featuring a 250-grain Keith-type bullet. My loads, although perhaps not dangerous, were definitely hard on my autoloaders and shortened their lives tremendously.

Beginners should start with a revolver if for no other reason than safety. A semiautomatic is always ready to fire again — whether the shooter is or is not. There is always a fresh cartridge under the firing pin, and the hammer is back, which should be a cause for concern. I find myself never taking my eyes off a new shooter with a self loader.

Whether or not bigger game should be hunted with handguns is for each to decide.

If a man chooses handguns as his hunting armament because he truly loves them, and he is dedicated enough to hold himself within the boundaries of limitations set by the use of that short-barreled gun — then I'm all for it.

If a shooter sets off to kill some outsized animal with a handgun because someone else did it — and for no other reason — I'm not on his side.

The author's two favorite .44 Magnum revolvers. Smith and Wesson's fine Model 29 at the top and Ruger's great Super Blackhawk. This Ruger was altered, so don't factory order one like it. Both wear Herrett's stocks custom made in their Jordan Trooper pattern.

Thompson/Center Contender decked out with Bushnell's scope on the .22 Hornet barrel and the interchangeable .44 Magnum barrel that shoots "Hot Shot" shotshells with the choke device attached or regular bulleted cartridges with it removed. A good duo for the hunting handgunner.

Swiggett's sitting position when no backrest is available. This can "smart" on the knee if a big gun isn't held firmly. Classified by the author as better than no rest at all.

Kneeling position used by Swiggett. Here you can get a good view of his two-hand hold. He doesn't just grip with both hands but uses the off-hand as a support as well.

Even the most potent handgun cartridges offer only token killing potential as compared to modern rifle cartridges. Actually, the much talked about .44 Magnum compares quite closely to the .44-40 of yesteryear, which makes it a definite second to the .30-30 insofar as true killing power is concerned.

Few people in their right mind would go into the wilds seeking a monster bruin of brown or white color, or an elk or moose, with either of those rifle cartridges, yet all too often .44 Magnums are listed as ample for the job.

In what way?

I don't mean this to belittle the sport of handgun hunting. I do a lot of it myself and have taken a considerable amount of game with one-hand-guns held in two hands. I hope to cause each of you thinking about undertaking this fascinating sport to think it out clearly. You must understand the limitations.

Set guidelines for yourself and stick to them. Only you, the shooter, knows exactly at what distance bullets can be precisely placed; how well you can track a wounded animal, and how you react in times of stress, for once a bullet is badly deposited in an animal's body that animal still has to be found and killed.

I'm not of the opinion that the .357 Magnum is adequate for whitetail deer, but every year they are successfully killed — so once again, each man must decide for himself. I tend to feel a bullet should be at least of .41 caliber and weigh at least 210 grains to be adequate for any fine game animal. Here I am referring to true handgun cartridges.

I also disagree with velocity at this point. The longer I shoot the more convinced I am that bullet weight has a lot more effect than does speed. I'm referring entirely to big animals where bullets must travel through many inches of bone and flesh to reach a kill area.

Fast, light bullets (to get one, you must have the other) will expand — no doubt about it. If you've done any research on the subject, you have noted that bullets with much expansion seldom penetrate very far. Caliber .357 bullets can be made to open up beautifully to the size of a .45, or even larger, but in so doing you will seldom find them deep enough to do much real damage. As the nose expands it is forced to push through flesh at the same time. It can't do both well.

A bullet of .44 or .45 caliber doesn't have to expand, so it can be heavy to utilize its weight to penetrate deeply. On this point let me explain one thing. Round-nosed bullets will penetrate deeply. They also push their way through rather than tear, or cut a path.

A flat-nosed bullet of .44 or .45 caliber will cut out a clean channel of that diameter however far it penetrates. This lets blood flow freely and in turn kills much quicker. Also, there is a lot more shock to the animal's system when hit with a flat-nosed bullet — the flat-nosed does real tissue damage while a round-nosed projectile only pushes the flesh aside.

Double-action shooters have an almost unlimited choice of guns in .357 caliber. Single-action fans have less choice but sufficient enough since two great companies offer "cock before shoot" guns.

Once progression upward reaches .41 caliber, choice of guns becomes rapidly more limited. Only Ruger, S&W, Thompson/Center and Auto Mag remain in the field.

If the choice has been self loaders there is only one — Auto Mag. This is a big semiautomatic chambered for .357 and .44 cartridges bearing their own Auto Mag headstamp. By the time this gets into print there may be others. The .30, .41 and .45 are slated for birth in due time.

The Auto Mag is a huge rotary-bolt design, shooting more like a short-barreled rifle which in reality it is, rather than a handgun. I have one with the 8½-inch barrel in .357 caliber that has produced 5-shot, 10-inch groups at 200 yards. Both 6½- and 10-inch barrels are also available.

Lee Jurras, in the development of the .357 AMP cartridge, dropped an antelope in New Mexico at something over 200 yards.

Though a handgun, this Auto Mag .357 develops nearly 2,000 feet per second which means that it practically shakes hands with the .30-30. This along with the 137-grain bullet is the only one proven practical for this cartridge so far. I find the .44 Auto Mag little different than a conventional .44 Magnum other than it is an autoloader. My preference of the two is definitely .357 AMP.

Double-action big-bore shooters can turn only to Smith & Wesson. Personally (and I shoot a Model 29 .44 Magnum a lot) I find them harder to handle than single actions basically because of the design. That hump on the backstrap does horrible things to my tender little hands. This can be tamed a good deal by installing custom stocks which cover that hump. Both my Model 29 S&W and my newest, extremely remodeled Super Blackhawk wear Herrett's Stocks of the Jordan Trooper design made to fit exactly my size seven-cadet hand.

These big guns are hard to handle in spite of what some of us might lead you to believe on occasion.

Single actions are limited to Ruger as far as I'm concerned. There are imports in these bigger calibers, but I suggest you look them over carefully before investing.

Clyde Fischer shows a good hunting position with his back against a tree for support, his forearms rest on the inside of his knees. A really solid position.

Ron White, biologist on the famous YO Ranch, takes advantage of a fallen tree for this shot with his S&W K38. Always use a rest of some sort unless there is absolutely none available.

This photo shows the use of Colonel Jack Cannon's "Dead Eye" pistol stock. A legal item since it does not attach to the gun. It is composed of a wristband with a socket in which the stock bar fits. The gun is then held in the hand normally.

Here the author demonstrates his sitting position when using guns of heavy recoil. In this case it's T/C's .30-30. Forearms across and on the inside of the knees. This is not one of his favorite positions.

Here Swiggett demonstrates how to use the side of a tree for a support. Don't let the gun touch anything hard. There is seldom a place where a rest of some sort isn't available. Then, and only then, shoot off-hand.

Here Swiggett shows the use of Colonel Jack Cannon's "Dead Eye" pistol stock. It is adjustable for either a far out hold or can be moved in closer to the eye so that even a rifle scope can be mounted on a handgun and safely fired. This is a legal handgun stock, because it does not attach to the handgun itself but plugs into a wrist device which serves to create a solid hold.

A shoulder holster is the only practical way to carry big hunting handguns. Here Swiggett's .357 Auto Mag is held ready for instant use in a rig by Bianchi.

I find the Blackhawk and still bigger Super Blackhawk much easier to shoot than my S&W. The guns roll back in the hand, making recoil much less apparent, which is the reason for smooth stocks on my heavily loaded single-action revolvers.

Though I've favored long barrels on handguns most of my life, I've recently become a full-fledged backslider. I sent a brand new Ruger Super Blackhawk with 7½-inch barrel, since that is all they turn out (.44 Magnum is the only caliber), to Trapper Alexiou, the fabulous Michigan gunsmith. He shortened the barrel to 4⅝ inches, inset a gold face into the ramp front sight, smoothed the inner workings, and then delivered it to Larry Kelly's Mag-Na-Port firm some eight or ten miles down the road for installation (I guess that's the word) of a pair of Mag-Na-Ports.

I haven't had it back long enough to be sure, but from all indications it is destined to become my number one hunting handgun.

Ruger has another offering of interest to many single-action big-bore shooters. This is the Blackhawk .45 Colt. It comes with an extra cylinder chambering the .45 ACP cartridge, but the longer Colt version is of special interest.

With this gun it is possible to handload 225-grain jacketed soft-point bullets to almost 1,400 feet per second, which means it is hard on the heels of the .44 Magnum. Don't for Heaven's sake, try this in any Colt single action or any of the imports. They will not stand this extra punishment.

I have one with a 7½-inch barrel topped with the fine little Hutson Handgunner 1X scope. It has taken a good deal of game and will take a lot more before I retire it.

Ruger won't admit to these heavy loads for obvious reasons, and neither will Thompson/Center but their great Contender single-shot pistol will also take these same heavy loads.

Again — DO NOT TRY THESE IN COLT OR IMPORTED .45's!

The Thompson/Center Contender is designed as a hunting arm and chambered for almost any cartridge you might think of. Many of T/C's chamberings are rifle cartridges and in reality these guns are "hand rifles." Also available from T/C are wildcat cartridges. Two of the favorites at the moment are .30 Herrett and .357 Herrett.

The T/C's stock in trade, of course, is the interchangeable barrel feature.

I own two frames and a drawer full of barrels, about half of which are scoped, but I limit my use to only a few for no particular reason other than they seem to fill the need.

The author with one of the many cottontails he has taken with his Hutson-Handgunner-sighted Charter Arms .22 rimfire revolver. It does an equally good job on squirrels and quail. A true hunting handgun.

My 5mm Remington and .22 Hornet barrels serve well as varmint getters. When I don't feel like a loading session, the 5mm is brought into play. It is deadly on jackrabbits out to 125 yards. My .30-30 barrel is used for all serious hunting where the T/C is concerned other than for birds. For these the .44 barrel, with its choke device for their fine "Hot Shot" shotshells, comes into use.

On many trips I take a small foam-lined case, one frame and three of these barrels. That way I'm ready for varmint and small game, big game or birds with only a little more weight than my big revolvers.

Barrels can be changed almost instantly which makes it truly the only really all-around handgun on the market.

Colt, High Standard, Llama and Dan Wesson plus the aforementioned Ruger and Smith & Wesson all serve well in the revolver field. Thompson/Center is the only single shot offered.

Autoloaders are plentiful: Colt, S&W, Star, Llama, and Browning to name the most popular. I have a scope mounted on the slide of a 9mm Star that has done a lot

of fine shooting. I've also done a lot of shooting with a pair of Llamas. One in .38 Super and the other the venerable .45 ACP. Each has taken its share of game. My favorite 9mm is a SIG P210-5 with the extra-length target barrel. This is the fine Swiss-made pistol.

In any of these handguns, tailor the ammunition to the gun by trying several brands of factory cartridges. One will shoot better than the others, as a rule.

There is one more range of hunting handguns to consider. Maybe you noticed the absence of .22 rimfire in these comments. That was for a reason.

Perhaps not considered as hunting handguns in the eyes of some, but more .22 rimfire ammo is expended than all other calibers combined. A lot of it is used in handguns, and much of it for hunting small game.

Whether the choice is a slick little autoloader or an inexpensive revolver, .22 Rimfire handguns have placed a lot of small game in the pot.

On top of this they serve superbly as training guns for beginning shooters. They also help pass away many hours as plinking guns because the expense is little.

In a pinch they serve as defense guns. Though not so potent as to be instant man-stoppers, they do a better

Allan Crawford, right, took this trophy wild goat with his Ruger Super Blackhawk .44 Magnum shooting Super Vel ammunition. His guide for this Telico Junction Hunting Preserve hunt in Tennessee was J. D. Jones, a three-time winner of the Outstanding American Handgunner Award.

Hal can hardly contain a smile here as he shows off a young gobbler dropped with a long shot from his Hutson-Handgunner-scoped Ruger Hawkeye .256 Winchester Magnum. This took place on one of his many hunts on the fabulous YO Ranch in Mountain Home, Texas. Swiggett's Hawkeye is retired now because of its rarity but still has to work on occasion for old time's sake.

A typical YO Ranch whitetail buck is this one taken by Swiggett shooting a Hutson-Handgunner-scoped .44 Magnum single action. The YO is located near Mountain Home, Texas, and is rated as the largest exotic game-hunting ranch in the world. Regrettably its great herds of whitetail and flocks of turkey often fail to get mentioned.

Swiggett and hog. That's Hal in back. He took this 200 pounder on the Telico Junction Hunting Preserve in Tennessee. His handgun is Thompson/Center's Contender .30-30 topped with Leupold's M8 2X scope. A favorite of Hal's for big-game hunting.

job than the .25's and .32's so often kept for that purpose. They would also do well as a survival gun because of the lightness of a plentiful supply of ammo. They can drop a cow, sheep or goat should serious survival be necessary. A carefully placed .22 rimfire bullet does a magnificent job in an emergency.

One of my prized possessions is a little Charter Arms Pocket Target, .22 which was the forerunner of their current Pathfinder. This little gun is topped with a Hutson Handgunner 1X scope and is absolutely deadly as a cottontail, squirrel and quail gun.

I own a lot of handguns covering most calibers and shoot them regularly. Like anybody else I would hate to have to limit my shooting to a single gun. But if that decision had to be made, I'd lean heavily towards a good .22 rimfire. On second thought I wouldn't lean— I'd grab it and never look back.

To me a good .22 Rimfire revolver is the nearest thing to the perfect "all-around" handgun. That means it is also a hunting handgun as far as I'm concerned— one of the best.

Charles Newton, Designer

by Robert H. Reagan

CHARLES NEWTON DESIGNED some of the finest cartridges in the world, and one of the best rifles ever built in the United States. Yet today his name is almost unknown — Newton was never able to produce very many of his rifles. His companies were plagued with bankruptcies. Parts of his rifle design may not have been amenable to the mass-production techniques of the 1920's. Either that, or Newton may not have been much of a production designer and factory manager. Still, he designed cartridges between 1900 and 1920 which have not been improved in their class since that time.

Roughly half of the rifles eventually sold as Newtons were assembled from rejected parts or were rejected rifles. Newton, himself, and his companies, while they were under his control, apparently sold only outstanding rifles, but dangerous rifles were sold by others using the Newton name and these gave all Newtons a bad reputation. Newton was probably ahead of his time both in cartridge and rifle design. The .25-06 he designed in 1912 is more modern than the one introduced in recent years. The Newton .25-06 has a sharper shoulder and less body taper. Some of his rifle designs, like interrupted screw bolt locking, have come on the market in recent years.

Charles Newton probably had a lot to do with one of the most famous cartridges of all time, the .30-06. Newton was employed at Springfield Arsenal during the redesign of the .30-03 cartridge into the .30-06. Knowledgeable men who had contact with Newton, such as A. O. Niedner, have said that Newton had quite a bit to do with the .30-06. Certainly, the .30-06 had a sharp shoulder and a short neck by the standards of the time. These design features were typical of most Newton designs.

The .22 Savage High Power is about the only Newton-designed cartridge now generally known that is really outdated. According to some authorities Newton designed the .22 High Power about 1905 and in the late 1890's according to others. One wonders if the High Power was a ballistic design at all. Certainly, the shell needed a fairly long neck, but the shallow shoulder angle and the sharply tapering case body may have been the easiest way to reduce case capacity of the basic brass and make the shell feed in the Savage 99. These features are unlike most of the other Newton designs.

About 1912 Newton designed a short little .25 Caliber shell with a short neck specifically for the 99 Savage —

the 250/3000. The 250/3000, or 250 Savage, was and is a heck of a good cartridge. Call for years, "the rifleman's cartridge," this little dude is one of those combinations that is just right. Newton designed his little 250 for a 100-grain bullet at about 2800 FPS muzzle velocity. Savage introduced the shell with an 87-grain bullet with its attendant 3000 FPS. In 1915, when the shell was announced, 3000 FPS at the muzzle was truly astonishing. Most riflemen of the day considered the 2200 FPS of the .30-30 or the .30-40 Krag to be high velocity.

Newton felt that Savage had made a mistake with the 87-grain loading, and a rifling twist that did not handle pointed 100-grain bullets well, but Savage liked their version of the shell. Unfortunately, Charles Newton died just before Peters introduced a 100-grain loading about 1933.

In some ways, both Savage and Newton were right. The 87-grain bullet likes the slow 1-in-14 rifling twist that Savage used with it. Small-to-medium-size deer shot in the chest with the 87 in the slow twist tend to fold up on the spot. With the older bullets, controlled expansion was rather difficult, but this combination worked very well. The 250/3000 leverguns often were deadly accurate. At one time I had a Savage 99 saddle carbine 250 that shot minute-of-angle, five-shot groups with selected reloads and one factory load clear out to the limit of testing (175 yards). Accuracy of this order from a lever action surpised me at the time and I re-checked it several times. This particular rifle had the 1-in-14 rifling twist. It never did well with 100-grain bullets of any description, but there weren't any big deer in that part of the world. The rifle was just right all over again for catch-as-catch-can coyote busting.

On the other side of the argument, a 250/3000 reloaded properly with 100-grain Sierras or Noslers equals at 300 yards the energy that the .30-30 carbine actually delivers at 100. The .30-30 has much more energy at the muzzle, but it loses that energy by the time it reaches the distances where the game is as a result of old-fashion bullet design. Sight a short-twist 250/3000 in for 275 yards after developing a good hot load for the 100-grain Sierra. The bullet will be about five inches high at 125 yards and about four inches low at 300. This will cover 99 per cent of all the deer hunting in North America; this is what Newton was thinking about.

Typically, the 250/3000 delivers its energy with pinpoint accuracy. Both in Michigan, where I was raised, and in the Arkansas hills, where I have guided, "the 250/3000 man" tended to be a special breed. They were and are riflemen. Most deer hunters let fly a salvo at the biggest part of their sighted departing whitetail

CHAS. NEWTON, President

deer and hope for the best. Most 250/3000 men pinpoint one shot and bring in their deer — often a deer with a broken neck.

In the gun room right now, there is a Ruger M77, 250/3000. This rifle has the 1-in-10 rifling twist that one associates with pointy 100-grain bullets or heavier bullets for that matter. One-inch groups and better came the first day on the range with three brands of 100-grain factory loads, two old standard 250/3000 reloads, and one newly figured 100-grain Sierra load at about 3000 FPS. In a good bolt action, there is little need to stick to the 44,000-pound loads that are normally recommended for the 250. Just remember as you get up above the manuals that the 1-in-10 twist develops more pressure than the 1-in-14 with a given load, and at the maximums pressures build quite quickly. Loading 250/3000 often is reminiscent of loading for the .222 Remington — both shells work well with approximately a case full of the right powders, and both tend to be deadly accurate.

Newton never pushed his .25 Special, which was a .25-06, although one of the several .25-06 Niedners was exactly the same shell. There were probably several reasons for this, but one of the main reasons was the .256 Newton. The .256 Newton was so good that one

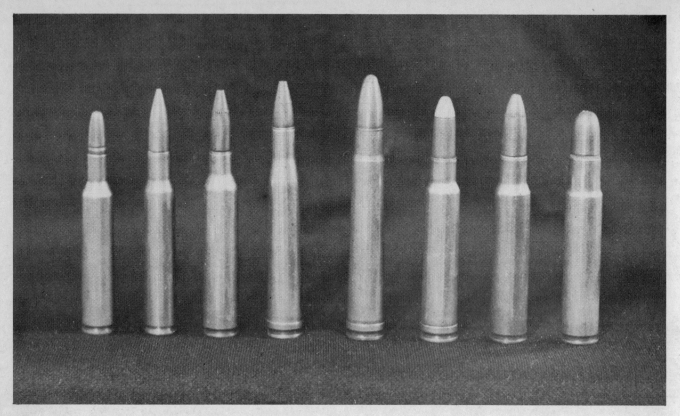

Left to right: 1. .25 Newton Special as made at Niedner Rifle Corp. in the late 1930's; This same reamer with a 6.5mm neck was the .256 Newton; 2. GI .30-06 for comparison; 3. .30 Newton; 4. .300 H&H—notice how much longer it is for the same case capacity; 5. .375 H&H; 6. .338 Winchester—note how it seems to fit in among the Newtons; 7. .35 Newton; 8. .40 Newton.

would think that there was never any need for any of the .257 Roberts, the .270 Winchester, or a sporting need for .30-06 on game up through elk.

This is a strong statement, but it is fairly easy to support. The .256 Newton shoots as flat as a .270 and delivers more energy than the .30-06. Although it is a 6.5mm and not a .25 caliber, it can be loaded down to .257 Roberts ballistics very successfully. Old .256 Newton ballistics (and remember the cartridge was introduced in 1914) equaled the later .270 in trajectory and beat the old .30-06 energies directly. Modern loadings for the .256 maintain this claim. With so many good 6.5mm bullets on the market now and really good slow powders around, my next custom rifle will probably be a .256 Newton. With a stock similar to the Ruger 77, a 24- or 25-inch slightly chunky barrel, and a balance like the old, 8½-pound Sedgley Spring-fields, this will be as close to an all-around rifle for North America as I can imagine.

The .30 Newton, which was introduced in a 1915 catalog, anticipated most of the .30 caliber magnum development since. This was a big-diameter case, not belted, and it had a case capacity very close to the .300 Holland & Holland and .300 Winchester Magnum.

Given the same components, the same pressures, and the same barrel lengths, the three cartridges will deliver the same ballistics. Old loading books and old factory-shell ballistics charts show the .30 Newton delivering better than 3200 FPS with 150-grain bullets, 3000 FPS with 172-grain bullets, and better than 2600 with the old 225-grain Western Tool and Copper Works bullet. Current .300 Winchester Magnum and .308 Norma Magnum do not beat these numbers by much. Pressures in the old Newton shells must have been very high. Still, the Newton rifle was designed for high pressures. When this rifle was properly made, it could and did hold all that pressure. For one thing, the Newton bolt has almost three times as much locking-lug bearing surface as a normal two-lug bolt, then or now.

The .35 Newton was a similar story on a .358 bore. It did about what the Norma .358 Magnum does now — better than 3000 FPS with 220-grain bullets and about 2750 with 250's. The Newton action was remarkably compact and, although very strong, relatively light. The rifles tended to weigh about 7½ pounds and the stocks were fairly straight. They *kicked*! One gun writer claimed that the .35 Newton kicked him three times every time he squeezed the trigger — once when

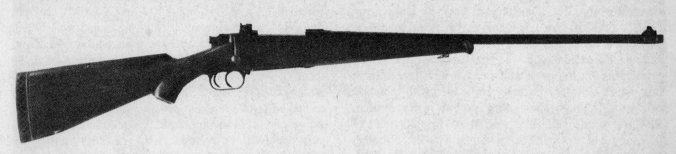

.35 Newton of the early type — light and potent.

the rifle recoiled and twice when he stood up and kicked himself for being damn fool enough to squeeze the trigger.

Short magnums with case capacities similar to the Newtons became available as wildcast in the late 1930's, roughly 20 years after Newton introduced his cartridges. Short magnums as factory loads did not become available until well after the end of World War II. The factory cartridges that competed directly with the big Newtons during the 1920's, 1930's, and 1940's were the .300 and .375 Holland & Holland. The .30 Newton and .300 H&H have very similar case capacities and were factory loaded to similar ballistics during the late 1930's, but the .300 H&H is not as good a cartridge as the .30 Newton. The .300 H&H loads were sometimes as much as 3.6 inches in overall length. This required a magnum-length action which the Newton didn't. With lots of taper in the body and a shallow-shoulder angle in the .300, reloaders found that brass stretched. Head separations as early as the third firing were relatively common unless the .300 was loaded down to roughly modern .30-06 ballistics.

The .375 H&H has more case capacity (up to 7½ per cent more) than the .35 Newton. With less taper than the .300, the .375 has always been a good reloader's cartridge. The .375 has a little more energy than the .35 Newton and trajectories are about the same. The Newton has the advantage of a shorter action, but making the Newton up in a light rifle resulted in more recoil than most people want to take. The .338 Winchester, made up on rifles somewhat heavier than the Newtons, has the reputation of being a "vicious kicker." Yet the Newtons were worse kickers. Competent riflemen will hit well with any of these big shells, but they are too much for the once-a-year hunter.

There was a .40 Newton. One source says four of them were made. It must have been some gun. Some gun writers doubt the existence of the .40 Newton even though it is known to have been advertised. However,

I have one cartridge of .40 caliber clearly headstamped "Western .35 Newt." Dimensionally, the .40 Newton head is the same as a .35. .30, .35, and .40 Newtons all had the same head; .40 Newtons were probably formed by opening up the necks of .35's. My father bought this shell along with some other collectors' cartridges from Tom Shellhammer at Niedner Rifle Corp. in the late 1930's.

At one time or another Charles Newton advertised, but — except for a sample or two — probably didn't make a .276 Newton and a .33 Newton. Apparently, demand for the .276 and the .33 was too little to justify the trouble in what had to have been seriously troubled companies.

My father has a .35 Newton of the early type. It has the interrupted screw bolt of the Newton-made Buffalo Newtons, but without the rather heavily cranked bolt handle associated with that type. Buffalo Newtons tend to have a reversed set-trigger arrangement. The rear trigger is set by pushing forward on a reversed trigger in the front of the trigger guard. Dad's Newton has a normal Mauser double-set trigger arrangement. His rifle is very nicely finished, although the stock needed refinishing when he bought it in the mid-1930's. Throughout fit is precise and the rifle is very accurate. Most .35 Newtons — in fact most Newton-made and Newton-sold Newtons — have a reputation for excellent accuracy. Benching one of these rifles is very difficult and I've never done it. This particular rifle was tested extensively at the old Niedner Rifle Corporation in Dowagiac, Michigan. They pronounced it very accurate, more accurate than most M70 Winchesters of the late 1930's, and so far, I have let it go at that. This rifle has figured prominently in the collecting of an outstanding number of Montana Elk and several other fine animals.

Reloaders who find themselves in possession of a Newton should proceed very cautiously. Chamber and barrel dimensions should be checked carefully by a top-notch gunsmith, who should also make sure that the locking lugs bear well on their mating surfaces. Cartridges for .256 Newton are easy to make from .30-06. Old .30 and .35 Newton cartridge cases are collectors' items and expensive. They may have been shot or stored too long with mercuric primers. These primers attack the brass and weaken it. I have a large number of old .45-70's that were loaded with mercuric primers. Although they were probably never fired, they are unsafe with any load. Brass for .30 and .35 Newtons can be made from belted H&H's, although sometimes this requires a little lathe work on the belts. In many cases, making big Newton brass is a simple as trimming, sizing, and fireforming according to the reference books. Cartridge cases made this way will have less case capacity than normal shells. Maximum loads will have to be reduced correspondingly. Fortunately, we have not had to do this. Dad bought a good supply of .30 and .35 Newton brass in around 1940, and we have taken good care of it. The brass was good Western brass in the first place, and it is still in use.

Newton used both arms history and thoughtful design to solve the rifle problems of his day. He developed a protected-point expanding bullet so that bullets could work well on game without battering themselves out of shape in the magazine of a hard-kicking rifle. One bullet had insulation between the jacket and the core so that cores would not melt. This is one of the things that we are going to need if we try to push big bullets much faster. Newton also developed some of the old-English rifling types into modern designs, or he re-invented them. There seems to be some question about whether he knew of or knew much about the old designs. The Newton rounded-corner segmental rifling, sometimes called Newton-Pope rifling, used ideas from old Lancaster and Metford rifling systems as well as some of Henry Pope's ideas. Newton finally developed what was supposed to be a very fine system of rifling using lands of parabolic section. I had at one time a well-made .256 Newton with this rifling. The rifle was very accurate and seemed to be accepting abnormally heavy loads without pressure signs. This rifling type had no sharp corners in it to catch fouling or wear out quickly. One would think that button rifling and parabolic lands would go together rather well. Both very high-velocity varmint rifles and very fast-firing machine cannons would seem to need a development similar to this. There was nothing new during Newton's time about interrupted screw bolting. The Canadian Ross Rifle had this feature before Newton produced his rifles and so did the breeches of many naval guns.

Modern rifle design seems to be trending towards more locking-lug bearing area. Newton did this successfully in a very compact action before World War I. Modern cartridges tend to have very little taper in the body of the shell, fairly sharp shoulders, and short necks. This describes Newton cartridges at about the time of World War I. One wonders why they didn't succeed. If those same designs are modern now, one wonders why weren't they appreciated then except by only the few purists who used them.

Table 1

Ballistics .256 Newton, .270 Winchester, .30-06 Old and New

| Cartridge and Bullet | Muzzle | | 300-Yard | | Mid-Range |
	Velocity	Energy	Velocity	Energy	Trajectory 300 Yard
.256 Newton* 123 Grain	3,100	2,560	2,518	1,690	4.99"
.256 Newton* 140 Grain	3,000	2,797	2,485	1,919	5.22
.30-06 (Old) 150 Grain	2,700	2,430	2,080	1,441	6.94
.30-06 (New) 150 Grain	2,970	2,930	2,240	1,670	6.0
.270 Winchester 130 Grain	3,140	2,850	2,450	1,700	5.3

*These must have been very high-pressure loads.
300-yard figures assume Sierra Bullets using the Sierra 120 grain for the first load.

Table 2
Old Loading Manual Loads for .256 Newton

Bullet Weight		Powder		Velocity in 24-inch barrel	Comments
100	DuPont	IMR 17½	45 Grains	3,100	Replaced by IMR 3031.
129		15½	50.4	3,000	Replaced by IMR 4064.
140		15½	49.5	2,875	We would tend to use slower powders today. See Schedules of Modern Starter Loads.

Table 3
Modern starter loads for .256 Newton; .270 and .30-06 figured on the same basis

Cartridge and Bullet Weight	Powder		Velocity in 24-inch barrel	Comments
.256 Newton				
120 Sierra	4831	56 Grains	3,050	
129 Hornady	4831	55	2,970	
140 Sierra	H 570			
	H 870	58.5	2,950	
.270 Winchester				These loads line up well with experience
130	4350	52	2,920	and what is in the manuals. Both these
	4831	54.5	3,000	and the Newton starter loads are relatively
.30-06				conservative in normal rifles.
150	4320	52	2,830	

Table 4
Old Newton Loads .30 and .35

.30 Newton				Comments
150	15½	71.7	3,150	**Caution:** Have your rifle checked carefully
172	15½	68.2	2,900	before firing it at all. Work up loads from below.
	HighVel 2	63.5	3,070	54,500 PSI according to Hercules.
180	15½	69.5	3,000	
	HighVel 2	63.0	3,035	55,000 PSI according to Hercules.
220	15½	62.5	2,510	
.35 Newton				
200	3031	78.0	3,030	These must have been very high-pressure loads.
250	3031	72.0	2,765	They look as if they might be considered about
275	3031	70.0	2,615	right today if they used 4350 instead of 3031.

Table 5
Modern starter loads for .30 and .35 Newton

	Gun Powder		Muzzle Velocity	Comments
.30 Newton				
150	4350	69	3,180	Notice the similiarity with .308 Norma
165	4350	69	3,130	Magnum starter loads.
200	4831	69	2,790	
.35 Newton				
200	4320	69	2,870	
250	4350	72.5	2,630	

What's New in Wheels for the Hunter

by Roger Barlow

SINCE MY COMPREHENSIVE report on full-time four-wheel-drive vehicles in last year's SHOOTER'S BIBLE, Dodge has brought out its own Blazer-like Ramcharger, and I drove one to South Dakota last fall for some sharptail grouse and pheasant hunting. Its full-time four-wheel-drive system and automatic transmission are above criticism. The Ramcharger may ride a bit better than the Blazer, but, unfortunately, it seems a little more directionally vague on the highway. However, where the going is rougher the steering is fine and the turning circle is surprisingly tight. It is no more economical than others of its type, averaging 8 to 11 mpg. It's a pity that these lovable brutes came on the market when the oil shortage hit. The Ramcharger feels indestructible, as do most Dodge commercial products, and it should prove to be a real workhorse.

The same basic vehicle is now offered by Plymouth under the very appropriate name of Trail Duster. Last year I complained because you could not set a cup of coffee on the curved cover of the box between the front seats of the Blazer. Well, Dodge and Plymouth have pleased me with two useful recesses made in that box for holding cups, cans or bottles. Small detail, perhaps, but it shows the more practical approach to styling matters at Dodge. Although the car I used still had its huge wheel and tire located inside, taking up room that the user needs, an optional outside mounting is now available, and no one should have one of these vehicles without it.

As with the great new British Range Rover, which we may never see on the US market, there is now an equally new and interesting four-wheel-drive job by Fiat we will probably never get to drive. The new Campagnola is remarkable in that it is fitted with soft independent suspension for all four wheels, providing a ride which is reported by those who have driven it over bumps, ruts and rocks to be incredibly comfortable and stable. Being lighter and fitted with a two-litre engine, this advanced four-wheel-drive vehicle should deliver between 18 and 22 mpg. Just as Fiat has been building a fully independently sprung vehicle of this type for the military for some years, this updated Campagnola with its even more modern suspension is also based upon solid experience.

Most of this report will deal with that ever-popular all-purpose hunter's vehicle — the station wagon.

I'm really not an admirer of the average family wagon, despite its evident popularity. First of all, the usable inside space of the really big, luxurious ones isn't nearly as large as one might expect from the outside dimensions. Both the sides and the rear usually slant inward to such a degree that a great deal of useable space is lost. Because most large wagons have doors and sides anywhere from six to twelve inches thick, a lot more useful space is foolishly wasted. But the worst failing of all from an outdoorsman's point of view is that when we actually make full use of the available space, the well-loaded family wagon settles

The new Dodge Ramcharger provided comfortable and practical transport for two hunters and two dogs plus all the needed gear for a trip to South Dakota for pheasants and sharptails.

down at the rear with its tailpipe and bumper virtually dragging the ground and the headlight beam up in the trees. Go through a dip in the driveway and the bumper scrapes with an ominous shudder for a couple of feet; and once you are on the highway you'll have even more problems.

The top of the compartment between the bucket seats of the Ramcharger and the Trail Duster is cleverly designed to hold a variety of objects. The actual cover can even double as a clipboard to hold maps or toll cards.

Of course, we can easily cure this problem by fitting a set of load-carrying rear shock absorbers such as the Gabriel Hi-Jackers or Delco's Jac Pac; these take care of the overloaded springs simply by the expedient of adding air to the shock absorbers. The Delco kit even comes with its own little engine-driven air compressor, and air can be fed into or released from the shocks by a control and gauge fitted to the dash. With the Gabriel units you can use the air hose at a gas station. Various types of small air bags are also available for taking some of the load off too-soft rear springs.

This year, for the first time this sort of simple leveling system is an optional factory-installed item on some Chrysler, Dodge and Plymouth wagons (as well as on some sedans). Actually this is a somewhat more sophisticated approach, for it is automatically self-leveling as the load varies. Unfortunately the public hasn't been told about this useful feature, perhaps because Chrysler's sales people either don't understand the value of this option, or they resent having to sell an engineering feature rather than the usual highly profitable sucker-oriented "trim packages" costing more and providing nothing useful.

Which reminds me to damn Nader once again, for there is yet another vehicle of genuine interest to hunters which carries this self-leveling feature to its logical ultimate application, but which will probably never be available here in the US because of our continually changing anti-pollution and safety requirements. I

One of the advantages of front-drive station wagons is that they have a low cargo floor without impairing ground clearance. This is the Citroen GS.

Straight sides and square end of the Volvo wagon give it immense carrying capacity for its size. It will negotiate ruts and gullies no full-size family wagon can manage, and take a hunter to a lot of off-the-road places.

Who hasn't been nearly scalped by walking into the raised tailgate of a number of economy wagons? The VW Dasher is welcome, for its rear door is high. This wagon, too, has a surprisingly large cargo area, despite its size and the considerable slant of its rear window. With its 26-30 mpg capability and superior handling characteristics both on and off the highway, its is a great economy wagon.

drove this truly remarkable smallish front-wheel-drive station wagon across England and back last year and can testify to its relatively immense load-carrying capacity and the effectiveness of its self-leveling front and rear suspension. This Citroen GS (newer and more advanced than the old Safari wagons once sold here) is one of the best-handling, safest and most comfortable cars I've ever driven. It is a wagon I would buy immediately if it were available, despite the fact that its 1220 cc engine is a bit small. It would run happily at 80 with another 13 mph still available and deliver over 25 miles per gallon at 70.

With gasoline prices being what they are today (and anticipating what they might be in the future), I've checked out for hunter's use a number of economy wagons for this report: like many others, I've had my fill of 10-to-14-mpg guzzlers!

Along with that fabulous but unavailable Citroen GS, I drove another outstanding front-drive wagon — the VW Dasher, which is on the US market. Although it does not boast self-leveling suspension, its rear springs are quite capable of dealing with full loads without set-

tling down to such an extent that its tailpipe is in danger of dragging. For anyone used to the ploughing and wallowing of our big wagons, driving the smaller, more agile and better-handling wagons like the Vega, Toyota, Datsun, Fiat, Hornet, Volvo, Renault, Pinto and especially the Dasher can be a revelation. It is not only the economy of up to more than twice the gas mileage which makes these wagons so great, but also the sheer driving pleasure and convenience they can provide. Not all these small wagons have the near-incredible road holding and cornering ability of the front-drive Dasher or the Citroen GS, which makes either of these wagons a very satisfactory substitute for a genuine sports car when not carrying a full load. Indeed, I took the empty Dasher over the Blue Ridge mountains faster and with less drama than any other sedan or wagon I've ever driven.

Of course, any station wagon used by a hunter, fisherman or camper has serious work to do in the field as well as being a pleasure to drive on the highway, so we must consider that aspect of the smaller economy wagons. I must admit to being prejudiced in a matter which

One of the very latest additions to the field of economy wagons is the new Audi Fox Wagon which is, in effect, the same vehicle as the XVW Dasher except for fuel injection and a deluxe interior. The result is a smallish wagon of Mercedes quality at a reasonable price, delivering remarkable gas mileage and performance.

Beneath the lockable steel hatch in the floor of the Hornet Sport-about wagon is a large compartment where guns, cameras and fishing equipment can travel unseen and very hard for a thief to get at. The Volvo wagon has a similar compartment, but not lockable.

relates to this subject — having had enough of communal living in the armed forces to last me a lifetime, I find that one of the great attractions of hunting is that it is basically a solitary sport, best savored alone or with a single companion — human or canine. As a hunting vehicle even the smallest wagons are more than adequate. Pinto, Datsun 610, Mazda, Colt, etc. will carry all your needed gear including a modern tent inside and a small boat on the roof. Their shorter wheelbase renders them less likely to get "high centered" on bad roads and trails, and reduced overhang guarantees that bumpers will not be continuously scraping the high spots.

The slightly larger examples like the Dasher can carry more than any two hunters and a dog can possibly need, and with intelligent planning could serve the needs of three hunters very nicely.

One of the best of the larger economy wagons is the Volvo, with its reputation for ruggedness and its sensible yet elegant square lines. Being a sort of Scandinavian Mercedes, it is one of the more expensive wagons. The economy comes from getting 18 to 21 mpg and a long life. It is really a very superior wagon with its unique

The AMC Hornet wagon does not utilize its space as well as it might (steeply raked rear hatch and high floor) but its four doors and very large under-the-floor compartment go a long way to compensate.

combination of toughness and luxury (no phony wood-trim package available here). I drove the latest version with its new continuous-flow fuel injection and automatic transmission for some 3,000 miles, and although it hasn't the sports car character and dash of the Dasher, it, nevertheless, has a lot of character of its own. It can boast an incredibly tight-turning circle which allows excellent quick-power steering letting one steer without effort. The hunter's wife will appreciate this quality when she takes this wagon on shopping trips.

With the Volvo's rear seat folded down, it will sleep a couple of six-footers in comfort. This cargo area is covered with a good quality indoor-outdoor carpet, firmly fixed in place and which cleans up most satisfactorily after hard use. Further aspects of the Volvo wagon which I found admirable were its ability to exclude water and dust to a degree which puts many others to shame. Splashed water is also kept from the engine compartment, for I hit many flooded sections of roads with water standing several inches deep at very high speeds without ever shorting out the new "electronic" ignition. (What a misuse of the term. All our ignition systems have been electronic since about 1890 when Gottlieb Daimler gave up the use of an externally flame-heated platinum tube in favor of a coil and spark plug.)

Another high-quality European wagon in this size group is the 504 Peugeot wagon which has even more comfortable fully reclining bucketseats than the Volvo. I hope to use the Peugeot diesel-powered wagon for an extended trip this fall, and I will have a report on it next year. It is also available with the smooth and lively four-cylinder gas engine which makes the sedan 504 one of my favorites.

One American wagon in the Peugeot's class is the Hornet Sportabout, which has been a disappointment to me despite my preference for this size vehicle. I took a look at it when it first came out, saw the steeply slanted rear hatch and high floor in the cargo area and decided that American Motors had goofed. It appeared as if they'd been unable to make up their mind as to whether they wanted a station wagon or a four-door hatchback coupé. Last week I decided I had better have a closer look at the Sportabout before writing it off as not being a practical hunter's compact wagon. Sure, that

The typical large station wagon with its rounded, thick sides and slanted rear door wastes a lot of potential cargo space for purely "styling" considerations. The rear overhang is a hazard when such a wagon is well loaded.

Ford claims to have moved the engine of the new 1975 van wagon farther forward, but these photos show that what they have actually done is to move the windscreen doors and front seats back about 18 inches! This gives easier access to the front seats and a much roomier area there as well as making the engine more easily serviced from the large new hood. Total cargo area is maintained because the chassis has been lengthened to compensate for the new position of the seats. The longer hood provides improved frontal crash protection.

This cut-away drawing of the new Fiat-Citroen front-wheel-drive van shows the conveniently low floor level of the cargo area and the good head room of 5 ft. 11½ in. in a vehicle with an outside height of 7 ft. 8½ in. when loaded. This would be an ideal chassis upon which to build a lightweight mini-motor home capable of delivering twice the highway gas mileage of our present ones. Floor is only 20 inches from road surface.

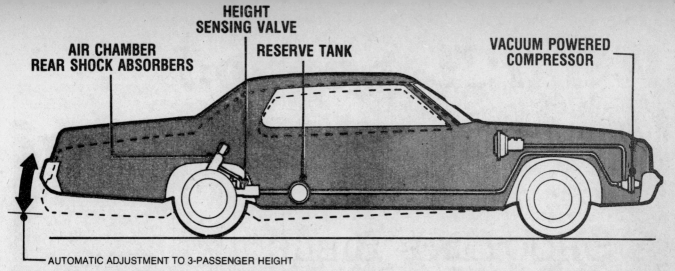

AIR CHAMBER REAR SHOCK ABSORBERS

HEIGHT SENSING VALVE

RESERVE TANK

VACUUM POWERED COMPRESSOR

AUTOMATIC ADJUSTMENT TO 3-PASSENGER HEIGHT

New automatic load-control option on some Chrysler, Dodge and Plymouth station wagons and sedans maintains normal bumper height and headlight aim when vehicle takes on weight up to full-rated load capacity. When a load lowers the rear height, a sensing valve opens to allow air from the reserve tank to enter air-chamber rear shock absorbers. As the load is reduced, the sensing valve vents air from the shocks. A built-in time delay ensures that road variations will not cause height adjustments.

steeply raked rear door reduces the amount of gear which can be stowed there, but the cargo area is long enough for sleeping when the rear seat is folded. Below the rather high floor is a really huge compartment hidden beneath the carpeting and covered by a lockable steel lid. It will hold and protect all the guns, ammo, and cameras a couple of hunters are likely to be carrying. With a six-cylinder engine, and the once-again-available overdrive, this Hornet wagon should prove as economical as many of the somewhat smaller imports, even though it doesn't steer and handle as well. This discovery on my part proves the old French proverb: "If you haven't tried it, don't knock it."

In my estimation, no wagon is a really useful station wagon if it has only two doors. The inconvenience of getting in and out of the rear seat doesn't bother me as much as trying to load a wagon properly from the rear hatch alone. Because the heaviest items should always go right behind the front seats to best distribute the load, it means an awkward lift; the heavy things are in the front and you are forced to reload from the back — perhaps ruining your own back. Having four doors makes it much easier to get at things in a hurry or to stow them for maximum accessibility.

When I actually need an immense amount of cargo space and simply can't manage with any of the economy wagons, I no longer even consider renting the very large station wagons or the oddly ugly Suburban wagons which ought to be right for this work. If I have to put up with 10 to 14 mpg, I want something more practical for my money and so I choose the van type of vehicle in station wagon format. These can carry an immense amount of cargo as well as numerous passengers. Of course, there is even one economy version of the van — the VW Micro-bus, which started the whole thing and gives bet-

ter than 20 mpg and more ground clearance than any of the rest.

This year Ford has done some interesting redesigning of their vans, moving the engine further forward for better accessibility and to provide more room in the cab area. A more convenient and comfortable swiveling front bucket seat is a welcome option. The chassis has also come in for a major change, probably to render it more suitable as a platform for mini-motor homes. Ford's new brochure shows one of the most handsome units ever. The van-type vehicles are far and away the most logical design for the ultimate station wagon. However, I'd like to see some new and slightly smaller, lighter vans on the market based upon a front-wheel-drive layout; then the floor level could be dropped almost a foot with the same ground clearance. This would result in even more interior space, more headroom, easier cargo loading and passenger entrance as well as vastly improved road holding.

I don't think Detroit will be bold enough to initiate something like this, even though GM has effectively demonstrated the virtues of this approach with their wonderful new motor home. However, just such an advanced front-drive van has already been jointly developed in Europe by Fiat and Citroen which went into production last year with a choice of a two-litre gasoline engine or a 2.2-litre Diesel. Depending upon engine type and load, fuel consumption should range between 20 and 25 mpg on the highway. Two basic versions are offered having payload capacity of 3300 or 4000 pounds. The platform chassis with cab should be ideal for a light "airstream" type of mini-motor home body of lightweight construction. However, I doubt that the manufacturers will consider the US market with its constantly changing Federal regulations.

What Happened to the Benders?

A SHOOTER'S BIBLE
Inquiry into History

by Robert Dana

Editor's Note: *In the preceding volume of the* SHOOTER'S BIBLE, *we published an article entitled, "Who Invented the Bowie Knife?" Reader response to it was so favorable that we have decided to make such an exploration of a historical mystery a regular feature.*

ABOUT A DOZEN miles west of Parsons, Kansas, the traveler along U.S. Highway 160 comes upon a series of low hills rising abruptly from the level plain. They are known locally as the Bender Mounds and take their name from the Bender family, who suddenly and mysteriously disappeared in 1873 from their nearby farm, alongside a wagon trail. This route was well traveled, for it led from Missouri through the Kansas towns of Fort Scott, Osage Mission, Parsons, Cherryvale, Independence, and on into the Indian Territory. The fate of the Benders has been the subject of speculation for over one hundred years. Today their story is a strange, confused jumble of legend and history.

In the 1870's, with the transfer of the remnants of the once numerous Osage Indians from their lands in the southeastern corner of Kansas to a new home in what is now the state of Oklahoma, the last barrier to settlement there by the white man was removed. Succeeding waves of settlement broke over this part of the frontier, and before long the bitter Civil War raids into "Bleeding Kansas" and the subsequent riotous days of railroad building were forgotten as the new settlers began to transform the prairie into prosperous farms.

To the good fortune of those who had filed first on the land, a steady stream of prospective farm and homestead buyers soon poured through the area with ready cash in their pockets. Only one thing disturbed the tranquillity of the scene. Directly to the south lay the lawless Indian Territory, a haven for criminals and wanted men who fled there for the safety it afforded from prosecution.

The attention of the residents of Labette County in southeastern Kansas was suddenly and dramatically focused on the Benders when, on Sunday, May 4, 1873, it was reported that cattle were wandering loose over the Bender farm and the Bender house was apparently deserted. Their neighbors were not long in recalling the circumstances of the Benders' arrival and particularly the many stories of mystery, murder, and the supernatural, which had become associated with the neighborhood since that time.

Although the Benders were unusually uncommunicative, the other settlers were able to piece together a few facts about them. The Bender family had come to Labette County to settle in 1870; it consisted of an old German couple, and two younger people who were reported to be a son and a daughter, but whose relationship to the older people was uncertain. The husband and wife were between fifty-five and sixty, stolid, peasant types, who spoke English only occasionally and then with a thick German accent. John Bender, the "son,"

"Ma" Bender

Kate Bender

was under thirty, a colorless fellow who spoke with only a slight accent and punctuated his statements with a disconcerting, aimless laugh. He seems to have been known locally as "John Gebhardt," as well. But it was the "daughter," Kate Bender, who stood out. She was about twenty, a statuesque, auburn-haired, shapely girl, with a remarkable beauty that caused many a traveler along the road to find an excuse for stopping at the Bender house. In addition to her physical attractiveness, Kate Bender's reputation as a medium made her a popular lecturer on spiritualism in nearby towns.

A notice printed for Kate Bender and distributed in neighboring towns curiously gave very exact directions for reaching the Bender house. It read:

PROF. MISS KATIE BENDER

Can heal all sorts of Diseases; can cure Blindness, Fits, Deafness and all such diseases, also Deaf and Dumbness.

Residence, 14 miles East of Independence, on the road from Independence to Osage Mission one and one-half miles South East of Morehead Station.

Like most of the other buildings on the frontier, where lumber was scarce, the Bender residence was small. It consisted of a roughly built frame house, only sixteen by twenty-four feet, whose interior was one large room, separated into two smaller rooms by means of an old canvas wagon cover hanging from the joists. The rear room was used as living quarters for the family, while the front room served as a combination store and restaurant where meals were served and lodging and supplies were provided for travelers along the road.

Outside the building a crudely lettered sign reading "Groceries" was hung, but the stock of provisions and tobacco on hand never amounted to more than a few dollars' worth. A hundred yards from the house stood a thatch-roofed stone barn, and adjoining this was a garden and orchard containing about fifty fruit trees. Although the male members of the family spent long hours plowing and harrowing there, their neighbors noticed that nothing ever seemed to come up.

In 1872 and the early part of 1873, a number of travelers disappeared along the route of the wagon trail that passed the Bender house. Among them was a physician, Dr. William H. York, who had been visiting his parents and brothers at Fort Scott. About March 9 or 10, 1873, Dr. York set out on horseback from Fort Scott for his home in Independence, and when he did

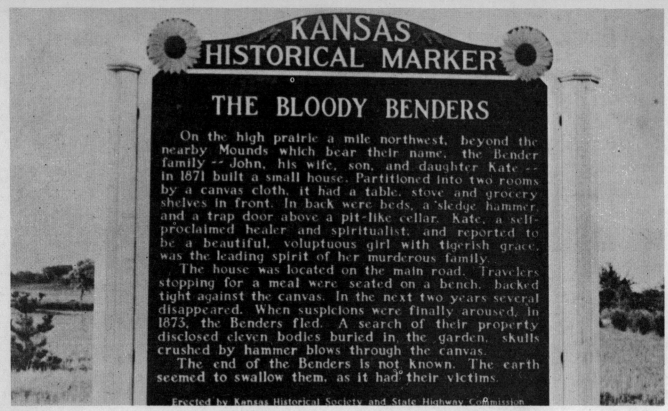

Highway historical marker near site of the Bender house.

not reach there, his brother, Colonel Alexander M. York, was notified at Fort Scott. Colonel York immediately started to search for the missing doctor, who was riding a large and conspicuous black horse, and followed his trail to the vicinity of the Bender farm. There it stopped cold.

The colonel, who took an active part in the rough-and-tumble Kansas politics of that time, was not one to give up easily and had already acquired a reputation along the frontier as a rather dangerous adversary. He immediately conferred with friends and law enforcement officers in Independence and in the nearby town of Cherryvale and discovered to his surprise that his brother was not the only person to have disappeared along the trail in the vicinity of the Bender farm. Piecing together the evidence from several sources, he learned that many travelers had reported suspicious happenings at the Bender farm; some even claimed to have been assaulted or threatened while stopping there.

Even though the Benders gave out very little information about themselves, everyone agreed that they were always intensely curious about their guests, particularly about such things as their destinations and financial status. Rumor also had it that weird sounds had been heard coming from the house. The Bender farm was indeed an unpopular place, and the air of gloom and

foreboding that seemed to hang over it caused many people to give the house a wide berth when traveling past it, especially at night.

Armed with this information, Colonel York, his younger brother, and a grim posse of what may have been as many as fifty of his friends, including several members of the local vigilance committee, set out for the Bender farm determined to solve the riddle of the vanished travelers. They questioned the sullen Benders in detail about the missing doctor and secured the rather nervous admission that he had eaten a meal at the house, watered his horse, purchased a few small items, and had ridden away.

Someone in the party must have recalled Kate Bender's talent as a spiritualist, for it was suggested that she place her services at their disposal to help in the search for the missing man. She begged off, however, saying that conditions were unfavorable for a successful seance and she would be troubled by the presence of so many men. She suggested significantly that Colonel York return the next day—alone—telling him, "I'll find your brother for you, even if he is in hell!" Despite this disquieting prophecy, the colonel promised he would return alone the next day and rode off with his friends.

Several days later a deserted wagon and team were found abandoned near the town of Thayer, about twelve

John Bender, Sr.

miles north of the Bender farm, and this fact was reported as a puzzling local mystery in the Thayer *Headlight* of April 9, 1873. On Sunday, May 4, when the startling discovery of the Benders' apparent disappearance was announced, their neighbors quickly gathered from the surrounding farms and congregated in the Bender yard in excited little groups to discuss the mystery. The first and most natural reaction was to include the Benders in the growing list of persons who had vanished in the vicinity. This latest disappearance was so disturbing that none of the farmers could get up enough courage to enter the Bender house.

Someone belatedly recalled the account in the Thayer newspaper of the previous month and suggested that the wagon and team described in it might have belonged to the Benders. They pointed out that the newspaper story had told of finding a wagon containing a sign with the word "Groceries" lettered on it and, strangely enough, such a sign was missing from the Bender house. A committee of two men was sent to Thayer, where they quickly identified the horses and wagon as the Benders'. In addition, they interviewed the Santa Fe ticket agent there, who distinctly recalled having sold tickets to a party of four Germans about three weeks earlier. Elated with their success, the committee rushed back to the Bender place with the information they had gathered.

The agitated people assembled there were now ready

to believe the worst about the Benders, and this confirmation of their flight was taken as evidence of their complicity in the other disappearances. Remembering his recent visit, they sent for Colonel York at Fort Scott. The colonel was unable to make the trip at that time, but his younger brother returned to the Bender farm on Tuesday, May 6, two days after the Benders' disappearance had been first noticed and almost a month after the Yorks' original visit in search of their missing brother.

Bolstered by the reassuring presence of one of the Yorks, a search party now entered the house and began a thorough examination of it. They found every evidence of what must have been a hurried flight, for clothing and utensils were scattered wildly about, and the furniture was overturned and broken. A bench and a table had stood against the canvas curtain separating the two rooms, and it was at this table that the meals had been served. In the floor of the combination store and dining room was a cleverly concealed trap door which opened on a damp and foul-smelling cellar. The stench coming from it was so great that an examination of the cellar had to be deferred until the house could be moved on rollers. When this was done, a few hardy volunteers entered the pit. Here they found the floor covered with stains of what might have been human blood. From the cellar a narrow passage led under the house and opened out into the garden and orchard behind it.

When the searchers turned their attention to the garden and orchard, the reason for the Benders' constant and careful cultivation of that spot became apparent, because there were several significant man-sized depressions visible in the now unbroken earth. The doctor's younger brother, probing the first of them with a wagon rod, found that it seemed to contain something. Spades and shovels were obtained quickly, and the men dug eagerly into the first depression. At the depth of a few feet a body was uncovered lying face down in the shallow grave. They lifted it out and his friends recognized the features of Doctor York, horribly distorted in death.

Word of the discovery of Doctor York's body spread immediately, and neighboring towns were alerted as fast as the news could be carried. The next morning digging was resumed with Colonel York on the scene, and the rest of the depressions were opened, as was the old well in the garden. When this work was completed, there was a long row of human bodies laid out behind the house. Whether eight, nine, eleven, or more bodies were discovered is difficult to determine, because accounts of the numbers and names of the victims are at variance. All but one of them were men; the last was a small child with long golden hair, the daughter of one of the murdered men. The skull of each of them had been crushed by blows from a blunt instrument, except that of the little girl, who had simply been buried alive. In the house was a heavy sledge hammer which exactly fitted the marks on the skull of the victims. The throats of most of them had been cut as well. The brutality of the crimes caused talk of lynching the Benders if they were caught.

Many travelers whose suspicions had been aroused by the strange and sometimes hostile actions of the Benders, and who had fled from the house to safety, now came forward with stories of their brushes with death.

Among the near victims was Father Paul M. Ponziglione, pioneer missionary to the Osage Indians at Osage Mission (now St. Paul), Kansas. Because of the large area covered by his missionary activities, Father Ponziglione spent much time in traveling through the frontier settlements and on several occasions stopped at the Bender place for a meal. On his last visit there in the spring of 1873, just as he was about to ask for a night's lodging, he decided to seek a more hospitable cabin in response to a premonition of danger. This decision, which may have saved his life, was helped by the sudden appearance of two large and vicious-looking dogs from the Bender house.

These accounts and the grisly discoveries enabled the investigators to piece together a picture of the Benders' method of operation. The unsuspecting traveler and prospective victim who was unlucky enough to stop at the house for a meal would be seated at the table in the front room with his back to the canvas curtain separating the two rooms. The Benders were either too much in a hurry or too unskilled to wait for information about a guest to come out in casual conversation. Consequently, they usually resorted to direct questioning in order to determine whether he should become the next victim, even though this practice scared more than one guest away from the house.

At a signal from Kate Bender, who always served the meals and engaged the diner in conversation while he was eating, one of the male members of the family would gently push the canvas curtain forward with his foot, outlining the body of the guest against it. Then the heavy sledge hammer would flash through the air, and the now unconscious diner would be dragged through the trap door into the cellar to be finished off later without fear of discovery.

The motive for the murders became clear when investigation revealed that most of the victims had been looking for farms in the vicinity and had been carrying large sums of money with which to make their purchases. Only strangers who might not soon be missed or traced were marked for death; two of them were never identified.

By tracing the movements of the Benders until the time when they had been last seen by their neighbors, and from the condition of the untended livestock on the farm, the investigators concluded that the Benders had fled about three weeks before their disappearance had been discovered.

A meeting in the local schoolhouse at which John Bender was present is sometimes advanced as the reason for the precipitous flight of the Benders. The purpose of this meeting is not clear; it may have been held to discuss the herd law or even to talk over the many strange disappearances. Some sources claim that the occasion was a local election. Whatever the original purpose of the meeting, the main topic of discussion seems to have been the growing number of mysterious disappearances.

Substantial rewards were offered for their capture and several posses were organized to conduct a systematic search of the surrounding country. Before long, bits of information began to trickle into Sheriff G. W. Franklin's office in Oswego, Kansas, the county seat and headquarters for the search. The Benders were reported to have purchased tickets at Thayer, Kansas, on the Atchison, Topeka & Santa Fe Railway to Humboldt, Kansas, where they may have boldly doubled back on their trail by boarding a train on the recently completed M. K. & T. Railroad south through the Indian Territory to Denison, Texas. The Santa Fe and M. K. & T. stations were only about a mile apart at Humboldt, and such a transfer would have been an easy one.

Accounts of the fate of the Benders are a tangled

Map of the Bender country.

skein of unverified claims, false clues and plain doubt, and it is difficult to tell where fact leaves off and legend begins. For example, one account describes how the posse which had taken a route south into the Indian Territory returned suddenly within a few days. The men comprising it explained that they had decided to give up the hunt for the Benders. This explanation was never really acceptable to their friends, who noticed that the subsequent speculation about the fate of the Benders did not seem to interest any of the members of this group.

Three years later, in a deathbed statement, a man in New Mexico is alleged to have admitted that he was one of the posse which had pursued the Benders into the Indian Territory. According to his statement, this posse overtook the fugitives and executed them. Among their effects was seven thousand dollars in cash, which was divided up among the eight members of the posse. Then each one is said to have taken a solemn oath never to reveal the killing of the Benders. Such an oath would have been hardly necessary, because the members of any posse to bring in the Benders dead or alive would have been received as heroes back in Labette County. Another version of the same story has the defiant, red-headed beauty, Kate, snarl to her captors just before they put her to death, "Shoot and be damned!"

The suspicion that the Benders had been part of a large and well-organized band of robbers received some support, for although most of their victims had been driving teams and wagons at the time of their disappearance, no one in any of the surrounding towns could be found who remembered that the Benders had ever tried to sell this equipment, nor could any of it ever be located. This led to the belief that the equipment had been passed along by accomplices and sold in another part of the Southwest. Some even suggested that this network might have aided the Benders in their escape by sheltering them by day and moving them out of the area by night — a sort of criminal underground railway. Other stories maintain that the bodies of the Benders lie at the bottom of the Verdigris River, or that they were buried in Texas, while still others claim that their bodies were burned.

What is probably the most interesting theory to explain the fate of the Benders, one that satisfies the age-old yearning for personal vengeance, hints that perhaps Colonel York kept the promise made to Kate Bender at the time of his first visit in search of information about his missing brother and that he returned the next day — but not alone and in the small hours of the morning. It suggests that the Benders, alarmed because the finger of suspicion had begun to point so accusingly at them, were surprised in the act of preparing to flee. If so, Colonel York and his men would have needed no other evidence to convince them that they had reached the end of the doctor's trail. The account intimates that a con-

Bender house after the discovery of the murders.

SCENE OF THE BENDER MURDERS.—[From a Sketch by JOHN W. DONLADY.]

1. Grave of Dr. York. 2. Grave of M'Kenzie. 3. Grave of M'Croatty. 4. Grave of Brown. 5. Grave of unknown. 6. Grave of unknown. 7. Grave of Longcors and child. 8. Pit or cellar in which bodies were cast.

fession was extracted from the Benders, and they were put to death on the very spot where they had killed so many others. Then the bodies were taken to an unmarked grave out on the lonely and unsettled prairie.

The members of Colonel York's posse must have known that people simply do not vanish without a clue, although the Benders seem to have believed that none of their victims would soon be missed or traced. Consequently, the stage was carefully set to suggest flight. The Benders' team and wagon were driven to Thayer and abandoned there. Next, four people speaking a carefully exhibited German accent bought tickets to Humbolt. It is said they never reached there, but left the train at New Chicago (now Chanute), from which place the "actors" playing the parts of the Benders unobtrusively dispersed to return to their homes.

In the welter of truths and half-truths told about the Benders and their crimes, one verifiable fact stands out: at some time before the Benders disappeared, they were visited by Colonel York and a posse of his friends searching for Doctor York. In most accounts, Colonel York is only described as a state senator, a lawyer, or, that most stinging of all epithets, a politician. What kind of a man was this colonel who had set out to find his missing brother? Politician he may have been, but he was certainly not an ordinary one.

As a youth, Alexander M. York had enlisted in the Union Army in the Civil War as a private, but soon rose to the rank of lieutenant colonel. After the war he established a successful law practice and was elected to the state senate. Only a few months before the disappearance of his brother, he caused a national sensation by blasting the political career of U.S. Senator Samuel C. Pomeroy. When Pomeroy had been elected to the United States Senate in 1861, there were faint rumors of bought votes. His reelection in 1867 was investigated by a committee of the legislature which reported unanimously that Pomeroy had bribed members of that body. In spite of this, it was generally agreed that Pomeroy's reelection for a third term by both houses of the Kansas legislature was assured, for he had 70 votes pledged to him and only 67 were needed. On January 28, 1873, just before the balloting was to begin in the state capitol in Topeka, Colonel York rose dramatically and walked to the speaker's rostrum to deposit a bundle of bills representing the first payment of a bribe he claimed to have received from Senator Pomeroy in return for the promise of York's vote. Although this drastic action ruined Pomeroy politically, it also wrote finis to York's own political career. The U.S. Senate committee which subsequently investigated the affair concluded that the whole thing seemed to have been a cleverly conceived plot to get Pomeroy.

This was not Pomeroy's first encounter with the impetuous York. The year before, York had been retained by the citizens of Independence, Kansas, and sent to Washington to attempt to secure the removal of the federal land office from the town of Neodesha to Independence. York successfully secured the coöperation of influential Senator Pomeroy, who found his arguments hard to resist. Before visiting Pomeroy with his request for the removal of the land office, York had carefully provided himself with affidavits showing that Pomeroy had previously spent a night in a Baltimore hotel with a woman who was not his wife. Stories of the Senator's indiscretions had been whispered about in the past, but Colonel York let it be known that he was now ready to publish the evidence.

It is not surprising, therefore, to discover that Colonel York accomplished his mission, and the land office was moved. During the subsequent investigation of the removal of the land office and the part he played in it, Colonel York was asked his opinion of the methods he had employed. He answered frankly and unashamedly, "They were questionable, but the people of Independence sent me to Washington to get the land office and I got it." This, then, was the man who had set out to find his missing brother.

Out of fairness to Colonel York, it must be said that in later years he always denied having avenged his brother's death. Several years after the disappearance of the Benders, he went to Denver, Colorado to live, where he engaged in the real estate business. In 1908, a newspaper story reported an account of the death of the Benders by George Evans Downer of Chicago. Downer had been a resident of Kansas in the 1870's and on his deathbed "confessed" to having been a member of the posse which had caught the Benders trying to escape from their house and had killed them. This account prompted a newspaper interview with Colonel York in Denver in which he questioned the truth of the so-called confession and once again denied being responsible for the death of the Benders. "It has been said at times that the Benders were killed by a posse and that I was one of the members of the posse. That is not true. Had I taken part in the killing of the Benders, I would have

been glad to have added this act to another one of the good deeds of my life," he told a reporter. This exchange of news stories set off a whole series of statements in support of each version.

After engaging in the real estate business for many years, Colonel York apparently left Denver about 1925, for his name disappears from the city directory for that year. While visiting friends in Denver, he died on February 25, 1928, just a few days short of ninety years of age. As might have been expected, his death touched off a last wave of speculation about the fate of the Benders.

In spite of the variety of the stories describing the death of the Benders, the belief that they were still alive persisted for almost fifty years after their disappearance. Let a family of four strangers, consisting of an old and a young couple, move into a rural neighborhood, and before many weeks had passed the sheriff of Labette County in Kansas would receive a telegram from a suspicious neighbor telling him to "come and get the Benders." In the beginning, the harassed sheriff and his deputies traveled to many parts of the West and Southwest in a futile chase after the elusive family, but in later years letters and telegrams were carefully investigated first, particularly those asking to have the standing rewards sent by the next mail.

In 1889, a woman and her daughter were brought to Kansas from Michigan and charged with the murder of Dr. York. Despite the fact that the older woman was as Yankee as apple pie and had no trace of a German accent, and the daughter did not even faintly resemble the beautiful, auburn-haired Kate, preparations were made for a trial. Feelings ran high in Labette County, where the citizens found themselves divided into two camps. Some testified vehemently that the women were the Benders, while others swore with equal certainty they were not, in a legal battle which almost reached comicopera proportions. Fortunately, Justice had her blindfold off this time, for the ludicrousness of the charge was apparent to almost everybody except a few diehards, and the case was dismissed before trial.

It is almost certain now that the true fate of the Benders will never be known. Did they escape to another part of the country to take up a respectable existence and to forget the brutal crimes they had committed in Kansas? Were they part of a large and well-organized band of robbers preying upon unsuspecting travelers, as some believed? And, if so, did these partners in crime assist them in their flight? Or will some farmer in what is now Oklahoma or Texas one day turn up four shallow graves as he plows his fields and pause to wonder at their grim contents? The past guards its secrets well, and the big question remains unanswered: *What really happened to the Benders?*

There's Gold in Them Thar

OUTSIDE OF FOOD, clothing and shelter, I feel the thing I'd miss most, if marooned somewhere, would be books. Books make anything possible —a good book can show you how to do anything that can be done; it can enable you to be anything, anywhere, any time, and can teach you the basics of any skill.

But not just any book. It must be an accurate book; it must read well; it must entertain as well as inform, and it must engender in you a faith in the author and a trust in his knowledge.

When we were kids (most of us, at least) we placed books in two categories—learning and adventure. The learning books were ones we studied more or less assiduously to bring home school grades of sufficient merit to keep parental tempers down. Adventure books were just that, adventure. They covered the truth or fiction about things, places, and people, heroes and villains, danger and intrigue. Gauntleted and helmeted knights of old or Buck Rogers in the 25th century, it made no difference—adventure was in those books, and not in the *learning* ones.

I was fortunate — I learned early that there is adventure in *all* books. I learned that, instead of merely seeing a few mundane words on paper, I could be there standing beside Newton when the legendary apple bounced off his head; I could feel first the frustration and then the triumph of the Curies; I could see the sunwink off helmets and shields in battle, and I could hear the clash of arms and cries of the doomed on the Horns of Hatten.

If there is all that adventure in the run-of-the-mill schoolbooks, how can there not be even more in what we call loosely "Gun Books" or "Hunting Books?"

You may buy and read books just to learn, just to find out how a P-38 Walther or a Colt Navy works. Maybe you do, but between the lines on those pages are the agonies, privations, and deaths of an entire army at Stalingrad. Or the accomplishments and adventures of a young Civil War cavalryman who made his way West in the 1860's, with nothing to stave off Indians, outlaws, animals, and starvation, except that battered Navy Colt. Gun books contain more adventure and history than nearly any other kind of book, for guns are objects used by people for the widest range of purposes imaginable.

Too many people buy gun books simply because, "If I need to look something up, I'll know where to find it." Assuming an individual can do that, he'll still miss the best part of the book. Most likely he won't be able to find much of what he wants in the book unless he's read through it a couple of times. A book waiting on the shelf, new and unread, is pure waste. The learning and the adventure go hand in hand, and can only be brought to life when the book is read and studied. The smudged and dog-eared pages of a book that is utilized become marks of honorable use.

"Gun books" is what we call them, but they don't deal with guns alone. The guns are there between the pages, of course, but often no more strongly presented than the boots the man wears, the binoculars he carries, the game he sees, or the country he covers. Perhaps even more important is that gun books deal mainly with people—those who have shaped and formed firearms during the past seven centuries; those who have benefitted or suffered from their use, and those who make them and use them whether for better or worse.

Gun books are literally crammed with: geography, history, philosophy, cooking, conservation, biology, weather, hiking, driving, boating, medicine, and human nature—just to name a few. If you look, you'll learn far more from a good gun book than

Books

by George C. Nonte, Jr.

the anti-gun reader will learn from his latest best seller that might be devoted to murder or perversion. Gun books record the technology of man for many centuries, for production of weapons has long received more attention than many other fields. In fact, you'll learn in gun books that modern mass-production and interchangeable parts first succeeded with guns.

Many other subjects are so akin to guns that an author simply can't write without including them. Yet the guns aren't overpowering—the gun lore, and the technical details are still all there. In the "Shooter's Bookshelf" section of the SHOOTER'S BIBLE, you'll find fine books by well-known authors on such subjects as:

Africa
Air guns
Alaska
Ammunition
Asia
Ballistics
Big game
Black powder and muzzle loading
Cooking
Dogs
Europe
Firearms identification
Frontier guns
Gunsmithing
Handguns

Handloading
Hunting
Military arms
Outdoor life
Rifles
Shotguns
Skeet and trap
Small game
Waterfowling
And many more.

There are so many gun books, in fact, that choosing those most suitable for your needs and your purse can be a trying chore. Just how does one pick from 50 to 100 titles in a given category? Latest isn't necessarily best, nor is the costliest. Even the best-known author may not produce the best work on a particular subject. I can recall thinking many times how much help it would be if there was someone who'd read most of the books and could or would make suggestions on what to buy.

Well, I've not read all those books, but a lot of them, and here are some suggestions I'll make. They are listed under specific subject headings:

RECOMMENDED READING

Gunsmithing
Gunsmith Kinks. F. R. Brownell. Montezuma, Iowa: F. Brownell & Sons, 1969. $9.95. Shop kinks, short cuts, techniques and useful advice from professional gunsmiths.

Gunsmithing Simplified. Harold E. McFarland. Cranbury, New Jersey: A. S. Barnes & Co., Inc. $8.95. Thorough and dependable and full of helpful short cuts.

Home Gun Care & Repair. P. O. Ackley, Harrisburg, Pennsylvania: Stackpole Books, 1974. pap. $2.95. A basic reference for fixing and converting rifles, shotguns and handguns.

Modern Gunsmith, 2 volumes. James V. Howe. New York: Funk & Wagnalls Publishing Co., 1970. $12.50 each volume; Set $25.00. A guide for professional gunsmiths covering firearms design, construction and repair.

Pistolsmithing. George C. Nonte. Harrisburg, Pennsylvania: Stackpole Books, 1974. $12.95.

Handguns
Firearms Assembly Handbook, Vol. II, *Handguns.* Washington, D.C.: National Rifle Association, 1974. mem. $3.00, non-mem. $4.00. Illustrated articles showing the takedown of 101 pistols and revolvers.

Pistol and Revolver Guide, 3rd ed. George C. Nonte. South Hackensack, New Jersey: Stoeger Publishing Company, 1975. $5.95.

Pistols, Revolvers, & Ammunition. Michel Josserand and Jan Stevenson. New York: Crown Publishers, Inc., 1972. $7.50. Basic information on the pistol and revolver with chapters on ammunition, ballistics and rules of safety.

Sixguns. Elmer Keith. Harrisburgh, Pennsylvania: Stackpole Books, 1968 reprint of 1961 edition (now out of print). First published in 1961, this handgun classic is still useful and fascinating.

Handloading

Complete Guide to Handloading, 3rd ed. Philip B. Sharpe. New York: Funk & Wagnalls Publishing Co., 1953. $10.00. Has been the handloader's bible since its first publication in 1937. Somewhat dated now but still useful.

Modern Handloading. George C. Nonte. New York: Winchester Press, 1972. $10.00.

N.R.A. Handloader's Guide. Washington, D.C.: National Rifle Association, 1974. mem. $4.00, non-mem. $5.00. A helpful guide for handloaders with safety as its main theme.

Principles & Practice of Loading Ammunition. Earl Naramore. Harrisburg, Pennsylvania: Stackpole Books, 1954. $14.95. An extensive coverage of loading ammunition, with 240 illustrations to help you along.

Military

Small Arms of the World. Joseph E. Smith. Harrisburg, Pennsylvania: Stackpole Books, 1973. $7.95. An interesting survey of arms from more than 42 different countries.

Muzzle-Loading

Black Powder Guide. George C. Nonte. South Hackensack, New Jersey: Stoeger Publishing Company, 1965. $5.95.

Black Powder Gun Digest. Toby Bridges, ed. Northfield, Illinois: Digest Books, Inc., 1972. $5.95. Another in the series of the well-known Digest books.

Rifles

The Accurate Rifle. Warren Page. South Hackensack, New Jersey: Stoeger Publishing Company, 1975. $5.95. Provides all shooters and hunters with practical information on the entire range of subjects effecting rifle accuracy.

The Hunting Rifle. Jack O'Connor. South Hackensack, New Jersey: Stoeger Publishing Company, 1975. $5.95. The old master himself analyzes modern rifles, cartridges and accessories in a work full of wit and wisdom.

Shooting

Complete Book of Shooting: Rifles, Shotguns, Handguns. Jack O'Connor. New York: The Times Mirror Co., 1965. $7.95. How to shoot with rifle, shotgun and handgun in the field and on the range.

Field Skeet and Trap Shooting, revised ed. Charles E. Chapel. Cranbury, New Jersey: A. S. Barnes & Co., Inc., 1962. $7.95. A masterful work on shotgun shooting covering gun types, ammunition, accessories and marksmanship.

A History of Marksmanship. Charles C. French. Chicago: Follet Publishing Co., 1972. $12.95. A comprehensive history of the art of shooting from the earliest times to the present day. Profusely illustrated and wide ranging.

Instinct Shooting, revised ed. Mike Jennings. New York: Dodd, Mead & Co., 1965. $3.95. Lucky McDaniel's aerial-shooting techniques that enable novice shooters to hit flying targets.

Kuhlhof on Guns. Pete Kuhlof. New York: Winchester Press, 1970. $5.95. Selected firearms articles by the late, great gun editor of *Argosy.*

Position Rifle Shooting. Bill Pullum and Frank T. Hanenkrat. South Hackensack, New Jersey: Stoeger Publishing Company, 1973. $5.95. This is the most complete, authoritative and up-to-date book for the competitive rifleman.

Shotguns

American Shotgun. David F. Butler. New York: Winchester Press, 1973. $15.00. Traces the development of the American shotgun and modern shotgun ammunition.

Golden Age of Shotgunning. Bob Hinman. New York: Winchester Press, 1972. $8.95. The fascinating story of American shotgun shooting and wing shooting between 1870 and 1900.

Gough Thomas's Gun Book. G. T. Garwood. New York: Winchester Press, 1970. $8.95. Articles originally published in *Shooting Times* by a well-known British authority.

Gough Thomas's Second Gun Book. G. T. Garwood. New York: Winchester Press, 1972. $8.95. More articles on the shotgun, its use, care and history.

Shotgun Book. Jack O'Connor. New York: Alfred A. Knopf, Inc., 1965. $10.00. A definitive work on shotgun makes, models and actions with chapters on wildfowling, upland hunting, and trap and skeet shooting.

Now, that extensive list doesn't mean you need all of those books—you only need one or two from each category in which you are most interested. That means that a dozen assorted, well-chosen volumes will form the basis for a library that you can add to over the years. Sure some of those books cost $10, $12, even $15 or more—but you can't read them all at once, so start with one. Maybe lay out a book budget allowing you one new volume each month, or every second month for the more expensive ones. Money can be saved by getting with a similarly interested friend and arranging for each of you to buy different books each month. That way there is twice as much reading for the same money—at least so long as you remain friends.

Don't be one of those people who thinks books must remain unmarked. Don't hesitate to annotate, underline or index-tab. Stick a few sheets of notepaper between the pages at the end of the chapters, and use them. Create from your book a useful tool to which you may return again and again for information. After all, the book is a tool, an indispensable tool of learning and knowledge.

Once you've acquired a new book, mark it well with your name and the date in several places—people who borrow books can't seem to remember the original owners. It is best not to loan books, but few of us can turn down an enquiring mind. To keep those enquiring minds alert and responsive, I write the title, date, and borrower's name on a file card and keep it handy. Then, when I need the book and it's not on the shelf (and it often isn't), I know who to call. Actually, it's a good idea to track down loaned-out books once a month—honest borrowers won't be offended, and the other's feelings don't count.

Hunting & Shooting Classics

The Muckle Hart of Benmore

H. C. Watson

ST. JOHN'S "WILD Sports of the Highlands," is a work peculiarly attractive, by the unaffected simplicity and honest cordiality which pervade it. The author's hand is evidently more familiar with the rod and rifle than with the pen – he gives a blunt country gentleman sort of detail of Highland sport by field and flood, and has an observant eye to the habits of the lower animals, and a kindly regard withal to the objects of the chase, which is ever characteristic of the legitimate sportsman. We extract, with slight abridgment, one of the most stirring incidents in the volume, the stalking of "The Muckle Hart of Benmore."

"Malcolm, the shepherd of the sheiling at the foot of Benmore, reported his having crossed in the hill a track of a hart of extraordinary size, and guessed it must be 'the muckle stag of Benmore.' This was an animal seldom seen, but which had long been the talk and marvel of the shepherds for its wonderful size and cunning. They love the marvellous, and in their report 'the muckle stag' bore a charmed life; he was unapproachable and invulnerable. I had heard of him too, and, having got the necessary information, resolved to try to break the charm, though it should cost me a day or two.

"*Monday*. – This morning, at sunrise, Mr. St. John with his rifle, Donald, an eccentric gillie, carrying his double-barreled gun, and Bran, his deer-hound, took their way up the glen to the sheiling at the foot of Benmore. After a fruitless beating of the glen, we turned, at nightfall, to the sheiling, rather disheartened; but the shepherd cheered us by the assurance that the hart was still in the district, and describing his track, which he said was like that of a good-sized heifer. Our spirits were quite restored by a meal of fresh caught trout, oat-cake, and milk, with a modicum of whiskey, which certainly was of unusual flavor and potency.

"*Tuesday*. – We were off again by daybreak. I will pass by several minor adventures, but one cannot be omitted. Malcolm went with us to show us where he had last seen the track. As we crossed a long reach of black and broken ground, the first ascent from the valley, two eagles rose out of a hollow at some distance. Their flight was lazy and heavy, as if gorged with food; and on examining the place, we found the carcass of a sheep half eaten, one of Malcolm's flock. He vowed vengeance; and merely pointed out to us our route, returned for a spade to dig a place of hiding near enough to the carcass to enable him to have a shot at the eagles if they should return. We held on our way, and the greater part of the day, without any luck to cheer us, my resolution 'not to be beat,' being, however, a good deal strengthened by the occasional grumbling of Donald. Towards the afternoon, when we had tired ourselves with looking with our glasses at every corrie in that side of the hill, at length, in crossing a bare and boggy piece of ground, Donald suddenly stopped, with a Gaelic exclamation, and pointed – and there, to be sure, was a full fresh footprint, the largest mark of a deer either of us had ever seen. There was no more grumbling. Both of us were instantly as much on the alert as when we started on the adventure. We traced the track as long as the ground would allow. Where we lost it, it seemed to point down the little burn, which soon lost itself to our view in a gorge of bare rocks. We proceeded now very cautiously, and taking up our station on a concealed ledge of rocks, began to search the valley below with our telescopes. It was difficult ground to see a deer in, if lying; and I had almost given up seeking, when Donald's glass became motionless, and he gave a sort of grunt as he changed his posture, but without taking the glass from his eye. "Ugh! I'm thinking yon's him, sir, I'm seeing his horns." I was at first incredulous; but the doubt was short. While we gazed, the stag rose and commenced feeding; at last I saw the great hart of Benmore! He was a long way off, perhaps a mile and a half, but in excellent ground for getting at him. Our plan was soon arranged. I was to stalk him with the rifle, while Donald, with my gun and Bran, was to get round, out of sight, to the pass by which the deer was likely to leave the valley. My task was apparently very easy. After getting down behind the rock, I had scarcely to stoop my head, but to walk up within shot, so favorable was the ground and the wind. I walked cautiously, however, and slowly, to give Donald time to reach the pass. I was now within three hundred yards of him, when, as I leant against a slab of stone, all hid below my eyes, I saw him give a sudden start, stop feeding, and look round suspiciously. What a noble beast! what a stretch of antler! with a mane like a lion! He stood for a minute or two, snuffing every breath. I could not guess the cause of this alarm; it was not myself; the light wind blew fair down from him upon me; and I knew Donald would give no inkling of his whereabouts. He presently began to move, and came at a slow trot toward me. My pulse beat high. Another hundred yards forward, and he is mine! But it was not so to be. He took the top of a steep bank which commanded my position, saw me in an instant, and was off, at the speed of twenty miles an hour, to a pass wide from that where Donald was hid. While clattering up the hill, scattering the loose stones behind him, two other stags joined him, which had evidently been put up by Donald, and had given the alarm to my quarry. It was then that his great size was conspicuous. I could see with my glass they were full-grown stags, and with good heads, but they looked like fallow deer as they followed him up the crag. I sat down, disappointed for the moment, and Donald soon joined me, much crestfallen, and cursing the stag in a curious variety of Gaelic oaths. Still it was something to have seen 'the muckle stag,' and *nil desperandum* was my motto. We had a long and weary walk to Malcolm's sheiling; and I was glad to get to my heather-bed, after arranging that I should occupy the hiding-place Malcolm had prepared near the dead sheep next morning.

"Wednesday. — After dispatching the plundering eagles in fine style, our hero and his redoubted gillie again set forth in quest of 'the muckle hart.' Our line of march today was over ground so high, that we came repeatedly into the midst of ptarmigan. On the very summit, Bran had a rencontre with an old mountain fox, toothless, yet very fat, which he made to bite the dust. We struck at one place the tracks of the three deer, but of the animals themselves we saw nothing. We kept exploring corrie after corrie till night fell; and as it was in vain to think of returning to the sheiling, which yet was the nearest roof, we were content to find a sort of niche in the rock, tolerably screened from all winds; and having almost filled it with long heather, flower upwards, we wrapped our plaids around us, and slept pretty comfortably.

"Thursday. — A dip in the burn below our bivouac renovated me. I did not observe that Donald followed my example in that; but he joined me in a hearty attack on the viands which still remained in our bag, and we started with renewed courage. About midday we came on a sheiling beside a long narrow loch, fringed with beautiful weeping birches, and there we found means to cook some grouse, which I had shot to supply our exhausted larder. The shepherd, who had 'no Sassenach,' cheered us by his report of 'the deer' being lately seen, described his usual haunts. Donald was plainly getting disgusted and homesick. For myself, I looked upon it as my fate that I must have that hart; so on we trudged. Repeatedly that afternoon we came on the fresh tracks of our chase, but still he remained invisible. As it got dark, the weather suddenly changed, and I was glad enough to let Donald seek for the bearings of a 'whisky bothy,' which he had heard of at our last stopping-place. While he was seeking for it, the rain began to fall heavily, and through the darkness we were just able to distinguish a dark object, which turned out to be a horse. 'The lads with the still be no far off,' said Donald. And so it turned out. But the rain had increased the darkness so much, that we should have searched in vain, if I had not distinguished at intervals, between the pelting of the rain and the

heavy rushing of a black burn that ran beside us, what appeared to me to be the shrill treble of a fiddle. I could scarcely believe my ears. But when I communicated the intelligence to Donald, whose ears were less acute, he jumped with joy. 'It's a' right enough, sir; just follow the sound. It's that drunken deevilish Sandy Ross; ye'll never haud a fiddle frae him, nor him frae a whisky-still.' It was clear that the sound came from across the black stream, and it looked formidable in the dark. However, there was no remedy. So grasping each other's collar, and holding our guns high overhead, we dashed in, and staggered through in safety, though the water was up to my waist, running like a mill-race, and the bottom was of round stones. Scrambling up the bank, and following the merry sound, we came to what seemed a mere hole in the bank, from which it proceeded. The hole was partially covered by a door woven of heather; and, looking through it, we saw a sight worthy of Teniers. On a barrel in the midst of the apartment — half hut, half cavern — stood aloft, fiddling with all his might, the identical Sandy Ross, while round him danced three unkempt savages; and another figure was stooping, employed over a fire in the corner, where the whisky-pot was in full operation. The fire, and a sliver or two of lighted bog-fir, gave light enough to see the whole, for the place was not above ten feet square. We made our approaches with becoming caution, and were, it is needless to say, hospitably received; for who ever heard of Highland smugglers refusing a welcome to sportsmen? We got food, rest, and fire — all that we required — and something more; for long after I had betaken me to the dry heather in the corner, I had disturbed visions of strange orgies in the bothy, and of sober Donald exhibiting curious antics on the top of a tub. These might have been the productions of a disturbed brain; but there is no doubt that, when daylight awoke me, the smugglers and Donald were all quiet and asleep, far past my efforts to rouse them, except one, who was still able to tend the fire under the large black pot.

"Friday. — From the state in which my trusty companion was, with his head on a heap of ashes, I saw it would serve no purpose to awake him, even if I were able to do so. It was quite clear that he could be good for nothing all day. I therefore secured some breakfast and provisions for the day, (part of them oat-cake, which I baked for myself,) tied up Bran to wait Donald's restoration, and departed with my rifle alone. The morning was bright and beautiful; the mountain streams overflowing with last night's rain. I was now thrown on my own resources, and my knowledge of the country, which, to say the truth, was far from minute or exact. 'Benna-skiach' was my object today, and the corries which lay beyond it, where at this season the large harts were said to resort. My way at first was dreary enough, over a long slop of boggy ground, enlivened, however, by a few traces of deer having crossed, though none of my 'chase.' I at length passed the slope, and soon topped the ridge, and was repaid for my labor by a view of glen, and wood, and water so beautiful, that I sat down to gaze at it, though anxious to get forward.

"While I lay above the lake, the day suddenly changed, and heavy wreaths of mist came down the mountain sides in rapid succession. They reached me soon, and I was inclosed in an atmosphere through which I could not see twenty yards. It was very cold, too, and I was obliged to move, though scarcely well knowing whither. I followed the course of the lake, and afterwards of the stream which flowed from it, for some time. Now and then a grouse would rise close to me, and, flying a few yards, light again on a hillock, crowing and croaking at the intruder. The heron, in the darkness, came flapping his great wings close past me; I almost fancied I could feel the movements they caused in the air. Nothing could be done in such weather, and I was not sure that I might not be going away from my object. It was getting late, too, and I had made up my mind that my most prudent plan was to arrange a bivouac before it became quite dark. My wallet was empty, except a few crumbs, the remains of my morning's baking. It was necessary to provide food; and just as the necessity occurred to me, I heard, through the mist, the call of a cock grouse as he lighted close to me. I contrived to get his head between me and the sky, as he was strutting and croaking on a hillock close at hand; and aiming at where his body ought be, I fired my rifle. On going up to the place, I found I had not only killed him, but also his mate, whom I had not seen. It was a commencement of good luck. Sitting down, I speedily skinned my birds, and took them down to the burn to wash them before cooking. In crossing a sandy spot beside the burn, I came upon — could I believe my eyes? — 'the track.' Like Robinson Crusoe in the same circumstances, I started back, but was speedily at work taking my information. There were prints enough to show the hart had crossed at a walk, leisurely. It must have been lately, for it was since the burn had returned to its natural size, after the last night's flood. But nothing could be done till morning, so I set about my cooking; and having, after some time, succeeded in lighting a fire, while my grouse were slowly broiling, I pulled a quantity of heather, which I spread in a corner, a little protected by an overhanging rock; I spread my plaid upon it, and over the plaid built another layer of heather. My supper ended, which was not epicurean, I crawled into my nest under my plaid, and, in spite of a rapid change from a dull foggy sky to a clear keen frost, was soon sound asleep.

"*Saturday*. — Need I say my first object was to go down and examine the track anew. There was no mistake. It was impossible to doubt that 'the muckle hart of Benmore' had actually walked through that burn a few hours before me, and in the same direction. I followed the track and breasted the opposite hill. Looking round from its summit, it appeared to me a familiar scene, and, on considering a moment, I found I overlooked, from a different quarter, the very same rocky plain and the two black lochs where I had seen my chase three days before. I had not gazed many minutes, when I saw a deer lying on a black hillock which was quite open. I lay down immediately, and with my glass made out at once the object of all my wandering. My joy was somewhat abated by his position, which was not easily approachable. My first object, however, was to withdraw myself out of his sight, which I did by crawling backwards down a little bank, till only the tips of his horns were visible, and they served to show me that he continued still. As he lay looking towards me, he commanded with his eye three-fourths of the circle; and the other quarter, where one might have got in upon him under cover of the little hillock, was unsafe, from the wind blowing in that direction. A burn ran between him and me, one turn of which seemed to come

within two hundred yards of him. It was my only chance; so, retreating about a half a mile, I got into the burn in hidden ground, and then crept up its channel with such caution, that I never allowed myself a sight of more than the tips of his horns till I reached the nearest bend to him. There looking through a tuft of rushes, I had a perfect view of the noble animal, lying on the open hillock, lazily stretched out at length, and only moving now and then to scratch his flank with his horns. I watched him for fully an hour, the water up to my knees all the time. At length he stirred, gathered his legs together, and rose; and arching his back, he stretched himself just as a bullock does when rising from his night's lair. My heart throbbed, as turning all round he seemed to try the wind for his security, and then walked straight to the burn, at a point about one hundred and fifty yards from me. I was much tempted, but had resolution to reserve my fire, reflecting that I had but one barrel. He went into the burn at a deep pool, and, standing in it up to his knees, took a long drink. I stooped to put on a new copper cap and prick the nipple of my rifle; and on looking up again, he was gone! I was in despair, and was on the point of moving rashly, when I saw his horns again appear a little farther off, but not more than fifty yards from the burn. By and by they lowered, and I judged he was lying down. 'You're mine at last,' I said; and I crept cautiously up the bed of the burn till I was opposite where he had lain down.

"I carefully, and inch by inch, placed my rifle over the bank, and then ventured to look along it. I could see only his horns, but within an easy shot. I was afraid to move higher up the bed of the burn, where I could have seen his body; the direction of the wind made that dangerous. I took breath for a moment, and screwed up my nerves; and then with my cocked rifle at my shoulder, and my finger on the trigger, I kicked a stone, which splashed into the water. He started up instantly; but exposed only his front towards me. Still he was very near, scarcely fifty yards, and I fired at his throat just where it joins the head. He dropped on his knees to my shot; but was up again in a moment, and went staggering up the hill. Oh for one hour of Bran! Although he kept on at a mad pace, I saw he was becoming too weak for the hill. He swerved, and turned back to the burn, and came headlong down within ten yards of me, tumbling into it apparently dead. Feeling confident, from the place my ball had taken effect, that he was dead, I threw down my rifle, and went up to him with my hunting knife. I found him stretched out, and, as I thought, dying; and I laid hold of his horns to bleed him. I had scarcely touched him when he sprang up, flinging me backwards on the stones. It was an awkward position. I was stunned by the violent fall; behind me a steep bank of seven or eight feet high; before me was the bleeding stag, with his horns levelled at me, and cutting me off from my rifle. In desperation I moved, when he instantly charged, but fortunately tumbled ere he quite reached me. He drew back again like a ram about to butt, and then stood still with his head lowered, and his eyes bloody and swelled, glaring upon me. We stood mutually at bay for some time, till, recovering myself, I jumped out of the burn so suddenly, that he had not time to run at me, and from the bank above I dashed my plaid over his head and eyes, and threw myself upon him. I cannot account for my folly, and it had nearly cost me dear. The poor beast struggled desperately, and his remaining strength foiled me in every attempt to stab him in front; and he at length made off, tumbling me down, but carrying with him a stab in the leg which lamed him. I ran and picked up my rifle, and then kept him in view as he rushed down the burn on three legs towards the loch. He took the water, and stood at bay up to his chest in it.

"As soon as he halted, I commenced loading my rifle, when, to my dismay, I found that all the balls I had remaining were for my double-barrel, and were a size too large for my rifle. I sat down and commenced scraping one to the right size, an operation that seemed interminable. At last I succeeded; and having loaded, the poor stag remaining perfectly still, I went up within twenty yards of him, and shot him through the head. He turned over and floated, perfectly dead. I waded in and towed him ashore, and then had leisure to look at my wounds and bruises, which were not serious, except my shin-bone, which was scraped from ankle to knee by his horn. I soon had cleaned my quarry, and stowed him away as safely as I could, and then turned down the glen at a gay pace. I found Donald, with Bran, reposing at Malcolm's sheiling; and for all reproaches on his misconduct, I was satisfied with sending him to bring home 'the muckle hart of Benmore,' a duty which he performed before nightfall."

An Old-Time Michigan Squirrel Shoot

Stanley Waterloo

THE MAN WHO was in his prime forty-five years ago, who had the sporting instinct in him, and who lived in the eastern tier of counties of southern Michigan, had annually a quality of enjoyment of one adorable autumn day denied to the sportsman of the present time. He could participate in a squirrel shoot, and a squirrel shoot was a thing to be remembered. It brought out an illustration of perfect knowledge of the wood and all its creatures. It brought out an exhibition of exquisite marksmanship with the old muzzle-loading rifle, carrying say ninety to the pound, or else of blazing murderous skill with an old shotgun having any kind of a bore, loaded first with any quantity of power topped by any fragment of a newspaper rammed down hard, burdened then by any part of a handful of shot, topped again by more newspaper, and backed by a "G" cap which generally worked well when smashed by a hammer which came down with vigor when the lockspring was in form.

Nowhere upon the face of the globe outside of the Eastern and Middle States has ever been afforded such area for the form of recreation known as a squirrel shoot. Sometimes it was a contest between picked hunters from adjacent townships, sometimes merely an offhand test between two groups of hunters — almost always farmers — living with their clearings close together throughout the township and pining for a day of recreation. Squirrel shoot was not an exact or proper name for the contest of woodcraft and good marksmanship, because other creatures than squirrels counted. A shoot being agreed upon, captains were sometimes selected before the event, that they might see to the success of the gathering in point of numbers, and then on a certain day the farmers met, the captains chose sides, and each party went out wherever it liked, returning at six o'clock in the evening to display its game and win or lose. The party making the lowest count paid for the big tavern dinner for both sides. This is about the manner in which the quarry counted:

Bear	100
Wolverine	75
Deer	50
Fox	20
Coon	15
Turkey	15
Ruffed Grouse — "Partridge"	10
Woodchuck	7
Quail	5
Barked Squirrel	3
Squirrel — black or gray	1

Each bird or beast named, little or big, was abundant in the forests of St. Clair County in the boyhood of men still in their prime, and on the occasion of one of these famous squirrel shoots, bear, deer, and turkey frequently added heavily to the scores. Ruffed grouse or "partridges," as they were called, were especially numerous and made a factor of importance in the count. It was the squirrels, though, upon whom each band of farmers-hunters chiefly relied for triumph. They existed in myriads, the gray and black, in that nut-blessed land of oak and beech and hickory, and the brush fences about the cornfields hewed into the forest were alive with the marauders. In numbers the black squirrel exceeded the gray, though now the black is practically extinct, his place being taken by the fox squirrel, which more readily adapts itself to forests less dense and to new sources of food supply. Each squirrel, however rudely killed, counted one; but a "barked" squirrel — that is, one thrown from the tree by a bullet placed between it and limb or bole, and so killed by the shock and fall, and showing no wound — counted always treble as a tribute to good marksmanship.

And a squirrel shoot was on which promised to be a record breaker. Was not one side to be captained by Lon Jones, popular farmer, great wrestler and excellent shot, and the other by Jim Granger of equally wide and excellent repute in the community? The shoot was to take place on Saturday, the place of assemblage was to be at Smith's Creek, a little woodland railroad station; the hunt was to begin at eight o'clock in the morning; and the count, as was the custom, to be made at six o'clock in the evening. Friday afternoon was one of the most glorious of all that rich October.

Both Jones and Granger were honest and honorable men. The word of either was as good as his bond, and either would scorn trickiness in any of the ordinary affairs of the droning life of every day. But, according to the ethics of the time and place, all was fair in love or war or a squirrel shoot.

So it came that on that yellow Friday afternoon neither

Jones nor Granger could be seen at work in any of his fields, and inquiry at their houses would have resulted in the information that Jones had gone with a plow-point to the blacksmith's, and that Granger had taken a load of staves to town.

At about three o'clock of that same afternoon a tall, fair-haired, bronzed man might have been seen sitting, immovable, upon a log in the midst of a thick beechwood and, at the same hour, a couple of miles away, a slight, dark-haired individual might have been noted, slipping along silently as an Indian and with upward gaze, through a flat in the forest where the hickory trees were so numerous as to form almost a grove. And each of these two men carried a rifle and a powderhorn and a coat-pocket full of bullets and a box of "G" caps; and another peculiarity about these gentlemen of the woods was that the first bore a striking resemblance to Lon Jones and the other to Jim Granger.

The afternoon waned, the shadows of the dead trees in the clearings became longer and the mid-day quietude was past. The creatures of the wood returned to active life again. There was rustling among the leaves and the patter of many feet; nutshells came dropping from the tree tops, and then from the beechwood and the hickory grove came faintly to the distant roadway what sounded like the repeated cracking of an ox-driver's whip. The rifles were at work. As evening fell the cracking ceased, and two men took their way from different points toward the hamlet of Smith's Creek. They were not a hundred yards apart when they paused and each made a cache, concealing his game under dead branches and a heap of leaves. Jones had twenty-one squirrels, seven of them barked; score, 35. Granger had only sixteen squirrels, two barked, but he had a grouse; score, 30. Honors were nearly even.

"I wish there was more," said Jones to himself, "but they'll help out."

"Thirty's better than nothing," chuckled Granger.

The game concealed, ready to be added surreptitiously to the morrow's bag, the two men, each unconscious of the other's presence, started for home in different directions.

And old man Hank Goodsell, out looking for his hogs, which were running wild in the woods that autumn and fattening on "mast," saw the performance of both from a huge log upon which he had climbed to get a better view in the woods, and ten minutes later was making his way home with a decent load upon his back. Next morning they had fried partridge at old man Goodsell's house and at the end of the week his hired man swore that he wouldn't stand squirrel for breakfast, squirrel for dinner, and squirrel for supper any longer!

It was a fine and flashing Saturday morning which dawned upon Smith's Creek. There could be no doubt of that. There was hoar frost upon the trees and fences, a land of silver, rapidly changing in appearance beneath the beams of the sun arisen in a cloudless eastern sky, while the temperature was just crisp enough to make activity a pleasure. The farmers assembled for the shoot were in a riotously good-natured mood; there was chaffing over crops, much horse-play among the younger men, and much jeering allusion as this man or that man was selected by the captains choosing sides, with such comment as: "Why, Joe, what's the use of you going squirrel hunting? You couldn't hit a cow!" or something not less personal. At the end of it all, the two companies, twenty-one men on a side, separated for the struggle of the day, the tavern-keeper having been meanwhile warned that the supper must be a mighty and a good one.

The two captains, Jones and Granger, conferred but briefly with their companies. Time was precious now. There was swift separation, and armed with anything, from some relic of the War of 1812 to the latest piece from the gun-smith, the men melted away into the woods, singly or by twos — for two men together can hunt squirrels most effectively — each lone man or two hurrying to some ground already decided upon where squirrels were thought to be most plentiful.

Within a radius of three or four miles about Smith's Creek that day the jays and woodpeckers must have thought that Fourth of July had come again, all out of season, for there was a roar and crackle throughout the forest everywhere, and the smell of powder was in the air.

To attempt to tell in detail of the incidents of that day among the forty-two hunters in the game-burdened woods of eastern Michigan forty-five years ago would be a task in vain. Incidents there were in abundance, some droll, some otherwise; but all strenuous, and all partaking of the spirit of the time and the surroundings and the bronzed, strong men. At a little before six o'clock in the evening they came streaming in — the hunters — and by six they were all at hand, for game brought in though but a moment after the appointed hour was not allowed to figure in the count.

There was a great enclosed shed near the tavern, where black-ash hoops for the market were stored in summer, which was now empty, and along each side of this, rude trestles with planks upon them had been placed for the exhibit of the game of the opposing companies. The Jones men came in and deposited their spoils on the trestles to the left, the Granger men placed theirs upon the trestles to the right. Soon each long narrow table had received its furry and feathered burden, and the sight was one calculated to make exceedingly wide open the eyes of the sportsman of to-day.

Meantime, while the hunters were filing in, each captain had disappeared for the time, with some commonplace excuse. Each visited his cache and each found his possession gone. Where were the squirrels of yesterday? The hard work and clever planning of the two honorable captains had already provided old Hank Goodsell with a good meal or two. The two men met in the tavern, each with a blazing face, each half suspicious of the other, took a drink together and went over to the shed.

It was a rule of the squirrel shoots that a committee of six — three from each side — should do the counting alone, the captains being, ex-officio, members of the two committees. The two remaining members from each company were promptly selected and count began. This was the result.

JONES COMPANY

Fox	2
Turkey	11
Ruffed Grouse	19
Woodchuck	1
Squirrel — "barked"	40
Squirrel	248
Total	770

GRANGER COMPANY	
Bear	1
Fox	1
Turkey	7
Ruffed Grouse	23
Quail	30
Squirrel — "barked"	25
Squirrel	90
Total	770

It was wonderful, but of course the committee could not know of this coming result until the end of the count was reached. Before that moment, though, the quick eye of Jones had noted that the summaries must be nearly even. Unseen, he thrust into his pocket a black squirrel from the long table of his adversaries. Small benefit seemed likely to accrue to him or his party from that deft feat, for it was the custom to search each man of the committee as he left the counting-place. It is well to be extremely careful, even among old friends, when great sporting events come off and excitement is running high.

The count went on, the end of the second table was nearly reached and Jones was thinking hard. He put his hands behind him as the men moved slowly along, the two committeemen doing the counting, and the captains lagging near and observing closely, and twisted his coat pocket around and got both hands into it, where lay his plunder. Strong fingers tore the skin of the squirrel apart at the back and stripped it clean from head to tail. The hair was swept from the tail by those same fingers and scattered along the earth; and the skin, torn into little patches, found the same resting place, to be ground into the soil of the unfloored shed by the soles of carefully adjusted heavy boots. It was so with the viscera. There remained in the pocket of Jones but a young black squirrel, all ready for the table, save that it was uncooked.

The end of the count was reached and the astonishing result declared. Each captain blazed out expressions of doubt and wrath; Granger, because he had relied upon the accidental bear slain by his party, and Jones for reasons more peculiarly his own. The count must be made over again to insure against all error, and the task was entered upon at once, the Jones game, as before, being counted first.

Lingering a little behind Granger as they followed the four counting and tallying members of the committee came the stalwart Jones. Again his sinewy hands reached the pocket drawn behind him; there was a twitch, a swift subsequent movement, and the hind quarter of a squirrel went into his roomy mouth. His jaws worked vigorously.

"Thought you'd stopped tobacco, Lon," said Granger carelessly, who, though he noted the mastication, was too intent upon the count to pay much attention to anything else.

"Did," was the response, "but I got a hankering and took it up again. Doesn't seem to hurt me any."

A moment later his fingers went swiftly to his mouth and a little handful of white bones was dropped to earth, to be ground as the skin had been beneath the soles of a pair of cowhide boots. And so went all the squirrel.

The end of the second count of the Granger game was reached and then the heavens fell! It did not correspond with the first enumeration. There was one squirrel short. Under the loud protests of Granger the work was repeated with the utmost thoroughness. The enumerators confessed that they must have made a mistake the first time. The Jones company were declared victors in the squirrel shoot by but a single unit, but victors still.

The rage of Granger was something worth the seeing. There had been trickery! The long, bare, floorless shed was searched, but no trace of a squirrel could be found; and besides, the committee had been together all the time. Then each man was searched as thoroughly as ever custom-house officer, keen for diamonds, might have searched some noted smuggler. As they rose — so pure proved they! The doors were opened, the six men filed out, and the result was shoutingly announced. There was silence on one side, wild yells from the other, and a rush for supper.

To tell of that supper and to do it justice would require the skill of him who wrote of one of "Cleopatra's Nights." It was not of the same order of feasting, but it was as enjoyable, and healthier. The moment of pique and anger of the losing party was forgotten. What tales of shots made that October day, and of forest triumphs in the past! What vast consumption of edibles which the tavern, somehow, made more toothsome than anything in the hotel can produce. And how absent-minded the men were next day in the little meeting-houses at the different crossroads. A squirrel shoot is almost a legend now, but a squirrel shoot was one of the days the passing country generation knew of as being as scarlet as the leaves of the October maple, as golden as those of the elm in the same crisp, mellow month.

The Conqueror

Maximilian Foster

AWAY BY the head of the forgotten Mamoziekel lies a barren — a gray solitude in the depths of the untraversed woods. Grim hills of mystery look down upon it, and the forest, pausing at its edge, overshadows quagmires working darkly like a witch's pot. Man is seldom there. Its waste is given over to the somber moose and to herds of woodland caribou, stray voyagers of the wilderness who track in from the runways leading to the south, and go unchallenged across its breadth.

There came a wind from the north. It drew down the flank of the mountain, sheeting the landscape with a pall of flying vapor, roared a moment on the forest edge, and swept across the barren. Night was falling. The last daylight glimmered in the west, and hastening clouds streaked the horizon in the van of the coming storm.

On the brink of the black pool at the center of the barren stood a herd of caribou, their heads uplifted, staring. A moment before there had been peace — quietly feeding, they had straggled across the bog. But now battle was in the air. On the flank of the band stood the herding bull — a great, white-maned creature, gray on the flanks, whose crowning antlers upreared over the cows like a guarding weapon. Beyond him pawed the challenger, once tolerated in the herd, but now, with the rut strong upon him, bawling defiance at the leader. They were sire and son. Across the shoulders of each ran a broad, white band, an unusual marking among the caribou. All day the younger had been beating the alders with his horns; now he was wildly eager for the fray. *Ruh-rr-r!* he bellowed gutturally.

The gale had lulled a moment, and in the sudden quiet, the sound volleyed across the interval. An uneasy tremor moved the herd; it bunched in its agitation, the cows huddling about their principal. The swollen neck of the herding bull bristled. Snorting in answer, he breasted the cows aside, his call of war ringing clear across the gathering night. Pawing the sodden earth, he pushed forward, "brattling" in rage. After years of mastery, should his sway be now disputed? Here was the bidding of Nature — once more the struggle for mastery.

Roaring, they crashed together. With a ringing stroke their antlers met, and, heads down, they wrestled across the mossy flooring of the bog. Their breaths whistled stridently, and the ground thudded beneath their quick-flying

strokes. Night resounded with the clang of horn on horn. Nervously the cows looked on, or, again, in the lulls of the combat, stamped the bog. Sometimes they trotted to and fro along the flanks of the combat; sometimes they blatted, their staccato complaint urging on the fighters.

Weakness fell upon the herding bull, long time master of the ranges. He felt his power slipping from him. Conqueror in half a hundred battles, he was himself to taste the bitterness of defeat. Against his stout antagonist, whose thews and sinews were an inheritance from himself, his stand was short. His breath failed, and every voice gasped agony as it whistled from his lungs. The younger bull plied on with added fierceness, hurling his bulk against the tottering defense, beating down the swaying head — striking, stabbing as he would. Roaring in frenzy, the older bull upreared, wavered, and crashed backward as the other goaded him with piercing tines. A moment he lay inert; then, tottering to his feet, he fled, his implacable enemy following, driving him from the place.

A sudden flaw swept again across the barren, and the wind hummed among the spruce like a sound of gales upon the sea. The cows had wandered on, and with backs to the gusts, were feeding before the storm, indifferent now to the outcome of the fray. They had passed the pond hole, when across the bog came a rattle of hoofs clicking like a dancer's castanets. They threw up their heads and tried the air. Then they faced the storm, and out of the blinding rain-sheets came the conqueror, his neck still ruffled and his eyes still red from rage. He called once, they answered softly, and they were gone together — fleeting specters vanishing into the gloom. It was but the way of Nature — the survival of the fittest.

With the deepening of the snows, the battling rage of the bull died out. Yet he still held sway over the herd, leading it proudly from range to range. Their old leader was gone — exiled, an outcast. Together the band tracked the wilderness — here one day and gone the next, yet ever returning to the big barren of the Mamoziekel. In broad daylight they kept to the open country, for their lord was not the usual caribou bull, who skulks halting through the bushes. His craft seemed infallible; his nose keen to detect danger in the wind. So he led bravely.

Through the long winter they hovered about the barren.

Sometimes, after a heavy wind, they voyaged through the forest to feed on the lichens blown down with broken limbs and treetops, but in the deep snow their usual food was the moss on the big barren. In its center were no drifts, and they pawed away the white covering and fed fatly upon the food beneath. Still wind and weather told. Before the new year had come, their coats were growing streaky yellow, the hair long and heavy, and their round barrels were gradually flattening out.

The bull no longer wore his crest with pride. It seemed a useless burden. He faced the wind with a lowered head, and about the bases of his horns crept an itching soreness. As he straggled into the wracked, distorted depths of a cedar swamp, he struck his antlers against a tree, and one antler dropped to the ground. Then he forged along, lop-eared and lop-headed, a most dejected-looking royalty — for all like a tipsy princeling with coronet askew. But a day later he revived; the other horn followed its mate, and, relieved of the uneven burden, he skipped across the barren at an eager pace, the snow flying in clouds under his cracking hoofs. The cows followed, and working to the northward he crossed the timbered valley, swung up over the ridges, and bore away to Nictau. Through the forest they kept their unbroken gait, their broad hoofs carrying them gallantly over the snowdrifts, and, at length, burst forth on the frozen surface of the lake. The sun shone, the air was crisp and invigorating. Like kittens they gambolled up and down the broad expanse. At night they fed in the black swamp at the eastward, and with the rising of the moon filed again across the ice, bound for a far-away range on the headwaters of the Sisson Branch.

The winter passed, and there was promise in the air. Flights of wild fowl, gossiping high overhead, sped northward to the breeding places; and on the mountain's southern slopes the ground was bursting with new life. The winter uneasiness of the herd had waned; they sought for a summer resting ground, and in swift passages southward drove the bewildered moose floundering from many a winter yard. But, after all the wandering, the herd returned once more to the big barren, and in a thick swamp just at its head cast themselves down to settle for the season.

Domestic affairs occupied their time. The bull's horns had just sprouted, when a heavy cow bore into the world a little awkward stranger. It was an uncouth youngling indeed. Its feet seemed out of all proportion; it was knock-kneed and hardly bigger than a dog. The bull clung about idly while this offspring was delivered into the world, and at dawn slouched into the covert where the mother cow lay huddled, the weakling at her side. He gazed at the calf — the clumsy, spindle-legged creature with the spreading, splay feet — and sniffed as if in scorn. But still the calf was big — a bull, and, like its sire, curiously marked with the band of white across its withers. It shuffled loosely to its knees as he loomed over it, and the cow, reaching forth, steadied it with her head until it stood, with legs far apart, for the first time on its feet.

Seemingly, the calf gave little concern to the bull, for the surly leader had troubles of his own. His head was swollen about the pedicles of the growing horns, and all his attention was required to pick a painless way for himself through the forest arches. Moreover, the flies had come with the first warm weather; life was hardly worth living when they grew attentive, and there was no peace without a lake or mud-wallow handy. Two pads of velvet on the sides of his head showed where the new antlers were sprouting and as they pushed forth he scratched them delicately with the point of his hoof. They were sore — very sore, indeed — and he moved about in moody dignity.

When the weather grew warm in earnest, and the calf was able to frisk about with his fellows, the herd's longing took them tripping from one lake to another. In the clear, cool water they swam and wallowed. Sometimes they fed on the water grasses, but their main food was still lichens. They did not often browse, as the moose do on the tender sprigs, and when they did, they plucked at the buds instead of nipping them clearly. An Indian, seeing their work, would have known it from the browsing of the moose. "Moose ben here, sartin" — pointing to a clean-cut twig. "Hunh! that caribow feller!" — pointing to a fractured one.

During the day they clung to the heart of the deepest swamps, and at night tracked the shores of the black ponds and pug-holes. There was one mud-pit in an opening on the ridges which they often favored, and here the bull, his cows, and the calves would wallow in pure delight. Garbed with black slime from head to foot, they were a rowdy crew, but the morning dip in the lake made them once more presentable. It was a grand life, and they waxed fat and happy.

One warm afternoon, just after the last snow had vanished from the hollows under the hills, the herd bore down the slope of Bald Mountain, and swung away toward Bathurst. When they struck into the flat lying between, the bull paused and threw up his head. A faint air strayed about the valley, and, as a cross-current swept overhead, the bull caught a warning scent — the rank taint that betrayed the presence of a foe. He sniffed heavily, his nose wrinkling as he sought another gust, and was just tentatively stepping onward, when there was a resounding crash in the bush.

A black form hurled itself upon him. He saw the creature jump — a great hulk of fur — saw its distended jaws and horrid shape. One instant he stood appalled, then with a violent thrill he leaped aside. It was a bear, a lean, ravenous creature, not long from its winter den, and wild with hunger. As the bull jumped the bear shot by, missed its stroke, but by chance gashed a cow cruelly along the shoulder. She was a big one, an anomaly that boasted a small set of horns. Bawling with fear, she wheeled and fled, a flap of skin hanging from her shoulder, and blood streaming along the brown forest. Crashing forward with frantic jumps, the herd cleared the perilous neighborhood, and once free from peril, dropped into their swinging trot, while from the rear came the bear's long-drawn howl of disappointment.

As they clattered along the back-trail fresh disaster awaited. Beyond the spur of the ridge, they crossed down toward the lake, and were clattering along the game trail at its edge, when the cows halted abruptly, spun about, and fled, the calves shambling at their heels. The bull stopped in wonder. He tried the air, and scented a strong pungent odor — saw a wisp of blue smoke crawling over the tree-tops, and, for the first time in his life, beheld a man. Cautiously he drew near, vainly trying for a scent. He saw the figure at the fire start up, and then a ripping crash thundered along the forest. The bull jumped. He did not know he had been fired on, and in mild curiosity skipped through the bush and circled the camp. There a sudden suspicion seized him; he plunged about, and in a long, swinging stride took away on the trail of the cows.

On the Bathurst carry he overtook them. The cows and calves were ambling along the open path, still nervous with vague terrors. They had escaped so far, but what was in store? The bull took his place at their head, resolved that peace and quiet must be sought far away from here. As they dipped down over the crest of the divide, and neared an abandoned beaver meadow, he swung out, mindful of his horns, from under a leaning tree trunk that had all the semblance of a windfall. But the cows kept straight on. Crash! The windfall fell thunderously, filling the silent forest with re-echoing noises. The bull leaped as if struck. Beneath the heavy tree lay the leading cow, her back broken, writhing in a last mortal effort. She had walked into the trap, sprung the trigger, and the deadfall had slain her, as its builders had devised. They were the poachers in camp on the lake — bear hunters — and this was their method of getting bait for bruin.

The bull circled about the dying cow, powerless to aid. He sniffed the air, and hung over his stricken mate, trotting to and fro with futile energy. A gust stirred the treetops, and whirling along the ridge, set down toward him. Snorting anew, he threw up his head and looked. He saw two figures running swiftly along the trail — saw them stoop and point forward, and once more the forest resounded with the rifle's deafening noise. The herd broke and ran in every direction, leaving him there alone. Once more there was a loud report, a gush of flame — the man had fired and missed again. But as the lead stirred the hair on the bull's shoulders, he shook himself together from this mad fascination and fled — away from the direful place and the cow heaving in a convulsion of death upon the forest floor.

The herd was gone, and he a wanderer alone. He followed to the north, searching far and wide. He tried the unknown barrens under the flank of Bald Mountain, swept about the edge of the long ridges, and circled the headwaters of the Mamoziekel. But they were gone, he knew not where. Alone and weary, he kept up the days of weary pursuit, felt the summer slip by, and, with the first frosts, was touched, once more, with the rutting wrath.

They told in the settlements of a caribou bull — a mighty straggler from the herds, bigger than any man had ever seen before. He was using along the great range westward of Nictau, and twice, they knew, he had been fired upon. Once blood had been drawn, but the men on the trail were no match in speed or stamina for this solitary, and had given up the chase after weary miles, convinced that the wound was slight. His antlers were a marvel, they spread like the brown roots of a hemlock windfall, and down the center of his nose ran a brow-palm, as big and broad, almost, as the shovel of a moose. Vainly they sought for a nearer shot, but his craft foiled them. At the first suggestion of danger he was gone, vanishing like a specter.

Fear had taught its lesson to the big bull. He had renounced his first swaggering indifference, and now skulked and treaded as timorously as any creature on the range. He followed the wind keenly, and on the rising ridges looked over for possible foes before revealing himself. He no longer swam the ponds in daylight, and rarely moved except at night. But among the caribou he was still master. He fought from range to range, forever looking for the lost herd, but the snows came again, and he had not found it. Sometimes he forgot his terrors, and ran through the forest, pausing on the ridges to roar a challenge of a call. But it was of no avail, and, at last, in a sudden access of fury, he fell upon the leader of a passing herd, beat him down, and, victorious, thrust his companionship upon the cows.

Year after year he kept on. His rage was masterful. He harried and abused and drove from the hills the bulls that sought to withstand him. He rounded his cows about roughly, hectoring them at every turn. At the beginning of every rut he fell in a fury upon the spike-horn yearlings, and gored cruelly, driving them from the herd. Perhaps he was in mind of how he himself had come into power over his own sire. In this warfare he wandered far from the barren of the Mamoziekel, carrying dismay before him. Yet in his heart there was ever a longing, a desire to return and once more be with the lost herd, to go back to the place of his birth as every caribou goes.

Years passed and he grew old. His horns had increased in size and strength while his vigor held, but now that age was coming, he noted a difference. At last one autumn found him with diminished weapons. In the place of the center palm was only a spindly tine. Moreover, his antlers did not reach so far, nor were they so stout about the beams. Still he felt no relaxing of his ugly humors, no weakening of his might. He held his sway unchecked, and when other bulls came up against him, he forced the conflict to a swift and powerful climax.

His fear of men had become a second nature. He steered wide of ranges where he had heard the rifle speak doom to other caribou. Nor did he relax his vigilance, like the other bulls, when law forbids the shooting. He took no chances, and so survived. Then one day the fit to wander homeward fell upon him. He shacked to his feet, and roared. The cows arose, and, at the sound, another bull came challenging up the slope of the ridges. He was big, and the battle waxed furious. At its height still another bull, an interloper, stole in and drove away the cows. Thus, when the conflict ended, and the challenging bull had been driven crashing through the thickets, he again found himself alone. He stood for a while and called. But there was no answer, no clatter of the brush betokening their return. Darkness fell upon the forest, and turning his head southward, he sped away, homeward — back to the black headwaters of the Mamoziekel and the big barren that still lay unchanged, to the forest where axe never sounded nor rifle spoke. Hope sprung high in his heart — the lost herd would be found.

Into this wild came, the day after, a man. He had followed the long valley of the stream that runs into Nictau, setting a course along the ridges that back up the southern slope of Bald Mountain. He pushed out upon the barren, and halted, studying the tracks that marked the black ooze of the quagmire. Presently he stooped, with wide eyes studying one great track that punctuated the writing of trafficking herds. The slot was big and broad, more than a hand's-breadth across, and, with the twin dots of the accessory hoofs, almost as long. Rising with a gesture of eagerness, he sped along, studying the ground.

Overhead, a skim of dull vapor cast across the zenith, and the wind, moaning fitfully among the tall spires of the pines and spruce, betokened the approach of snow. Abruptly the man turned aside from the trail, plunged into the edge of the forest, and threw down his pack. Pushing aside the bush, he crouched there, his rifle ready.

In a thicket farther up the bog lay the big bull. Here in this retreat he was nursing the wounds of battle — stiff and sore and ugly.

A twig cracked on the hillside. His neck bristled, and he heaved himself to his feet. Across the open he saw a cow steal to the edge of the woods and peep forth. Another followed, then came a pair of skipping calves and two more cows, one a shoulder-scarred creature with small horns. A tremor seized him. He saw the familiar forms, the gray figures of old, the calves band-streaked across the withers — the lost herd! He pushed from the thicket, calling madly, and at the same moment another bull stepped into the open in the train of the advancing cows.

Across the shoulders of the newcomer was that same distinctive mark. His own memory went back to the day when this great, gallant creature was but a weakling come into the world in this same swamp. And now it had grown to this proud estate! Year after year it had clung to the herd. As a yearling it had been tolerated by the ursurper who had found the stray herd when they lost their leader in the disaster of the trap. But with its second year and its first long spikes, it had been browbeaten, pushed, and driven about. Still it had kept by the same little family, returning in peace when the rut was past. Again in the third year it had fought and failed; but in the fourth it arose, mighty in strength, well armed and headed, and falling upon the bullying lord of the herd, drove him forth, stricken and cowed.

At a sharp trot the band moved down the wind. Forward stepped the old bull. His head was uplifted with its still mighty crest, and there was a new fire in his eye. He gazed at the cows and at their leader. He stretched his throat and called anew, and at the racketing call, they halted in their tracks.

The younger bull stopped, stamping. The hair on his neck ruffled; he spread his feet and bellowed a challenge. Who was this come to dispute his sway? His petulant hoof pawed the earth, and gutturally he gave the call of war.

The sound rang down the barren, stirring the man crouching in the thicket. At the challenge the old bull tossed his antlers. Before, he had never hesitated; but now he did not rush to battle. Old memories, perhaps, were in his mind, and in his heart peace. But the challenge was renewed; the other was advancing. With lowered head the younger bull stepped along, fire in his eyes. *Ruh-rr-r!* he roared — *ruh!*

They advanced, the old bull half temporizing. He called plaintively, but the other took no notice of the appeal. Nearer he came — nearer and nearer, and the man, crouching in the thicket, cocked his rifle, waiting.

A sudden scurry of hoofs beat upon the bog. With a frenzied effort the younger bull burst upon the other. The big one fell back, unwilling for combat, but once more the young one charged. Startled, the old bull recoiled again, and the younger, breaking through his guard, stabbed him on the flank.

A pang rang through the old caribou's nerves, and a roar escaped him. He forgot all; his wrath, his fear, perhaps, aroused. Once more the blood ran hotly through his veins, and he turned upon his antagonist, mad for the fight.

Their heads shocked together, and the forest threw back the sound in clattering echoes. The torn and trampled moss flew about and blood-streaked froth flecked their heaving shoulders. Again they lunged, the antlers locked — one striving for mastery; the other — knowing it — for life. Once the old bull was forced back upon his haunches, and was all but lost. By a mighty effort he writhed free and recovered. Then he whirled upon the other, and strove to beat down his crest. He was sublime, yet he failed — and terror choked him.

A flurry of snow sped across the bog, the first of the dying year. It wheeled across the landscape for an instant, blotting out the fray. The man, crouching in the thicket, drew a hand across his eyes, almost appalled at the fierceness of this strife. Slipping out upon the barren, he crawled toward them.

The younger bull drew on. With unabated strength he beat and battered at the swaying antlers of his adversary, and inch by inch drove him back. His rage was direful. The cows, trotting up and down the arena, called piteously; yet the strife went on. At last, with an overwhelming effort, the younger bull drove upon the other. He hunched his shoulders, struck with destroying force, and as the old bull staggered for an instant, half-reared, and turned aside, he struck still again, another mighty blow. Down went the old bull, a brow-tine piercing him in the vitals. He struggled once to his knees, turned with a despairing call to the cows, and died.

Back from the forest blew the wind, laden with a terrifying taint. One breath of it sent the cows streaming in every direction. But the conqueror gave no heed. He stood over the dead, lifted his crest, and gave the call. Blood and froth flecked his white mane; the steam spumed from his wide-pressed nostrils.

A moments silence — then from down the bog streamed a spear of flame. The hills harked back with thundering echoes. Again a shot! High into the air leaped the conquering bull, and fell, kicking spasmodically, across the form of the other.

The Plural of Moose is Mise

Irvin S. Cobb

AT THE OUTSET, when our expedition was still in the preparatory stages, we collectively knew a few sketchy details regarding the general architectural plan and outward aspect of the moose. One of us had once upon a time, years and years before, shot at or into — this point being debatable — a moose up in Maine. Another professed that in his youth he had seriously annoyed a moose with buckshot somewhere in Quebec. The rest of us had met the moose only in zoos with iron bars between us and him or in dining halls, where his head, projecting in a stuffed and mounted condition from the wall, gave one the feeling of dining with somebody out of the Old Testament. Speaking with regard to his family history, we understood he was closely allied to the European elk — the Unabridged told us that — and we gathered that, viewed at a distance, he rather suggested a large black mule with a pronounced Roman nose and a rustic hatrack sprouted out between his ears. Also, through our reading upon the subject, we knew that next to the buffalo he was the largest vegetarian in North America and, next to a man who believes in the forecast of a campaign manager on the eve of an election, the stupidest native mammal that we have. By hearsay we had been made aware that he possessed a magnificent sense of smell and a perfectly wonderful sense of hearing, but was woefully shy on the faculty of thought, the result being that while by the aid of his nose and his ear he might all day elude you, if then perchance you did succeed in getting within gunning range of him he was prone to remain right where he was, peering blandly at you and accommodatingly shifting his position so as to bring his shape broadside on, thereby offering a better target until you, mastering the tremors of eagerness, succeeded in implanting a leaden slug in one of his vital areas.

But, offhand, we couldn't decide what the plural of him was. Still if the plural of goose were geese and the plural of mouse were mice it seemed reasonable to assume that the plural of moose should be mise. Besides, we figured that when we had returned and met friends and told them about our trip it would sound more impressive, in fact more plural, to say that we had slain mise rather than that we had slaughtered moose. In the common acceptance of the term as now used, moose might mean one moose or a herd of them, but mise would mean at least a bag of two of these mighty creatures and from two on up to any imaginable number.

One mentally framed the conversation:

"Well, I hear you've been up in Canada moose hunting." This is the other fellow speaking. "Kill any moose?"

"Kill any moose? Huh, we did better than that — we killed mise."

So by agreement we arranged that mise it should be. This being settled we went ahead with plans for outfitting ourselves against our foray into the game country. We equipped ourselves with high-powered rifles, with patent bedding rolls, with fanciful conceits in high boots and blanket overcoats. We bought everything that the clerk in the shop, who probably had never ventured north of the Bronx in all the days of his sheltered life, thought we should buy, including wicked-looking sheath knives and hand axes to be carried in the belt, tomahawk fashion, and pocket compasses. Personally, I have never been able to figure out the exact value of a compass to a man adrift in a strange country. What is the use of knowing where north is if you don't know where *you* are? Nevertheless, I was prevailed upon to purchase a compass, along with upward of a great gross of other articles large and small which the clerk believed would be needful to one starting upon such an expedition as we contemplated.

On my account he did a deal of thinking. Not since the fall of 1917, when we were making the world safe for the sporting-goods dealers of America, could he have spent so busy and so happy an afternoon as the afternoon when I dropped in on him.

By past experience I should have known better than to permit myself to be swept off my feet by this tradesman's flood of suggestions and recommendations. Already I had an ample supply of khaki shirts that were endeared to me by associations of duck-hunting forays in North Carolina and chill evenings in an Adirondack camp and a memorable journey to Wyoming, where the sage hen abides. I treasured a pair of comfortable hunting boots that had gone twice to European battlefields and down into the Grand Canyon and up again and across the California desert, without ever breeding a blister or chafing a shin. Among my most valued possessions I counted an ancient shooting coat, wearing which I had missed quail in Kentucky, snipe on Long Island, grouse in Connecticut, doves in Georgia, and woodcock in New York State. Finally, had I but taken time for sober second consideration, I should have recalled that the guides I have from time to time known considered themselves properly accoutered for the chase when they put on the oldest suit of store clothes they owned and stuck an extra pair of wool socks in their pockets. But to the city-bred sportsman half the joy of going on a camping trip consists in getting ready for it. So eminent an authority as Emerson Hough is much given to warning the amateur sportsman against burdening himself with vain adornments, and yet I am reliably informed that the said Hough has a larger individual collection of pretty devices in canvas and leather than any person in this republic.

That clerk had a seductive way about him; he had a positive gift. Otherwise I suppose he would have been handling some line which practically sells itself, such as oil stocks or mining shares. Under the influence of his blandishments I invested in a sweater of a pattern which he assured me was being favored by the really prominent moose hunters in the current season, and a pair of corduroy hunting pants which, when walked in, gave off a pleasant swishing sound like a soft-shoe dancer starting to do a sand jig. I was particularly drawn to these latter garments as being the most vocal pants I had ever seen. As I said before, I bought ever and ever so many other things; I am merely mentioning some of the main items.

We assembled the most impassive group of guides in the whole Dominion — men who, filled with the spirit of the majestic wilds, had never been known publicly to laugh at the expense of a tender-footed stranger. They did not laugh at Harry Leon Wilson's conception of the proper equipment for a man starting upon such an excursion as this one. Wilson on being wired an invitation to go on a hunt for moose promptly telegraphed back that to the best of his recollection he had not lost any moose, but that if any of his friends had been so unfortunate or so careless as to mislay one he would gladly join in the quest for the missing. He brought along an electric flashlight, in case the search should be prolonged after nightfall, a trout rod and a camera. The guides did not laugh at Colonel Tillinghast Houston's unique notion of buying an expensive rifle and a hundred rounds of ammunition and then spending his days in camp sitting in a tent reading a history of the Maritime Provinces in two large volumes. They did not laugh at Colonel Bozeman Bulger's overseas puttees or at Damon Runyon's bowie knife, or at Major McGeehan's eight-pound cartridge belt — it weighed more than that when loaded; I am speaking of it, *net* — or at Frank Stevens' sleeping cap or at Bill MacBeth's going-away haircut — the handiwork of a barber who was a person looking with abhorrence upon the thought of leaving any hair upon the human neck when it is so easy to shave all exposed surfaces smooth and clean from a point drawn across the back of the head at the level of the tops of the ears on down as far as the rear collar button. He must have been a lover of the nude in necks, that barber.

The guides did not laugh even at my vociferous corduroys, which at every step I took, went *hist, hist,* as though entreating their wearer to be more quiet so they might the better be heard.

By a series of relay journeys we moved up across the line into Quebec, thence back again below the boundary and across the state of Maine, thence out of Maine into New Brunswick and to the thriving city of St. John, with its justly celebrated reversible falls which, by reason of the eccentricities of the tide, tumble upstream part of the time and downstream part of the time, thence by steamer across that temperamental body of water known as the Bay of Fundy, and so on into the interior of Nova Scotia. If anywhere on this continent there is a lovelier spot than the southern part of Nova Scotia in mid-fall I earnestly desire that, come next October, someone shall take me by the hand and lead me to it and let me rave. It used to be the land of Evangeline and the Acadians; now it is the land of the apple. You ran out of the finnan-haddie belt in and around Digby into the wonderful valley of the apples. On every hand are apples — on this side of the right-of-way, orchards stretching down to the blue waters of one of the most beautiful rivers in America, on that side, orchards climbing up the flanks of the rolling hills to where the combing of thick timber comes down and meets them; and everywhere, at roadside, on the verges of thickets, in pastures and old fields, are seedlings growing singly, in pairs and in clumps. They told us that the valley scenically considered is at its best in the spring after the bloom bursts out upon the trees and the whole countryside turns to one vast pink and white bridal bouquet, but hardly can one picture it revealing itself as a more delectable vision than when the first frosts have fallen and every bough of every tree is studded with red and green and yellow globes and the scent of the ripened fruit rises like an incense of spices and wine.

The transition from the pastoral to the wilderness is abrupt. You leave Annapolis Royal in a motor car — that is, you do if you follow in our footsteps — and almost immediately you strike into the big game country. Not that the big game does not lap over into the settlements and even into the larger towns on occasion, for it does. It is recorded that on a certain day a full-grown moose — and a full-grown moose is almost the largest full-grown thing you ever saw — strolled through one of the principal streets of St. John and sought to enter — this being in the old sinful times — a leading saloon. A prominent lawyer of the same city told me that some four weeks before our arrival a woman client of his, living some two miles from the corporate limits, called him on the telephone at his office to ask his professional advice as to how legally she might go about getting rid of a bull moose which insisted on frequenting her orchard and frightening her children when they went to gather pippins. She felt, she said, that a lawyer was the proper person to seek in the emergency that had arisen, seeing that the closed season for moose was still on and it would be unlawful to take a shot at the intruder, so what she particularly desired to know was whether she couldn't have him impounded for trespass or something of that nature.

But such things as these do not happen every day. Probably a man could spend months on end in St John without seeing the first of the above-mentioned animals rambling down the sidewalk in the manner of a young moose-about-town and trying to drop into the place where the saloon used to be, only to back out again, with chagrin writ large upon his features, upon discovering that the establishment in question had been transformed into a hat store.

To meet the moose where frequently he is and not merely where occasionally he is, one must go beyond the outlying orchards and on into the vasty expanse of the real moose country — hundreds of hundreds of miles of virgin waste, trackless except for game trails and portages across the ridges between waterways. It is a country of tamaracks and hemlocks, of maples and beech and birch, of berries and flowering shrubs, of bogs and barrens and swampy swales, of great granite boulders left behind by the glaciers when the world was young and thawing, of countless lakes and brawling white rapids and deep blue pools where, in the spawning season, the speckled trout are so thick that the small trout have to travel on the backs of the larger ones to avoid being crushed in the jam. I did not see this last myself; my authority for the statement is my friend the veracious lawyer of St. John. But I saw all the rest of it — the woods wearing the flaunting war-paint colors of the wonderful Canadian Indian summer — crimson of huckleberry, tawny of tamarack, yellow of birch, scarlet of maple; the ruffed grouse strutting, unafraid as barnyard fowl and, thanks be to a three-year period of protection, almost as numerous as sparrows in a city street; the signs of hoofed and padded creatures crossing and crisscrossing wherever the earth was soft enough to register the foot tracks of wild things.

And if you want to know how interior New Brunswick looked after Nova Scotia, you are respectfully requested to reread the foregoing paragraph, merely leaving out some of the lakes and most of the boulders.

On a flawless morning, in a motorboat we crossed a certain lake, and I wish I knew the language that might serve to describe the glory of the colors that ringed that lake around and were reflected, to the last flame-tipped leaf and the last smooth white column of birchen trunk in its still waters, but I don't. I'll go further and say I can't believe Noah Webster had the words to form the picture, and he had more words than anybody up to the time William J. Bryan went actively into politics. As for myself, I can only say that these colors fairly crackled. There were hues and combinations of hues, shadings and contrasts such as no artist ever has painted and no artist will care to paint, either, for fear of being called a nature faker.

The scene shifts to our main camp. We have met our guides and have marveled at their ability to trot over steep up-and-down-hill portages carrying, each one of them, upon his back a load which no humane man would put on a mule, and have marveled still more when these men, having deposited their mountainous burdens at the farther end of the carry, go hurrying back across the ridge presently to reappear bearing upon their shoulders upturned canoes, their heads hidden inside the inverted interiors and yet by some magic gift peculiar to their craft, managing somehow to dodge the overhanging boughs of trees and without losing speed or changing gait to skip along from one slick round-topped boulder top to another.

Now we are in the deep woods, fifty miles from a railroad and thirty miles from a farmhouse. We sleep at night in canvas lean-tos, with log fires at our feet; we wash our faces and hands in the lake and make high resolves — which we never carry out — to take dips in that same frosty water;

we breakfast at sun-up and sup at dusk in a log shanty set behind the cluster of tents, and between breakfast and supper we seek, under guidance, for fresh meat and dining-room trophies.

We have come too late for the calling season, it seems. In the calling season Mr. Moose desires female society, and by all accounts desires it mightily. So the guide takes a mean advantage of his social cravings. Generally afoot, but sometimes in a canoe, he escorts the gunner to a likely feeding ground or a drinking place and through a scroll of birch bark rolled up in a megaphone shape, he delivers a creditable imitation of the call of the flirtatious cow moose. There are guides who can sound the love note through their cupped hands, but most of the fraternity favor the birchen cornucopia. The sound — part lonely bleat, part plaintive bellow — travels across the silent reaches for an incredible distance. Once when the wind was right here is record of a moose call having been heard six miles away from where it was uttered, but in this case the instrumentalist was Louis Harlowe, a half-breed Micmac Indian, the champion moose caller of Nova Scotia and perhaps the world.

In the bog where he is lying, or on the edge of the barren where he is feeding, the bull hears the pleading entreaty and thereby is most grossly deceived. Forgetting the caution which guides his course at other times, he hurries to where the deceiver awaits him, in his haste smashing down saplings, clattering his great horns against the tree boles, splashing through the brooks. And then when he bursts forth into the open, snorting and puffing and grunting, the hunter beholds before him a target which in that setting and with that background must loom up like a grain elevator. Yet at a distance of twenty yards or thirty, he has been known to miss the mark clean and to keep on missing it, while the vast creature stands there, its dull brain filled with wonder that the expected cow should not be where he had every vocal assurance that she would be, and seemingly only mildly disturbed by the crashing voice of the repeater and by the unseen, mysterious things which pass whistling over his back or under his belly as the gun quivers in the uncertain grasp of the overanxious or mayhap the buckague-stricken sportsman.

Once though he has made up his sluggish mind that all is not well for him in that immediate vicinity, he vanishes into deep cover as silently as smoke and as suddenly as a wink.

The mating time comes in mid-September and lasts about a month, more or less; and since the open season does not begin until October the first, it behooves the hunter who wishes to bag his moose with the least amount of physical exertion to be in camp during the first two weeks of October, for after that the bull moose is reverting to bachelorhood again. He may answer the call, but the chances are that he will not.

A little later on, after the snows have come, one may trail him with comparative ease. Besides, he is browsing more liberally then and consequently is moving pretty consistently. But between the time when the leaves begin to fall and the time when the snow begins to fly he is much given to staying in the densest coverts he can find and doing the bulk of his grazing by night.

So he must be still-hunted, as the saying goes, and it was still-hunting that we were called upon to do. The guide takes his birch-bark horn along each morning when he starts out, carrying it under one arm and an axe under the other, and upon his back a pouch containing the ingredients for a midday lunch and the inevitable fire-blackened teapot, which he calls by the affectionate name of "kittle." He never speaks of stopping for lunch. When the sun stands overhead and your foreshortened shadow has snuggled up close beneath your feet like a friendly black puppy, he suggests the advisability of "biling a kittle," by which he means building a fire and making tea. So the pack between his shoulders is necessary but the moose call is largely ornamental; it is habit for him to tote it and tote it he does; but mainly he depends upon his eyes and his ears and his uncanny knowledge of the ways of the thing we aim to destroy.

Yes, they call it still-hunting and still-hunting it truly is so far as Louis Harlowe, the half-breed, or Sam Glode, the full-blooded Micmac, or Charley Charlton, the head guide, is concerned, as he goes worming his way through the undergrowth in his soft-soled moccasins, instinctively avoiding the rotted twig, the loose bit of stone and the swishy bough. But the pair of us, following in his footsteps, in our hard-bottomed, hobnailed boots, our creaky leather gear and our noisy waterproofed nether garments, cannot, by the wildest latitude in descriptive terminology, be called still-hunters. Carrying small avalanches with us, we slide down rocky slopes which the guide on ahead of us negotiated in pussy-footed style; and we blunder into undergrowth; and we trip over logs and we flounder into bogs and out of them again with loud, churning sounds. Going into second on a hillside we pant like switch engines. I was two weeks behind with my panting when I came out of Canada and at odd times now I still pant briskly, trying to catch up.

Reaching level ground we reverse gears and halt to blow. Toward mid-afternoon, on the homebound hike, our weary legs creak audibly at the joints and our tired feet blunder and fumble among the dried leaves. We create all the racket which, without recourse to bass drums or slide trombones, it is humanly possible for a brace of overdressed, city-softened sojourners to create in deep woods. And still our guide — that person so utterly lacking in a sense of humor — speaks of our endeavor as still-hunting. If an ethical Nova Scotian guide — and all professional guides everywhere, so far as I have observed, are most ethical — were hired to chaperon Sousa's band on a still-hunt through the wilderness and on the way Mr. Sousa should think up a new march full of oompahs and everything, and the band should practice it while cruising from bog to barren, the guide, returning to the settlements after the outing, would undoubtedly refer to it as a still-hunt.

In our own case, I trust that our eagerness in some measure compensated for our awkwardness. At least, we worked hard — worked until muscles that we never knew before we had achingly forced themselves upon our attention. Yes, if for the first day or two our exertion brought us no reward in the shape of antlered frontlets or great black pelts drying on the rocks at the canoe landing or savory moose steaks in the frying pan; if it seemed that after all we would have to content ourselves with taking home a stuffed guide's head or so; if twilight found us reuniting at the supper table each with tales of endless miles of tramping to our credit but no game, nevertheless and notwithstanding, the labor we spent was not without its plenteous compensations.

To begin with, there was ever the hope that beyond the next thicket or across the next swale old Mr. Sixty Inch Spread would be browsing about waiting for us to come stealing upon him with all the stealthy approach of a runaway moving van and blow him over. There was the joy of watching our guide trailing, he reading the woods as a scholar reads a book and seeing there plain as print what we never would have seen — the impress of a great splayed hoof in the yellowed moss, the freshly gnawed twigs of the moose wood, the scarred bark high up on a maple to show that here a bull had whetted his horns, the scuffed earth where a bear had been digging for grubs, the wallow a buck deer had made at a crossing. And when he told us that the moose had passed this way, trotting, less than an hour before, but that the deer's bed was at least two nights old, while the bear's scratching dated back for days, we knew that he knew. Real efficiency in any line carries its own credentials and needs no bolstering affidavits. There may be better eyes in some human head than the pair Louis Harlowe owns or than that equally keen pair belonging to Harry Allen, the dean of New Brunswick guides, but I have yet to see their owner, and I am quite sure that for woodcraft there are no better equipped men anywhere than the two I have named.

We couldn't decide which was the finer — the supper at night with a great log fire chasing back the dense shadows, and the baked beans and the talk and the crisp bacon and the innocent lies passing back and forth or the midday lunch out in the tangy, painted forest, miles and miles away from anywhere at all, with the chickadees and the snowbirds and the robins flittering about, waiting their chance to gather the crumbs they knew we would leave behind for them, and with the moose birds informally dropping in on us before ever the kettle had begun to sing.

Naturalists know the moose bird, I believe, as the Canada jay and over the line in the States they call him the venison hawk, but by any name he is a handsome, saucy chap, as smart as Satan and as impudent as they make 'em. The first thin wisp of your fire, rising above the undergrowth, is his signal. For some of the denizens of the wilderness it may be just twelve o'clock, but to him it's feeding time. Here he comes in his swooping flight, a graceful, slate-blue figure with his snowy bib and tucker like a trencherman prepared. And there, following close behind him, are other members of his tribe. There always is one in the flock more daring than the rest. If you sit quietly, this fellow will flit closer and closer, his head cocked on one side, uttering half-doubtful, half-confident cheeps until he is snatching up provender right under your feet or even out of your hand. His preference is for meat — raw meat for choice, but his taste is catholic; he'll eat anything. Small morsels he swallows on the spot, larger tidbits he takes in his bill and flies away with to hide in a nearby tree crotch. His friends watch him, and by the time he has returned for another helping they have stolen his cache, so that chiefly what he gets out of the burden of his thrifty industry is the exercise. I do not know whether this should teach us that it is better to strive to lay something against a rainy day and take a chance on the honesty of the neighbors or to seize our pleasure when and where we find it and forget the morrow. Aesop might be able to figure it out, but, being no Aesop, I must continue to register uncertainty.

Campfire suppers and high noon barbecues and glorious sunrises and shooting the rapids in the rivers and paddling across the blue lake, scaring up the black duck and the loons from before us, and all rest of it, was fine enough in its way, but it was not killing the bull moose. So we hunted and we hunted. We dragged our reluctant feet through moose bogs — beaver meadows these are in the Adirondacks — and we ranged the high ground and the low. Cow moose we encountered frequently and calves aplenty. But the adult male was what we sought.

We had several close calls, or perhaps I should say he did. One of our outfit — nameless here because I have no desire to heap shame upon an otherwise well-meaning and always dependable companion — had been cruising through thick timber all day without seeing anything to fire at. Emerging into an open glade on a ridge above Little Red Lake, he was moved to try his new and virgin automatic at a target. So he loosed off at one of the big black crows of the North that was perched, like a disconsolate undertaker, with bunched shoulders and drooping head, on a dead tamarack fifty yards away. He did not hit Brother Corbie but he tore the top out of the tamarack snag. And then when he and the guide had rounded the shoulder of the little hill and descended to a swamp below they read in certain telltale signs a story which came near to moving the marksman to tears.

Moving up the slope from the other side the guide had been calling, a bull moose — and a whaling big one, to judge by his hoof marks — had been stirred to inquire into the circumstances. He had quitted the swamp and had ambled up the hill to within a hundred yards of the crest when — as the guide deduced it — the sound of the shot just above caused him to halt and swing about and depart from that neighborhood at his very best gait. But for that unlucky rifle report he probably would have walked right into the enemy. My friend does not now feel toward crows as he formerly felt. He thinks they should be abolished.

An experience of mine was likewise fraught with the germs of a tragic disappointment. In a densely thicketed district, my guide, with a view to getting a view of the surrounding terrain above the tops of the saplings, scaled the steep side of a boulder that was as big as an icehouse and then beckoned to me to follow.

But as a scaler I am not a conspicuous success. By main strength and awkwardness I managed to clamber up. Just as I reached the top and put my rifle down so that I might fan breath into myself with both hands, my boot soles slipped off the uncertain surface and I slid off my perch into space. Wildly I threw out both arms in a general direction. My clutching fingers closed on a limb of a maple which overshadowed the rock and I swung out into the air twelve feet or so above the inhospitable earth, utterly unable to reach with my convulsively groping feet the nearermost juts of granite. For an agonized moment it seemed probable that the only thing that might break my fall would be myself. But I kept my presence of mind. I flatter myself that in emergencies I am a quick thinker. As I dangled there an expedient came to me. I let go gradually.

And then as I plumped with a dull sickening thud into the herbage below and lay there weaponless, windless and jarred I saw, vanishing into the scrub not a hundred feet away, the black shape of a big and startled moose. I caught one fleeting glimpse of an enormous head, of a profile which might have belonged to one of the major prophets, of a set of horns outspreading even as the fronded palm outspread itself, of a switching tail and slab-sided rump, and then the shielding bushes closed and the apparition was gone, and gone for keeps. For my part there was nothing to do but to sit there for a spell and cherish regrets. Under the circumstances, trailing a frightened bull moose would have been about as satisfactory as trailing a comet, and probably not a bit more successful as to results.

For the majority of the members of our troupe the duration of the hunt had a time limit. On the afternoon of the last day in camp two of the party strolled into the immediate presence of a fair-sized bull and, firing together, one of them put a slug of lead in a twitching ear which he turned toward them. It must have been his deaf ear, else he would have been aware of their approach long before. But one moose was singular and the achievement of the plural number was our ambition. So four of us crossed back into New Brunswick, where, according to all native New Brunswickers, the moose grow larger than they do in the sister province, Nova Scotians taking the opposing side and being willing to argue it at all times.

With unabated determination the gallant quartet of us hunted and hunted. Three big deer died to make holiday for us but the moose displayed a coyness and diffidence which might be accountered for only on the ground that they heard we were coming. Indeed they could not very well help hearing it.

Each morning under the influence of the frost the flaming frost colors showed a dimming hue. Day before yesterday they had been like burning brands, yesterday there were dulled embers, today smoldering coals; and tomorrow they would be as dead ashes. Each night the sun went down in a nimbus of cold gray clouds. There was a taste and a smell as of snow in the air. The last tardy robin packed up and went south; the swarms of juncos grew thicker; wedge-shaped flights of coot and black duck passed overhead, their bills all pointing toward the Gulf of Mexico. Then on the last day there fell a rain which turned to sleet and the sleet to snow — four inches of it — and in the snow on that last day the reward which comes — sometimes — to the persevering was ours.

To know the climactic sensation which filled the triumphant amateur you must first of all care for the outdoors and for big-game shooting, and in the second place you must have known the feeling of hope deferred, and in the third place you must have reached the eleventh hour, so to speak, of your stay in these parts with the anticipation you had been nuturing for all these weeks since the trip was first proposed still unrealized in your soul.

You and your camp mate and your guide were on the last lap of the journey back to camp; the sun was slipping down the western wall of the horizon; the shadows were deepening under the spruces; you rounded the shoulder of a ridge and stood for a moment at your guide's back looking across a fire-burned barren. He stiffened like a pointer on a warm scent and pointed straight ahead. Your eye followed where his finger aimed, and two hundred yards away you saw a dark blot against a background of faded tamarack — a bull standing head-on. You shot together, you and your companion. Apparently the animal swung himself about and started moving at the seemingly languid lope of the moose, which really is a faster gait than you would suppose until you measure the length of his stride. You kept on firing, both of you, as rapidly almost as you could pull the triggers of your automatics. Twice he shoot himself and humped his hindquarters as though stung, but he did not check his speed. You emptied your magazine, five shots. Your mate's fifth shell jammed in the chamber, putting him out of the running for the moment. In desperate haste you fumbled one more shell into your rifle, and just as the fugitive topped a little rise before disappearing for good into the shrouding second growth you got your sight full on the mark and sent a farewell bullet whistling on its way. The black hulk vanished magically.

"That'll do," said your guide, grinning broadly. "You got

'im. But load up again before we go down there. He's down and down for keeps, I think, judgin' by the way he flopped, but he might get up again."

But he didn't get up again. You came on him where he lay, still feebly twitching, with two flesh wounds in his flanks and a third hole right through him behind the shoulders — a thousand pounds of meat, a head worth saving and mounting and bragging about in the years to come, a pelt as big as a double blanket and at last the accomplished plural of moose was mise.

So then you did what man generally does when language fails to express what he feels. You harked back sundry thousands of years and you did as your remote ancestors, the cave dweller, did when he slew the sabretoothed what-youmaycallhim. About the carcass of your kill you executed a war dance; at least you did if you chambered the emotions which filled the present writer to the choking point.

And then the next day, back in the settlements, when you reunited with the two remaining members of the outfit who had been in camp eight miles away from the camp where you stayed, and when you learned that now there was a total tally of three deceased beasties, the war dance was repeated, only this time it was a four-handed movement instead of a solo number.

Two Eyes that Shone as One

Edmund Ware Smith

UNCLE JEFF COONGATE was depressed. He sat in a rocker in the front room of Zack Bourne's cabin, responding gloomily to Zack's conversation. The origin of Uncle Jeff's mood was, to him, so hideous and shameful that he hated to think of it. The fact was that yesterday he had deliberately missed a standing shot at a buck deer. He had willfully fired his rifle into the air. This act of mercy, being without precedent in the one-eyed poacher's career, made him suspect that his mind was going. Even granting that the buck was a very particular one, Uncle Jeff could neither condone nor comprehend his own softness. It humiliated and distressed him. He now lived in constant dread lest Zack discover his chicken-hearted secret and expose him to ridicule throughout the lake country.

Zack perched on a bench, his rifle across his lap, his voice merry with self-esteem. Zack was fitting a wire frame to the receiver of his rifle. The frame was cunningly designed to hold a flashlight in position to shine not only the front and rear sights, but the eyes of a deer in the dark. Come nightfall, Zack, never doubting Jeff's enthusiastic aid, proposed to use the device in laying low the very buck that the one-eyed poacher had spared. To Zack, it was unthinkable that his old comrade might revolt at the idea. Zack monologued blissfully:

"Dang shame a feller couldn't patint a rig like this. I'd call her the Zack Bourne Dead Shot Jacklightin' Frame. We'll test her out tonight on that old buck. Bet he'll dress two hundrid, easy."

At the mention of the buck, Uncle Jeff winced imperceptibly. "You couldn't patint that rig this side of hell," he muttered.

Zack tightened a screw and spoke himself a word of congratulation, while Uncle Jeff's good eye rested sorrowfully on a faded print entitled *The Fiancee*, from a drawing by Edouard Bisson, 1891. The Fiancee was bushel-bosomed. She appeared to be dreaming of dignified passions. A couple of overstuffed cherubim floated in her background. Uncle Jeff snorted, and remarked: "Besides, the chances is I scairt that buck clear'n out of the country yest'dy afternoon."

"Nope," contradicted Zack. "He'll likely hang 'round till a good frost starts him ridge-runnin' after does. How close did you get onto him, d'you say?"

"Right handy," said Uncle Jeff, squirming.

"Can't see how come you to miss him."

"Tripped over a damn root, like I told you," lied the old poacher. "Jest's I pulled the tricker."

"Huh. Well, sir, I'l jest nail him cold tonight. An' I won't trip over no root, neither. I'll lay off shore a ways in my canoe, an' shine him. First blood for the Dead Shot Jacklightin' Frame."

Uncle Jeff Coongate was by now completely miserable. He pushed back his high-crowned felt hat and stroked his forehead with his wrist. He yearned to unburden, to tell Zack the truth and call the whole thing off. But he knew he would never hear the last of it. Truth was, Uncle Jeff could not bring himself to kill the buck. He would even go to dangerous extremes to prevent anyone else killing it. And the reason was that both he and the buck had lost an eye!

The common injury had given Jeff the deer's point of view for the first time in his bloodthirsty career. The shock had unnerved him. But how could he save the deer's life without losing his own reputation?

The old woodsman dismally recalled that he had invited himself to Zack's cabin for the purpose of hunting this very buck. It was to have been a heartwarming reunion, following their recent feud over the chicken shoot at Jumbo Tethergood's.

On that bitter occasion at Jumbo's, Jeff had won both chickens, not so much by superior marksmanship as by means of a pint of Old Flat-Spin rye to which he had introduced Zack an hour before firing time. Onlookers joyously proclaimed that Zack was shooting blanks. Zack himself had asserted that his rear sight looked as big as Yellowhead Pass, and in the notch his front sight towered like a chimbley.

Since Zack was considered by himself and everyone else to be the best offhand rifle shot in the country, he had been furious. For weeks afterward he had not spoken to his old crony. But recently they had met on the main street of Privilege. For a moment, their quarrel still rankling, they had exchanged sulky stares. Then their natures overcame the grudge, and they had charged one another, arms flailing.

"You old tomcat!"

"Why, you danged outlaw, you."

"How's Sarah?"

"Down to her folks. I'm dreadful lonesome."

"Me, too. Ain't seen a real friend for a month."

"Say, was them chickens of Jumbo's any good?"

"Turrible! Scrawniest a man ever set tooth into!"

They had tested their renewed friendship by poking one another in the ribs. Both stood the test. Then Uncle Jeff leaned close to Zack's ear, and whispered: "You got any prime wild meat located uplake? I ain't et a thing but pork an' baloney since them hellish chickens. I'm droolin' for a junk of loin."

Zack had clutched his friend's sleeve: "Jeff, boy — I got my eye on the biggest buck ever this country heard tell of. Been fattin' in the wild medder grass in the cove. Ain't half a mile from my door."

"Dear Lord, leave me at 'im," Uncle Jeff had supplicated, his eye teary with anticipation. "Wait'll I git my rifle."

Later, his rifle barrel down his pants leg, and the stock and forearms concealed under his coat, Jeff rejoined his partner. In poker-faced innocence, they had strolled past the game warden's house and on to the canoe landing without attracting official notice.

It was on the following afternoon, in the cedar thicket bordering the wild meadow, that Uncle Jeff and the magnificent buck met eye-to-eye at a distance of ten yards. The buck had been lying down, napping. Startled by the woodsman's approach, the deer had leaped straight into the air and come to earth, legs braced, distended nostrils whistling.

For a long instant Uncle Jeff and the buck had stared at each other. The old poacher's teeth bared in his ruthless kill-grin. "Jest hold quiet another second," he growled, "till I blast you between the eyes!" Then, suddenly noticing the buck's lone eye, Uncle Jeff had begun to tremble. He couldn't understand it. He had always been cool and merciless in the presence of illegal game. He tried to pull the trigger. He couldn't. Here was the standing shot of a lifetime, but it was no use.

"You poor old feller," murmured the one-eyed poacher. "You got on'y one eye, too."

Then he elevated his rifle muzzle, fired into the air, and hissed: "Go to it, boy. Git out of here."

The buck cleared an eight-foot blowdown on the first jump, and by the third was making forty miles an hour in dense cover. Zack was stationed on a stump in an old chopping. He reported subsequently that he had seen nothing but a reddish-white flash as the buck sailed across. . . .

Now, in the cabin, the hot breeze humming in the screens, Uncle Jeff thought tenderly of the buck, while Zack Bourne assembled his deadly jacklighting frame. The seeds of a scheme had sprouted slowly in the one-eyed poacher's mind. If the sprouts flowered, the buck would be spared, or at least its death indefinitely postponed. And Zack never would be the wiser.

Zack taped the flashlight to the frame and sighted along the cabin wall. "She's a humdinger," he declared.

Uncle Jeff coughed, but withheld comment.

"Lines up jest perfick," Zack announced.

Uncle Jeff uttered a low moan, and Zack pricked up his ears. "Say, you got a misery? You been mopin' all mornin'. What ails you? Heat?"

The old poacher bowed his head, as if in agonized embarrassment. "I guess it's jest my dang conscience, gnawing at my innards."

"Your what?" asked Zack, astounded."

"Conscience."

"Christ A'mighty, since when . . .?"

Uncle Jeff held up his hand for silence. "I ain't been square with you, Zack. I been holdin' back on you. After

you invitin' me here to share in that buck, too."

"Holdin' back what?" grunted Zack, laying his rifle on the bench at his side.

Uncle Jeff hitched in his chair. He passed his hand across his chin. "I'm scared to tell you, Zack."

"Why?"

"Might mean we'd have to leave that buck go awhile."

"Why so? What you drivin' at?"

Uncle Jeff's head jerked. A jet of Strong Jaw tobacco juice splashed through the lower draft of the cold stove. "Cause in this weather, meat don't keep good. Flyblows. An' you can't keep no buck deer in Ruffy Dixon's icehouse in September. Too dang risky."

"Who said anything about puttin' our buck in any icehouse?"

The one-eyed poacher winced, as if his conscience had struck him a mortal blow. "No. But you can hang a veal calf in Ruffy's icehouse. All clear an legal, too."

"Who's got any veal calf?"

"You," said Uncle Jeff contritely. "I practickly stole it from you, too. On'y I couldn't — not after what I done to you at Tethergood's chicken shoot."

Zack was thoroughly perplexed. He was also interested. He loved veal. "You say you stole a veal calf off me that I never had in the first place?"

"Yuh. I dang near did, on'y for my conscience. Tomorrow, after we'd killed that buck, I was goin' down to Jumbo Tethergood's an' win your calf in the big shoot."

Zack was deeply impressed. "Jumbo puttin up a veal calf?"

"Yuh, tomorrow. An' I never said a word to you about it, 'cause" — Uncle Jeff swallowed noisily — "you're the on'y one in the country can beat me shottin'.".

Flattered by his old friend's regard for his marksmanship, and cheered by prospects of tender veal, Zack said: "You're a mighty square friend, Jeff. I'll give you half the meat."

"I couldnt take it from you," Uncle Jeff sighed. "On'y just a little junk of loin. 'Nough for two feeds. I — I feel like I'd ought to pay your entry fee to the shoot, too, Zack."

"Couldn't let you do that."

Zack sat for a time in deep thought. "Maybe," he said at last, "we'd ought to let that one-eyed buck roam for a spell. If we killed him tonight, he'd fly-blow while we was eatin' veal."

"I was a-feared of it," mourned Uncle Jeff. "I hate awful to pass him up, but still an' all" — he sighed heavily — "I see the sense to it. He'd be maggoty in three-four days."

"Well, look. I'll give you a quarter of the veal, Jeff."

"Couldn't take it."

"I'll make you take it!"

"Well, all right," conceded the one-eyed poacher. "Mighty white of you Zack."

"Which calf is it?" Zack inquired.

"The spotted one. The bull."

Zack rolled his eyes in bliss. "I can smell the gravy now."

"I seen the calf in Ruffy's icehouse. Dressed a hundrid and eighty," informed Uncle Jeff. "Fat as butter. But I'd ruther a loin steak off that buck, any day."

"What? Venison off an old buck, 'stead of veal? You're crazy."

With an air of heavy sacrifice, Uncle Jeff changed the subject: "Maybe, if you're aimin' to appear at Jumbo's shoot, you better unscrew that jacklightin' frame off your rifle. That young game warden Tom Corn's li'ble to be there."

The weather for Tethergood's shoot broke clear and windless. Zack and Uncle Jeff Coongate arrived by canoe about noon, Zack carrying some rope and a bundle of sacking in which to wrap that portion of the prize which, in Dixon's icehouse, he would carve off after the shoot was over.

Sixty-five competitors had paid the one dollar entry fee. Those who knew of Zack's skill moaned when he appeared on the scene. Zack grinned and patted his rifle. "She ain't shootin' blanks today, boys!"

The target, set a hundred yards from the firing line, had a five-inch bull's-eye. Each contestant was allowed ten shots. The competition was keen, but Zack Bourne was determined to wipe out the shame of his performance at the chicken shoot while under the spell of Old Flat-Spin rye. He and Jeff Coongate joyfully watched the targets come in. The only one which was going to bother Zack was Stumpy Coldwillow's. Stumpy had nine shots in the black.

"Beat that, Zack," Stumpy said.

The shoot was practically over. The onlookers crowded close to watch Zack perform. Uncle Jeff stood at his elbow, whispering words of encouragement. Zack settled and began firing. He put ten shots into the black — all of them cleanly save for one, which broke a trifle into the white. Uncle Jeff Coongate whooped with triumph. His one-eyed buck was spared. Zack waved his rifle, kissed its hot barrel, and yelled: "Jumbo! Gimme the key to Ruffy's icehouse. I want my veal."

"Just a minute," Jumbo said. "One more feller to shoot yet."

A small, apologetic man stepped to the firing line. He was a stranger. He wore a curious-looking coat, heavily padded at the elbows. Nothing like it had been seen in the surrounding country. The stranger's rifle, too, seemed odd. It had set triggers. The barrel was very heavy. The caliber was twenty-two, and the sights telescopic. The stranger's ten shots simply cut the center out of the bull's-eye. Zack Bourne got second prize, which was a tub of lard. Uncle Jeff felt so sick that he bought a pint of medicine from Jumbo Tethergood. It was Old Flat-Spin.

On the way down to the canoe landing, he spoke disconsolately to Zack. "Tub of lard, an' nothin' to fry in it."

Zack swore savagely. He gripped his friend by the elbow and snarled: "Looks like you're goin' to have a chance at that one-eyed buck after all. If I can't shoot for veal, I can kill deer. I'd like to kill about six, jest to git even with my feelin's. That buck-ll be jest a starter. Come on!"

Reluctantly, his feet leaden and his heart sad, Uncle Jeff got into the canoe. They reached Zack's cabin after dark. The night was cloudy and dead still — perfect conditions for jacklighting. In the cabin, by them lamp, Zack hummed "The Church in the Wildwood" as he refitted the Dead Shot Frame to his rifle. Jeff took his first gulp of Old Flat-Spin, and choked. "I got the cholery — summer cholery!"

"Take a swallow of kerosene," Zack advised.

"This is stronger," said Uncle Jeff, taking another jolt, "but it don't taste so good."

The whiskey seemed only to intensify Uncle Jeff's sympathy for all one-eyed creatures, especially himself and the buck. As he listened to Zack's plan of strategy the old poacher grieved sorely. Zack was to take his canoe and paddle along the cove, about fifty yards off shore. He was almost certain to shine the eye of the gigantic buck,

and almost certain to drill him cleanly when he did. But in case of a miss, the buck would run across the chopping on his regular route. There with the second flashlight, Uncle Jeff was to be stationed. He would hear the buck coming, perhaps stall him with a sudden blaze of light, and get a quick shot.

In the darkness the oldtimers crept down to the canoe. Zack laid his rifle on the floor of the craft.

"Git in," he whispered. "I'll leave you ashore down a ways. No sense walkin' that fer."

Presently Zack sided in to shore. Uncle Jeff got out on a sand spit.

"I'll give you ten minutes to get set in the choppin'," Zack whispered. "Then I'll turn on my light an' start rakin' the shore for his eye!"

The paddle dripped as Zack eased the canoe out into the lake. Uncle Jeff stood alone in the darkness, just inside the seawall growth. He knew the country well. His moccasins felt for the little path used by deer. He didn't use his light. He crept forward, a hand up to fend the branches from his face. He paused and took a mammoth gurgle of Old Flat-Spin. The shock made him close his eye. When he opened it, he saw the long, sharply focused beam of Zack's light. Zack was a considerable distance behind him and coming slowly.

Uncle Jeff intended to jump the deer somewhere close to shore. He did not propose to go anywhere near the chopping. All he wanted to do was frighten the deer, somehow, so that Zack wouldn't get a shot. But Zack was getting closer. He was within hearing. If Uncle Jeff yelled or crashed about in the brush, Zack would be suspicious. If he fired his rifle, Zack would mistrust him, and ask questions as to what he was doing in the shore growth, when he should be a quarter of a mile away by the runway in the chopping. No! The only thing to do was to make Zack fire *his* rifle.

Zack was now so close that his light gleamed occasionally on the undersides of cedar fronds. Uncle Jeff crept a bit nearer shore. He concealed his body behind an old spruce blowdown, and stood to his full height. He moved his head, so that a hemlock branch all but hid his face. Confident that he would be invisible to Zack, Jeff took another slug of whiskey, muttered a prayer, and waited.

Slowly the light beam played along the shore, always a little closer. Once or twice it slanted into the sky, as Zack laid his rifle against a thwart and paddled a few strokes. Now the beam glowed on a birch trunk ten feet away. Behind him, Uncle Jeff heard a branch crackle. His heart pounded. The one-eyed buck was near.

The next instant, from his cover, Uncle Jeff Coongate looked fair into the beam of Zack's light. From out on the lake came a metallic click as Zack cocked his rifle. Uncle Jeff thirsted for one more searing swallow of Old Flat-Spin, but he dared not move a finger. The light beam had steadied.

Zack's rifle shot ripped open the stillness of the night, re-echoing from the steep shores of the lake. Uncle Jeff stooped, clutched his hat, and dodged back, deeper into the forest. He had made but a few yards when he heard a buck whistle. The buck was warned now. He was gone. Safe.

Uncle Jeff slunk back to the cabin. He had just lighted the lamp when Zack came in, his face like a squall cloud.

"I missed him! Shone his eye plumb fair! So help me, it glowed like a 'lectric bulb, an' I missed!"

Uncle Jeff teetered over to the rocking chair and sat down a little off center. "Nope, Zack," he remarked wearily, "you never missed that buck. You missed me."

"I tell you I shined that buck's eye."

"No you didn't, neither," corrected Uncle Jeff. "What you shined was my glass eye."

Zack's lips twitched. "How'd I shine your eye, an' you a quarter mile back there, in the choppin'?"

Uncle Jeff significantly stroked his stomach, and moaned: "I never got to the choppin'. I was took with a turrible cholery cramp, an' had to lay down. Didn't dast yell to you, for fear I'd scare that buck. I must of kind of fainted for a spell. 'Cause when I come to, an' stood up, I was lookin' right into your light. Next thing I knowed you'd fired. Your shoot scared the buck, an' he run. Oh, ain't it cruel! Cruel! If he'd of been a few steps nearer the shore, just a little mite sooner, we'd been rollin' out his entr'ls right now."

Zack Bourne's face had turned ash white. He sank down on the bench. "My God! I might of killed you!"

"Well, you didn't. Feller's gen'ally apt to shoot high over a jacklight, I allus say." The one-eyed poacher picked up his hat and stuck his thumbs through the bullet holes in the crown. "You had the line jest perfick," he complimented, showing Zack the holes, "but you was about two inches high. I dunno how many times I've told you to hold down, shootin' over a light."

Zack's forehead had broken out in a cold, glistening sweat. "So help me, I'll never shoot at a one-eyed buck again — never! It might be you!"

"Take a lick of this," said Jeff, offering Zack the whiskey.

Zack accepted the bottle. It rattled against his teeth as he drank. "Look, Jeff," he begged, "can't we leave that one-eyed buck go? Prob'ly be tough as snowshoe fillin' anyways."

"Well," shrugged Uncle Jeff, "'course if you feel that way, I know where we might shoot a dry doe tomorrow."

"Let's do it. I don't want no more of that buck."

"Jest's you say," sighed the one-eyed poacher. "Guess I'll open a can of beans for us to eat tonight."

The Alaskan Grizzly

Harold McCracken

THE GREAT ALASKAN grizzly — the Kodiak brown bear (*Ursus middendorffi*) and its even larger Alaska Peninsula brother (*Ursus gyas*) — is probably as far famed as either the African lion or the Bengal tiger. And yet, probably less is known of its life history than of any of the other larger mammals. He is, nevertheless, a sort of fictitious byword at the hearths of all those hunter-sportsmen who enjoy the savor of genuine hazard in their quest for sport and trophies. A beast whom most prefer to "talk" about hunting, rather than face in mortal combat. And his one thousand to two thousand pounds of brawn and power is unquestionably the embodiment of all that even the most adventurous care to seek. He is supreme in size, in brute power, as well as in physical dexterity, sagacity, and pernicious damnableness in the animal kingdom. And this, not in the mere belief of a casual observer, but weighed and tried on the scales of science. To go into details regarding the life history, the "whys" and "whens" and "hows" of his life career, would entail a goodly volume, which, though immensely interesting in every detail, would be far too cumbersome in such a place as this.

His home is that long, slighly curved arm that reaches out from the southwestern corner of Alaska, separating the North Pacific Ocean from the Bering Sea, and dabbling off in the spattered Aleutian Islands. The Alaska Peninsula is today one of the most wild, least visited and less known of all the districts on this continent.

But in reality, the Alaska Peninsula is, for the most part, a terribly wild Garden of Eden. Its waterways boast more fine fish than any other similar sized section of the globe; on its rounded undulating hills and tundra lands are great herds of caribou, the finest of edible flesh; it is carpeted with berry bushes; there are fine furred animals in abundance; millions of wildfowl, duck, geese, eiders, seals, sea lions; big bears — everything necessary for the welfare and happiness of primitive man. It is a truly primitive land.

While the great Alaska Peninsula bear is a carnivore, or flesh-eater — and what applies to his bear also applies in many respects to his brothers, the sub- and sub-sub-species of other districts of Alaska — yet he has frequently and correctly been called "the great grass-eating bear" and also "the great fish-eating bear." All animals subsist in the manner and on the foods that demand the least efforts, hazard and inconvenience to their life and comforts. Thus the bears of the Alaskan Peninsula have chosen fish and grass and berries as their main diet of food, varied with an occasional caribou, a seal or meal from the carcass of a dead whale or walrus washed up on the beach. During most of the months of the year, the streams are choked with salmon, affording him an inexhaustible supply until well into the middle of the winter. And as hibernation is for the most part only an alternative for existing under winter conditions, when it is hard or sometimes impossible to get food, and as the Alaska Peninsula is in winter moderated by the warming Japan Current, making it quite mild and livable for old Gyas, he is forced to spend but a relatively short period in the "long sleep." This increased activity, together with the abundance of fine food, accounts for the unusual size to which the bears of that district grow.

And he is very much aware of his size and strength; and the fact that he has had no outside natural enemy through the line of his ancestors has made him aggressive, haughty and overbearing, fearing nothing and crushing all that impedes his way.

Thus the Alaska Peninsula grizzly is to be found a most unscrupulous fighter, and his acquaintance with man and his high-powered rifles is as yet too short and limited to have impressed upon his brute mind that here is a most powerful mortal enemy. He usually charges when wounded, more than frequently when a female with very young cubs is suddenly surprised or attacked, and occasionally when watching a fresh "kill" or "cache" and surprised. And if old Gyas decides to fight, woe betide our bold Nimrod unless he is a good shot and non-excitable, or accompanied by someone who possesses these valuable faculties. For a wounded grizzly will not stop for one to reload his gun, nor pause to be shot at until the vital spot is struck. He means blood! Fifty bullets that are not placed in the proper place will not stop him; and you can't back out once he accepts your challenge. Not that one is certain of being charged by every Alaskan grizzly that he fells; I have had even females retreat until knocked down. But these cases are really the exception, and the experiences of practically all the old bear hunters of that district — I have known most of them — will bear me out in the statement that these Alaskan grizzlies almost invariably charge under the three circumstances I have cited.

The natives of Alaska do not often go to look for these big bears. They have a great deal of respect for them — as all others have who know them.

We are at King Cove, a native village near the site of the once famous village of Belkovski, center of the sea otter hunting grounds of old. We are about six hundred miles southwest of Kodiak, the nearest town of over fifteen white inhabitants, and very near the extreme western end of the Alaska Peninsula, and almost due north of Honolulu by location. And here, where the traveler is almost never seen, we will start out to hunt for the biggest of carnivora — start it by incidentally being shipwrecked, almost drowned and getting a foot severely frozen.

It was on the morning of Wednesday, November 1, 1916, that I left King Cove in a twenty-eight-foot covered-over powerboat with Captain Charlie Madsen. We headed for the Isanotski Straits, at the end of the peninsula, and the Bering Sea country, where I intended hunting Grant's Barren Ground caribou and the big grizzlies at several desirable localities near the end of the peninsula.

It was cloudy; looked like another snowstorm; but the wind being from the north, rave it might and the low hills of the mainland would protect us until we reached the end of the peninsula, where we could hunt bear and wait for more favorable winds. But the winds of the North are most fickle!

It was a most magnetic sight as we plied out towards the cape at the entrance of the bay, sending flock after flock of salt-water ducks flopping off over the swelling surface of the blue-green sea. An occasional seal could be seen plunging headlong into the water from the jut of a reef or an outcrop of the rocky shoreline. The hills were gray, dappled with the first settling snows of winter, and the clouds were heavy and leaden-looking.

As we rounded the cape the swells became more pronounced, carrying a deep, rolling, green-sided trough. But our boat plied steadily on, plunging its nose fearlessly into the rising waves.

Breasting some five miles of rock coastline, we rounded the second cape at the entrance to Cold (Morofski) Bay, which protrudes some twenty-five miles back into the peninsula, almost making what is to the west an island and what is to the east the end of the peninsula. As we had expected, the wind was raging out of the bay to seaward. But heading the boat's nose towards Thin Point, about ten miles distant, we started fighting our way to the protection of the opposite cape.

Madsen had been watching the sky with misgiving and shortly announced that the wind was changing to the southwest.

I naturally inquired what would be the best course to pursue, knowing that it undoubtedly meant more storm and that we would soon be in the thick of it.

"Cap" decided we would take a chance on reaching Thin Point before the wind had swung to the southwest and thrown the storm in our faces. Once behind the cape we would be safe.

But we were not halfway across when the wind, swinging out past the protection of the peninsula and clashing against the tide, was soon lashing the sea into a stormy havoc. Diving into one great swell, the wind toppled its crest over the boat, washing overboard the hatch-cover and pouring a volume of water into the hold upon our supplies and outfit. I got on deck and endeavored to get a piece of canvas nailed over the open hatchway before another big one should pour its volume into the boat, at the same time clinging as best I could to the pitching vessel.

In the midst of all this, and as if to impress more forcibly upon us our insignificance in this big affair, our engine stopped. Gas engines are hellish things anyhow, and always buck in just the wrong place. But one must act quickly in a case such as this, and almost before I knew it the boat's sail was up and we were racing before the wind, toward the entrance to the bay we had not long left.

I took the rope and wheel, while Madsen endeavored to get the engine running again, though vainly. But the wind was now coming in such gusts that each one nigh turned our boat onto its nose. It was also snowing and sleeting, almost hiding the outline of the coast.

A gust hit our sail, turning the boat clear on its side, taking water over the rail, and we narrowly escaped finding ourselves in the arms of Neptune himself. Madsen left the engine and decided we would run before the wind and tack into King Cove Bay.

We crossed the entrance to the bay, driven at top speed towards the opposite cape and the line of rocky reefs.

Going as close to as safe, the sail was drawn in with an endeavor to throw it to the opposite side, thus turning the boat. But the wind was too strong and the sea too rough, and try as we might, we would only be driven helplessly on towards the reef where the waves were dashing their foam and spray high in the air. Then a big wave took the flopping sail, pulling the boat over onto its side until the canvas was torn from end to end. As a last resort, the anchor was thrown out; this failed to catch sufficiently to hold us and was regained at great difficulty when we saw that hitting the reef was inevitable.

The first rock of the reef that the boat hit jammed its head through the bottom of the hull and we clambered out into the big dory we were towing and started for shore through the narrow, raging channels in the reef. But this being an open boat, it soon swamped in the breakers and we were forced to take to the water and make shore as best we could. Swimming was impossible, but keeping our heads above the water as best we could, and riding the waves, we were soon washed up on the rocky shore, like half-drowned rats.

To build a fire was impossible for lack of material; we must wait until the boat washed over the reef and was driven ashore. So, wet and cold, and facing a biting snow and sleet and rain-pelted wind, we walked back and forth over the rocks and waited.

Through all this, while we had been battling with the elements, for our very lives, I had noticed with no small interest how very little the storming and havoc had inconvenienced the little creatures that made their homes in or about the sea. The ducks swam about, quacking, and apparently thoroughly enjoying their buoyant existence. So even storms at sea, it seemed, were a mere matter of relativity and part of the everyday life of those that made their home thereon.

Eventually the boat came ashore — it was fortunately high tide — and getting aboard we got out block and tackle, sunk our anchor as a deadman, and pulled the boat up as best we could. Supplies and everything were drenched and several planks in the hull were smashed.

When we had done all that we could we started for the village — a hard hike. It was well after dark when we reached the squatty barrabaras, or native dirt huts, of King Cove, and we were wet and tired and miserable — ready for a meal and the blankets.

As I began to thaw out, however, I found that part of my right foot had frozen — the leather boots I had been wearing having shrunk and stopped the circulation of blood, causing the freezing. I was laid up for over a week with my foot, though it took Madsen, with the assistance of several natives, somewhat longer to get the boat repaired and back to the village.

Such are but a bit of the "pleasures" that often come with hunting big bear at the western end of the Alaskan Peninsula.

I was especially fortunate in making a one-day bag of four of these Alaska Peninsula bears, a big female and her three yearling cubs, the latter being as large as quite mature Southern brown bears I have gotten.

Deciding to spend a day alone in the hills after caribou, I took the .30-40 Winchester — in consideration of the bear — and followed the beach of a lagoon or bay to its head about two and half miles from the village. From the head of the lagoon a valley rose at an easy pitch for about two miles to a low divide on the opposite side of which was a large valley extending out onto the Pacific. This was a very good place for caribou.

At the head of the lagoon I stopped to shoot some salt-water ducks with a .22 Colt revolver, but had fired but a few shots when I was attracted by the bawling of a bear. Glancing in the direction of the sound, I saw a brown bear making a speedy, somewhat noisy, getaway up through the alders from where he had been no doubt eating salmon in the creek a few hundred yards upvalley from me. He was then a good five hundred yards distant and in the alders. I fired, hoping at least to turn him back down the hillside, but he made the top of the ridge and went over it out of sight. I started a speedy climb up through the alders towards the top, not far from where he went over. By the time I reached this, Mr. Ursus had gone down the other side and was making a "hiyu clattewa" along the opposite side of the valley. I started up the ridge toward an open space in the alders with the intent of hurrying down to the creek and descending it with hopes of heading the bear off or getting a shot at him while crossing a wide rock slide a few hundred yards below. But I had not gone a dozen steps when I saw three other bears coming along at a good pace on quite the same course that Number One had taken. This was somewhat more of a "bear party" than I had really anticipated inviting myself to!

I felt quite certain that they would cross a small saddle through which the previous one had passed, and I decided to wait until they had come out of this and were somewhat below me before chancing a shot. I was alone, I remembered.

Squatting down in the alders, I waited with gun ready and, I must say, nerves tense. The first one to come through the saddle was the old female, a big, high-shouldered brute that strode in a manner indicating it was looking for me every bit as much as I was waiting for it. She was followed by her other two yearlings — big fellows almost as tall and as broad as they were long. Being alone, and feeling that the female would undoubtedly fight, I deemed it most wise to play doubly safe. Conditions were fortunately in my favor. The wind was from seaward, and the alders were heavy enough

to conceal me from her none-too-good eyesight, and it would be difficult for her to determine from just which direction the report of my rifle came. The dispatching of the old one was of course my first move. The rest would be comparatively easy. I did not have an opportunity of a good shot, however, until the three had reached the creek bed and crossed and started up along the other side. I slipped into a heavy clump of alders and waited. She was not then, I was quite sure, aware of my whereabouts at least. She lumbered slowly along, yet ever watchful, I could see. Coming out in a little open space she stopped and made an apparent survey of the surrounding vicinity. I took a coarse bead and let drive at her shoulder. I could fairly hear the bullet slip into her. With a nasal bellow she wheeled and made a vicious swipe at the nearest yearling. I fired again, at which she wheeled and charged madly along the hillside opposite me. She went into a small ravine and in a moment came up into sight on one side and stopped, snout swaying high in the air to catch a scent of danger. I steadied my aim, and at the report she went down in a heap and rolled out of sight. "A bullseye!" I thought, and breathed a sigh of relief.

The two cubs had made off in the opposite direction, stopping occasionally to look about. I knocked down one of these at the second shot, breaking his back, though he raised on his forelegs and bawled for all he was worth. I was about to let him have another, when out of the ravine came Mrs. Ursus, mad and apparently as much alive as ever, although dragging her right foreleg. She scrambled through the alders straight for the bawling cub. Greatly surprised and a little uneasy, I again let drive at her. She threw her head to one side, at the same time letting forth another nasal cry. At my next shot she wheeled completely around and charged along the mountainside for a short distance with head held high and every nerve strained to its utmost to locate the cause of her molestation — snarling and bawling in a manner that made me perspire uncomfortably. She was desperate and no doubt calling upon the souls of all her past ancestors to assist her in locating the peculiar new enemy. Then she charged back to the cub. Finally she made a dash almost straight in my direction.

One does not fully appreciate the thrills of real bear hunting until he has experienced just such circumstances as this. To be alone in such a case is a quite different matter from being in company — poor though it may be.

She at last came to a standstill, standing half sidelong to me, and I clamped the gold bead square on her neck and let drive. She went down, got up and, tearing a few alders up by the roots, unwillingly sank in a heap. She had finished her career as a big brown bear on the Alaska Peninsula.

The rest was quite easy and uneventful.

With the assistance of three natives I skinned the four, took the necessary measurements for mounting, and brought the pelts in by boat. The natives, however, made a second trip, bringing in every bit of the meat of all four, salting it down for winter use. The pelts were in fine condition and beautiful specimens, the large one measuring a full ten feet. They were now in the Ohio State Museum.

It was on Sunday, November 19, 1916, that I bagged the original "bearcat" — one of the largest bears ever killed on the continent.

We were hunting around the eastern side of Frosty Peak, a high volcanic mountain towering between Morzhovi and Morofski Bays and about ten miles from the Pacific. This is about twenty miles from King Cove, near the end of the peninsula, and a very good place for big bears. It was a *big* one that I wanted now; and though numerous tracks and one medium-sized bear were seen, none were bothered until the original "bearcat" was found. That took two days under Old Frosty.

I had previously been hunting Grant's Barren Ground caribou on the Bearing Sea side of the peninsula and before we landed at the foot of Frosty Peak on our return there was a good twelve inches of snow on the ground. In places it had already drifted to a depth of five feet. Bear hunting was quite an easy matter — though a little unpleasant on account of the snow and cold — as it was a small matter to track the animals. The streams were still open and full of salmon, but a small percentage of the bruins had sought their winter quarters, the pads of their big clawed feet having beaten paths along the iced shores of the stream where they came periodically to gorge themselves.

It was late afternoon of the second day under Frosty Peak that we found the fresh trail of our longed-for quarry. We had been investigating the broad alder-patched table of one of the valleys that cut up toward the pinnacle of Old Frosty. There were numerous tracks along the creek where the brownies had been feasting on the silver salmon, though no fresh ones of a really large bear. But as we came well up to the head of the valley we saw the well-distinguished trail of an unquestionably large bear where it had made its way up through the snow on the mountainside into a heavy growth of alders. This was at the very foot of the peak and in the highest growth of alders. Upon reaching the tracks we were well satisfied that they could have been made only by the paw and claw of just the bear that we were seeking. Although it was evident that he had been in no special hurry in making the climb, yet it was all that a six-foot man could possibly do to step from one track to the next.

To the left of the alder patch was a comparatively open track of rocky ground, with only a spare patch of brush here and there. It was certain that he could not, if still in the thicket, escape in that direction without being noticed. But on the right there was a low ridge, the opposite side of which dipped down into a deep wide ravine. The alders extended to within a few yards of this ridge, and to see the other side it was necessary to mount to the top of it. Also, it was quite probable that the bear had already gone over this ridge and might then be high up in the canyon near to its hibernation quarters.

Being unable to locate the bear with my glasses, I decided to make a complete detour around the patch, to be assured whether or not he was still in there.

So leaving Charlie on the flat below, I took the two natives and started up through the alders on the trail of old Ursus. As soon as possible, we mounted the ridge at the right and went along the extent of it to assure ourselves that the bear had not crossed. This he had not. But to make doubly sure that he was still in the alder patch, we went above and around it to complete the circle about the place. He was without question lying somewhere in that thicket.

Upon reaching the flat, and as a last resource, we fired several volleys up through the alders. Then one of the natives spotted him standing in a thick growth of the alders, where he had gotten up and was looking inquiringly down at us. We moved down opposite to him and I fired from the shoulder. He started off along the mountainside, like an animal that has just broken from its cage. Then I fired again.

Mounting a little knoll in the open, he peered dubiously down at us — in unmistakable defiance. I held on him full in the chest for my next shot, at which he let out a bellow and came for us.

My shots had hit, though he had not so much as bit or clawed at the wound on either occasion — merely jumped slightly. He was then about 200 yards distant, though I was well aware of the short time that it would take him to cover that distance. And he was a big fellow — looked more like a load of hay than a bear, coming down the mountainside.

I had previously told the others not to shoot until I called for help, as I was anxious to fell this big brute singlehanded. But on he came, and though try as I might, I could not stop him. My shots seemed to be taking no effect whatever. And then, when he had come about half the distance, I yelled "Shoot!" And I'd have liked to have done so long before. The four guns spoke simultaneously, but old Gyas kept coming.

I squatted down in the snow, and resting my elbows on my knees, decided to take the long chance — a shot for the head. I was confident that Madsen could stop him before he reached us, and determined to take a chance shot of dropping him in a heap. The two natives, however, were not so confident and began to move backward, shooting as they went.

He turned an angle to cross a small ravine, and while he was mounting the opposite side at a decreased pace I held just forward of the snout. The first shot missed, as I saw a small flit of snow where it hit just in front of him. But at the second shot he dropped in a heap, falling on his belly with his nose run into the snow. After waiting for some moments to make certain he was beyond the trouble point, we climbed up through the alders to where he lay. The others stood by with guns ready while I went up and poked him with the end of my own gun. He was dead.

This had all taken but a few moments, though relatively it seemed a great deal longer.

He was indeed a big fellow — a genuine bearcat. We gutted him, and as it was then getting late, hit for camp. The next morning we went back to skin the animal —and no small task it was!

He had been hit twelve times, we found. Nine of the shots had entered the neck and shoulder and two in the head and one in the abdomen. One bullet had hit him squarely in the mouth, shattering the tops of his lower teeth on one side, piercing the tongue and lodging in the back of his throat. Four of the .30 caliber leads were retrieved from the shoulder, where they had not so much as reached the bone. The shot that stopped him struck well up on the brain box, but squarely enough to break the casing of the bone and penetrate the skull though only a part of the lead entered the brain, the most of it spattering off in the fleshy part of the head. It was a luck shot on an even more lucky day!

We estimated his live weight at from 1,600 to 1,800 pounds, and the skin at twelve feet in length. The actual measurements of the tanned skin, however, as made by Chas. A. Ziege, noted taxidermist of Spokane, Wash., are: eleven feet four inches maximum length, by ten feet six inches spread of forelegs. The skull, measured one year after killing, eighteen and one-quarter inches, or one-half inch under the world record, according to Washington, D.C. authorities.

The Case of the Seven Good Hunters

Rufus King

THE LAKE HELD a heliotrope flush of dawn, and it was very cold, very still. Fragile ice rimmed its edges, tentatively seeking a glaze for the late fall's first imprisonment of the water.

The crack of a single rifleshot came clear, down from westward.

Gertrude Enford woke up. There was no blurred transition from slumber about it. She knew exactly where she was. She knew the day. She knew the time of day. She suspected that the source of her awakening had been a shot.

Gertrude was an odd woman, lean and stringy, tough in her fibers, and indefinably smart, no matter what she wore or how she put it on. There was a great assurance in all of her movements; and her voice (which she never bothered to lower) was decisive, final and clipped. Gertrude's age was forty-seven. Her hair, which she wore rather long, and arranged with an artful simplicity, still excitingly retained its natural deep-auburn tones. She was very rich.

You had to be rich to stay at the Lodge, for its tariff was stiff, and you either paid it and liked it, or else you stayed away. The Jenklins owned it, Jerry and Sara: a rambling estate in the heart of the Adirondack Mountains, having its own lake, four hundred acres, and the best deer hunting in the north country.

Gertrude never minced decisions. In spite of the earliness of the hour, she decided to get up. She had had enough sleep, and her nerves were in excellent condition. She dressed. She looked at herself critically in a mirror. Her face, she decided, was in shape: colorless, ageless, with interesting wide frank eyes and a mouth whose shading held a dash of fuchsia in its red.

She went through the living room of her suite and out into a central hallway, darkly paneled, dark with the obscurity of the day's pale dawn, and down stairs of waxed oak. Lighted candles were somber in the main hall (the Jenklins leaned heavily on atmosphere), and she saw the stranger vaguely, standing before a large open hearth where birch logs flamed.

She said: "I'm Gertrude Enford. When did you get in?"

"I came on the morning train. The one that dumps you out at half-past four. I'm Colin Starr."

"Oh, yes. They said you were coming — but they said next week."

"It's hard for me to arrange anything definitely."

"Yes, I suppose that would be so."

Gertrude stared at Starr openly, taking him all in, his compact tall vigor and brief ugliness of features which gave to his face a curious effect of charm. One of those healthy animals, she thought, who live in the eternal forties, with digestions like clockwork. A server, a good man. A keen, kind, honest man and to hell with him. One who from birth would have lived on the proper emotional side of the tracks, in a lovely house of clear-white glass bricks secure on a foundation of ethics. She thought: "What I need is a couple of cups of strong black coffee."

Gertrude sketchily recalled Dr. Starr's dossier as she had obliquely learned it: his home was in Ohio, in one of those settled small towns which you sometimes see at fairs done in miniature, a well-cleaned, polished microcosm of all that was sturdiest and best in the nation. The name, if she remembered, was Laurel Falls. He was a doctor of considerable repute, a repute that reached beyond any local or state boundaries, a man of wealth, and a man with a strange aptitude for the medico-legal angles of his profession. This, in the sense of his having been instrumental in the unmasking of several apparently natural deaths and stamping them as murder.

"I understand you have been here before, Doctor."

"Yes, several times. Whenever I can arrange to, in fact. The Jenklins are old friends." Starr considered Gertrude's turnout, its severe smartness, the inappropriateness of her shoes. "You're not going out this morning?"

"I don't hunt. I'm here with Jack, my brother, and a friend of his — an intense young thing by the name of Mason Hallway, whose family is involved with soaps. Jack hopes to bag a twelve-point buck. I've no objection to his mounting the heads — we live on Long Island, a little town called Mealand, and his den is littered with antlers — but I do object to his making us eat up the rest of them. Jack thinks it's the only sporting thing to do. Would that be atavism or just a plain obsession, Doctor?"

"Perhaps just a healthy appetite?"

"Well, if it's healthy, it's the —"

The main door opened and Bill, one of the guides, came in: a hardened youngster, leathery, and with deep-blue, vital eyes. Hard running had left him breathless.

He said to Gertrude: "Where's Mr. Jenklin, Miss Enford? Mr. Singmen's been shot. He's bad."

Gertrude's pale long fingers clutched the back of a chair for support, and Starr observed her sudden convulsive trembling, and thought her about to faint.

She said: "Mr. Singmen — Mr. Singmen is dead?"

"No, he ain't dead, but he's near enough to make no difference. They're bringing him in. I got to find Mr. Jenklin. I got to find a doctor."

"I'm a doctor."

Bill looked relievedly at Starr.

"Maybe you can fix him up?"

"Maybe I can."

But he couldn't. Nothing could. Starr knew that when Singmen was brought in and carried up to a bed. Singmen was of medium build, a middle-aged man wearing corduroys, stout boots, a gray hunting jacket and a red cap. He had been shot through the back. There was not, on the gray hunting jacket, much blood, and Starr believed shortly that an internal hemorrhage would make death a matter of minutes or of an hour or so at most.

Singmen's eyes were cloudly and almost absurdly kind. They gave his pleasant face a stricken spaniel look. He said to Starr: "I should have worn my red hunting jacket after all, not that gray one. The red cap wasn't enough."

("There's no use," Starr thought, "in making him preserve his ebbing strength. He might as well talk, and keep his mind occupied. There's nothing at all I can do.")

"Who shot you, Mr. Singmen?"

"I don't know."

"Do you mean to say whoever did it didn't come to your help?"

"Yes. Too frightened, I guess. A couple of the guides found me and brought me in." Singmen sighed gently and closed his cloudy eyes. "It's a funny thing how excited some men will get when they think they see a buck."

"Were you in brush or on a trail?"

"A trail, Doctor."

"Fairly straight?"

"Yes, right along there it was, for almost a hundred yards or so. But you know how it is with buck fever."

"Look here, Singmen, that shot went directly through your back in a straight line. Surely whoever fired must have seen you pretty clearly. Tell me this —"

"I'm very tired, Doctor."

"I know you are. But tell me, of the people who are up here, of the men out hunting this morning, has any one of them anything against you?"

"Me? Lord no, Doctor. I've always been my own worst enemy." Singmen smiled feebly at this feeble airing of the bromide. "Don't get any notion like that in your head."

"Was any one of them using the same trail you were on?"

"No. I did meet Mason Hallway for a minute at the fork, where there's a cross trail of sorts, but he hit on off to the left up toward the ridge. He's that young friend of Jack Enford. Enford has a nice sister, by the way. A very interesting woman. She's staying here. You'll meet her."

"I have. Was Mason Hallway the only man you saw?"

"That's right, Doctor. It couldn't have been he who caused this accident, because he knew the way I was heading. Just how bad am I, Doctor?"

"You are all right." And Singmen was . . . He was dead.

Starr talked with Sara Jenklin while they were waiting for the sheriff. Gray peppered Sara's dark sleek hair, and her animated eyes were heavy with shock and worry.

Seven hunters (Sara said) were out that morning, in-
cluding Singmen, who was dead. None of the others had as yet returned, including Mason Hallway, whom Singmen had met at the fork and who had branched off to hit it up for the ridge. No concerted drive had been set for the morning. Each man had started off on his own. The guides were out now, bringing them in.

"Tell me, Sara, something about Singmen."

"There isn't much, Colin. He was a widower. No children. His wife was Alice Dobbs. Alice and I went to school together, which is how Arthur started coming up here."

"What did he do?"

"Arthur? Nothing. He had a good income, and more or less budgeted it. He owned a co-operative apartment in New York, just a good, plain fine one with nothing bizarre about it — old stuff, old silver. He kept a place on the beach at Miami." Sara looked at Starr earnestly. "He couldn't have been a kinder man, or more harmless."

"You're puzzled, Sara, too?"

"Naturally I'm puzzled. I know the place in the trail where he was shot. There's a good clear view for quite a stretch back. Anyhow, every man who went out this morning is experienced. I just can't believe that any one of them would get buck fever."

"What of Mason Hallway, Sara?"

"I don't know, except that I like him. It's his first time here. He came with the Enfords. I've known them, of course, for several years. Jack met him sometime last spring, I understand, when both of them were applying for the Reserve Corps. Each was turned down for some reason or other, and it seemed, well, to form a bond. They became quite friendly."

"Did Hallway know Singmen?"

"Only in the sense of their having met two days ago."

Starr thought back upon Gertrude Enford's convulsive trembling, the sharp clutch of her fingers upon the chair when the guide had told them about Singmen having been shot. It had struck him as far too sharp a reaction at news concerning a stranger, no matter how shocking. There was a connection with Singmen, he felt, either through Hallway or through the Enfords themselves.

"Tell me about Jack Enford. I've met his sister."

Sara thought for a while, staring contemplatively at Starr with her dark-gray animated eyes.

"Jack's all right."

"That suggests reservations."

"Yes, I know it does. Jack's the type of man whom all sorts of things are said about. But nothing's ever proved. I feel sorry for him because you know how that sort of thing goes. How it spreads. He's a magnet for innuendoes."

"Unpleasant ones?"

"Some. Very."

"Moral? Ethical? Financial?"

"Oh, they run the whole list. His job's promoting things. Sometimes they come off; more frequently they don't — leaving a lot of bag-holders."

"Including, perhaps, Singmen?"

"No; I'm sure about that. Jack and his sister only met Arthur two days ago, too."

"I've still a feeling that there's some connection. I gathered that from Miss Enford's reaction to the news."

Sara leaned forward and said earnestly: "Colin, Arthur Singmen never harmed anyone in his life. There's not even anyone I know of left who will gain by his death. He told me last season that he was leaving his money to charity.

Now if it had been Jack —" She bit her lip, and stopped abruptly.

"Yes, Sara?"

"I'm doing exactly what I've just complained about in others. Going in for innuendoes. You see, with the exception of Arthur and Mason Hallway, Jack knows the other men who were out this morning fairly well. And I mean by that, of course, that they know him. Frankly, they don't like him. And to be still more frank about it, I think that each has been bitten by one or another of his promotion schemes."

"Deeply enough to want to take a pot-shot at him?"

Sara hesitated.

"Who can ever tell about that? But it wasn't Jack who was shot; it was Arthur."

"Did you see them when they left this morning, Sara?"

"Yes."

"What sort of hunting jacket was Jack Enford wearing?" Starr asked.

"His regular red one."

"Then that knocks out that thought. Singmen's was gray."

They were sitting in Sara's living room: a pleasant clear place of pickled pine, with casement windows having a magnificent view across a valley that was flooding with the rising sun. A maid came in without knocking. She said to Sara: "It's Miss Enford, ma'am. I think she's got hysterics. Anyhow, she's screeching awfully."

Gertrude had them, all right. Severely. And there was little that Starr could do but give her an opiate to knock her out. He observed the usual disjointed mélange of sense and nonsense to her ravings: a mélange of fears and remembrances, all uprooted from the sable caves of her subconscious mind, and brokenly shrieked out.

He felt strongly disturbed, more so even than was usual with him during such exhibitions. He thought: "She thinks that it was murder, all right. Her brother's on her mind like an obsession. It must be that she thinks that the shot was meant for her brother — as Sara did."

Sara stood watching Gertrude quiet down; then a man stepped into the room very softly. His face was deadly pale, and stamped with a weak prettiness that contrasted oddly with his large, rangy build.

He said to Starr: "Oh, you're the doctor, aren't you?"

"Yes."

"I'm her brother. How is she?"

"She has had a bad shock, Mr. Enford."

"Yes, I know. Look here — nothing will happen to her, will it?"

"No, she'll get over it."

Jack felt sweat on his forehead. He found it distasteful, and wiped it away petulantly.

"Awful thing. Awful thing about Arthur Singmen."

"Very."

"You were with him, weren't you? I mean when he died."

"Yes."

"Well — did he say anything?"

"He did speak of having met your friend Mr. Hallway along the trail. He mentioned a fork."

"Yes? He didn't imply — I mean he didn't seem to feel that Mason was responsible, did he?"

"No, on the contrary. He felt strongly that Mr. Hallway could not have been."

"It's funny that whoever did fire the shot didn't come forward — right away — and help Singmen. I suppose it was panic at the accident."

"I suppose it was."

"It makes me awkward."

"Awkward, Mr. Enford?"

"Sure, for the rest of us."

"Your sister seemed to feel — I don't know exactly how to put this, but I got the impression that she, well, has her own rather strong ideas about this business."

"Yes?"

Both of them stared down at the bed, at Gertrude with her lips a little parted over sharp white teeth, with her breath coming through them in the first deep plunge into the opiate sleep.

"Your sister — I almost gathered that she was inclined to consider it murder, but that the bullet wasn't meant for Singmen."

"Gertrude? She said that?"

"Not in so many words. I felt it implied, rather, in her hysteria."

"Look, Doctor, that's all that it was. Just hysteria. I know Gertrude, and she gets that way. She's highly strung. She goes right off her bat sometimes just over trifles." Jack's hand was petulant again with sweat. "It isn't only Gertrude. Our family has always been that way. I am myself sometimes. High-strung."

"Was that why they rejected you for the Reserves last spring, Mr. Enford?"

"Well, not entirely." Jack smiled. There was some syrup on the smile's deprecatory sweetness. "I believe they just considered me as temperamentally unfit."

"I understand that Mr. Hallway was rejected at the same time, that that was how you met. Was he rejected on the same grounds?"

Jack suddenly stopped being pleasant.

"Why do you harp on him? Singmen gave him a clean slate, didn't he? Well, isn't that good enough for you?"

"Sorry, Mr. Enford."

"That's all right. So am I. I told you that I — that it ran in the family. Forget it, Doctor."

Four men stood in the main hall.

Welford, a banker from Boston, dominated the others in appearance: strikingly silver-haired, thin, and tall to the point of gauntness, with sharply chiseled ears and nose and lips. They gave him (as he very well knew) the patrician look. He also knew its value to him in business, even though it amused him considerably when he considered his private vices, which were pigs' knuckles, Western novels, and gin mixed with plain water and no ice.

He observed Jack Enford coming into the room with a stranger. He did not see the stranger very clearly, because his fine bold eyes were concentrating so sharply on Enford. Their expression was not pleasant. He thought: "You wait!"

Burkell stood beside Welford. Denwood Burkell was a novelist of a brief repute whose flair lay in calling soil *soil*. He was a little man, barely five feet two inches in his lifts, and still he publicized himself amazingly as a sportsman: big fish, big game. Secretly it bored him stiff, but his agent thought it useful with his public and for his press. The hours were the things that "got his goat." It irked him constantly that no animal of the slightest publicity value could, apparently, be bagged at noon.

Haskell Fortescu was on Welford's other side. He was a corporation counsel for a general-utilities outfit in the South: a stout man, rotund all over, with limpid little eyes and a merry mouth. People thought him famously jolly. His reaction to Enford was a little smile.

The fourth man, Hallway, was very much the intense young thing that Gertrude had called him. You got that from the deep burning look in his dark eyes rather than from his build, which was medium and placid enough. But his eyes were extraordinary and Starr read in them, as he shook hands, a hint of emotionalism, the suggestion of the dreamer or the fanatic, say in the sense of a hero-worshiper who would let his god or enthusiasm of the hour go to good lengths before admitting even the possibility of any feet of clay.

Starr met them and noted that they wore, to a man, hunting jackets of assorted reds. He acknowledged the usual perfunctory generalities: *"Terrible. . . . Fine man, Singmen. . . . Can't understand it. . . . Happens every year — terrible. You would think that by now . . . Buck fever — you might expect it in a novice, but not one of us — terrible!"* Then he went into a small lounge room where he saw Jerry Jenklin.

Jerry, Sara's husband, seemed lethargic when you first met him, which wasn't so. He was like an animal that way, slipping from a lounge into the most fluid physical sort of activity without any consciousness on the part of anyone watching him of the transition. Everything about him looked sleepy and somewhat sultry and slow. You expected him to scratch himself and continuously yawn.

He said to Starr: "You've still got to meet McDuff."

"The seventh hunter?"

"Yes. He'll be along soon. Well?"

"Well?"

Jerry continued to slouch and look sleepy. He offered Starr a cigarette, lit one himself, and let it dangle.

"This is bad, Colin. It's murder. And there's one thing that makes it pretty convincing that Singmen was meant to be the victim. He's the only one of the lot who wore a gray hunting jacket. They all must have known that, because they started out together. Still, you've been talking with Sara. I can only emphasize what she told you, that there's no sane reason why anybody here or anywhere else would want to kill Singmen — but someone did. So that leaves us what?"

"It leaves us with Miss Enford in hysteria."

"Yes, Sara told me that, too. Jack's at the bottom of that. She's pretty blind about him, but she can't be so utterly blind as not to realize what a more rational victim he would have made than Singmen. Or than anybody else who's here."

"She seems quite a good deal older."

"She is. She's always dominated him. She brought him up."

"From childhood?"

"Nearly. He was eleven when their parents died. Gertrude was going on nineteen. She made a fine mess of it, if you ask me." Jerry leisurely turned his head. "That's McDuff now. Hey, McDuff!"

McDuff came in. He was a huge, raw-boned, beef-skinned, red-nosed man and, Starr realized, full of Scotch. He was dour. He walked with precise care. He shook hands with Starr, and lowered himself into a chair, and said: "I've been up all night." His eyes looked it. They were as red as his hunting jacket. "You're the doctor. Why couldn't you pull old Singmen through?"

"It was too late."

"Who was the fool who got buck fever?"

"No one's saying."

"He will." McDuff stuck a bony finger out at Starr. "You know that, Doctor. No man can escape from a consciousness of guilt."

"I'm afraid they've been known to, Mr. McDuff. Some-times it has to be smoked out."

Starr sent a wire. He sent it to the proper department of the Reserve Corps at which Enford and Hallway had applied. He wanted to know on what grounds the two men had been rejected. He wanted to know whether there was any record on the files about a man named Arthur Singmen. As a right to the courtesy of this information, he referred to himself as a friend of the Adjutant General.

It was, he felt, an arrow shot into the air but it was impossible to get rid of the belief that Jack Enford was a focal point in the case. It was impossible to forget that Jack's friend Mason Hallway had met and talked with Singmen just before the shot was fired. It seemed of pressing importance to get all of the information about Enford and Hallway and Singmen that he could.

The sheriff was starting to spread out his bag of tricks in the main hall. Starr joined the group and was introduced. He liked the sheriff for his air of plain forthrightness, and the healthy color of his skin, and (in spite of the air of forthrightness) his political ability to skate with dexterity over these assembled surfaces of human importance and considerable wealth. He followed the sheriff's casual but pertinent questions carefully.

"Well, gentlemen," the sheriff said in conclusion, "I think it's murder, all right; and because of any seeming lack of motive, I think that Mr. Singmen was murdered by mistake. Now there's only one thing that made him look different from the rest of you at any distance away in the woods, and that was his gray jacket. All the rest of you had on some shade of red. The point as I see it is this: was that Mr. Singmen's jacket? Was it the one he wore habitually, or did he borrow it from somebody else?"

McDuff aroused.

"That gray jacket was mine. I was up all night and saw Singmen when he came down this morning. He had ripped the sleeve of his own jacket yesterday and was looking for one of the maids to sew it. I suggested he leave it and borrow that gray one of mine. Gentlemen — I sent that man to his death."

"No, I'd hardly say that, Mr. McDuff. The question seems to be, did you sometimes wear that gray jacket yourself?"

"Certainly. I wore it every day last week. I'd ordered a red one, but it only came through last night."

The sheriff was pleased.

"Well, now we seem to be getting some place."

McDuff, who was not so pleased, began to get the impact of the drift.

"Me? That shot was meant for me?"

"After all, Mr. McDuff, it was aimed at the only gray jacket in camp."

Starr thought: "Wait — this is wrong; you've gone off the track somewhere. They all started off together this morning; they would have known that Singmen was wearing the gray jacket, not McDuff." Then he felt a presence behind him, and turned, and saw Gertrude Enford in the doorway. She was looking at the sheriff with her wide, frank eyes. Then she turned them on McDuff. Then she started to laugh hysterically.

The answering wire came toward late afternoon.

No one by the name of Arthur Singmen, Starr read, was listed or known. Mason Hallway rejected under suspicion of an incipient psychopathological trend. Jack Enford rejected for deuteranopia, but recent experiments in the detection of camouflage made it desirable Enford apply again.

Starr thought carefully for a long time. So it was like that.

He folded the telegram and put it in his pocket. He looked up the sheriff. He looked up Bill, the guide who had found Singmen that morning. He asked Bill to take them over the trail which Singmen had followed. The sun was sinking below the top of the range. Pine and balsam needles offered a silent, pungent strip of carpeting for their steps, while Starr talked with the sheriff.

It was, Starr said to the sheriff, one of the oddest cases he had ever come upon. At least he thought so. He asked the sheriff to take the five protagonists: a kindly man who was dead; a local, easy-going character who had loaned the kindly man a gray hunting jacket; an idealist who touched on being a zealot and who was thought to have a psychopathological trend; a weakling, and a woman who feared desperately for this weakling whom she herself had brought up. The case should, he thought, be speedily cleared up. For he believed that there was danger still.

They came to the "cross trail of sorts" which Singmen had mentioned, and where there was a definite fork to the left. It was here that Singmen had met and spoken briefly with Hallway. They stood at the fork and Starr explained to the sheriff his theory of what could have occurred.

He suggested that they observe the trail along which they had just come: it was a winding one, and masked by a turn as closely as ten yards back.

They observed the "trail of sorts" which Hallway had used that morning. It was too tortuous, and from their viewpoint briefly obscured.

He indicated then the trail which forked to the left, the one which Hallway had taken after his chat with Singmen: he point out that you could not see any farther than several yards along it at the most.

On the other hand, the right fork, which Singmen had continued upon, held a straight and unobstructed stretch through the woods for possibly a hundred yards; and therein, Starr suggested to the sheriff, could lie the answer to the case.

He suggested that they return to the Lodge. He suggested that the sheriff put some pressure to bear upon young Hallway. . . . He suggested that they borrow seven coats.

Gertrude decided on a jade-green net. It offset her hair. She fixed her face carefully so the jade didn't also offset her skin. Pretty good. They'd have to get out of here on the morning train. Get right out and away from here, if that milk-fed sheriff didn't force them to stay. Nice guy, the sheriff. A he-man. With a whittler's delicate touch. And, no doubt, a rattler's fang. Tooth? No, fang. She felt that every hour they stayed there spelled, for Jack, the most desperate sort of danger. . . . Gertrude shuddered.

She'd been shuddering a lot all through the day, and even seven old-fashioneds hadn't soothed the jitters. She clasped an emerald necklace about her throat. What would an eighth old-fashioned do? Well, what would it do?

She went downstairs, a smart, flowing shaft of jade.

All right. Why not? If he wanted to sit beside her and watch her down her eighth, let him.

"Sit down, Doctor Starr. I'm thinking of a cocktail. I'm still on the first today — the first dozen. — Jane!"

"Miss?"

"An old-fashioned."

"Yes, miss. And you, sir?"

Starr would, he said, have an old-fashioned too.

"I missed you this afternoon, Doctor. I haven't thanked you yet for your kindness this morning."

"Not at all, Miss Enford. Any St. Bernard in a storm."

"I go off that way all the time. People get so they supply other house-guests with that stuff you stuff in your ears to keep out street noises."

"Haven't you ever done anything about it?"

"Of course I have. I've been to every psychiatrist in town. My major reaction was that most of the psychiatrists needed *me*. Honestly, Doctor, there was one man who had the infernal nerve to ask me how I would handle the situation if the *Normandie* started sailing up Broadway."

"Of course you told him?"

"Explicitly. After I got home, I sent him a bill for twenty-five dollars." *(I wish that old-fashioned would come. I can't keep this up much longer. I'll start shuddering again.)* "Tell me — you've been talking with the sheriff; has he found anything out?"

"About Singmen?"

"About his murder."

Starr looked evasive.

"I'm afraid the case is in his hands."

"Oh — then there is a case?"

"He thinks so. He plans to conduct a little experiment."

"Really? Of what nature, Doctor?"

"I understand it has to do with the selection of a hunting jacket."

"Are you being serious?"

"Very serious, Miss Enford."

"The maid is taking a wretched time with those old-fashioneds."

Gertrude looked toward the door hopefully, on the last outpost of her nerves. There were people coming in, but there were no old-fashioneds, and there was no maid. The sheriff came first carrying, amazingly, some hunting jackets on his arm. The six men left from the morning hunt trailed him. They grouped, with awkward reticence, near the blazing hearth. The Jenklins, with odd formality, came in and sat on a settee near the doorway.

It's like a tableau, Gertrude thought: *stilted. Jack looks terrible. I wish he'd look at me.* She examined Hallway. *He's worse off than Jack,* she decided. A chill ran through Gertrude and she thought, still covertly examining Hallway: *He's talked. He's spilled it.* Then the future became a tunnel through which she was entering into bitter darkness.

The sheriff was folding the hunting jackets lengthwise and placing them side by side on a lounge. Odd — six of them were in different shades of red, ranging from maroon to vivid scarlet, but the seventh one was gray. The sheriff was speaking, and Gertrude listened with a feverish impatience to this prelude which, from the look on Mason Hallway's tortured face, she had already discounted.

"— defalcation," the sheriff was saying, "— outright theft of a good many thousands of dollars, nearly two hundred, to be exact — a swindle perpetrated by Mr. Enford and achieved partly through the influential and trusted position of his friend Mr. Hallway. There was no doubt but that Mr. Hallway had been completely deceived as to the transaction, but Mr. Hallway had ultimately discovered its criminal nature and had insisted that the miserable business be exposed, even though he himself would also be subject to prosecution and disgrace. Mr. Hallway was that kind of man — an idealist."

(*Yes,* Gertrude thought, *we know all that. Get on with it. Get* through *with it.*)

There was, the sheriff said, a curious angle about the matter which gave it a classic touch: the strange power of domination which Miss Enford held over her young brother, who all of his life had been a moral weakling. It was a power, in Doctor Starr's opinion, analogous to that exercised over her husband by Lady Macbeth, in the sense that Miss Enford had planted in her brother's mind the seed of murder. A seed which she had then nurtured into fruition.

(Gertrude thought: *Give us your proof. It was still a hunting accident, and nothing can make it come out differently*.)

Mr. Hallway had admitted to him, the sheriff said, that he had agreed to accompany Miss Enford and her brother on this hunting trip, so that they could all talk things over. Miss Enford had pleaded that her own disgrace at her brother's exposure would be as deep as theirs. She had begged Mr. Hallway not to force her into social ostracism. She had insisted that a reasoned discussion of the disgraceful affair would show them some honorable way out. That, of course, was nothing but a lure. Mr. Hallway had been deliberately brought up here to be "accidentally" shot and killed — to silence him and his zealous moral qualms. Mr. Singmen had unhappily been shot instead. Perhaps Doctor Starr would offer his conclusions about that?

Starr was nervously depressed. It affected him this way — the end of a chase, and any psychological trick devised to cause a suspect to crack. He sensed the virulence in Gertrude, her fierce mental intention to make her brother look at her so that she could control him. Starr spoke to her directly, forcing her to attend to him.

"Miss Enford, your brother followed Mr. Hallway this morning, staying at a careful distance behind. By the time your brother reached the fork, Mr. Hallway had completed his brief talk with Mr. Singmen and was already lost to view behind the first turning of the trail that leads up to the ridge. On the other hand, Mr. Singmen was still in view, say a hundred yards or more away, at the farther end of the clear stretch of the right-hand trail. Your brother took it for granted that Mr. Singmen was Mr. Hallway and followed him. He shot him. His mistake was a natural one, because of all the men who were out hunting this morning only Mr. Singmen and Mr. Hallway had similar builds."

Gertrude's head was shot with sharp pain. Her eyes, in memory, compared Singmen's body with Mason's. All right. That much was true. Both were of medium build, whereas the others grouped by the fire were a varied assortment of gaunt, of small, of large size, of fat. And still all right. She looked at Jack. That was true, too. He was a weakling, and a flash of honesty made Gertrude admit that perhaps it was she who had made him one. Then the hunting jackets neatly lined up on the lounge began to fascinate her.

She said desperately: "You're wrong, Doctor. Mason wore a red hunting jacket, whereas Mr. Singmen's jacket was gray. No matter what the distance, no matter what the similarity in their builds, Jack would have noticed that. He would have known by the jacket alone that Mr. Singmen couldn't have been Mason."

Starr crossed to the hearth.

He said: "Mr. Enford, there are six coats on that lounge of varying shades of red. There is one coat there that is gray. Will you indicate the gray one, please?"

Sweat was unpleasant on Jack's face. His lips felt abominably loose, and he was terrified at the thought that he was about to cry. One chance in seven. Like that ordeal-by-fire stuff, and other tests for guilt or innocence of the Middle Ages. It suddenly didn't matter — nothing. Singmen, he remembered absently, had given several convulsive twists before he had fallen. Even Gertrude seemed a long distance away.

He pointed to the end jacket on the left.

He said: "That's the gray one."

Gertrude looked at him for a breathless second; then she screamed.

"*No*, Jack — that one is red."

Starr held her firmly by the shoulders.

"Not to your brother, Miss Enford. I suppose his vanity prevented him from ever telling you. He's color-blind, you see. He *knows no red*."

The Best Wingshot in the United States

Ed Zern

BACK IN FRANK KING's market-hunting days, he was somehow appointed one of the assessors for the township — probably because he knew every inch of it thoroughly, and if his respect for property lines was not highly developed, his knowledge of them was unsurpassed.

It happened that a portion of an immense private shooting preserve, owned by a wealthy New York sportsman named Milford, lay within the township boundaries, and also that a great many of the deer and grouse Frank shipped to market came from within its closely patrolled confines.

In pursuance of his official duties, Frank learned that Milford was present at the main lodge one day, and so he put on his best bib and tucker, carefully picking off any stray partridge feathers that adhered thereto, and drove over to discuss the property's assessment with the owner.

The owner explained to Frank that he kept the place merely as a shooting preserve, primarily for the large numbers of grouse it harbored, and politely inquired whether Frank ever did any bird-shooting. Frank looked at the city man suspiciously, but when it seemed clear that the question was asked out of prime innocence, Frank allowed that he sometimes fooled around with a scattergun, and knew a grouse from a groundhog.

The owner then went on to remark that he considered himself the best wingshot in the United States. Frank pricked up his ears, and allowed that the United States was a pretty big country. "I know it's a big country," said the owner, "but I've shot birds from one end of it to the other, and always with the best wingshots in the area, and I've yet to meet a man I couldn't outshoot. And the same holds true for England and Scotland."

"Of course," he explained, "I *ought* to be the best wingshot in the country. I've never done anything else since I was a youngster, except fish for salmon. Got my first English shotgun as a gift on my twelfth birthday, and been shooting upland and lowland ever since."

"Well now," said Frank, "mebbe you *are* the best wingshot in the United States. Like you say, you *ought* to be. But if you're the best, I figure I'm a real close *second*-best."

"Really?" said the owner. "Well, Mr. King, I'll tell you what. I'll wager one hundred dollars that we can shoot grouse over the same dog for one day, and I'll grass two birds to your one. How does that strike you?"

"It strikes me fine," said Frank. "When would you like to settle this here wager?"

"How does Saturday suit you?" Milford said. "I've a fine grouse dog up with me that needs a workout, and we'll make a day of it."

Thus the next Saturday morning found Frank and Milford setting out from the lodge with a good English setter, and it was a matter of minutes before the dog came to point on birds.

"How do you want to work this, Mr. Milford?" Frank asked. "If we're shooting alternate points, you take the first one."

"None of that, Mr. King!" chuckled the owner. "I'm not going to do you any favors, and I don't want you to do any for me. When those birds flush, you shoot as many as you can, and I'll do the same. This is every man for himself."

"Suits me," Frank said. (Afterwards Frank said, "That's where that feller made his mistake. For ten years back I hadn't never let a ruff fly more than eight — ten feet, and mostly I hit 'em less than five.")

When three grouse flushed, Frank doubled on the two that came up on Milford's side while Milford was still bringing his gun up — and by eleven o'clock Frank had killed twenty-seven birds to Milford's three.

"It looks like you've won yourself a hundred dollars, Mr. King," Milford said. "Let's go back and have lunch. And may I say that this has been one of the most disconcerting days of my life, and that you, sir, are beyond the slightest shadow of doubt the greatest wingshot in the world."

"You'd better not tell that to nobody around these parts," said Frank. "Some of these Sullivan County boys can *really* shoot."

After lunch, Frank took the hundred dollars, thanked his host for a pleasant morning's shoot, and drove home. That afternoon the head gamekeeper of the preserve appeared at the lodge in a black fury, and announced his resignation. "What's the matter?" Milford asked his usually mild-mannered minion.

"Matter?" screamed the enraged bailiff. "Yesterday I hired two extra watchmen to keep Frank King off this place — and today you *invite* him in!"

Once a year thereafter, until his death, Milford (which isn't his name, of course) invited Frank to the lodge for a day of companionable (and noncompetitive) shooting. "It's the only way I can give the watchmen a day off," he explained one time to Frank, and they both chuckled.

Mollie

Paul Hyde Bonner

IT WAS NOT until the season had closed on March fifteenth that Purvey began to realize the change that had come over Mollie. The very first day out with the plow he had noticed that she was not pulling her weight. It was on the twenty-acre piece that he had figured on switching from corn to tobacco because it lay in low ground along the branch where there was always good drainage and the soil was a mixture of rich dark loam and sand. He could tell at once by the way her traces sagged and he had to lean on the right handle to keep the share-cutting straight. He had slapped her with the reins for three lengths of the field, then he had cut a nice limber sucker from a sweetgum in the woody copse that followed the course of the branch and given her a good smart lick with it every time her traces were not as taut as Mike's.

When he had bought Mike and Mollie from a dealer up at Andrews three years before, his neighbors had shaken their heads and clucked their tongues. Pretty looking, yes, they had said down at the store, but too small, too neat and fancy for mules that have to be plowing and hauling and doing a day's work. Purvey had not argued. He had known what he was doing. That pair was just what he had been looking for — strong enough to work his land, which was so full of sand it turned soft and easy, and small enough so that the gentlemen whose quail leases he looked after could mount into the saddle without him having to give them a leg up. He used to have horses for the gentlemen, horses he rented for the season, but they never worked out right. There would always be one that was skittish and shied at every shoat, or one that was so lazy on its feet that it stumbled into every stump hole. And the gentlemen were always complaining and saying, Purvey, why can't you get us some decent nags to ride? Why, hell, mules would be better than these bucking bronchos.

That had given him the idea, and it had worked out just fine. He had paid Mr. Fletcher, the dealer, two hundred and forty dollars for the pair, which was a bargain because nobody wanted mules that size even though they were perfectly matched, sound as two new-minted dollars, and only four years old. Mr. Jessup had been the first of the gentlemen to shoot that season. He had come down in early December and brought a friend with him. When he had gotten out of the car at the little church for colored folks where they always met to shoot the Rutledge property, he had slapped Purvey on the back and let out a whoop like a schoolboy. That's the slickest pair of mules I ever laid my eyes on, he had said,

patting Mollie's shining neck. Don't ever let the Duke of Alba see that pair. He'd give a thousand dollars for them.

Purvey had no idea who the Duke of Alba was, nor why he would fancy mules enough to pay big money for them, but he was pleased by the reception. He had had to admit to Bessie, his wife, when he had ridden off that morning, he on his little gray mare, leading Mollie and Mike, that they looked as pretty as anything in the circus. He had curried and brushed them until their smooth mahogany coats shone like patent leather. Nor had Mr. Jessup's enthusiasm waned after a day in the saddle. They had turned out to be quick, careful walkers who cutely dodged every stump hole and delicately picked their feet over fallen logs. When the dogs had a point, there was no need to tie them up or carry the reins for Purvey to hold. Just dismount and leave them and they would stand there, stanch and immobile.

When, later on in the season, Mr. Dodge and Mr. Weatherby, the two other members of the syndicate, came down for their shooting, they were prepared to admire, for Mr. Jessup had written them glowing accounts of Mollie and Mike. And it had gone on like that for two seasons, everybody happy about the mules and complaints reduced to the behavior of the dogs, which could not be blamed on Purvey as the gentlemen supplied their own and all he had to do was feed and kennel them from Thanksgiving to March fifteenth. Of course Purvey also handled them in the field. He was good with dogs, talking to them mostly and never beating them real hard when they jumped a covey. Just a light whack or two on their hind quarters and a real sharp scolding while they lay in the grass and cringed. Dogs knew when they had done wrong, just as well as people, and it often wasn't their fault. Coming down fast on the lea of a covey, they sometimes wouldn't get the scent until they were right on one of the outlying birds, and when he flushed the whole covey was sure to follow.

There were only two out of the six that were what you could call real downright reliable bird dogs. They were Brownie, a small rangy pointer who was three-quarters covered with liver-colored spots that made it difficult to keep an eye on him in the high broomsedge, and Tess, a big white setter bitch with a black patch over one eye that made her look like Lew Douglas or the Hathaway shirt man. The others were tempermental, sometimes flashy, sometimes messing everything up.

Of course all three of the gentlemen wanted to hunt Tess and Brownie every day. But Purvey was stubborn on that point. Even though it was their leases and their dogs, as long as he was guide and handler all six dogs had to take their half-days in rotation, so they wouldn't get tuckered out and lame and not be able to get through the season. But no matter how often he explained this to them in his soft voice, they would always say to Bessie when they stopped by at the farm to pick up the pair for the morning, what's the matter, Mrs. Gourdine? Why aren't we taking Brownie and Tess? Because Purvey says it's to be Jack and Sunset, Bessie would tell them, because Brownie and Tess was out yesterday and they ain't due to go hunting again until after tomorrow. They grumbled a bit, but they know that Purvey was right and they respected him for it.

The business with Mollie was all the fault of Mr. Christie. He was the new member who had taken Mr. Weatherby's place in the syndicate when Weatherby had had to give up quail shooting because of a stroke. He had come down for the first time in the early part of February, after Mr. Jessup and Mr. Dodge had had their quota of days in the field and had gone back to Cleveland where they both were something big in the steel industry. This Christie wasn't a Clevelander. He was a New York lawyer, who, according to what he said, handled some legal matter for Jessup and Dodge. He brought his wife down with him, a well-set-up blonde woman he called Gertrude who could ride and shoot as well as any man Purvey had ever guided. They put up at a motel near Georgetown and motored over every day for the two weeks they were down, that is, every day but Sundays.

Purvey took a fancy to the Christies from the start. There was no fuss and feathers about them the way there is about some of the northerners who come to hunt quail in the Low Country of South Carolina during the winters. They were full of beans and fun, liked to horse around and say silly things, kidding and sassing each other, and Purvey. And they were both real smart with a gun — quick and deadly. They used double-barreled sixteens which they said they had had made to measure in England. With those four barrels they could kill more birds in a day than Jessup and Dodge with their automatics could kill in a week. Maybe there was something to that made-to-measure business. More times than not there were four birds to pick up after a covey rise.

It was because he liked Christie that Purvey felt so mean about Mollie. For it was Mr. Christie who had ruined her, made a trollop out of a good steady mule. If he hadn't given her to Christie on that very first day, all might have been well. He had given Mike to Mrs. Christie because Mike's saddle holster was newer and nicer looking. Well, that was the big mistake. He had not known then that Christie was one of those city fellows who just can't help spoiling animals. Anything with four legs made him go soft. He just couldn't bring himself to cross that mule on one little thing. If Mollie wanted to go around a tree to the right, he let her go to the right. If Mollie stopped and ate cane, fine. If Mollie looked longingly at a streamer of Florida moss that was hanging out of her reach, Mr. Christie would reach it for her and lean over in the saddle so that she could take it in her dainty, gunmetal lips. He brought a pocketful of sugar every day to feed her, and gave her half his lunch. No Duke of Alba was ever more stuck on a mule than Mr. Christie was on Mollie. It got to be so that Mrs. Christie would look disgusted and say, why Dan, anyone would think you were in love with that mule, and Christie would whoop and shout, love her? I adore her. Don't I, my sweet little Mollie?

By the time March first had come around and the Christies had said good-bye and Christie had kissed Mollie on the nose, she was the most ornery, stuck-up mule in Williamsburg County. She wouldn't work. She wouldn't eat unless there was some cane in the hay, and she treated Mike like she'd never been in harness with him. Let him swing his nose over towards her and her ears would go back and one of those little black hooves on her back feet would flash out so fast you couldn't follow it with your eye.

"Look, Bessie," Purvey Gourdine said to his wife one evening in late April when the tobacco was all set out and he was resting up to plant the cotton. "There ain't nothin' to it, I jes got to get rid of Mollie. She's ruint, plum ruint. She won't work. She's ornery. Kicks Mike or any other animal gets near her. It's all right havin' a mule that the gentlemen likes to ride huntin', but I didn't buy that pair jes for the saddle. From March to November they got to do their share of the work around the farm. I ain't in no position like Jake Ferrier over to the Longleaf Plantation who ain't got nothin' to do the year round but plantin' lespedeza and shootin' hawks when he ain't takin' the gentlemen out huntin'. I ain't paid on that basis. I got my farm to run if you and me and the kids ain't goin' to starve. Jake's got horses in the barn that never carries nothin' but a saddle, but my mules has got to work when there's work to be done."

"Mebbe you could trade her with Mr. Fletcher for another the same size," Bessie suggested as she cut a piece of denim from a pair of old overalls which was going to patch another, less old pair.

"Yeah, well mebbe I could," Purvey said, with doubt in his voice.

"Mollie's a right pretty lookin' mule," Bessie commented, having noted her husband's hesitancy.

"But she ain't got a good reputation," Purvey said.

Bessie Gourdine looked up from her sewing and smiled at Purvey. "I do believe you're carryin' on like Mr. Christie, talkin' about Mollie havin' a reputation jest as if she were some slut of a girl."

"Things like that gets around," Purvey said, moodily.

"Shucks, Purvey," Bessie said impatiently, "who-all knows about Mollie not workin' right except you and me and our kids and old Jim?"

"They're laughin' about it down to the store," Purvey said sorrowfully. "I heard 'em. They was sayin' how Mr. Christie has ruint her for work."

"Tst, tst," Bessie clucked, "You reckon the story's got as far as Andrews?"

"I reckon it has. Seems like it's some kind of big joke on me. Mr. Fletcher's likely to be laughin' fit to burst his collar."

There was a long silence while Purvey sucked on his pipe and Bessie sewed on the patch.

"Maybe Jake Ferrier might use her over to Longleaf Plantation," Bessie said finally.

"I done spoke to him a'ready. He says his gentlemen ain't ridin' no mules."

"My, oh my!" Bessie murmured and sighed.

That summer seemed the longest that Purvey Gourdine could remember. Though his son Harry, a strapping boy of eighteen, and old Jim, the colored hand, were willing, they could be of little help except to work Mike alone or run the pick-up truck. Mollie would not work for them at all, and if neither of them came near her, she just kept turning her rear artillery in their direction. Purvey was the only one who could get her to move, and to do that he had to keep after her every minute with a stout, limber switch. You might have thought she would come out of it, forget about Mr. Christie and his sugar and his patting, but not Mollie. She had a long memory and she knew well that, come the first frost of November, she'd have that saddle on again and would be lazing her way across the savannahs, through the longleaf saplings, snipping dainty bits here and there when the fancy took her, and smelling the sweet scent of warm dead partridge in her saddle bag. Those were the days she waited for in her pettish, ornery, feminine way.

Sure enough, the day Purvey and his son came back from Monks Corner with the six crates of bird dogs in the pick-up and set them loose in the kennels, Mollie trotted across the small field where she and Mike and the gray mare were pastured with her big ears up and forward like twin bayonets. She stuck her head over the wire fence and started a song that was half bray and half whinny. From that moment she was a redeemed animal, sweet and gentle as a kitten. Anyone, Harry or old Jim, could walk up to her in the field and toss a halter over her head. And she took to nuzzling Mike again, something she hadn't done since March. But Purvey was not fooled. He knew that the change of heart would only last as long as the bird season, that next spring she would be worse than ever.

When Mr. Dodge and Mr. Jessup came down together in early December, Purvey could hardly wait to tell them his sad tale. They met at the Simons farm on the first day. Because Purvey knew that there were at least ten coveys using there, he started them off with Brownie and Tess. The day was bright and sunny, with a scattering of fleecy clouds blowing high from the west, and the night dew had been heavy enough to leave a good scent. Everything was perfect for a good day's sport except the state of Purvey's mind.

As they rode out through the back gate of the farm into a broad savannah, Purvey turned in his saddle and spoke to Mr. Jessup, who was behind him on Mollie. "That mule you're ridin' like to ruin my summer," he said with feeling.

Mr. Jesup chuckled. "Mollie? Why, what's she been up to?"

"She won't do a lick of work no more, and she's got so ornery she'll kick anyone who gets in range of her."

"She was as gentle as a lamb when I mounted her," Mr. Jessup said, patting Mollie's neck reassuringly.

"Sure, she's all right now, now that the huntin' season's on. She likes you gentlemen fine, and following the dogs suits her, but she's got it into her mind she's too good to pull a wagon or a plow."

Mr. Jessup roared with laughter and turned in his saddle to Mr. Dodge who was following on Mike. "Did you hear that, Jerry?" he said. "Purvey says that Mollie has delusions of grandeur. She only likes to go shooting with us. Won't work anymore."

"I always said that was a damn smart mule," Mr. Dodge said, and they both laughed loud and long.

"Next year she'll be wanting to spend the summer at Newport," Mr. Jessup said, wiping the tears from his eyes.

Purvey was disturbed. No one wanted to take his problem seriously. It was just a big joke, and he was the butt of it. "With me it ain't so funny as it sounds, Mr. Jessup," he said earnestly. "I've got me a farm to run. I can't afford to feed no mule as thinks she's too good to work. If she cuts up next spring the way she did last, I'm goin' to find me another mule."

Mollie stopped to pluck a bunch of laurel leaves. Mr. Jessup jerked her head up and kicked her with his heels, but she did not move until the branch was secure in her mouth. "Come on, Mollie," Mr. Jessup commanded, "no feminine temperament. You're out hunting now."

Purvey shook his head. "You see what I mean, Mr. Jessup."

But they never really did believe the story of her wickedness. How could they, when she was always so docile, so clever on her feet, so stanch when the guns were firing and she was left alone? They put it down to Purvey's natural pessimism, the pessimism of a man who spends his life in a struggle with Nature. It delighted them that Mollie had the instincts of a lady and preferred the sporting life to the drudgery of the farm. It was a story they would tell and retell back home on Shaker Heights.

Purvey's gloom persisted in spite of fine days with many coveys found. The gentlemen were happy even though they fired four shells for every bird killed. It was the pines against the blue and the dogs racing back and forth in the wind-billowed broomsedge that thrilled them as much as the shot fired. But poor Purvey knew that in another two weeks Mr. and Mrs. Christie would arrive and that would be the end of any chance to retrieve Mollie from her path of glory.

How right he was! The morning the Christies arrived, as they stepped out of their station wagon at the colored church, Mollie, who was tethered to the fence under the chinaberry tree, lifted her head, her ears forward, and gave forth with her combination bray-whinny.

"Mollie, sweet Mollie!" Mr. Christie called, and forgetting his wife and the yelping dogs in the back of the car, rushed across the yard and flung his arms around Mollie's neck. The mule pushed at his pocket with her nose. "Oh, it's sugar you want, my Mollie-O." He pulled out a lump and she picked it daintily from his palm. "What a mule! What a memory! Did you see that, Gertrude? Did you hear her call to me? She knew me the minute I stepped out of the car. Oh, Mollie, if you could only talk." Mollie let out a low snort. "By God, Purvey, she understands me. She tried to answer."

Purvey Gourdine, who was slipping the guns into the saddle holsters, grunted. "I reckon she knows what you're sayin' aw right. That's the trouble with that mule, she knows more'n is good for her."

Mrs. Christie laughed. "Now don't tell me she gossips, Purvey."

Purvey walked over to the station wagon, opened the rear window and let the dogs out. They were Flotsam and Blitz, a pair of fast, unreliable pointers. He was saving Brownie and Tess for the next day when they would be shooting the paper company lease where there were at least twelve coveys using. Purvey watched the dogs race around the church yard. He was worried. He liked the Christies. They were nice, kindly folk, and they shot like masters. Yet they, that is, he was the cause of all the trouble. He hated to disappoint him after that greeting with Mollie, but it was no use, he had to tell him sooner or later, and it might as well be now.

"Ma'am," he said to Mrs. Christie, "that mule is doin' the last bit of huntin' she's ever goin' to do on my property. She's so spoilt she won't do a lick of work outside of ridin' gentlemen after birds. When the season's over, I'm gettin' rid of her. I jes can't afford to own a mule that won't do her share."

"What's that? What's that?" Christie asked in astonishment. "You're going to get rid of Mollie?"

"Yes, sir, Mr. Christie," Purvey said firmly. "She's gettin' too smart for her own good."

"Now listen, Purvey," Christie said genially. "Let's not talk about this now. Gertrude and I have come down for a pleasant two weeks of sport and we don't want any sorrows hanging over it. Just give Mollie another chance for the moment. Let me talk to her. Then if she doesn't behave, you can have a second look at the problem."

"Jest as you say, Mr. Christie," Purvey said skeptically. "Only I'm warnin' you, and —" he nodded toward Mollie — "her too, that she's got to pull that plow and keep her hind feet on the ground or else."

As usual Flotsam and Blitz ranged so wide that they were out of sight half of the time. Purvey did not worry so much about Blitz, who he knew would hold stanch if he did find a covey, which was not too often as he preferred to range the cotton fields and corn stubble where quail are seldom found. It was Flotsam he was not sure of. He had a suspicion that this dog liked to get out of sight for the express purpose of flushing coveys. More than once he had seen birds flying from a direction where Flotsam had been heading. He told the Christies to keep an eye on Blitz while he trotted off to see what Flotsam was up to.

Christie and his wife had ridden on a hundred yards or so, whistling for Blitz whom they could see far off on the right, racing across a plowed field as if he were a sweepstake greyhound, when Mollie lifted her head, shot her ears forward, and gave a little rattling snort with her nostrils.

"She's worried about Purvey and the grey mare leaving us," Gertrude Christie said.

Christie patted Mollie's neck. "Never mind, old girl," he said, "they'll be back in a minute."

Mollie stopped, her head still high, her nostrils still fluttering. Christie paid no attention. He was intent on getting Blitz out of the plow and back to the feed patch of lespedeza which was just ahead. He put the whistle between his lips again and blew two long sharp blasts. Blitz must have heeded finally, for they could see him turn sharply, bound the low hedge that bordered the plow, and come racing towards them.

"Come on, Mollie," Christie said, giving her a gentle tap with his heels.

Gertrude Christie reined in Mike and turned in her saddle. "What's got into Mollie?" she asked. "What's she looking at?"

"I can't imagine," her husband replied. "She seems to be watching Blitz."

When Blitz was about fifty yards from them, bowling along, he suddenly jammed on his brakes and froze. The point was a solid one. Every muscle of the dog was petrified into the final attitude of stopping, his front feet thrust forward, his head down, his tail rigid as a bent stick.

"Down we get," Christie said to his wife, excited. "This is it. No stink bird this time."

They both slid out of the saddles, pulled the guns out of the holsters and loaded.

"I think we had better lead the mules around behind Blitz so they won't be facing us when the birds get up," Mrs. Christie said.

Christie pulled on Mollie's bridle. "Come, girl," he urged. But she did not move. Her head was still high, her ears still forward. She was as frozen as Blitz. Christie gave the bridle a yank. "Come on! What are you frightened of?" It was useless. He might as well have tried to move a bronze statue. "She's not going to move," he said to his wife.

"Well, leave her, then," Gertrude Christie said impa-

tiently. "If she gets a pellet in her hide, it's her own stubborn fault. I'm beginning to see what Purvey was talking about."

The Christies took a wide circle and came up behind Blitz, who had never moved a muscle. Christie came well forward on the left side of the dog in the hope of making the birds break away from the direction of the mules. When a lone cock quail rose at Gertrude's feet, she nailed it. Then the whole covey exploded and Gertrude dropped another, while Christie missed with his first shot and killed one with his left barrel. They both stood where they had fired, intently watching to mark where the birds would settle.

Christie tried to call in Blitz to retrieve the dead birds, but he found it hopeless. The overexcited dog was racing in circles like a chicken with its head cut off. So he and Gertrude did their own picking up, which was not to difficult on the sparse ground.

Mollie was eating grass when Christie came up to her, carrying the three dead birds. "You know, Gertrude," he said, "I wonder if Mollie was pointing that covey."

"Don't be an idiot," Mrs. Christie said crossly.

Christie dangled the birds in front of Mollie. She lifted her head and sniffed them deeply, then ruffled their feathers with her prehensile lips. "Did you smell 'em, Mollie?" he asked. "Did you get that point? Was Blitz only backing you up?"

Purvey came riding up with Flotsam running behind him. "I seen where some of your birds lit," he said. "I got 'em marked good. How many did you get?"

"The little lady got two, but I muffed my right barrel. Too excited," Christie said, and mounted into the saddle. "Okay, let's go. I want to get that bird I missed."

They rode over to a spot where the pines grew closer together, Purvey keeping the dogs in at heel. Finally Purvey halted and told them to dismount. "They're right in there by them saplin's," he said, pointing to a cluster of young longleaf pines that looked like green brooms up-ended. Purvey dismounted too, walking between them, talking to the dogs, cautioning them to take it easy and hunt close. Christie and his wife went forward cautiously, guns ready, as the dogs worked back and forth in front of them, noses to the ground. Flotsam was the first to get a point and Christie took it. A single bird rose up, curled, and flew back over their heads. Christie wheeled and killed it high and far out. He was surprised to see that it dropped near Mollie. Then he realized that she had moved, that she had left Mike and the grey mare and had wandered fifty yards to the right. That was unlike her. Never before had she budged from the spot where he had left her. He walked over to pick up the dead bird and Blitz followed him.

He was about to scold Mollie when he saw that she had again assumed the rigid, watching posture, with her head high and her ears forward. Blitz galloped up beside her and froze to a point. Christie turned to Purvey and his wife. "Look at that!" he called excitedly. "Mollie's pointing a single and Blitz is backing her up again."

"More'n like she smells a snake," Purvey said.

"Do be careful," Gertrude warned.

"Blitz he's pointin' your dead birds," Purvey said.

"No he isn't," Christie said, walking forward. "That bird of mine is right here," he stooped down and picked it up. "Blitz ran right over it." Stuffing the bird quickly into his pocket he moved forward cautiously, edging between Mollie and Blitz, his eyes on the ground, fearing it might be a snake after all.

When the quail flushed, Christie took his time and killed it neatly, then he turned and came up to Mollie whose ears were drooping mulewise now. He put his cheek on her soft nose. "Mollie, my lass, you're the wonder of the age," he crooned. "You found a covey and you found a single. And those dumb people wouldn't believe you. They thought you were just ornery. They thought you were seeing snakes. Well, we'll show 'em who's the best damn quail hound in South Carolina. Come on, Mollie."

He walked in the direction of the dead bird, Mollie coming along behind him, nuzzling the pocket where he kept the sugar. Stopping a few yards from the spot where the quail had fallen, he pointed. "Now fetch it, Mollie," he said. "Fetch dead and you get your lump of sugar."

Mollie looked at him, then punched her nose hard against his pocket.

Christie shook his head. "No, Mollie, not until you fetch that bird."

Mollie hesitated, then out of the corner of her eyes she saw Flotsam running over to the spot where the dead bird lay. With a spring she jumped forward, pushed the dog away with her head and picked up the quail in her lips. Tossing her head as if in triumph and snorting through her nostrils, she brought it back to Christie. He took it with his left hand and offered her a lump with his right.

"Nobody's going to sell you down the river," he whispered to her, stroking her sleek neck.

Mrs. Christie and Purvey had come up, looking bewildered.

"This is weird," Mrs. Christie said. "It's fantastic!" She turned to Purvey. "Tell me, did you ever hear of a mule pointing birds?"

Purvey shook his head. "No, ma'am, I can't rightly say as I have. It don't look to me as if it's quite natural."

"You saw it, didn't you?" Christie asked.

"Yes, sir, I saw what looked like it," Purvey admitted.

"And Gertrude, you saw her point the covey, didn't you?" Christie asked his wife.

"I suppose I did, but I still think I dreamt it," Gertrude said.

"What did you pay for Mollie, Purvey?" Christie asked.

"I give Mr. Fletcher two hundred and forty for the pair," Purvey replied.

"Well, you can keep Mike, I'm giving you three hundred dollars for Mollie this very day," Christie said, with the smile of a man who as acquired a masterpiece. "And what's more, I'm paying you for her feed and keep." He turned to Mollie. "No more bloody plowing for you, my Mollie-O."

"It's sure kind of you, Mr. Christie," Purvey said, embarrassed, "but I don't reckon there is a mule on earth worth . . ."

"Says you!" Christie shouted with a whoop at the end. "Wait till the Duke of Alba hears about Mollie. He'll pay anything to get her for his partridge shoot in Andalusia."

"Yeah?" Purvey said skeptically, taking off his cap and scratching his head. "Mr. Jessup was speakin' about that Dook. He must be powerful fond of mules."

Reference

Weapons Museums of the United States and Canada

ALABAMA

Birmingham

ARLINGTON ANTEBELLUM HOME AND GARDENS, 331 Cotton Ave., S.W. 35211. Tel.: (205) 788-6155. *Founded:* 1953. *Historic House Museum:* Built 1822. *Collections:* Civil War weapons. *Hours & Admission Prices:* Tues.-Sat. 9-5; Sun. 1-6; adults $1.50; children 75¢. Closed Mondays; Xmas.

Mobile

THE MOBILE ART GALLERY, Langan Park. 33608. Tel.: (205) 342-4642. *Founded:* 1964. *Art Gallery. Collections:* Armor and weapons. *Hours & Admission Prices:* Mon.-Sat. 10-5; Sun. 12-5. No charge. Closed New Year's; Mardi Gras; July 4; Labor Day; Thanksgiving; Xmas.

USS ALABAMA BATTLESHIP COMMISSION, P.O. Box 65. 36601. *Founded:* 1963. *Historic Ship Museum. Collections:* 1942 *USS Alabama* Battleship; 1941 *USS Drum* Submarine; army and marine weapons and field equipment. *Hours & Admission Prices:* Daily 8-Sunset; adults $2; children 6-11 50¢.

ARIZONA

Camp Verde

FORT VERDE STATE HISTORIC PARK, P.O. Box 397. 86322. Tel.: (602) 567-3275. *Founded:* 1956. *State Park General Museum:* Located on original site of Forte Verde, Ariz. *Collections:* Military hardware; guns. *Historic Buildings:* 1871-1872 three officers quarters and adjutants building. *Hours & Admission Prices:* Daily 8-5:30. $1 per car or 50¢ per person; children under 14 no charge. Closed Xmas.

Ganado

HUBBELL TRADING POST NATIONAL HISTORIC SITE, Box 298. 86505. Tel.: (602) 755-3475. *Founded:* 1876. *History Museum. Collections:* Military; guns. *Hours & Admission Prices:* Winter: Daily 8-5; Summer: Daily 8-6. No charge. Hubbell House tour 50¢; no charge for children under 16. Closed New Year's; Thanksgiving; Xmas.

Nogales

PETE KITCHEN MUSEUM, Pete Kitchen Ranch-Highway 89. 85621. Tel.: (602) 287-2019. *Founded:* 1954. *Historic House Museum:* The oldest ranch in Arizona located at the western gateway to Mexico, 1854. *Collections:* Armor; Spanish Colonial weapons; pioneer guns. *Hours & Admission Prices:* Tues.-Sun. 10-5; adults 50¢; children under 12 no charge. Closed Mondays; Xmas.

Tucson

ARIZONA HISTORICAL SOCIETY, 949 E. 2nd St. 85719. Tel.: (602) 622-3202. *Founded:* 1884. *History Museum. Collections:* American military weapons. *Hours & Admission Prices:* Mon.-Fri. 9-5; Sat. 9-1; Sun., Holidays 2-5. No charge. Closed New Year's; Easter; July 4; Xmas.

ARKANSAS

Berryville

SAUNDERS MEMORIAL MUSEUM, 113-15 Madison St. 72616. Tel.: (501) 423-2563. *Founded:* 1956. *Gun Museum. Collections:* Colonel C. Burton Saunder's gun collection; history of gunmaking display. *Hours & Admission Prices:* Mon.-Sat. 9-5; Sun. 1-5; adults 75¢; children 25¢. Closed November-March 15.

Fort Smith

MUSEUM OF SCIENCE AND NATURAL HISTORY, MacArthur Park. 72202. Tel.: (501) 376-4321. *Founded:* 1924. *General Museum:* Housed in 1838 Old Little Rock Arsenal located in park where the original arsenal was located. *Collections:* Firearms. *Hours & Admission Prices:* Tues.-Sat. 10-5; Sun. 2-5. No charge. Closed Mondays; New Year's; Memorial Day; July 4; Labor Day; Thanksgiving Day; Xmas.

Rogers

DAISY INTERNATIONAL AIR GUN MUSEUM, U.S. Hwy. 71 South. 72756. Tel.: (501) 636-1200. *Founded:* 1966. *Gun Museum. Collections:* Non-powder guns. *Hours & Admission Prices:* Mon.-Fri. 9-5. No Charge.

Washington

PIONEER WASHINGTON RESTORATION FOUNDATION. 71862. Tel.: (501) 983-2466. *Founded:* 1958. *History Museum. Collections:* Weapons. *Hours & Admission Prices:* Mon.-Sat. 9-5; Sun., Holidays 9:30-5; State Capitol: no charge; Garland House: adults 75¢; children 35¢; Other Houses: adults 50¢; children 25¢. Closed Xmas.

CALIFORNIA

Amador City

GOLD RUSH MUSEUM, Corner Fleeheart and Main. 95601. Tel.: (209) 267-0260. *Founded:* 1960. *History Museum. Collections:* Guns; Wells Fargo Office. *Hours & Admission Prices:* Fri-Sun. 10-5; adults 10¢; children no charge. Closed January-February.

Bakersfield

KERN COUNTY MUSEUM, 3801 Chester Ave. 93309. Tel.: (805) 861-2133. *Founded* 1941. *Local History Museum. Collections:* Firearms. *Hours & Admission Prices:* Museum: Mon.-Fri. 8-5; Sat.-Sun., Holidays 12-5; Summer: Daily 12-7. Outdoor Museum: Mon.-Fri. 8-3:30; Sat.-Sun., Holidays 12-3:30; Summer: Daily 12-5:30; adults 50¢; students 35¢; children 6-12 25¢. Closed New Year's; Thanksgiving; Xmas.

Bevery Hills

THE FRANCIS E. FOWLER, JR. FOUNDATION MUSEUM, 9215 Wilshire Blvd. 90210. Tel.: (213) 278-8010. *Founded:* 1953. *Art Museum. Collections:* Antique firearms; edge weapons; cannon models. *Hours & Admission Prices:* Mon.-Sat. 1-5. No charge. Closed Sundays; Legal Holidays.

Dorris

HERMAN'S HOUSE OF GUNS, 204 S. Oregon St. 96023. Tel.: (916) 397-2611. *Gun and History Museum. Collections:* Shoulder and hand guns; cannon and related items; military. *Hours & Admission Prices:* Daily 8-8. No charge.

El Monte

EL MONTE HISTORICAL MUSEUM, 3100 N. Tyler Ave. 91731. Tel.: (213) 444-3813. *Founded* 1958. *General Museum. Collections:* Guns. *Hours & Admission Prices:* Mon. 1-4; Tues.-Fri. 10-4. No charge. Closed Saturdays; Sundays; August; Legal Holidays.

Fort Jones

FORT JONES MUSEUM, Main St. 96032. Tel.: (916) 468-2302. *Founded:* 1952. *Historical Museum. Collections:* Guns. *Hours & Admission Prices:* Mon.-Fri. 10-5; Sat. 10-5; and Sun. and Holidays by appointment. No charge.

Lakeport

LAKE COUNTY MUSEUM, 175 Third St. 95453. Tel.: (707) 263-5461. *Founded:* 1936. *General Museum. Collections:* Old guns. *Hours & Admission Prices:* Mon.-Fri. 1-4; Sat. 11-4. No charge. Closed Sundays; Holidays.

Monterey

MONTEREY STATE HISTORIC PARK, 210 Olivier. 93940. Tel.: (408) 373-2103. *Founded:* 1938. *State Historic Park Museum. Collections:* Spanish gun collection. *Hours & Admission Prices: Larkin House:* Wed.-Mon. 9-4; California's First Theatre: Tues.-Sun. 9-5; Pacific House, Casa del Oro, Stevenson House and Custom House: Daily 9-5; adults 25¢; children no charge. Closed New Year's; Thanksgiving; Xmas.

Port Hueneme

CIVIL ENGINEER CORPS/SEABEE MUSEUM, Naval Construction Battalion Center, Code 2232. 93041. Tel.: (805) 982-5163. *Founded:* 1947. *Military Museum. Collections:* Military weapons; uniforms; models of military equipment; personal papers and books of high-ranking officers; unit plaques and flags. *Hours & Admission Prices:* Mon.-Fri. 8-4:30; Sat. 9-4:30; Sun. 12:30-4:30. No charge. Closed Holidays.

San Diego

SAN DIEGO HISTORICAL SOCIETY, SERRA MUSEUM, LIBRARY AND TOWER GALLERY, 2727 Presidio Dr., Presidio Park. 92138. Tel.: (714) 297-3258. *Founded:* 1928. *History Museum:* Located on the site of the first mission and presidio in Alta Calif. founded by Fray Junipero Serra and Governor-Captain Gaspar de Portola in July, 1769. *Collections:* Firearms. *Hours & Admission Prices:* Tues.-Sun. 10-5. No charge. Closed Mondays; New Year's; Thanksgiving; Xmas.

San Francisco

WELLS FARGO BANK HISTORY ROOM, 420 Montgomery St. 94104. Tel.: (415) 396-2648. *Founded:* 1941. *Company History Museum. Collections:* Guns. *Hours & Admission Prices:* Mon.-Fri. 10-3. No charge. Closed National Holidays.

Shasta

SHASTA STATE HISTORIC PARK, P.O. Box 507. 96807. Tel.: (916) 243-8194. *Founded:* 1950. *State Park Museum. Collections:* Gun collection. *Hours & Admission Prices:* Daily 10-5; adults 25¢; children under 18 no charge. Closed New Year's; Thanksgiving; Xmas.

Woodside

WOODSIDE STORE, 471 Kings Mountain Rd. 94062. Tel.: (415) 851-7615. *Founded:* 1940. *Historic Store:* c. 1853. *Collections:* Guns. *Hours & Admission Prices:* Wed.-Sun. 10-12 & 1-5. No charge. Closed Mondays; Tuesdays; National Holidays.

COLORADO

Colorado Springs

PIONEERS' MUSEUM, 25 West Kiowa. 80902. Tel.: (303) 471-6650. *Founded:* 1908. *History Museum. Collections:* Weapons. *Hours & Admission Prices:* Tues.-Sat. 10-5; Sun. 2-5. No charge. Closed National Holidays.

Estes Park

ESTES PARK AREA HISTORICAL MUSEUM, Hghwy. 36. 80517. *Founded:* 1962. *General Museum. Collections:* Guns. *Hours & Admission Prices:* Memorial Day-Labor Day Mon.-Sat. 10-12 & 2-5; Sun. 2-5. No charge. Closed winters.

Fort Carson

FORT CARSON VISITORS CENTER AND MUSEUM, 849 Oconnel Blvd. 80913. Tel.: (303) 579-2908. *Founded:* 1957. *Military Museum. Collections:* Weapons; uniforms. *Hours & Admission Prices:* Daily 9-5. No charge. Closed National Holidays.

LaVeta

FORT FRANCISCO MUSEUM. 81055. *Founded:* 1947. *Historic Site Museum:* 1862 Fort. *Collections:* Guns. *Hours & Admission Prices:* Memorial Day-Oct. 1 Daily, Holidays 9-5. Donations accepted. Closed Oct. 2-Memorial Day.

Meeker

THE WHITE RIVER MUSEUM, 565 Park St. 81641. Tel.: (303) 878-9982. *Founded:* 1956. *Folk Type Museum.* Housed in 1880 Officer's Quarters, built after Meeker Massacre. *Collection:* Guns. *Hours & Admission Prices:* Daily 10-12 & 1-4. No charge. Closed New Year's; Xmas.

Sterling

OVERLAND TRAIL MUSEUM, Junction I-80S and Highway 6 East. 80751. Tel.: (303) 522-3895. *Founded:* 1936. *General Museum:* Located on the site of the Overland Trail, near the the Valley Station of Ben Holladay Stage line. *Collections:* Frontier rifles and shot guns; relics of Civil, Spanish-American, and later wars. *Hours & Admission Prices:* Mon.-Sat. 9:30-5; Sun., Holidays 10-5. No charge. Closed September 15-May 1.

CONNECTICUT

Guilford

HENRY WHITFIELD MUSEUM, Whitfield St. 06437. Tel.: (203) 453-2457. *Founded:* 1903. *Historic House:* The oldest house in New England, built in 1639 by founders of Guilford as home for pastor, meeting house, fort and church; located on land purchased from Indian Sachem Squaw. *Collections:* Relics; firearms. *Hours & Admission Prices:* May 1-Oct. 31 Wed.-Sun., Holidays 10-5; Nov. 1-April 30 Sat & Sun. 10-4 and by appointment; adults 50¢. Closed Thanksgiving; December 15-January 15.

Hartford

CONNECTICUT STATE LIBRARY MUSEUM, 231 Capital Ave. 06115. Tel.: (203) 566-3056. *Founded:* 1910. *History Museum. Collections:* Colt firearms; military relics; World War I posters. *Hours & Admission Prices:* Mon.-Fri. 9-5; Sat. 9-1. No charge. Closed Sundays; National and State Holidays.

WADSWORTH ATHENEUM, 600 Main St. 06103. Tel.: (203) 278-2670. *Founded:* 1842. *Art Museum. Collections:* European arms and armor; Colt collection of firearms. *Hours & Admission Prices:* Museum: Tues.-Sat. 11-4; Sun. 1-5; No charge. Closed Mondays; New Year's; July 4; Thanksgiving; Xmas.

Meriden

MERIDEN HISTORICAL SOCIETY, INC., 424 W. Main St. 06450. Tel.: (203) 237-5079. *Founded:* 1893. *General Museum. Collections:* Firearms. *Hours & Admission Prices:* Sun., Wed. 2-5; other times by appointment; adults $1; children no charge. Closed Veteran's Day; Thanksgiving; Xmas.

New Haven

WINCHESTER GUN MUSEUM, 275 Winchester Ave. 06504. Tel.: (203) 777-7911. *Founded:* 1866. *Gun Museum. Collections:* Firearms and accessories from 15th century to present; 4-barrelled European repeating hand gun from 1450: 2,000-year old Chinese crossbow trigger mechanism; Italian breechloading flint lock rifle 1683; U.S. martial arms; history of firearms. *Hours & Admission Prices:* Mon.-Sat. 9-4. No charge. Closed Sundays; National Holidays.

Norwich

THE SLATER MEMORIAL MUSEUM, 108 Crescent St. 06360. Tel.: (203) 887-2505. *Founded:* 1888. *Art Museum. Collections:* Guns. *Hours & Admission Prices:* Sept.-May Mon.-Fri. 9-4; Sat.-Sun. 2-5; June-Aug. Tues.-Sun. 1-4. No charge. Closed Holidays.

Torrington

TURNER MUSEUM, Torrington Library, 12 Daycoeton Pl. 06790. Tel.: (203) 489-6684. *Founded:* 1900. *China, Glass, Silver Museum. Collections:* Guns. *Hours & Admission Prices:* Sat.; other times by appointment.

DISTRICT OF COLUMBIA

Washington

ANDERSON HOUSE, HEADQUARTERS AND MUSEUM OF THE SOCIETY OF THE CINCINNATI, 2118 Massachusetts Ave., N.W. 20008. Tel.: (202) 785-2040. *Founded:* 1783. *History and Art Museum. Collections:* Swords and firearms. *Hours & Admission Prices:* Tues.-Sun. 2-4. No charge. Closed Mondays; Thanksgiving; Xmas.

DAUGHTERS OF THE AMERICAN REVOLUTION MUSEUM, 1776 D St., N.W. 20006. (202) 628-4980. *Founded:* 1890. *Decorative Arts Museum. Collections:* Guns; military; Revolutionary War artifacts. *Hours & Admission Prices:* Mon.-Fri. 9-4. No charge. Closed one week in April; Saturdays; Sundays; National Holidays.

NATIONAL RIFLE ASSOCIATION FIREARMS MUSEUM, 1600 Rhode Island Ave., N.W. 20036. Tel.: (202) 783-6505. *Founded:* 1871. *Firearms Museum. Collections:* More than 1,200 firearms including antique and modern shotguns, rifles and pistols, both foreign and U.S. make. *Hours & Admission Prices:* Daily 10-4. No charge. Closed New Year's; Easter; Xmas.

U.S. NAVY MEMORIAL MUSEUM, Bldg. 76, Washington Navy Yard. 20390. Tel.: (202) 433-2651. *Founded:* 1961. *Naval History Museum:* Housed in the former 1828 Breech Mechanism Shop of the old Naval Gun Factory. *Collections:* Weapons; relics; memorabilia of Navy. *Hours & Admission Prices:* Mon.-Fri. 9-4; Sat.-Sun., Holidays 10-5. No charge. Closed New Year's; Thanksgiving; Xmas.

FLORIDA

Jacksonville

FORT CAROLINE NATIONAL MEMORIAL, 12713 Fort Caroline Rd. 32225. Tel.: (904) 724-8337. *Founded:* 1953. *Historic Site Museum. Collections:* Armor; spears; guns; helmets. *Hours & Admission Prices:* Daily 8-5. No charge. Closed Xmas.

Key West

MARTELLO GALLERY AND MUSEUM, S. Roosevelt Blvd., 33040. Tel.: (305) 296-3913. *Founded:* 1951. *General Museum. Collections:* Naval exhibits; Scuba gear; Japanese submarine; anchor; steam driven torpedos; pictorial exhibit of the growth of Key West Naval Station; destroyers; scale model aircraft; weapons. *Hours & Admission Prices:* Daily, Holidays 9:30-5; adults $1; children 7-16 25¢. Closed Xmas.

Orlando

ORANGE COUNTY HISTORICAL COMMISSION, 27 E. Central Blvd. 32801. Tel.: (305) 849-3598. *Founded:* 1957. *Historical Commission Museum. Collections:* Firearms. *Hours & Admission Prices:* Mon.-Wed., Fri. 2-5. No charge. Closed National Holidays.

St. Petersburg

ST. PETERSBURG HISTORICAL MUSEUM, 335 2nd Ave., N.E. 33701. Tel.: (813) 894-1401. *Founded:* 1920. *General Museum. Collections:* Civil War mementos, uniforms; guns. *Hours & Admission Prices:* Mon.-Sat. 11-5; Sun. 1-5; adults 75¢; children over 4 25¢. Closed Thanksgiving; Xmas.

GEORGIA

Atlanta

ATLANTA MUSEUM, 537-39 Peach St., N.E. 30308. Tel.: (404) 872-8233. *Founded:* 1938. *General Museum. Collections:* First captured Japanese Zero plane; Eli Whitney gun collection. *Hours & Admission Prices:* Mon.-Fri. 9-4:30; adults $1; children 25¢. Closed Saturdays; Sundays; New Year's; July 4; Labor Day; Thanksgiving; Xmas.

CYCLORAMA, Boulevard at Atlanta. 30303. *Founded:* 1898. *Park Museum. Collections:* Painting depicting the Battle of Atlanta; Civil War documents; uniforms; weapons. *Hours & Admission Prices:* Daily, Holidays 9-5; adults $1.25; children 75¢. Closed Xmas.

Columbus

COLUMBUS MUSEUM OF ARTS AND CRAFTS, INC., 1251 Wynnton Rd. 31906. *Founded:* 1952. *General Museum. Collections:* Antique American guns. *Hours & Admission Prices:* Tues.-Sat. 10-5; Sun. 2-5. No charge. Closed Mondays; New Year's; July 4; Thanksgiving; Xmas.

Fort Benning

UNITED STATES ARMY INFANTRY MUSEUM, U.S. Army Infantry Center. 31905. Tel.: (404) 545-5413. *Founded:* 1959. *Military Museum. Collections:* Military weapons; military art; early military archeological materials; archives of photographs; collection of firearms including experimental US items and Japanese firearms. *Hours & Admission Prices:* Tues.-Fri. 10-4:30; Sat.-Sun. 12:30-4:30. No charge. Closed Mondays; New Year's; Xmas.

Fort Ogelthorpe

CHICKAMAUGA-CHATTANOOGA NATIONAL MILITARY PARK. 30741. Tel.: (404) 866-9241. *Founded:* 1890. *Military Museum. Collections:* Civil War relics; Fuller gun collection of American military shoulder arms. *Hours & Admission Prices:* Daily, Holidays 8-5. No charge. Closed Xmas.

Irwinville

JEFFERSON DAVIS STATE PARK, off Route 32. 31760. Tel.: (912) 831-2335. *Founded:* c. 1940. *Collections:* Confederate relics; guns; flags. *Hours & Admission Prices:* Tues.-Sat. 9-12, 1-5; Sun. 1-5. No charge.

Marietta

KENNESAW MOUNTAIN NATIONAL BATTLEFIELD PARK, Jct. Stilesboro Rd. and Old Hwy. 41. 30060. Tel.: (404) 427-4686. *Founded:* 1899. *Civil War History Museum:* Located on the site of a Civil War battle. *Collections:* Dress and weapons of Civil War soldiers. *Hours & Admission Prices:* Mon.-Sat. 8:30-5; Sun. 9:30-6. No charge. Closed Xmas.

HAWAII

Honolulu

PEARL HARBOR MEMORIAL MUSEUM, 821 Mililani St. 96813. Tel.: (808) 847-1660. *Founded:* 1973. *Military Museum. Collections:* Uniforms; weapons; badges; decorations; military equipment used in WW II in the Pacific; artillery pieces; a submarine; tanks. *Hours & Admission Prices:* Daily 8:30-5; adults $1; children 50¢; students 75¢.

IDAHO

Rexburg

UPPER SNAKE RIVER VALLEY HISTORICAL SOCIETY, Rte. 2, Box 12 D. 83440. Tel.: (208) 356-7030. *Founded:* 1965. *Historic Research Institute. Collections:* Guns. *Hours & Admission Prices:* Mon.-Fri. 9-5. No charge. Closed Saturday; Sunday; National Holidays.

ILLINOIS

Aurora

AURORA HISTORICAL MUSEUM, 304 Oak Ave. 60506. Tel.: (312) 897-9029. *Founded:* 1906. *General Museum. Collections:* Guns. *Hours & Admission Prices:* Wed., Sun. 2-4:30; Tues.-Fri. by appointment; Main Building; no charge; Carriage House; adults 25¢; children 10¢. Closed National Holidays.

Chicago

CHICAGO HISTORICAL SOCIETY, Clark Street at North Ave. 60614. Tel.: (312) 642-4600. *Founded:* 1856. *History Museum. Collections:* Weapons; military; Civil War uniforms; flags; Lincoln material. *Hours & Admission Prices:* Mon.-Sat. 9:30-4:30; Sun., Holidays 12:30-5:30; families $1; adults 50¢; children 25¢; Mondays no charge. Closed New Year's; Thanksgiving; Xmas.

GEORGE F. HARDING MUSEUM, 86 E. Randolph St. 60601. Tel.: (312) 332-4803. *History Museum. Collections:* Armor and weapons. *Hours & Admission Prices:* Hours by appointment. No charge.

Edwardsville

MADISON COUNTY HISTORICAL MUSEUM, 715 N. Main St. 62025. Tel.: (618) 656-7562. *Founded:* 1924. *Historical Society Museum. Collections:* Guns. *Hours & Admission Prices:* Wed. 9-5, Sat. 1-5, Sun. 2-5. No charge. Closed Legal Holidays.

Prairie du Rocher

FORT DE CHARTRES STATE PARK MUSEUM, Fort de Chartres State Park. 62277. Tel.: (618) 284-3486. *Founded:* 1917. *State Park Museum:* Located on the original site of an 18th century stone French Fort de Chartres built 1753-56. *Collections:* Original powder magazine; military; weapons. *Hours & Admission Prices:* Daily 9-5. No charge. Closed New Year's; Thanksgiving; Xmas.

Rock Island

JOHN M. BROWNING MEMORIAL MUSEUM. 61201. Tel.: (309) 794-5021. *Founded:* 1905. *Military Museum. Collections:* Weapons; equipment; small arms; artillery; field equipment; automatic rifles developed by John N. Browning. *Hours & Admission Prices:* Wed.-Sun. 11-4. No charge. Closed New Year's; Thanksgiving; Xmas.

Sandwich

SANDWICH HISTORICAL SOCIETY, 704 N. Main St. 60548. Tel.: (815) 786-4571. *Founded:* 1965. *General Museum. Collections:* Guns; swords. *Hours & Admission Prices:* Sun. 1-5; adults 50¢; children 10¢.

Wheaton

DUPAGE COUNTY HISTORICAL MUSEUM, 102 E. Wesley St. 60187. Tel.: (312) 682-7343. *Founded:* 1967. *General Museum. Collections:* Flags; guns. *Hours & Admission Prices:* Mon., Wed., Fri.-Sat. 10-4. No charge. Closed Holidays.

INDIANA

Columbus

BARTHOLOMEW COUNTY HISTORICAL SOCIETY, 524 Third St. 47201. Tel.: (812) 372-3541. *Founded:* 1921. *Local History Museum. Collections:* Guns. *Hours & Admission Prices:* Tues.-Sat. 12:30-4:30.

Franklin

JOHNSON COUNTY HISTORICAL MUSEUM, 150 W. Madison St. 46131. Tel.: (317) 535-8604. *Founded:* 1923. *General Museum. Collections:* World War I and II guns and equipment; Civil War items. *Hours & Admission Prices:* Thurs. 2-4 & 7-9; other days by appointment only. Donations accepted.

Kokomo

HOWARD COUNTY HISTORICAL MUSEUM, 1200 W. Sycamore St. 47901. Tel.: (317) 452-4314. *Founded:* 1916. *General Museum. Collections:* Military; guns. *Hours & Admission Prices:* Mon., Wed., Fri. 1-4; Sun. 2-4, No charge. Closed National Holidays.

La Porte

LA PORTE COUNTY HISTORICAL MUSEUM, Court House Basement-Lincolnway. 46350. Tel.: (219) 362-8676. *Founded:* 1906. *History Museum. Collections:* Jones collection of firearms. *Hours & Admission Prices:* Mon.-Fri. 10-4:30. No charge. Closed National Holidays.

Richmond

WAYNE COUNTY HISTORICAL MUSEUM, 1150 North "A" St. 47374. Tel.: (317) 962-5756. *Founded:* 1929. *General Museum. Collections:* Guns. *Hours & Admission Prices:* Tues.-Fri. 12-4; Sat.-Sun. 1-5; Vacation Time: Tues.-Sun. 1-5; adults $1; children 50¢. Closed Mondays; National Holidays; Xmas-mid-February.

Salem

WASHINGTON COUNTY HISTORICAL SOCIETY, INC., 307 E. Market St. 47167. Tel.: (812) 883-6495. *Founded:* 1897. *General Museum. Collections:* Wars; guns. *Hours & Admission Prices:* Tues.-Sun. 1-5 adults 50¢ children under 12 no charge. Closed Mondays.

Vincennes

GEORGE ROGERS CLARK NATIONAL HISTORIC PARK, 115 Du Bois Street. 47591. Tel.: (812) 882-1176. *History Museum:* Museum commemorates the winning of old Northwest Territory and the achievement of Clark and his associates during the American Revolution. *Activities:* Musket demonstration, Sunday. *Hours & Admission Prices:* Winter Daily 8:30-5; Summer Daily 8:30-6. No charge.

IOWA

Decorah

NORWEGIAN-AMERICAN MUSEUM, 502 W. Water St. 52101. Tel.: (319) 382-3856. *Founded:* 1877. *Ethnic Museum. Collections:* Guns. *Hours & Admission Prices:* May-June, Sept.-Oct. Daily 10-4; July-Aug. 9-5; adults $1; children under 15 75¢; children under 6 no charge. Closed Nov.-Apr.

Des Moines

DEPARTMENT OF HISTORY AND ARCHIVES, E. 12th and Grand Aves. 50319. Tel.: (515) 281-5111. *Founded:* 1892. *General Museum. Collections:* Guns. *Hours & Admission Prices:* Daily 8-4. No charge.

Glenwood

MILLS COUNTY HISTORICAL SOCIETY AND MUSEUM, 211 N. Chestnut St. 51534. Tel.: (712) 527-4584. *Founded:* 1957. *General Museum. Collections:* Guns. *Hours & Admission Prices:* May-Sept. Mon.-Sat. by appointment; Sun., Holidays 1:30-5:30; adults 25¢; children under 12 no charge when accompanied by adults. Closed October-April.

Osage

MITCHELL COUNTY HISTORICAL MUSEUM, North 6th. 50461. Tel.: (515) 732-3082. *Founded:* 1965. *General Museum. Collections:* Guns. *Hours & Admission Prices:* May 15-Oct. 1 Fri.-Sun., Holidays 2-5. No charge.

Sibley

McCALLUM MUSEUM, City Park. 51249. *Founded:* 1956. *General Museum. Collections:* Civil War guns, swords, bayonets, ammunition cases and uniforms; World War I and II items. *Hours & Admission Prices:* May-Sept., Sun. 2-5; other times by appointment. No charge.

KANSAS

Abilene

DICKINSON COUNTY HISTORICAL SOCIETY, 412 S. Campbell St., P.O. Box 506. 67410. Tel.: (913) 263-2681. *Founded:* 1928. *History Museum. Collections:* Guns; cattle drive memorabilia. *Hours & Admission Prices:* Mon.-Sat. 10-4:30; Sun. 1-4:30; Dec.-Mar. Sat., Sun. 1-4:30. Donations accepted.

Ashland

PIONEER MUSEUM, Hwy. 160. 67831. Tel.: (316) 635-2570. *Founded:* 1939. *General Museum. Collections:* Guns. *Hours & Admission Prices:* Summer: Mon.-Sat. 10:30-6; Sun. 12:30-4:30; Winter: Daily 12:30-4:30. Donations accepted. Closed Xmas.

Baldwin City

OLD CASTLE MUSEUM, 5th and Dearborn Sts. 66006. Tel.: (913) 594-6451, ext. 483. *Founded:* 1952. *Collections:* Early Kansas weapons; arrowheads; Civil War relics. *Hours & Admission Prices:* Tues.-Sun. 2-5. Donations accepted. Closed Mondays.

Chanute

MARTIN AND OSA JOHNSON SAFARI MUSEUM, INC., 16 S. Grant St. 66720. Tel.: (316) 431-9708. *Founded:* 1961. *African History. Collections:* Trophies collected by Martin and Osa Johnson. *Hours & Admission Prices:* Mon.-Sat. 10-5:30; Sun., Holidays 12-5:30; adults 50¢; children under 12 10¢; no charge if accompanied by parents. Closed Xmas.

Garnett

ANDERSON COUNTY HISTORICAL MUSEUM, Court House. 66032. *Founded:* 1968. *Local History Museum. Collections:* Guns. *Hours & Admission Prices:* Mon.-Fri. 1:30-4. No charge.

Kanopolis

FORT HARKER MUSEUM. 67454. *Founded:* 1920. *Military Museum. Collections:* Guns and war equipment of 1870's; uniforms. Historic House: 1867 Fort Harker Guardhouse. *Hours & Admission Prices:* Winter: Sat. 10-12 & 1-5; Sun. 1-5; Summer: Tues.-Sat. 10-12 & 1-5; Sun. 1-5. No charge. Closed New Year's; Thanksgiving; Xmas.

Larned

FORT LARNED NATIONAL HISTORIC SITE, Rte. 3. 67550. Tel.: (316) 285-3571. *Founded:* 1966. *Historic Buildings:* 1886 old commissary; 1867 quartermaster depot; 1867-68 three officer's quarters; infantry barracks; 1868 shops; 1868 new commissary. *Collections:* Military and pioneer firearms of the Indian War period; military exhibits. *Hours & Admission Prices:* Park Daily 8-5. No charge. All buildings open to the public every day of the year. No charge.

Manhattan

RILEY COUNTY HISTORICAL MUSEUM, Memorial Auditorium Building, 11th and Poyntz Ave. 66502. Tel.: (913) 537-2210. *Founded:* 1914. *History Museum. Collections:* Weapons. *Hours & Admission Prices:* Tues.-Sat. 1-5; Sun., Holidays 2-4:30. No charge. Closed Mondays; New Year's; Easter; Thanksgiving; Xmas.

Marysville

ORIGINAL PONY EXPRESS HOME STATION, INC., 809 North St. 66508. Tel.: (913) 562-9874. *Founded:* 1967. *History Museum. Collections:* Guns. *Hours & Admission Prices:* May-Sept. 1 Mon.-Sat. 9-12 & 1-5; Sun. 2-5.

Meade

DALTON GANG HIDEOUT MUSEUM, Highway 54. 67864. Tel.: (316) 873-2731. *Collections:* Guns. *Facilities:* Escape tunnel from house to barn. *Hours & Admission Prices:* Mon.-Fri. 10-12, 1-5; Sat. 10-5; tunnel trip 25¢.

Minneapolis

OTTAWA COUNTY HISTORICAL MUSEUM, 101 W. Second St. 67467. *Founded:* 1966. *General Museum. Collections:* Guns. *Hours & Admission Prices:* Tues.-Sat. 10-12 & 1-5; Sun. 1-5. No charge. Closed Mondays; Holidays.

North Newton

KAUFFMAN MUSEUM, E. 27th St. 67117. Tel.: (316) 283-2500. *Founded:* 1940. *General Museum. Collections:* Firearms. *Hours & Admission Prices:* Mon.-Fri. 8:30-5; Sat. 8:30-12; Sun. 1-5; adults $1; children 50¢. Closed Easter; Xmas.

Osawatomie

JOHN BROWN CABIN, 10th and Main Sts. 66064. Tel.: (913) 755-4384. *Founded:* 1912. *Historic House:* 1854 John Brown Cabin. *Collections:* Guns. *Hours & Admission Prices:* Tues.-Sat. 10-5; Sun. 1-5. No charge.

Phillipsburg

OLD FORT BISSELL. 67661. *Founded:* 1961. *General Museum. Collections:* Old guns. *Hours & Admission Prices:* Memorial Day-Labor Day Daily 9-9. No charge.

Salina

SMOKY HILL HISTORICAL MUSEUM, Oakdale Park. 67401. Tel.: (913) 827-3958. *Founded:* 1935. *History Museum. Collections:* Guns. *Hours & Admission Prices:* Tues.-Sun., Holidays 1-5. No charge. Closed New Year's; Xmas.

Wichita

WICHITA HISTORICAL MUSEUM ASSOCIATION, 3751 E. Douglas Ave. 67218. Tel.: (316) 686-0915. *Founded:* 1939. *History Museum. Collections:* Military; guns. *Hours & Admission Prices:* Tues.-Sat. 11-5; Sun. 1-5; adults 50¢; children 25¢. Closed Mondays; National Holidays.

KENTUCKY

Bowling Green

KENTUCKY MUSEUM, Western Kentucky University. 42101. Tel.: (502) 745-4771. *Founded:* 1930. *General Museum. Collections:* Firearms. *Hours & Admission Prices:* Mon.-Fri. 9-5; Sat. 9-4; Sun. 2-4. No charge. Closed University Holidays.

Fort Knox

PATTON MUSEUM OF CAVALRY AND ARMOR, Old Ironsides Ave. 40121. Tel.: (502) 624-3812. *Founded:* 1948. *Military Museum. Collections:* Tanks; artillery; armored cavalry; vehicles; firearms; medals and decorations; Gen. Patton memorabilia; paintings. *Hours & Admission Prices:* Daily 9-4:30. No charge. Closed Dec. 24-25; Dec. 31-Jan. 1.

Frankfort

KENTUCKY HISTORICAL SOCIETY, 200 Broadway, Box H. 40601. Tel.: (502) 564-3106. *Founded:* 1836. *State History Museum. Collections:* Civil War artifacts; papers of Jefferson Davis and Abraham Lincoln; letters by George Washington; firearms collection, including Daniel Boone's rifle; pistol with which Aaron Burr killed Alexander Hamilton; Kentucky long rifles. *Hours & Admission Prices:* Mon.-Sat. 9-4; Sun., Holidays 1-5. No charge. Closed Xmas; New Years.

London

MOUNTAIN LIFE MUSEUM, Levi Jackson Wilderness Road State Park. 40741. *Founded:* 1929. *State Park Museum. Collections:* Guns. *Hours & Admission Prices:* May-Aug. Mon.-Sat. 9-5; Sept. Sun. 9-5; adults 50¢; children 25¢.

Louisville

THE FILSON CLUB, 118 W. Breckinridge St. 40203. Tel.: (502) 582-3727. *Founded:* 1884. *History Museum. Collections:* Guns and rifles. *Hours & Admission Prices:* Oct.-June Mon.-Fri. 9-5; Sat. 9-12; July-Sept. Mon.-Fri. 9-5. No charge. Closed National Holidays.

MUSEUM OF SCIENCE AND HISTORY, 743 S. 5th St. 40203. Tel.: (502) 587-1666. *Founded:* 1872. *General Museum. Collections:* Guns. *Hours & Admission Prices:* Mon.-Fri. 9-5. No charge. Closed Saturdays; Sundays; Holidays.

Richmond

JOHATHAN TRUMAN DORRIS MUSEUM, Eastern Kentucky University, John Grant Crabbe Library, University Dr. 40475. Tel.: (606) 622-5585. *Founded:* 1926. *History Museum. Collections:* Firearms and edged weapons; Civil War relics; Revolutionary War uniforms; 1789 drum. *Hours & Admission Prices:* Mon.-Fri. 9-4; Sat.-Sun. by appointment. No charge. Closed University Holidays and Vacations.

LOUISIANA

Arabi

CHALMETTE NATIONAL HISTORICAL PARK, P.O. Box 429. 70032. Tel.: (504) 271-2412. *Founded:* 1939. *Military Museum:* Housed in c. 1832 Beauregard House located on the site of last decisive battle between American and British forces in War of 1812. *Collections:* Weapons and ammunition used in Battle for New Orleans; diorama of the battle; military history of War of 1812. Historic Site: 1864 National Cemetery for Union soldiers of Civil War; interment of Americans from major battles including Vietnam. *Hours & Admission Prices:* Sept.-May 8-5; June-Aug. 8-6. No charge. Closed Mardi Gras; Xmas.

Mansfield

MANSFIELD BATTLE PARK, Rte. 2, Box 252. 71052. Tel.: (318) 872-1474. *Founded:* 1957. *History Museum. Collections:* Scale model of Gettysburg Memorial Monument of State of Louisiana; mementos of the Civil War; Civil War weapons; small arms; field guns; swords; shells; uniforms. *Hours & Admission Prices:* Tues.-Fri. 9-5; Sun. 1-5. Closed Mondays; children under 12 no charge when accompanied by adult; 12 and older 50¢. Closed Xmas.

Mary

FT. JESUP STATE PARK, Rte. #2. 71449. Tel.: (318) 256-5480. *Founded:* 1960. *Historic Military Museum:* Housed in 1822 Army Kitchen located on the site of a Military Outpost established in 1822 by Zachary Taylor. *Collections:* Army desk; pots; rifles and metal items found on site. *Hours & Admission Prices:* Tues.-Sat. 8:30-4:30; Sun. 1-5; adults 53¢; children under 12 no charge. Closed Mondays.

New Orleans

CONFEDERATE MUSEUM, 929 Camp St. 70130. Tel.: (504) 523-4522. *Founded:* 1891. *Military Museum. Collections:* Weapons; memorabilia; of early Louisiana and Civil War history. *Hours & Admission Prices:* Mon.-Sat. 10-4; adults 50¢; students 25¢; children 10¢. Closed Sundays; New Year's; Mardi Gras Day; Labor Day; Thanksgiving; Xmas.

MAINE

Newfield

WILLOWBROOK AT NEWFIELD, Elm St. 04056. Tel.: (207) 793-2784. *Founded:* 1970. *19th Century General Museum. Collections:* Guns. *Hours & Admission Prices:* May 15-Oct. 1 Daily 10-5; adults $2.50; children 6-14 $1; under 6 no charge. Closed winter months.

Portland

MAINE HISTORICAL SOCIETY, 485 Congress St. 04111. Tel.: (207) 774-9351. *Founded:* 1822. *General Museum. Collections:* Firearms; arms. *Hours & Admission Prices:* June-Sept. Mon.-Fri. 10-5; Oct.-May Sat. 12-5. No charge. Closed State and Federal Holidays.

MARYLAND

Aberdeen Proving Ground

U.S. ARMY ORDNANCE MUSEUM, c/o U.S. Army Ordnance Center and School. 21040. Tel.: (301) 278-3602. *Founded:* 1926. *Military Museum. Collections:* Ordnance equipment from many countries and wars; extensive collection of foreign military equipment captured in S.E. Asia; small arms from 16th century to present; body armor; artillery tanks; tank destroyers; ammunition explosives; ordnance archives; war history; military transportation. *Hours & Admission Prices:* Outdoor Display: Daily during daylight hours; Indoor Display: Tues.-Fri. 12-5; Sat.-Sun. 10-5. No charge. Closed Mondays; National Holidays except: Armed Forces Day; Memorial Day; Independence Day; Veterans Day and Labor Day.

Baltimore

FORT McHENRY NATIONAL MONUMENT AND HISTORIC SHRINE. 21230. Tel.: (301) 539-2248. *Founded:* 1925. *Historic Site:* 1814 site of bombardment which inspired Francis Scott Key to write "The Star Spangled Banner." *Collections:* Military artifacts. Historic Buildings: 1814 guardhouses; 1830 soldiers barracks. *Activities:* Musket firing demonstrations. *Hours & Admission Prices:* Labor Day-June Daily 9-5; July-Aug. Daily 8-8. No charge. Closed Xmas.

MARYLAND SUBMARINE MEMORIAL, U.S.S. TORSK, Pier 4, Pratt St. 21202. Tel.: (301) 837-7770 or 837-1776. *Founded:* 1972. *Submarine Museum. Collections:* Battle flags; pictoral views and plans of submarines from 1779-1972; medals and captured weapons from enemy submarines and surface ships. *Hours & Admission Prices:* Summer Daily 11-6. Winter, Labor Day-June 20 weekends 11-6. Adults $1; children 50¢. Closed New Year's; Good Friday; Xmas.

STAR-SPANGLED BANNER FLAG HOUSE, 844 E. Pratt St. 21202. Tel.: (301) 837-1793. *Founded:* 1927. *History Museum:* Housed in 1793 home of Mary Pickersgill, maker of the banner which flew over Fort McHenry during the War of 1812 and inspired Francis Scott Key to pen his famous poem. *Collections:* New and old flags of historic importance; firearms; uniforms; War of 1812 artifacts. *Hours & Admission Prices:* Tues.-Sat. 10-4; Sun. 2-4:30; adults $1; children under 16 and students no charge. Closed Mondays; New Year's; Easter; Thanksgiving; Xmas.

UNITED STATES FRIGATE CONSTELLATION, Constellation Dock Pier, One Pratt St. 21202. Tel.: (301) 539-1797. *Founded:* 1953. *Historic Ship:* Authorized 1794, launched 1797, the first of six frigates designed and built for the navy to put to sea June 1798, in commission 1798-1955. *Collections:* Marine; naval; uniforms; weapons. *Activities:* Cannon demonstration. *Hours & Admission Prices:* June-Sept. Mon.-Sat. 10-6; Sundays, Holidays 12-6; Sept.-May Mon.-Sat. 10-4; Sundays, Holidays 12-5; adults $1; children under 12 50¢. Closed New Year's; Xmas.

Big Pool

FORT FREDERICK STATE PARK. 21711. Tel.: (301) 842-2504. *History Museum. Collections:* Early firearms. *Hours & Admission Prices:* Apr. 15-Nov. 1. Daily 10-9. No charge.

Burkittsville

GATHLAND STATE PARK, Gapland Road. 21718. Tel.: (301) 371-6630. *Historic House and Park Museum. Collections:* Firearms; Civil War mementos. *Hours & Admission Prices:* Sat. and Sun. 9-7. No charge.

Fort George G. Meade

FIRST U.S. ARMY MUSEUM, Bldg. T 4674. 20755. Tel.: (301) 677-6966. *Founded:* 1966. *Military Museum. Collections:* German War art; W.P.A. art; firearms; uniforms; flags. *Hours & Admission Prices:* Wed.-Fri. 1-4:30; Sat. 11-4; Sun. 1-4. No charge. Closed Mondays; Tuesdays; National Holidays.

St. Michaels

CHESAPEAKE BAY MARITIME MUSEUM, P.O. Box 636. 21663. Tel.: (301) 745-2916. *Founded:* 1965. *Maritime History Museum:* Battle site of War of 1812. *Collections:* Water fowling. Historic House: 1879 Hooper Strait Lighthouse. *Hours & Admission Prices:* Winter: Tues.-Sun., Holidays 10-4; Summer: Daily 10-5; adults $1.50; children 6-16 50¢; children under 6 and members no charge. Closed Xmas.

Sharpsburg

ANTIETAM NATIONAL BATTLEFIELD SITE-VISITOR CENTER, P.O. Box 158. 21782. Tel.: (301) 432-5124. *Founded:* 1890. *Historic Site Museum:* Site of Civil War battle of Antietam or Sharpsburg, 1862. *Collections:* Civil War weapons; military uniforms and equipment, relics; military and personal papers of Henry Kyd Douglas; Cope-Carmen Battlefield maps. Historic House: Gen. McClellan's headquarters. *Activities:* Firearm demonstration. *Hours & Admission Prices:* Winter: Daily 8:30-5; Summer: Daily 8-6. No charge. Closed New Year's; Thanksgiving; Xmas.

MASSACHUSETTS

Beverly

BEVERLY HISTORICAL SOCIETY, 117 Cabot St. 01915. Tel.: (617) 922-1186. *Founded:* 1891. *General Museum. Collections:* Military; guns. *Hours & Admission Prices:* Sept.-June Mon., Wed., Fri.-Sat. 10-4; July-Aug. Mon.-Sat. 10-4. Adults 50¢; children under 14 25¢. Closed Holidays.

Canton

CANTON HISTORICAL SOCIETY, 1400 Washington St. 02021. Tel.: (617) 828-4962. *Founded:* 1893. *History Museum. Collections:* Gun exhibit; Civil War relics. *Hours & Admission Prices:* By appointment only.

Danvers

DANVERS HISTORICAL SOCIETY, 13 Page St. 01923. Tel.: (617) 777-2821. *Founded:* 1889. *General Museum. Collections:* Military uniforms; guns. *Hours & Admission Prices:* June 15-Aug. 15 Wed. 2-4; other times by appointment. Donations accepted. Closed Sept.-May.

Fall River

FALL RIVER HISTORICAL SOCIETY, 451 Rock St. 02720. Tel.: (617) 677-9291. *Founded:* 1921. *Historical Society Museum:* Site of 1778 Battle of Fall River. *Collections:* Guns. *Hours & Admission Prices:* Tues.-Fri. 9-4:30; Sat. 9-12; Sun. 2-4. No charge. Closed Holidays.

Middleborough

MIDDLEBOROUGH HISTORICAL ASSOCIATION, INC., Jackson St. 02346. *Founded:* 1960. *General Museum. Collections:* G.A.R. collection including rifles. *Hours & Admission Prices:* Sept.-Oct. 15, June 15-July 1 Sun. 1-5; July-Aug. Wed., Fri., Sun. 1-5; adults $1; children 25¢. Closed Holidays.

Sandwich

HERITAGE PLANTATION OF SANDWICH, Grove St. 02563. Tel.: (617) 888-3300. *Founded:* 1969. *General Museum. Collections:* Military miniatures; weapons. *Hours & Admission Prices:* May-Oct. Daily 10-5; adults $2.50; children 75¢.

South Carver

EDAVILLE RAILROAD MUSEUM, Rochester Rd., P.O. Box 7. 02566. Tel.: (617) 866-4526. *Founded:* 1946. *Railroad Museum. Collections:* Antique guns. *Hours & Admission Prices:* Apr. 7, 14, 15, 21, 28; May 5, 12, 19, 25, 26, 27; June 1, 2; 12-5; June 8-Labor Day Mon.-Sat. 10-5:30; Sun. 12-5:30; open every Wed. July & Aug. 9:00 p.m. Labor Day-Oct. 14th Mon.-Fri. 10:30-3 (diesel) Sat.-Sun., Holidays 12-5 (steam) Oct. 12, 13, 19, 20, 21, 26, 27; 12 Noon-5 p.m. Nov. 3, 10, 17, 24; 12-4; Nov. 29, thru Jan. 5 4-9 p.m. weekdays; 2-9 p.m. weekends. Combination Tickets For Train and Museum: adults $2.40; children $1.20. Closed Xmas.

Springfield

SPRINGFIELD ARMORY MUSEUM, INC., P.O. Box 515. 01101. Tel.: (413) 734-6477. *Founded:* 1871. *Gun Museum:* Housed in 1847 Springfield Armory established national landmark in 1962 by the Dept. of Interior. *Collections:* Military small arms. *Hours & Admission Prices:* Mon.-Sat. 10-5; Sun. 1-5; adults $1; children no charge. Closed New Year's; Thanksgiving; Xmas.

Sturbridge

OLD STURBRIDGE VILLAGE. 01566: Tel.: (617) 347-3362. *Founded:* 1938. *Village Museum. Collections:* Firearms. *Hours & Admission Prices:* Mid-March-Nov. Daily 9:30-5:30; Dec.-mid-March 10-4; adults $4.00; children $1.25. Closed New Year's; Xmas.

Taunton

OLD COLONY HISTORICAL SOCIETY, 66 Church Green. 02780. Tel.: (617) 822-1622. *Founded:* 1853. *Historical Society Museum: Collections:* Indian relics; guns; swords; uniforms. *Hours & Admission Prices:* Tues.-Sat. 10-4; adults $1.00; children 50¢.

Worcester

JOHN WOODMAN HIGGINS ARMORY, INC., 100 Barber Ave. 01606. Tel.: (617) 853-6015. *Founded:* 1928. *Armor Museum. Collections:* Ancient Medieval & Renaissance arms and armor; firearms. *Hours & Admission Prices:* Tues.-Fri. 9-4; Sat. 10-3; Sun. 1-5; adults 75¢; children and students 10¢. Closed Mondays; National Holidays.

MICHIGAN

Escanaba

DELTA COUNTY HISTORICAL SOCIETY, Ludington Park. 49829. Tel.: (906) 786-3428. *Founded:* 1947. *General Museum. Collections:* Firearms. *Hours & Admission Prices:* July 1-Sept. 1 Daily 1-9; May 20-July 1 Sat.-Sun. 1-9. Donations accepted. Closed Sept. 1-first week in May except by appointment.

Hastings

CHARLTON PARK VILLAGE AND MUSEUM, 2545 S. Charlton Park Rd. 49058. Tel.: (616) 945-3775. *Founded:* 1936. *History Museum. Collections:* Military; weapons. *Hours & Admission Prices:* Museum: June-Oct. Mon.-Fri. 9-5; Sat., Sun. 1-5; Oct.-May Mon.-Fri. 9-5; Park: Daily 8-sundown; per car $1.

Niles

FORT ST. JOSEPH MUSEUM, 508 E. Main St. 49120. Tel.: (616) 683-4702. *Founded:* 1932. *General Museum. Collections:* Guns; Fort St. Joseph artifacts. *Hours & Admission Prices:* Mon.-Sat. 1-5. No charge. Closed Sundays; Holidays.

MINNESOTA

Brainerd

CROW WING COUNTY HISTORICAL SOCIETY, Court House. 56401. *Founded:* 1927. *General Museum. Collections:* Guns. *Hours & Admission Prices:* June-Labor Day Tues.-Fri. 1-5; Labor Day-May Tues.-Thur. 1-5. No charge. Closed Mondays.

Henderson

SIBLEY COUNTY HISTORICAL SOCIETY. 56044. *Founded:* 1940. *History Museum. Collections:* Guns. *Hours & Admission Prices:* Last Sun. in May-last Sun. in Oct. Daily 2-5; other times by appointment. Donations accepted.

Windom

COTTONWOOD COUNTY HISTORICAL SOCIETY, 1157 River Rd. 56101. Tel.: (507) 831-3166. *Founded:* 1901. *General Museum. Collections:* Guns; Civil War. *Hours & Admission Prices:* Summer: Wed., Sat. 1-5; Holidays by request. No charge.

MISSISSIPPI

Biloxi

JEFFERSON DAVIS SHRINE AND MEMORIAL GARDENS, 200 West Beach Street. 39530. Tel.: (601) 388-1313. *Founded:* 1941. *Historic House:* (Last home of Jefferson Davis, only president of the Confederacy.) *Collections:* Firearms. *Hours & Admission Prices:* Daily 8:30-5; adults $2.50; children $1; under 8 free; Active Military $1.50.

Pascagoula

OLD SPANISH FORT AND MUSEUM, 4602 Fort St., No. 39567. Tel.: (601) 769-1505. *Founded:* 1949. *General Museum. Collections:* Military; Revolutionary and Civil War weapons. *Hours & Admission Prices:* Daily, Holidays 9-5; adults $1; children 50¢.

MISSOURI

Arrow Rock

JOHN P. SITES GUNSHOP. 65320. *Founded:* 1968. *Gun Museum. Collections:* Gunsmith tools of 1850 period. *Hours & Admission Prices:* Apr.-Sept. 1 Mon.-Fri., Sun. 10-3. No charge. Closed Saturdays.

Butler

MUSEUM OF PIONEER HISTORY, East Fort Scott St. 64730. Tel.: (816) 679-3791. *Founded:* 1961. *History Museum. Collections:* Civil War guns. *Hours & Admission Prices:* May-Nov. Daily 1-5; other times by appointment; Non-members 50¢.

Clayton

GENERAL DANIEL BISSELL HOME, JEFFERSON BARRACKS HISTORICAL PARK, 7900 Forsythe. 63105. Tel.: (314) 889-3196. *Founded:* 1958. *Military Museum. Collections:* Military guns and uniforms of 1826-1946. *Hours & Admission Prices:* Wed.-Sat. 8-5; Sun., Holidays 1-5; adults 50¢; children 25¢. Closed Mondays; Tuesdays; New Year's; Xmas.

Hazelwood

LITTLE RED SCHOOL HOUSE, 450 Brookes Lane. 63042. Tel.: (314) 731-1589. *Founded:* 1960. *Historical Society Museum. Collections:* Antique gun collection. *Hours & Admission Prices:* By appointment. No charge.

Kansas City

LIBERTY MEMORIAL, 100 West 26th St. 64108. Tel.: (816) 274-1675. *Founded:* 1919. *Military Museum:* Built in 1920's as a memorial to those who served in World War I. *Collections:* World I relics. *Hours & Admission Prices:* Tues.-Sun. 9:30-4:30. No charge. Closed Mondays; New Year's; Thanksgiving; Xmas.

St. Louis

SOLDIERS' MEMORIAL, 1315 Chestnut St. 63103. Tel.: (314) 453-4550. *Founded:* 1938. *Military Museum. Collections:* Mementos of different wars including pistols; medals; maps; insignia; uniforms; helmets; papers; photos displayed with name of serviceman as a memorial to him. *Hours & Admission Prices:* Daily 10-4:30. No charge.

Vienna

OLD JAIL MUSEUM AND FELKER HOUSE. 65582. Tel.: (314) 422-3602. *Founded:* 1955. *General Museum:* Housed in 1855 Jail and 1855 Felker House. *Collections:* Guns; Civil War mementos. *Hours & Admission Prices:* Daily, Holidays 8-5; adults 25¢; children 10¢.

MONTANA

Billings

YELLOWSTONE COUNTY MUSEUM, Logan Field, P.O. Box 959. 59103. Tel.: (406) 248-6341. *Founded:* 1953. *General Museum. Collections:* Guns. *Hours & Admission Prices:* Tues.-Sat. 10:30-12 & 1-5; Sun. 2-5. No charge. Closed Thanksgiving; Xmas.

Helena

MONTANA HISTORICAL SOCIETY, 225 N. Roberts. 59601. Tel.: (406) 449-2695. *Founded:* 1865. *General Museum. Collections:* Military; Johns gun collection. *Hours & Admission Prices:* Labor Day-Memorial Day, Mon.-Fri. 8-5; Sat.-Sun. 12-5; Memorial Day-Labor Day, Daily 8-8. No charge. Closed New Year's; Thanksgiving; Xmas.

Sydney

J. K. RALSTON MUSEUM & ART CENTER, 221 Fifth S.W. 59270. Tel.: (406) 482-3500. *Founded:* 1971. *General Museum. Collections:* Guns; gun shop; sheriff's office. *Hours & Admission Prices:* Tues.-Fri. 10-12 and 1-5 and 6-8; Sat. 10-12 and 1-5; Sun. 1-4. No charge. Closed Mondays.

Wisdom

BIG HOLE NATIONAL BATTLEFIELD, P.O. Box 237. 59761. Tel.: (406) 689-2530. *Founded:* 1910. *Visitor Center Exhibit Hall:* Located on land which includes all major sites relating to the 1877 Battle of the Big Hole between the Nez Perce Indians and the 7th U.S. Infantry, plus a small number of citizen volunteers. *Collections:* Army accoutrements, equipment, uniforms and firearms. *Hours & Admission Prices:* Daily 8-5. No charge.

NEBRASKA

Broken Bow

CUSTER COUNTY MUSEUM AND LIBRARY, 225 S. 10th Ave. 68822. Tel.: (308) 872-2203. *Founded:* 1962. *General Museum. Collections:* Guns. *Hours & Admission Prices:* Mon.-Sat. No charge. Closed Sundays; National Holidays.

Central City

MERRICK COUNTY HISTORICAL MUSEUM, INC., 822 C Ave. 68826. Tel.: (308) 946-2773. *Founded:* 1969. *General Museum. Collections:* Guns. *Hours & Admission Prices:* Sun. 2-5; other times by appointment. No charge.

Chadron

MUSEUM OF THE FUR TRADE, Rte. 2, Box 18. 69337. Tel.: (308) 432-3843. *Founded:* 1949. *History Museum. Collections:* Indian trade guns. *Hours & Admission Prices:* Daily 8-6; Non-member adults 50¢; children free with parents, otherwise 15¢. Closed Tuesdays after Labor Day-May except by appointment.

Fort Calhoun

WASHINGTON COUNTY HISTORICAL MUSEUM, 14th and Monroe Sts. 68023. Tel.: (402) 468-5740. *Founded:* 1938. *General Museum. Collections:* Fort Atkinson relics and records; weapons associated with exploration and settlement of area. *Hours & Admission Prices:* Wed., Fri., Sat.-Sun. 1:30-4:30. No charge. Closed December-March except by appointment.

Gering

NORTH PLATTE VALLEY HISTORICAL ASSOCIATION, INC., 1349 10th St. 69341. Tel.: (308) 436-5411. *Founded:* 1969. *General Museum. Collections:* Guns. *Hours & Admission Prices:* June 1-Labor Day daily 8-5; after Labor Day-May 31 Tues. and Thurs. 9-12 and 1-5. Sun. and Holidays 2-5.

Gothenburg

PONY EXPRESS STATION, Ehmen Park. 69138. Tel.: (308) 537-2881. *Founded:* 1954. *Historic Building Museum. Collections:* Guns. *Hours & Admission Prices:* June-Sept. 10 8 am-9 pm Sept. 10-Oct. 1 & May 1-June 1 8-5:30 No charge. Closed October-May 1.

Hastings

HASTINGS MUSEUM, 1330 N. Burlington. 68901. Tel.: (402) 463-7126. *Founded:* 1926. *General Museum. Collections:* George W. Cole Smith and Wesson guns; Richard T. Conroy big-game trophies. *Hours & Admission Prices:* Sept.-May Mon.-Sat. 8-5; Sun. 1-5; Holidays 1-5; June-Aug. Mon.-Sat. 8-8; Sun. 1-5; Holidays 1-5; adults 75¢; children 25¢; children under 6 no charge. Closed Thanksgiving; New Year's; Xmas.

Ogallala

TRAILS MUSEUM, Route 2. 69153. Tel.: (308) 284-2237. *Founded:* 1965. *General Museum. Collections:* Guns. *Hours & Admission Prices:* April-Dec. Daily, Holidays 9-9. No charge. Closed Jan.-March.

Omaha

UNION PACIFIC HISTORICAL MUSEUM, 15th and Dodge Sts. 68102. Tel.: (402) 271-3530. *Founded:* 1939. *History Museum: Collections:* Lincoln; guns. *Hours & Admission Prices:* Mon.-Fri. 9-5; Sat. 9-1. No charge.

Wilber

WILBER CZECH MUSEUM, Box 217. 68465. Tel.: (402) 821-9891. *Founded:* 1962. *General Museum. Collections:* Guns. *Activities:* Guided tours; permanent and temporary exhibitions. *Hours & Admission Prices:* Sun. 2-5; other times by appointment. Donations accepted. Closed National Holidays.

York

DAUGHTERS OF AMERICAN REVOLUTION MUSEUM, Community Center, 211 East 7th Street. 68467. Tel.: (402) 362-5549. *History Museum: Collections:* Civil War firearms; Spanish-American War and World War I relics. *Hours & Admission Prices:* Mon.-Sat. 9-5. No charge.

NEVADA

Reno

NEVADA HISTORICAL SOCIETY, 1650 N. Virginia St., P.O. Box 1129. 89504. Tel.: (702) 784-6397. *Founded:* 1904. *History Museum. Collections:* Guns. *Hours & Admission Prices:* Mon.-Fri. 8-5; Sat. 9-5. No charge. Closed National Holidays; Nevada's Admission Day Oct. 31st.

NEW HAMPSHIRE

Charlestown

OLD FORT NUMBER 4 ASSOCIATES, Rte. 11. 03603. Tel.: (603) 826-5516. *Founded:* 1948. *Historic Site Museum:* Granted in 1737 by Massachusetts Bay Colony completed as a fort about 1745. *Collections:* Weapons; seven reconstructed fort buildings. *Hours & Admission Prices:* June 13-Labor Day Daily 11-5; May 13-June 12, Labor Day-Oct. 22 Sat.-Sun. 11-5; adults $1.50; children 7-12 75¢; under 7 no charge.

Dover

ANNIE E. WOODMAN INSTITUTE, 182-192 Central Ave. 03820. Tel.: (603) 742-1038. *Founded:* 1916. *General Museum. Collections:* Guns. *Hours & Admission Prices:* Tues.-Sun. 2-5. No charge. Closed Mondays; Thanksgiving; Xmas.

Manchester

MANCHESTER HISTORIC ASSOCIATION, 125 Amherst St. 03104. Tel.: (603) 622-7531. *Founded:* 1896. *Local History Museum. Collections:* Guns. *Hours & Admission Prices:* Tues.-Fri. 9-4; Sat. 10-4. No charge. Closed Sundays; Mondays; National Holidays; Tuesday following Monday Holidays.

Newport

NEWPORT CLOCK MUSEUM, 43 Park St. 03773. Tel.: (603) 863-3610. *Founded:* 1962. *Hobby Museum. Collections:* Pistols. *Hours & Admission Prices:* Summer: Mon.-Sat., Holidays 9-4; Sun. 1-4; Winter: by appointment; adults 95¢; children 50¢.

Portsmouth

PORTSMOUTH HISTORICAL SOCIETY, 43 Middle St. 03801. Tel.: (603) 436-8420. *Founded:* 1920. *Historic House Museum:* 1758 John Paul Jones House. *Collections:* Guns. *Hours & Admission Prices:* May 15-Oct. 1 Mon.-Sat. 10-5; adults $1; children 6-14 50¢; children under 6 no charge. Closed October 2-May 14.

NEW JERSEY

Cape May Court House

CAPE MAY COUNTY HISTORICAL MUSEUM, Main St. 08210. Tel.: (609) 465-7111. *Founded:* 1927. *History Museum. Collections:* World War I and II exhibits; Civil War, Revolutionary and War of 1812 items; guns; Merrimac flag. *Hours & Admission Prices:* Mon.-Sat. 9-12 & 1-4; donation 25¢. Closed Holidays.

Freehold

MONMOUTH COUNTY HISTORICAL ASSOCIATION, 70 Court St. 07728. Tel.: (201) 462-1466. *Founded:* 1898. *History Museum. Collections:* Revolutionary and Civil War relics; guns and military equipment. *Hours & Admission Prices:* Tues.-Sat. 10-5; Sun. 2-5. Closed Mondays; New Year's; July 15-31; Thanksgiving; December 15-31.

Morristown

MORRISTOWN NATIONAL HISTORICAL PARK, P.O. Box 1136R. 07960. Tel.: (201) 539-2016. *Founded:* 1933. *History Museum:* Housed in 1774 Ford Mansion used as Washington's Headquarters during the American Revolution. *Collections:* Military weapons. *Hours & Admission Prices:* Daily 10-5; adults 50¢; children under 16 no charge. Closed New Year's; Thanksgiving; Xmas.

Paterson

THE PASSAIC COUNTY HISTORICAL SOCIETY, Lambert Castle, Garret Mountain Reservation, 07509. Tel.: (201) 523-9883. *Founded:* 1926. *General Museum. Collections:* Weapons; Civil War uniforms; Spanish-American War books and manuscripts.

Ringwood

RINGWOOD MANOR HOUSE MUSEUM, Sloatsburg Rd., 07456. Tel.: (201) 962-7031. *Founded:* 1935. *Historic House Museum. Collections:* Firearms; Revolutionary iron relics. *Hours & Admission Prices:* May-Oct. Tues.-Fri. 10-4; Sat.-Sun. Holidays 10-5; adults 25¢; children no charge.

Trenton

OLD BARRACKS ASSOCIATION, S. Willow St. 08608. Tel.: (609) 396-1776. *Founded:* 1902. *Military History Museum:* Housed in 1758 Barracks used during the French and Indian and Revolutionary Wars located on the site of the Battle of Trenton, fought in 1776. *Collections:* Early firearms; dioramas illustrating the Battles of Trenton and Princeton; recreated barracks room. *Hours & Admission Prices:* May-Oct. Mon.-Sat. 10-5; Sun. 1-5; Nov.-April Mon.-Sat. 10-4:30; Sun. 1-4; adults 75¢; children 25¢; maximum family group $2. Closed New Year's; Washington's Birthday; Thanksgiving; December 24; Xmas.

NEW MEXICO

Columbus

PANCHO VILLA MUSEUM, Lima St. 88029. Tel.: (505) 531-2217. *Founded:* 1960. *Military Museum. Collections:* Photographs, guns and other relics of Pancho Villa; uniforms of the Civil War period. *Hours & Admission Prices:* Mon.-Sat. 9-5; adults 50¢; children no charge; tour 25¢. Closed Sundays; New Year's; Easter; Thanksgiving; Xmas.

Lincoln

OLD LINCOLN COUNTY COURTHOUSE MUSEUM. 88338. Tel.: (505) 653-4381. *Founded:* 1937. *History Museum. Collections:* Guns. *Hours & Admission Prices:* Summer: Daily 8-5:30; Winter: Daily 9-4:30; admission 50¢; children under 6 no charge. Closed Xmas.

Taos

GOVERNOR BENT MUSEUM, Bent St. 87571. Tel.: (505) 758-2376. *Founded:* 1958. *History Museum. Collections:* Guns. *Hours & Admission Prices:* Daily 9-5; adults 40¢; children 8-15 15¢; children under 8 with parents no charge. Closed January; February.

Watrous

FORT UNION NATIONAL MONUMENT. 87753. Tel.: (505) 425-8025. *Founded:* 1956. *Military Museum. Collections:* Weapons; history of the fort, 1851-1891, and its significance in the development of the Santa Fe trade; Civil War. Historic Building: 1851 Fort Union. *Hours & Admission Prices:* Memorial Day-Labor Day 8-8, rest of year—most daylight hours. Individual 50¢; Carload $1.

NEW YORK

Batavia

HOLLAND LAND OFFICE MUSEUM, 131 W. Main St. 14020. Tel.: (716) 343-4727. *Founded:* 1894. *General Museum. Collections:* Military; guns. *Hours & Admission Prices:* Mon.-Sat. 10-5; Sun. 2-5. No charge. Closed National Holidays.

Clayton

1000 ISLANDS MUSEUM, 401 Riverside Dr., Old Town Hall. 13624. Tel.: (315) 686-5794. *Founded:* 1964. *General Museum. Collections:* Gun room; wildlife room. *Hours & Admission Prices:* Daily, Holidays 9-9; adults 75¢; children 25¢.

East Durham

DURHAM CENTER MUSEUM, INC. 12423. Tel.: (518) 239-8461. *Founded:* 1960. *General Museum. Collections:* Indian and pioneer weapons; military. *Hours & Admission Prices:* May 30-Labor Day Sat.-Sun. 9-5. No charge.

Fabius

PIONEER'S MUSEUM, Highland Forest, Box 31. 13063. Tel.: (315) 683-5550. *Founded:* 1959. *History Museum. Collections:* Guns and military. *Hours & Admission Prices:* May-Nov. Mon.-Fri. 1-4; Sat.-Sun., Holidays 10-6. No charge. Closed December-April.

Fort Johnson

MONTGOMERY COUNTY HISTORICAL SOCIETY, N.Y. Rte. 5. 12070. Tel.: (518) 842-0683. *Founded:* 1904. *General Museum. Collections:* Civil War costumes; Mohawk Valley weapons from 17th-19th century. *Hours & Admission Prices:* May-June, Sept.-Oct. Daily, Holidays 1-5; July-Aug. Mon.-Sat. 10-5; Sun., Holidays 1-5; adults $1; children under 12 no charge. Closed November-April.

Ilion

REMINGTON GUN MUSEUM, Hofler Ave. 13357. Tel.: (315) 894-9961. *Founded:* 1959. *Gun Museum. Collections:* Remington firearms and artifacts from 1840's to the present. *Hours & Admission Prices:* Daily 9-9. No charge.

Lake George

FORT WILLIAM HENRY MUSEUM, Canada St. 12845. Tel.: (518) 668-5168. *Founded:* 1952. *Historic Site Museum:* Housed in restored c. 1750 Fort William Henry. *Collections:* Weapons; Colonial Wars of Lake George region; military relics and artifacts excavated from the fort site and adjacent area; French and Indian War. *Hours & Admission Prices:* May, June, Sept., Oct. Daily 9-5; July-Aug. Daily 9 am-10pm; adults $2.50; children 6-11 $1.25; children under 6 free. Senior citizens $2.00. Closed November-May.

Little Falls

GENERAL HERKIMER HOME, Route 169. 13365. Tel.: (315) 823-0398. *Founded:* 1914. *Historic House Museum. Collections:* Revolutionary War; firearms. *Hours & Admission Prices:* April 15-Oct. 31; Mon.-Sat. 9-5; Sun. 1-5. No charge. Open holidays during season. Closed November 1-April 15 except by appointment.

Narrowsburg

FORT DELAWARE. 12764. Tel.: (914) 252-6660. *Founded:* 1957. *History Museum. Collections:* Stout stockade; blockhouses; gun platform; armory; flintlock muskets; rifles, fowling pieces. *Hours & Admission Prices:* Last Sat. in June-Labor Day Mon.-Sat. 10-6; Sun. 12-6; June, Sept. Sat.-Sun.; adults $1.25; children 8-16 60¢; children under 8 no charge; family $3.50.

New York

FRAUNCES TAVERN MUSEUM, 54 Pearl St. 10004. Tel.: (212) 425-1776. *History Museum. Collections:* Revolutionary War relics; George Washington memorabilia (site of farewell to his officers); muskets. *Hours & Admission Prices:* Mon.-Fri. 10-4; Sat.-Sun. 1-4. No charge.

NEW YORK CITY POLICE MUSEUM, 235 E. 20th St. 10003. Tel.: (212) 677-1133, ext. 300. *Founded:* 1930. *Police Department Museum. Collections:* Old time uniforms; unusual weapons. *Hours & Admission Prices:* Mon.-Fri. 9-5; tours 10 & 1. No charge. Closed Saturdays; Sundays.

Oswego

FORT ONTARIO. 13126. Tel.: (315) 343-4711. *Founded:* 1949. *Military Museum:* Located on the sites of various battles, Indian conferences and military encampments. *Collections:* military furnishings, firearms, equipment, uniforms, accoutrements, prints, paintings and other items pertaining to fortifications development and military activities at the mouth of the Oswego River 1727-1946. Historic Buildings: 1842-1844 enlisted men's barracks, a magazine, two officer's quarters with outbuildings, post headquarters; 1863-1872 two guardhouses and a series of casemates; 1821 post hospital. *Hours & Admission Prices:* April-Oct. Mon.-Sat. 9-5; Sun. 1-5. No charge. Closed Easter.

Owego

TIOGA COUNTY HISTORICAL SOCIETY MUSEUM, 110 Front St. 13827. Tel.: (607) 687-2460. *Founded:* 1914. *History Museum. Collections:* Military; Civil War items; guns; flags. *Hours & Admission Prices:* Tues.-Fri. 10-12 & 1:30-4:30; Sat.-Sun. 1:30-4:30. No charge. Closed Mondays; New Year's; Good Friday; Easter Sunday; Memorial Day; July 4; Thanksgiving; Xmas.

Oyster Bay

SAGAMORE HILL NATIONAL HISTORIC SITE, Mtd. Route, Box 304. 11771. Tel.: (516) 922-4447. *Founded:* 1963. *Historic House Museum:* 1884 Sagamore Hill, home of Theodore Roosevelt. *Collections:* Military; big-game hunting. *Hours & Admission Prices:* July 1-Labor Day Daily 9-6; Labor Day-June 30 Daily 9-5; adults 50¢; children under 16 no charge. Closed New Year's; Thanksgiving; Xmas.

Riverhead

SUFFOLK COUNTY HISTORICAL SOCIETY, 300 W. Main St. 11901. Tel.: (516) 727-2881. *Founded:* 1886. *Historical Museum. Collections:* Revolutionary flags and firearms; guns. *Hours & Admission Prices:* Summer: Mon.-Sat. 1-5; Winter: Mon.-Sat. 12-4. No charge. Closed Sundays; Legal Holidays.

Rochester

ROCHESTER HISTORICAL SOCIETY, 485 East Ave. 14607. Tel.: (716) 271-2705. *Founded:* 1861. *Historical Society. Collections:* Guns; swords; medals. *Hours & Admission Prices:* Mon.-Fri. 10-4:30. No charge. Closed Saturdays; Sundays; New Year's; Easter; July 4; Thanksgiving; Xmas.

Sackets Harbor

SACKETS HARBOR BATTLEFIELD STATE PARK, Box 48. 13685. Tel.: (315) 646-3634. *Founded:* 1966. *History Museum:* Housed in six buildings: 1818 Hotel; 1850 Farmhouse; 1848 Commandant's House; 1849 Lieutenant's House; 1850 Stable; 1850 Ice House located on the site of the War of 1812 shipyard, fortifications and battlefield; 19th century naval station. *Collections:* War of 1812 weapons, uniforms and accoutrements. *Hours & Admission Prices:* June-Sept. Daily 9-9. No charge. Closed October-May except by special appointment.

Schenectady

SCHENECTADY COUNTY HISTORICAL SOCIETY, 32 Washington Ave. 12305. Tel.: (518) 374-0263. *Founded:* 1906. *General Museum:* Located within the stockade area of early settlement of Schenectady by the Dutch in 1661. *Collections:* Guns. *Hours & Admission Prices:* Mon.-Sat. 12:30-5:30; Sun. 1-5. No charge. Closed National Holidays.

Scoharie

OLD STONE FORT MUSEUM & WILLIAM W. BADGLEY HISTORICAL MUSEUM, N. Main St. 12157. Tel.: (518) 295-7192. *Founded:* 1889. *General Museum:* Housed in 1772 church, later used as a fort. *Collections:* Firearms. *Hours & Admission Prices:* June-Aug. Daily, Holidays 10-5; May, Sept.-Oct. Tues.-Sun. 10-5; adults $1; children 25¢. Closed November-April.

Tarrytown

THE HISTORICAL SOCIETY OF THE TARRYTOWNS, INC., 1 Grove St. 10591. Tel.: (914) 631-8374. *Founded:* 1889. *General History Museum. Collections:* American Revolution; 1780 capture of Major John Andre at Tarrytown; military; firearms. *Hours & Admission Prices:* Tues.-Sat. 2-4. No charge. Closed Sundays; Mondays; July 4; Thanksgiving; Xmas; New Year's.

Ticonderoga

FORT MT. HOPE, Burgoyne Rd. 12883. Tel.: (518) 585-4477. *Founded:* 1947. *Historic Site. Collections:* Guns; artifacts; cannon; relics, restored blockhouse; guardhouse. *Hours & Admission Prices:* Daily; Holidays 8-dark. No charge. Closed Columbus Day weekend.

Warwick

WARWICK HISTORICAL SOCIETY, Main St. 10990. Tel.: (914) 986-1686. *Founded:* 1906. *General Museum. Collections:* Guns and sports equipment of sportsman-author, William H. Herbert (pen name "Frank Forester"). *Hours & Admission Prices:* Tues., Sat. 2-4. No charge.

West Point

WEST POINT MUSEUM, United States Military Academy. 10996. Tel.: (914) 938-2203. *Founded:* 1854. *Military History Museum. Collections:* International military history; civil history; American and foreign military ordnance; dress, accoutrements. *Hours & Admission Prices:* Daily, Holidays 10:30-4:15. No charge. Closed New Year's; Xmas.

NORTH CAROLINA

Currie

MOORE'S CREEK NATIONAL MILITARY PARK, Box 69. 28435. Tel.: (919) 283-5591. *Founded:* 1926. *Military Museum:* Located on the site of the Battle of Widow Moore's Creek Bridge, Feb. 27, 1776. *Collections:* Weapons; diorama. *Activities:* Demonstrations of weapons. *Hours & Admission Prices:* Daily 8-5. No charge. Closed Xmas; New Year's.

Greensboro

GUILFORD COURTHOUSE NATIONAL MILITARY PARK. New Garden Rd. & Old Battleground Rd. 27408. Tel.: (919) 288-1776. *Founded:* 1917. *Military Museum. Collections:* Revolutionary War weapons; cannon; surrender terms of British at Yorktown; diorama of battle; electric map. *Activities:* Demonstrations of 18th century musket and cannon firing during the summer on weekends only. *Hours & Admission Prices:* Sept.-June 14 Daily 8:30-5; June 15-Sept. 1 Daily 8:30-6. No charge. Closed New Year's; Xmas.

Hickory

THE HICKORY MUSEUM OF ART, 3rd St. & First Ave., N.W. 28601. Tel.: (704) 327-8576. *Founded:* 1944. *Art Museum. Collections:* Guns. *Hours & Admission Prices:* Mon.-Fri. 10-5; Sun., Holidays 3-5. No charge. Closed August; Easter; July 4; Thanksgiving; Xmas.

Murfreesboro

MURFREESBORO, NORTH CAROLINA MUSEUM, P.O. Box 3. 27855. Tel.: (919) 398-4886. *Founded:* 1967. *Preservation Project. Collections:* Richard J. Gatling Room (inventor of the Gatling gun); Gatling artifacts and exhibits on Gatling family. *Hours & Admission Prices:* By appointment only.

Raleigh

NORTH CAROLINA MUSEUM OF HISTORY. 109 E. Jones St. 27611. Tel.: (919) 829-3894. *Founded:* 1903. *General History Museum. Collections:* Uniforms; weapons; military. *Hours & Admission Prices:* Sept.May Mon.-Sat. 8:30-5:30; Sun. 2-5; June-Aug. Mon.Sat. 85. No charge. Closed New Year's; Thanksgiving; Xmas.

Wilmington

WILMINGTON-NEW HANOVER MUSEUM, 814 Market St. 28401. Tel.: (919) 763-0852. *Founded:* 1898. *Regional History Museum. Collections:* Weapons, equipment, personal items from Civil War to present. *Hours & Admission Prices:* Tues.-Sat. 10-5; Sun. 2-5. No charge. Closed Mondays; National Holidays.

NORTH DAKOTA

Bismark

STATE HISTORICAL SOCIETY OF NORTH DAKOTA, Liberty Memorial Bldg. 58501. Tel.: (701) 224-2666. *Founded:* 1895. *General Museum. Collections:* Firearms.

OHIO

Burton

GEAUGA COUNTY HISTORICAL SOCIETY CENTURY VILLAGE, 14653 E. Park St. 44021. Tel.: (216) 834-4012. *Founded:* 1938. *Historic Village Museum. Collections:* Firearms. *Hours & Admission Prices:* March-Dec. Tues.-Sat. 10-5, Sun. 1-5; adults $1.50; students 75¢; children under 12 free when accompanied by adult. Closed Mondays; January; February; Thanksgiving; Xmas; New Year's; Easter.

Fremont

THE RUTHERFORD B. HAYES LIBRARY AND MUSEUM, 1337 Hayes Ave. 43420. Tel.: (419) 332-2081. *Founded:* 1911. *U.S. Presidential Library and Museum. Collections:* Civil War relics; weapons. *Hours & Admission Prices:* Mon.-Sat. 9-5; Sun. Holidays 1:30-5; adults $2 for museum and residence tours; children $1. Closed New Year's; Thanksgiving; Xmas.

Piqua

HISTORIC INDIAN MUSEUM, N. Hardin Rd. 45356. Tel.: (513) 773-2522. *Founded:* 1973. *History Museum:* Adjacent to site of Fort Pickawillany, first Indian-White contact point in present Ohio. *Collections:* Weapons. *Hours & Admission Prices:* April 1-Oct. 31 daily 10-5; adults $1.

Wooster

WAYNE COUNTY HISTORICAL SOCIETY, 546 E. Bowman St. 44691. Tel.: (216) 264-8856. *Founded:* 1954. *General Museum. Collections:* Mounted birds and small animals; military equipment. *Hours & Admission Prices:* Tues.-Sun. 2-4:30. No charge. Closed National Holidays.

Wright-Patterson AFB

UNITED STATES AIR FORCE MUSEUM. 45433. Tel.: (513) 255-3284. *Founded:* 1923. *Military Museum:* Located at historic Wright Field where much early aviation pioneering was accomplished. *Collections:* 150 aircraft and major missiles; uniforms; personal military related memorabilia; aviation guns and instruments; aircraft squadron insignia; military badges; space hardware and foods; model collections. *Hours & Admission Prices:* Weekdays 9-5; Sat.-Sun. 10-6. Holidays 9-5. No charge. Closed Xmas.

Zanesfield

LOGAN COUNTY HISTORICAL SOCIETY, P.O. Box 45. 43360. Tel.: (513) 592-5201. *Founded:* 1945. *General Museum. Collections:* Firearms; uniforms and other insignia. *Hours & Admission Prices:* Sun. 2-4; other times by appointment. No charge.

OKLAHOMA

Claremore

J. M. DAVIS GUN MUSEUM, Fifth and Hwy. 66. 74017. Tel.: (918) 341-5707. *Founded:* 1965. *General Museum. Collections:* Guns; animal horns; trophy heads; swords and knives. *Hours & Admission Prices:* Mon.-Sat. 8:30-5; Sun. 1-5. No charge. Closed Xmas.

Fort Sill

U.S. ARMY FIELD ARTILLERY AND FORT SILL MUSEUM. 73503. Tel.: (405) 351-5123. *Founded:* 1934. *Military Museum:* Housed in several of the 1869-75 original stone buildings of Fort Sill's Old Post in Indian Territory. *Collections:* U.S. Army field artillery for all periods; U.S. Cavalry, Infantry and Indian items for Western frontier period; military ordnance, small arms and edged weapons; uniforms, equipment, horse furnishings, vehicles; Indian War items. Historic Building: 1909 1st headquarters of the School of Fire for Field Artillery. *Hours & Admission Prices:* Daily, Holidays 9-4:30. No charge. Closed December 24-25; January 1-2.

Oklahoma City

NATIONAL COWBOY HALL OF FAME AND WESTERN HERITAGE CENTER, 1700 N.E. 63rd St. 73111. Tel.: (405) 478-2250. *Founded:* 1955. *Memorial Shrine to Great Westerners. Collections:* Guns. *Hours & Admission Prices:* Daily 9:30-5:30; adults $1.50; children 50¢. Closed New Year's; Xmas.

Tishomingo

CHICKASAW COUNCIL HOUSE MUSEUM, Rt. 1, Box 14. 73460. Tel.: (405) 371-3351. *Founded:* 1970. *Indian Museum. Collections:* Firearms. *Hours & Admission Prices:* Tues.-Fri. 9-5; Sat.-Sun. 2-5. No charge.

OREGON

Haines

EASTERN OREGON MUSEUM, Rte. 1, Box 109. 97833. Tel.: (503) 856-3568. *Founded:* 1958. *General Museum. Collections:* Uniforms; guns; arrowheads. *Hours & Admission Prices:* May-Oct. Daily 9-5. Donations accepted.

Lakeview

SCHMINCK MEMORIAL MUSEUM, 128 S. "E" St. 97630. Tel.: (503) 947-3134. *Founded:* 1936. *General Museum. Collections:* Guns. *Hours & Admission Prices:* Mon., Wed.-Fri. 9-5; Tues. 1:30-5; other times by appointment; adults 50¢; children 25¢. Closed Thanksgiving; December 23-28.

Portland

PORTLAND CHILDREN'S MUSEUM, 3037 S. W. 2nd Ave. 97201. Tel.: (503) 227-1505. *Founded:* 1949. *General Children's Museum. Collections:* Live animals; guns. *Hours & Admission Prices:* Jan.-Aug., Oct.-Dec. Mon.-Fri. 10-6; Sat. 10-3. No charge. Closed September; National Holidays.

Roseburg

DOUGLAS COUNTY MUSEUM, Box 1550, County Fairgrounds. 97470. Tel.: (503) 672-5961. *Founded:* 1968. *General Museum. Collections:* Guns; native birds and animals. *Hours & Admission Prices:* Daily 8:30-5. No charge. Closed Legal Holidays.

PENNSYLVANIA

Athens

TIOGA POINT MUSEUM, 724 South Main St. 18810. Tel.: (717) 882-5493. *Founded* 1895. *General Museum. Collections:* Guns; Revolutionary War; Civil War. *Hours & Admission Prices:* Mon. 7-9; Wed., Sat. 2-5; Tues., Thurs., Fri. by appointment only. Donations accepted. Closed Sundays; National Holidays.

Brookville

E. M. PARKER INDIAN MUSEUM, 247 E. Main St. 15825. Tel.: (814) 849-2151. *Founded:* 1924. *General Museum. Collections:* Guns. *Hours & Admission Prices:* By appointment only.

Carlisle Barracks

HESSIAN GUARDHOUSE MUSEUM. 17013. Tel.: (717) 245-3600. *Founded:* 1948. *Military Museum:* Housed in 1777 building used as a powder magazine for the Continental Army, later used as a post guardhouse by Cavalry School and Indian School. *Collections:* U.S. Army weapons; rifles; pistols; daggers; medals; uniforms, archives and other items pertaining to history of Carlisle Barracks. *Hours & Admission Prices:* Museum: May-Sept. Sat.-Sun. 1-4:30. Library: Mon.-Fri. 8-5. No charge.

Haverford

HAVERFORD TOWNSHIP HISTORICAL SOCIETY, Karakung Dr., Powder Mills Park. 19083. Tel.: (215) 446-1026. *Founded:* 1939. *Local History Museum. Collections:* Black powder. Historic building: 1810 Nitre Hall, home of the Powder Master. *Hours & Admission Prices:* Sun. 2-4; other times by appointment. No charge. Closed mid-November-May.

Hellertown

GILMAN MUSEUM, at the Cave. 18055. Tel.: (215) 838-8767. *Founded:* 1955. *General Museum. Collections:* Guns; fossils; weaponry. *Hours & Admission Prices:* Daily 9-9. No charge. Closed Xmas; New Year's.

Meadville

BALDWIN-REYNOLDS HOUSE MUSEUM, 639 Terrace St. 16335. Tel.: (814) 724-6080. *Founded:* 1963. *General Museum. Collections:* Guns. *Hours & Admission Prices:* Museum: June-Aug. Wed., Sat.-Sun. 2-5; Adults $1; children 50¢. Archives: Mon.-Sat. 1-5. Closed November-May.

Philadelphia

WAR LIBRARY AND MUSEUM OF THE MILITARY ORDER OF THE LOYAL LEGION OF THE UNITED STATES, 1805 Pine St. 19103. Tel.: (215) 735-8196. *Founded:* 1886. *Military Museum:* Housed in 1857 building of the Civil War period. *Collections:* Uniforms; weapons; portraits; Lincoln items; Civil War relics. *Hours & Admission Prices:* Mon., Wed., Fri. 11-3. No charge. Closed Tuesdays; Thursdays; Saturdays; Sundays; National Holidays.

Valley Forge

THE VALLEY FORGE HISTORICAL SOCIETY, Valley Forge State Park. 19481. Tel.: (215) 783-0535. *Founded:* 1918. *History Museum:* Located on the site of Valley Forge encampment area. *Collections:* Washingtoniana; Revolutionary firearms. *Hours & Admission Prices:* Mon.-Sat. 9-4:30; Sun. 1-5; adults 25¢; children under 10 no charge. Closed Thanksgiving; Xmas.

SOUTH CAROLINA

Beaufort

BEAUFORT MUSEUM, Craven St. 29902. Tel.: (803) 524-8339. *General Museum. Collections:* Civil War relics; cannons; firearms. *Hours & Admission Prices:* Mon.-Fri. 9-4; Sat.-Sun. 1-4:30. Donations accepted. Closed National Holidays.

Camden

CAMDEN DISTRICT HERITAGE FOUNDATION, HISTORIC CAMDEN, P.O. Box 710. 29020. Tel.: (803) 432-9841. *Founded:* 1970. *History Museum. Collections:* Artifacts of the Revolutionary period; weapons; dioramas; maps. *Hours & Admission Prices:* Winter: Tues.-Fri. 10-4; Sat. 10-5; Sun., Holidays 1-5. Summer: Tues.-Fri. 10-5; Sat. 10-6; Sun. 1-6; adults $1; children 50¢.

Charleston

CITADEL ARCHIVES-MUSEUM, The Citadel. 29409. Tel.: (803) 723-0611, ext. 324. *Founded:* 1961. *Military Museum. Collections:* Collections of Generals Mark W. Clark; Hugh P. Harris; Charles Summerall; Admiral Arleigh Burke; Vice Admiral Friedrich Ruge; uniforms; weapons; medals. *Hours & Admission Prices:* Mon.-Fri., Sun. 10-5; Sat. 9-5. No charge. Closed New Year's; Xmas.

Columbia

SOUTH CAROLINA CONFEDERATE REL!C ROOM AND MUSEUM, World War Memorial Building, Sumter at Pendleton. 29201. Tel.: (803) 758-2144. *Founded:* 1896. *History Museum. Collections:* Military uniforms; weapons. *Hours & Admission Prices:* Mon.-Fri. 9-5; Sat. by appointment. No charge. Closed New Year's; Jan. 19; 3rd Monday in Feb.; May 10; June 3; July 4; Labor Day, General Election Day; 4th Mon. in Oct.; Thanksgiving; Dec. 25 & 26.

Greenwood

THE MUSEUM, Phoenix St. 29646. Tel.: (803) 229-7093. *Founded:* 1968. *General Museum. Collections:* Shells; firearms; war relics; zoology; mounted birds; animals; animal heads. *Hours & Admission Prices:* Mon.-Fri. 9-5; Sun. 2-5; other times by appointment. No charge. Closed Saturdays; Easter; Thanksgiving; Xmas.

Kings Creek

KINGS MOUNTAIN NATIONAL MILITARY PARK, Kings Mountain. 28086. Tel.: (803) 936-7508. *Founded:* 1931. *Military Park Museum. Collections:* Military; Revolutionary War. *Activities:* Weapons demonstration. *Hours & Admission Prices:* Mon.-Sat. 8:30-5; Sun., Holidays 9-5:30. No charge. Closed Xmas.

SOUTH DAKOTA

St. Francis

PETTIGREW MUSEUM, 131 N. Duluth. 57104. Tel.: (605) 336-6272. *Founded:* 1926. *General Museum. Collections:* Birds; guns. *Hours & Admission Prices:* Mon.-Sat. 9-12 & 1:30-5, Sun. 2-5. No charge. Closed New Year's; Thanksgiving; Xmas.

TENNESSEE

Franklin

CARTER HOUSE, 1140 Columbia Ave. 37064. Tel.: (615) 794-1733. *Founded:* 1951. *History Museum:* Housed in Union Command Post located on the site of the Battle of Franklin during Civil War. *Collections:* Civil War relics; uniforms; guns. *Hours & Admission Prices:* Mon.-Sat. 9-4; Sun., Holidays 2-4; adults $1; children under 16 25¢. Closed Xmas.

Smyrna

SAM DAVIS HOME, Route 1. 37167. Tel.: (615) GL 9-2431. *Founded:* 1927. *Historic House:* 1810 home of Sam Davis, Confederate hero. *Collections:* Confederate veterans magazines; clothing; firearms; other items of Civil War period. *Hours & Admission Prices:* Mon.-Sat. 9-5; Sun. 1-5; adults $1.00; children 50¢.

TEXAS

Austin

TEXAS STATE LIBRARY, 1201 Brazos St. 78711. Tel.: (512) 475-2445. *Founded:* 1839. *History Museum. Collections:* Firearms. *Hours & Admission Prices:* Mon.-Fri. 8-5. No charge. Closed Saturday; Sunday; State Holidays.

Comfort

COMFORT HISTORICAL MUSEUM, High and 8th Sts. 78013. *Founded:* 1934. *Local History Museum. Collections:* Guns. *Hours & Admission Prices:* Sat. 1-5. Donations accepted.

Crosbyton

CROSBY COUNTY PIONEER MEMORIAL MUSEUM, 101 Main (U.S. 82) on Plains Trail. 79322. Tel.: (806) 675-2331. *Founded:* 1957. *Historic House Museum. Collections:* Civil War; guns. *Hours & Admission Prices:* Tues.-Sat. 9-12 & 2-5; Sun., Holidays 2-4. No charge. Closed Mondays; National Holidays.

Del Rio

WHITEHEAD MEMORIAL MUSEUM, 1308 S. Main St. 78840. Tel.: (512) 775-6911. *Founded:* 1962. *General Museum. Collections:* Border War items; firearms; marine. *Hours & Admission Prices:* Mon.-Fri. 9-11 & 3-5; adults 50¢; children 25¢.

Denton

NORTH TEXAS STATE UNIVERSITY HISTORICAL COLLECTION, West Mulberry and Ave. A. 76203. Tel.: (817) 788-2386. *Founded:* 1930. *General Museum. Collections:* Military; antique weapons. *Hours & Admission Prices:* Mon.-Sat. 2-5. No charge. Closed University Vacations.

Egypt

NORTHINGTON-HEARD MEMORIAL MUSEUM, Box 35. 77436. *Founded:* 1947. *General Museum. Collections:* Guns. *Hours & Admission Prices:* Mon.-Sat. No charge.

Falfurrias

THE HERITAGE MUSEUM AT FALFURRIAS, INC., Box 86. 78355. Tel.: (512) 325-3333. *Founded:* 1965. *General Museum. Collections:* Guns. *Hours & Admission Prices:* Mon.-Fri. 9-5. No charge. Closed Saturdays; Sundays.

Fort Davis

FORT DAVIS NATIONAL HISTORIC SITE, Box 785. 79734. Tel.: (915) 426-3225. *Founded:* 1963. *Military Museum:* Housed in a former enlisted men's barracks located on the site of Fort Davis. *Collections:* Period weapons; regimental records. Historic Buildings: 1854-91, 85 fort structures. *Hours & Admission Prices:* Winter: Daily, Holidays 8:30-5:30; Summer: 8-8; adults 50¢; children no charge; family carload $1.

Fort Worth

FORT WORTH MUSEUM OF SCIENCE AND HISTORY, 1501 Montgomery St. 76107. Tel.: (817) 732-1631. *Founded:* 1939. *General Museum. Collections:* Firearms. *Hours & Admission Prices:* Mon.-Sat. 9-5; Sun. 2-5; June-Aug. Sun. 2-6; No charge. Closed New Year's; July 4; Labor Day; Thanksgiving; Xmas.

Hillsboro

CONFEDERATE RESEARCH CENTER AND GUN MUSEUM, P.O. Box 619. 76645. *Founded:* 1964. *Military Library Museum. Collections:* Hood's Texas Brigade; Civil War guns; artifacts; 2,500 books on the Confederacy-especially Texas available for inter-library loan. *Hours & Admission Prices:* Mon.-Fri. 8-5. No charge. Closed National and School Holidays.

Levelland

SOUTH PLAINS MUSEUM ASSOCIATION, 608 Ave. H. 79336. Tel.: (806) 894-7547. *Founded:* 1968. *Natural Science and History Museum. Collections:* North American Big Game mounted. *Hours & Admission Prices:* Tues.-Sat. 2-5; other times by appointment. No charge. Closed Thanksgiving; Xmas.

Nacogdoches

STONE FORT MUSEUM, P.O. Box 6075, Stephen F. Austin University. 75961. Tel.: (713) 569-2408. *Founded:* 1936. *History Museum. Collections:* Indian arrowheads; guns. Historic Buildings: 1913 original Old Stone Fort. *Hours & Admission Prices:* Mon.-Sat. 9-12 & 1-5; Sun. 1-5. No charge. Closed New Year's; Thanksgiving; Xmas.

New Braunfels

SOPHIENBURG MUSEUM, 401 W. Coll St. 78130. *Founded:* 1932. *History Museum. Collections:* Guns; pistols. *Hours & Admission Prices:* Summer: Mon.-Sat. 3-5; Sun., Holidays 2-6; Winter: Wed., Fri. 3-5; Sun. 2-6; adults 25¢; children 10¢. Closed Xmas.

Newcastle

FORT BELKNAP MUSEUM AND ARCHIVES, Box 68. 76372. *Founded:* 1856. *General and Military Museum. Collections:* Military; guns; swords. Historic Houses: 1853 Corn House, officer's quarters, magazine; army barracks #1, #2 and #4. *Hours & Admission Prices:* Mon.-Thurs., Sat.-Sun. 8-5. No charge. Closed Fridays; Xmas.

San Antonio

LONE STAR BREWING COMPANY, BUCKHORN HALL OF HORNS, FINS, FEATHERS AND BOAR'S NEST, 600 Lone Star Blvd. 78297. Tel.: (512) 226-8301. *Founded:* 1881. *Natural History Museum. Collections:* Wildlife; marine; birds; firearms. *Hours & Admission Prices:* Daily 9:30-5:30. No charge.

Uvalde

GARNER MEMORIAL MUSEUM, 333 N. Park St. 78801. Tel.: (512) 278-5018. *Founded:* 1960. *Historic House. Collections:* Guns; arrowheads. *Hours & Admission Prices:* Mon.-Sat. 9-5; Holidays 1-5. No charge. Closed Sundays; New Year's; Easter; Thanksgiving; Xmas.

UTAH

Cove Fort

OLD COVE FORT MUSEUM. 84713. *Founded:* 1867. *Antiques Museum:* Located on the site of 1867 rock fort. *Collections:* Guns. *Hours & Admission Prices:* Daily, Holidays 7-8; adults 75¢; children 25¢.

Ogden

JOHN M. BROWNING ARMORY, 625 East 5300 South. 84403. Tel.: (801) 392-4075. *Founded:* 1960. *Collections:* Firearms invented by and associated with John M. Browning. *Hours & Admission Prices:* Mon.-Fri. 8:30-4:30. No charge.

VERMONT

Montpelier

VERMONT MUSEUM, Pavilion Bldg. 05602. Tel.: (802) 828-2291. *Founded:* 1838. *Historical Museum. Collections:* Firearms. *Hours & Admission Prices:* Year-round Mon.-Fri. 8-4:30; also July-Aug. Sat.-Sun. 1-4:30. No charge, donation. Closed Holidays.

Northfield

NORWICH UNIVERSITY MUSEUM, on Rte. 12 (Main St.) 1/4 mile north of Jct. 12 & 12A. 05663. Tel.: (802) 485-8011, ext. 40. *Founded:* 1819. *Military Museum. Collections:* Personal memorabilia of founder Alden Partridge; Adm. George Dewey; Gen. Alonzo Jackman; Gen. Grenville Dodge, builder of the Union-Pacific railroad; Maj. Gen. Ernest N. Harmon. Special collections include: Norwich uniforms; flags; Wilson globes; Indian weapons; W.W. II trophies. *Hours & Admission Prices:* Sept.-May Daily 8-4; summer: Mon.-Fri. 8-12, 1-3:30; other times by appointment. No Charge.

Windsor

AMERICAN PRECISION MUSEUM, INC. 05089. *Founded:* 1966. *Industrial Museum. Collections:* Gun-making machines. *Hours & Admission Prices:* May 30-Oct. 15 Daily 12-5; adults $1; children 12-16 25¢.

OLD CONSTITUTION HOUSE, North Main St. 05089. *Founded:* 1777. *State Historic Site. Collections:* Civil War; firearms. *Hours & Admission Prices:* Mid-May-mid-Oct. Daily 10-6; except Mondays. Donations accepted.

VIRGINIA

Norfolk

NAVAL AMPHIBIOUS MUSEUM, NAB Little Creek. 23521. Tel.: (804) 464-8130. *Founded:* 1970. *Military Museum. Collections:* Naval uniforms; marine uniforms; flags; U.S. and Foreign weapons; equipment; tanks; landing craft; helicopter. *Hours & Admission Prices:* Sat.-Sun.-Holidays 1-5; tours by appointment. No Charge. Closed Thanksgiving; Xmas; New Years.

Petersburg

CENTRE HILL MANSION, MUSEUM, Franklin St. 23803. Tel.: (703) 732-8081. *Founded:* 1950. *Historic House. Collections:* Uniforms; rare maps; swords; pistols. *Hours & Admission Prices:* Tues.-Sat. 10-1 & 2-5; Sun. 2:30-5. No charge. Closed New Year's; Xmas.

PETERSBURG NATIONAL BATTLEFIELD, Box 549. 23803. Tel.: (703) 732-3531. *Founded:* 1926. *Military Museum:* Located on Petersburg Battlefield. *Collections:* Military history of campaign for Petersburg; artillery; maps; uniforms; ordnance. *Hours & Admission Prices:* Labor Day-Memorial Day Daily 8-5; Memorial Day-Labor Day Daily 8-8. No charge. Closed New Year's; Xmas.

Portsmouth

PORTSMOUTH NAVAL MUSEUM, 2 High St., P.O. Box 248. 23705. Tel.: (804) 393-8591. *Founded:* 1949. *Maritime Museum. Collections:* History of the Naval Shipyard, Portsmouth area and the armed forces of the locality; the CSS Virginia, also known as the Merrimac; ship models; uniforms; flags; arms of all types from early muskets to the Polaris missile; model aeronautical planes. *Hours & Admission Prices:* Tues.-Sat. 10-5; Sun. 2-5. No charge. Closed New Year's; Xmas.

Quantico

UNITED STATES MARINE CORPS MUSEUM, Marine Corps Base. 22134. Tel.: (703) 640-2606. *Founded:* 1940. *Military Museum. Collections:* Automatic weapons development specimens and early models; marine corps history; flags; uniforms. Historic Houses: 1800 Marine Barracks, Washington, D.C. 1803 Commandant's House. *Hours & Admission Prices:* Mon.-Fri. 9-6; Sat. 9-5; Sun., Holidays 12-4. No charge. Closed New Year's; Xmas.

Richmond

VIRGINIA HISTORICAL SOCIETY, 428 North Blvd. 23221. Tel.: (804) 358-4901. *Founded:* 1831. *Library with Collection other than Books:* Housed in 1450 Warwick Priory "Virginia House" was brought to U.S. from England as Confederate Memorial, 1912, the site was formerly occupied by the Confederate Old Soldiers' Home. *Collections:* Firearms; flags. *Hours & Admission Prices:* Mon.-Fri. 9-5; Sat.-Sun. 2-5; admission $1. Closed National Holidays.

Winchester

WINCHESTER-FREDERICK COUNTY HISTORICAL SOCIETY, 610 Tennyson Ave. 22601. Tel.: (303) 662-6752. *Founded:* 1930. *History Museum. Collections:* Civil War relics; firearms; swords. *Historic House:* 1746 George Washington's office. *Hours & Admission Prices:* Apr. 30-Nov. 1 Mon.-Sat. 9-5; Sun. 2-5; adults 50¢; children 25¢. Closed November 1-April 30.

Yorktown

COLONIAL NATIONAL HISTORICAL PARK, P.O. Box 210. 23490. Tel.: (703) 887-2241. *Founded:* 1930. *Historic Park. Collections:* 18th century arms and artifacts. *Hours & Admission Prices:* Daily. No charge. Closed Xmas.

WASHINGTON

Fort Lewis

FORT LEWIS MILITARY MUSEUM, Bldg. T4320. 98433. Tel.: (206) 968-4796; 968-5835. *Founded:* 1970. *Military Museum. Collections:* Uniforms; equipment; weapons; military history of the Northwest from Lewis and Clark to present day. *Activities:* Soviet weapons class. *Hours & Admission Prices:* Tues.-Sun. 12-4. No charge. Closed Mondays; Thanksgiving; Xmas; New Year's.

Maryhill

MARYHILL MUSEUM OF FINE ARTS. 98620. Tel.: (509) 773-4792. *Founded:* 1922. *Art Museum. Collections:* Antique guns. *Hours & Admission Prices:* March 15-Nov. 14 9-5:30; adults 75¢; students 40¢; children under 12 no charge.

North Bend

SNOQUALMIE VALLEY HISTORICAL MUSEUM, 112 N. Ballarat St. 98045. *Founded:* 1960. *General Museum. Collections:* Military; guns. *Hours & Admission Prices:* Sat.-Sun. 1-5; other times by appointment. No charge. Closed National Holidays.

Prosser

BENTON COUNTY HISTORICAL MUSEUM, P.O. Box 591. 99350. *Founded:* 1968. *General Museum. Collections:* Guns. *Hours & Admission Prices:* Tues.-Sat. 10-4; Sun., Holidays 1-5; adults 50¢; children 25¢. Closed Thanksgiving; Xmas.

Seattle

MUSEUM OF HISTORY AND INDUSTRY, 2161 E. Hamlin St. 98112. Tel.: (206) 324-1125. *Founded:* 1914. *General Museum. Collections:* Maritime; aeronautics; guns. *Hours & Admission Prices:* Tues.-Fri. 11-5; Sat. 10-5; Sun. 12-5. No charge. Closed Mondays; New Year's; Memorial Day; Thanksgiving; Xmas.

Waterville

DOUGLAS COUNTY HISTORICAL SOCIETY, P.O. Box 308. 98858. Tel.: (509) 745-2581. *Founded:* 1959. *Antiques Museum. Collections:* Firearms. *Hours & Admission Prices:* June-Sept. Daily, Holidays 11-5; other times by request. Donations.

WEST VIRGINIA

Ansted

HAWK'S NEST MUSEUM, Hawk's Nest State Park, U.S. Highway 60. 25812. Tel.: (304) 658-5196 (state park). *Founded:* 1940. *Collections:* Civil War and Pioneer items including gun exhibit. *Hours & Admission Prices:* Daily 9-5. No charge.

Charleston

WEST VIRGINIA STATE GOVERNMENT, ARCHIVES AND HISTORY MUSEUM, 400 E. State Capitol. 25305. Tel.: (304) 348-2276. *Founded:* 1905. *History Museum. Collections:* Stuffed animals and birds; Civil War regimental flags; firearms; Daniel Boone collection. *Hours & Admission Prices:* Mon.-Sat. 9-5; Sun., Holidays 1-5. No charge. Closed New Year's; Xmas.

Harpers Ferry

HARPERS FERRY NATIONAL HISTORICAL PARK, Shenandoah St. 25424. Tel.: (304) 535-6371, ext. 222. *Founded:* 1944. *Historic Site:* Location of approx. 40 restored and partially restored historic buildings and Civil War fortifications. *Collections:* Harpers Ferry arms; John Brown; Civil War. *Hours & Admission Prices:* Winter: Daily 8-5; Summer: Daily 8-8. No charge. Closed New Year's; Xmas.

Wheeling

OGLEBAY INSTITUTE-MANSION MUSEUM, Oglebay Park. 26003. Tel.: (304) 242-7272. *Founded:* 1930. *History Museum. Collections:* Firearms. *Hours & Admission Prices:* Sept. 2-July 1 Mon.-Sat. 9:30-5; Sun., Holidays 1:30-5; July 2-Sept. 1 Daily 9:30-8; adults $1.25; children under 12 no charge. Closed National Holidays.

WISCONSIN

Jamesville

ROCK COUNTY HISTORICAL SOCIETY, 440 N. Jackson St. 53545. Tel.: (608) 752-4519. *Founded:* 1948. *Historic House Museum. Collections:* Firearms; station of Underground Railroad. *Hours & Admission Prices:* May, Sept., Oct. Mon.-Fri. by appointment; Sat.-Sun. 11-4; Memorial Day-Labor Day Tues.-Fri. 1-4; Sat.-Sun. 11-4; adults $1.50; students 75¢.

Kenosha

KENOSHA COUNTY HISTORICAL MUSEUM, 6300 3rd Ave. 53140. Tel.: (414) 654-5770. *Founded:* 1878. *General Museum. Collections:* Guns. *Hours & Admission Prices:* Tues., Thurs., first Sun. of each month 2-4:30. No charge. Closed Holidays.

Madison

STATE HISTORICAL SOCIETY OF WISCONSIN, 816 State St. 53706. Tel.: (608) 262-2704. *Founded:* 1846. *General Museum. Collections:* Firearms; Civil War items. *Hours & Admission Prices:* Mon.-Fri. 8 am-10 pm; Sat. 8-4. No charge. Closed National Holidays.

New Glarus

CHALET OF THE GOLDEN FLEECE, 618 2nd St. 53574. Tel.: (608) 527-2614. *Founded:* 1955. *Historic House Museum. Collections:* Weapons. *Hours & Admission Prices:* Apr.-Oct. Daily 9-4:30; adults $1; children under 12 50¢; children under 6 no charge.

Oshkosh

OSHKOSH PUBLIC MUSEUM, 1331 Algoma Blvd. 54901. Tel.: (414) 231-2010. *Founded:* 1911. *General Museum. Collections:* Guns. *Hours & Admission Prices:* Tues.-Sat. 9-5; Sun. 1-5. No charge. Closed Mondays; National Holidays.

Superior

DOUGLAS COUNTY HISTORICAL MUSEUM, 906 E. 2nd St. 54880. Tel.: (715) 394-5712. *Founded:* 1931. *General Museum. Collections:* Firearms. *Hours & Admission Prices:* Tues.-Fri. 10-12 & 1-5; Sun. 2-5; other times by appointment. No charge. Closed Mondays; New Year's; Memorial Day; Labor Day; Thanksgiving; December 15-December 25.

WYOMING

Cody

BUFFALO BILL HISTORICAL CENTER, Box 1020. 82414. Tel.: (307) 587-2777. *Founded:* 1917. *General Museum. Collections:* Firearms; items relating to Wild West Show. *Hours & Admission Prices:* May, Sept. Daily 8-5; June-Aug. Daily 7 am-10 pm; admission subject to change; under 6 no charge.

Fort Laramie

FORT LARAMIE NATIONAL HISTORIC SITE. 82212. Tel.: (307) 837-2704. *Founded:* 1938. *Historic Site. Collections:* Army equipment and accoutrements; ammunition and components. Historic Buildings (refurnished); 1855 bachelor officer quarters in Bedlam; 1864 commanding officer's quarters and post head-quarters in Bedlam; 1870 captain's quarters in OQ "A"; 1876 Post Trader's store; 1880 Post Surgeon's quarters in OQ "E"; 1883 Post Office, enlisted men's bar and officer's club; 1888 Lieutenant Colonel's quarters. *Hours & Admission Prices:* Labor Day-June 15: Daily, Holidays 8-4:30; June15-Labor-Day: Daily, Holidays 7-7. No charge. Closed New Year's; Xmas.

Gilette

WELTNER WONDER MUSEUM, I90 & So. 59, Hwy. Exit. 82716. Tel.: (307) 682-3705. *Founded:* 1950. *General Museum. Collections:* Guns; preserved animals. *Hours & Admission Prices:* May 1-Nov. 3; Sun. 12-5. Daily 9-9; Jan.-March by appointment only; adults $1; children under 12 50¢; students 25¢.

Green River

SWEETWATER COUNTY MUSEUM, 50 W. Flaming Gorge Way. 82935. Tel.: (307) 875-2611. *Founded:* 1967. *History Museum. Collections:* Guns. *Hours & Admission Prices:* Mon.-Fri. 10-4:30. No charge. Closed Saturdays; Sundays; Holidays.

Jackson

JACKSON HOLE HISTORICAL MUSEUM, 101 N. Glenwood. 83001. Tel.: (307) 733-2414. *Founded:* 1958. *General Museum. Collections:* Firearms. *Hours & Admission Prices:* May 15-Sept. 15 Daily 9-9; adults $1; children 50¢; family $2. Closed September 16-May 14.

Rawlins

RAWLINS NATIONAL BANK MUSEUM, 220 5th St. 82301. Tel.: (307) 324-2731. *Founded:* 1899. *General Museum. Collections:* Guns. *Hours & Admission Prices:* Mon.-Thurs. 9-3; Fri. 9-5. No charge. Closed Holidays.

CANADA

ALBERTA

Calgary

KING'S OWN RIFLES OF CANADA, CALGARY REGIMENT MUSEUM, Department of National Defense Building. Tel.: (403) CH 2-1161, loc. 525. *Founded:* 1957. *Collections:* Canadian military and civilian articles and documents; weapons; badges; photographs; films; tape recordings; uniforms and relics of the King's Own Rifles. *Hours & Admission Prices:* By appointment only. No charge.

Smoky Lake

FORT VICTORIA MUSEUM, Box 178. *Founded:* 1962. *General Museum. Collections:* Guns; mounted wildgame heads; mounted small animals; mounted fish and birds; taxidermy.

Wetaskiwin

REYNOLDS MUSEUM, Hwy. 2A. Tel.: (403) 352-5201. *Founded:* 1954. *General Museum. Collections:* Weapons. *Hours & Admission Prices:* May-Sept. Daily 10-5; adults $1.50; students $1; children under 12 50¢; children under 6 no charge.

BRITISH COLUMBIA

Penticton

PENTICTON MUSEUM AND ARCHIVES, Main Street. Tel.: (604) 492-6025. *Founded:* 1957. *Collections:* Indian artifacts; guns. *Hours & Admission Prices:* Tues.-Sat. 2-5. No charge.

Prince Rupert

MUSEUM OF NORTHERN BRITISH COLUMBIA, Corner McBride St. and First Ave. Tel.: (604) 624-5637. *Founded:* 1924. *General Museum. Collections:* Guns. *Hours & Admission Prices:* Summer: Daily 9-9; Winter: Mon.-Sat.; 9-4. No charge. Closed New Year's; Good Friday; Xmas.

Vancouver

PACIFIC NATIONAL EXHIBITION, British Columbia Pavilion, Exhibition Park. Tel.: (604) 253-2311. *Founded:* 1941. *Natural History Museum. Collections:* Hager collection of big-game trophies. *Hours & Admission Prices:* Mon.-Fri. 9:15-4:45; Sun. 1-4:45. No charge. Closed Saturdays.

MANITOBA

Shilo

ROYAL CANADIAN ARTILLERY MUSEUM, Canadian Forces Base. *Founded:* 1962. *Military Museum. Collections:* Uniforms; weapons; accoutrements and badge displays of Canadian artillery through the ages. *Hours & Admission Prices:* Mon.-Fri. 10:30-4:30. No charge. Closed Holidays

NEWFOUNDLAND

St. John's

NEWFOUNDLAND NAVAL AND MILITARY MUSEUM, Confederation Building. Tel.: (709) 722-0711. *Founded:* 1963. *Collections:* Swords; guns; uniforms; model forts. *Hours & Admission Prices:* Mon.-Fri. 8:30-4:30; Sun. 2:30-4:30; Sat. 9:30-12:45, 2:30-4:30. No charge.

NOVA SCOTIA

Halifax

ARMY MUSEUM-HALIFAX CITADEL, P.O. Box 3418, South Postal Station. Tel.: (902) 422-5979. *Founded:* 1953. *Military Museum. Collections:* Shoulder and hand-fired guns; swords; pole-arms; period uniforms and headgear; general militaria. *Hours & Admission Prices:* Summer: Daily 9-8; Winter: Mon.-Sat. 10-5; Sun. 12-5. No charge. Closed New Year's; Xmas.

ONTARIO

Alliston

SOUTH SIMCOE PIONEER MUSEUM, Municipal Office. Tel.: (705) 435-6471. *Founded:* 1960. *Pioneer History Museum. Collections:* Guns. *Hours & Admission Prices:* July-Aug. Tues.-Sun. 12-8; other times by appointment; adults 50¢; young children 10¢; students 25¢. Closed September-June.

Borden

WASHINGTON MILITARY MUSEUM AND WORTHINGTON PARK, Canadian Forces Base. *Military Museum. Collections:* World War I and II fighting vehicles; military history; military vehicles and guns; equipment relating to the development of armor and other military corps in the Canadian forces. *Hours & Admission Prices:* Mon.-Fri. 9-12 & 1-4:30; Sat.-Sun. 1:30-4:30.

Dundas

DUNDAS HISTORICAL SOCIETY MUSEUM, 139 Park St., W. Tel.: (416) 627-7412. *Founded:* 1956. *Local History Museum. Collections:* Military; firearms. *Hours & Admission Prices:* Mon.-Fri. 10-12 & 1-4; Sun. 2-5; other times by appointment. No charge. Closed Holidays.

Dunvegan

GLENGARRY SCOTTISH MUSEUM. *Founded:* 1962. *General Museum. Collections:* Guns. *Hours & Admission Prices:* Victoria Day-end of June Sat.-Sun. 1:30-5:30; July-Aug. Tues.-Sun. 1:30-5:30; Labor Day-Thanksgiving, Sat.-Sun. 1:30-5:30; Holiday weekends open Mon. 1:30-5:30; adults 50¢; children 12-16 25¢; children under 12 no charge. Closed Tues.; Thanksgiving-May 24.

London

UNIVERSITY OF WESTERN ONTARIO, MUSEUM OF INDIAN ARCHAEOLOGY AND PIONEER LIFE. Tel.: (519) 679-3437. *Collections:* Guns. *Hours & Admission Prices:* Hours correspond to University schedule. No charge.

Ottawa

GOVERNOR GENERAL'S FOOT GUARDS MUSEUM, Drill Hall, Cartier Sq. Tel.: (613) 992-3807. *Founded:* 1953. *Military Museum:* Housed in 1879 Drill Hall. *Collections:* Artifacts of regimental interest over the past 100 years: weapons, uniforms, medals, badges, trophies and souvenirs of campaigns and wars. *Hours & Admission Prices:* Jan.-June, Sept.-Dec. Tues., Fri. 8 pm-10 pm. No charge.

Prescott

FORT WELLINGTON NATIONAL HISTORIC PARK, 400 Dibble St., E. Tel.: (613) 925-3211. *Founded:* 1921. *National Historic Site:* 1838 Fort Wellington. *Collections:* Military; relics from the Battle of the Windmill; British arms 1812-1918. *Hours & Admission Prices:* May 1-June 15 weekdays 10 am-5 pm; Sundays 12 pm-5 pm June 16-Labor Day 9 am-8 pm Daily. Day after Labor Day-Oct. 31 weekdays 10 am-5 pm; Sundays 12 pm-5 pm. No charge.

Sutton

EILDON HALL, SIBBALD MEMORIAL MUSEUM, Sibbald Point Park, R.R. 2. Tel.: (416) 722-5182. *Founded:* 1959. *General Museum. Collections:* Firearms and weapons; military equipment. *Hours & Admission Prices:* May 25-mid-June Sat.-Sun. 10-6; mid-June-Sept. 6 Daily 10-6. No charge. Closed September 6-May 20.

Windsor

HIRAM WALKER HISTORICAL MUSEUM, 254 Pitt St. W. Tel.: (519) 253-1812. *Founded:* 1958. *General Museum:* Housed in 1812 Francis Baby House used as the American headquarters at opening of War of 1812. *Collections:* Firearms. *Hours & Admission Prices:* Tues.-Sat. 9-5; Sun. 2-5. No charge. Closed Mondays; Easter weekend; Statutory Holidays; Dec. 15-Dec. 27.

PRINCE EDWARD ISLAND

Rocky Point

FORT AMHERST NATIONAL HISTORIC PARK. *Founded:* 1967. *Historic Park Museum. Collections:* Military; firearms. *Hours & Admission Prices:* Apr.-June 14, Labor Day-Nov. Daily 10-5; June 15-Labor Day Daily 9-8. No charge.

QUEBEC

Montreal

ROYAL CANADIAN ORDNANCE CORPS MUSEUM, 6560 Hochelaga St. Tel.: (514) 255-8811. *Founded:* 1962. *Military Museum. Collections:* Weapons; ammunition; military clothing; uniforms; models; badges; insignia; medals; flags. *Hours & Admission Prices:* Mon.-Fri. 10-3; Sat.-Sun., Holidays by appointment. No charge.

THE SOCIETY OF THE MONTREAL MILITARY AND MARITIME MUSEUM, St. Helen's Island. Tel.: (514) 521-7172. *Founded:* 1960. *Military Museum:* Housed in c. 1820 the Old Fort at the recommendation of Duke of Wellington used as a military garrison to protect Montreal from attack, located on St. Helen's Island used since 1611 as a military base until evacuated by French in 1760. Used by British garrison until 1870. *Collections:* Firearms; uniforms; original documents; the Amherst Cannon. *Hours and Admission Prices:* May-Sept. Daily 10-5; adults 50¢; children 25¢. Closed October-April.

SASKATCHEWAN

Battleford

BATTLEFORD NATIONAL HISTORIC PARK, Box 479. Tel.: (306) 937-2144. *Founded:* 1951. *General Museum. Collections:* North-West Rebellion; militaria; firearms. *Historic Buildings:* 1876 commanding officer residence; 1886 officers quarters; 1886 #5 barracks; 1887 guardhouse. *Hours & Admission Prices:* May-June, Sept.-Oct. Mon.-Sat. 9-5; Sun., Holidays 10-6; July-Aug. 9-8; other times by appointment. No charge. Closed November-April.

Where to Hunt What in the World:
A Guide for All Who Hunt with Gun or Camera

NORTH AMERICA

Alaska
Deer, moose, caribou, mountain goat, mountain sheep, musk ox, bison, brown and grizzly bear, black bear, polar bear, wolf, wolverine, mink, marten, weasel, lynx, land otter, red, blue and white fox, muskrat, beaver, squirrel, coyote, grouse, ptarmigan, hare, rabbit, walrus, sea lion, porpoise, beluga, seal and waterfowl.

Canada
ALBERTA: Buffalo, moose, white-tailed deer, Rocky Mountain mule deer, elk, bighorn sheep, mountain goat, grizzly and black bear, mallard, pintail, blue-winged and green-winged teal, gadwall, baldpate and shoveller, Canadian goose, snow goose and white-front goose, sharp-tailed grouse, Hungarian partridge, blue grouse, Franklin grouse and ptarmigan.

BRITISH COLUMBIA: Moose, wapiti, caribou, wolf, mountain sheep, mountain goat, mule deer, white-tailed deer, grizzly and black bear, ptarmigan, prairie chicken, grouse, duck, goose, snipe, pheasant, partridge and quail.

MANITOBA: Moose, white-tailed deer, mule deer, bear, wolf, small game and wildfowl.

NEW BRUNSWICK: White-tailed deer, black bear, woodcock, partridge, ruffed grouse, duck and goose.

NEWFOUNDLAND: Moose, caribou, black bear, rabbit, snipe, wild goose and wild duck.

NORTHWEST TERRITORIES: Seal, moose, caribou, elk, grizzly and black bear, mountain sheep and mountain goat, upland game birds and waterfowl.

NOVA SCOTIA: Moose, white-tailed deer, black bear, wildcat, fox, raccoon, rabbit, woodcock, snipe, black duck, grouse, partridge, pheasant and Canadian wild goose.

ONTARIO: Deer, wolf, bear, moose, grouse, pheasant, woodcock, Hungarian partridge, quail, European hare, snowshoe and cottontail rabbits, blue goose, snow goose, Canada goose, pintail and black duck.

PRINCE EDWARD ISLAND: Hungarian partridge, ruffed grouse, ring-necked pheasant, wild duck and goose.

QUEBEC: Deer, black bear, wolf, wild duck, goose and partridge.

SASKATCHEWAN: Moose, black bear, mallard and pintail, Canadian and white-front goose, sharp-tailed grouse, Hungarian partridge, rough, spruce and sage grouse, willow ptarmigan, ring-necked pheasant, whitetail and mule deer.

YUKON TERRITORY: Mountain sheep, mountain goat, moose, barrenground and Osborn caribou, grizzly and black bear, grouse, ptarmigan, waterfowl.

THE CARIBBEAN AND THE BAHAMAS

Antigua
Deer (on the island of Barbuda).

Bahamas
Wild hog (on the islands of Abaco, Andros and Inagua).

Dominica
Wild hog, agouti and manique.

Martinique
Turtle dove, wood piegon, small heron and a few species of North American duck.

Puerto Rico
Waterfowl, dove and pigeon.

Trinidad and Tobago
Agouti, armadillo, alligator, deer, lappe, opossum, mongoose, wild hog, squirrel, duck, crane, heron, the scarlet ibis and parrot.

U.S. Virgin Islands
ST. CROIX: Deer, dove and pigeon.

MEXICO AND CENTRAL AMERICA

British Honduras
Jaguar, puma, tapir, deer, antelope, ocelot, wild pig, monkey, iguana, alligator, crane and snakes.

Costa Rica
Deer, wild pig, saino, tapir, puma, jaguar, tepezquintle, rabbit, fox, ocelot, raccoon, wild goat, pizote, muskrat, ferret, otter, opossum, weasel, wild turkey, duck, quail, snipe, wild hen, band-tailed pigeon and the purple dove.

Guatemala
Jaguar, puma, javelina, deer, wild pig, wild turkey, monkey, alligator, quail, white-wing pigeon, dove, parrot and turtle.

Honduras
Jaguar, puma, wild pig, whitetail deer, monkey, wild turkey, alligator, quail, white-winged pigeon, parrot and waterfowl.

Mexico
Agouti, armadillo, bobcat, ring-tailed cat, chachalaca, coati, coyote, crane, curassow, brocket deer, whitetail deer, mule deer, dove, duck, gray fox, kit fox, goose grison, crested guan, iguana, jackrabbit, jaguar, jaguarundi, kinkajou, margay, ocelot, opossum, paca, collared peccary, white-lipped peccary, pigeon, upland plover, puma, quail, rabbit, raccoon, desert sheep, snipe, squirrel, tayra, tinamou, ocellated turkey, wild turkey, weasel and wolf.

Panama
Jaguar, black jaguar, ocelot, mangle cat, paca, agouti, deer, tapir, peccary, white-lipped peccary, wild turkey, alligator, iguana, pigeon, dove, grouse and duck.

SOUTH AMERICA

Bolivia
Jaguar, ocelot, puma, anteater, alligator, anaconda python, tapir, deer, wild boar, vicuña, guanaco, wolf, American tiger, bear and game birds.

Brazil
Tapir, otter, water buffalo, wild dog, wild pig, capivara, cotia, wildcat, arara, toucan, mutum, parrot, snowy owl, ocelot, alligator, wolf, painted jaguar, black jaguar, paca, sloth, fox, turtle, anteater, deer, stork, crane, flamingo, duck, pheasant, partridge and snake.

Colombia
Jaguar, puma, tapir, wild boar, deer, water hog, ape, alligator, anaconda, anteater, antelope, wild duck and wild turkey.

Guyana
Jaguar, puma, alligator, capybara, white-lipped peccary, monkey, parrot, lizard, several large bush fowl and snake.

Surinam
Deer, jaguar, tapir, alligator, wild boar, ocelot, black jaguar, puma, jungle hare, water buffalo, monkey, wild fox, otter, duck, parrot and tropical birds.

EUROPE

Austria
Roebuck, stag, chamois, red deer, moufflon, snipe, mountain and blackcock, pheasant, partridge, marmot, wild boar, fox, polecat, wild rabbit, weasel, sparrow hawk and heron.

Belgium
Stag, wild boar, ferret, badger, fox, partridge, pheasant, hare and rabbit.

Britain and Ireland
England and Wales: stag, hind, grouse and rabbit. Scotland: stag, hind, and grouse. Ireland: stag, hind, grouse, snipe, plover, duck, goose, pheasant and partridge.

Bulgaria
Stag, deer, fallow deer, wild boar, pheasant, hare, partridge and quail.

Czechoslovakia
Deer, fallow deer, moufflon, roe deer, wild boar, chamois, hare, wild rabbit, lynx, fox, bear, wood grouse, black grouse, the rare bustard, pheasant, partridge, snipe, lark.

Denmark
Hare, pheasant, fox.

Finland
Moose, lynx, hare, wolverine, wood grouse, heath grouse, ruffed grouse, white ptarmigan, wild duck.

France
Stag, deer, wild boar, wild hare, pheasant, quail, wild duck, moufflon, chamois, various partridge, plover, snipe, lark.

Germany
Red deer, fallow and sika deer, roe deer, wild boar, moufflon, chamois, marmot, hare, badger, otter, capercailzie, blackcock, hazel grouse, partridge, pheasant, wild pigeon, woodcock, snipe, wild goose, wild duck, buzzard and sea gull.

Hungary
Red deer, roe deer, fallow deer, wild pig, moufflon, hare, pheasant, wild bustard, wild duck and goose.

Iceland
Arctic ptarmigan, wild goose, wild duck, reindeer and sea birds.

Norway
Moose, reindeer, stag, polar bear, roe deer, fallow deer, capercailzie, black grouse, hazel grouse, ptarmigan, partridge, pheasant, snipe, woodcock, wild duck, wild goose, hare, fox and seal.

Poland
Red deer, fallow deer, roe deer, wild boar, lynx, wolf, fox, hare, rabbit, capercailzie, blackcock, hazelcock, pheasant, partridge, woodcock, ruff, snipe, wild duck and wild goose.

Portugal
Hare, turtledove, quail, snipe, wood pigeon, duck, woodcock, partridge, bustard and thrush.

Soviet Union
Stag, roebuck and wild boar.

Spain
Deer, buck, roebuck, wild goat, wild pig, bear, partridge, quail, turtledove, pheasant, grouse, wild rabbit, wild hare, dove, wild duck and goose.

Sweden
Moose, elk, stag, hare, woodcock, partridge, pheasant, duck.

Switzerland
Chamois, marmot, stag, buck, hare, wild duck, fox, badger, wild boar, pheasant, partridge, ibex, eagle, mountain cock and blackcock.

Yugoslavia
Stag, roebuck, chamois, bear, wild boar, hare, wood grouse, blackcock, pheasant, field and rock partridge, quail, snipe, hazel grouse, wild duck, wild goose, pigeon, turtledove.

ASIA

India
Tiger, panther, sambar, chital, blue bull, chinkara, black buck, wild pig, gaur, wild buffalo, wild bear, sloth bear, barking deer, four-horned deer, crocodile, pheasant, partridge, pigeon, quail, duck, goose and dozens of other bird species.

Indonesia
Barking deer, Java deer, wild pig, tiger, water buffalo, panther, elephant, dwarf deer, monkey, orangutan, crocodile, giant lizard, parrot, bird of paradise, cassowary, waterfowl and reptiles.

Iran
Red, fallow, spotted and roe deer, wild ass, gazelle, tiger, cheetah, wild sheep, wild goat, bear, leopard, wildcat, wolf, fox, jackal, hyena, wild boar, lynx, porcupine, pheasant, francolin, chukker partridge, all European waterfowl, sand grouse, wild pigeon, woodcock, snow partridge and quail.

Iraq
Wild boar, desert rabbit and duck.

Japan

Bear, brown bear, wild boar, deer, fox, racoon dog, badger, common and giant flying squirrel, marten, nutria, chipmunk, mink, hare, white-fronted and eastern bean goose, smew, three types of snipe, two types of sparrow, two types of crow, raven, woodcock, duck, pheasant, hazel grouse, quail, bamboo partridge, heron, coot and moor hen.

Jordan

Wild boar, ibex, gazelle, hare, lynx, porcupine, bustard, common partridge, sand partridge, rock dove, lark, sand grouse, coot, snipe, crane, quail, duck and goose.

Malaysia and Singapore

Tiger, leopard, wild boar and mouse deer.

Nepal

Tiger rhino, panther, black lepoard, snow leopard, clouded leopard, sambar, swamp deer, musk deer, spotted deer, hog deer, barking deer, black buck, four-horned antelope, blue bull, blue sheep, Himalayan tahr, wild boar, sloth bear, elephant, bison, crocodile, peacock, swan, pheasant, marsh mugger, peafowl, duck and goose.

The Philippines

Carabao or water buffalo, wild boar, deer, crocodile, mouse deer, squirrel, anteater, porcupine, bearcat, pheasant, snipe, plover, sandpiper, curlew, godwit, jacana, lemur, dove, pigeon, partridge, quail, coot, rail, hornbill and wild duck.

Turkey

Bear, wild boar, red deer, ibex, wolf, dove, quail, chukar partridge, duck, goose and woodcock.

AFRICA

Algeria

Redleg partridge, hare, pin-tailed grouse, quail, turtledove, gazelle, snipe, pigeon, wild boar, starling, sheep and wild duck.

Angola

Elephant, buffalo, rhino, lion, leopard, sassaby, cape eland, wildebeest, impala, reedbuck, rean Antelope, red Lechwe, duiker steinbock, oribi, greater kudu, sable antelope, situtunga, warthog, cape buffalo, crocodile, partridge and guinea-fowl.

Botswana

Elephant, sable, black-maned lion, buffalo, greater kudu, situtunga, red lechwe, gemsbok, springbok and red hartebeest.

Cameroon

Giant eland, dwarf buffalo, roan, topis, waterbuck, giraffe, elephant, hippo, gorilla and birds.

Central African Republic

Elephant, bongo, situtunga, giant forest hog, red dwarf buffalo, red river hog, gorilla, bushbuck, duiker and small antelope.

Chad

White oryx, gazelle, Barbary sheep, cheetah, ostrich, bat-eared fox, antbear, wild dog and many varieties of birds in the desert. Giant eland, elephant, buffalo, lion, leopard, greater kudu, hippo, giraffe, roan, waterbuck, hartebeest, warthog, crocodile, python, goose and duck elsewhere.

Ethiopia

Nubian ibex, mountain nyala, Nile lichwe, oryx beisa, Soemmering's gazelle, gerenuk, roan antelope, greater and lesser kudu, elephant, buffalo, bushbuck, giant forest hog, waterbuck, hartebeest, tiang, hippopotamus, warthog, lion, leopard and game birds.

Gabon

Elephant, hippo, buffalo, situtunga, waterbuck, gorilla, panther, bush pig, bongo and chimpanzee.

Gambia

Hartebeest, duiker, Gambian oribi, waterbuck, cob, reedbuck, antelope, bushbuck, river hog, giraffe, eland, elephant, hippo, Congo-Senegambian buffalo, waterfowl and plumed birds.

Kenya

Lion, cheetah, elephant, leopard, buffalo, gerenuk, eland, reedbuck, bushbuck, waterbuck, gazelle, oryx, hartebeest, zebra, blue and red duiker, impala, warthog, rhinoceros, hippopotamus, giraffe, ostrich, bongo, monkey and birds.

Libya

Partridge and gazelle.

Morocco

Wild boar, hare, partridge, turtledove, ring dove, thrush, wildfowl and fowl of passage.

Mozambique

The greater kudu, pitch-black sable, nyala, giraffe, rhino, lion, leopard, eland, zebra, duiker, crocodile, hippo and birds.

Rhodesia

Buffalo, bushbuck, duiker, eland, elephant, impala, kudu, leopard, lion, sable, antelope, warthog, waterbuck, wildebeest, zebra and game birds.

Senegal

Lion, panther, hippo, lamantin, chimpanzee, elephant, giraffe, derby eland, gazelle, buffalo, bubale, wild sheep, ostrich, stork, flamingo, aigrette, heron, pelican, jabiru, marabou, duck, alligator, warthog and hare.

Somali Republic

47 different species are found here, ranging from the rabbit to the elephant. Other animals include the bat-eared fox, lynx, crocodile, zebra, guenon, klipspringer, leopard, lion, kudu, porcupine and mongoose.

South Africa

Elephant, giraffe, rhino, eland, gemsbok, buffalo, hippo, lion, chettah, impala, kudu, zebra, blue wildebeest, reedbuck and birds.

South-West Africa

Giant oryx, greater kudu, cape hartebeest, mountain zebra, springbok, duiker, wildebeest, ostrich, eland, steinbok, and birds.

Sudan

Bushbuck, bush pig, many species of cob, dik-dik, four kinds of duiker, eland, gazelle, hartebeest, hippo, ibex, klipspringer, kudu, leopard, giraffe, cheetah, rhino and zebra.

Tanzania

Buffalo, elephant, lion, giraffe, rhino, hippo, zebra, dik-dik, rock rabbit, topi, pygmy antelope, birds and waterfowl.

Tunisia

Wild boar, hare, partridge, turtledove, ring dove, thrush, wildfowl and fowl of passage.

Uganda

Lion, cheetah, elephant, leopard, buffalo, gerenuk, eland, reedbuck, bushbuck, waterbuck, gazelle, oryx, hartebeest, zebra, blue and red duiker, impala, warthog, rhinoceros, hippopatamus, giraffe, ostrich, bongo, monkey, mountain gorilla and birds.

Zambia

Lion, sable, puku, oribi, elephant, warthog, cheetah, hartebeest, zebra, crocodile, leopard, roan, lechwe, duiker, hippo, eland, impala and buffalo.

AUSTRALIA, NEW ZEALAND AND HAWAII

Australia

Kangaroo, fox, dingo, camel, deer, goat, hare, buffalo wild pig, wallaby, donkey, crocodile, snipe, wedge-tail eagle, duck and goose.

New Zealand

Wapiti (elk), red deer, fallow deer, Virginia deer, Japanese deer, rusa deer, sambar deer, chamois, tahr, wild boar, Australian wallaby, and ferrel goat.

Hawaii

Axis deer, wild goat, wild pig, wild sheep, ring-necked pheasant, Japanese blue pheasant, California quail, Japanese quail, lace-necked dove, barred dove, chukar partridge and wild pigeon.

Endangered Bird and Mammal Species of the World

BIRDS (Class Aves/Phylum Chordata)

Penguins (Order: Sphenisciformes)
Penguin, Galapagos, *Spheniscus mendiculus.* Galapagos Islands

Ostriches (Order: Struthioniformes)
Ostrich, Arabian, *Struthio camelus syriacus.* Jordan/ Saudia Arabia/Spanish Sahara
Ostrich, West African, *Struthio camelus spatzi.* Jordan/ Saudi Arabia/Spanish Sahara

Rheas (Order: Rheiformes)
Rhea, Darwin's, *Pterocnemia pennata.* Argentina/Peru/ Uruguay/Bolivia

Grebes (Order: Podicipediformes)
Grebe, Atitlan, *Podilymbus gigas.* Guatemala

Albatrosses, Petrels & Relatives (Order: Procellariiformes)
Albatross, Short-tailed, *Diomedea albatrus.* Japan
Cahow (Bermuda petrel), *Pterodroma cahow.* Bermuda
Petrel, Hawaiian dark-rumped, *Pterodroma phaeopygia sandiwichensis.* USA (Hawaii)

Pelicans (Order: Pelecaniformes)
Pelican, Brown, *Pelecanus occidentalis.* USA/ W. Indies/ Coastal Central & South America

Herons, Storks, Flamingos, & Relatives (Order: Ciconiiformes)
Egret, Chinese, *Egretta eulophotes.* People's Republic China/Korea
Ibis, Japanese crested, *Nipponia nippon.* Japan/Korea/ USSR/People's Rep. China
Stork, White, Oriental, *Ciconia ciconia boyciana.* Japan/ Korea/USSR/People's Rep. China

Ducks, Geese, Swans & Relatives (Order: Anseriformes)
Duck, Hawaiian (koloa), *Anas wyvilliana,* USA (Hawaii)
Duck, Laysan, *Anas laysanensis.* USA (Hawaii)
Duck, Mexican, *Anas diazi.* USA (Texas, Arizona, Mexico)
Duck, White-winged wood, *Cairina scutulata.* Southeast Asia
Goose, Alutian Canada, *Branta canadensis leucopareia.* USA (Western)/Japan
Goose, Hawaiian (nene), *Branta sandvicensis.* USA (Hawaii)

Eagles, Falcons, Vultures, & Relatives (Order: Falconiformes)
Condor, Andean, *Vultur gryphus.* W. So. Amer: Columbia/ Ecuador/Peru/Argentina
Condor, California, *Gymnogyps californianus.* USA (California)
Eagle, Monkey-eating, *Pithecophaga jefferyi.* Phillippines
Eagle, Southern bald, *Haliaeetus leucocephalus leucocephalus.* USA (So. of 40th Parallel)
Eagle, Spanish imperial, *Aquila heliaca adalberti.* Spain/Morocco/Algeria
Falcon, American peregrine, *Falco peregrinus anatum.* Canada/USA/Mexico
Falcon, Arctic peregrine, *Falco peregrinus tundrius.* Canada/USA/Mexico
Goshawk, Christmas Island, *Accipiter fasciatus natalis.* Christmas Island
Hawk, Anjouan Island sparrow, *Accipiter francesii pusillus.* Comoro Islands
Hawk, Galapagos, *Buteo galapagoensis.* Galapagos Islands
Hawk, Hawaiian (io), *Buteo solitarius.* USA (Hawaii)
Kestrel, Mauritius, *Falco punctatus.* Mascarene Is.
Kestrel, Seychelles, *Falco araea.* Seychelles
Kite, Cuba hook-billed, *Chondrohierax wilsonii.* Cuba
Kite, Grenada hook-billed, *Chondrohierax uncinatus mirus.* West Indies
Kite, Florida Everglades (snail kite), *Rostrhamus sociabilis plumbeus.* USA (Florida)

Pheasants, Grouse, Curassows, & Relatives (Order: Galliformes)
Curassow, Red-billed, *Crax blumenbachii.* Brazil
Curassow, Trinidad white-headed, *Pipile pipile pipile.* Trinidad
Guan, horned, *Oreophasis derbianus.* Guatamala/Mexico
Magapode, Maleo, *Macrocephalon maleo.* Indonesia
Megapode, LaPerouse's, *Megapodius laperouse.* Palau Is./Mariana Is.
Pheasant, Bar-tailed, *Syrmaticus humiae.* Burma/People's Rep. China
Pheasant, Blyth's tragopan, *Tragopan blythii.* People's Rep. China/Burma/India
Pheasant, Brown-eared, *Crossoptilon mantchuricum.* People's Rep. China
Pheasant, Cabot's Tragopan, *Tragopan caboti.* People's Rep. China
Pheasant, Chinese monal, *Lophophorus lhuysii.* People's Rep. China
Pheasant, Edward's, *Lophura edwardsi.* Vietnam
Pheasant, Imperial, *Lophura imperialis.* Vietnam
Pheasant, Mikado, *Syrmaticus mikado.* Taiwan
Pheasant, Palawan peacock, *Polyplectron emphanum.* Philippines
Pheasant, Sclater's monal, *Lophophorus sclateri.* People's Rep. China/Burma/India
Pheasant, Sinhoe's, *Lophura swinhoii.* Taiwan
Pheasant, Western tragopan, *Tragopan melanocephalus.* India/Pakistan
Pheasant, White-eared, *Crossoptilon crossoptilon.* Tibet/India
Prairie Chicken, Attwater's greater, *Tympanuchus cupido attwateri.* USA (Texas)
Quail, Masked bobwhite, *Colinus virginianus ridgwayi.* Northern Mexico/USA (Arizona, New Mexico)

Cranes, Rails, Bustards, & Relatives (Order: Gruiformes)
Bustard, Great Indian, *Choriotis nigriceps.* India/Pakinstan
Coot, Hawaiian, *Fulica americana alai.* USA (Hawaii)
Crane, Hooded, *Grus monachus.* Japan/USSR
Crane, Japanese, *Grus japaonensis.* Japan/People's Rep. China/Korea/USSR
Crane, Mississippi sandhill, *Grus canadensis pulla.* USA (Mississippi)
Carne, Siberian white, *Grus leucogeranus.* Eastern USSR to India
Crane, Whooping, *Grus americana.* Canada/USA
Gallinule, Hawaiian, *Gallinula chloropus sandvicensis.* USA (Hawaii)
Kagu (rail), *Rhynochetos jubatus.* New Caledonia
Rail, Auckland Island, *Rallus pectoralis muelleri.* New Zealand
Rail, California clapper, *Rallus longirostris obsoletus.* USA (California)
Rail, Light-footed clapper, *Rallus longirostris levipes.* Mexico/USA (California)
Rail, Yuma clapper, *Rallus longirostris yumanensis.* Mexico/USA (California, Arizona)
Wanderer, Plains, *Pedionomus torquatus.* Australia

Plovers, Snipes, Gulls, & Relatives (Order: Charadriiformes)
Curlew, Eskimo, *Numenius borealis.* Canada to Argentina
Gull, Audouin's, *Larus audouinii.* Mediterranean Ocean & adjacent lands
Plover, New Zealand shore, *Thinornis novae-seelandiae.* New Zealand
Stilt, Hawaiian, *Himantopus himantopus knudseni.* USA (Hawaii)
Tern, California least, *Sterna albifrons browni.* Mexico/USA

Pigeons, Doves, Sandgrouse, & Relatives (Order: Columbiformes)
Dove, Cloven-feathered, *Drepanoptila holosericea.* New Caledonia
Dove, Grenada, *Leptotila wellsi.* Grenada

Pigeons, Doves, Sandgrouse, & Relatives (Cont'd)

Dove, Palau ground, *Gallicolumba canifrons*. Paulau Islands
Pigeon, Azores wood, *Columba palumbus azorica*. Azores
Pigeon, Chatham Island, *Hemiphaga novaeseelandiae chathamensis*. New Zealand
Pigeon, Puerto Rican plain, *Columba inornata wetmorei*. Puerto Rico

Parrots, Parakeets, & Relatives (Order: Psittaciformes)

Parakeet, Forbes', *Cyanoramphus auriceps forbesi*. New Zealand
Parakeet, Golden-shouldered, *Psephotus chrysopterygius*. Australia
Parakeet, Mauritius ring-necked, *Psittacula krameri echo*. Mascarene Is.
Parakeet, Ochre-marked, *Pyrrhura cruentata*. Brazil
Parakeet, Orange-bellied, *Neophema chrysogaster*. Australia
Parakeet, Paradise, *Psephotus pulcherrimus*. Australia
Parakeet, Scarlet-chested, *Neophema splendida*. Australia
Parakeet, Turquoise, *Neophema pulchella*. Australia
Parrot, Bahamas, *Amazona leucocephala bahamensis*. Bahamas
Parrot, Ground, *Pezoporus wallicus*. Australia
Parrot, Imperial, *Amazona imperialis*. Dominica Is.
Parrot, Night, *Geopsittacus occidentalis*. Australia
Parrot, Owl (kakapo), *Strigops habroptilus*. New Zealand
Parrot, Puerto Rican, *Amazona vittata*. Puerto Rico
Parrot, Red-browed, *Amazona rhodocorytha*. Brazil
Parrot, St. Lucia, *Amazona versicolor*. St. Lucia
Parrot, St. Vincent, *Amazona guildingii*. St. Vincent
Parrot, Thick-billed, *Rhynchopsitta pachyrhyncha*. Mexico/USA (Arizona, New Mexico)

Cuckoos, Road-Runners, & Relatives (Order: Cuculiformes)

Malkoha, Red-faced, *Phaenicophaeus pyrrhocephalus*. Ceylon

Owls (Order: Strigiformes)

Owl, Anjouan scops, *Otus rutilus capnodes*. Comoro Islands
Owl, Palau, *Otus podargina*. Palau Islands
Owl, Seychelles, *Otus insularis*. Seychelles
Owlet, Mrs. Morden's, *Otus ireneae*. Kenya

Goatsuckers & Relatives (Order: Caprimulgiformes)

Whip-poor-will, Puerto Rican, *Caprimulgus noctitherus*. Puerto Rico

Kingfishers, Bee-Eaters, & Relatives (Order: Coraciiformes)

Roller, Long-tailed ground, *Uratelornis chimaera*. Madagascar

Woodpeckers, Puffbirds, Barbets, & Relatives (Order: Piciformes)

Woodpecker, Imperial, *Campephilus imperialis*. Mexico
Woodpecker, Ivory-billed, *Campephilus principalis*. Southern USA/Cuba
Woodpecker, Red cockaded, *Dendrocopus borealis*. Southern USA
Woodpecker, Tristram's, *Dryocopus javensis richardsi*. Korea

Perching Birds—Sparrows, Larks, Thrushes, & Relatives (Order: Passeriformes)

Bulbul, Mauritius olivaceous, *Hypsipetes borbonicus olivaceus*. Mascarene Is.
Crow, Hawaiian (alala), *Corvus tropicus*. USA (Hawaii)
Cuckoo-Shrike, Maritius, *Coquus typicus*. Mascarene Is.
Cuckoo-Shrike, Renuion, *Coquus newtoni*. Mascarene Is.
Finch, Sao Miguel bullfinch, *Pyrrhula pyrrhula murina*. Azores
Flycatcher, Chatham Island robin, *Petroica traversi*. New Zealand
Flycatcher, Eyrean grass-wren, *Amytornis goyderi*. Australia
Flycatcher, Grey-necked rock-fowl, *Picathartes oreas*. Cameroon
Flycatcher, Palau fantail, *Rhipidura lepida*. Palau Islands
Flycatcher, Seychelles black, *Terpsiphone corvina*. Seychelles
Flycatcher, Tahiti, *Pomarea nigra nigra*. Tahiti
Flycatcher, Western bristlebird, *Dasyornis brachypterus longirostris*. Australia
Flycatcher, White-necked rock-fowl, *Picathartes gymnocephalus*. Togo to Sierra Leone

Perching Birds (Cont'd)

Flycatcher (Tyrant), Euler's, *Empidonax euleri johnstonei*. Grenada
Flycatcher (Tyrant), Scarlet-breasted robin, *Petroica multicolor multicolor*. Australia (Norfolk Island)
Flycatcher (Tyrant), Tinian monarch, *Monarcha takatsukasae*. Mariana Is.
Grackle, Slender-billed, *Cassidix palustris*. Mexico
Honeycreeper, Akiapolaau, *Hemignathus wilsoni*. USA (Hawaii)
Honeycreeper, Crested (akohekohe), *Palmeria dolei*. USA (Hawaii)
Honeycreeper, Hawaii akepa (akepa), *Loxops coccinea coccinea*. USA (Hawaii)
Honeycreeper, Kauai akialoa, *Hemignathus procerus*. USA (Hawaii)
Honeycreeper, Maui parrotbill, *Pseudonestor xanthorphrys*. USA (Hawaii)
Honeycreeper, Maui akepa (akepuie), *Loxops coccinea ochraceu*. USA (Hawaii)
Honeycreeper, Molokai creeper (kakawahie), *Loxops maculata flammea*. USA (Hawaii)
Honeycreeper, Oahu creeper (alauwahio), *Loxops maculata maculata*. USA (Hawaii)
Honeycreeper, Ou, *Psittirostra psittacea*. USA (Hawaii)
Honeycreeper, Palila, *Psittirostra bailleui*. USA (Hawaii)
Honeycreepers, Laysan & Nihoa finches, *Psittirostra cantans*. USA (Hawaii)
Honeycreepers, Kauai & Maui nukupuus, *Hemignathus lucidus*. USA (Hawaii)
Honey-eater, Helmeted, *Meliphaga cassidix*. Australia
Honey-eater, Kauai Oo (oo aa), *Moho braccatus*. USA (Hawaii)
Scrub-bird, Noisy, *Atrichornis clamosus*. Australia
Sparrow, Cape sable, *Ammospiza maritima mirabilis*. USA (Florida)
Sparrow, Dusky seaside, *Ammospiza maritima nigrescens*. USA (Florida)
Sparrow, Santa Barbara, *Melospiza melodia graminea*. USA (California)
Starling, Ponape Mountain, *Aplonis pelzelni*. Caroline Is. (Ponape)
Starling, Rothschild's (myna), *Leucopsar rothschildi*. Indonesia (Bali)
Thrasher, White-breasted, *Ramphocinclus brachyurus*. Martinique/St. Lucia
Trembler, Martinique brown, *Cinclocerthia ruficauda gutturalis*. Martinique
Thrush, Cebu black shama, *Copsychus niger cebuensis*. Philippines
Thrush, Large Kauai, *Phaeornis obscurus myadestina*. USA (Hawaii)
Thrush, Molokai (olomau), *Phaeornis obscurus rutha*. USA (Hawaii)
Thrush, Seychelles magpie-robin, *Copsychus seychellarum*. Seychelles
Thrush, Small Kauai (puaiohi), *Phaeornis palmeri*. USA (Hawaii)
Thrush, Western whipbird, *Psophodes nigrogularis*. Australia
Warbler, Nihoa millerbird, *Acrocephalus kingi*. USA (Hawaii)
Warbler, Reed, *Acrocephalus luscinia*. Mariana Islands
Warbler, Rodrigues, *Bebrornis rodericanus*. Rodrigues Island
Warbler, Semper's, *Leucopeza semperi*. St. Lucia
Warbler, Seychelles, *Bebrornis sechellensis*. Seychelles
Warbler (Wood), Bachman's, *Vermivora bachmanii*. Cuba/USA (Southeastern States)
Warbler (Wood), Barbados yellow, *Dendroica petechia petechia*. Barbados
Warbler (Wood), Kirtland's, *Dendroica kirtlandii*. USA/Bahamas
White-eye, Ponape great, *Rukia sanfordi*. Caroline Is. (Ponape)
White-eye, Seychelles, *Zosterops modestus*. Seychelles
Wren (Bush), New Zealand, *Xenicus longipes*. New Zealand
Wren, Guadeloupe house, *Troglodytes aedon guadeloupensis*. Guadeloupe
Wren, St. Lucia, *Troglodytes aedon mesoleucus*. St. Lucia
Wattlebird, Kokako, *Callaeas cinerea*. New Zealand

Perching Birds (Cont'd)

Wattlebird, Piopio, *Turnagra capensis.* Mascarene Is.
Weaver-finch, Seychelles fody, *Foudia sechellarum.* Seychelles

MAMMALS (Class Mammalia/Phylum Chordata)

Marsupials or Pouched Mammals (Order: Marsupialia)

Bandicoot, Barred, *Perameles bougainville.* Australia
Bandicoot, Desert, *Perameles eremiana.* Australia
Bandicoot, Rabbit, *Macrotis lagotis.* Australia
Bandicoot, Lesser rabbit, *Macrotis leucura.* Australia
Bandicoot, Pig-footed, *Chaeropus ecaudatus.* Australia
Dibbler, *Antechinus apicalis.* Australia
Forester, Tasmanian, *Macropus giganteus tasmaniensis.* Australia
Marsupial, Eastern jerboa, *Antechinomys langier.* Australia
Marsupial-mouse, Large desert, *Sminthopsis psammophila.* Australia
Marsupial-mouse, Long-tailed, *Sminthopsis longicaudata.* Australia
Native-cat, Eastern, *Dasyurus viverrinus.* Australia
Numbat, *Myrmecobius fasciatus.* Australia
Planigale, Little, *Planigale subtilissima.* Australia
Planigale, Southern, *Planigale tenuirostris.* Australia
Possum, Mountain pigmy, *Burramys parvus.* Australia
Possum, Scaly-tailed, *Wyulda squamicaudata.* Australia
Quokka, *Setonix brachyurus.* Australia
Rat-kangaroo, Brush-tailed, *Bettongia penicillata.* Australia
Rat-kangaroo, Gaimard's, *Bettongia gaimardi.* Australia
Rat-kangaroo, Lesueur's, *Bettongia lesueur.* Australia
Rat-kangaroo, Plain, *Caloprymnus campestris.* Australia
Rat-kangaroo, Queensland, *Bettongia tropica.* Australia

Tiger, Tasmanian (Thylacine), *Thylacinus cynocephalus.* Australia
Wallaby, Banded hare, *Lagostrophus fasciatus.* Australia
Wallaby, Bridled nail-tail, *Onychogalea frenata.* Australia
Wallaby, Crescent nail-tail, *Onychogalea lunata.* Australia
Wallaby, Parma, *Macopus parma.* Australia
Wallaby, Western hare, *Lagorchestes hirsutus.* Australia
Wallaby, Yellow-footed rock, *Petrogale xanthopus.* Australia
Wombat, Barnard's, *Lasiorhinus barnardi.* Australia
Wombat, Queensland hairy-nosed, *Lasiorhinus gillespiei,* Australia

Insect-Eating Mammals (Order: Insectivora)

Solenodon, Cuban, *Atopogale cubana.* Cuba
Solenodon, Haitian, *Solenodon paradoxus.* Dominican Republic (Haiti)

Bats (Order: Chiroptera)

Bat, Hawaiian hoary, *Lasiurus cinereus semotus.* USA (Hawaii)
Bat, Indiana, *Myotis sodalis.* USA (Midwest & East)

Primates (Order: Primates)

Avahis, *Avahi* spp. (All Species). Madagascar
Aye-aye, *Daubentonia madagascariensis.* Madagascar
Colobus, Red, *Colobus badius rufomitratus.* Kenya
Colobus, Zanzibar red, *Colobus badius kirkii.* Tanzania/Zanzibar
Gibbon, Kloss, *Hylobates klossi.* Indonesia
Gibbon, Pileated, *Hylobates pileatus.* Laos/Thailand/Cambodia
Gorilla, *Gorilla gorilla.* Central & Western Africa
Indris, *Indri* spp. (All Species). Madagascar
Langur, Douc, *Pygathrix nemaeus.* Indochina/People's Rep. China (Hainan)
Langur, Pagi Island, *Simias concolor.* Indonesia
Lemurs, *Lemurs* spp. (All Species). Madagascar & Comoro Is.
Lemurs, Gentle, *Hapalemur* spp. (All Species). Madagascar & Comoro Is.
Lemurs, Sportive & Weasel, *Lepilemur* spp. (All Species). Madagascar & Comoro Is.
Lemurs, Dwarf, *Cheirogaleus* spp. (All Species). Madagascar & Comoro Is.

Primates (Cont'd)

Lemurs, Mouse, *Microcebus* spp. (All Species). Madagascar & Comoro Is.
Lemurs, Fork-marked, *Phancer furcifer.* Madagascar & Comoro Is.
Macaque, Lion-tailed, *Macaca silenus.* India
Mangabey, Tana River, *Cercocebus galeritus galeritus.* Kenya
Marmoset, Goeldi's, *Callimico goeldii.* Brazil/Colombia/Ecuador/Peru
Monkey, Spider, *Ateles geoffroyi frontatus.* Costa Rica/Nicaragua
Monkey, Spider, *Ateles geoffroyi panamensis.* Costa Rica/Panama
Monkey, Red-backed squirrel, *Saimiri oerstedii (S. sciureus oerstedii).* Costa Rica/Panama
Monkey, Woolly spider, *Brachyteles arachnoides.* Brazil
Orangutan, *Pongo pygmaeus.* Indonesia/Malaysia
Saki, White-nose, *Chiropotes albinasus.* Brazil
Sifakas, *Propithecus* spp. (All Species). Madagascar
Tamarins, Golden-rumped (Golden Marmosets), *Leontideus* spp. (All Species). Brazil
Uakari, *Cacajao* spp. (All Species). Northwestern Brazil and adjacent territories

Sloth, Anteaters, & Armadillos (Order: Edentata)

Armadillo, Pink fairy, *Chlamyphorus truncatus.* Argentina
Sloth, Brazilian three-toed, *Bradypus torquatus.* Brazil

Pikas, Rabbits, & Hares (Order: Lagomorpha)

Rabbit, Volcano, *Romerolagus diazi.* Mexico

Rodents (Order: Rodentia)

Kangaroo Rat, Morro Bay, *Dipodomys heermanni morroensis.* USA (California)
Mouse, Field's, *Pseudomys fieldi.* Australia
Mouse, Gould's, *Pseudomys gouldii.* Australia
Mouse, New Holland, *Pseudomys novaehollandiae.* Australia
Mouse, Salt marsh harvest, *Reithrodontomys raviventris.* USA (California)
Mouse, Shark Bay, *Pseudomys praeconis.* Australia
Mouse, Shortridge's, *Pseudomys shortridgei.* Australia
Mouse, Smoky, *Pseudomys fumeus.* Australia
Mouse, Western, *Pseudomys occidentalis.* Australia
Porcupine, Thin-spined, *Chaetomys subspinosus.* Brazil
Prairie Dog, Mexican, *Cynomys mexicanus.* Mexico
Prairie Dog, Utah, *Cynomys parvidens.* USA (Utah)
Rat, False water, *Xeromys myoides.* Australia
Rat, Stick-nest, *Leporillus conditor.* Australia
Squirrel, Delmarva Peninsula fox, *Sciurus niger cinereus.* USA (Maryland)

Whales, Dolphins, & Porpoises (Order: Cetacea)

Whale, Blue, *Balaenoptera musculus.* Oceanic
Whale, Bowhead, *Balaena mysticetus.* Oceanic
Whale, Finback, *Balaenoptera physalus.* Oceanic
Whale, Gray, *Eschrichtius gibbosus.* Oceanic
Whale, Humpback, *Megaptera novaeangliae.* Oceanic
Whale, Right, *Eubalaena* spp. (All Species). Oceanic
Whale, Sei, *Balaenoptera borealis.* Oceanic
Whale, Sperm, *Physeter catodon.* Oceanic

Carnivores (Order: Carnivora)

Bear, Mexican grizzly, *Ursus arctos nelsoni.* Mexico
Cat, Tiger, *Felis tigrina.* Costa Rica to Northern South America
Cheetah, *Acinonyx jubatus.* Africa/Middle East/India
Cougar, Eastern, *Felis concolor cougar.* USA (Eastern)
Dog, Asiatic wild, *Cuon alpinus.* USSR/India
Ferret, Black-footed, *Mustela nigripes.* Western USA/Western Canada
Fox, Northern kit, *Vulpes velox hebes.* Western Canada
Fox, San Joaquin kit, *Vulpes macrotis mutica.* USA (California)
Hyaena, Barbary, *Hyaena hyaena barabara.* Morocco
Hyaena, Brown, *Hyaena brunnea.* South African Republic
Jaguar, *Panthera onca.* Mexico to southern South America
Leopard, *Panthera pardus.* Africa/Asia

Carnivores (Cont'd)

Leopard, Formosan clouded, *Neofelis nebulosa brachyurus*. Taiwan
Leopard, Snow, *Panthera uncia*. Central Asia
Lion, Asiatic, *Panthera leo persica*. India
Lynx, Spanish, *Felis lynx pardina*. Spain
Margay, *Felis wiedii*. Mexico/South America
Marten, Formosan yellow-throated, *Martes flavigula chrysospila*. Republic China (Taiwan)
Ocelot, *Felis pardalis*. Mexico/South America
Otter, Cameroon clawless, *Paraonyx microdon*. Cameroon
Otter, Giant, *Pteronura brasiliensis*. South America
Otter, La Plata, *Lutra platensis*. Uruguay/Argentina/Bolivia/Brazil
Panther, Florida, *Felis concolor coryi*. USA (Florida)
Serval, Barbary, *Felis serval constantina*. Algeria
Tiger, *Panthera tigris*. Temperate and Tropical Asia
Wolf, Eastern timber, *Canis lupus lycaon*. Eastern Canada/USA (Minnesota, Michigan)
Wolf, Northern Rocky Mountain, *Canis lupus irremotus*. USA (Wyoming, Montana)
Wolf, Red, *Canis rufus*. USA (Texas, Louisiana)
Wolf, Maned, *Chrysocyon brachyurus*. Brazil/Bolivia/Paraguay/Argentina

Seals, Sea Lions, & Walruses (Order: Pinnipedia)

Seal, Mediterranean monk, *Monachus monachus*. Black Sea/Mediterranean/Northwestern Africa (Coastal)

Dugongs & Manatees (Order: Sirenia)

Dugong, *Dugong dugon*. Indian/Pacific Oceans (Coastal)
Manatee, Amazonian, *Trichechus inunguis*. South America (Amazon Basin)
Manatee, West Indian (Florida), *Trichechus manatus*. Caribbean/Adjacent Atlantic (Coastal)

Odd-Toed Ungulates (Order: Perissodactyla)

Ass, African wild, *Equus asinus*. Ethiopia/Somalia/Sudan
Ass, Asian wild, *Equus hemionus*. Southwestern & Central Asia
Rhinoceros, Great Indian, *Rhinoceros unicornis*. India/Nepal
Rhinoceros, Javan, *Rhinoceros sondaicus*. Burma, Thailand
Rhinoceros, Northern white, *Ceratotherium simum cottoni*. Zaire/Uganda/Sudan
Rhinoceros, Sumatran, *Didermoceros sumatrensis*. Southeastern Asia
Tapir, Brazilian, *Tapirus terrestris*. Colombia/Venezuela to Paraguay

Odd-Toed Ungulates (Cont'd)

Tapir, Central America, *Tapirus bairdii*. Southern Mexico/Central America/Colombia/Ecuador
Tapir, Mountain, *Tapirus pinchaque*. Colombia/Ecuador/Peru

Even-Toed Ungulates (Order: Artiodactyla)

Anoa, *Anoa depressicornis*. Indonesia
Banteng, *Bibos banteng*. Southeast Asia
Bison, Wood, *Bison bison athabascae*. Canada
Deer, Bawean, *Helaphus kuhli (Cervus kuhli)*. Indonesia
Deer, Brow-antlered (Eld's), *Cervus eldi*. India/Southeastern Asia
Deer, Columbian white-tailed, *Odocoileus virginianus leucurus*. USA (Oregon, Washington)
Deer, Key, *Odocoileus virginianus clavium*. USA (Florida)
Deer, Marsh, *Blastocerus dichotomus*. Argentina/Uruguay/Brazil/Paraguay
Deer, McNeill's, *Cervus elaphus macneilli*. Tibet
Deer, Persian fallow, *Dama dama mesoptoamica*, Iraq/Iran
Deer, Swamp, *Cervus duvauceli*. India/Nepal
Gazelle, Clark's (Dibatag), *Ammodorcas clarkii*. Somalia/Ethiopia
Gazelle, Cuviers, *Gazella cuvieri*. Morocco/Tunisia
Gazelle, Mhorr, *Gazella dama mhorr*. Morocco
Gazelle, Moroccan dorcas, *Gazella dorcas massaesyla*. Morocco/Algeria
Gazelle, Rio de Oro dama, *Gazella dama lozanoi*. Spanish Sahara
Gazelle, Slender-horned (Rhim), *Gazella leptoceros*. Sudan/Algeria/Egypt/Libya
Hartebeest, Swayne's, *Alcelaphus buselaphus swaynei*. Ethiopia
Hog, Pygmy, *Sus salvanius*. India/Nepal/Bhutan/Sikkim
Ibex, Pyrenean, *Capra pyrenaica pyrenaica*. Spain
Ibex, Walia, *Capra walie*. Ethiopia
Impala, Black-faced, *Aepyceros melampus petersi*. Angola
Kouprey, *Bos sauveli*, Cambodia
Lechwe, Black, *Kobus leche smithemani*. Zambia
Oryx, Arabian, *Oryx leucoryx*. Arabian Peninsula
Pronghorn, Sonoran, *Antilocapra americana sonoriensis*. Mexico/USA
Seladang (Gaur), *Bos gaurus*. India/Bangladesh/Southeastern Asia
Shou, *Cervus elaphus wallichi*. Tibet/Bhutan
Stag, Barbary, *Cervus elaphus barbarus*. Tunisia/Algeria
Stag, Kashmir, *Cervus elaphus hanglu*. India (Kashmir)
Tamaraw, *Anoa mindorensis*. Philippines
Vicuna, *Vicugna vicugna*. Argentina
Yak, Wild, *Bos grunniens mutus*. Tibet/India

Federal, State and Provincial Agencies Concerned with Wildlife Protection and Exploitation

FEDERAL GOVERNMENT

Bureau of Sport Fisheries and Wildlife
Fish and Wildlife Service
Department of the Interior
18th and C Streets, N.W.
Washington, D.C. 20240

Environmental Protection Agency
401 M Street, S.W.
Washington, D.C. 20460

Forest Service
Department of Agriculture
Building E
Rosslyn Plaza
Rosslyn, Virginia 22209

Migratory Bird Conservation
    Commission
Department of the Interior Building
Washington, D.C. 20240

National Zoological Park
Smithsonian Institution
Adams Mill Rd.
Washington, D.C. 20009

STATE GOVERNMENTS

ALABAMA
Game and Fish Division
Department of Conservation and
    Natural Resources
64 North Union Street
Montgomery, Alabama 36104

ALASKA
Department of Fish and Game
Subport Building
Juneau, Alaska 99801

ARIZONA
Game and Fish Department
2222 West Greenway Road
Phoenix, Arizona 85203

ARKANSAS
Game and Fish Commission
Game and Fish Commission Building
Little Rock, Arkansas 72201

CALIFORNIA
Department of Fish and Game
Resources Agency
1416 Ninth Street
Sacramento, California 95814

Wildlife Conservation Board
Resources Agency
1416 Ninth Street
Sacramento, California 95814

COLORADO
Division of Wildlife
Department of Natural Resources
6060 Broadway
Denver, Colorado 80216

CONNECTICUT
Fish and Wildlife Unit
Department of Environmental
    Protection
State Office Building
165 Capitol Avenue
Hartford, Connecticut 06115

DELAWARE
Division of Fish and Wildlife
Department of Natural Resources and
    Environmental Control
Tatnall Building
Legislative Avenue and D Street
Dover, Delaware 19901

DISTRICT OF COLUMBIA
Department of Environmental Services
1875 Connecticut Avenue, N.W.
Washington, D.C. 20009

FLORIDA
Game and Fresh Water Fish
    Commission
Farris Bryant Building
620 South Meridian Street
Tallahassee, Florida 32304

GEORGIA
Game and Fish Division
Department of Natural Resources
270 Washington Street, S.W.
Atlanta, Georgia 30334

HAWAII
Fish and Game Division
Department of Land and Natural
    Resources
1179 Punchbowl Street
Honolulu, Hawaii 96813

IDAHO
Fish and Game Department
600 South Walnut
P.O. Box 25
Boise, Idaho 83707

ILLINOIS
Wildlife Resources Division
Department of Conservation
605 State Office Building
400 South Spring Street
Springfield, Illinois 62706

INDIANA
Fish and Wildlife Division
Department of Natural Resources
State Office Building
Indianapolis, Indiana 46204

Land, Forests, and Wildlife
Resources Advisory Council
Department of Natural Resources
State Office Building
Indianapolis, Indiana 46204

IOWA
Fish and Wildlife Division
Conservation Commission
300 Fourth Street
Des Moines, Iowa 50319

KANSAS
Forestry, Fish and Game Commission
P.O. Box 1028
Pratt, Kansas 67124

KENTUCKY
Department of Fish and Wildlife
    Resources
State Office Building Annex
Frankfort, Kentucky 40601

LOUISIANA
Game Division
Wildlife and Fisheries Commission
Box 44095
Capitol Station
Baton Rouge, Louisiana 70804

MAINE
Department of Inland Fisheries
    and Game
284 State Street
Augusta, Maine 04330

MARYLAND
Wildlife Administration
Department of Natural Resources
Tawes State Office Building
580 Taylor Avenue
Annapolis, Maryland 21401

MASSACHUSETTS
Department of Natural Resources
Leverett Saltonstall Building
100 Cambridge Street
Boston, Massachusetts 02202

MICHIGAN
Wildlife Division
Department of Natural Resources
Stevens T. Mason Building
Lansing, Michigan 48926

MINNESOTA
Game and Fish Division
Department of Natural Resources
Centennial Office Building
St. Paul, Minnesota 55155

MISSISSIPPI
Game and Fish Commission
Game and Fish Building
402 High Street
P.O. Box 451
Jackson, Mississippi 39205.

MISSOURI
Game Division
Department of Conservation
2901 North Ten Mile Drive
P.O. Box 180
Jefferson City, Missouri 65101

MONTANA
Game Management Division
Department of Fish and Game
Helena, Montana 59601

NEBRASKA
Game and Parks Commission
2200 North 33rd Street
P.O. Box 30370
Lincoln, Nebraska 68503

NEVADA
Department of Fish and Game
P.O. Box 10678
Reno, Nevada 89510

NEW HAMPSHIRE
Game Management and Research
    Division
Department of Fish and Game
34 Bridge Street
Concord, New Hampshire 03301

NEW JERSEY
Wildlife Management Bureau
Fish, Game and Shellfisheries Division
Department of Environmental
    Protection
Labor and Industry Building
P.O. Box 1390
Trenton, New Jersey 08625

NEW MEXICO
Game Management Division
Department of Game and Fish
State Capitol
Sante Fe, New Mexico 87503

NEW YORK
Division of Fish and Wildlife
Department of Environmental
    Conservation
50 Wolf Road
Albany, New York 12233

NORTH CAROLINA
Wildlife Resources Commission
Albermarle Building
325 North Salisbury Street
P.O. Box 27687
Raleigh, North Carolina 27611

NORTH DAKOTA
Department of Game and Fish
2121 Lovett Avenue
Bismarck, North Dakota 58501

OHIO
Wildlife Division
Department of Natural Resources
1500 Dublin Road
Columbus, Ohio 43224

OKLAHOMA
Department of Wildlife Conservation
1801 North Lincoln Boulevard
P.O. Box 53465
Oklahoma City, Oklahoma 73105

OREGON
Wildlife Commission
1634 Southwest Alder Street
P.O. Box 3503
Portland, Oregon 97208

PENNSYLVANIA
Game Commission
P.O. Box 1567
Harrisburg, Pennsylvania 17120

RHODE ISLAND
Division of Fish and Wildlife
Department of Natural Resources
83 Park Street
Providence, Rhode Island 02903

SOUTH CAROLINA
Department of Wildlife Resources
1015 Main Street
P.O. Box 167
Columbia, South Carolina 29202

SOUTH DAKOTA
Department of Game, Fish and Parks
State Office Building No. 1
Pierre, South Dakota 57501

TENNESSEE
Game and Fish Commission
Ellington Agricultural Center
P.O. Box 40747
Nashville, Tennessee 37220

TEXAS
Fish and Wildlife Division
Parks and Wildlife Department
John H. Reagan State Office Building
Austin, Texas 78701

UTAH
Division of Wildlife Resources
Department of Natural Resources
1596 West North Temple
Salt Lake City, Utah 84116

VERMONT
Department of Fish and Game
Agency of Environmental Conservation
Montpelier, Vermont 05602

VIRGINIA
Commission of Game and Inland
    Fisheries
4010 West Broad Street
P.O. Box 11104
Richmond, Virginia 23230

WASHINGTON
Department of Game
600 North Capitol Way
Olympia, Washington 98504

WEST VIRGINIA
Division of Wildlife Resources
Department of Natural Resources
1800 Washington Street, East
Charleston, West Virginia 25305

WISCONSIN
Game Management Bureau
Forestry, Wildlife, and Recreation
    Division
Department of Natural Resources
P.O. Box 450
Madison, Wisconsin 53701

WYOMING
Game and Fish Division
P.O. Box 1589
Cheyenne, Wyoming 82001

CANADA

ALBERTA
Alberta Fish and Wildlife Division
Natural Resources Building
9833 - 109th Street
Edmonton, Alberta T5K 2E1

BRITISH COLUMBIA
Environment and Land Use
    Commission
Parliament Building
Victoria, British Columbia

Department of Land, Forest and
    Water Resources
Parliament Building
Victoria, British Columbia

MANITOBA
Department of Lands, Forests and
  Wildlife Resources
9-989 Century Street
Winnipeg, Manitoba R3H 0W4

NEWFOUNDLAND
Canadian Wildlife Service
Sir Humphrey Gilbert Building
Duckworth St.
St. John's, Newfoundland

Department of Tourism
Wildlife Division
Confederation Building, 5th Floor
St. John's, Newfoundland

NORTHWEST TERRITORIES
Game Management Branch
Government of the Northwest
  Territories
Yellowknife, Northwest Territories

NOVA SCOTIA
Department of Environment
Box 2107
Halifax, Nova Scotia

Department of Land and Forests
Dennis Building
Granville Street
Halifax, Nova Scotia

ONTARIO
Wildlife Branch
Ministry of Natural Resources
Whitney Block
Toronto, Ontario M7A 1W3

PRINCE EDWARD ISLAND
Department of Fish and Wildlife
Environmental Control Commission
Box 2000
Charlottetown, Prince Edward Island

Department of Environment and
  Tourism
Box 2000
Charlottetown, Prince Edward Island

QUEBEC
Department of Tourism, Fish and
  Game
150 St. Cyrille East - 15th Floor
Quebec, Quebec G1R 4Y3

SASKATCHEWAN
Department of Natural Resources
Fisheries and Wildlife Branch
Administrative Building
Regina, Saskatchewan

YUKON TERRITORY
Game Branch
Government of the Yukon Territory
Whitehorse, Yukon Territory

Organizations and Associations of Interest to the Hunter and Shooter

AMATEUR TRAPSHOOTING ASSOCIATION
P.O. Box 246, West National Road   Phone: (513) 898-4171
Vandalia, Ohio 45377
Hugh L. McKinley, Manager
Founded: 1923
Members: 65,000
Persons interested in the sport of trapshooting. Sanctions and determines rules governing-shoots held by local, state, and provincial trapshooting associations: maintains permanent records for each shooter participating in 16 yard, handicap and doubles classifications in registered class competitions in state and provincial meets. Sponsor of Grand American Trapshooting Tournament held annually at Vandalia, Ohio, where historical exhibit and Hall of Fame are maintained. Publications: (1) *Trap and Field Magazine,* monthly; (2) *Official Trapshooting Rules,* annual; (3) *Trap and Field Official ATA Averages,* annual.

AMERICAN ASSOCIATION FOR CONSERVATION INFORMATION
c/o Allan S. Murray
Conservation Extension, Box 11
139 Tuxedo Blvd.
Winnipeg, Manitoba, Canada
J. W. Sizer, Pres.
Founded: 1938
Members: 68
Professional society of officials of state and provincial conservation agencies. Sponsors annual awards program whereby winners in various categories of conservation education work are selected by a panel of judges. Publications: (1) *Balance Wheel,* bimonthly; (2) *Yearbook.* Convention/Meeting: Annual – always June.

AMERICAN COMMITTEE FOR INTL. WILD LIFE PROTECTION
c/o The Wildlife Society   Phone: (202) 363-2435
3900 Wisconsin Ave., N.W., Suite S-176
Washington, D.C. 20016
Fred G. Evenden, Sec.-Treas.
Founded: 1930
Members: 55
Persons interested in conservation and preservation of wildlife of the world; stimulate, promote and finance research into status and ecology of threatened species; lend assistance to national and international organizations concerned with wildlife conservation, outside the U.S.

AMERICAN CONSERVATION ASSOCIATION
30 Rockefeller Plaza
New York, N.Y. 10020
Gene W. Setzer, Exec. V. Pres.
Founded: 1958
Trustees: 11
Not a membership group. A private foundation established "to advance knowledge and understanding of conservation and to preserve and develop natural and living resources for public use, either directly or in cooperation with federal, state, local and private conservation agencies."

AMERICAN DEFENSE PREPAREDNESS ASSOCIATION
819 Union Trust Bldg.   Phone: (202) 347-7250
Washington, D.C. 20005
Jean E. Engler, Exec. V. Pres.
Founded: 1919
Members: 43,000
Staff: 28

American Defense Preparedness Association (Cont'd)
Local groups: 44
Manufacturers, military personnel and engineers interested in industrial preparedness for the national defense of the United States. Divisions: Air Armament; Artillery; Chemical-Biological; Combat and Surface Mobility; Electronics; Fire Control; Management; Materials; Missiles and Astronautics; Mobilization Readiness; Packaging, Handling, and Transportability; Quality and Reliability; Research; Small Arms Systems; Standards and Metrology; Technical Documentation; Underwater Ordnance; Value Engineering. Publications: (1) *Common Defense,* monthly; (2) *National Defense,* bimonthly; (3) *Armament— Progress and Readiness,* bimonthly. Formerly: American Ordnance Association. Absorbed: (1965) Armed Forces Chemical Association. Convention/Meeting: Annual—1975 May 15, Washington, D.C.

AMERICAN INSTITUTE OF BIOLOGICAL SCIENCES
3900 Wisconsin Ave., N.W.   Phone: (202) 244-5581
Washington, D.C. 20016
John R. Olive, Dir.
Founded: 1948
Members: 14,500
Federation of professional biological associations and individuals with an interest in the life sciences. To promote unity and effectiveness of effort among persons engaged in biological research, teaching or application of biological data; to further the relationships of biological sciences to other sciences, the arts, and industries. Conducts symposium series; arranges for prominent biologists to lecture at small liberal arts colleges and radiation biologists to visit certain medical schools; provides advisory committees and other services to the Atomic Energy Commission, Office of Naval Research, and National Aeronautics and Space Administration. Created in 1966 an Office of Biological Education which serves as a clearing-house for information and conducts programs relative to several facets of biological education. Offers annual award for outstanding vegetable research. Maintains placement service. Committees: Behavioral Biology; Bioinstrumentation; Education; Environmental Biology; Exobiology; Hydrobiology; Microbiology; Oceanic Biology; Physiology; Planetary Quarantine; Public Responsibilities; Publications; Radiation Pasteurization of Foods; Scientific Manpower Commission; Theoretical Biology. Publications: (1) *BioScience,* monthly; (2) *Directory of Bioscience Departments in the U.S. and Canada,* every 2 years; also, symposia proceedings, AEC-AIBS monographs, and select single titles. Absorbed: (1969) American Society of Professional Biologists. Convention/Meeting: Annual.

AMERICAN PHEASANT AND WATERFOWL SOCIETY
c/o Richard E. Burger   Phone: (302) 994-0508
Stranton-Ogletown Rd.
Route 3
Newark, Del. 19711
Irene H. Jones, Sec.-Treas.
Founded: 1936
Members: 450
Hobbyists, aviculturists, zoos. To perpetuate all varieties of upland game, ornamental birds and waterfowl. Publications: (1) *Bulletin,* bimonthly; (2) *Membership Roster,* annual. Formerly: (1962) American Pheasant Society. Convention/Meeting: Annual.

AMERICAN SINGLE SHOT RIFLE ASSOCIATION
11439 Wicker Ave.   Phone: (219) 365-5074
Cedar Lake, Ind. 46303
Gilbert H. Crontz, Sec.

American Single Shot Rifle Association (Cont'd)
Founded: 1946
Members: 342
State groups: 2
Persons interested in use, study and preservation of single shot rifles developed in the period between the close of the Civil War and the onset of World War I (1865-1915). Sponsors competitions and awards; conducts educational meetings. Publications: (1) *American Single Shot Rifle News,* bimonthly; (2) *Membership Roster.* Convention/Meeting: Annual—always the second weekend in June, in Michigan City, Ind.

AMERICAN SOCIETY OF ARMS COLLECTORS
Markesan, Wis. 53946
Samual E. Smith, Pres.
Founded: 1954
Members: 218
Membership by invitation only. Advanced collectors, museum curators, writers, and others interested in antique arms and weapons.

ASSOCIATION OF AMERICAN ROD AND GUN CLUBS, EUROPE OCPA,
Headquarters USAREUR/7A
APO New York, N.Y. 09403
Michael P. Klimaszewski, Exec.-Sec. Custodian
Founded: 1952
Members: 65,000
Local groups: 85
Federation of rod and gun clubs connected with American military forces in Europe, North Africa and the Near East. To encourage hunting, fishing, archery and allied sports; to promote the principles of sportsmanship and game conservation. Maintains library on conservation and European wildlife, with majority of books in German language. Publication: *Rod and Gun,* monthly. Convention/Meeting: Annual.

ASSOCIATION OF MIDWEST FISH AND GAME COMMISSIONERS
c/o Fred Warders   Phone: (303) 825-1192x212
Kansas Fish and Game Commission
P.O. Box 1028
Pratt, Kansas 67124
Fred Warders, Sec.-Treas.
Founded: 1934
Members: 17
Fish and game commissioners and directors of 15 midwestern states and 2 Canadian provinces. Promotes conservation of wildlife and outdoor recreation. Sponsors Midwest Pheasant Council; Dove Committee. Committees: Federal-State Relations; Federal Aid; Legislation; Federal Farm Program; Wetlands. Publication: *Proceedings,* annual. Convention/Meeting: Annual.

BIG THICKET ASSOCIATION
Box 377   Phone: (713) 274-2971
Saratoga, Tex. 77585
Pete A. Gunter, Pres.
Founded: 1964
Members: 700
Conservationists and others interested in preserving the wilderness area of southeast Texas known as the "Big Thicket." The Thicket is one of the major resting places along the Gulf Coast for migratory birds; in addition, at least 300 species live there permanently, many of them endangered species. Members of the Association are working to have the area declared a national park. Other activities include assisting scientists with research projects, operating a tourguide service, helping to maintain a Big Thicket collection at the Lamar University Library in Beaumont, Tex., and coordinating programs aimed at preserving the area with other conservation organizations. Publication: *Big Thicket Bulletin,* quarterly; also publishes informational pamphlets, a

Big Thicket Association (Cont'd)
bibliography and other materials. Convention/Meeting: Annual—always May or June, Saratoga, Tex.

BOUNTY INFORMATION SERVICE
c/o Stephens College Post Office   Phone: (314) 442-2211
Columbia, Mo. 65201   x473
H. Charles Laun, Dir.
Founded: 1965
Members: 2000
Individuals interested in the removal of wildlife bounties in the U.S. and Canada. Organizes bounty removal programs, publishes literature on the bounty system and methods for removal, compiles yearly summary of bounties in North America and executes individual studies of areas (i.e. cougar bounty in Texas). Maintains library. Publications: *Bounty News,* 1-3/year; has also published *"Guide for the Removal of Bounties"* and *"A Decade of Bounties."* Convention/Meeting: Annual or Biennial.

CITIZENS COMMITTEE FOR THE RIGHT TO KEEP AND BEAR ARMS
1601 114th S.E.   Phone: (206) 454-4911
Bellevue, Washington 98004
Alan M. Gottlieb, Executive Director
Founded: 1971
Members: 51,000
Staff: 4
A national independent non-profit mass membership organization concerned solely with preserving the right to keep and bear arms. Arthur Godfrey serves as Honorary National Chairman of the Committee's National Advisory Council, made up of businessmen, educators, legislators, religious leaders, and includes 14 members of the U.S. Congress. Issues action bulletins, pro-gun rights brochures, bumper strips, decals, buttons and patches, and legislative action materials. Supported by membership fees and voluntary contributions. Publication: *Point Blank,* monthly.

CITIZENS COMMITTEE ON NATURAL RESOURCES
1346 Connecticut Ave., N.W.   Phone: (202) 785-1261
Washington, D.C. 20036
Spencer M. Smith, Jr., Sec.
Founded: 1954
Directors: 50
Staff: 2
Individuals interested in lobbying in behalf of conservation program dealing with government departments.

COMPANY OF MILITARY HISTORIANS
287 Thayer St.   Phone: (401) 421-7713
Providence, R.I. 02906
W. Ogden McCagg, Admin.
Founded: 1951
Members: 2000
Staff: 2
Professional society of military historians, museologists, artists, writers, and private collectors interested in the history of American military units, organization, tactics, uniforms, arms, and equipment. Publications: (1) *Military Collector and Historian,* quarterly; (2) *Military Uniforms in America,* quarterly; (3) *Military Music in America* (records), irregular. Formerly: (1962) Company of Military Collectors and Historians. Convention/Meeting: Annual.

CONSERVATION EDUCATION ASSOCIATION
c/o Robert O. Ellingson
Box 450
Madison, Wis. 53701
Robert O. Ellingson, Sec.-Treas.
Founded: 1947
Members: 950
Conservationists, educators and others interested in improving

Conservation Education Association (Cont'd)

conservation education in public schools, teacher training institutions, and organization programs. Outstanding state, local and organizational conservation publications, especially those of normally limited distribution, are circulated bimonthly to members. Publications: (1) *Newsletter,* bimonthly; (2) *Proceedings,* annual. Formerly: (1953) National Committee on Policies in Conservation Education. Convention/Meeting: Annual — always August.

CONSERVATION FOUNDATION
1717 Massachusetts Ave., N.W.　　　Phone: (202) 265-8882
Washington, D.C. 20036
Sydney Howe, Pres.
Founded: 1948
Staff: 42

Not a membership organization. Conducts research, education and information programs to develop knowledge, improve techniques, and stimulate public and private decision-making and action to improve the quality of the environment. Carries out environmental studies, demonstration planning programs, and offers a variety of conservation services at home and abroad. Divisions: Conservation Services; Education; Energy; International Programs; Planning; Policy Studies; Public Affairs. Publication: *CF Letter,* monthly; also publishes books, pamphlets, studies.

CONSERVATION LAW SOCIETY OF AMERICA
1500 Mills Tower, 220 Bush St.　　　Phone: (415) 981-7800
San Francisco, Calif. 94104
Robert W. Jasperson, Gen. Coun.
Founded: 1963
Members: 105
Staff: 1

Lawyers and other individuals interested in conservation. Provides the services on a fee basis of a legal staff to research the laws, decision, and other precedents relating to conservation problems; advises conservation groups on the basis of such research, and represents these groups in court if necessary. Aids groups interested in preservation of the forest, wildlife, water, wildnerness, and natural resources of the United States, especially park, recreational, and open space areas. Active in defense of public interest lands in Western states and other areas.

CONSERVATION AND RESEARCH FOUNDATION
Department of Botany　　　Phone: (203) 442-5391 x306
Connecticut College
New London, Conn. 06320
Richard H. Goodwin, Pres.
Founded: 1953

Not a membership organization. To encourage biological research and promote conservation of renewable natural resources. Makes research grants; offers Jeanette Siron Pelton Award for outstanding published contributions in experimental plant morphology. Publishes *A Ten Year Report* (last one in 1963). Convention/Meeting: Annual.

CONSERVATION SERVICES, INC.
South Great Road　　　Phone: (617) 259-9500
Lincoln, Mass. 01773
Allen H. Morgan, Exec. Dir.
Founded: 1965
Members: 5
Staff: 5

Small Audubon and conservation groups, comprising 34,000 individual members. Purpose is to publish magazines, newsletters and environmental brochures for New England conservation organizations, and to develop television, radio and audiovisual materials that can be used in New England. Maintains extensive source files. Publications: (1) *Massachusetts Audubon Society Newsletter,* 10/year; (2) *Man and Nature* (magazine), quarterly. Formerly: Conservation Services Center.

COUNCIL OF CONSERVATIONISTS
201 East 62nd St.　　　Phone: (212) 838-4883
New York, N.Y. 10021
Fred Smith, Dir.
Founded: 1949

Coordinating organization for groups seeking to conserve and properly utilize water, parks, recreation facilities, forests, etc., through legislation and education. Publishes occasional bulletins and booklets on conservation.

DEFENDERS OF WILDLIFE
2000 N St., N.W.　　　Phone: (202) 223-1993
Washington, D.C. 20036
Mary Hazel Harris, Exec. Dir.
Founded: 1925
Members: 35,000

Persons interested in wildlife and conservation. To promote, through education and research, the protection and humane treatment of all mammals, birds, fish and other wildlife, and the elimination of painful methods of trapping, capturing and killing wildlife. Publication: *Defenders of Wildlife News,* bi-monthly. Formerly: Anti-Steel-Trap League; Defenders of Furbearers. Convention/Meeting: Annual.

DESERT PROTECTIVE COUNCIL
P.O. Box 33
Banning, Calif. 92220
Robert G. Bear, Exec. Dir.
Founded: 1954
Members: 700

Persons interested in safeguarding desert areas that are of unique scenic, scientific, historical, spiritual, and recreational value. Seeks to educate children and adults to a better understanding of the desert. Works to bring about establishment of wildlife sanctuaries for protection of indigenous plants and animals. The Desert Protective Council Education Foundation, a subdivision of the Council formed in 1960, handles educational activities and distributes reprints of desert and wildlife conservation articles. Publication: *El Paisano* (by Foundation), quarterly. Convention/Meeting: Annual—second Sunday in Oct.

DUCKS UNLIMITED
P.O. Box 66300　　　Phone: (312) 299-3334
Chicago, Ill. 60666
Dale E. Whitesell, Exec. V. Pres.
Founded: 1937
Members: 70,000
Staff: 15
State groups: 54

Conservationists in the United States and Canada interested in migratory waterfowl conservation. To restore or build natural breeding areas for migratory waterfowl primarily in the prairie provinces of Canada, which provides 75% of North America's wild geese and ducks. The American group raises funds for this construction and rehabilitation work, carried on by the field operating unit in Canada. Publications: (1) *Ducks Unlimited Magazine,* quarterly; (2) *Annual Report;* also publishes *The Ducks Unlimited Story.* Affiliated with: Ducks Unlimited (Canada). Absorbed: (1936) More Game Birds in America. Convention/Meeting: Annual.

FEDERATION OF WESTERN OUTDOOR CLUBS
Box 548
Bozeman, Mont. 59715
Kenneth Baldwin, Pres.
Founded: 1932
Members: 1341

Outdoor clubs (41) in western United States with combined membership of 48,000, associate members 1300. Promotes conservation of forests, wildlife, and natural features. Publication: *Western Outdoor Quarterly.* Convention/Meeting: Annual — always Labor Day weekend.

FRIENDS OF THE EARTH

529 Commercial St. Phone: (212) 687-8747, 691-2130
San Francisco, Calif. 94111
David Brower, Founder
Founded: 1969
International conservation organization which concentrates on legislative and political activities in this field.

FRIENDS OF NATURE, INC.

Brooksville, Me. 04617
Martin R. Haase, Exec. Sec.
Founded: 1953
Conservationists "dedicated to maintaining the balance of nature for the mutual benefit of man and his plant and animal friends." Carries on educational work and maintains several nature sanctuaries. Holds annual meeting.

FRIENDS OF THE WILDERNESS

3515 East Fourth St. Phone: (218) 724-7227
Duluth, Minn. 55804
William H. Magie, Exec. Sec.
Founded: 1949
Members: 17,364
Persons interested in preservation of the Boundary Water Canoe Area of Minnesota, the wildnerness canoe country of the Superior National Forest. Maintains library of 400 volumes pertaining to the area. Holds annual meeting.

FRUGAL BRUGAL SOCIETY

Claybrook Rd.
Dover, Me. 02030
Frederick N. Blodgett, Pres.
Founded: 1932
Members: 100
Sportsmen from four countries, primarily those interested in fishing and shooting. (A Frugal Brugal is a drink made with unsweetened grapefruit juice and Brugal rum.) Purposes are: promotion of conviviality and camaraderie among fellow sportsmen; conservation of woodcock, partridge and ducks by strict adherence to game laws and the ability to cope therewith; improvement of game habitats in selected areas. Convention/Meeting: Annual — always Oct.

INTERNATIONAL ASSN. OF GAME, FISH AND CONSERVATION COMMISSIONERS

1412 16th St., N.W. Phone: (202) 232-1652
Washington, D.C. 20036
John S. Gottschalk, Exec. V. Pres.
Founded: 1902
Members: 377
State and provincial game, fish and conservation departments (61) and officials (316). To educate the public to the economic importance of conserving natural resources and managing wildlife properly as a source of recreation and a food supply; to seek better conservation legislation, administration and enforcement. Publications: (1) *Proceedings,* annual; (2) *Newsletter,* irregular. Formerly: (1917) National Association of Game Commissioners and Wardens. Convention/Meeting: Annual — always second Monday in Sept.

INTERNATIONAL BENCHREST SHOOTERS

RD 1, Robinson Rd. Phone: (315) 866-1769
Mohawk, N.Y. 13407
Mrs. James Stekl, Rec. Sec.
Founded: 1970
Members: 1000
Staff: 1
Gunsmiths, research engineers, gun writers, other interested persons. "To develop the ultimate in gun accuracy." Sponsors tournaments with demonstrations of new inventions or idea developments in the field. Also sponsors seminars. Publication: *Precision Shooting Magazine,* monthly. Convention/Meeting: Annual.

INTERNATIONAL UNION FOR CONSERVATION OF NATURE AND NATURAL RESOURCES

P.O. Box 19347 Phone: (703) 280-4086
Washington, D.C. 20036
Harold J. Coolidge, Pres.
Founded: 1948
Members: 266
International federation of national governments (29) and national and international organizations (228) in 61 countries. For the preservation of the natural environment of man and the conservation of the world's natural resources. Serves as a forum for discussion of conservation problems and studies; sponsors international youth camps; intercedes with governments on conservation matters; maintains Van Tienhoven Library. Conducts research on measures to promote and protect national parks, nature reserves, wildlife and its habitat. Provides advisory field missions. International headquarters located in Morges, Switzerland. Technical Commissions: Conservation Education; Ecology; Environmental Policy, Law, and Administration; Landscape Planning; Law and Administration; National Parks; Survival Service. Publications: (1) *IUCN Bulletin,* quarterly; (2) *Proceedings* (of conferences); also publishes *Red Data Book* (endangered species), technical reports and a UN List of National Parks and Equivalent Reserves. Formerly: (1956) International Union for the Protection of Nature. General Assembly/Technical Meeting: Triennial.

INTERNATIONAL WILD WATERFOWL ASSOCIATION (IWWA)

c/o Carl E. Strutz Phone: (701) 252-1239
Box 1075
Jamestown, N.D. 58401
Carl E. Strutz, Sec.
Founded: 1958
Members: 500
Persons concerned with conservation and the preservation of wild waterfowl. Works toward protection, conservation and reproduction of any species considered in danger of eventual extinction; encourages the breeding of well known and rare species in captivity so that more people may learn about them by observation and enjoy them in the natural habitats created for this purpose. Has established Avicultural Hall of Fame. Publications: (1) *Bulletin,* bimonthly; (2) *Membership list,* annual; has published books on keeping cranes, wild geese, and wild ducks in captivity. Convention/Meeting: Annual—1974 Oct., Philadelphia, Pa.

IZAAK WALTON LEAGUE OF AMERICA

1800 N. Kent St., Suite 806 Phone: (703) 528-1818
Arlington, Va. 22209
Jack Lorenz, Exec. Dir.
Founded: 1922
Members: 50,000
Staff: 16
State divisions: 22
Local chapters: 600
Promotes means and opportunities for educating the public to conserve, maintain, protect and restore the soil, forest, water and other natural resources of the U.S. and promotes the enjoyment and wholesome utilization of those resources. Committees: Air Quality; Clean Water; Conservation Education; Public Lands. Publications: (1) *The Izaak Walton Magazine,* monthly; (2) *National Bulletin,* monthly; (3) *Outdoor America.* Absorbed: (1962) Friends of the Land. Convention/Meeting: Annual — always July.

J. N. "DING" DARLING FOUNDATION

c/o Central National Bank Phone: (515) 243-8181
Des Moines, Iowa 50304
Mr. Sherry R. Fisher, Chm.
Founded: 1962
Trustees: 50

J. N. "Ding" Darling Foundation (Cont'd)

"To initiate plans and to coordinate, guide and expedite programs, research and education which will bring about conservation and sound management of water, woods and soil; to restore and preserve historical sites; to create and assist in wildlife management plans; to improve and assure outdoor recreational opportunities for present and future generations." Established 1700-acre wildlife and waterfowl sanctuary on Sanibel Island, off the west coast of Florida. Awards scholarships at Iowa State University for wildlife management students. Named for the late J. N. "Ding" Darling, a professional cartoonist long active in conservation activities. Holds annual meeting.

LEAGUE TO SAVE LAKE TAHOE

74 Los Altos Square   Phone: (414) 941-3943
Los Altos, Calif. 94022
Donald G. Ellis, Pres.
Staff: 1
Membership comprised of individuals and organizations who give financial support to the League. Purpose is to "do all things and to perform all acts necessary to keep Lake Tahoe blue and to protect and preserve the natural beauty and grandeur of the Lake Tahoe area of California and Nevada; to promote and encourage the concept that all developments, improvements and man-made changes of any kind, which may be required to accommodate the proper and desirable growth of the area and provide the maximum recreational values, should place primary emphasis on preserving the natural beauty of the lake." Publication: *Newsletter*, quarterly. Convention/Meeting: Annual.

NATIONAL ASSOCIATION OF FEDERALLY LICENSED FIREARMS DEALERS

7001 North Clark   Phone: (312) 338-7600
Chicago, Illinois 60626
Andrew Molchan, Administrator
Founded: 1972
Members: 8,000
Staff: 4
An independent tax-paying group supported by membership fees and industry contributions. Its basic purpose is to expand the legal rights of firearms dealers and the firearms industry. Publication: *American Firearms Industry*, monthly. Holds annual directors' meeting.

NATIONAL AUDUBON SOCIETY

950 Third Ave.   Phone: (212) 369-3200
New York, N.Y. 10022
Elvis J. Stahr, Pres.
Founded: 1905
Members: 200,000
Staff: 225
Chapters: 250
Affiliated groups: 275
Persons interested in conservation and restoration of natural resources, with emphasis on wildlife, wildlife habitats, soil, water, and forests. Sponsors four Audubon camps for teachers and youth leaders; nature lectures; and wildlife tours. Supports a force of 18 wardens to patrol wildlife refuge areas and sanctuaries; produces films, posters and teaching materials for schools. Divisions: Educational Services; Lecture; Nature Centers; Research; Sanctuary; Service. Publications: (1) *Audubon Leader*, semimonthly; (2) *Audubon Magazine*, bimonthly; (3) *American Birds*, bimonthly; (4) *Nature Bulletins*, irregular. Formerly: (1935) National Association of Audubon Societies for the Protection of wild Birds and Animals, Inc. Convention/Meeting: Annual.

NATIONAL BENCHREST SHOOTERS ASSOCIATION

607 West Line St.   Phone: (216) 868-6132
Minerva, Ohio 44657
Bernice McMullen, Sec.-Treas.
Founded: 1951

National Benchrest Shooters Association (Cont'd)

Rifle enthusiasts interested in precision shooting. Conducts registered shoots and certifies records. Sections: Bench Rest Rifle; Heavy Varmint; Light Varmint; Sporter Classes. Publication: *Rifle*, bimonthly. Holds annual directors' meeting.

NATIONAL BOARD FOR THE PROMOTION OF RIFLE PRACTICE

Forrestal Bldg. (West) Room 1E053   Phone: (202) 693-6460
Washington, D.C. 20314
LTC Frank T. Lohmann, Exec. Off.
Founded: 1903
Members: 25
Staff: 9
Local clubs: 3,200
Civilian shooting clubs and marksmanship clubs in high schools and colleges. An agency of the U.S. Department of the Army, "to promote marksmanship training with rifled arms among able bodied citizens of the U.S. and to provide citizens outside the active services of the Armed Forces with means whereby they may become proficient with such arms." Provides arms and ammunition to member clubs; exhibits national marksmanship trophies; maintains records and distributes awards for national and international marksmanship competitions. Publication: *National Board Directory*. Convention/Meeting: Annual—always Washington, D.C.

NATIONAL MUZZLE LOADING RIFLE ASSOCIATION

Friendship, Ind. 47021   Phone: (812) 667-4631
Mrs. Maxine Moss, Office Mgr.-Editor
Founded: 1933
Members: 8,700
Local clubs: 168
Persons interested in black powder shooting. To preserve the heritage left to us by our forefathers, and to promote safety in the use of arms. Maintains National Range located at Friendship, Ind. Sponsors Beef Shoot in Jan., Spring Shoot, National Shoot in the fall, and Turkey Shoot in Oct. Committees: Long Range Planning; Property; Fund Raising; Range Officers; Grounds; Commercial Row; Traffic; Safety; Camping; Memorial; Public Relations; Scoring; Award. *Muzzle Blasts*, monthly. Convention/Meeting: Annual.

NATIONAL PRAIRIE GROUSE TECHNICAL COUNCIL

Colorado Division of Wildlife   Phone: (303) 484-2836
Box 567
Fort Collins, Colo. 80521
Donald M. Hoffman, Chm.
Founded: 1952
Sponsors biennial meeting for technical personnel and administrators of state, provincial and federal agencies, and individuals from private groups involved in preservation, research, and management of the prairie chicken and sharp-tailed grouse. Conference makes possible exchange of information on current research and management of these species and reviews local and national legislation affecting the prairie grouse resource. Publications: (1) *P.G. News*, semiannual; (2) *Proceedings*, biennial. Formerly: (1956) National Committee on the Prairie Chicken; (1961) Prairie Chicken Technical Committee. Conference: Biennial—next 1975.

NATIONAL RIFLE ASSOCIATION OF AMERICA

1600 Rhode Island Ave., N.W.   Phone: (202) 783-6505
Washington, D.C. 20036
Maj. Gen. Maxwell Rich, Exec. V. Pres.
Founded: 1871
Members: 1,050,000
Staff: 292
State groups: 52
Local groups: 12,000
Target shooters, hunters, gun collectors, gunsmiths, police offi-

National Rifle Association of America (Cont'd)

cers, and others interested in firearms. Promotes rifle, pistol, and shotgun shooting, hunting, gun collecting, hunter and home firearms safety, conservation, etc. Encourages civilian marksmanship in interests of national defense. Maintains national records of shooting competitions; sponors teams to compete in the Olympic Games and other world championships. Collects, tabulates, and compiles information on hunting casualties in the United States and Canada. Committees: Competition Rules and Firearms Legislation; Gun Collectors; High Power Rifle; Home Firearms Safety; Hunting and Game Conservation; Junior and College; National Match Policy; Pistol and Revolver; Shotgun Committee; Smallbore Rifle. Publications: (1) *The American Rifleman,* monthly; (2) *Tournament News,* monthly; (3) *Uniform Hunter Casualty Report,* semiannual. Convention/Meeting: Annual—always April: 1975 San Diego, Calif.; 1976 Indianapolis, Ind.

NATIONAL SHOOTING SPORTS FOUNDATION

1075 Post Road   Phone: (203) 637-3618
Riverside, Conn. 06878
Warren Page, Pres.
Founded: 1961
Members: 114
Staff: 12
Manufacturers of firearms and ammunition, accessories, components, gun sights, hunting clothes, and other "reputable firms that make a profit from hunting and shooting"; includes outdoor and gun magazine publishers. "To foster in the American public a better understanding and more active participation in the shooting sports." Publications: (1) *Newsletter,* irregular; (2) *National Shooting Preserve Directory,* annual; also publishes brochures and booklets on proper gun handling, gun clubs, quail and pheasant hunting; game breeding and shooting preserves, shooting safety, and films for sportsmen; also distributes ranger targets. Absorbed: (1963) Sportsmen's Service Bureau. Holds annual meeting, always Feb., Chicago, Ill.

NATIONAL SKEET SHOOTING ASSOCIATION

P.O. Box 28188   Phone: (512) 688-3371
San Antonio, Tex. 78228
James M. Leer, Jr., Exec. Dir.
Founded: 1935
Members: 18,500
Staff: 12
State groups: 54
Local groups: 715
Amateur skeet shooters. Registers competitive shoots and supervises them through formulation and enforcement of rules. Publication: *Skeet Shooting Review,* monthly. Convention/Meeting (World Championship Shoot): Annual.

NATIONAL WATERFOWL COUNCIL

c/o R. A. Hodgins, Dir.   Phone (605) 224-3387
S. D. Division of Game Fish and Parks
State Office Bldg. No. 1
Pierre, S.D. 57501
Members: 50
State and provincial fish and game departments. To coordinate waterfowl planning, research, and management. Convention/Meeting: Semiannual—Mar. and Aug., held in conjunction with conventions of North American Wildlife Conference and Bureau of Sport Fish and Wildlife Service Waterfowl Regulations.

NATIONAL WILDLIFE FEDERATION

1412 16th St., N.W.   Phone: (202) 483-1550
Washington, D.C. 20036
Thomas L. Kimball, Exec. V. Pres.
Founded: 1936
State affiliate members: 52
Associate members: 700,000
Staff: 20
Local chapters: 6,500

National Wildlife Federation (Cont'd)

Federation of 52 state conservation organizations and 700,000 associate members, plus individual conservationist-contributors. Represents in its structure 3 million supporters. To encourage the intelligent management of the life-sustaining resources of the earth, and to promote a greater appreciation of these resources, their community relationship and wise use.

Gives organizational and financial help to local conservation projects; annually awards fellowships for graduate study of conservation; publishes conservation-education teaching materials. Compiles and distributes annual survey of compensation in the fields of fish and wildlife management. Maintains library of conservation publications. Sponsors National Wildlife Week; many public service television and radio announcements. Activities are financed by sales of Wildlife Conservation Stamps and nature-related materials. Publications: (1) *Conservation Report,* weekly; (2) *Conservation News,* semimonthly; (3) *Ranger Rick's Nature Magazine,* 10/year; (4) *National Wildlife Magazine,* bimonthly; (5) *International Wildlife Magazine,* bimonthly; (6) *Conservation Directory,* annual; also publishes numerous free and lowcost conservation materials. Convention/Meeting: Annual.

NATURAL RESOURCES COUNCIL OF AMERICA

1025 Connecticut Ave., N.W.   Phone: (202) 223-1536
Suite 911
Washington, D.C. 20036
Hamilton K. Pyles, Exec. Sec.
Founded: 1946
Members: 45
Federation of national and regional conservation organizations and scientific societies interested in conservation of natural resources. Sponsors special natural resource studies and surveys. Committee: Scientific Advisory. Publications: (1) *Legislative News Service* (actions taken by Congress on natural resources), weekly; (2) *Executive News Service* (actions taken by Executive Branch on natural resources), weekly; also publishes books on selected natural resource topics. Convention/Meeting: Semiannual — always held with North American Wildlife and Natural Resources Conference.

NEW ENGLAND ADVISORY BOARD
FOR FISH AND GAME PROBLEMS

25 Franklin St.   Phone: (603) 224-1245
Concord, N.H. 03301
Robert C. Hill, Sec.
Founded: 1951
Members: 102
Sportsmen. To promote and improve conservation, hunting, fishing and recreation in New England. Convention/Meeting: 3/year.

NORTH AMERICAN WILDLIFE FOUNDATION

709 Wire Bldg.   Phone: (202) 347-1774
Washington, D.C. 20005
C. R. Gutermuth, Sec.
Founded: 1911
Contributing members: 376
Trustees: 30
"To insure, through financial support, the continuity of practical and systematic investigation into management practices and techniques throughout North America, to the end that the latest, most effective local, national, and international programs for wildlife and other natural resources will be adopted in the public interest." Foundation is not an action organization and does not attempt the actual mechanics of wildlife restoration; works through cooperating agencies, organizations, institutions. Owns Delta Waterfowl Research Station in Manitoba, Canada. Maintains library of 450 volumes on natural science subjects and wildlife restoration and management. Formerly: (1935) American Game Protective Association; (1946) American Wildlife Institute; (1951) American Wildlife Foundation.

NORTH-SOUTH SKIRMISH ASSOCIATION

3062 N. 54th Street   Phone: (414) 278-3098
Milwaukee, Wis. 53210
William J. K. Beaudot, Co-editor
Frank W. Schoch, Commander
Founded: 1950
Members: 2,500
Local groups: 150
"To pay tribute to the soldier on both sides in the War Between the States; to show the use of his weapons and equipment." Sponsors semiannual marksmanship match (National Skirmish) at Fort Shenandoah, Virginia, in which competitors, wearing uniforms and using arms of the period (1861-1865), fire weapons in team (8-man) competition for rifle and (6-man) artillery. Publication: *Skirmish Line Magazine,* bimonthly. Affiliated with: National Rifle Association of America.

OUTDOOR RECREATION INSTITUTE

5003 Wapakoneta
Washington, D.C. 20016
Dr. Radcliffe F. Robinson, Pres.
To advance outdoor recreational interests at all levels — family, local, state, and national; to emphasize recreational objectives of natural resource conservation, through technical research and educational activities. Provides information service on recreational equipment; answers technical inquiries; gives talks to groups on recreation, nutrition, foods, camping, etc.; conducts research in biology, pollution, recreational equipment, and other topics. Divisions: Research; Educational; Consulting. Publication: *ORI Newsletter,* quarterly.

OUTDOOR WRITERS ASSOCIATION OF AMERICA

4141 W. Bradley Rd.   Phone: (414) 354-9690
Milwaukee, Wis. 53209
Edwin W. Hanson, Exec. Dir.
Founded: 1927
Members: 1400
Staff: 3
Professional organization of newspaper, magazine, radio, television, and motion picture writers and photographers (both staff and free-lance) on outdoor recreation and conservation. Gives awards for outstanding writing and films in the field; conducts surveys for educational and industrial organizations; compiles market data for writer members, and offers liaison aid in writer assignments. Committees: Awards; Educational and Scholarship; Ethics; Youth Program. Publications: (1) *Outdoors Unlimited,* monthly; (2) *Spotlight,* quarterly; (3) *National Directory of Outdoor Writers,* annual; (4) *Standard Check List of Common Names for Principal American Sport Fishes,* revised periodically; also publishes a youth education manual. Convention/Meeting: Annual.

PACIFIC INTERNATIONAL TRAPSHOOTING ASSOCIATION

3847 Glenwood Loop, S.E.   Phone: (503) 364-1042
Salem, Ore. 97301
Gordon E. Hull, Sec.-Mgr.
Founded: 1928
Members: 6,000
Sponsors state, provincial, and individual registered trapshoots. Convention/Meeting: Annual—always July, Reno, Nev.

PHEASANT TRUST

Great Witchingham
Norwich, Norfolk, England
Philip Wayre, Hon. Dir.
Founded: 1959
Members: 500
Staff: 3
Purposes are: to breed and rear rare and threatened species of game birds in suitable reserves in their native lands; to main-

Pheasant Trust (Cont'd)

tain the world's largest collection of rare pheasants for education and scientific research; to promote the conservation of rare game birds throughout the world. Has received several first breeding awards from Agricultural Society of Great Britain. Publication: Annual report. Formerly: Ornamental Pheasant Trust.

PRAIRIE CHICKEN FOUNDATION

4122 Mineral Point Rd.   Phone: (608) 233-5474
Madison, Wis. 53705
Paul J. Olson, Pres.
Founded: 1958
Persons dedicated to preservation of the prairie chicken in Wisconsin. Raises funds and acquires land to develop prairie chicken habitat in the state. Owns some 5000 acres, at a cost of $200,000; makes some purchases cooperatively with the Society Tympanuchus Cupido Pinnatus. Publication: *Prairie Chicken,* irregular.

RUFFED GROUSE SOCIETY OF NORTH AMERICA (RGSNA)

4515 Culver Rd.   Phone: (716) 467-3230
Rochester, N.Y. 14622
George E. Ford, Pres.
Founded: 1961
Members: 3,000
State chapters: 10
International chapter: 1
Ruffed grouse hunters; game biologists; conservationists. Actively supports ruffed grouse and woodcock research and habitat improvement. Cooperates with state conservation departments, paper and pulp industries, and strip mining companies in habitat improvement and encourages conservation measures. Endows research into ecological aspects of the ruffed grouse and woodcock. Publication: *Magazine of the RGSNA,* semiannual. Convention/Meeting: Annual.

SAINT HUBERT SOCIETY OF AMERICA

c/o Mrs. Herbert Allan Dingwall   Phone: (212) YU 6-2989
5 Tudor City Place
New York, N.Y. 10017
George V. Lenher, Sec.
Founded: 1958
Members: 131
Individuals interested in wildlife, conservation, hunting, and the lore of the outdoors. "Dedicated to the promulgation of conservation, hunting, fishing, and the preservation of the great American heritage of the outdoors and those traditions of sportsmanship and fair play which have become associated with the American way of life." Sponsors outings for members including shoots, hunts, and fishing expeditions. Named in honor of the patron saint of hunters who was born in Belgium in the middle of the seventh century. Similar organizations have been in existence in Europe since the eighth century. Meet bimonthly.

SHOOTERS CLUB OF AMERICA

8150 North Central Park Ave.
Skokie, Ill. 60076
E. F. Becker, Membership Chm.
Founded: 1963
Members: 12,000
Staff: 3
Hunters, shooters, gun dealers, collectors, industry personnel, and others interested in "protecting the fundamental right of citizens to keep and bear arms and in combatting restrictive anti-gun legislation on local, state, and national levels." Conducts educational and public relations program on behalf of gun sportsmen and in support of "pro-gun" legislation.

SIERRA CLUB

1050 Mills Tower   Phone: (415) 981-8634
San Francisco, Calif. 94104
J. Michael McCloskey, Exec. Dir.
Members: 135,000
Staff: 90
Regional chapters: 42

All who feel the need to know more of nature, and know that this need is basic to man. "To protect and conserve the natural resources of the Sierra Nevada, the United States and the World; to undertake and publish scientific and educational studies concerning all aspects of man's environment and the natural ecosystems of the World; and to educate the people of the United States and the World to the need to preserve and restore the quality of that environment and the integrity of those ecosystems." Works on urgent campaigns to save threatened areas, wildlife, and resources; conducts annual environmental workshops for educators; schedules wilderness outings; presents awards; maintains library. Chapters and committees schedule talks, films, exhibits, and conferences. Committees: Economics; Energy; Environmental Education; Environmental Research; Forest Practices; International Environment; Mountaineering; National Land Use; National Water Resources; Native American Issues; Outings; Population; Wilderness; Wildlife and Endangered Species. Departments: Conservation; Publications; Outings. Publications: (1) *National News Report,* weekly; (2) *Sierra Club Bulletin,* monthly; (3) *Ascent,* Sierra Club mountaineering journal, annual; also publishes books and produces films, posters, and exhibits. Member of: United Nations (with non-government organization status). Convention/Meeting (Wilderness Conference): Biennial.

SOCIETY FOR THE PRESERVATION OF BIRDS OF PREY

P.O. Box 293   Phone: (213) 454-0403
Pacific Palisades, Calif. 90272
J. Richard Hilton, Pres.
Founded: 1966
Members: 180
Staff: 1

Professional ornithologists, bird watchers, and raptor enthusiasts. Seeks to stress the value of birds of prey (raptors) and to encourage their protection and preservation; disseminate information and promote communication among members; discourage harvesting of raptorial birds for purposes of falconry and research; denounce caging, selling and trading, display, or exhibition of the birds; urge reasonable and biologically sound pest control measures and support abolition of use of accumulative, wide-target insecticides. Plans to open a museum in 1974. Maintains library of books on birds of prey. Maintains a 24 hour raptor rescue program in the greater Los Angeles area which handles about 40 birds of prey annually; operates a raptor rehabilitation center in Lancaster, Calif. Publications: *The California Condor,* 5/year; also publishes numerous bulletins and pamphlets. Formerly: (1966) Palisades Hawking Club. Convention/Meeting: Annual—always third Tuesday in November, Santa Monica, Calif.

SOCIETY OF TYMPANUCHUS CUPIDO PINNATUS

c/o Willis G. Sullivan
9400 North Lake Drive
Milwaukee, Wis. 53217
Willis G. Sullivan, Pres.
Founded: 1960

Sportsmen dedicated to preserving the prairie chicken and to "doing so with humor, excellent taste, and efficiency—at the same time having a bit of fun along the way." (The prairie chicken or prairie hen, also called a pinneated grouse, is a game bird of the northern hemisphere, related to the pheasant and having mottled plumage. The Society calls itself by the scientific name for the prairie chicken.) Members' contributions are used to buy land for prairie chicken habitat, specifically to add acres to the Buena Vista Reservation in Portage County, Wisconsin. As of June,

Society of Tympanuchus Cupido Pinnatus (Cont'd)

1971, the Society had bought over 6300 acres of land, which is leased to the Wisconsin Conservation Department for clearing, restoration, and maintenance on chicken range. Only other organized activity is an annual cocktail party and business meeting held in December in Milwaukee where many of the members live. Publications: (1) *Boom,* quarterly; (2) *Membership Roll.*

SOUTHEASTERN ASSOCIATION OF GAME AND FISH COMMISSIONERS

c/o Arnold L. Mitchell
Dept. of Fish and Wildlife Resources
State Office Bldg. Annex
Frankfort, Ky. 40601
Arnold L. Mitchell, Sec.-Treas.
Founded: 1947
Members: 16

Directors of state game and fish commissions in 16 southern states. To protect the right of jurisdiction of southeastern states over their wildlife resources on public and private lands; study state and federal wildlife legislation and regulations as they affect the area; consult with and make recommendations to federal wildlife and public land agencies on federal management programs and programs involving federal aid to southeastern states; serve as a clearing house for exchange of ideas on wildlife management and research techniques. Sponsors statistical studies at North Carolina.

SPORTING ARMS AND AMMUNITION MANUFACTURERS INSTITUTE

420 Lexington Ave.   Phone: (212) 689-3237
New York, N.Y. 10017
Harry L. Hampton, Jr., Secretary-Treasurer
Founded: 1926
Members: 13
Staff: 7

Manufacturers of sporting firearms, ammunition and powder. Promotes shooting sports, safe handling of firearms, technical research, etc. Committees: Legislative and Legal Affairs; National Defense; Promotional Guidance; Statistical and Logistical; Technical. Convention/Meeting: Semi-annual.

UNITED STATES REVOLVER ASSOCIATION

59 Alvin St.   Phone: (413) 734-5725
Springfield, Mass. 01104
Stanley A. Sprague, Exec. Sec.
Founded: 1900
Members: 1500
Staff: 2

To foster and develop revolver and pistol shooting; to establish and preserve records; and to encourage and conduct pistol matches between members and clubs of this country as well as marksmen of other countries. Publication: *U.S. Handgunner,* bimonthly. Convention/Meeting: Annual—always Springfield, Mass.

WATERFOWL ADVISORY COMMITTEE

Group of thirteen national organizations interested in waterfowl management. Meets each Aug. in Washington, D.C. to hear reports on the status of waterfowl, and to recommend annual hunting regulations to the director of Bureau of Sports Fisheries and Wildlife of U.S. Department of the Interior.

WESTERN ASSN. OF STATE GAME AND FISH COMMISSIONERS

c/o Robert L. Salter   Phone: (208) 384-3771 ext. 50
Box 25
600 S. Walnut St.
Boise, Idaho 83707
Robert L. Salter, Sec.-Treas.
Founded: 1920
Members: 17

Western Assn. of State Game and Fish Commissioners (Cont'd)
Officials of state and provincial game and fish agencies of western states and provinces. Promotes fish and game conservation in West. Publication: *Proceedings of WASGFC,* annual. Convention/Meeting: Annual.

WILDERNESS SOCIETY

729 15th St., N.W.   Phone: (202) 347-4132
Washington, D.C. 20005
Stewart M. Brandborg, Exec. Dir.
Founded: 1935
Members: 77,000
Staff: 35
Persons interested in preserving wilderness through educational programs, scientific studies, and cooperation with local and state citizen organizations in resisting the destruction of wildland resources and wildlife. Conducts leadership training programs for citizen conservationists. Sponsors book award program for young people. Sponsors "A Way to the Wilderness" trip program. Publication: *Living Wilderness,* quarterly; also publishes *Wilderness Reports,* notices, and conservation alerts on critical conservation issues. Convention/Meeting: Annual.

WILDLIFE MANAGEMENT INSTITUTE

709 Wire Bldg.   Phone: (202) 347-1774
Washington, D.C. 20005
Daniel A. Poole, Pres.
Founded: 1946
Staff: 22
To promote better management and wise utilization of all renewable natural resources in the public interest. Sponsors annual North American Wildlife and Natural Resources Conference for government conservation administrators, technicians, scientists, educators and others interested in wildlife conservation. Publications: (1) *Outdoor News Bulletin,* biweekly; (2) *Transactions of Annual North American Wildlife and Natural Resources Conference* (and cumulative index); also publishes various books and monographs. Holds annual conference.

WILDLIFE SOCIETY

3900 Wisconsin Ave., Suite S-176   Phone: (202) 363-2435

Wildlife Society (Cont'd)
Washington, D.C. 20016
Dr. Fred G. Evenden, Exec. Dir.
Founded: 1936
Members: 7000
Sectional groups: 7
Professional society of wildlife biologists and others interested in resource conservation and wildlife management on a sound biological basis. Publications: (1) *Journal of Wildlife Management,* quarterly; (2) *Wildlife Society News,* bimonthly; (3) *Wildlife Monographs,* irregular. Formerly: (1937) Society of Wildlife Specialists. Convention/Meeting: Annual — held with North American Wildlife and Natural Resources Conference.

WORLD WILDLIFE FUND

910 17th St., N.W., Suite 619   Phone: (202) 296-0422
Washington, D.C. 20006
William C. Scheele, Exec. Dir.
Founded: 1961
Staff: 13
Supported by contributions from individuals, funds, corporations, and foundations with a concern for conservation of wildlife and its habitat. Emphasizes preservation of endangered and vanishing species of wildlife anywhere in the world. Programs include public education, promoting law enforcement, initiating ecological and biological research, providing data on endangered species, buying land for nature reserves, and propagating threatened species in captivity. Support is given existing conservation societies, agencies, and governments to carry out projects and services. Maintains small library. Committee: Scientific Advisory. Affiliated with: World Wildlife Fund, International, and International Union for Conservation of Nature and Natural Resources, both headquartered at Morges, Switzerland. Holds semiannual board meeting.

(NOTE: Organizations and associations which are national in scope and who desire to be listed in this directory should send detailed information about themselves in the format shown here. Address: The Editor, SHOOTER'S BIBLE, 55 Ruta Court, South Hackensack, N.J. 07606.)

The Shooter's Bookshelf

Ammunition

Amber, John T. **Handloader's Digest.** 6th ed. 1972. pap. 5.95. Follett.

Collins, Whit, ed. **Guns & Ammo Annual 1974.** 6th ed. (Illus.). 1973. pap. 3.95. Petersen Pub.

Josserand, Michael & Stevenson, Jan. **Pistols, Revolvers & Ammunition.** (Illus.). 1972. 7.50. Crown.

Naramore, Earl. **Principles & Practice of Loading Ammunition.** (Illus.). 1954. 14.95. Stackpole.

Ripey, Warren. **Artillery & Ammunition of the Civil War.** 1973. 22.50. Swallow.

Sharpe, Philip B. **Complete Guide to Handloading.** 3rd rev. ed. (Illus.). 1953. 10.00. Funk & W.

Wallack, Robert L. **Anatomy of Firearms.** 1965. 6.95. S&S.

Woods, Jim. **Guns & Ammo Complete Guide to Blackpowder.** (Illus.). 1974. pap. 4.95. Petersen Pub.

Antelopes

Bere, Rennie. **Antelopes.** (Illus.). 1971. 3.95. Arco.

Skirka, Peter & Swank, Wendell. **African Antelope.** 1971. 27.50. Winchester Pr.

Anti-Tank Guns

Chamberlain, Peter & Gander, Terry. **Anti-Tank Weapons.** (Illus.). 1974. 5.95. pap. 3.95. Arco.

Hoffschmidt, Edward J. & Tantum, William H. **German Tank & Antitank Guns of World War Two.** 1968. 9.95. We Inc.

Archery

American Alliance for Health, Physical Education & Recreation. **Archery: A Planning Guide for Group & Individual Instruction.** 1972. pap. 3.25. AAHPER. **Archery Selected Articles, 1971.** pap. 1.50. AAHPER.

Annarino, A. **Archery: Individualized Instructional Program.** 1973. pap. text ed. 1.95. P-H.

Ascham, Roger. **Toxophilus.** 1968. Repr. of 1545 ed. 7.00. Shumway. **Toxophilus.** Repr. of 1788 ed. 5.00. British Bk Ctr. **Toxophilus, 1845.** Arber, Edward, ed. 1971. Repr. of 1895 ed. 8.00. Scholarly.

Barrett, Jean A. **Archery.** 2nd ed. 1973. pap. text ed. 2.25. Goodyear. **Archery.** 1969. pap. text ed. 1.85. Goodyear.

Bear, Fred. **Archer's Bible.** (Illus.). 1968. Repr. softbound 2.50. Doubleday.

Burke, Edmund. **Archery.** (Illus.). 1963. pap. 1.45. Arc Bks.

Burke, Edmund H. **Archery Handbook.** (Illus.). 1954. 3.50. Arco. **Field & Target Archery.** (Illus.). 1961. 4.00. Arco. **History of Archery.** 1971. Repr. of 1957 ed. text ed. 12.25. Greenwood.

Butler, David F. **The New Archery.** rev. ed. (Illus.). 1973. 5.95. A S Barnes.

Campbell, Donald W. **Archery.** 1970. ref. ed. 4.95. pap. 1.85. ref. ed. P-H.

Forbes, Thomas A. **New Guide to Better Archery.** rev. & enl. ed. 1962. pap. 1.50. Macmillan.

Ford, Horace A. **Archery, Its Theory & Practice.** 1971. Repr. of 1856 ed. 6.00. Shumway.

Foy, Tom. **Beginner's Guide to Archery.** 8.75. Transatlantic.

Gillelan, G. Howard. **Archery.** 1972. pap. 1.25. Cornerstone.

Heath, E. G. **A History of Target Archery.** (Illus.). 1974. 7.95. A S Barnes.

Herrigel, Eugen. **Zen in the Art of Archery.** 1953. 4.95. Pantheon.

Hochman, Louis. **Complete Archery Book.** (Illus.). 1957. 3.95. Arco.

Hougham, Paul. **Encyclopedia of Archery.** (Illus.). 1957. 5.00. A S Barnes.

Klann, Margaret L. **Target Archery.** 1970. pap. 3.50. A-W.

Latham, J. D., ed. **Saracen Archery.** Paterson, W. F. (Illus.). 20.00. Saifer.

Laycock, George & Bauer, Erwin. **Hunting with Bow & Arrow.** 1965. 3.95. Arco.

Learn, C. R. **Bowhunter's Digest.** pap. 6.95. Digest Bks.

Longman, Charles J. & Walrond, H. **Archery.** 1967. 12.00. Ungar.

McKinney, Wayne C. **Archery.** 2nd. ed. Lockhart, Aileene, ed. 1971. pap. text ed. 1.25. Wm. C Brown.

Markham, Gervase. **The Art of Archerie.** facs. ed. (Limited ed. of 400). 1968. Repr. of 1634 ed. 12.00. Shumway.

Neade, William. **The Double Armed Man.** facsimile ed. (Illus., Limited ed. of 300). 1971. 6.00. Shumway.

Niemeyer, Roy K. **Beginning Archery.** rev. ed. (Illus.). 1968. pap. text ed. 2.25. Wadsworth Pub.

Pszczola, Lorraine. **Archery.** (Illus.). 1971. pap. text ed. 2.25. Saunders.

Reichart, N. & Keasey, G. **Archery.** 3rd ed. (Illus.). 1961. 5.95. Ronald.

Sigler, Howard T. **Pocket Guide to Archery.** (Illus.). 1967. 2.95. Stackpole.

Sollier, Andre & Gyorbiro, Zsolt. **Japanese Archery: Zen in Action.** (Illus.). 1969. 6.50. Weatherhill.

Stamp, Don. **Archery—an Expert's Guide.** pap. 2.00. Wilshire. **Challenge of Archery.** (Illus.). 1971. 10.00. Intl. Pubns. Serv.

Tinsley, Russell. **Bow Hunter's Guide.** (Illus.). 1975. softbound 5.95. Stoeger.

Wood, William. **The Bowman's Glory.** facs. ed. 1969. Repr. of 1682 ed. 6.00. Shumway. **Bowman's Glory.** Repr. of 1682 ed. 4.00. British Bk Ctr.

Arms and Armor

Albion, Robert G. **Introduction to Military History.** (Illus.). 1971. Repr. 11.50. AMS Pr.

Ashdown, Charles H. **British & Continental Arms & Armour.** (Illus.). 6.00. Peter Smith. **British & Continental Arms & Armour.** (Illus.). 1970. pap. 4.00. Dover.

Barker, A. J. **Russian Infantry Weapons of World War Two.** 1970. 3.50. Arco.

Blackmore, Howard L. **Arms & Armour.** (Illus.). pap. 1.95. Dutton.

Blair, Claude. **European Armour.** (Illus.). 1972. 10.50. Crane-Russak Co.

Boeheim, W. & Koetschau, K., eds. **Zeitschrift Fur Historiche Waffen: Und Kostumkunde 1897-1920,** (Illus.). 1973. Repr. 375.00. Arma Pr.

Brinckerhoff, Sidney B. & Chamberlain, Pierce A. **Spanish Military Weapons in Colonial America 1700-1821.** 1972. 14.95. Stackpole.

Brodie, Bernard & Brodie, Fawn M. **From Crossbow to H-Bomb.** rev. enl. ed. (Illus.). 1973. 7.95. pap. 2.95. Ind U Pr.

Buehr, Walter. **Warriors' Weapons.** (Illus.). 1963. 5.95. T Y Crowell.

Cleator, P. E. **Weapons of War.** (Illus.). 1968. 6.95 T Y Crowell.

Control of Weapons & World Peace: Improving Administration of Justice, How Can the Administration of Justice Be Improved in the U.S. 1971. pap. 3.00. Mid-West.

De Gheyn, Jacob. **The Exercise of Armes.** 1973. 45.00. Arma Pr.

Dillion, Harold A. **Armour.** 1968. softbound 4.00. Shumway.

Foulkes, Charles. **Armour & Weapons.** (Illus.). 1974. Repr. of 1909 ed. 7.50. Rowman.

Ffoulkes, Charles & Hopkinson, E. C. **Sword, Lance & Bayonet.** (Illus.). 1967. 7.50. Arco.

Ffoulkes, Charles J. **Armourer & His Craft.** 1967. Repr. 18.50. Blom. **Armourer & His Craft, from the Eleventh to the Sixteenth Century.** (Illus.). 18.50. Ungar.

Franklin, Charles A. **The Bearing of Coat Armour by Ladies.** 1923. Repr. 12.00. Finch Pr.

Gruzanski, C. V. **Spike & Chain.** 5.25. Wehman.

Hakuseki, Arai. **Armour Book in Honcho-Gunkiko.** (Illus.). 1964. bds. 20.00. C. E. Tuttle.

Hawley, W. M. **Introduction to Japanese Swords.** 1973. pap. 2.00. Hawley.

Held, Robert. **Arms & Armor Annual.** 1973. 14.95. pap. 9.95. Follett.

Hewitt, John. **Ancient Armour & Weapons in Europe,** 3 vols. (Illus.). 1973. 75.00. Arma Pr.

Hogg, Ian & Weeks, Joseph. **Military Small Arms of the Twentieth Century.** 1973. 7.95. Follett.

Hughes, B. P. **Firepower: Weapon Effectiveness on the Battlefield, 1630-1815.** 1974. 12.50. Scribner.

Journal of the Arms & Armour Society, Vol. 1. 1970. 8.00. Shumway.

Keller, May L. **The Anglo-Saxon Weapon Names, Treated Archaeologically & Etymologically.** 1967. Repr. of 1906 ed. 24.00. Intl Pubns Serv.

Kelly, Francis M. & Schwabe, Randolph. **Short History of Costume & Armour, Chiefly in England 1066-1800,** 2 Vols. in 1. (Illus.). 1968. Repr. of 1931 ed. 13.75. Blom.

Kelly, Francis M. & Schwabe, Randolph. **A Short History of Costume & Armour. 1066-1800,** 2 vols. in 1 (Illus.). 1973. 12.50. Arco.

Lindsay, Merrill. **Miniature Arms.** (Illus.). 1973. 7.95. Arma Pr. **Twenty Great American Guns.** (Illus.). Repr. pap. 1.75. Arma Pr.

Martin, Paul. **Arms & Armour from the Ninth to the Seventeenth Century.** (Illus.). 1968. 15.00. C E Tuttle.

Mason, Richard O. **Use of the Long Bow with the Pike.** 1970. limited ed. 6.00. Shumway.

Moyer, Frank A. **Special Forces Foreign Weapons Handbook.** new ed. (Illus.). 1970. 12.95. Paladin Pr.

Neal, W. Keith & Back, D. H. **A History of British Gunmaking Seventeen Hundred Forty-Ninety.** (Illus.). 1974. 55.00. S P Bernet.

Neumann, George C. **History of the Weapons of the American Revolution.** 1967. 15.00. Har-Row.

Norman, A. V. & Pottinger, Don. **History of War & Weapons 449-1600: English Warfare from the Anglo-Saxons to Cromwell.** Orig. Title: **Warrior to Soldier: 449-1660.** 1967. 7.95. T Y Crowell.

Orgill, Douglas. **German Armor.** Pitt, Barrie & Courrier, David, eds. 1974. pap. 2.00. Ballantine.

Pinches, Rosemary, et al, eds. **A European Armorial: An Armorial of Knights of the Golden Fleece & 15th Century Europe, from a Contemporary Manuscript.** (Illus.). 1971. 18.00. Gale.

Pretty, R. T. & Archer, D. H., eds. **Jane's Weapon Systems, 1973-1974.** (Illus.). 1974. 65.00. McGraw.

Robinson, H. Russell. **The Armour of Imperial Rome.** (Illus.). 1974. 17.50 Scribner.
The Armour of Imperial Rome. 1974. 17.50. Scribner.
Sakakibara, Kozan. **Manufacture of Armour & Helmets in Sixteenth Century Japan.** (Illus.). 1963. bds. 20.00. C E Tuttle.
Saxtorph, Niels M. **Warriors & Weapons of Early Times.** (Illus.). 1972. 4.95. Macmillan.
Schevitz, Jeffrey. **Weapons Makers.** 1975. 12.50; pap. 5.95. Schenkman.
Schuyler-Hartley-Graham Military Furnishers. **Illustrated Catalog Arms & Military Goods.** facsimile ed. (Illus.). 1864. 9.50. Flayderman.
Shepperd, G. A. **A History of War & Weapons, 1660-1918.** (Illus.). 1972. 7.95. T Y Crowell.
Snodgrass, A. M. **Arms & Armour of the Greeks** (Illus.). 1967. 7.50. Cornell U Pr.
Snodgrass, Anthony. **Early Greek Armour & Weapons: From the End of the Bronze Age to 600 BC.** (Illus.). 11.25. Aldine.
Thomas, Donald G. **U.S. Silencer Patents,** 2 vols. new ed. Brown, Robert K. & Lund Peter C., eds. Incl. Vol. 1. 1888-1935. 15.95. Vol. 2. 1936-1972. 15.95. (Illus.). 1973. Set. 29.95. Paladin Pr.
Truby, David J. **Silencers, Snipers & Assassins.** Brown, Robert K. & Lund, Peder C., eds. (Illus.). 1972. 15.95. Paladin Pr.
Truby, J. David. **Quiet Killers** (Illus.). 1972. 5.95. pap. 4.00. Paladin Pr.
U.S. Army Munitions Command. **Silencers.** (Illus.). 1971. 9.95. pap. 4.95. Paladin Pr.
U.S. Army Sniper Training Manual. (Illus.). 1971. 11.95. Paladin Pr.
Vangen. Roland D. **Indian Weapons.** (Illus.). 1972. 4.00. pap. 1.25. Filter.
Werner, E. T. **Chinese Weapons.** 3.50. Wehman.
Wilkinson, Frederick. **Arms & Armour.** 1973. pap. 1.45. Bantam.
Battle Dress: A Gallery of Military Style & Ornament. (Illus.). 1971. 12.95. Doubleday.
Edged Weapons. (Illus.). 1970. 6.95. Doubleday.
Wintringham, Thomas H. **Story of Weapons & Tactics.** facs. ed. 1943. 9.75. Bks for Libs.

Artillery
Batchelor, John. **Fighter.** 1973. 7.95. Scribner.
Batchelor, John & Hogg, Ian. **Artillery.** (Illus.). 1972. 9.95. Scribner.
Foss, Christopher. **Artillery of the World.** 1974. 6.95. Scribner.
Artillery of the World. (Illus.). 1974. 6.95. Scribner.
Gibbon, John, ed. **Artillerist's Manual.** Repr. of 1860 ed. 29.50. Greenwood.
Hogg, Ian V. **The Guns: 1939-45.** (Illus.). 1973. pap. 1.00. Ballantine.
Hogg, O. F. **Artillery: Its Origin, Heyday, & Decline.** (Illus.). 1970. 12.50. Shoe String.
Hughes, B. P. **Firepower: Weapon Effectiveness on the Battlefield, 1630-1815.** (Illus.). 1974. 12.50. Scribner.
Marsden, E. W. **Greek & Roman Artillery: Technical Treatises.** 1971. 16.00. Oxford U Pr.
Patrick, John M. **Artillery & Warfare During the Thirteenth & Fourteenth Centuries.** 1961. pap. 2.00. Utah St U Pr.
Peterson, Harold L. **Round Shot & Rammers: An Introduction to Muzzle-Loading Land Artillery in the U. S.** (Illus.). 1969. 9.95. Stackpole.
Ripey, Warren. **Artillery & Ammunition of the Civil War.** 1973. 22.50. Swallow.
Rogers, H. B. **A History of Artillery.** (Illus.). 1974. 7.95. Citadel Pr.
Simienowicz, C. **Great Art of Artillery.** (Illus.). 17.50. Saifer.

Simienowicz, Casimir. **The Great Art of Artillery.** Chevlet, George, tr. from Fr. 1973. Repr. of 1729 ed. 17.95. British Bk Ctr.
Tousard, Louis De. **American Artillerists Companion,** 3 vols. 1809-1813. Repr. Set. 106.00. Greenwood.

Ballistics
Lowry, E. D. **Interior Ballistics: How a Gun Converts Chemical Energy into Projectile Motion.** (Illus.). 1968. 4.50. Doubleday.
McShane. **Exterior Ballistics.** 2.00. Swallow.

Bayonets
Angolia, John R. **Daggers, Bayonets & Fighting Knives of Hitler's Germany.** (Illus.). 15.00. Quaker.
Carter, Anthony. **The Bayonet: The History & Development of the Sword, Sabre & Knife Bayonet 1850-1973.** (Illus.). 1974. 8.95. Scribner.
Carter, J. Anthony, **Allied Bayonets of World War Two.** (Illus.). 1969. 3.50. Arco.

Bird Dogs
Brown, William F. **National Field Trial Champions. 1956-1966.** (Illus.). 1966. 10.00. A S Barnes.
Davis, Henry P. **Training Your Own Bird Dog.** rev. ed. (Illus.). 1970. 5.95. Putnam.
Mueller, Larry. **Bird Dogs.** (Illus.). 1973. softbound 5.95. Stoeger.

Bow and Arrow
Hamilton, T. M. **Native American Bows: Their Types & Relationships.** (Illus.). 1972. 10.00. Shumway.
Hurley, Vic. **Arrows Against Steel: The History of the Bow.** (Illus.). 1974. 9.95. Mason & Lipscomb.
Lewis, Jack. **Bow & Arrow Archers' Digest.** 1971. 5.95. Follet.
Mason, Richard O. **Use of the Long Bow with the Pike.** 1970. limited ed. 6.00. Shumway.
Murdock, John. **Study of the Eskimo Bows in the U. S. National Museum.** facs. ed. (Illus.). 1884. pap. 1.50. Shorey.
Pope, Saxton T. **Bows & Arrows.** 1962. pap. 1.50. U of Cal Pr.
Smythe, John. **Bow Versus Gun.** 1974. Repr. of 1590 ed. text ed. 12.50. British Bk Ctr.
Tinsley, Russell. **Bow Hunter's Guide.** (Illus.). 1975. softbound 5.95. Stoeger.

Caribou
Georgeson, C. C. **Reindeer & Caribou.** facs. ed. (Illus.). 1904. pap. 1.50. Shorey.
Murie, Olaus J. **Alaska Yukon Caribou.** facsimile ed. (Illus.). 1935 pap. 10.00. Shorey.

Cartridges
Barnes, Frank C. **Cartridges of the World.** 3rd ed. (Illus.). 1972. pap. 6.95. Follett.
Bartlett, W. A. & Gallatin, D. B. **B & G Cartridge Manual.** 2.00. Pioneer Pr.
Borden's Catalog of Collector's Cartridges. 9.95. Borden.
Cartridge Manual: An Illustrated Digest. (Illus.). 2.00. Pioneer Pr.
Datig, Fred A. **Cartridges for Collectors,** 3 Vols. 7.50 ea. Borden.
Lewis, Berkeley R. **Small Arms & Ammunition in the United States Service** 1776-1865. (Illus.). 1956. 12.50. Smithsonian.
Nonte, George C., Jr. **Home Guide to Cartridge Conversion.** 2nd ed. 1967. 8.95. Stackpole.
Sharpe, Philip B. **Complete Guide to Handloading.** 3rd rev. ed. (Illus.). 1953. 10.00. Funk & W.

Steindler, R. A. **Reloader's Guide.** 3rd ed. (Illus.). 1968. softbound 5.95. Stoeger.
Suydam. **American Cartridge.** 8.50. Borden.
Treadwell. **Cartridges, Regulation & Experimental.** 2.00. Pioneer Pr.
Whelen, Townsend. **Why Not Load Your Own.** (Illus.). 6.95. A S Barnes.
White, Henry P. & Munhall, Burton D. **Centerfire Pistol & Revolver Cartridges.** rev. ed. 10.00. A S Barnes.

Colt Revolvers
Bady, Donald B. **Colt Automatic Pistols,** rev. ed. 1973. 9.95. Borden.
Larson, E. Dixon. **Colt Tips.** 3.95. Pioneer Pr.
Shumaker, P. L. **Colt's Variations of the Old Model Pocket Pistol.** 1957. 6.00. Borden.
Swayze, Nathan L. **Fifty One Colt Navies.** (Illus.). 1967. 15.00. Gun Hill.

Colt's Patent Firm Arms Manufacturing Co.
Parsons, John E. **Peacemaker & Its Rivals: An Account of the Single Action Colt.** (Illus.). 1950. 7.50. Morrow.

Crossbows
Payne-Gallwey, R. **Crossbow.** 27.50. Newbury Bks Inc.
Payne-Gallwey, Ralph. **Cross-Bow, Medieval & Modern.** 25.00. Saifer.
Wilbur, C. Martin. **History of the Crossbow.** (Illus.). 1936. pap. 1.50. Shorey.

Daggers
Angolia, John R. **Daggers, Bayonets & Fighting Knives of Hitler's Germany.** (Illus.). 15.00. Quaker.
Atwood, James P. **Daggers & Edged Weapons of Hitler's Germany.** 16.50. Borden.
Wallace, John. **Scottish Swords & Dirks.** (Illus.). 1970. 4.95. Stackpole.

Damascening
Smith, Cyril S. **History of Metallography.** (Illus.). 1960. 12.00. U of Chicago Pr.

Decoys
Barber, Joel. **Wild Fowl Decoys.** (Illus.). pap. 4.00. Dover.
Wild Fowl Decoys. (Illus.). 6.50. Peter Smith.
Becker, A. C., Jr. **Decoying Waterfowl.** (Illus.). 1973. 12.00. A S Barnes.
Brown, Ercil. **Thrills of the Duck Hunt.** 1973. 2.50. Dorrance.
Connett, Eugene. **Duck Decoys.** 9.50. Durrell.
Coykendall, Ralf. **Duck Decoys & How to Rig Them.** (Illus.). 1965. 6.95. HR&W.
Earnest, Adele. **Art of the Decoy: American Bird Carvings.** (Illus.). 1970. 10.00. Potter.
Mackey, William J., Jr. **American Bird Decoys.** (Illus.). 12.50. Dutton.
Parmalee, Paul W. & Loomis, Forrest D. **Decoys & Decoy Carvers of Illinois.** (Illus.). 1969. 17.50. N Ill U Pr.
Richardson, R. H., ed. **Chesapeake Bay Decoys: The Men Who Made & Used Them.** (Illus.). 1973. 12.00. Cornell Maritime.
Starr, George. **Decoys of the Atlantic Flyway.** (Illus.). 1974. limited ed. 50.00. Winchester Pr.
Webster, David S. & Kehoe, William. **Decoys at Shelburne Museum.** 1961. pap. 5.50. Hobby Hse.
Weiler, Milton C. & Mackey, W., Jr. **Classic Shorebird Decoys.** (Illus.). 1971. 100.00. Winchester Pr.
Zern, Ed. **Classic Decoy Series.** (Illus.). 1969. 100.00. Winchester Pr.

Deer Hunting

Conway, Bryant W. **Successful Hints on Hunting White Tail Deer.** 2nd ed. 1967. pap. 1.98. Claitors.

Cox, Alex. **Deer Hunting in Texas.** rev. ed. (Illus.). 1971. 6.95. Naylor.

Dalrymple, Byron W. **Complete Book of Deer Hunting.** 1973. 5.95 pap. Stoeger.

Freeman, Edward A. **How to Hunt Deer.** 1962. pap. 0.95. Macmillan.

Heuser, Ken. **The Whitetail Deer Guide.** (Illus.). 1972. 6.95. HR&W.

Hewitt, H. P. **Fairest Hunting: Hunting & Watching Exmoor Deer.** 1974. pap. 4.50. British Bk Ctr.

Koller, Lawrence R. **Shots at Whitetails.** rev. ed. (Illus.). 1970. 7.95. Knopf.

Laycock, George. **Deer Hunter's Bible.** rev. ed. (Illus.). 1971. softbound 2.50. Doubleday.

McNair, Jack. **Shooting for the Skipper: Memories of a Veteran Deerstalker.** (Illus.). 1971. 8.50. Reed.

Outdoor Life. **Outdoor Life's Deer Hunting Book.** (Illus.). 1974. 7.95. Times Mirror Mag.

Page, Warren. **The Field & Stream Guide to Deer Hunting.** 1973. pap. 1.25. Popular Lib.

Sell, Francis E. **Art of Successful Deer Hunting.** Orig. Title: **Deer Hunter's Guide.** (Illus.). 1971. pap. 2.95. Stackpole.

Tillett, Paul. **Doe Day: The Antlerless Deer Controversy in New Jersey.** 1963. 6.00. pap. 2.75. Rutgers U Pr.

Tinsley, Russell. **Hunting the Whitetail Deer.** 1965. 4.50. Times Mirror Mag.

Wambold, Homer R. **Bowhunting for Deer.** (Illus.). 1964. 5.95. Stackpole.

Duck Shooting

Barber, Joel. **Wild Fowl Decoys.** (Illus.). 6.50. Peter Smith.
Wild Fowl Decoys (Illus.). pap. 4.00. Dover.

Coykendall, Ralf. **Duck Decoys & How to Rig Them.** (Illus.). 1965. 6.95. HR&W.

Gresham, Grits. **Complete Wildfowler.** 1973. 8.95. Winchester Pr.

Hinman, Bob. **The Duck Hunter's Handbook.** 1974. 8.95. Winchester Pr.

Short & Cartwright. **Sports Afield Know Your Ducks & Geese.** 1943. 19.95. Hearst Bks.

Ducks

Cornell Laboratory of Ornithology. **Dawn in a Duckblind.** 6.95. HM.

Dethier, Vincent G. **Fairweather Duck.** 1970. 4.95. Walker & Co.

Ellis, Melvin R. **Peg Leg Pete.** 1973. 5.95. HR&W.

Fraser, Bryce. **Sitting Duck.** (Illus.). 1970. 5.95. Stein & Day.

Hester, F. Eugene & Dermid, Jack. **The World of the Wood Duck.** (Illus.). 1973. 5.95. Lippincott.

Hyde, Dayton. **Raising Wild Ducks in Captivity.** 1974. 15.00. Dutton.

Jaques, Florence P. **Geese Fly High.** (Illus.). 1964. Repr. of 1939 ed. 5.50. U of Minn. Pr.

McKane, John G. **Ducks of the Mississippi Flyway.** (Illus.). 1969. deluxe ed. 4.95. pap. 2.98. North Star.

Merne, O. **Ducks, Geese, Swan.** 1974. 6.95. St. Martin.

Ripley, Dillon. **Paddling of Ducks.** (Illus.). 1969. 5.95. Smithsonian.

Dueling

Baldick, Robert. **The Duel: A History of Duelling.** (Illus.). 8.50. Potter.

Bennetton, Norman A. **Social Significance of the Duel in Seventeenth Century Drama.** Repr. of 1938 ed. 13.50. Greenwood.

Burr, Samuel E., Jr. **The Burr-Hamilton Duel.** 1971. 4.95. pap. 2.95. Naylor.

Coleman, J. Winston. **Famous Kentucky Duels.** (Illus.). 1969. 3.95. Henry Clay.

De Massi, Coustard. **The History of Dueling.** 1880. Repr. Finch Pr.

Gamble, Thomas. **Savannah Duels & Duellists: 1733-1877.** (Illus.). 1974. Repr. of 1923 ed. 15.00. Reprint.

The Gunfighters. 1974. lib. bdg. 7.95. Silver.

Hutton, Alfred. **The Sword & the Centuries; or, Old Sword Days & Old Sword Ways.** (Illus.). 1973. Repr. of 1901 ed. 8.50. C E Tuttle.

Melville, Lewis & Hargreaves, Reginald. **Famous Duels & Assassinations.** (Illus.). 1972. Repr. of 1929 ed. 14.00. Singing Tree.

Sabine, Lorenzo. **Notes on Duels & Dueling.** 1973. Repr. of 1855 ed. 35.00. Milford Hse.
Notes on Duels & Dueling: Alphabetically Arranged with a Preliminary Historical Essay. 1973. Repr. of 1854 ed. 17.00. Bks for Lbs.

Seitz, Don C. **Famous American Duels.** facs. ed. 1929. 11.75. Bks for Lbs.

Thimm, Carl A. **Complete Bibliography of Fencing & Dueling.** 1968. Repr. of 1846 ed. 15.00. Blom.

Truman, Benjamin C. **The Field of Honor: Being a History of Dueling.** 1884. Repr. 22.00. Finch Pr.

Falconry

American Falconer's Club Journals: 1941-1961. 1971. 32.50. Falcon Head Pr.

Ap Evans, Humphrey. **Falconry.** (Illus.). 1974. 12.95. Arco.

Beebe, Frank L. & Webster, Harold M. **North American Falconry & Hunting Hawks.** 3rd ed. 1970. 25.00. North Am. Fal Hunt.

Blaine, Gilbert. **Falconry.** 1970. 5.50. Branford.

Brander, Michael. **Dictionary of Sporting Terms.** (Illus.). 1968. 6.50. Fernhill.

Bruce, David. **The Bird of Jove.** (Illus.). 1971. 5.95. Putnam.

Burton, Richard F. **Falconry in the Valley of the Indus.** 1971. 13.50. Falcon Head Pr.

Evans, Humphrey. **Falconry for You.** 4.95. Branford.

Fisher, Charles H. **Reminiscences of a Falconer.** 1972. 15.00; deluxe ed. 25.00. Falcon Head Pr.

Fleming, Arnold. **Falconry & Falcons: Sport of Fight.** Repr. text ed. 17.50. British Bk Ctr.

Frederick Second of Hohenstaufen. **The Art of Falconry.** Wood, Casey A. & Fyfe, F. Marjorie, eds. (Illus.) 1943. 20.00 Stanford U. Pr.

Freeman, Gage E. **Practical Falconry.** 1972. Repr. of 1869 ed. 10.00. W R Hecht.

Freeman, Gage E. & Salvin, Francis H. **Falconry: Its Claims, History & Practice.** 1972. 12.50. deluxe ed. 25.00. Falcon Head Pr.

Illingworth, Frank. **Falcons & Falconry.** 3rd rev. ed. 1964. 6.95. British Bk Ctr.

Lascelles, Gerald. **Art of Falconry.** (Illus.). 1971. Repr. of 1895 ed. 5.50. Branford.

Madden, D. H. **Chanter of Mediaeval History.** 1969. Repr. of 1924 ed. 12.50. Kennikat.

Mellor, J. E. **Mellor's Notes on Falconry.** 8.50. Falcon Head Pr.

Michell, E. B. **Art & Practice of Hawking.** 7.00. Bradford.

Salvin, Francis H. & Broderick, William. **Falconry in the British Isles.** 1970. Repr. of 1855 ed. 22.50. North Am Fal Hunt.

Schlegel, H. & Wulverhorst, A. H. **Traite De Fauconnerie.** Hanlon, Thomas, tr. (Illus.) 1973. 32.50. Chasse Pubns.

Stevens, Ronald. **Observations on Modern Falconry.** Repr. of 1956 ed. 12.50. W R Hecht.

Summers, Gerald. **The Lure of the Falcon.** 1973. 7.95. S&S.

Woodford, Michael H. **Manual of Falconry.** 7.25. Branford.

Firearms

Ackley, Parker O. **Home Gun Care & Repair.** (Illus.). 1974. pap. 2.95. Stackpole.

Amber, John T. **Gun Digest.** 28th ed. (Illus.). 1974 pap. 7.95. Follett.

Amber, John T., ed. **Gun Digest.** 29th ed. 1974. pap. 7.95. Digest Bks.
Gun Digest Treasury. 4th ed. (Illus.). 1972. pap. 5.95. Follett.

Handloader's Digest, 6th ed. pap. 5.95 Digest Bks.

Bailey, DeWitt. **British Military Longarms, 1715-1815.** (Illus.). 1971. 4.95. Stackpole.
British Military Longarms, 1815-1864. 1972. 4.95. Stackpole.

Blackmore, Howard L. **Guns & Rifles of the World.** (Illus.). 1965. 30.00. Viking Pr.

Boothroyd, Geoffrey. **The Handgun.** (Illus.). 1970. 19.95. Crown.

Bowman, Hank W. **Famous Guns from the Winchester Collection.** (Illus.). 1958. 3.50. Arco.

Bridges, Toby. **Black Powder Gun Digest.** (Illus.). 1972. pap. 5.95. Follett.

Bristow, Allen P. **The Search for an Effective Police Handgun.** (Illus.). 1973. 15.75. C C Thomas.

Browne, Bellmore H. **Guns & Gunning.** (Illus.). 1908. ae. 6.00. Shorey.

Carey, A. Merwyn. **English, Irish & Scottish Firearms Makers.** (Illus.). 1967. 6.50. Arco.

Chapel, Charles L. **Complete Guide to Gunsmithing, Gun Care & Repair.** rev. ed. (Illus.). 1962. 7.95. A S Barnes.

Collins, Whit. ed. **Guns & Ammo Annual 1974.** 6th ed. (Illus.). 1973. pap. 3.95. Petersen Pub.

Consumer Guide. **The Consumer Guide: Guns.** 1972. pap. 1.95. PB.

Cormack, A. J. **Small Arms in Profile,** Vol. 1. (Illus.). 1973. 22.50. Doubleday.

Davis, John E. **Introduction to Tool Marks, Firearms & the Striagraph.** (Illus.). 1958. 8.50. C C Thomas.

Dunlap, Roy. **The Gunowner's Book of Care, Repair & Improvement.** (Illus.). 1974. 9.95. Har-Row.

Dunlap, Roy F. **Gun Owner's Book of Care, Repair , & Improvement.** (Illus.). 1974. 9.95. Times Mirror Mag.

Garwood, G. T. **Gough Thomas's Gun Book.** (Illus.). 1970. 8.95. Winchester Pr.

Glendinning, Ian. **British Pistols & Guns, 1640-1840.** (Illus.). 1967. 7.50. Arco.

Grant, Matt & Grant, Bruce. **The Sharp Shooter: How to Get the Best Out of Rifles & Ammunition.** (Illus.). 1972. 8.95. Reed.

Grennell, Dean A. **A B C's of Reloading.** pap. 6.95. Digest Bks.

Gun Digest Editors. **Guns Illustrated.** 5th ed. 1973. pap. 3.95. Digest Bks.

Hamilton, Donald. **Donald Hamilton on Guns & Hunting.** 1970. pap. 0.75. Fawcett World.

Hatcher, Julian S. **Hatcher's Notebook,** rev. ed. (Illus.). 1962. 11.95. Stackpole.

Held, Robert. **Age of Firearms.** 2nd ed. Amber, John T., ed. pap. 4.95. Digest Bks.

Hoffschmidt, Edward J. & Tantum, William H., 4th. **Second World War Combat Weapons,** 2 vols. Incl. Vol. 1. **German Combat Weapons;** Vol. 2. **Japanese Combat Weapons.** (Illus.). 7.95 ea. We Inc.

Hogg, Ian V. & Weeks, John S. **Military Small Arms of the Twentieth Century.** pap. 7.95. Digest Bks.

Howe, James V. **Amateur Guncraftsman.** (Illus.). 1967. pap. 1.95. Funk & W.

Howe, Walter J. **Professional Gunsmithing.** (Illus.). 1946. 10.00. Stackpole.

Huntington, R. T. **Hall's Breechloaders: John H. Hall's Invention & Development of a Breechloading Rifle with Precision-Made Interchangeable Parts, & Its Introduction into the United States Service.** (Illus.). 1972. 15.00, softbound 10.00. Shumway.

Journal of the Historical Firearms Society
of South Africa, Vol. 1. (Illus.). 1964.
Repr. of 1958 ed. 6.32. Verry.

Kennedy, Monty. Checkering & Carving of
Gunstocks, rev. ed. (Illus.). 1952. 10.00.
Stackpole.

Koller, Larry. The Golden Guide to Guns.
rev. ed. 1974. pap. 3.95. Western Pub.

Kuhlhoff, Pete. Kuhlhoff on Guns. (Illus.).
1970. 5.95. Winchester Pr.

Lavin, James D. History of Spanish Firearms.
(Illus.). 1965. 9.95. Arco.

Lenk, Torsten. Flintlock: Its Origin &
Development. 30.00. Saifer.

Lewis, Berkeley R. Small Arms &
Ammunition in the United States Service
1776-1865. (Illus.). 1956. 12.50.
Smithsonian.

Moreton, Dave, ed. Gun Talk: Practical
Advice from America's Greatest Gun &
Shooting Writers. 1973. 7.95. Winchester
Pr.

Mueller, Chester & Olson, John. Small Arms
Lexicon. 1968. pap. 5.95. Follett.

Murtz, Harold A. Guns Illustrated. 7th ed.
1974. pap. 5.95. Digest Bks.

Murtz, Harold A., ed. Gun Digest Book
of Exploded Firearms Drawings. pap.
5.95. Digest Bks.

Nonte, George. Firearms Encyclopedia.
(Illus.). 1973. 11.95. Times Mirror Mag.

Peterson, Harold L. Encyclopedia of
Firearms. (Illus.). 1964. 16.95. Dutton.

Pollard, Hugh B. The History of Firearms.
1974. lib. bdg. 22.50. B. Franklin.

R. W. Norton Art Gallery. E. C.
Prudhomme: Master Gun Engraver.
(Illus.). 1973. pap. 3.00. Norton Art.

Rice, F. Philip. The Data Book of Guns,
Ammunition & Shooting. (Illus.).
Times Mirror Mag.

Riviere, Bill. The Gunner's Bible. rev. ed.
1973. pap. 2.50. Doubleday.

Roberts, Willis J. & Bristow, Allen P.
Introduction to Modern Police Firearms.
Gourley, Douglas, ed. (Illus.). 1969. text
ed. 8.95. Glencoe.

Russel, Carl. Firearms, Trap & Tools of
the Mountain Men. (Illus.). 1967. 15.00.
Knopf.

Rywell, Martin. The Powder Flask. 1.50.
Pioneer Pr.

Schroeder, Joseph J., Jr., ed. Gun
Collector's Digest. 1st ed. pap. 6.95.
Digest Bks.

Sell. Handguns Americana. 1973. 8.50.
Borden.

Sherrill, Robert. The Saturday Night Special.
1973. 8.95. Charterhouse.

Shooter's Bible, No. 67. Bicentennial ed.
1976. 7.95. Stoeger.

Smith, Joseph E. Small Arms of the World.
rev. ed. (Illus.). 1973. 7.95. Stackpole.

Smith, W. H. Mauser, Walther & Mannlicher
Firearms. (Illus.). 1971. 14.95. Stackpole.

Stanford, J. K. Complex Gun. 12.50. Soccer.

Steindler, R. A. Firearms Dictionary. (Illus.).
1970. 7.95. Stackpole.
Modern ABC's of Guns. (Illus.). 1965.
4.95. Stackpole.
Reloader's Guide. 2nd ed. 1968. pap.
4.95. Follett.

Stockbridge, V. D. Digest of U. S. Patents
Relating to Breech-Loading & Magazine
Small Arms, 1836-1873. (Illus.). 1963.
12.50. Flayderman.

Tanner, Hans, ed. Basic Gun Repair. (Illus.).
1973. pap. 3.95. Petersen Pub.
Guns of the World. (Illus.). 1972. pap.
6.95. Petersen Pub.

Van Rensselaer, Stephen. Colt Firearms.
(Illus.). 6.00. Century Hse.

Walker, Ralph. Hobby Gunsmithing. Lewis,
Jack, ed. 1972. pap. 5.95. Digest Bks.

Wallack, Robert L. Anatomy of Firearms.
1965. 6.95. S&S.

Waterworth, Cyril. Reloading Simplified.
(Illus.). 1970. pap. 4.50. Reed.

Wels, Byron G. Fell's Guide to Guns &
How to Use Them Safely, Legally,
Responsibly. 1969. 5.95. Fell.

West, Bill. Know Your Winchesters: General
Use, All Models & Types, 1849-1969.
(Illus.). 10.00. B West.
Winchester-Complete: All Wins &
Forerunners, 1849-1970. (Illus.). 1972.
20.00. B West.
Winchester Encyclopedia. (Illus.). 12.00.
B West.
Winchester Lever-Action Handbook.
(Illus.). 22.00. B West.
The Winchester Single Shot. (Illus.) 12.00.
B West.
Winchester, Cartridges, & History. (Illus.).
20.00. B West.

Wilkinson, Frederick. Firearms. (Illus.).
1973. 2.95. Western Pub.

Willet, Roderick. Gun Safety. (Illus.). 1967.
5.25. Intl Pubns Serv.

Wycoff, James. Famous Guns That Won
the West. (Photos). 1968. Repr. of 1966
ed. lib. bdg. 3.50. Arco.

Firearms—Catalogs

Chapel, Charles E. Gun Collector's
Handbook of Values. 9th rev. ed. (Illus.).
1970. 12.50. Coward.
The Gun Collector's Handbook of Values.
10th rev. ed. 1972. 12.50. Coward.

Nonte, George. The Firearms Encyclopedia.
(Illus.). 1973. 11.95. Times Mirror Mag.

Remington Gun Catalog 1877. 1.95. Pioneer
Pr.

Schroeder, John G., Jr. Guns Illustrated.
6th ed. (Illus.). 1974. pap. 4.95. Follett.

Schroeder, John G., Jr. Guns Illustrated.

Schroeder, Joseph J., Jr. ed. Arms of the
World. 1911. pap. 5.95. Digest Bks.

Tarassuk, L. Antique European & American
Firearms at the Heritage Museum.
Drapkin, R., tr. (Illus., Eng. & Rus.).
1973. 20.00. Arco.

U. S. Cartridge Company's Collection of
Firearms. 1971. 6.00. We Inc.

West, Bill. Remington Arms Catalogues.
1877-1899. 1st ed. (Illus.). 1971. 10.00.
B West.
Stevens Arms Catalogues, 1877-1899.
1st ed. (Illus.). 1971. 10.00. B West.

Firearms—Collectors and Collecting

Akehurst, Richard. Antique Weapons.
(Illus.). 1969. 5.95. Arco.

Bowman, Hank W. Antique Guns from the
Stagecoach Collection. (Illus.). 1964. lib.
bdg. 3.50. Arco.

Chapel, Charles E. Complete Book of Gun
Collecting (Illus.). 1961. 5.95. Coward.
Gun Collector's Handbook of Values.
9th rev. ed. (Illus.). 1970. 12.50. Coward.
The Gun Collector's Handbook of Values.
10th rev. ed. 1972. 12.50. Coward.

Dixie Gun Works Antique Arms Catalog.
0.50. Pioneer Pr.

Grancsay, Stephen. Early Firearms of Great
Britain & Ireland from the Collection of
Clay P. Bedford. (Illus.). 1971. 17.50. pap.
4.95 Metro Mus Art.

Hawkins, P. Price Guide to Antique Guns
& Pistols. (Illus.). 32.50. Newbury
Bks. Inc.

Kennard, A. M. French Pistols & Sporting
Guns. 1972. 2.95. Transatlantic.

Neal, Robert J. & Jinks, Roy G. Smith &
Wesson, 1857-1945. 1973. 25.00. A S
Barnes.

Pyne Press Editors. Guns & Hunting
Supplies 1890: John P. Lovell Arms Co.
(Illus.). 1971. pap. 5.95. Pyne Pr.

Rywell, Martin. Fell's Collector's Guide to
American Antique Firearms. 1973. pap.
2.45. Fell.
Gun Collector's Guide. 3.95. Pioneer Pr.

Shumaker, P. L. Colt's Variations of the
Old Model Pocket Pistol. 1957. 6.00.
Borden.

Tarassuk, L. Antique European & American
Firearms at the Hermitage Museum.
Drapkin, R., tr. (Illus., Eng. & Rus.).
1973. 20.00. Arco.

U.S. Cartridge Company's Collection of
Firearms. 1971. 6.00. We Inc.

Wahl, Paul. Gun Trader's Guide. 6th ed.
(Illus.). 1973. 6.95. Stoeger.

Firearms—History

Askins, Charles. Texans, Guns & History.
1970. 8.95. Winchester Pr.

Blackmore, Howard L. Guns & Rifles of the
World (Illus.). 1965. 30.00. Viking Pr.

Bowman, Hank W. Antique Guns from the
Stagecoach Collection. (Illus.). 1964. 3.50.
Arco.
Famous Guns from the Smithsonian
Collection. (Illus.). 1966. Arco.

Bowman, Hank W. & Cary, Lucian. Antique
Guns. (Illus.). 1953. 3.50. Arco.

Buchele, W. & Shumway, G. Recreating the
American Longrifle. (Illus.). 1973. pap. 6.50.
Shumway.

Burrell, Brian. Combat Weapons: Handguns
& Shoulder Arms of World War 2.
(Illus.). 1974. 9.50. Transatlantic.

Butler, David F. U. S. Firearms: The First
Century, 1776-1875. (Illus.). 15.00.
Winchester Pr.

Fuller, Claud E. Breech-Loader in the
Service 1816-1917. (Illus.). 1965. 14.50.
Flayderman.

Greener, William W. The Gun & Its
Development. 1881. 26.00. Finch Pr.

Hanauer, Elsie. Guns of the Wild West.
(Illus.). 1973. 12.00. A S Barnes.

Held, Robert. Age of Firearms. (Illus.). 1957.
12.50. Har-Row.

Hetrick, Calvin. The Bedford County Rifle &
Its Makers. (Illus.). 1973. pap. 4.00.
Shumway.

Jackson, Melvin H. & De Beer, Charles.
Eighteenth Century Gunfounding:
(Illus.). 1974. 15.00. Smithsonian.

Koller, Larry. Fireside Book of Guns. 1959.
12.95. S&S.
The Golden Guide to Guns. rev. ed.
(Illus.). 1974. pap. 3.95. Western Pub.

Lindsay, Merrill. One Hundred Great Guns.
(Illus.). 1967. 25.00. Walker & Co.

Neal, Keith W. & Back, D. H. A History
of English Gunmaking 1740-1790: John
Twigg & the Packington Story. (Illus.).
1974. 55.00. S P Bernet.

Peterson, Harold L. & Elman, Robert.
Great Guns. (Illus.). 1971. 14.95. G&D.

Pollard, Hugh B. History of Firearms.
(Illus.). 1974. 22.50. B. Franklin.

Rosebush, Waldo E. American Firearms &
the Changing Frontier. 1962. pap. 2.00.
Eastern Wash.

Rywell, Martin. American Antique Pistols.
2.00. Pioneer Pr.
Confederate Guns. 2.00. Pioneer Pr.

Smythe, John & Barwick, Humphrey. Bow
Versus Gun: Certain Discourses, & a
Breefe Discourse. 1974. 8.00. Shumway.

Tarassuk, Leonid. Antique European &
American Firearms at the Hermitage
Museum. limited ed. (Illus., Eng & Rus.).
1973. 30.00. Arma Pr.

Tout, Thomas F. Firearms in England in the
Fourteenth Century. (Illus.). 1969.
softbound 4.00. Shumway.

West, Bill. Browning Arms & History,
1847-1973. (Illus.). 1972. 20.00. B West.
Marlin & Ballard, Arms & History.
1861-1971. (Illus.). 1972. 22.00. B West.
Remington Arms & History, 1816-1971.
(Illus.). 1972. 20.00. B West.
Savage & Stevens, Arms & History,
1849-1971. (Illus.). 1971. 22.00. B West.
Winchester-Complete: All Wins &
Forerunners, 1849-1970. (Illus.). 1972.
20.00. B West.

Wilkinson, F. **Flintlock Guns & Rifles.** (Illus.). 1971. 4.95. Stackpole.
Williamson, Harry F. **Winchester: The Gun That Won the West.** (Illus.). 5.98. A S Barnes.

Firearms—Identification

Mathews, J. Howard. **Firearms Identification: Original Photographs & Other Illustrations of Hand Guns,** Vol. 2. 1973. Repr. of 1962 ed. 44.75. C C Thomas.
Firearms Identification: Original Photographs & Other Illustrations of Hand Guns. Data of Rifling Characteristics of Hand Guns & Rifles. Vol. 3. Wilimovsky, Allan E., ed. (Illus.). 1973. 69.50. C C Thomas.
Firearms Identification: The Laboratory Examination of Small Arms, Rifling Characteristics in Hand Guns, & Notes on Automatic Pistols. Vol. 1. 1972. Repr. of 1962 ed. 44.75. C C Thomas.

Firearms—Industry and Trade

Albaugh, William A., 3rd, et al. **Confederate Handguns: Concerning the Guns, the Men Who Made Them, the Times of Their Use.** (Illus.). 1963. 1963 first ed. 12.00. 1969 ed. 9.00. Shumway.
Bakal, Carl. **Right to Bear Arms.** 1966. 6.95. McGraw.
Carey, A. Merwyn. **English, Irish & Scottish Firearms Makers.** (Illus.). 1967. 6.50. Arco.
Deyrup, Felicia J. **Arms Making in the Connecticut Valley.** 2nd ed. (Illus.). 1970. 10.00. Shumway.
Grancsay, Stephen V. & Lindsay, Merrill. **Illustrated British Firearms Patents 1718-1853.** limited ed. (Illus.). 75.00. Arma Pr.
Hanifhen, Frank C. & Engelbrecht, Helmuth C. **Merchants of Death: A Study of the International Armaments Industry.** lib. bdg. 16.00. Garland Pub.
Hartzler, Daniel D. **Arms Makers of Maryland.** 1974. 27.50. Shumway.
Kirkland, Turner. **Southern Derringers of the Mississippi Valley.** 2.00. Pioneer Pr.
Lavin, James D. **History of Spanish Firearms** (Illus.). 1965. 9.95. Arco.
Lindsay, Merrill. **One Hundred Great Guns.** (Illus.). 1967. 25.00. Walker & Co.
Noel-Baker, Philip. **Private Manufacture of Armaments.** 1971. pap. 6.00. Dover.
Russell, Carl P. **Guns of the Early Frontier.** 5.00. Peter Smith.
Shumway, George. **Arms Makers of Philadelphia.** Shumway.
Thayer, George. **War Business.** 1969. 6.95. S & S.
West, Bill. **Browning Arms & History, Eighteen Forty-Two to Nineteen Seventy-Three.** (Illus.). 1972. 22.00. B West.

Fowling

Bauer, Edwin A. **Duck Hunter's Bible.** softbound 2.50. Doubleday.
Becker, A. C., Jr. **Waterfowl in the Marshes.** (Illus.). 1969. 7.50. A S Barnes.
Bourjaily, Vance. **Unnatural Enemy.** (Illus.). 1963. 6.95. Dial.
Carroll, Hanson, et al. **Waterfowler's World,** 1973. 12.95. Winchester Pr.
Day, J. Wentworth. **The Modern Fowler.** 1973. Repr. of 1934 ed. 13.95. British Bk Ctr.
Duffey, David M. **Bird Hunting Know-How.** 1968. 5.95. Van Nos Reinhold.
Gresham, Grits. **Complete Wildfowler.** 1973. pap. 5.95. Stoeger.
Rice, F. Philip & Dahl, John. **Game Bird Hunting.** 1965. pap. 2.95. Times Mirror Mag.
Russell, Dan M. **Dove Shooter's Handbook.** 1974. 6.95. Winchester Pr.
Waterman, Charles F. **Hunting Upland Birds.** 1972. 8.95. Winchester Pr.

Waterman, Charles F. **Hunting Upland Birds.** 1972. 5.95. Stoeger.

Game and Game Birds

Bauer, Erwin. **Treasury of Big Game Animals.** (Illus.). 1972. 12.50. Har-Row.
Treasury of Big Game Animals. (Illus.). 1972. 12.50. Times Mirror Mag.
Becker, A. C., Jr. **Game & Bird Calling.** (Illus.). 1972. 7.95. A S Barnes.
Belton, I. M. **Poultry & Game.** (Illus.). 4.00. Soccer.
Bishop, Richard E. & Williams, Russ. **The Ways of the Wildfowl.** (Illus.). 1971. 24.95. Doubleday.
Brusewitz, Gunnar. **Hunting.** (Illus.). 1969. 25.00. Stein & Day.
Burk, Bruce. **Game Bird Carving.** (Illus.). 1972. 12.50. Winchester Pr.
Dasmann, Raymond F. **Wildlife Biology.** (Illus.). 1964. 9.75. Wiley.
Edminster, Frank C. **American Game Birds of Field & Forest.** 1971. 17.50. Scribner.
Evans, George B. **Upland Shooting Life.** (Illus.). 1971. 10.00. Knopf.
Gooch, B. **Squirrels & Squirrel Hunting.** 6.00. Cornell Maritime.
Hagerbaumer, David. **Selected American Game Birds.** 1972. 30.00. Caxton.
Henderson, J. Y. & Taplinger, Richard. **Circus Doctor.** (Illus.). 1951. 5.95. Little.
McCristal, Vic. **Top End Safari.** 7.50. Soccer.
Ormond, Clyde. **Small Game Hunting.** (Illus.). 1974. pap. 1.95. B&N.
Pray, Leon. **Nineteen Sixty-Five Bird Mounting Book.** 1965. 2.00. Reel Trophy.
Rue, Leonard L. **Sportsman's Guide to Game Animals.** (Illus.). 1968. 7.95. Har-Row.
Rue, Leonard L., III. **Game Birds of North America.** (Illus.). 1973. 12.50. Times Mirror Mag.
Scott, P. **Coloured Key to the Wildfowl of the World.** rev. ed. (Illus.). Repr. 7.50. Heinman.
Scott, Peter. **A Coloured Key to the Wildfowl of the World.** rev. ed. (Illus.). 1972. 8.50. Intl Pubns Serv.
Waterman, Charles F. **Hunting Upland Birds.** 1972. 5.95. pap. Stoeger.

Game and Game Birds—Africa

Clancey, P. A. **Gamebirds of South Africa.** 15.75. Purnell Lib. Serv.

Game and Game Birds—France

Villenave, G. M. **Chasse.** (Illus., Fr.). 18.50. Larousse.

Game and Game Birds—New Zealand

Poole, A. L. **Wild Animals in New Zealand.** (Illus.). 1969. 10.95. Reed.

Game and Game Birds—North America

Conley, Clare. **The Field & Stream Guide to Upland Game Birds.** 1973. pap. 1.25. Popular Lib.
Holland, Dan. **Upland Game Hunter's Bible.** (Illus.). softbound 2.50. Doubleday.
Jaques, Florence P. **Geese Fly High.** (Illus.). 1964 Repr. of 1939 ed. 5.50. U of Minn Pr.
Knap, Jerome. **The Hunter's Handbook.** (Illus.). 1973. 7.95. Scribner.
Leopold, A. Starker & Darling, F. Fraser. **Wildlife in Alaska.** 1973. Repr. of 1953 ed. 9.25. Greenwood.
Leopold, Aldo. **Game Management.** (Illus.). 1933. pap. text ed. 5.95. Scribner.
Miracle, Leonard, et al. **New Hunter's Encyclopedia.** rev. ed. 1965. 24.95. Stackpole.
Rice, F. Philip & Dahl, John. **Game Bird Hunting.** 1965. pap. 2.95. Times Mirror Mag.

Rue, Leonard L., 3rd. **Sportsman's Guide to Game Animals.** (Illus.). 1968. 7.95. Times Mirror Mag.
Strung, M. **Hunter's Almanac.** 1971. 4.95. Macmillan.
Walsh, H. D. **Outlaw Gunner.** 1971. 8.50. Cornell Maritime.
Walsh, Roy E. **Gunning the Chesapeake.** 1960. 7.00. Cornell Maritime.
Waterman, Charles F. **Hunting Upland Birds.** 1972. 5.95. pap. Stoeger.
Zim, Herbert S. & Sprunt, Alexander, 4th. **Game Birds.** 1961. 4.95; pap. 1.50. Western Pub.

Gatling Guns

Wahl, Paul & Toppel, Donald R. **Gatling Gun.** (Illus.). 1965. 5.95. Arco.

Guns

Daenhardt, Rainer. **Espingarda Perfeyta: or the Perfect Gun: Rules of Its Use Together with Necessary Instructions for Its Construction & Precepts for Good Aiming.** Daenhardt, Rainer, tr. from Port (Illus., Eng. & Port.). 1974. 22.50. S P Bernet.
George, John N. **English Pistols & Revolvers.** 10.00. Saifer.
Kuhlhoff, Pete. **Kuhlhoff on Guns.** (Illus.). 1970. 5.95. Winchester Pr.
Nonte, George C., Jr. **Home Guide to Muzzle Loaders.** 1974. 6.95. Stackpole.
Peterson, Harold. **Historical Treasury of American Guns.** pap. 4.95. Benjamin Co.

Gunsmithing

Ackley, Parker O. **Home Gun Care & Repair.** (Illus.). 1974. 2.95. Stackpole.
Angier, R. H. **Firearms Blueing & Browning.** 1936. 5.00. Stackpole.
Bish, Tommy L. **Home Gunsmithing Digest.** Lewis, Jack. ed. 1970. pap. 5.95. Digest Bks.
Demeritt, Dwight B., Jr. **Maine Made Guns & Their Makers.** (Illus.). 22.00. Maine St Mus.
Dunlap, Roy F. **Gunsmithing.** 1963. 10.00. Stackpole.
Gill, Harold B., Jr. **Gunsmith in Colonial Virginia.** (Illus.). 7.50. pap. 4.50. U Pr of Va.
Grancsay. Stephen A. & Lindsay, Merrill. **Master French Gunsmith's Designs: From the Twelfth to Fourteenth Century.** limited ed. (Illus.). 89.00. Arma Pr.
Gun Digest Editors, ed. **NRA Collector's Series: 1885-1888 1906-1923.** 1970 pap. 2.95. Digest Bks.
Hartzler, Daniel D. **Arms Makers of Maryland.** (Illus.). 1974. 27.50. Shumway.
Howe, James V. **Amateur Guncraftsman.** (Illus.). 1967. pap. 1.95. Funk & W.
Modern Gunsmith. 2 Vols. (Illus.). 1970. 12.50 ea. Vol. 1. Vol. 2. 25.00, boxed set. Funk & W.
Howe, Walter J. **Professional Gunsmithing.** (Illus.). 1946. 10.00. Stackpole.
Hutslar, Donald A. **Gunsmiths of Ohio: 18th & 19th Centuries** (Illus.). 1973. 29.50. Shumway.
Kauffman, Henry J. **Gunsmith: Early American Occupation.** pap. 3.00. Century Hse.
Kist, J. B., et al. **Dutch Muskets & Pistols: An Illustrated History of 17th Century Gunmaking in the Low Countries.** (Illus.). 1974. casebound 20.00. Shumway.
MacFarland, Harold E. **Gunsmithing Simplified.** (Illus.). 8.95. A S Barnes.
Introduction to Modern Gunsmithing. (Illus.). 1965. 6.95. Stackpole.
Newell, A. Donald. **Gunstock Finishing & Care.** (Illus.). 1949. 9.50. Stackpole.
Norton Art Gallery. **Artistry in Arms: The Art of Gunsmithing & Gun Engraving.** (Illus.). 1971. pap. 2.50. Norton Art.

Shumway, George. **Longrifles of Note Pennsylvania.** (Illus.) 1968. softbound 3.95. Shumway.

Walker, Ralph. **Hobby Gunsmithing.** (Illus.). 1972. pap. 5.95. Follett.

Gunstocks

Arthur, Robert. **Shotgun Stock: Design, Construction & Embellishment.** (Illus.). 1970. 15.00. A S Barnes.

Hawken Rifles

Baird, John D. **Fifteen Years in the Hawken Lode.** (Illus.). 1971. 10.00. Buckskin Pr.
Hawken Rifles: The Mountain Man's Choice. 1968. 10.00. Buckskin Pr.

Hunting

Babcock, Havilah. **Jaybirds Go to Hell on Friday.** 1964. 4.95. HR&W.

Baily's Hunting Directory, 1973-1974. annual (Illus.). 1974. 19.95. British Bk Ctr.

Bashline, L. James, ed. **The Eastern Trail.** (Illus.). 1972. 8.95. Freshet Pr.

Bauer, Erwin. **Treasury of Big Game Animals.** (Illus.). 1972. 12.50. Har-Row.

Bauer, Erwin A. **Hunter's Digest.** 1973. 6.95. Follett.

Beckford, Peter. **Thoughts on Hunting.** (Illus.). 1972. Repr. 4.50. British Bk Ctr.

Bourjaily, Vance. **Country Matters: Collected Reports from the Fields & Streams of Iowa & Other Places.** 1973. 8.95. Dial.

Brander, Michael. **Hunting & Shooting.** (Illus.). 1971. 13.95. Putnam.

Buckle, Esme. **Dams of National Hunt Winners.** Incl. 1955-60. 20.00; Supplement 1, 1963-64. 4.50; Supplement 2. 4.50. 1972. British Bk Ctr.

Buckman, C. T. **Seventy-Five Years with the Shotgun.** (Illus.). 1974. 5.95. Valley Calif.

Cabell, Charles A., 3rd & St. Clair, David. **Safari: Pan Am's Guide to Hunting with Gun & Camera Round the World.** (Illus.). 1969. 5.95. Doubleday.

Carlisle, Norman & Michelsohn, David. **The Complete Guide to Treasure Hunting.** (Illus.). 1973. 8.95. Regnery.

Churchill, Robert. **Game Shooting: Churchill's Guide.** Hastings, Macdonald, ed. 1972. 9.95. Stackpole.

Clarke, I. A. **An Introduction to Beagling.** (Illus.) 1974. 4.95. British Bk Ctr.

Clayton, Michael. **A-Hunting We Will Go.** 1972. 5.95 British Bk Ctr.

Cone, Arthur L., Jr. **Complete Guide to Hunting.** (Illus.) 1970. 6.95. Macmillan.

Cramond, Michael. **Hunting & Fishing in North America.** (Illus.). 1953. 9.95. U. of Okla Pr.

Dalrymple, Byron H. **North American Big Game Hunting.** 1974. 5.95. pap. Stoeger.

Dickey, Charles. **Charley Dickey's Quail Hunting.** 1974. pap. 2.95. Stoeger.

Dodd, Ed. **Mark Trail's Hunting Tips.** (Illus.). 1969. pap. 1.00. S & S.

East, Ben. **The Ben East Hunting Book.** (Illus.). 1974. 13.95. Har-Row.

Elliott, Charles. **Outdoor Observer: How to See, Hear & Interpret in the Natural World.** 1970. 4.50. Dutton.

Elman, Robert. **The Hunter's Field Guide.** 1973. 12.50. Knopf.

Field & Stream. **Field & Stream Reader.** facs. ed. 1946. 13.50. Bks for Libs.

Gordon-Cumming, Rouleyn G. **The Lion Hunter of South Africa.** 1972. Repr. of 1850 ed. 18.50. Bks for Libs.

Gorman, Gerd, ed. **Hunter & Hunted.** 1974. pap. 2.95. (Delta). Dell.

Grey, Hugh, ed. **Field & Stream Treasury.** 1971. 12.95. HR&W.

Grinnell, George B. & Sheldon, Charles, eds. **Hunting & Conservation.** 1970. Repr. of 1925 ed. 25.00. Arno.

Hamilton, Donald. **Donald Hamilton on Guns & Hunting.** 1970. pap. 0.75. Fawcett World.

Heuser, Ken. **The Whitetail Deer Guide.** (Illus.). 1972. 6.95. HR&W.

Hill, Gene. **A Hunter's Fireside Book: Tales of Dogs, Ducks, Birds & Guns.** (Illus.). 1972. 7.95. Winchester Pr.

Hinman, Bob. **The Duck Hunter's Handbook.** 1974. 8.95. Winchester Pr.

Holden, Philip. **Hunter by Profession.** (Illus.). 1974. 9.90. Intl Pubns Serv.

Jaipal, Major. **Great Hunt.** 4.75. Cariton.

James, David & Stephens, Wilson, eds. **In Praise of Hunting.** (Illus.). 1961. 10.00 Devin.

Johnson, et al. **Outdoor Tips: A Remington Sportsmen's Library Bk.** pap. 2.95. Benjamin Co.

Kaye, Alex. **Hunting for All Seasons.** (Illus.). 1973. pap. 1.50. Stadia Sports Pub.

Klineburger, Bert & Hurst, Vernon W. **Big Game Hunting Around the World.** (Illus.). 1969. 15.00. Exposition.

Knap, Jerome. **The Hunter's Handbook.** (Illus.). 1973. 7.95. Scribner.

Knap, Jerome & Knap, Alyson. **Training the Versatile Gun Dog.** (Illus.). 1974. 7.95. Scribner.

Koller, Larry. **Fireside Book of Guns.** 1959. 12.95. S&S.

Laycock, George. **Shotgunner's Bible.** (Illus.) 1969. softbound 2.50. Doubleday.

Lindner, Kurt. **The Second Hunting Book of Wolfgang Birkner.** (Illus.). 1973. with case 175.00. Arma Pr.

Lockard, John R. **Bee Hunting.** pap. 0.60. Fur-Fish-Game.

McCristal, Vic. **Top End Safari.** 7.50. Soccer.

McGrail, William & McGrail, Joie. **Catch & the Feast.** (Illus.). 1969. 20.00. Weybright.

Madden, D. H. **Chapter of Mediaeval History.** 1969. Repr. of 1924 ed. 12.50. Kennikat.

Madden, Dodgson H. **Diary of Master William Silence: A Study of Shakespeare & Elizabethan Sport.** 1970. Repr. of 1897 ed. 17.95. Haskell.

Mannix, Daniel P. **Sporting Chance, Unusual Methods of Hunting.** (Illus.). 1967. 7.95. Dutton.

Merrill, William K. **Hunter's Bible.** (Illus.). 1968. 2.50. Doubleday.

Needwork. **The Hunting Quiz Book.** pap. 2.95. British Bk Ctr.

O'Connor, Jack, et al. **Complete Book of Shooting: Rifles, Shotguns, Handguns.** (Illus.). 1965. 7.95. Times Mirror Mag.

Ormond, Clyde. **Complete Book of Hunting.** rev. ed. (Illus.). 1972. 7.95 Harper & Row. **Small Game Hunting.** 1970. 4.95. Dutton.

Ortega Y Gasset, Jose. **Meditations on Hunting.** 1972. 9.95. Scribner.

Page, Warren. **One Man's Wilderness.** 1973. 8.95. HR&W.

Peper, Eric & Rikhoff, Jim, eds. **Hunting & Fishing Moments of Truth.** 1973. limited ed. 25.00. Winchester Pr. **Hunting Moments of Truths.** 1973. 8.95. Winchester Pr.

Petzal, David E., ed. **Experts' Book of the Shooting Sports.** 9.95. S&S

Pollard, Hugh B. **The Mystery of Scent.** 1972. 4.95. British Bk Ctr.

Pollard, Jack. **Straight Shooting.** 9.00. Soccer.

Pryce, Dick. **Safe Hunting: An Introduction to Hunting, Guns, & Gun Safety.** (Illus.). 1974. 6.95. McKay.

Pulling, Pierre. **Game & the Gunner: Common-Sense Observations on the Practice of Game Conservation & Sport Hunting.** 1973. 8.95. Winchester Pr.

Randolph, J. W. **World of Wood, Field & Stream.** 1962. 3.95. HR&W.

Reiger, George, ed. **Zane Grey: Outdoorsman.** (Illus.). 1972. 9.95. P-H.

Rudner, Ione & Rudner, Jalmar. **Hunter & His Art—A survey of Rock Art in Southern Africa.** (Illus.). 1970. 35.00. Verry.

Scharff, Robert. **Hunter's Game, Gun & Dog Guide.** 1963. pap. 1.95. Macmillan.

Schwenk, Sigrid, et al, eds. **Multum et Multa: Beitraege zur Literatur, Geschichte und Kultur der Jagd.** (Illus.). 1971. 50.00. De Gruyter.

Sell, Francis. **Art of Small Game Hunting.** new ed. 1973. pap. 2.95. Stackpole.

Severinsen, Keith. **Hunt the Far Mountain.** (Illus.). 1970. 7.50. Reed.

Sharp, Hal. **Sportsman's Digest of Hunting.** 1963. pap. 1.75. B&N.

Situacion Demografica: **No. 1 Agricultura, Ganaderia, Silvicultura, Caza y Pesca.** (America En Cifras Ser., 1970). (Span.). 1.00. OAS.

Sparano, Vin T. **The Complete Outdoors Encyclopedia.** (Illus.). 1973. 13.95. Har-Row.

Spiller, Burton. **Grouse Feathers.** (Sportsmen's Classics Ser). (Illus.). 1972. 7.50. Crown.

Spiller, Burton L. **More Grouse Feathers.** (Illus.). 1972. 7.50. Crown.

Stehsel, Donald L. **Hunting the California Black Bear.** (Illus.). pap. 4.95. Stehsel.

Strung, Norman. **Deer Hunting.** (Illus.) 1973. 7.95. Lippincott.

Stung, N. **Hunter's Almanac.** 1971. 4.95. Macmilan.

Tapply, Horace G. **Sportsman's Notebook.** 1964. 7.95. HR&W.

Taylor, Zack. **Successful Waterfowling.** (Illus.). 1974. 8.95. Crown.

Van Der Post, Laurens. **The Heart of the Hunter.** (Illus.). 1971, pap. 2.50. Morrow.

Washburn, O. A. **General Red.** (Illus.). 5.50. Jenkins.

Waterman, Charles F. **Hunter's World.** (Illus.). 1970. 15.00. Random. **Hunting in America.** new ed. (Illus.). 1973. 16.95. HR&W.

Willett, Roderick. **Gun Safety.** (Illus.). 1967. 5.25. Intl. Pubns Serv.

Wilson, James. **The Rod & the Gun.** (Illus.). 1973. Repr. of 1844 ed. 16.95. British Bk Ctr.

Woodcock, E. N. **Fifty Years a Hunter & Trapper.** pap. 2.00. Fur-Fish-Game.

Woolner, Frank. **Timberdoodle: A Thorough Guide to Woodcock Hunting.** (Illus.). 1974. 7.95. Crown.

Woolner, Lionel. **Hunting of the Hare.** 1972. 7.50. British Bk Ctr.

Hunting—Dictionaries

Brander, Michael. **Dictionary of Sporting Terms.** (Illus.). 1968. text ed. 6.50. Fernhill.

Burnand, Tony. **Dictionnaire Chasse.** (Fr.) 1970. 4.75. Larousse.

Hunting—History

Brusewitz, Gunnar. **Hunting.** (Illus.). 1969. 25.00. Stein & Day.

Hunting—Africa

Cloudsley-Thompson, J. L. **Animal Twilight, Man & Game in Eastern Africa.** (Illus.) 1967. 7.95. Dufour.

Findlay, Frederick R. N. & Schreiner, Olive. **Account of Shooting Trips in the Cheringoma & Gorongoza Divisions of Portuguese South-East Africa & in Zululand.** Repr. of 1903 ed. 32.50. Bks for Libs.

Gillmore, Parker. **Days & Nights by the Desert.** Repr. of 1888 ed. 16.50 Bks for Libs.

Haardt, Georges M. & Audouin-Dubreuil, Louis. **Black Journey: Across Central Africa with Citroen Expedition.** (Illus.). Repr. of 1927 ed. 18.25. Negro U Pr.

Hemingway, Ernest. **Green Hills of Africa.** 1935. 6.95; pap. 2.65. Scribner.

Holman, Dennis. **Inside Safari Hunting.** Rundgren, Eric. ed. (Illus.). 1970. 6.95. Putnam.

Holub, Emil. **Seven Years in South Africa.** 2 Vols. 1881. Set. 39.50. Scholarly.

MacQueen, Peter. **In Wildest Africa.** 1909. 21.50. Scholarly.

Mohr, Jack. **Hyenas in My Bedroom.** (Illus.). 1969. 5.95. A S Barnes.

Nassau, Robert H. **In an Elephant Corral: And Other Tales of West African Experiences.** Repr. of 1912 ed. 8.00. Negro U Pr.

Ruark, Robert. **Horn of the Hunter.** 1970. pap. 0.95. Fawcett World.

Hunting—Alaska

Hubback, T. R. **Ten Thousand Miles to Alaska for Moose & Sheep.** facs. ed. 1921. 6.00. pap. 4.00. Shorey.

Waugh, Hal & Keim. **Charles J. Fair Chase with Alaskan Guides.** (Illus.). 1972. pap. 3.95. Alaska Northwest.

Hunting—Arctic Regions

Nelson, Richard K. **Hunters of the Northern Ice.** 1969. 12.50. U. of Chicago Pr.

Stefansson, Vilhjalmur. **Hunters of the Great North.** 1922. 22.00. AMS Pr.

Hunting—Asia

Gates, Elgin. **Trophy Hunter in Asia.** (Illus.). 1971. 12.50. Winchester Pr.

Girsham, Jack & Thomas, Lowell. **Burma Jack.** 1971. 5.95. Norton.

Hunting—Australia

Byrne. **Duckshooting Down Under.** 1974. 8.95. Reed.

Stewart, Allan. **The Green Eyes Are Buffalos.** 13.25. Soccer.

Hunting—France

Villenave, G. M. **Chasse.** (Illus., Fr.). 18.50. Larousse.

Hunting—Germany

Dalby, David. **Lexicon of the Mediaeval German Hunt: A Lexicon of Middle High German Terms, 1050-1500, Associated with the Chase, Hunting with Bows, Falconry, Trapping & Fowling.** 1965. 60.00. DeGruyter.

Hunting—Great Britain

Edward of Norwich. **Master of Game: Oldest English Book on Hunting.** Baillie-Grohman, William A. & Baillie-Grohman, F., eds. (Illus.). Repr. of 1904 ed. 45.00. AMS Pr.

Hewitt, H. P. **Fairest Hunting: Hunting & Watching Exmoor Deer.** pap. 4.50. British Bk Ctr.

Knutsford, Viscount. **The Haunted Hunt: A Story of the Hunting Field.** 8.50. British Bk Ctr.

Hunting—Greece

Hull, Denison B. **Hounds & Hunting in Ancient Greece.** (Illus.). 1964. 15.00. U of Chicago Pr.

Hunting—India

Corbett, Jim. **Man-Eaters of India.** 1957. 8.50. Oxford U Pr.

Singh, Kesri. **Hints on Tiger Shooting.** 1969. pap. 1.50. InterCulture.
The Tiger of Rajasthan. 1967. pap. 1.50. InterCulture.

Turner, J.E. **Man-Eaters & Memories.** 1967. pap. 1.50. InterCulture.

Hunting—North America

Alaska Magazine Editors. **Alaska Magazine's Alaska Hunting Guide.** 1973. pap. 3.95. Alaska Northwest.

Anderson, Luther A. **How to Hunt American Small Game.** (Illus.). 1969. 5.95. Funk & W.

Dalrymple, Byron W. **North American Big Game Hunting.** 1974. 10.00. Winchester Pr.

Duffy, M. **Hunting & Fishing in Louisiana.** 1969. 3.95. Pelican.

Holland, Dan. **Upland Game Hunter's Bible.** (Illus.). softbound 2.50. Doubleday.

Hunter, Rodello. **Wyoming Wife.** 1969. 5.95. Knopf.

Knap, Jerome. **The Hunter's Handbook.** (Illus.). 1973. 7.95. Scribner.
Where to Fish & Hunt in North America: A Complete Sportsmen's Guide. (Illus.). 7.95. Pagurian.

Leopold, Luna B., ed. **Round River: From The Journals of Aldo Leopold.** (Illus.). 1972. pap. 1.75. Oxford U Pr.

Mathiessen, Peter. **Wildlife in America.** (Illus.). 1964. pap. 2.25. Viking Pr.

Miracle, Leonard, et al. **New Hunter's Encyclopedia.** rev. ed. 1965. 24.95. Stackpole.

O'Connor, Jack. **The Art of Hunting Big Game in North America.** 1967. 8.95. Popular Sci.

Rearden, Jim. **Alaska Magazine's Alaska Hunting Guide.** 1973. pap. 3.95. Alaska Northwest.

Hunting—U.S.

Babcock, H. **My Health Is Better in November.** (Illus.). 1960. 5.95. HR&W.

Cadbury, Warder, intro. by. **Journal of a Hunting Excursion to Louis Lake. 1851.** (Illus.). 1961. 4.95. Syracuse U Pr.

Calkins, Frank J. **Rocky Mountain Warden.** (Illus.). 1971. 6.95. Knopf.

Cory, Charles B. **Hunting & Fishing in Florida, Including a Key to the Water Birds.** 1970. Repr. of 1896 ed. 11.00. Arno.

Cox, Alex. **Deer Hunting in Texas.** rev. ed. (Illus.). 1971. 6.95. Naylor.

Dalrymple, Byron. **Complete Guide to Hunting Across America.** (Illus.). 1970. 10.00. Popular Sci.

Dietz. Lew. **Touch of Wilderness: A Maine Woods Journal.** 1970. 5.95. HR&W.

Dodge, Richard I. **Hunting Grounds of the Great West.** Repr. of 1878 ed. 18.00. Finch Pr.

Foster, William H. **New England Grouse Shooting.** (Illus.) 1970. 12.50. Scribner.

Gohdes, Clarence, ed. **Hunting in the Old South: Original Narratives of the Hunters.** (Illus.). 1967. 7.50. La State U Pr.

Jefferson, John. **Hunter's Guide to Texas.** (Illus.). 3.95. Jenkins.

Lang, Varley. **Follow the Water.** (Illus.). 1961. 4.50. Blair.

McTeer, Ed. **Adventures in the Woods & Waters of the Low Country.** 4.95. Beaufort.

Murray, William H. **Adventures in the Wilderness.** Verner, William K., ed. (Illus.). 1970. Repr. 10.50. Syracuse U Pr.

Palliser, John. **Solitary Rambles & Adventures of a Hunter in the Prairies.** (Illus.). 1969. Repr. of 1853 ed. 5.00. C E Tuttle.

Podge, Richard I. **Hunting Grounds of the Great West.** Repr. of 1878 ed. 18.00. Finch Pr.

Roosevelt, Theodore. **Hunting Trips of a Ranchman.** 1970. Repr. of 1885 ed. 12.50. Gregg.
Outdoor Pastimes of an American Hunter. 1970. Repr. of 1905 ed. 16.00. Arno.
Ranch Life & the Hunting-Trail. 1970. Repr. of 1901 ed. 8.00. Arno.
Ranch Life & the Hunting-Trail. 1966. Repr. of 1899 ed. 8.95. Univ Microfilms.
Ranch Life in the Far West. (Illus.). 1968. 6.00. Northland.
Theodore Roosevelt's America. Wiley. Farida, ed. (Illus.) 1955. 7.50. Devin.

Roosevelt, Theodore. (Cont'd)
Wilderness Hunt. 1970. Repr. of 1900 ed. 11.00. Gregg.

Tillett, Paul. **Doe Day: The Antlerless Deer Controversy in New Jersey.** 1963. 6.00; pap. 2.75. Rutgers U Pr.

Tome, Philip. **Pioneer Life or Thirty Years a Hunter: Being Scenes & Adventures in the Life of Philip Tome.** (Illus.). 1971. Repr. of 1854 ed. 10.00. Arno.

Waterman, Charles F. **Hunting in America.** new ed. (Illus.). 1973. 16.95. HR&W.

Hunting—Primitive

Coon, Carleton. **The Hunting Peoples.** 1971. 10.00, pap. 3.95. Little.

Lee, Richard B. & De Vore, Irven, eds. **Man the Hunter.** 1968. 12.50; pap. 4.95. Aldine.

Oswalt, Wendell. **Habitat & Technology.** 1973. text ed. 7.00. HR&W.

Service, Elman R. **Hunters.** (Illus.). 1966. pap. 2.40. P-H.

Hunting Dogs

Bernard, Art. **Dog Days.** 1969. 5.95. Caxton.

Duffey, Dave. **Hunting Dog Know-How.** (Illus.). 1972. 5.95. Winchester Pr.
Hunting Hounds: How to Choose, Train & Handle America's Trail & Tree Hounds. (Illus.) 1972. 5.95. Winchester Pr.

Falk, John R. **Practical Hunter's Dog Book.** (Illus.). 1971. 5.95. pap. Stoeger.

Griffen, Jeff. **Hunting Dogs of America.** (Illus.). 1964. 4.95. Doubleday.

Hartley, Oliver. **Hunting Dogs.** pap. 2.00. Fur-Fish-Game.

Henschel, Stan. **How to Raise & Train a Chesapeake Bay Retriever.** 1965. pap. 1.50. TFH Pubns.
How to Raise & Train a Coonhound. pap. 1.50. TFH Pubns.
How to Raise & Train a Labrador Retriever. (Illus.). pap. 1.29. TFH Pubns.

Modern Dog Encyclopedia Staff. **Hunting Dogs & Their Uses.** (Illus) 1962. pap. 0.95. Macmillan.
Training Hunting Dogs. (Illus.). 1962. pap. 0.95. Macmillan.

Monk, John. **Gundogs.** (Illus.). 1969. 5.50. C. E. Tuttle.

Rice, F. Philip & Dahl, John. **Hunting Dogs.** 1967. 4.95. Har-Row.

Stetson. **Hunting with Scenthounds.** 1965. pap. 1.50. TFH Pubns.

Stetson, Joe. **Handbook of Gundogs.** 1965. pap. 1.50. TFH Pubns.
Hunting with Flushing Dogs. 1965. pap. 1.50. TFH Pubns.

Whitney, Leon F. & Underwood, Acil B. **Coon Hunter's Handbook.** Hart, Ernest, ed. (Illus.). 1952. 4.95. HR&W.

Wolters, Richard A. **Gun Dog. Revolutionary Rapid Training Method.** (Illus.). 1961. 6.95. Dutton.

Hunting Dogs—Pointers

Hart, Ernest H. **How to Raise & Train a Pointer.** (Illus.). 1966. pap. 1.00. TFH Pubns.

Johns, Richard S. **German Shorthaired Pointers.** (Illus.). 1974. pap. 2.95. TFH Pubns.

Pet Library Ltd. **Know Your Setters & Pointers.** (Illus.). softbound 1.00. Doubleday.

Stetson, Joe. **Hunting with Pointing Dogs.** 1965. pap. TFH Pubns.

Hunting Dogs—Retrievers

Coykendall, Ralph W., Jr. **You & Your Retriever.** (Illus.) 1963. 4.95. Doubleday.

Fowler, Ann & Walters, D. K., eds. **Charles Morgan on Retrievers.** (Illus.) 1968. 12.50. October.

Free, James L. **Training Your Retriever.** 3rd rev. ed. (Illus.). 1970. 6.95. Coward.

Kersley, J. A. **Training the Retriever: A Manual** (Illus). 1971. 7.95. Howell Bk.

Leclerc, Maurice J. **Retriever Trainer's Manual.** (Illus). 1962. 8.50. Ronald.

Pet Library Ltd. **Know Your Retriever.** (Illus). softbound 1.00. Doubleday.

Shoemaker, Paul E. **Training Retrievers for Field Trials & Hunting.** 1970. 12.95. Superior Pub.

Stetson, Joe. **Hunting with Retrievers.** pap. 1.00. TFH Pubns.

Terroux, Sally J. **How to Raise & Train a Flatcoated Retriever.** (Illus). 1968. pap. 1.50. TFH Pubns.

Wolters, Richard A. **Water Dog.** (Illus). 6.95. Dutton.

Hunting Dogs—Setters

Pet Library Ltd. **Know Your Setters & Pointer.** (Illus). softbound 1.00. Doubleday.

Hunting Stories

Brister, Bob. **Moss, Mallards & Mules: And Other Hunting & Fishing Stories.** 1973. 8.95. Winchester Pr.

Ford, Corey. **You Can Always Tell A Fisherman.** (Illus). 1959. 2.95. HR&W.

Neasham, V. Aubrey. **Wild Legacy: California Hunting & Fishing Tales.** (Illus). 1973. 6.50. Howell-North.

Hunting with Bow and Arrow

Bear, Fred. **Archer's Bible.** (Illus). 1968. softbound 2.50. Doubleday.

James, M. R. **Bowhunting for Whitetail & Mule Deer.** (Illus). 1974. 7.95. pap. 5.95. O'Hara.

Laycock, George & Bauer, Erwin. **Hunting with Bow & Arrow.** 1965. 3.95. Arco.

Schuyler, Keith C. **Bow Hunting for Big Game.** (Illus). 1974. 8.95. Stackpole.

Wambold, Homer R. **Bowhunting for Deer.** (Illus). 1964. 5.95. Stackpole.

Knife Throwing

McEvoy, Harry K. **Knife Throwing: A Practical Guide.** (Illus). 1973. 2.95. C E Tuttle.

Knives

Cassidy, William. **Knife Digest.** Peterson, Harold L., et al. eds. (Illus). 1974. 15.00. pap. 5.95. Ten Speed Pr.

Ehrhardt, Larry. **Encyclopedia of Pocket Knives: Winchester & Marbles Hardware Collectibles, Book 3.** (Illus). 1974. pap. 6.95. Heart Am Pr.

Ehrhardt, Roy. **Encyclopedia of Pocket Knives: Book Three Price Guide.** (Illus). 6.95. Heart Am Pr.

Encyclopedia of Pocket Knives: Book One & Book Two Combined. (Illus). plastic ring 5.95. Heart Am Pr.

Hughes, B. R. **American Hand-Made Knives of Today.** 2.95. Pioneer Pr.

Hughes, B. R. & Lewis, Jack. **Gun Digest Book of Knives.** pap. 5.95. Digest Bks.

Latham, Sid. **Knives & Knifemakers.** (Illus). 1974. pap. 4.95. Macmillan.

Latham, Sid. **Knives & Knifemakers.** 1973. 15.00. Winchester Pr.

Peterson, Harold L. **American Knives.** (Illus). 1958. 5.95. Scribner.

Woods, Jim. **Guns & Ammo Guidebook to Knives & Edged Weapons.** (Illus). 1974. pap. 4.95. Petersen Pub.

Lee-Enfield Rifles

Reynolds, Edmund G. **Lee-Enfield Rifle.** 1963. 9.50. Arco.

Chamberlain, Peter & Gander, Terry. **Machine Guns.** (Fact Files on World War I Ser.). (Illus). 1974. 5.95 pap. 3.95. Arco.

Mauser Pistols

Belford & Dunlap. **Mauser Self-Loading Pistol.** 12.50. Borden.

Holland, Claude V. **The Military Four.** 4.95; pap. 2.98. C V Holland.

Pender. **Mauser Pocket Pistols: 1910-1946.** 14.50. Borden.

Moose

Peterson, Randolph L. **North American Moose.** (Illus). 1955. 19.00. U of Toronto Pr.

Van Wormer, Joe. **The World of the Moose.** (Living World Ser). (Illus). 1972. lib. bdg. 5.82. Lippincott.

Natural History—Outdoor Books

Bedichek, Roy. **Adventures with a Texas Naturalist.** (Illus). 1961. 6.50 U of Tex Pr.

Beston, Henry. **Outermost House.** 1971. pap. 0.95. Ballantine.

Borland, Hal. **Beyond Your Doorstep: A Handbook to the Country.** (Illus). 1962. 6.95. Knopf.

Borland, Hal G. **This Hill, This Valley.** 1963. 10.00. Lippincott.

Burroughs, John. **Under the Apple-Trees.** 1916. lib. bdg. 15.00. Folcroft.
Under the Maples. 1921. lib. bdg. 15.00. Folcroft.
Wake-Robin. 1896. lib. bdg. 15.00. Folcroft.
Winter Sunshine. 1879. lib. bdg. 15.00. Folcroft.
A Year in the Fields. 1901. lib. bdg. 15.00. Folcroft.

Cooper, Susan F. **Rural Hours.** (Illus). 1968. Repr. of 1887 ed. 6.95. Syracuse U Pr.

Davids, Richard C. **How to Talk to Birds & Other Uncommon Ways of Enjoying Nature the Year Round.** (Illus). 1972. 6.95. Knopf.

Errington, Paul L. **The Red Gods Call.** (Illus). 1973. 5.95. Iowa St U Pr.

Fuller, Raymond T. **Now That We Have to Walk: Exploring the Out-of-Doors.** facsimile ed. Repr. of 1943 ed. 10.75. Bks for Libs.

Gibbons, Euell. **Euell Gibbons' Beachcombers Handbook: Field Guide Edition.** 1972. pap. 2.95. McKay.

Gresham, Grits. **The Sportsman & His Family Outdoors.** (Illus). 1969. 4.50. Popular Sci.

Halle, Louis J. **Spring in Washington.** 4.00. Peter Smith.
Spring in Washington. (Illus). 1963. pap. 1.25. Atheneum.

Jefferies, Richard. **Old House at Coate.** 1948. 10.50. Bks for Libs.

Kieran, John F. **Nature Notes.** facs. ed. 1941. 8.75. Bks for Libs.

Leopold, Aldo. **Sand County Almanac: With Other Essays on Conservation from Round River.** (Illus). 1966. 7.95. Oxford. U Pr.

Macleod, Fiona, pseud. **Where the Forest Murmurs.** 1906. 13.25. Bks for Libs.

Madson, John. **Stories from Under the Sky.** (Illus). 1961. 1.00. Iowa St U Pr.

Olson, Sigurd F. **Listening Point.** (Illus). 1958. 5.95. Knopf.
Open Horizons. (Illus). 1969. 5.95. Knopf.
Singing Wilderness. (Illus). 1956. 5.95. Knopf.
Sigurd F. Olson's Wilderness Days. (Illus). 1972. 12.50. deluxe ed. 25.00. Knopf.

Ormond, Clyde. **Complete Book of Outdoor Lore.** (Illus). 1964. 7.95. Popular Sci.

Pearson, Haydn S. **Sea Flavor.** facs. ed. 1948. 9.25. Bks for Libs.

Rood, Ronald, et al. **Vermont Life Book of Nature.** Hard, Walter, Jr., ed. (Illus). 1967. 6.95. Greene.

Sharp, William. **Where the Forest Murmurs.** 1906. 13.25. Bks for Libs.

Sharp, Dallas L. **Face of the Fields.** facs. ed. 1911. 9.00. Bks for Libs.
Sanctuary! Sanctuary! facs. ed. 1926. 9.75. Bks for Libs.

Shepard, Odell. **Harvest of a Quiet Eye: A Book of Digressions.** facsimile ed. Repr. of 1927 ed. 13.00. Bks for Libs.

Shepherd, Anthony. **Flight of the Unicorns.** (Illus). 1966. 5.25. Abelard.

Teale, Edwin W. **Adventures in Nature.** pap. 1.95. Apollo Eds.
American Seasons. 4 Vols. (Illus). 1966. Set. 40.00; 7.95 ea. Dodd.
Autumn Across America. (Illus). 1956. 10.00. Dodd.
Journey into Summer. (Illus). 1960. 10.00. Dodd.
Lost Woods: Adventures of a Naturalist. (Illus). 1961. 6.95. Dodd.
North with the Spring. (Illus). 1951. 10.00. Dodd.
Wandering Through Winter. (Illus). 1965. 10.00. Dodd.

Terres, John K. **From Laurel Hill to Siler's Bog: The Walking Adventures of a Naturalist.** (Illus). 1969. 6.95. Knopf.

Ordnance

Bruce, Robert V. **Lincoln & the Tools of War.** (Illus). 1974. Repr. of 1956 ed. text ed. 15.00. Greenwood.

Carman, W. Y. **History of Firearms from Earliest Times to 1914.** 1955. 6.50. St. Martin.

Cipolla, Carlo M. **Guns, Sails & Empires: Technological Innovation & the Early Phases of European Expansion.** 1966. 7.50. Pantheon.

Cleator, P. E. **Weapons of War.** (Illus). 1968. 6.95. T Y Crowell.

Ffoulkes, Charles. **The Gun Founders of England.** (Illus). 1969. 10.00. Shumway.

Hoffschmidt, Edward J. & Tantum, William H., 4th. **Second World War Combat Weapons,** 2 vols. Incl. Vol. 1. **German Combat Weapons;** Vol. 2. **Japanese Combat Weapons.** (Illus). 7.95. ea. We Inc.

Office Strategic Services. **S S Sabotage & Demolition Manual.** (Illus). 1973. pap. 12.95. Paladin Pr.

Orientation

Biology Colloquium—Oregon State University—1966: **Animal Orientation & Navigation: Proceedings.** Storm, Robert M., ed. Orig. Title: **Animal Migrations.** (Illus). 1967. 5.00. Oreg St U Pr.

Burton, Maurice. **The Sixth Sense of Animals.** 6622. (Illus). 1973. 7.95. Taplinger.

Disley, John. **Orienteering.** (Illus). 1973. pap. 2.95. Stackpole.

Fraenkel. Gottfried & Dunn. Donald L. **Orientation of Animals.** 1961. 5.50. Peter Smith.

Fraenkel, Gottfried S. & Dunn, Donald L. **Orientation of Animals: Kineses, Taxes & Compass Reactions.** pap. 3.50. Dover.

Kjelistrom, Bjorn. **Be Expert with Map & Compass: The Orienteering Handbook.** 1972. pap. 3.50. Scribner.

Mooers. Robert L., Jr. **Finding Your Way in the Outdoors.** (Illus). Popular Sci.

Ratliff, Donald E. **Map, Compass & Campfire.** (Illus). 1970. pap. 1.50. Binfords.

Rutstrum, Calvin. **Wilderness Route Finder.** 1967. 4.95. Macmillan.

Symposium On Animal Orientation—Garmisch-Partenkirchen—1962. **Animal Orientation: Proceedings.** Autrum, H., et al, eds. 1963. 23.80. Springer-Verlag.

Von Frisch, Karl. **Dance Language & Orientation of Bees.** Chadwick, Leigh E., tr. (Illus). 1967. 17.00. (Belknap Pr). Harvard U Pr.

Outdoor Cookery

Ames, Mark & Ames, Roberta. **Barbecues.** new ed. 1973. pap. 0.95. Paperback Lib.

Angier, Bradford. **Food-from-the-Woods-Cooking.** (Illus.). 1973. pap. 1.50. Macmillan.
Wilderness Cookery. (Illus.). 1970. pap. 1.95. Stackpole.

Banks, James E. **Alferd Packer's Wilderness Cookbook.** (Illus.). 1969. 4.00; pap. 1.00. Filter.

Bartmess, Marilyn A, ed. **Woodall's Campsite Cookbook.** 1971. pap. 2.95. S&S.

Bates, Joseph D., Jr.. **Outdoor Cook's Bible.** (Illus.). 1964. softbound 2.50. Doubleday.

Beard, James A. **Fireside Cookbook.** (Illus.). 1969. 10.00. S&S.

Berglund, Berndt & Bolsby, Clare. **Wilderness Cooking.** 1973. 7.95. Scribner.

Better Homes & Gardens Editors. **The Better Homes & Gardens Barbecue Book.** 1972. pap. 1.25. Bantam.

Betty Crocker's Cookbook for Family Camping. 1974. pap. 1.00 (Golden Pr). Western Pub.

Brent, Carol D., ed. **Barbecue: The Fine Art of Charcoal, Gas & Hibachi Outdoor Cooking.** (Illus.). 1971. 3.95. Doubleday.

Brown, Helen E. **Patio Cookbook for Outdoor Entertaining.** 1972. pap. text ed. 2.95. Ritchie.

Brown, Helen E. & Brown, Philip S. **Cookout Book.** (Illus.). 1961. pap. 3.50. Ritchie.

Bunnelle, Hasse. **Food for Knapsackers: And Other Trail Travelers.** pap. 1.95. Sierra.

Carhart, Arthur H. **Outdoorsman's Cookbook.** rev. ed. 1962. pap. 0.95 Macmillan.

Dawson, Charlotte. **Recreational Vehicle Cookbook.** Nulsen, David, tr. (Illus., Orig.). 1970. 3.95. Trail-R.
Trailerists Cookbook. 2.50. Trail-R.

Dodd, Ed. **Mark Trail's Cooking Tips.** 1971. pap. 1.00. S&S.

Douglas, Luther A. & Douglas, Conda E. **The Explorers Cookbook.** (Illus.). 1971. 14.95. Caxton.

Farmer, Charles J. **Campground Cooking.** 1974. pap. 5.95. Digest Bks.

Fiske, Jean & Cross; Margaret, **Backpack Cookbook.** 1973. 7.95. pap. 3.00. Ten Speed Pr.

Fitzgerald. **Easy to Bar-B-Q Cook Book: A Guide to Better Barbecuing.** pap. 2.95. Pacifica.

Holm, Don. **Old-Fashioned Dutch Oven Cookbook.** 1969. pap. 3.95. Caxton.

Kamins, James. **The Cookout Conspiracy.** 1974. 7.95. Ashley Bks.

McElfresh, Beth. **Chuck Wagon Cookbook.** pap. 1.95. Swallow.

Marshall, Mel. **Cooking over Coals.** 1971. 5.95. pap. Stoeger.

Martin, George W. **The Complete Book of Outdoor Cooking.** (Illus.). 1974. 6.95. A S Barnes.

Mendenhall, Ruth D. **Backpack Cookery.** (Illus.). 1966. pap. 1.50. La Siesta.

Messner, Yvonne. **Campfire Cooking.** new ed. (Illus., Orig.). 1973. pap. 1.95. Cook.

Morris, Dan & Morris, Inez. **Complete Outdoor Cookbook.** 1970. 8.95. Hawthorn.

Riviere, William A. **Family Campers' Cookbook.** (Illus.). 1965. 4.95. HR&W.

Schubert, Ruth L. **The Camper's Cookbook.** 1974. pap. 3.50. Little.

Steindler, Geraldine. **Game Cookbook.** (Illus.). 1965. softbound 4.95. Stoeger.

Stephens, Mae W. & Wells, G. S. **Coping with Camp Cooking.** 1968. 2.95. Stackpole.

Strom, Arlene. **Cooking on Wheels.** (Illus.). 1970. 4.95; pap. 2.25. Wheelwright.

Tarr, Yvonne Y. **The Complete Outdoor Cookbook.** (Illus.). 1973. 8.95. Quadrangle.

Thomas Dian. **Roughing It Easy: A Unique Ideabook on Camping & Cooking.** (Illus.). 1974. 7.95. pap. 4.95. Brigham.

Woodall's Campsite Cookbook. pap. 2.95. Woodall.

Wooding, Loyta. **Meals on Wheels: A Guide to Delicious On-The-Go Meals.** 1972. 7.95. Nash Pub.

Outdoor Life

Angier, Bradford. **Food-from-the-Woods-Cooking.** (Illus.). 1973. pap. 1.50. Macmillan.
How to Stay Alive in the Woods. Orig. Title. **Living off the Country.** 1966. pap. 0.95. Macmillan.
One Acre & Security: How to Live off the Earth Without Ruining It. 1972. 6.95. Stackpole.
Skills for Taming the Wilds. (Illus.). 1967. 6.95. Stackpole.
Skills for Taming Wilds: A Handbook of Woodcraft Wisdom. 1972. pap. 1.25. PB.
Survival with Style. (Illus.). 1972. 6.95. Stackpole.
Wilderness Gear You Can Make Yourself. (Illus.). 1973. 6.95; pap. 2.93. Stackpole.

Bacon, Thorn. **Weather for the Sportsman.** 1973. 6.95. Motor Boating.

Bourjaily, Vance. **Country Matters: Collected Reports from the Fields & Streams of Iowa & Other Places.** 1973. 8.95. Dial.

Bradner, Enos. **Inside on the Outdoors.** (Illus.). 1973. 9.95. Superior Pub.

Brown, Vinson. **Knowing the Outdoors in the Dark.** (Illus.). 1973. pap. 2.95. Macmillan.
Knowing the Outdoors in the Dark. 6.95. Stackpole.

Burch, Monte. **Outdoorsman's Fix-It-Book.** (Illus.). 1971. 6.95. Popular Sci.

Caffey, David L. **Head for the High Country.** (Illus.). 1973. pap. 2.95. Abingdon.

Carrighar, Sally. **Home to the Wilderness.** 1973. 7.95. HM.

Collins, Chase. **The Country Guide for City People.** (Illus.). 1973. 5.95. Stein & Day.

Dalrymple, Byron. **Survival in the Outdoors.** (Illus.). 1972. 6.95. Popular Sci.

Explorers Limited, compiled by. **Explorers Ltd. Source Book.** (Illus.). 1973. pap. 4.95. Har-Row.

Fear, Daniel E., ed. **Surviving the Unexpected: A Curriculum Guide for Wilderness Survival & Survival from Natural & Man Made Disasters.** (Illus.). 1971. spiral bdg. 2.50. Survival Ed Assoc.

Fredrickson, Olive A. & East, Ben. **The Silence of the North.** 1973. pap. 1.25. Paperback Lib.

Frisbie, Richard P. **It's a Wise Woodsman Who Knows What's Biting Him.** 1969. 4.95. Doubleday.

Galton, Lawrence. **Outdoorsman's Fitness & Medical Guide.** (Illus.). 1966. 4.95. Popular Sci.

Gearing, Catherine. **Field Guide to Wilderness Living.** 1973. pap. 3.95. Southern Pub.

Gresham, Grits. **Sportsman & His Family Outdoors.** 1970. 4.50. Dutton.

Hamper, Stanley R. **Wilderness Survival.** 1973. Repr. of 1963 ed. 1.29. Peddlers Wagon.

Hardacre, J. V. **Woodland Nuggets of Gold.** 1974. 7.50. Holland Hse Pr.

Henderson, Luis M. **Campers' Guide to Woodcraft & Outdoor Life.** Orig. Title: **Outdoor Guide.** 1972. pap. 3.00. Dover.

Hood, Mary V. & Hood, A. William. **Nature & the Camper: A Guide to Safety & Enjoyment for Campers, Hikers, Hunters & Fishermen.** (Illus.). 1966. pap. 1.95. Ritchie.

Hunter, Rodello. **Wyoming Wife.** 1969. 5.95. Knopf.

Johnson, et al. **Outdoor Tips: A Remington Sportsmen's Library Bk.** pap. 2.95. Benjamin Co.

Joseph, James. **Careers Outdoors.** rev. ed. 1969. 5.95. Nelson.

Kephart, Horace. **Camping & Woodcraft.** (Illus.). 1948. 6.95. Macmillan.

Knap, Jerome. **Complete Outdoorsman's Handbook.** (Illus.). 7.95. Pagurian.

Kodet, E. Russel & Angier, Bradford. **Being Your Own Wilderness Doctor.** (Illus.). 1968. 3.95. Stackpole.

Merrill, W. K. **The Survival Handbook.** (Illus.). 1972. 5.95. Winchester Pr.

Miracle, Leonard. **Sportsman's Camping Guide.** 1965. pap. 4.50. Popular Sci.

Olsen, Larry D. **Outdoor Survival Skills.** 1967. 6.95; pap. 3.95. Brigham.

Ormond, Clyde. **Complete Book of Outdoor Lore.** (Illus.). 1965. 7.95 Har-Row.
Outdoorsman's Handbook. (Illus.). 1971. 5.95. Popular Sci.
Outdoorman's Handbook. 1971. 5.95. Dutton.

Patmore, J. Allan. **Land & Leisure.** 1971. 18.00. Fairleigh Dickinson.

Rawick, George P. **From Sundown to Sunup.** 1972. 10.00. Greenwood.

Robinson, David. **The Complete Homesteading Book: Proven Methods for Self-Sufficient Living.** 7.95. pap. 4.95. Garden Way Pub.

Rutstrum, Calvin. **New Way of the Wilderness.** (Illus.). 1966. 4.95; pap. 2.95. Macmillan.

Ruxton, George F. **Adventures in Mexico & the Rocky Mountains.** 10.00. Rio Grande.

Sparano, Vin T. **Complete Outdoors Encyclopedia.** (Illus.). 1972. 13.95. Popular Sci.

Symons, R. D. **The Broken Snare.** 1972. pap. 0.95. Curtis.

Van Der Smissen, Betty, et al. **Leader's Guide to Nature-Oriented Activities** 2nd ed. (Illus.). 1968. pap. 4.50. Iowa St U Pr.

Waterman, Charles F. **The Part I Remember.** (Illus.). 1974. 8.95. Winchester Pr.

Whelen, Townsend & Angier, Bradford. **On Your Own in the Wilderness.** 1958. 7.95. Stackpole.

Williams, Herb. **Outdoor Adventures.** 1973. pap. 1.95. H M Gousha.

Woolner, Frank. **My New England.** new ed. (Illus.). 1972. 6.50. Stone Wall Pr.

Wurman, Richard S., et al. **The Nature of Recreation: A Handbook & a Tribute to Frederick Law Olmsted.** 1973. pap. 4.95. MIT Pr.

Pistols

Best, Charles W. **Cast Iron Toy Pistols. 1870-1940: A Collector's Guide.** (Illus.). 1973. 15.00. Rocky Mtn Arms.

Blair, Claude. **Pistols of the World.** (Illus.). 1969. 30.00. Viking Pr.

Boothroyd, Geoffrey. **Handgun.** (Illus.). 1970. 19.95. Crown.

Datig, Fred A. **Luger Pistol.** rev. ed. 8.50. Borden.

Dixon, Norman. **Georgian Pistols: The Art & Craft of the Flintlock Pistol 1715-1840.** (Illus.). 1973. 22.50. British Bk Ctr.
Georgian Pistols: The Art & Craft of the Flintlock Pistol, 1715-1840. 1972. 14.00. Shumway.

Dunlap, H. J. **American, British & Continental Pepperbox Firearms.** (Illus.). 1964. Repr. 15.00. Pacific Bks.

Dyke, Samuel E. **Thoughts on the American Flintlock Pistol.** (Illus.). 1974. pap. 5.00 softbound. Shumway.

Glendenning, Ian. **British Pistols & Guns, 1640-1840.** (Illus.). 1967. 7.50. Arco.

Grennell, Dean & Williams, Mason. **Law Enforcement Handgun Digest.** 1972. pap. 5.95. Follett.

Hertzberg, Robert. **Modern Handgun.** (Illus.). 1965. 3.50. Arco.

Hogg, I. V. **Military Pistols & Revolvers.** (Illus.). 1970. pap. 1.95. Arco.

Holland, Claude V. **The Military Four.** 4.95; pap. 2.98. C V Holland.

Josserand, Michael & Stevenson, Jan. **Pistols, Revolvers, & Ammunition.** (Illus.). 1972. 7.50. Crown.

Kirkland, Turner. **Southern Derringers of the Mississippi Valley.** 2.00. Pioneer Pr.

Lachuk, John & Guns & Ammo Editors. **Wonderful World of the Twenty-Two.** (Illus.). 1972. pap. 2.95. Petersen Pub.

Leithe. **Japanese Hand Pistols.** 8.50. Borden.

Luger Manual. (Reprint of original English-language edition.) 1964. paper 1.95. Stoeger.

Nonte, George. **Pistol & Revolver Guide.** 3rd ed. (Illus.). 1974. softbound 5.95. Stoeger.

Nonte, George C., Jr. **Pistolsmithing.** (Illus.). 1974. 12.95. Stackpole.

Parsons, John E. **Henry Deringer's Pocket Pistol.** (Illus.). 1952. 7.50. Morrow.

Pollard, H. B. **Automatic Pistols.** (Illus.). 1970. Repr. of 1921 ed. 5.95. We Inc.

Reese, Michael. **Collector's Guide to Luger Values'.** 1972. pap. 1.00. Pelican.

Sawyer, Charles W. **United States Single Shot Martial Pistols.** 1971. 5.00. We Inc.

Smith, W. H. **Book of Pistols & Revolvers.** rev. ed. Smith, Joseph E., ed. (Illus.). 1972. 6.95. Stackpole.

Tarassuk, Leonid. **Russian Pistols in the Seventeenth Century.** (Illus.). 1968. Repr. softbound 4.00. Shumway.

Wilkinson, Frederick. **British & American Flintlocks.** 1972. 2.95. Transatlantic.

Revolvers

Hertzberg, Robert. **Modern Handgun.** (Illus.). 1965. 3.50. Arco.

Hogg, I. V. **Military Pistols & Revolvers.** (Illus.). 1970. 3.50; pap. 1.95. Arco.

Hogg, Ian V. **German Pistols & Revolvers, 1871-1945** (Illus.). 1971. 12.95. Stackpole.

Josserand, Michel & Stevenson, Jan. **Pistols, Revolvers, & Ammunition.** (Illus.). 1972. 7.50. Crown.

Nonte, George. **Pistol and Revolver Guide.** 3rd ed. (Illus.). 1974. softbound 5.95. Stoeger.

Parsons, John E. **Peacemaker & Its Rivals: An Account of the Single Action Colt.** (Illus.). 1950. 7.50. Morrow.

Rywell, Martin. **American Nickel Plated Revolver.** 1.25. Pioneer Pr.

Smith, W. H. **Book of Pistols & Revolvers.** rev. ed. Smith, Joseph E., ed. (Illus.). 1972. 6.95. Stackpole.

Rifles

Baird, John D **Fifteen Years in the Hawken Lode.** (Illus.). 1971. 10.00. Buckskin Pr. **Hawken Rifles: The Mountain Man's Choice.** 1968. 10.00. Buckskin Pr.

Buchele, William & Shumway, George. **Recreating the American Longrifle.** Orig. Title: **Recreating the Kentucky Rifle.** (Illus.). 1973. pap. 6.50. Shumway.

De Haas. Frank. **Bolt Action Rifles.** Amber, John T., ed. 1971. pap. 6.95. Follett. **Bolt Action Rifles.** Amber, John T., ed. pap. 6.95. Digest Bks.

Dillin, John G. **The Kentucky Rifle.** 5th ed. (Illus.). 1967. 20.00; deluxe limited ed. 35.00 Shumway.

Dunathan, Arni T. **American B.B. Gun: A Collector's Guide.** (Illus.). 1971. 12.00. A S Barnes.

Kindig, Joe, Jr. **Thoughts on the Kentucky Rifle in Its Golden Age.** 2nd. enl. ed. (Illus.). 1971. 20.00. Shumway.

Lachuk. John & Guns & Ammo Editors. **Wonderful World of the Twenty-Two.** (Illus.). 1972. pap. 2.95. Petersen Pub.

O'Connor, Jack, et al. **Complete Book of Rifles & Shotguns,** rev. ed. 1965. 7.95. Times Mirror Mag.

O'Connor, Jack. **Big-Game Rifle.** (Illus.). 1952. 10.00. Knopf. **Complete Book of Rifles & Shotguns.** rev. ed. (Illus.). 1966. 7.95. Popular Sci. **Hunting Rifle.** (Illus.). 1970. 5.95. pap. Stoeger. **Rifle Book.** 2nd ed. rev. ed. (Illus.). 1964. 10.00. Knopf.

Olson, John. **John Olson's Book of the Rifle.** (Illus.). 1974. 9.95. pap. 5.95. O'Hara.

Page, Warren. **The Accurate Rifle.** 1973. 5.95. pap. Stoeger.

Petzal, David. **The Point Twenty-Two Rifle.** (Illus.). 1973. 5.95. Winchester Pr.

Pullum, Bill & Hanenkrat, Frank T. **Position Rifle Shooting.** 1973. 5.95. pap. Stoeger.

Rywell, Martin. **American Antique Rifles.** 2.00. Pioneer Pr. **U.S. Muskets, Rifles & Carbines.** 2.00. Pioneer Pr.

Sharpe, Philip B. **Complete Guide to Handloading.** 3rd rev. ed. (Illus.). 1953. 10.00. Funk & W.

Shumway, George. **Longrifles of Note** (Illus.). 1968. softbound 3.95. Shumway.

Smith, Walter H. & Smith, Joseph E. **Book of Rifles.** rev. ed. 1972. 6.95. Stackpole.

Swenson, G. W. **Pictorial History of the Rifle.** (Illus.). 1972. 7.95. Drake Pubs.

U. S. Rifle Caliber .30 Model 1903. 2.00. Pioneer Pr.

U. S. Rifle Model 1866 Springfield. 0.75. Pioneer Pr.

U. S. Rifle Model 1870 Remington. 0.75. Pioneer Pr.

Wahl, Paul. **Carbine Handbook.** (Illus.). 1964. 6.00; pap. 3.95. Arco.

Sharps Rifles

Manual of Arms for the Sharps Rifle. 1.50. Pioneer Pr.

Rywell, Martin. **Sharps Rifle: The Gun That Shaped American Destiny.** 2.95. Pioneer Pr.

Smith, Winston O. **Sharps Rifle: Its History, Development & Operation.** (Illus.). 1966. Repr. of 1943 ed. 10.00. Morrow.

Shields

Davison, Betsy. **Shields of Ancient Rome.** (Illus.). 1969. pap. 2.00. Malter-Westerfield.

Shooting

Anderson, Gary. **Marksmanship.** 1972. 4.95. S&S.

Arnold, Richard. **Clay Pigeon Shooting.** (Illus.). 1974. 9.00. Intl Pubns Serv. **Clay Pigeon Shooting.** (Illus.). 1974. text ed. 11.50. Soccer.

Baird, John D. **Fifteen Years in the Hawken Lode.** (Illus.). 1971. 10.00. Buckskin Pr.

Brander. Michael. **Hunting & Shooting.** (Illus.). 1971. 13.95. Putnam.

Chapel, Charles E. **Field, Skeet & Trapshooting.** rev. ed. (Illus.). 1962. 7.95. A S Barnes.

Jennings, Mike. **Instinct Shooting.** rev. ed. (Illus.). 1965. 3.95. Dodd.

Kuhlhoff, Pete. **Kuhlhoff on Guns.** (Illus.). 1970. 5.95. Winchester Pr.

Lind, Ernie. **Complete Book of Trick & Fancy Shooting.** (Illus.). 1972. 5.95. Winchester Pr.

Montague, Andrew A. **Successful Shotgun Shooting.** (Illus.). 1971. 5.95. Winchester Pr.

O'Connor, Jack. **Complete Book of Shooting: Rifles, Shotguns, Handguns.** (Illus.). 1966. 7.95. Popular Sci. **Rifle Book.** 2nd ed. rev. ed. (Illus.). 1964. 10.00. Knopf. **Shotgun Book.** (Illus.). 1965. 10.00. Knopf.

Page, Warren. **The Accurate Rifle.** 5.95. pap. Stoeger.

Petzal, David E., ed., **Experts' Book of the Shooting Sports.** 9.95. S&S.

Riviere, Bill. **Gunner's Bible.** 1965. softbound 2.50. Doubleday.

Roberts, Willis J. & Bristow, Allen P. **Introduction to Modern Firearms.** Gourley, Douglas, ed. (Illus.). 1969. 8.95. Glencoe.

Stanbury, Percy & Carlisle, G. L. **Shotgun Marksmanship.** rev. ed. (Illus.). 1971. 6.95. A S Barnes.

Trench, Charles C. **A History of Marksmanship.** (Illus.). 1972. 12.95. Follett.

Shotguns

Arnold, Richard. **Automatic & Repeating Shotguns.** (Illus.). 1974. 10.00. Intl Pubns Serv.

Arthur, Robert. **Shotgun Stock: Design, Construction & Embellishment.** (Illus.). 1970. 15.00. A S Barnes.

Barker, A. J. **Shotguns & Shooting.** new ed. Brown, Robert K. & Lund, Peter C., eds. (Illus.). 1973. 4.95. pap. 2.50. Paladin Pr.

Boy Scouts Of America. **Rifle & Shotgun Shooting.** (Illus.). 1967. pap. 0.55. BSA.

Butler, David F. **The American Shotgun.** 1973. 15.00. Winchester Pr.

Garwood, G. T. **Gough Thomas's Gun Book.** (Illus.). 1970. 8.95. Winchester Pr. **Gough Thomas's Second Gun Book.** (Illus.). 1972. 8.95. Winchester Pr.

Hinman, Bob. **Golden Age of Shotgunning.** (Illus.). 1972. 8.95. Winchester Pr.

Knight, Richard A. **Mastering the Shotgun.** (Illus.). 1967. 4.95. Dutton.

Laycock, George. **Shotgunner's Bible.** (Illus.). 1969. softbound 2.50. Doubleday.

O'Connor, Jack. **Shotgun Book.** (Illus.). 1965. 10.00. Knopf.

O'Connor, Jack, et al. **Complete Book of Shooting: Rifles & Shotguns, Handguns.** rev. ed. 1965. 7.95. Popular Sci.

Robinson, Robert H. **The Police Shotgun Manual.** (Illus.). 1973. 10.50. C C Thomas.

Stanbury, Percy & Carlisle, G. L. **Shotgun Marksmanship.** rev. ed. (Illus.). 1971. 6.95. A S Barnes.

Swords

Akehurst, Richard **Antique Weapons.** (Illus.). 1969. 5.95. Arco.

Burton, Richard F. **Book of the Sword.** (Illus.). 1972. Repr. of 1884 ed. 13.50. B&N.

Castle, Egerton. **Schools & Masters of Fence from the Middle Ages to the Eighteenth Century.** (Illus.). 1969. 15.00. Shumway.

Dobree, Alfred. **Japanese Sword Blades.** 3rd ed. 1971. softbound 4.00. Shumway.

Foulkes, Charles & Hopkinson, E. C. **Sword, Lance & Bayonet.** (Illus.). 1967. 7.50. Arco.

Gunsaulus, H. C. **Japanese Sword-Mounts.** (Illus.). 1923. pap. 12.00. Kaus Repr.

Hamilton, John. **Collection of Japanese Sword Guards with Selected Pieces of Sword Furniture.** 1973-74. pap. price not set. Peabody Mus Salem.

Hawley, Willis, M. **Japanese Swordsmiths,** 2 Vols. 1966-67. Vol. 1. 15.00; Vol. 2. 10.00. Hawley.

Hutton, Alfred. **The Sword & the Centuries; or, Old Sword Days & Old Sword Ways.** (Illus.). 1973. Repr of 1901 ed. 8.50. C E Tuttle.

Joly, Henri. **Shosankenshu: Japanese Sword Mounts.** 18.00. Saifer.

Rankin, Robert H. **Small Arms of the Sea Services: A History of the Firearms & Edged Weapons of the U. S. Navy, Marine Corps & Coast Guard from the Revolution to the Present.** (Illus.). 1972. 14.50. Flayderman.

Rawson, Philip S. **Indian Sword.** (Illus.). 1967. 8.50. Arco.

Robinson, B. W. **Arts of the Japanese Sword.** (Illus.). 1971. 17.50. C E Tuttle.

Sasano, Massayuki. **Early Japanese Sword Guards: Sukashi Tsuba** (Pierced Work) (Illus.) 1972. 15.00. Japan Pubns.

Wallace, John. **Scottish Swords & Dirks.** (Illus.). 1970. 4.95. Stackpole.
Yumoto, John M. **Samuari Sword: A Handbook.** (Illus.). 1958. 7.25. C E Tuttle.

Survival

Angier, Bradford. **How to Stay Alive in the Woods.** Orig. Title: **Living off the Country.** 1966. pap. 0.95. Macmillan.
Armstrong, Charles W. **The Survival of the Unfittest.** 28.00. Gordon Pr.
Bailey, Maralyn & Bailey, Maurice. **Staying Alive.** 1974. 6.95. McKay.
Barker, Ralph. **Against the Sea: True Stories of Disaster & Survival.** (Illus.). 1972. 6.95. St. Martin.
Best, Herbert. **Parachute to Survival.** (Illus.). 1964. 4.95. John Day.
Brandner, Gary. **Living off the Land.** 1972. pap. 1.95. Nash Pub.
Craighead, Frank C., Jr. & Craighead, John J. **How to Survive on Land & Sea.** 3rd ed. (Illus.). 1956. pap. 5.50. Naval Inst. Pr.
Cunningham, Richard. **The Place Where the World Ends: A Modern Story of Human Courage & Cannibalism.** (Illus.). 1973. 5.95. Sheed.
Dalrymple, Byron. **Survival in the Outdoors.** 1972. 6.95. Dutton.
Dennis, Lawrence. **Operational Thinking for Survival.** 1969. 5.95. R. Myles.
East, Ben. **Survival.** (Illus.). 5.95. Dutton.
East, Ben. **Survival: Twenty-Three True Sportsmen's Adventures.** (Illus.). 1967. 5.95. Popular Sci.
Fear, Daniel E.; ed. **Surviving the Unexpected: A Curriculum Guide for Wilderness Survival & Survival from Natural & Man Made Disasters.** (Illus.). Rev. ed. 1974. spiral bdg. 2.50. Survival Ed. Assoc.
Fear, Eugene H. **Surviving the Unexpected Wilderness Emergency,** rev. ed. (Illus.). 1974. pap. 3.95. Survival Ed. Assoc.
Fear, Gene. **Where Am I: A text & Workbook for Personal Navigation Anywhere.** 1974. pap. 4.50. Survival Ed. Assoc.
Fenn, Charles. **Journal of a Voyage to Nowhere.** 1972. Repr. 5.95. Norton.
Fitch, Ken. **Survival.** (Illus., Orig.). 1974. pap. 1.50. Stadia Sports Pub.
Gibbons, Euell. **Stalking the Good Life.** 1971. 7.95. McKay.
Gibbs, Jim. **Disaster Log of Ships.** (Illus.). 1971. 12.95. Superior Pub.
Graves, Richard. **Bushcraft: A Serious Guide to Survival & Camping.** (Illus.). 1972. 10.00; pap. 3.95. Schocken.
Hamilton, Margaret L. **Is Survival a Fact?** 5.00. Branden.
Hersey, John R. **Here to Stay.** 1963. 6.95. Knopf.
Kilbourne, James W. **Escape & Evasion: Seventeen Stories of Downed Pilots Who Made It Back.** Glines, Carrol V., ed. (Illus.). 1973. 5.95. Macmillan.
Lee, E. C. & Lee, Kenneth. **Safety & Survival at Sea.** (Illus.). 1972. 8.25. Norton.
Lopez, Enrique H. **They Lived on Human Flesh.** 1973. pap. 1.25. PB
Merrill, Bill. **The Survival Handbook.** 1974. pap. 1.95. Arc Bks.
Nesbitt, Paul, et al. **Survival Book.** (Illus.). 1969. pap. 1.95. Funk & W.
Olsen, Larry D. **Outdoor Survival Skills.** 1967. 6.95; pap. 3.95. Brigham.
Read, Piers Paul. **Alive: The Story of the Andes Survivors.** (Illus.). 1974. 10.00. Lippincott.
Richards, Philip & Banigan, John J. **How to Abandon Ship.** (Illus.). 1943. 2.00. Cornell Maritime.
Robertson, Dougal. **Survive the Savage Sea.** (Illus.). 1973. 7.95. Praeger.

Saturday Evening Post Editors. **Post True Stories of Courage & Survival.** 1968. pap. 0.75. Popular Lib.
Shockley, Robert O. & Fox, Charles K. **Survival in the Wilds.** (Illus.). 1970. 6.95. A S Barnes.
Szczelkun, Stefan A. **Survival Scrapbook 1: Shelter.** (Illus.). 1974. pap. 3.95. Schocken.
Troebst, Cord-Christian. **Art of Survival.** 5.95. Doubleday.
Western Electric. **Survival in the North.** 4.50. Wehman.

Taxidermy

Berndt, A. C. **Taxidermy Tips.** 1966. 2.00. Reel Trophy.
Bruchac, Joseph, ed. **Professional Taxidermy Tips.** 1970. 2.00. Reel Trophy.
Cappel, Leo J. **A Guide to Model Making & Taxidermy.** (Illus.). 1973. pap. 5.50. Reed.
Casting in Clear Plastic. 1972. 1.50. Reel Trophy.
Farnham, Albert B. **Home Taxidermy for Pleasure & Profit.** (Illus.). pap. 2.00. Fur-Fish-Game.
Grantz, Gerald J. **Home Book of Taxidermy & Tanning.** (Illus.). 1970. 8.50. Stackpole.
Hardin, Cleo. **How to Preserve Animal & Other Specimens in Clear Plastic.** (Illus.). 1963. 2.00. Reel Trophy.
Labrie, Jean. **The Amateur Taxidermist.** (Illus.). 1972. 7.50; pap. 2.95. Hart.
Landforce, Andrew S. **Boning Out Your Deer.** (Illus.). 1968. 1.00. Reel Trophy.
Migdalski, Edward G. **How to Make Fish Mounts & Other Fish Trophies.** 7.50. Reel Trophy.
Moyer, John W. **Practical Taxidermy: A Working Guide.** (Illus.). 1953. 6.75. Ronald.
Pray, Leon. **American Game Head Studies.** 1961. 2.00. Reel Trophy.
Big Game Taxidermy Methods. (Illus.). 1951. 2.00. Reel Trophy.
Borax Moth Proofing Book. 1956. 2.00. Reel Trophy.
Modern Taxidermy Tips. 1964. 2.00. Reel Trophy.
Nineteen Sixty-Five Bird Mounting Book. 1965. 2.00. Reel Trophy.
Nineteen Sixty-Five Fish Mounting Book. rev. & enl. ed. 1965. 2.00. Reel Trophy.
Nineteen Sixty-Six Mammal Mounting Book. 1966. 2.00. Reel Trophy.
Pheasant Mounting Book. 1956. 2.00. Reel Trophy.
Squirrel Mounting Book. 1956. 2.00. Reel Trophy.
Taxidermy. (Illus.). 4.00. Reel Trophy.
Pray, Leon L. **Taxidermy.** (Illus.). 1943. 3.95. Macmillan.
Tinsley, Russell. **Taxidermy Guide.** (Illus.). hard 6.95. 1967. softbound 3.95. Stoeger.
Tinsley, Russell. **Shooter's Bible of Taxidermy.** 4.00. Reel Trophy.
White, J. Bob. **Paper Sculpture Taxidermy Methods.** (Illus.). 1962. 2.00. Reel Trophy.

Trap and Skeet Shooting

Campbell, Robert, ed. **Skeet Shooting with D. Lee Braun: A Remington Sportsmen's Library Bk.** 5.95; pap. 2.95. Benjamin Co. **Trapshooting with D. Lee Braun & the Remington Pros:** A Remington Sportsmen's Library Bk. 5.95; pap. 2.95. Benjamin Co.
Hartman, Barney. **Hartman on Skeet.** (Illus.). 1973. 7.95. Stackpole.
Missildine, Fred. **Score Better at Trap.** Karas, Nicholas, ed. (Illus.). 1970. 5.95; pap. 2.95. Winchester Pr.
Missildine, Fred & Karas, Nick. **Score Better at Skeet.** (Illus.). 1973. 5.95; pap. 2.95. Winchester Pr.

Trapping

Baird, John D. **Who's Who in Buckskins.** 1973. 10.00 Buckskin Pr.

Bateman, James A. **Animal Traps & Trapping.** (Illus.). 1971. 8.50. Stackpole.
Dearborn, Ned. **Trapping on the Farm.** Repr. of 1910 ed. 4.00; pap. 2.00. Shorey.
Harbottle, Jeanne & Credeur, Fern. **Woman in the Bush.** 6.00. Pelican.
Harding, A. R. **Deadfalls & Snares.** (Illus.). pap. 2.00. Fur-Fish-Game.
Fox Trapping. (Illus.). pap. 2.00. Fur-Fish-Game.
Mink Trapping. (Illus.). pap. 2.00. Fur-Fish-Game.
Steel Traps. (Illus.). pap. 2.00. Fur-Fish-Game.
Wolf & Coyote Trapping. (Illus.). pap. 2.00. Fur-Fish-Game.
Karras, A. L. **North to Cree Lake.** (Illus.). 1971. 7.95. Trident.
Kreps, E. **Science of Trapping.** (Illus.). pap. 2.00. Fur-Fish-Game.
Lynch, V. E. **Trails to Successful Trapping.** pap. 2.00. Fur-Fish-Game.
McCracken, Harold & Van Cleve, Harry. **Trapping.** (Illus.). 6.95. A S Barnes.
Mason, Otis T. **Traps of the American Indians.** facs. ed. (Illus.). 1901. pap. 1.25. Shorey.
Newhouse, Sewell. **The Trapper's Guide.** 1973. Repr. of 1869 ed. 8.95. Buckskin Pr.
Russell, Andy. **Trails of a Wilderness Wanderer.** 1971. 6.95. Knopf.
Russell, Carl. **Firearms, Traps & Tools of the Mountain Men.** (Illus.). 1967. 15.00. Knopf.
The Trapper's Companion. (Illus.). pap. 1.50. Fur-Fish-Game.
Woodcock, E. N. **Fifty Years a Hunter & Trapper.,** pap. 2.00. Fur-Fish-Game.

White-Tailed Deer

Anderson, Luther A. **How to Hunt Whitetail Deer.** (Illus.). 1968. 5.95. Funk & W.
Conway, Bryant W. **Successful Hints on Hunting White Tail Deer.** 2nd ed. 1967. pap. 1.98. Claitors.
Koller, Lawrence R. **Shots at Whitetails.** rev. ed. (Illus.). 1970. 7.95. Knopf.
Mattis, George. **Whitetail Fundamentals & Fine Points for the Hunter.** (Illus.). 1969. 7.95. Popular Sci.
Pray, Leon. **White Tail Deer Studies.** 1944. 2.00. Reel Trophy.
Rue, Leonard L. **World of the White-Tailed Deer.** 1962. 5.95. Lippincott.
Tinsley, Russel. **Hunting the Whitetail Deer.** 1965. 4.50. Popular Sci.
Weis, Norman D. **All About the White-Tailed Deer.** 1969. 1.50. Denlingers.

Winchester Rifles

Butler, David F. **Winchester Nineteen Seventy-Three & Seventy-Six: The First Repeating Centerfire Rifles** (Illus.). 1970. 7.95. Winchester Pr.
Madis, George. **Winchester Book.** 3rd ed. (Illus.). 1971. 25.00. Art & Ref.
Parsons, John E. **First Winchester Story of the 1866 Repeating Rifle.** rev. ed. 1955. Repr. of 1955 ed. 8.95. Winchester Pr.
Watrous, George R. **History of Winchester Firearms 1866-1966.** 2nd ed. 1966. 10.00. Winchester Pr.
West, Bill. **Know Your Winchesters: General Use. All Models & Types,** 1849-1969. (Illus.). 12.00. B West.
Winchester-Complete: All Wins & Forerunners, 1849-1970. (Illus.). 1972. 22.00. B West.
Winchester Encyclopedia. (Illus.). 12.00. B West.
Winchester Lever-Action Handbook. (Illus.). 22.00. B West.
The Winchester, Single Shot. (Illus.). 12.00. B West.
Winchester, Cartridges & History. (Illus.). 20.00. B West.
Williamson, Harry F. **Winchester: The Gun That Won the West.** (Illus.). 5.98. A S Barnes.

Magazines and Periodicals of Interest to the Hunter and Shooter

Alaska Geographic (Q)
Established 1973
Circulation: 2,165
Robert A. Henning, Editor
Alaska Northwest Publishing Company
Box 4-EEE
Anchorage, Alaska 99509
(907) 279-1723

All Outdoors Magazine (M)
Established 1947
Circulation: 165,250
Ralph Dice, Editor
Southwestern Associates, Inc., Publisher
P.O. Box 700
Denison, Texas 75020
(214) 463-2440

American Field (W)
Established 1874
Circulation: 14,803
W. F. Brown, Editor
American Field Publishing Company
222 West Adams Street
Chicago, Illinois 60606
(312) 372-1383

American Firearms Industry (M)
Established 1973
Circulation: 19,000
Andrew Molchan, Editor and Publisher
American Press-Media Associates, Inc.
7001 North Clark Street
Chicago, Illinois 60626
(312) 338-7601

The American Hunter (M)
Established 1973
Circulation: 130,000
Ken Warner, Editor
National Rifle Association
1600 Rhode Island Avenue, N.W.
Washington, D.C. 20036
(202) 783-6505

The American Rifleman (M)
Established 1885
Circulation: 1,026,571
Ashley Halsey, Jr., Editor
National Rifle Association
1600 Rhode Island Avenue
Washington, D.C. 20036
(202) 783-6505

The American Shotgunner (M)
Established 1973
Circulation: 65,340
Bob Thurston, Editor and Publisher
P.O. Box 3351
Reno, Nevada 89505
(702) 329-2521

The American West (BM)
Established 1964
Circulation: 29,513
George Pfeiffer, III, Editor and Publisher
American West Publishing Company
599 College Avenue
Palo Alto, California 94306
(415) 327-4660

Argosy (M)
Established 1882
Circulation: 967,404
Gil Paust, Editor
Popular Publications, Inc.
420 Lexington Ave.
New York, N.Y. 10017
(212) 689-4900

Arms Gazette (M)
Established 1973
Circulation: n.s.
Wallace Beinfeld, Editor and Publisher
13222 Saticoy Street
North Hollywood, California 91605
(213) 982-3700

Army (M)
Established 1904
Circulation: 92,142
L. James Binder, Editor-in-Chief
Association of the U.S. Army
1529 18th Street, N.W.
Washington, D.C. 20036
(202) 483-1800

Ducks Unlimited (Q)
Established 1938
Circulation: 128,811
Denton H. Hartley, Editor
Ducks Unlimited, Inc.
P.O. Box 66300
Chicago, Illinois 60666
(312) 299-3334

Field & Stream (M)
Established 1895
Circulation: 1,894,889
Jack Samson, Editor
CBS Publications
383 Madison Avenue
New York, N.Y. 10017
(212) 688-9100

Fishing and Hunting News (W)
Established 1944
Circulation: 108,670
Ken McDonald, Editor
Fishing and Hunting News, Inc., Publisher
511 Eastlake E.
Seattle, Washington 98109
(206) 624-3845

Fur-Fish-Game (Harding's Magazine) (M)
Established 1905
Circulation: 163,332
A. R. Harding, Editor
A. R. Harding Publishing Co.
2878 East Main Street
Columbus, Ohio 43209
(614) 231-9585

Great Lakes Sportsman (BM)
Established 1970
Circulation: 200,654
Harold Dobrowa, Editor
Sportsman Publications, Inc.
26555 Evergreen Road, Suite 410
Southfield, Michigan 48076
(313) 355-1270

The Gun Report (M)
Established 1955
Circulation: 9,700
Kenneth W. Liggett, Editor and Publisher
110 South College Avenue
Aledo, Illinois 61231
(309) 582-5311

Gunsport and Gun Collector (M)
Established 1958
Circulation: n.s
Leisure Publishing Company, Publisher
711 Penn Ave.
Pittsburgh, Pennsylvania 15222
(412) 281-7777

Gun Week (W)
Established 1966
Circulation: 32,000
J. O. Ames, Acting Editor
911 Vandemark Road
Sidney, Ohio 45365
(513) 492-4141

Gun World (M)
Established 1960
Circulation: 126,149
Jack Lewis, Editor
Gallant Publishing Company, Inc.
130 Olinda Place; P.O. Box 325
Brea, California 92621
(714) 493-2101

Guns and Ammo (including
Guns and Hunting) (M)
Established 1958
Circulation: 293,891
Howard French, Editor
Petersen Publishing Company
8490 Sunset Boulevard
Los Angeles, California 90069
(213) 657-5100

Guns Magazine (M)
Established 1954
Circulation: 123,900
Jerome Rakusan, Editor
Publisher Development Corporation
8150 North Central Park Boulevard
Skokie, Illinois 60076
(312) 675-6010

The Handloader (BM)
Established 1965
Circulation: 33,892
Neal Knox, Editor
David R. Wolfe, Publisher
Box 30-30
Prescott, Arizona 86301
(602) 445-7810

Hobbies, The Magazine for Collectors (M)
Established 1931
Circulation: n.s.
Pearl Ann Reeder, Editor
Lightner Publishing Company
1006 South Michigan Avenue
Chicago, Illinois 60605
(312) WE 9-4767

Hunting (M)
Established 1973
Circulation: n.s.
Ken Elliott, Editor
Petersen Publishing Company
8490 Sunset Boulevard
Los Angeles, California 90069
(213) 657-5100

KaHagon (M)
Established 1969
Circulation: n.s.
Gene Coleman, Editor
George E. Zorgo, Sr., Publisher
131 North Main Street
Pittston, Pennsylvania 18640
(717) 654-8831

Law and Order (M)
Established 1953
Circulation: 24,742
Frank G. MacAloon, Editor
Will Copp, Publisher
37 West 38th Street
New York, N.Y. 10018
(212) 239-8080

Michigan Out-of-Doors (M)
Established 1947
Circulation: 126,329
James V. Stabile, Editor
Michigan United Conservation Clubs, Inc.
P.O. Box 2235
Lansing, Michigan 48911
(517) 371-1041

Muzzle Blasts (M)
Established 1932
Circulation: 18,500
Maxine Moss, Editor
Franklin Printing Company, Inc., Publisher
P.O. Box 67
Friendship, Indiana 47021
(812) 667-4631

National Defense (BM)
Established 1920
Circulation: 33,000
R. E. Lewis, Editor
American Defense Preparedness
    Association, Publisher
819 Union Trust Building
740 15th Street, N.W.
Washington, D.C. 20005
(202) 347-7250

New England Sportsman (BM)
Established 1973
Circulation: 100,276
Sportsman Publications, Inc.
26555 Evergreen Road, Suite 410
Southfield, Michigan 48076
(313) 355-1270

Outdoor Arizona (M)
Established 1928
Circulation: 37,821
Robert L. Hirsch, Editor
Phoenix Publishing, Inc.
1230 East Camelback Road
Phoenix, Arizona 85014
(602) 248-8900

Outdoor Life (M)
Established 1898
Circulation: 1,901,536
Chat Fish, Editor
Times Mirror Magazines, Inc.
380 Madison Avenue
New York, N.Y. 10017
(212) 687-3000

Outdoor Press (W)
Established 1966
Circulation: 23,923
Fred L. Peterson, Editor
The Outdoor Press, Inc.
N. 2012 Ruby Street
Spokane, Washington 99207
(509) 328-9392

Outdoor World (BM)
Established 1968
Circulation: 50,000
Robert L. Polley, Editor
Country Beautiful Corporation
24198 W. Bluemound Road
Waukesha, Wisconsin 53186
(414) 542-9361

Outdoors Today (W)
Established 1970
Circulation: 93,427
Earl A. Shelsby, Editor
Outdoors Today, Inc.
P.O. Box 6852
St. Louis, Missouri 63144
(314) 727-2722

Pennsylvania's Outdoor People (SM)
Established 1959
Circulation: 27,121
G. M. Dennis and A. Dardanell, Editors
Dardanell Publications, Inc.
610 Beatty Road
Monroeville, Pennsylvania 15146
(412) 373-7900

Point Blank (M)
Established 1971
Circulation: 31,000
J. Nicholas Cannon, Editor
Citizens Committee for the Right
    to Keep and Bear Arms, Publisher
1601 114th S.E.,
Bellevue, Washington 98004
(206) 454-4911

Police Times (M)
Established 1966
Circulation: 88,000
Gerald S. Arenberg, Editor
American Federation of Police
1100 N.E. 125th Street
North Miami, Florida 33161
(305) 891-1700

Popular Mechanics (M)
Established 1902
Circulation: 1,750,486
Jim Liston, Editor
The Hearst Corporation, Publisher
224 West 57th Street
New York, N.Y. 10019
(212) 262-4282

Popular Science (M)
Established 1872
Circulation: 1,799,840
Hubert P. Luckett, Editor
Times Mirror Magazines, Inc.
380 Madison Avenue
New York, N.Y. 10017
(212) 687-3000

Precision Shooting (M)
Established 1956
Circulation: n.s.
Ritchie Moorehead, Editor
Precision Shooting, Inc.
Box 6
Athens, Pa. 18810
(717) 888-7801

The Rifle Magazine (BM)
Established 1968
Circulation: 23,714
Neal Knox, Editor
David R. Wolfe, Publisher
Box 30-30
Prescott, Arizona 86301
(602) 445-7810

Saga (M)
Established 1950
Circulation: 142,900
Martin M. Singer, Editor
Gambi Publishing Corporation
333 Johnson Avenue
Brooklyn, N.Y. 11026
(212) 456-8600

The Shooting Industry (M)
Established 1956
Circulation: 18,500
Jerome Rakusan, Editor
Publishers Development Corporation
8150 North Central Park Boulevard
Skokie, Illinois 60076
(312) 675-6010

Shooting Times (M)
Established 1960
Circulation: 123,198
Alex Bartimo, Editor
P.S.J. Publications
News Plaza
Peoria, Illinois 61601
(309) 682-6626

Shotgun News (SM)
Established 1946
Circulation: 87,000
Jim Weaver, Editor
Robert M. Snell, Publisher
Box 1147
Hastings, Nebraska 68901
(402) 463-4589

Skeet Shooting Review (M)
Established 1946
Circulation: 18,458
Ford W. Hubbert, Jr., Editor
National Skeet Shooting Association,
    Publisher
P.O. Box 28188
San Antonio, Texas 78228
(512) 688-3560

Southern Outdoors (BM)
Established 1953
Circulation: 100,442
Bob Cobb, Editor
Ray Scott, Publisher
P.O. Box 3543
Montgomery, Alabama 36109
(205) 277-3940

Sporting Goods Business (M)
Established 1968
Circulation: 23,244
Robert E. Carr, Editor
Gralla Publications
1515 Broadway
New York, N.Y. 10036
(212) 869-1300

Sporting Goods Dealer (M)
Established 1899
Circulation: 14,526
C. C. Johnson Spink, Editor and
  Publisher
1212 North Lindbergh Boulevard
St. Louis, Missouri 63166
(314) 997-7111

Sports Afield (M)
Established 1887
Circulation: 1,317,402
Lamar Underwood, Editor
The Hearst Corporation, Publisher
250 West 55th Street
New York, N.Y. 10019
(212) 262-8852

Sports and Recreation (BM)
Established 1946
Circulation: n.s.
Robert Bushnell, Editor
Roland E. Nystrom, Publisher
207 South Manitoba Avenue
Wayzata, Minnesota 55391
(612) 545-9182, 473-8595

Sports Illustrated (W)
Established 1954
Circulation: 2,277,801
Roy Terrell, Editor
Time, Inc., Publisher
1271 Ave. of the Americas
New York, N.Y. 10020
(212) JU 6-1212

Trap and Field (M)
Established 1890
Circulation: 18,500
Betty Ann Foxworthy, Editor
Curtis Publishing Company
1100 Waterway Boulevard
Indianapolis, Indiana 46202
(317) 634-1100

True (M)
Established 1937
Circulation: 1,096,444
Clare Conley, Editor
Petersen Publishing Co., Inc.
8490 Sunset Boulevard
Los Angeles, California 90069
(213) 657-5100

Western Outdoor News (W)
Established 1953
Circulation: 79,076
Western Outdoors Publications
3939 Birch Street
Newport Beach, California 92660
(714) 546-4370

Western Outdoors (M)
Established 1960
Circulation: 110,180
Western Outdoors Publications
3939 Birch Street
Newport Beach, California 92660
(714) 546-4370

West Virginia Hills and Streams (M)
Established 1971
Circulation: 3,000
Leo Young, Editor
West Virginia Hills and Streams, Inc.,
  Publisher
Box 38
Durbin, West Virginia 26264
(304) 456-4366

Canadian Periodicals
Alberta Sportsman (6 x yr.)
Established 1966
Circulation: 6,170
Railton Publications, Ltd.
125 Talisman Avenue
Vancouver, British Columbia
(604) 876-3535

B.C. Outdoors (BM)
Established 1945
Circulation: 23,432
A. G. Downs, Editor
Northwest Digest, Ltd., Publisher
Box 900, Station A
Surrey, British Columbia V3S 4P4
(604) 574-5211

Fish and Game Sportsman (Q)
Established 1969
Circulation: 10,500
J. B. Wilkinson, Editor
Nimrod Publications, Ltd.
P.O. Box 1654
Regina, Saskatchewan
(306) 523-8384

Northwest Sportsman (6 x yr.)
Established 1946
Circulation: 9,823
Jim Railton, Editor
Railton Publications, Ltd.
125 Talisman Avenue
Vancouver, British Columbia
(604) 876-3535

Sporting Goods Trade (BM)
Established 1928
Circulation: 9,900
William Schabas, Editor
David Wells, Publisher
300 Decarie Blvd.
Montreal 379, Quebec
(514) 748-8728

Quebec Chasse et Peche (M) (French)
Established 1971
Circulation: 15,500
Henri Ponpart, Editor
Les Publications Plein Air, Inc.
3339 Desmartean Street
Montreal, Quebec
(514) 845-5141

Western Fish and Wildlife (BM)
Established 1965
Circulation: 10,354
J. L. Grundle, Editor and Publisher
1591 Bowser Street
Vancouver, British Columbia
(604) 980-5821

Wildlife Crusader (M)
Established 1944
Circulation: 38,416
Paul F. Murphy, Editor
Manitoba Wildlife Federation, Publisher
St. James and Notre Dame
Winnipeg, Manitoba
(204) 774-2926

Explanation of Symbols:
(M) Monthly; (BM) Bi-monthly; (SM) Semi-monthly; (W) Weekly;(Q) Quarterly; (n.s.) circulation not specified.

Firearms, Ammunition and Accessory Manufacturers

A

American Heritage Arms, Inc.
Route 44
P.O. Box 95
West Willington, Connecticut 06279

Anschutz
(see Savage Arms Co.)

Astra
(see Garcia)

B

Bausch & Lomb
1400 North Goodman
Rochester, New York 14602

Benjamin Air Rifle Co.
1525 South 8th St.
St. Louis, Missouri 63104

Beretta
(see Garcia)

Bernardelli
(see Charles Daly)

Bonanza Sports, Inc.
412 Western Ave.
Faribault, Minnesota 55021

Browning Arms Co.
Route 1
Morgan, Utah 84050

BSA
Air guns (see Ithaca)

Maynard P. Buehler, Inc.
17 Orinda Way
Orinda, California 94563

Bushnell Optical Co.
2828 East Foothill Blvd.
Pasadena, California 91107

C

Charter Arms Corp.
430 Sniffens Lane
Stratford, Connecticut 06497

Colts Firearms Div.
150 Huyshope Ave.
Hartford ,Connecticut 06102

Crosman Arms Co.
980 Turk Hill Rd.
Fairport, New York 14450

D-E

Daisy Mfg. Co.
Rogers, Arkansas 72756

Charles Daly
Sloan's Sporting Goods Co., Inc.
10 South St.
Ridgefield, Connecticut 06877

Day Arms Corp.
7515 Stagecoach Lane
San Antonio, Texas 78227

E. I. Du Pont de Nemours & Co., Inc.
Explosives Department
Wilmington, Delaware 19898

F

Falconet
(see Stoeger Industries)

Federal Cartridge Corp.
2700 Foshay Tower
Minneapolis, Minnesota 55402

Franchi
(see Stoeger Industries)

Freeland's Scope Stands, Inc.
3737 14th Ave.
Rock Island, Illinois 61201

G

J. L. Galef & Sons, Inc.
85 Chambers St.
New York, New York 10007

Garcia Corp.
329 Alfred Ave.
Teaneck, New Jersey 07666

Carl Gustaf
(see Stoeger Industries)

H

Harrington & Richardson, Inc.
Industrial Rowe
Gardner, Massachusetts 01440

Hercules, Inc.
910 Market St.
Wilmington, Delaware 19899

High Standard Mfg. Corp.
1817 Dixwell Ave.
Hamden, Connecticut 06514

B. E. Hodgdon, Inc.
7710 West 50 Highway
Shawnee Mission, Kansas 66202

Hopkins & Allen
(see High Standard Mfg. Corp.)

Hornady Mfg. Co.
P.O. Box 1848
Grand Island, Nebraska 68801

Hy-Score Arms Co.
200 Tillary St.
Brooklyn, New York 11201

I

Interarms
10 Prince St.
Alexandria, Virginia 22313

Ithaca Gun Co., Inc.
123 Lake St.
Ithaca, New York 14850

Iver Johnson's Arms, Inc.
109 River St.
Fitchburg, Massachusetts 01420

J

Paul Jaeger, Inc.
Box 67
Jengintown, Pennsylvania 19046

K

Krieghoff Gun Co.
P.O. Box 48-1367
Miami, Florida 33148

L

Leupold & Stevens
P.O. Box 688
Beaverton, Oregon 97005

Llama
(see Stoeger Industries)

Luger
(see Stoeger Industries)

Lyman Products for Shooters
Route 147
Middlefield, Connecticut 06455

M

Marksman Products
P.O. Box 2983
Torrance, California 90509

Marlin Firearms Co.
100 Kenna Dr.
North Haven, Connecticut 06473

Marubeni America Corp.
200 Park Ave.
New York, New York 10017

Mauser Pistols
(see Interarms)

MEC
Mayville Engineering Co., Inc.
P.O. Box 267
Mayville, Wisconsin 53050

Merit Gun Sight Co.
P.O. Box 995
Sequim, Washington 98382

Micro Sight Co.
242 Harbor Blvd.
Belmont, California 94002

O. F. Mossberg & Sons, Inc.
7 Grasso Ave.
North Haven, Connecticut 06473

N-O

National Rifle Association
1600 Rhode Island Ave.
Washington, D.C. 20036

Navy Arms Co.
689 Bergen Blvd.
Ridgefield, New Jersey 07657

Norma Precision, Inc.
P.O. Box E
Lansing, New York 14882

Nosler Bullets, Inc.
Box 688
Beaverton, Oregon 97005

Numrich Arms Corp.
Box ZG
West Hurley, New York 12491

Ohaus Scale Corp.
29 Hanover Rd.
Florham Park, New Jersey 07932

P-Q

Pachmayr Gun Works
1220 South Grand Ave.
Los Angeles, California 90015

Pacific Tool Co.
P.O. Drawer 2048
Grand Island, Nebraska 68801

Pedersen
(see Mossberg)

Peters
(see Remington)

Ponsness-Warren, Inc.
P.O. Box 1818
Eugene, Oregon 97401

R

RCBS
P.O. Box 1919
Oroville, California 95965

Realist Inc.
North 93 West 16288 Megal Dr.
Menomonee Falls, Wisconsin 53051

Redding-Hunter, Inc.
114 Starr Rd.
Cortland, New York 13045

Redfield Gun Sight Co.
5800 East Jewell Ave.
Denver, Colorado 80222

Remington Arms Co.
939 Barnum Ave.
Bridgeport, Connecticut 06602

Rossi
(see Garcia)

S

Sako
(see Garcia)

Savage Arms Co.
Westfield, Massachusetts 01085

Security Industries of America
31 Bergen Turnpike
Little Ferry, New Jersey 07643

Sheridan Products, Inc.
3205 Sheridan Rd.
Racine, Wisconsin 53403

Sierra Bullets, Inc.
Santa Fe Springs, California 90670

Smith & Wesson
2100 Roosevelt Ave.
Springfield, Massachusetts 01101

Smith & Wesson-Air Gun Division
2100 Roosevelt Ave.
Springfield, Massachusetts 01101

Smith & Wesson Ammunition Co.
Foreman Rd.
Rock Creek, Ohio 44084

Speer, Inc.
Box 896
Lewiston, Idaho 83501

Springfield Armory
Creneseo, Illinois 61254

Star
(see Garcia)

Stering Arms
4436 Prospect St.
Gasport, New York 14067

Stoeger Industries
55 Ruta Court
South Hackensack, New Jersey 07606

Sturm, Ruger & Co., Inc.
Southport, Connecticut 06490

T

Thompson/Center Arms
Farmington Rd.
Rochester, New Hampshire 03867

U-V

Virginian
(see Interarms)

W-X-Y-Z

Walther Pistols
(see Interarms)

Weatherby's, Inc.
2781 Firestone Blvd.
South Gate, California 90280

W. R. Weaver Co.
7125 Industrial Ave.
El Paso, Texas 79915

Dan Wesson Arms, Inc.
293 Main St.
Monson, Massachusetts 01057

Western
(see Winchester-Western)

Williams Gun Sight Co.
7389 Lapeer Rd.
Davidson, Michigan 48423

Winchester-Western
275 Winchester Ave.
New Haven, Connecticut 06504

Handguns

ASTRA PISTOL & REVOLVERS

ASTRA 357, 357 MAG. & 38 SPECIAL

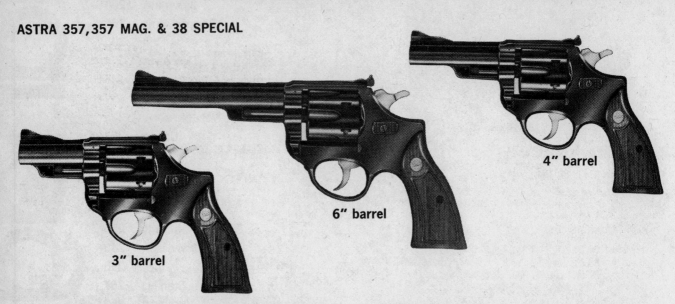

4" barrel

6" barrel

3" barrel

Potent, powerful, and smooth as silk: the Astra 357. Chambered for the hot 357 Magnum cartridge, this large-frame revolver also handles the popular 38 Special, making it equally suitable for the serious target shooter and for the sportsman.

All forged steel, and highly polished to a rich blue, the Astra 357 has a heavyweight barrel with integral rib and ejector shroud. The rear sight is click-adjustable for windage and elevation. The hammer is of the wide-spur target type, and the trigger is grooved. The grips are of checkered hardwood. The cylinder is recessed, and the gun utilizes a spring-loaded, floating firing pin for additional safety.

The internal lockwork of the Astra 357 is as finely fitted and finished as the exterior, giving it a smoothness second to none. There's even a four-stage adjustment to control spring tension on the hammer.

The Astra 357 is available with 3", 4", or 6" barrel. The 4" and 6" barreled models have square butts and are supplied with comfortable, hand-filling oversized grips. The 3" version has the more compact round butt with magna-style grips. Length overall with 6" barrel is 11¼".

Astra 357 . . . . **$185.00**

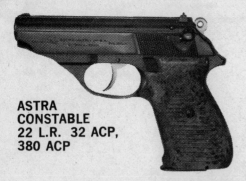

**ASTRA
CONSTABLE
22 L.R. 32 ACP,
380 ACP**

**F.I. MODEL D
380 ACP**

The Astra Constable is a double-action, all steel small-frame auto, so you can safely carry it fully loaded with a round in the chamber and the safety off. A single pull of the trigger then cocks and fires the pistol without the necessity of cocking the hammer manually, as is necessary with most autos. The thumb safety completely blocks the hammer and actually locks the firing pin in place until released. The barrel is rigidly mounted in the frame for greater accuracy and the gun features quick, no-tool takedown, integral non-glare rib on the slide, push-button magazine release, and a round, non-snagging hammer spur.

22 L.R., 32 ACP & 380 ACP **$150.00**
380 Chrome **$165.00**

All steel, all American-made, and chambered for the hot 380 ACP, the F.I. Model D combines power with compactness.

The Model D holds 6 rounds in the magazine and one in the chamber, yet it's only a hair over 6" long and 4" high. For maximum security it has an inertia firing pin, and the large thumb safety actually cams the hammer out of contact with the sear. The windage-adjustable rear sight is rounded on its outer dimensions so it won't snag on clothing. The grips are of checkered walnut, and the backstrap of the Model D is extra-long to protect even the fleshiest hand from being "bitten" by the hammer.

380 ACP **$150.00**

BERETTA AUTOMATIC PISTOLS

BERETTA MODEL 951

(9mm Parabellum)

$260.00

BERETTA MODEL 951

Specifications:

CALIBER	9mm Parabellum (Luger)
BARREL LENGTH	4½"
OVERALL LENGTH	8"
WEIGHT	31 oz.
SIGHTS	Fixed
MAGAZINE CAPACITY	8 rounds
MAGAZINE RELEASE	Pushbutton
SAFETY	Crossbolt
HAMMER	External, grooved
FINISH	Blue
GRIPS	Two-piece wrap-around, non-slip
SLIDE	Stays open on last shot

BERETTA MODEL 70S

(.380 Automatic)

$145.00

Specifications:

CALIBER	.380
BARREL LENGTH	3⅜"
OVERALL LENGTH	6¼"
WEIGHT	23¼ oz.
SIGHTS	Fixed
MAGAZINE CAPACITY	7 rounds
MAGAZINE RELEASE	Pushbutton
SAFETY	Thumb
HAMMER	External, grooved
FINISH	Blue
GRIPS	Two-piece wrap-around, non-slip
SLIDE	Stays open on last shot

BERETTA MODEL 76

(.22 Long Rifle)

$175.00

BERETTA MODEL 76

Specifications:

CALIBER	.22 Long Rifle
BARREL LENGTH	6"
OVERALL LENGTH	9½"
WEIGHT	35 oz.
SIGHTS	Adjustable rear, 3 interchangeable front blades
MAGAZINE CAPACITY	10 rounds
MAGAZINE RELEASE	Pushbutton
SAFETY	Thumb
HAMMER	External, grooved
FINISH	Blue
GRIPS	Two-piece wrap-around, checkered
SLIDE	Stays open on last shot

BERETTA MODEL DA

(380 Automatic)

PRICE NOT SET

Specifications:

CALIBER	380 ACP
BARREL LENGTH	3¾"
OVERALL LENGTH	6½"
WEIGHT	22½ oz.
MAGAZINE CAPACITY	13
MAGAZINE RELEASE	Convertible right hand/left hand
SAFETY	Right hand/left hand release
HAMMER	Round spur, non-snagging
FINISH	Blue
GRIPS	Walnut, Smooth

BROWNING AUTOMATIC PISTOLS

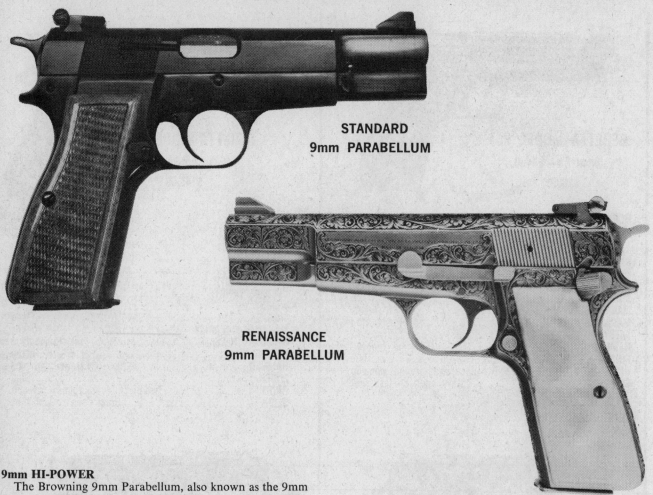

STANDARD
9mm PARABELLUM

RENAISSANCE
9mm PARABELLUM

9mm HI-POWER

The Browning 9mm Parabellum, also known as the 9mm Browning Hi-Power has a 14-cartridge capacity and weighs two pounds. The push-button magazine release permits swift, convenient withdrawal of the magazine.

The 9mm is available with either a fixed blade front sight and a windage adjustable rear sight or a non-glare rear sight, screw adjustable for both windage and elevation. The front sight is a ⅛-inch wide blade mounted on a ramp. The rear surface of the blade is serrated to prevent glare.

In addition to the manual safety, the firing mechanism includes an external hammer so it is easy to ascertain whether the pistol is cocked.

Standard	$254.50
Standard with adjustable sights	$274.50
Extra magazine	$ 19.00

RENAISSANCE ENGRAVED MODEL is finished with silver-grey, leaf-scroll metal frame, pure-white Nacrolac pearl grips and a gold-plated trigger. It is available with either fixed or adjustable sights.

Renaissance	$800.00
Renaissance with adjustable sights	$825.00
Extra magazine	$ 35.00

	9mm Hi-Power	
	Fixed Sights	**Adjustable Sights**
Capacity of Magazine	13	13
Overall Length	7¾″	7¾″
Barrel Length	4²¹/₃₂″	4²¹/₃₂″
Height	5″	5″
Weight (Empty)	32 oz.	32.8 oz.
Sight Radius	6⁵/₁₆″	6⅜″
Ammunition	9mm Parabellum/9mm Luger	
Grips	Checkered Walnut (Standard) Nacrolac Pearl (Renaissance)	
Front Sights	Fixed Blade	⅛″ wide blade on ramp
Rear Sights	Windage adjustable	Screw adjustable horizontal & vertical
Grades Available	Standard and Renaissance	Standard and Renaissance

CHARTER ARMS REVOLVER

UNDERCOVERETTE .32 S & W Long

Blue finish with Regular grips **$105.00**
Blue finish with Bulldog grips **$112.00**

SPECIFICATIONS:
Caliber: 32 S & W Long. **Type of Action:** 6 Shot, double action. **Barrel Length:** 2". **Overall Length:** 6¼". **Height:** 4⅛". **Weight:** 16½ ounces. **Grips:** Oiled American walnut, uncheckered. (Optional Bulldog grips.) **Sights:** Fixed, 9/64". **Rifling:** One turn in 17", right hand twist. **Finish:** High-luster Police Blue.

PATHFINDER .22 L.R.

Blue finish with Regular grips **$114.00**
Blue finish with Bulldog grips **$121.00**

SPECIFICATIONS:
Caliber: 22 Long Rifle. **Type of Action:** 6 shot, double action. **Barrel Length:** 3 inches. **Overall Length:** 7⅜ inches. **Height:** 4⅛ inches. **Weight:** 18½ ounces. **Grips:** Oiled American walnut, uncheckered. Optional: Bulldog grips American walnut hand-checkered. **Sights:** fully adjustable rear. 9/64-inch serrated ramp front. **Rifling:** one turn in 16 inches, right hand twist. **Finish:** High-luster Police Blue.

UNDERCOVER .38 Special

2" barrel Blue finish with Regular grips
........................**$104.00**
2" barrel Blue finish with Bulldog grips
........................**$111.00**
2" barrel Nickel finish with Regular grips
........................**$115.00**
2" barrel Nickel finish with Bulldog grips
........................**$122.00**
3" barrel Blue finish with Regular grips
........................**$104.00**
3" barrel Blue finish with Bulldog grips
........................**$111.00**

SPECIFICATIONS:
Caliber: 38 Special (Mid-Range & Standard). **Type of Action:** 5 shots, double action. **Barrel Length:** 2". **Overall Length:** 6¼" (2"bbl.), 7⅜" (3" bbl.). **Height** 4⅛". **Weight:** 16 oz. **Grips:** Smooth American walnut (Bulldog grips optional). **Sights:** Fixed 9/64" matte ramp front, square-notched rear. **Finish:** High-luster Police Blue or Nickle.

BULLDOG .44 SPL.

Blue finish with Bulldog grips **$138.00**

SPECIFICATIONS:
Caliber: 44 SPL. **Type of Action:** 5 shot, double action. **Barrel length:** 3 inches. **Overall Length:** 7½ inches. **Height:** 4½ inches. **Weight:** 19 ounces. **Grips:** Bulldog grips, American walnut hand-checkered. **Sights:** Partridge-type, 9/64-inch wide, full-length serrated ramp front sight; square-notched rear. **Finish:** High-luster Police Blue.

CHARTER ARMS REVOLVERS

CHARTER ARMS POLICE BULLDOG
38 SPECIAL 6-SHOT REVOLVER

SPECIFICATIONS:
Caliber: 38 Special. **Type of Action:** 6-shot single and double action. **Barrel length:** 4 inches. **Overall length:** 8½ inches. **Height:** 4½ inches. **Weight:** 20½ ounces. **Grips:** Bulldog grips, American walnut hand-checkered. **Sights:** Full-length ramp front; fully adjustable compat rear. **Finish:** High-luster Police Blue.

Blue finish with Bulldog grips **$135.00**

COLT REVOLVERS

TROOPER MK III

.357 Mag., Barrels: 4″, 6″

Tremendous penetrating power in the Magnum caliber makes this handgun suitable for hunters of big game or for police officers. Its quick draw type, ramp-style front sight and adjustable rear sight makes this a target-sighted general purpose revolver. Features include: wide target trigger; wide serrated hammer; full checkered walnut stocks. Trooper MK 111, .357 Magnum, 4″ or 6″ barrel:
W/Tgt. Stocks & Hammer, Target Trigger, Blue............ **$188.00**
W/Tgt. Stocks & Hammer, Target Trigger, Nickel.......... **$200.00**

Trooper Specifications: Caliber: .357 Magnum. **Barrel Lgth.:** 4″, 6″. With target stocks: ⅛″ longer. **Weight (Oz.):** 39 oz. with 4″ bbl. 42 oz. with 6″ bbl. **Sights:** Fixed ramp-type front sight with ⅛″ blade. Rear sight adjustable for windage and elevation. **Trigger:** Wide target trigger. **Hammer:** Wide checkered spur on target hammer. Target—case hardened finish. **Stocks:** Target stocks, checkered walnut. **Finish:** Colt blue and polished nickel finishes. **Cylinder Capacity:** 6 shot counterbored. **Overall Length:** 9½″ with 4″ barrel.

.357 Magnum

OFFICIAL POLICE MK III

.38 Spec.—Barrels: 4″

The Official Police MK III revolver is made in .38 Special caliber and is available in 4″ barrel length. Features include: glare-proofed fixed type front sight; wide target trigger; walnut stocks—fully checkered and target type hammer with wide checkered spur. Official Police MK 111, .38 Special, 4″, Blue **$147.00**

Official Police Specifications: Caliber: .38 Special. **Barrel Lgth.:** 4″ Taper. **Overall Lgth.:** With service stocks 9¼″. **Weight (Oz.):** 33 oz. **Sights:** Fixed ramp-type front sight with ⅛″ blade. Fixed rear open sight. **Trigger:** Wide target trigger; smooth or serrated service trigger. **Hammer:** Wide checkered spur on target hammer. Narrow serrated spur on service hammer. Target—case hardened finish. Service—metallic finish. **Stocks:** Checkered Walnut service stocks. **Finish:** Colt blue. **Cylinder Capacity:** 6 shot counterbored. **Finish:** Colt blue. **Overall Length:** 9⅜″.

.38 Special (mid-range, regular & hi-speed).

COLT DIAMONDBACK
.22 L.R., 4" bbl.,
   blue $176.00
.38 Spec., 2½" & 4"
   bbl., blue $176.00
.38 Spec., 4" bbl.
   polished nickel $188.00

The Colt Diamondback all-steel revolver was designed along the lines of the Python and includes the features of the bigger Python on a medium-size frame. These features include the ventilated rib, which dissipates barrel heat, reduces mirage effect and provides the preferred flat sighting plane . . . the wide spur target hammer which has a new cross-cut design which assures non-slip cocking . . . a grooved trigger and shrouded ejector rod, which protects the ejector rod and minimizes "barrel bounce."

The Diamondback is equipped with a fully adjustable rear sight for windage and elevation. The front sight is an integral ramp type.

The 4" barreled model comes with a checkered walnut target stock, while the 2½" barreled model is fitted with a fully checkered walnut service stock. Available with Colt blue finish only in .22 Long Rifle (also handles the .22 Short and Long) and .38 Special caliber, with a choice of a 2½" or 4" barrel in Colt blue and polished nickel finishes.

SPECIFICATIONS:
Calibers: .22 L.R. and .38 Special. **Barrel Lengths:** 2½" and 4". **Sights:** Adjustable rear sight, ramp-type front. **Trigger:** Smooth. **Hammer:** Wide-spur, checkered. **Stocks:** 4": Checkered walnut target stock. 2½": fully checkered walnut service stock. **Weights:** 2½" bbl. .38 Spec. (25 ozs.); 2½" bbl. .22 L.R. (28¼ ozs.); 4" bbl. .38 Spec. (28½ ozs.); 4" bbl. .22 L.R. (31¾ ozs.). **Finish:** Colt Blue. Polished nickel.

COLT
DETECTIVE SPECIAL
IN .38 SPECIAL
WITH 2" BARREL
(All Steel)

Blue Finish $140.00
Polished Nickel $149.50

SPECIFICATIONS:
Caliber: .38 Special. **Barrel Length:** 2" barrel. **Overall Length:** 6⅝". **Weight:** 22 ounces. **Sights:** Fixed-type ramp-style, glare proofed. **Trigger:** Smooth. **Stocks:** Full checkered walnut, round butt. **Finish:** Colt Blue. Polished Nickel.

COLT LAWMAN MK III
.357 MAGNUM REVOLVER
Barrel: 2", 4"

SPECIFICATIONS: Caliber: .357 Mag. **Barrel Lgth.:** 2" & 4" heavy barrel **Overall Lgth.:** With service stocks: 9¼" With target stocks: 9⅜" **Weight (Oz.):** 36 oz. **Sights:** Fixed quick-draw, ramp-style front-sight with ⅛" wide blade. Fixed open rear sight notch—.136". **Trigger:** Wide target trigger; smooth or serrated service trigger. **Hammer:** Wide checkered spur on target hammer. Narrow serrated spur on service hammer. Target is case hardened finish. Service is metallic finish. **Stocks:** Service stocks: Relief checkered genuine walnut (standard). Target stocks: Target grip configuration, relief checkered genuine walnut (optional). **Finish:** Colt blue. Polished nickel. **Cylinder Capacity:** 6 shot counter-bored.

Blue Finish $149.50
Polished Nickel $158.50

Government Model Mk IV/Series '70

Full-size automatic with 5" barrel. Available in .45 ACP, 9 MM Parabellum and .38 Super.

Features:
Fixed military sights, grip and thumb safeties, grooved trigger, sand-blasted walnut stocks and Accurizor barrel and bushing. Colt Blue or Polished Nickel finishes.

Weight: 39 oz. in .45 ACP
Overall Length: 8⅜"
Magazine Capacity: .45 ACP-7 rounds, .38 Super and 9 MM-9 rounds

Government Model
Blue finish (all calibers) $175.50
Polished Nickel (.45 A.C.P.) $192.00

MK IV/Series '70 GOVERNMENT MODEL
.45 Automatic, .38 Super Automatic and 9 mm Luger
(With Accurizor barrel and bushing)

Lightweight Commander

This lightweight, shorter version of the Government Model offers increased ease of carrying with the firepower of .45 ACP, 9 MM Parabellum, and .38 Super.

Features:
Alloy frame, fixed style sights, grooved trigger, and lanyard style hammer. Colt Blue with Walnut stocks.

Weight: 27 oz.
Overall Length: 7⅞"
Magazine Capacity: 7 rounds in .45 ACP
9 rounds in 9mm Parabellum, .38 Super

Lightweight Commander
Blue $175.50

LIGHTWEIGHT COMMANDER
(Alloy Frame)
.45 Automatic
.38 Super Auto
9m/m Luger

Combat Commander

An all-steel frame gives the stocky Combat Commander extra heft and stability. Genuine walnut sand-blasted stocks embedded with the Colt medallion. Available in .45 ACP, 9 MM Parabellum and .38 Super cartridges.

Features:
Fixed style sights, thumb safety and grip safety. In Colt Blue or Satin Nickel finishes.

Weight: 35 oz. in .45 ACP
Overall Length: 7⅞"
Magazine Capacity: .45 ACP-7 rounds, .38 Super and 9 MM-9 rounds

Combat Commander
Blue or Satin Nickel $175.50

COMBAT COMMANDER
(All Steel)
.45 Automatic
.38 Super Auto
9m/m Luger

Colt MK IV/Series '70
Gold Cup National Match

*With group tightening
Accurizor barrel and bushing.*

.45 A.C.P.

Gold Cup National Match MKIV/Series '70
.45 ACP centerfire target pistol with improved barrel and bushing.

Features:
Sear depressor, grooved front straps, special exterior finish, all hand-fitted parts, 5" barrel. Colt-Elliason adjustable rear sight, undercut front sight, solid rib, wide grooved trigger, serrated hammer, checkered walnut stocks flat grip housing.

Gold Cup National Match Mark IV/Series '70 Specifications:

MAGAZINE CAPACITY: 7 rounds. BARREL LENGTH: 5".
LENGTH OVERALL: 8⅜". WEIGHT: 38½ oz.
SIGHTS: Front sight, vertical rear face. Adjutable rear sight.
Sighting radius, 5" barrel—6.55".
HOUSING: .45 Flat, .38 Flat (arched available).
SAFETY: Standard .45 Grip and Thumb Safety. HAMMER: Serrated.
STOCKS: WALNUT with gold plated medallion. FINISH: Royal Blue.

45 GOLD CUP NATIONAL MATCH Mark IV/Series '70 . . . . **$256.00**

BALLISTICS PERFORMANCE

CARTRIDGES	BULLET		VELOCITY—FEET PER SECOND			ENERGY—FOOT POUNDS			MID-RANGE TRAJECTORY		TEST BARREL LGTH.
	WGT.-GRS.	STYLE	MUZZLE	50 YDS.	100 YDS.	MUZZLE	50 YDS.	100 YDS.	50 YDS.	100 YDS.	
45 AUTOMATIC	230	Metal Case	850	810	775	370	335	305	1.6"	6.5"	5"
	185*	Metal Case Wad Cutter	775	695	625	245	200	160	2.0"	9.0"	5"
	230	Metal Case, Targetmaster	850	810	775	370	335	305	1.6"	6.5"	5"

COLT SINGLE ACTION REVOLVERS

PEACEMAKER .22

22 Long Rifle/Magnum—Barrel: 4⅜″, 6″, 7½″

An all steel, true .22 caliber version of the Colt .45 caliber
"Peacemaker", a color case hardened frame; blued barrel,
trigger guard and backstrap. In 4⅜″, 6″, and 7½″ barrel
lengths, the Peacemaker .22 comes with an extra interchangeable .22 Magnum cylinder. Length overall, with 6″
barrel, 11¼″. Weight, with 4¾″ barrel, 30½ ounces.
Sights are of the fixed type, featuring a blade front sight.
Peacemaker .22 L.R., w/.22 Mag. dual cylinder, 4⅜″ or 6″
bbl., blue **$96.50**
Peacemaker .22 L.R., Buntline, w/.22 Mag. dual cylinder,
7½″ bbl., blue **$102.50**

NEW FRONTIER .22

22 Long Rifle/Magnum—Barrel: 4⅜″, 6″, 7½″

Steel frame .22 caliber version of the Colt New Frontier
Model, boasting ramped front sight and adjustable rear
sight, as well as a color case hardened frame. The New
Frontier .22 comes with an extra interchangeable .22 Magnum cylinder. Made in 4⅜″, 6″ and 7½″ barrel lengths;
the length overall, with 4⅜″ barrel, is 9⁹⁄₁₆″, and weighs in
at 31 ounces.
New Frontier .22 L.R., w/.22 Mag. dual cylinder, 4⅜″ or
6″ bbl., blue **$108.00**
New Frontier .22 L.R., Buntline, w/.22 Mag. dual cylinder, 7½″ bbl., blue **$113.50**

BUNTLINE SPECIAL

.45 Colt—Barrel: 12″

This .45 Colt, designed by Colt for Ned Buntline, the famous Western
writer of the 1870's, has an overall length of 17½″, and its 12″ barrel
provides a longer sight radius, higher bullet velocity and muzzle energy
for rifle-like accuracy.

Features:

Blade front sight, Colt Blue finish with color case hardened frame and
walnut stocks. Weight: 42 oz. Overall Length: 17½″ **Special Order Only**

COLT AUTOMATIC PISTOLS

WOODSMAN MATCH TARGET
.22 L.R.—Barrels: 4½" & 6"

CALIBER: .22 Long Rifle.
MAGAZINE CAPACITY: 10 rounds.
LENGTH OF BARREL: 4½" or 6",
LENGTH OVERALL: 9" with 4½" bbl., 12" with 6" bbl.
WEIGHTS: 39 oz. with 6" bbl., 36 oz. with 4½" bbl.
SIGHTS: Adjustable rear sight. ⅛" standard. Ramp-type front sight with removable undercut blade. Sighting radius: 4½" barrel—7⅜"; 6" barrel—8.75".
TRIGGER: Wide.
FINISH: Blue. SLIDE STOP: Automatic. STOCKS: Walnut with Thumbrest.

**WOODSMAN MATCH TARGET
.22 L.R. CALIBER
$164.95**

WOODSMAN SPORT MODEL
.22 L.R.—Barrel: 4"

CALIBER: .22 Long Rifle.
MAGAZINE CAPACITY: 10 rounds.
LENGTH OF BARREL: 4".
LENGTH OVERALL: 9".
WEIGHT: 32 ounces.
SIGHTS: Adjustable rear sight. Ramp-type front sight with removable blade. Sighting radius, 4½" barrel—7.35".
TRIGGER: Wide.
SLIDE STOP: Automatic.
STOCKS: Walnut with Thumbrest. FINISH: Blue.

**WOODSMAN SPORT MODEL
.22 L.R. CALIBER
$147.50**

WOODSMAN TARGET MODEL (not illustrated)
.22 L.R.—Barrel: 6"

Specifications: Same as above but with 6" barrel, sighting radius, 6" barrel—8.75". Weight, 35 oz. **$124.50**

TARGETSMAN
.22 L.R.—Barrel: 6"

CALIBER: .22 Long Rifle.
MAGAZINE CAPACITY: 10 rounds.
LENGTH OF BARREL: 6".
LENGTH OVERALL: 10⅞".
WEIGHT: 3! ounces.
SIGHTS: Adjustable rear sight. Sighting radius, 6" barrel—9.1".
TRIGGER: Wide.
STOCKS: Walnut with Thumbrest.
FINISH: Blue.

**TARGETSMAN
.22 L.R. CALIBER
$125.00**

HUNTSMAN
.22 L.R.—Barrel: 4" & 6"

CALIBER: .22 Long Rifle.
MAGAZINE CAPACITY: 10 rounds.
LENGTH OF BARREL: 4" or 6".
LENGTH OVERALL: 9" with 4" bbl., 10½" with 6" bbl.
WEIGHTS: 31 oz. with 4½" bbl., 31½ oz. with 6" bbl.
SIGHTS: Fixed. Sighting radius: 4" barrel—7.3"; 6" barrel—8.75".
TRIGGER: Wide.
STOCKS: Walnut. FINISH: Blue.

**HUNTSMAN
.22 L.R. CALIBER
$109.50**

COLT REVOLVERS

PYTHON .357 MAGNUM

.357 Magnum—Barrels: 2½″, 4″, 6″

**PYTHON
6-INCH BARREL**

The Colt Python revolver is chambered for the powerful .357 Magnum cartridge, suitable for hunting, target shooting and police use. Made in 2½″, 4″ and 6″ barrel lengths, every contact part is hand honed, hand-fitted. Features include: ventilated rib; fast-cooking, wide-spur hammer; shrouded ejector rod; target hammer, trigger and grips; adjustable rear and ramp-type front sights. Shoots both .357 Mag. and .38 Spec. loads.

Sights consist of an adjustable rear sight, and ramp-type front sight, ⅛″ wide. The sighting radius with 2½″ barrel is 4.4″; 4″ barrel—5.7″; and 6″ barrel—7.65″. The Python comes fitted with full-checkered walnut, square butt, target stocks. Length overall with 2½″ barrel—7¼″; 4″ barrel—9¼″; and 6″ barrel—11¼″. Weights: with 2½″ barrel—38 ounces; 4″ barrel—41 ounces; and 6″ barrel—43½ ounces. Finish—Colt royal blue or polished nickel.

Python, w/2½″, 4″, or 6″ barrel, blue finish ... $253.00

Python, w/4″, or 6″ barrel, polished nickel ... $282.00

**PYTHON
4-INCH BARREL**

**PYTHON
2½-INCH BARREL**

AGENT

.38 Special

Caliber: .38 Special.
Length of Barrel: 2″.
Length Overall: 6⅝″.
Weight: 16 oz.
Sights: Fixed type, ramp-style, glare-proofed. Front blade. .110″. Rear notch .135″. Sighting radius 3.5″.
Trigger: Smooth.
Stocks: Full-checkered walnut, round butt.
Finish: Blue.
Agent $141.00
With Shroud $146.00

COBRA

Caliber: .38 Special.
Length of Barrel: 2″
Length Overall 6⅝″.
Weight: 16½oz.
Sights: Fixed-type ramp-style, glare-proofed. Sighting radius 3.5″.
Trigger: Grooved.
Finish: Blue, or Nickel
Cobra, blue finish $143.00
Cobra, nickel finish $162.00

Made in .38 Special

COLT SINGLE ACTION REVOLVERS

NEW FRONTIER SINGLE ACTION ARMY

.45 Colt, .357 Mag.—Barrels: 5½", 7½"

.45 Colt, .357 Magnum

The Colt New Frontier Single Action Army Revolver is made in two calibers—.45 Colt and .357 Magnum, with a choice of 5½-inch or 7½-inch barrels. It features an adjustable rear sight, with flat top frame and ramp front sight. The sighting radius with the 5½-inch barrel is 6.5", and 8.45" with the 7½-inch barrel. Additional features include smooth trigger, knurled hammer spur and walnut stocks.

NEW FRONTIER SINGLE ACTION ARMY, .45 Colt or .357 Mag., **$294.00**

SPECIFICATIONS

CALIBERS: .45 Colt & .357 Magnum.
LENGTH OF BARREL: 5½" and 7½" in above calibers.
LENGTH OVERALL: 10⅞" with 5½" bbl.; 13½" with 7½" bbl.
WEIGHTS: .45 cal. with 5½" bbl., 3½ lbs., with 7½" bbl., 4 lbs. & .357 Magnum with 5½" bbl., 3¾ lbs., with 7½" bbl., 4½ lbs.

SIGHTS: Ramp front. Adjustable rear.
SIGHT RADIUS: With 5½" barrel—6.5".
With 7½" barrel—8.45".
FINISH: Case hardened frame; blued barrel, cylinder, trigger guard & backstrap.
STOCKS: Walnut.

SINGLE ACTION ARMY

.45 Colt, .357 Mag.—Barrels: 4¾", 5½", 7½"

The Colt Single Action Army, also known as the original "Peacemaker" is available in .45 Colt and .357 Magnum calibers. The .45 Colt and .357 Magnum models come in 4¾", 5½" and 7½" barrel lengths. The sights are fixed type with a 5.9" sighting radius for the 4¾" barrel, 6.5" for the 5½" barrel and 8.45" for the 7½" barrel. With color case hardened frame, blued barrel, cylinder, trigger guard and backstrap. The Colt Single Action Army is also available with a polished nickel finish in .45 caliber and comes with walnut stocks.

S.A. Army .45 Colt or .357 Mag., w/4¾" or 5½" bbl., Blue **$246.50**
S.A. Army .45 Colt or .357 Mag., w/7½" bbl., Blue **$253.50**
S.A. Army .45 Colt, w/7½" bbl., Polished Nickel **$294.00**

SPECIFICATIONS

CALIBERS: .45 Colt, & .357 Magnum.
LENGTH OF BARRELS: 4¾", 5½" & 7½" in .45 Colt & .357 Magnum.
LENGTH OVERALL: 11½" with 5½" bbl.; 12⅞" with 7½" bbl.; 10¾" with 4¾" bbl.
WEIGHTS: .45 cal. with 5½" bbl., 3½ lbs., with 7½" bbl., 4 lbs. & .357 Mag. with 5½" bbl., 3¾ lbs., with 7½" bbl., 4½ lbs.

SIGHTS: Fixed type.
SIGHT RADIUS: With 4¾" barrel—5.9"; with 5½" barrel—6.5"; with 7½" barrel—8.45".
FINISH: Case hardened frame; blued barrel, cylinder trigger guard & backstrap.
STOCKS: Square butt with checkered ebony rubber.

DELUXE COLT SINGLE ACTION REVOLVERS

Deluxe Colt Single Action revolvers are also available in highly decorated form. Degree of decoration is dependent only on the individual customer's taste. Colt Single Action Army illustrated at left provides coverage of approximately two thirds of the barrel, portions of the cylinder and partial coverage of the frame and sideplate.

More highly decorated models provide larger coverage of engraving, including the side of the top strap, the backstrap down to the stock, the butt, trigger guard and the crane.

DAY ARMS CONVERSION UNITS

30-X .22 TARGET CONVERSION FOR THE .45 & .38 AUTOMATIC

DAY ARMS "30-X" CONVERSION
(5" or 6" Barrel Lengths)
$99.50

• Converts .45 or .38 Government Model to .22 target pistol • No alterations to pistol • X-ring accuracy at fifty yard • Shoot the same trigger in all matches • Comes with two special five shot magazine adaptors. Converts .45 magazine to .22 caliber • Stationary Douglas premium grade "Ultra-Rifled" barrel • Fully adjustable, deluxe type target sights installed on a stationary steel rib • Changes back instantly for center-fire • No special tools necessary.

A target grade .22 LR Conversion Kit for the Colt Govt. Model 45 and 38 Super pistols is available from the Day Arms Corporation. The Day Conversion comes complete with two 5 shot magazine adaptors. This unit can turn the Colt Auto into a .22 caliber target pistol in less than 60 seconds without alteration to the gun. No special fitting is necessary and the pistol can be changed back to the original caliber just as quickly. It is possible for the serious competitor to shoot the same receiver in 22, centerfire, and 45 matches, and allow practice and sport shooting with .22 LR ammo. **General Specifications:** The Day 30-X Conversion is available in either 5 or 6 inch barrel lengths. Douglas Premium Grade barrels are used. The unit has a heavy rib type sighting system equipped with deluxe target sights and is attached directly to the barrel housing. Sight radius is 7" on the 5" barrel model and 8⅛" on the 6". The slide operates independently of the sights and barrel. The assembled unit is secured to the receiver by means of a three point spring loaded suspension system that accommodates minor receiver irregularities while providing the rigid mounting necessary for accuracy. The weight of the complete pistol with the 5" model installed and one magazine and adaptor is 40 oz.

The 6" model is 44 oz. All safties function normally on the pistol however the slide must be locked to the rear manually after the last shot.

The Day 30-X Conversion will fit all Govt. Model pistols manufactured by Colt from the Mod. 1911 through the new Mark IV Series 70, including the Gold Cups. In addition it will fit most of these that have been accurized. It will not fit the Commander models nor any of the foreign or domestic copies.

The "El Macho" (.22 conversion unit) is a plinker version, in 5" barrel length only, without the rib; however, it comes equipped with deluxe adjustable sights, and is priced at **$89.50**.

H&R REVOLVERS

H&R Revolver Models 929, 925, 926

Model 929 being a 9-shot .22 for target shooting, plinking and small game hunting. Model 926 is available as a 9-shot .22 or 5-shot .38 caliber, features checkered walnut grips. Model 925 is a .38 caliber, 5-shot revolver designed for police, security guard and sporting use. All three models feature single and double action and H&R Crown-Lustre blue finish.

H&R Model 929
Sidekick 9-Shot Revolver

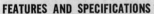

9-Shot .22 Long Rifle—Barrel: 2½″, 4″, & 6″

H&R's Model 929 "Sidekick" revolver features a 9-shot swing-out cylinder. Made in .22 caliber, it is available with 2½″, 4″ and 6″ barrel lengths. The 4″ and 6″ barrels have windage adjustment on rear sight. Blue finish **$62.50**
Model 930 has identical features, but is finished in durable, protective nickel, and comes with 2½″ or 4″ barrel. Matte finish on top frame. **$69.50**

FEATURES AND SPECIFICATIONS

Caliber:	.22 short, long, and long rifle; standard or high velocity.	**Weight:**	22 oz., 26 oz., and 28 oz.
Capacity:	9 shots.	**Action:**	Single and double. Swing-out cylinder.
Grips:	Black Cycolac.	**Sights:**	4″ and 6″ barrels have windage adjustment on rear sight.
Barrel Length:	2½″, 4″, and 6″.	**Finish:**	H&R Crown-Lustre Blue.

H&R Model 925 Defender
5-Shot Revolver

.38 S&W—Barrel: 2½″

Designed for police, security guard and sporting use, the H&R Defender combines firepower, accuracy and total dependability. It's perfectly balanced, easy to handle and chambered for the powerful .38 caliber S&W cartridge **$79.50**

FEATURES AND SPECIFICATIONS

Caliber:	.38 S&W.	**Action:**	Single and double. Top break-open.
Capacity:	5 shots.	**Sights:**	Fixed front; adjustable rear sight.
Grips:	One-piece wrap-around.	**Finish:**	H&R Crown-Lustre Blue.
Barrel Length:	2½″.		
Weight:	22 oz.		

H&R Model 926 Revolver

.22 Long Rifle, .38 S&W—Barrel: 4″

The compact Model 926 is suited for small game hunting, or just for occasional plinking. Features include hand checkered, walnut grips and trigger guard extension. With 4″ barrel, the Model 926 is available in .22 Long Rifle or .38 S&W .. **$84.50**

FEATURES AND SPECIFICATIONS

Caliber:	.22 short, long, and long rifle, and .38 S&W.	**Weight:**	31 oz.
Capacity:	9 shots .22 cal., 5 shots .38 S&W.	**Action:**	Single and double. Top break-open.
Grips:	Hand checkered walnut.	**Sights:**	Fixed front; adjustable rear sight.
Barrel Length:	4″.	**Finish:**	H&R Crown-Lustre Blue.

H&R REVOLVERS

H&R Revolver Models 922, 732, 733

Model 922 is available in a choice of three barrel lengths. Models 732 and 733 are both six-shot, .32 caliber revolvers with swing-out cylinder. The 732 has a Crown-Lustre blue finish while the 733 is plated in protective nickel.

H&R Model 922
9-Shot Revolver
9-Shot .22 Long Rifle—Barrel: 2½", 4", & 6"

The **H&R Model 922,** is a 9-shot single and double action .22 caliber revolver which handles .22 short, long, and long rifle, standard or high velocity, and features a safety rim cylinder. Available in 2½", 4", and 6" barrel lengths. Blue finish **$54.50**

FEATURES AND SPECIFICATIONS
Caliber: .22 short, long, and long rifle; standard or high velocity.
Capacity: 9 shots.
Grips: Black Cycolac.
Barrel Length: 2½", 4", and 6".
Weight: 20 oz., 24 oz., and 26 oz.
Action: Single and double.
Sights: Blade front sight.
Finish: H&R Crown-Lustre Blue

H&R Model 732 Guardsman
6-Shot Revolver

.32 S&W & .32 S&W Long—Barrel: 2½", 4"

The Guardsman features the easy-loading swing-out cylinder and comes with either 2½ or 4-inch barrel in blue finish **$62.50**

FEATURES AND SPECIFICATIONS
Caliber: .32 S&W and .32 S&W long.
Capacity: 6 shots.
Grips: Black Cycolac.
Barrel Length: 2½" and 4".
Action: Single and double. Swing-out cylinder.
Sights: 4" barrels have windage adjustment on rear sight.
Finish: H&R Crown-Lustre Blue.
Weight: 23½ oz., and 26 oz.

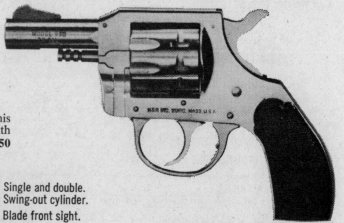

H&R Model 733 Guardsman
6-Shot Revolver

.32 S&W & .32 S&W Long—Barrel: 2½"

Model 733: Offering the same features as the Model 732, this revolver is finished in a high-lustre, protective nickel. With 2½" barrel only **$69.50**

FEATURES AND SPECIFICATIONS
Caliber: .32 S&W and .32 S&W long.
Capacity: 6 shots.
Grips: Black Cycolac.
Barrel Length: 2½".
Action: Single and double. Swing-out cylinder.
Sights: Blade front sight.
Finish: Nickel.
Weight: 23½ oz.

H&R REVOLVERS

H&R Revolver Models 999, 949, 939

A trio of 9-shot, .22 caliber revolvers from H&R including Model 999 with 6″ barrel and ventilated rib, checkered walnut grips and adjustable sights. Model 949 features authentic Western styling, automatic rebound hammer and one-piece walnut grip. Model 939 with 6″ target weight barrel and ventilated rib has an exclusive lock and key feature for maximum safety.

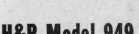

H&R Model 999
Deluxe Sportsman

9-Shot .22 Long Rifle—Barrel: 6″

HR's **Model 999 Deluxe Sportsman** is a break-open type 9-shot revolver, featuring a wide hammer spur for fast and easy cocking. Made with unbreakable coil springs throughout. With 6″ ventilated rib barrel................$89.50

FEATURES AND SPECIFICATIONS

Caliber:	.22 short, long, and long rifle; standard or high velocity.
Capacity:	9 shots.
Grips:	Checkered walnut.
Barrel Length:	6″ ventilated.

Weight:	30 oz.
Action:	Single and double. Top break-open.
Sights:	Adjustable front and rear.
Finish:	H&R Crown-Lustre Blue.

H&R Model 949
Forty-Niner

9-Shot .22 Long Rifle—Barrel: 5½″

H&R's **Forty-Niner** is a modern 9-shot .22 caliber revolver with frontier features. With automatic rebound hammer, wide cocking spur and unbreakable coil spring construction $59.50

FEATURES AND SPECIFICATIONS

Caliber:	.22 short, long, and long rifle; standard or high velocity.
Capacity:	9 shots.
Grips:	One-piece walnut grip.
Barrel Length:	5½″.
Weight:	31 oz.

Action:	Single and double. Side loading and ejection.
Sights:	Adjustable rear sight; Western type front blade sight.
Finish:	H&R Crown-Lustre Blue; (or nickel—Model 950 $69.50).

H&R Model 939
Ultra Sidekick

9-Shot .22 Long Rifle—Barrel: 6″

The **Ultra Sidekick** revolver comes equipped with a precision adjustable rear sight, and ventilated rib barrel. Features include a safety lock device which prevents unauthorized persons from firing your revolver $82.50

FEATURES AND SPECIFICATIONS

Caliber:	.22 short, long, and long rifle; standard or high velocity.
Capacity:	9 shots.
Grips:	Checkered walnut with contoured thumb rest.
Barrel Length:	6″ target weight; ventilated rib.
Weight:	33 oz.

Action:	Single and double. Swing-out cylinder.
Sights:	Fixed front. Rear sight adjustable for windage and elevation.
Finish:	H&R Crown-Lustre Blue.

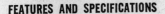

H&R REVOLVERS

H&R Revolver Models 970, 622, 632, 940

Designed for athletic events and theatrical use, Model 970 Starter Revolver is a 9-shot .22 blank-firing pistol. Also available as Model 960 in .32 caliber for louder report. Model 622 is a single and double action, 6-shot .22 with pull pin cylinder. Also available in .32 caliber as Model 632. The Model 940 is a 9-shot .22 with exclusive safety lock and key to prevent unauthorized use.

H&R Model 970

Starter Revolver

9-Shot .22 Blank—Barrel: 2½"

For use as a signaling device for all types of athletic events, or for realism in theatrical use, the Model 970 fires rimfire, blank ammunition. **$42.50**

FEATURES AND SPECIFICATIONS
Caliber: .22 blank. **Capacity:** 9 shots. **Grips:** Black Cycolac. **Barrel Length:** 2½". **Weight:** 19 oz. **Action:** Single and double. Pull pin cylinder. **Finish:** H&R Crown-Lustre Blue.

NOTE: *If a louder report is required, the 6-shot Model 960 is available at the same price, and with features identical to those of the Model 970. It is chambered for .32 caliber S&W center-fire, blank cartridges. . . . $42.50*

H&R Model 622

6-Shot Revolver

6-Shot 22 Long Rifle—Barrel: 2½" & 4"

The H&R Model 622, is a 6-shot single and double action .22 caliber revolver which handles .22 short, long, and long rifle, standard or high velocity, and features a safety rim cylinder. Available in 2½", and 4" barrel lengths. Blue finish **$51.00**

FEATURES AND SPECIFICATIONS

Caliber: .22 short, long, and long rifle; standard or high velocity.
Capacity: 6 shots.
Grips: Black Cycolac. Round Butt.
Barrel Length: 2½" and 4".

Weight: 22 oz. and 26 oz.
Action: Single and double. Pull pin cylinder.
Sights: Blade front sigrt.
Finish: Satin finished frame. H&R Crown-Lustre Blue barrel.

> Also in .32 S&W & .32 S&W Long as Model 632 Price . . . **$54.50** 2½" & 4". Blue Finish.

Model 940

9-Shot Revolver

The Model 940 features a swing-out 9-shot cylinder, and comes equipped with H&R's exclusive safety lock that prevents anyone from using the gun unless the owner gives them the key. The round, target weight barrel assures steady holding, and a trigger guard extension combined with the thumb rest on the grips makes the Model 940 well suited for target work. **$79.50**

FEATURES AND SPECIFICATIONS

Caliber: .22 short, long, and long rifle; standard or high velocity.
Capacity: 9 shots.
Grips: Checkered walnut with contoured thumb rest.
Barrel Length: 6" target weight; ventilated rib.

Weight: 33 oz.
Action: Single and double. Swing-out cylinder.
Sights: Fixed front sight. Rear sight adjustable for windage and elevation.
Finish: H&R Crown-Lustre Blue.

HIGH-STANDARD AUTO PISTOLS

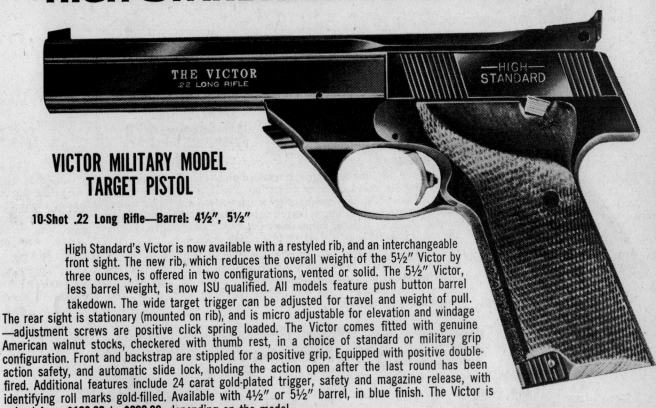

VICTOR MILITARY MODEL TARGET PISTOL

10-Shot .22 Long Rifle—Barrel: 4½", 5½"

High Standard's Victor is now available with a restyled rib, and an interchangeable front sight. The new rib, which reduces the overall weight of the 5½" Victor by three ounces, is offered in two configurations, vented or solid. The 5½" Victor, less barrel weight, is now ISU qualified. All models feature push button barrel takedown. The wide target trigger can be adjusted for travel and weight of pull. The rear sight is stationary (mounted on rib), and is micro adjustable for elevation and windage —adjustment screws are positive click spring loaded. The Victor comes fitted with genuine American walnut stocks, checkered with thumb rest, in a choice of standard or military grip configuration. Front and backstrap are stippled for a positive grip. Equipped with positive double-action safety, and automatic slide lock, holding the action open after the last round has been fired. Additional features include 24 carat gold-plated trigger, safety and magazine release, with identifying roll marks gold-filled. Available with 4½" or 5½" barrel, in blue finish. The Victor is priced from **$198.00** to **$209.00**, depending on the model.

FEATURES AND SPECIFICATIONS: Caliber: .22 L.R. **Capacity:** 10 rounds. **Barrel:** 4½ inch and 5½ inch, specially molded and contoured barrels. **Sights:** Adjustable micrometer rear sight mounted on rib. **Trigger:** Wide target trigger—2-2¼ lb. pull. **Grips:** Checkered walnut military. **Weight:** 48 oz. for 4½ inch model; 52 oz. for 5½ inch model. **Overall Length:** 8¾" for 4½ inch model; 9¾" for 5½ inch model. **Finish:** Blue.

OLYMPIC I.S.U. TARGET MODELS IN .22 SHORT CALIBER

OLYMPIC ISU*
WITH 6¾" TAPERED BARREL
(10-Shot .22 Short)
$204.00

CALIBER: .22 Short only **CAPACITY:** 10 rounds.
BARREL: 6¾" tapered barrel, with integral stabilizer and 2 removable weights.
SIGHTS: Recoil proof, wide square-notched rear sight with indexed positive-click adjustment. Undercut ramp front sight. Sight radius, 9½".
TRIGGER: Wide target trigger with anti-backlash trigger-screw adjustment.
GRIPS: Deeply checkered thumbrest walnut grips.
WEIGHT: 40 ozs. **OVERALL LENGTH:** 11¼". **FINISH:** Blue.
*Complies with all rapid fire pistol International Shooting Union Regulations.

OLYMPIC I.S.U. MILITARY*
10 Shot .22 Short
6¾" TAPERED BARREL
$204.00

CALIBER: .22 Short only. **CAPACITY:** 10 rounds.
BARREL: 6¾" tapered barrel, with integral stabilizer and 2 removable weights.
SIGHTS: Stationary adjustable rear sight; deep notched. Undercut ramp front sight. Sight radius, 9.9".
TRIGGER: Wide target trigger with anti-backlash trigger-screw adjustment.
GRIPS: Military type checkered American walnut with thumb rest.
WEIGHT: 40.5 ozs. **OVERALL LENGTH:** 11". **FINISH:** Blue.
*Complies with all rapid fire pistol International Shooting Union Regulations.

HIGH-STANDARD AUTO PISTOLS

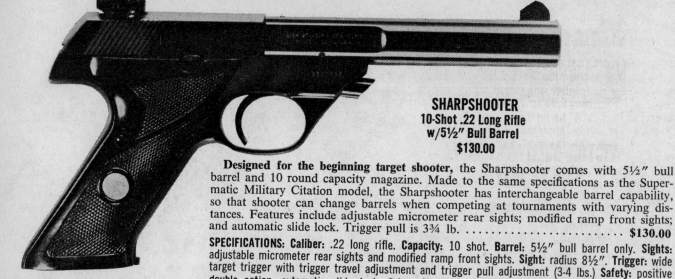

SHARPSHOOTER
10-Shot .22 Long Rifle
w/5½" Bull Barrel
$130.00

Designed for the beginning target shooter, the Sharpshooter comes with 5½" bull barrel and 10 round capacity magazine. Made to the same specifications as the Supermatic Military Citation model, the Sharpshooter has interchangeable barrel capability, so that shooter can change barrels when competing at tournaments with varying distances. Features include adjustable micrometer rear sights; modified ramp front sights; and automatic slide lock. Trigger pull is 3¾ lb. **$130.00**

SPECIFICATIONS: Caliber: .22 long rifle. **Capacity:** 10 shot. **Barrel:** 5½" bull barrel only. **Sights:** adjustable micrometer rear sights and modified ramp front sights. **Sight:** radius 8½". **Trigger:** wide target trigger with trigger travel adjustment and trigger pull adjustment (3-4 lbs.) **Safety:** positive double action; automatic slide lock. **Grips:** Checkered walnut grips. **Length overall:** 10 inches. **Weight:** 42 oz. **Finish:** blue.

SPORT KING
10-Shot .22 Long Rifle
w/4½" or 6¾" Barrel
Blue $99.95
Nickel $109.95

High-Standard's Sport King .22 caliber automatic pistol is available in standard blue, or nickel finish, with choice of 4½" or 6¾" barrel lengths. It comes with hard durable checkered plastic grips and features the push button barrel takedown. It comes equipped with fixed sights—fixed front and square-notched rear sight.
Blue finish **$99.95**
Nickel finish **$109.95**

SPECIFICATIONS: Caliber: .22 caliber long rifle. **Capacity:** 10 round. **Barrel:** 4½" or 6¾", quick takedown barrel, interchangeable. **Sights:** fixed front and square notched rear sight. **Trigger:** wide contour serrated trigger. **Safety:** double-acting safety. **Grips:** hard durable checkered plastic. **Weight:** with 4½" barrel—39 oz; with 6¾" barrel—42 oz. **Overall length:** with 4½" barrel—9"; with 6¾" barrel—11¼". **Finish:** blue or nickel.

DERRINGERS
.22 Long Rifle; .22 R. F. Magnum
w/3½" 2-Shot Dual Barrels

The Derringers from High Standard offer the traditional look of the old, with the safety design features of the new. They feature hammerless design.

Their double action is safety-engineered—the High Standard Derringer cannot ever fire accidentally—even if dropped.

They're available in either onyx black with ivory type grips or polished nickel with ebony grips. These derringers, have an overall width of less than 1" and weigh 11 oz. Chambered to fire .22 shorts, longs or long rifle, or, for .22 magnum.

NO. 9305 STANDARD DERRINGER*

No.	Cal.	Cap.	Finish	Grips	Lgth. Bbl.	Full Lgth.	Wt. Oz.	Retail
9193	.22	2	Blue	Ivory	3½"	5"	11	$74.00
9305	.22	2	Nickel	Ebony	3½"	5"	11	$87.00

Fire long rifle, longs or shorts.

NO. 9306 MAGNUM DERRINGER

No.	Cal.	Cap.	Finish	Grips	Lgth. Bbl.	Full Lgth.	Wt. Oz.	Retail
9194	.22 Mag.	2	Blue	Ivory	3½"	5"	11	$74.00
9306	.22 Mag.	2	Nickel	Ebony	3½"	5"	11	$87.00

Set of magnums in presentation case, $125.00.

HIGH-STANDARD REVOLVERS

Rim Fire Revolvers

Sentinel Mark I and Mark IV

A completely redesigned and improved version of the .22 caliber rim fire Sentinel revolver, the Sentinel Mark I and Mark II is now a steel framed revolver with classic styling, and is chambered for .22 Long Rifle or .22 Magnum rim fire cartridges. Available in 2″, 3″ or 4″ barrel lengths, with fixed or adjustable rear sights. Impressive ballistics of the .22 Magnum rim fire, coupled with the mild recoil, make it a suitable off-duty gun for policemen or policewomen. Available in trophy blue or nickel finish, with wrap around American walnut stocks. White outline rear sight with red ramp front sight comes standard with nickel finish adjustable sight models.

Sentinel Mark I—22 Long Rifle caliber: 2″ & 4″, with fixed sights, blue, **$109.00**; 2″ & 4″, with fixed sights, nickel, **$119.00**; 3″ & 4″, with adj. rear sight, blue, **$119.00**; 4″, with adj. rear sight, nickel, **$129.00**.
Sentinel Mark IV—22 Magnum rimfire caliber: 2″, 3″ & 4″, with fixed sights, blue, **$109.00**; 2″, 3″ & 4″, with fixed sights, nickel, **$119.00**; 3″ & 4″, with adj. rear sight, blue, **$119.00**; 3″ & 4″, with adj. rear sight, nickel, **$129.00**.

Center Fire Revolvers

Sentinel Mark II and Mark III—

A heavy duty .357 double action revolver, available in standard or Trophy blue finish, fixed or adjustable rear sight, with service or target grips.

Featuring a smooth, crisp trigger pull, and

SENTINEL MARK II
(with fixed sights)
6-shot .357 Magnum
Barrel: 2¼″, 4″ & 6″
Blue finish $120.00

SENTINEL MARK III
(with adustable rear sight)
6-shot .357 Magnum
Barrel: 2¼″, 4″ & 6″
Trophy blue finish $154.95

fast lock-up time.

With front cylinder release latch, and full case ejection, the Sentinel is available in 2½″, 4″ or 6″ barrel length.

Features include full wrap around walnut grips with backstrap checkering.

Center Fire Revolvers

MODEL NO.	NAME	FEATURES	FINISH	CAL.	BBL. LGTH.
9401	Sentinel Mark II	Fixed Sights	Blue	.357	2½″
9402	Sentinel Mark II	Fixed Sights	Blue	.357	4″
9403	Sentinel Mark II	Fixed Sights	Blue	.357	6″
9407	Sentinel Mark III	Adj. Rear Sight	Trophy Blue	.357	2½″
9408	Sentinel Mark III	Adj. Rear Sight	Trophy Blue	.357	4″
9409	Sentinel Mark III	Adj. Rear Sight	Trophy Blue	.357	6″

HIGH-STANDARD AUTO PISTOLS

TROPHY GRADE—MILITARY MODEL AUTOMATICS

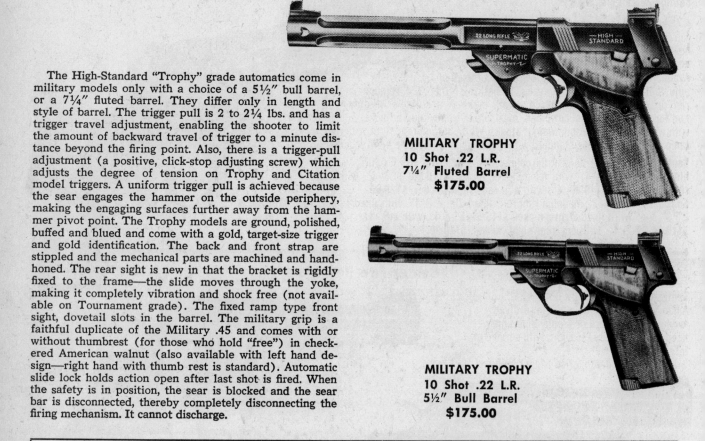

MILITARY TROPHY
10 Shot .22 L.R.
7¼″ Fluted Barrel
$175.00

MILITARY TROPHY
10 Shot .22 L.R.
5½″ Bull Barrel
$175.00

The High-Standard "Trophy" grade automatics come in military models only with a choice of a 5½″ bull barrel, or a 7¼″ fluted barrel. They differ only in length and style of barrel. The trigger pull is 2 to 2¼ lbs. and has a trigger travel adjustment, enabling the shooter to limit the amount of backward travel of trigger to a minute distance beyond the firing point. Also, there is a trigger-pull adjustment (a positive, click-stop adjusting screw) which adjusts the degree of tension on Trophy and Citation model triggers. A uniform trigger pull is achieved because the sear engages the hammer on the outside periphery, making the engaging surfaces further away from the hammer pivot point. The Trophy models are ground, polished, buffed and blued and come with a gold, target-size trigger and gold identification. The back and front strap are stippled and the mechanical parts are machined and hand-honed. The rear sight is new in that the bracket is rigidly fixed to the frame—the slide moves through the yoke, making it completely vibration and shock free (not available on Tournament grade). The fixed ramp type front sight, dovetail slots in the barrel. The military grip is a faithful duplicate of the Military .45 and comes with or without thumbrest (for those who hold "free") in checkered American walnut (also available with left hand design—right hand with thumb rest is standard). Automatic slide lock holds action open after last shot is fired. When the safety is in position, the sear is blocked and the sear bar is disconnected, thereby completely disconnecting the firing mechanism. It cannot discharge.

SPECIFICATIONS FOR MILITARY TROPHY MODELS (5½″ & 7¼″ BARRELS)

CALIBER: .22 Long Rifle.
CAPACITY: 10 shot.
BARREL: 5½″ bull barrel; 7¼″ fluted barrel.
SIGHTS: Stationary bracket type, deep notched rear; fixed ramp type dovetail front sight.
SIGHT RADIUS: With 5½″ barrel—8¾″; with 7¼″ barrel—10″.

TRIGGER: Wide target trigger, with trigger travel adjustment and trigger-pull adjustment (2-2¼ lbs.).
SAFETY: Double acting safety. Automatic side lock.
LENGTH OVERALL: With 5½″ bbl.—9¾″; with 7¼″ bbl.—11½″.
WEIGHT: 44.5 ounces for both models.
FINISH: Ground, polished, buffed and blued.

STANDARD-CITATION GRADE WITH 5½″ BULL BARREL

CALIBER: .22 Long Rifle.
CAPACITY: 10 rounds.
BARREL: 5½″ bull barrel.
SIGHTS: Recoil-proof wide rear sight mounted on slide, square-notched with indexed click-adjustments. Undercut ramp front sight.
SIGHT RADIUS: 8½″
TRIGGER: Wide target trigger with anti-backlash trigger-screw adjustment.
FRAME: Back and front straps serrated.
SAFETY: Double-acting safety. Rebounding firing pin.
GRIPS: Checkered Walnut grip with built-in thumbrest.
WEIGHT: 42 ozs.   OVERALL LENGTH: 10″.   FINISH: Blue.

SUPERMATIC CITATION
WITH 5½″ BULL BARREL
(10-Shot .22 Long Rifle)
$169.50

HIGH-STANDARD AUTO PISTOLS

CITATION MILITARY MODEL AUTOMATICS

CITATION MILITARY
10 Shot .22 Long Rifle
7¼" Fluted Barrel . . . $169.50

CITATION MILITARY
10 Shot .22 Long Rifle
5½" Bull Barrel . . . $169.50

The Supermatic "Citation" grade military models are available in two barrel lengths—5½" bull barrel, and 7¼" fluted barrel. The trigger pull and trigger travel adjustment are standard on all Citation models. The military models have a stationery type near sight with a dovetail, fixed ramp type front sight. Back and front straps are stippled. The grips are checkered American walnut and come with or without thumb rest, in right or left hand design. All Citation models come with positive, double action safety and side lock features. Barrel interchangeability is also standard with all Citation models. Mechanical parts are machined and hand-honed.

SPECIFICATIONS

CALIBER: .22 Long Rifle.
CAPACITY: 10 shot.
BARREL: 5½" bull barrel; 7¼" fluted barrel.
SIGHTS: Stationary bracket type, deep notched rear; fixed ramp type dovetail front sight.
SIGHT RADIUS: With 5½" barrel—8¾"; with 7¼" barrel—10".
TRIGGER: Wide target trigger, with trigger travel adjustment and trigger-pull adjustment (2-2¼ lbs.).
SAFETY: Positive, double action. Side lock.
GRIPS: Military type checkered American walnut with thumb rest.
LENGTH OVERALL: With 5½" barrel—9¾"; with 7¼" barrel—11½".
WEIGHT: 44.5 ounces for both models.
FINISH: Ground, polished, blued.

HIGH-STANDARD REVOLVERS

HIGH SIERRA
9-SHOT .22 LONG RIFLE
7" OCTAGONAL BARREL

The High Sierra Western-style revolver features a steel frame and comes with a 7" octagonal barrel with a custom blue finish, complemented by hand-rubbed walnut grips. Trigger guard and backstraps are gold-plated. Available with dual cylinders (22L.R./22 Magnum). High Sierra deluxe comes equipped with an adjustable rear sight. Price: High Sierra with fixed sights and two cylinders (22LR/mag), **$122.00;** adjustable rear sight and two cylinders (22LR/mag), **$127.95.**

The Double Nine with steel frame and 5½" barrel, comes with interchangeable cylinders for standard 22 L.R. and 22 Magnum ammunition. Features include nine-shot capacity, double action and swing out cylinders. With fixed sights, the Double Nine sells for **$112.00** in blue finish and **$122.00** in nickel finish. Also available with adjustable rear sight in blue finish, priced at **$127.00.**

The Longhorn, with 9½" barrel and fixed sights comes in blue finish only, and is priced at **$102.00;** with two cylinders, **$122.00.** Other features are the same as the Double Nine.

Western Revolvers (9-shot) Double Action

MODEL NO.	NAME	FEATURES	FINISH	CAL.	BBL. LGTH.
9320	Double Nine	Fixed Sights	Trophy Blue	2 Cyl .22 LR/mag	5½"
9322	Double Nine	Fixed Sights	Nickel	2 Cyl .22 LR/mag	5½"
9324	Double Nine Deluxe	Adj. Rear Sight	Trophy Blue	2 Cyl .22 LR/mag	5½"
9326	Longhorn	Fixed Sights	Trophy Blue	2 Cyl .22 LR/mag	9½"
9314	High Sierra	Fixed Sights	Trophy Blue	2 Cyl .22 LR/mag	7" Oct
9315	High Sierra Deluxe	Adj. Rear Sight	Trophy Blue	2 Cyl .22 LR/mag	7" Oct

IVER JOHNSON "CATTLEMAN" SINGLE-ACTION REVOLVERS

CATTLEMAN
(with fixed sights)
Calibers: .357 Magnum,
.45 Long Colt & .44 Magnum

The Cattleman Magnum single action revolver is available in .357 Magnum, .45 Long Colt and .44 Magnum calibers, and comes with fixed sights. Finished in a high luster custom blue on the cylinder and barrel, while the forged frame is color case hardened. The backstrap and trigger guard are made from highly polished solid brass. Featured is a unique safety system positively locking on the hammer so that the gun cannot fire, even if dropped. The Cattleman comes fitted with genuine walnut grips. The .357 Magnum and .45 Long Colt calibers are available in 4¾", 5½" and 7¼" barrel lengths; .44 Magnum caliber is available in 4¾", 6" and 7¼" barrel lengths. Cattleman with fixed sights, .357 Magnum and .45 Long Colt calibers, 4¾", 5½" & 7¼" barrel, blue **$151.75**
Cattleman with fixed sights, .44 Magnum caliber, 4¾", 6" & 7¼" barrel, blue **$175.95**

CATTLEMAN BUCKHORN MAGNUM
(with adjustable sights)
Calibers: .357 Magnum,
.45 Long Colt & .44 Magnum

The Cattlemen Buckhorn Magnum is manufactured from forgings and contains no castings. Available in calibers .357 Magnum, .45 Long Colt and .44 Magnum, the Buckhorn features a specially designed frame with adjustable target sights. The backstrap and frame are made from highly polished solid brass complementing the color case hardened frame. Weight is 2 lbs. 12 oz.
Buckhorn with adustable sights, .357 Magnum and .45 Long Colt calibers, 5¾" & 7½" barrel, blue **$166.95**
Buckhorn with adjustable sights, .44 Magnum caliber, 4¾", 6" & 7½" barrel, blue **$191.25**

THE ENGRAVED CATTLEMAN SINGLE ACTION REVOLVER
($500 price in addition to cost of gun)

The engraved Cattleman single action revolver comes with a finely engraved frame, barrel, cylinder, hammer, trigger guard and back strap. The cylinder and hammer is finished in polished blue steel, and the frame in polished natural steel. Together with the solid brass trigger guard and back strap, the engraved Cattleman is a superb blend of European craftsmanship and artistry. Available in calibers: .357 Magnum, .45 Long Colt, .44 Magnum, .22 Long Rifle and .22 Magnum rim fire. Every Cattleman is proof tested and proof marked.

IVER JOHNSON "CATTLEMAN" SINGLE ACTION REVOLVERS

CATTLEMAN BUNTLINE
SINGLE ACTION REVOLVER WITH SHOULDER STOCK & 18" BARREL

CATTLEMAN BUNTLINE BUCKHORN MAGNUM

A big precision rifled ordnance steel 18" barrel with adjustable target sights. Ideal choice for handgun hunting or long range handgun shooting. The forged frame is handsomely color case hardened with a brilliant custom blue on barrel and frame. The backstrap is cut so that a shoulder stock can easily be fitted. Every single action fan, whether collector or shooter, will want to own this unusual, fine revolver. Weight about 3 lbs. 8 oz. Available in .357, .38 and .44 magnum and .45 long colt.

The Buntline comes furnished with an oil finished shoulder stock made from beautifully grained genuine walnut. The fittings are highly polished brass. A stocked handgun is an interesting display item and makes for a high point in any collection.

Buntline w/stock
Calibers:
.357 Magnum $316.20
.45 Long Colt $316.20
.44 Magnum $339.95

SPECIFICATIONS:

Calibers: .45 Colt, .357 Magnum & .44 Magnum
Sights: Front & rear dovetailed. Rear—deep rectangular notch.
Barrel Length: 18-inches only.
Overall Length: 24-inches.
Overall Length: w/Stock: 36½-inches.
Weight: approximately 3 lbs. 15 ozs. (varies according to caliber).
Stock Weight: approximately 1 lb. 12 ozs.

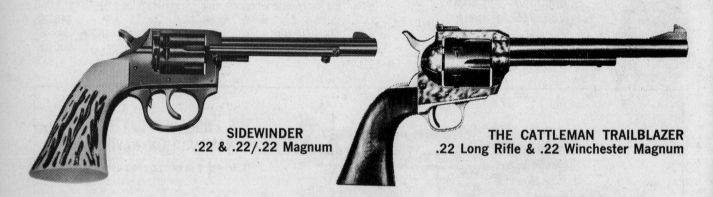

SIDEWINDER
.22 & .22/.22 Magnum

THE CATTLEMAN TRAILBLAZER
.22 Long Rifle & .22 Winchester Magnum

A .22 caliber revolver styled with the tradition and flavor of the old west. A well-balanced, ruggedly constructed revolver featuring a wider hammer spur, half-cock safety, and the availability of a magnum caliber cylinder. Available with either 4¾" or 6" barrel in .22 L.F. or .22/.22 Magnum.

.22 .... $56.60
.22/.22 Magnum $60.35

DELUXE SIDEWINDER. Same as Sidewinder with adjustable sights.
.22 .... $66.25
.22/.22 Magnum $73.00

A great idea in .22 caliber rimfire revolvers. In a matter of seconds the Trailblazer converts from an economical plinker to a serious varmint-control weapon with the interchangeable cylinder in .22 Winchester Magnum. A big, heavier built gun with the exact same finish and quality as found on magnum revolvers. The highly polished solid-brass backstrap and trigger guard are complemented by deep rich color case hardening on the forged frame. The precision-rifled ordnance steel barrel is available in 5½" and 6½" lengths. Weight about 2½ lbs.

Trailblazer .22/22 Mag. w/5½" barrel & adjustable sights **$132.00**
Trailblazer .22/22 Mag. w/6½" barrel & adjustable sights **$132.00**

IVER JOHNSON REVOLVERS

SPORTSMAN TARGET REVOLVER
8-Shot .22 Long Rifle
Barrel: 4¾", 6"
$53.75

**MODEL 57-A TARGET REVOLVER
WITH FRONT & REAR ADJUSTABLE SIGHTS**
8-Shot 22 Long Rifle—-Barrel: 4¾", 6"
$57.75

MODEL 55S-A "CADET"
8-Shot .22 Long Rifle—Barrel: 2½"
8-shot .22 Magnum—Barrel: 2½"
5-Shot .32 .38 S&W—Barrel: 2½"
$52.00
(5-shot .38 Special $59.75)

MODEL 56-A "STARTER"
8-Shot .22 Blanks
5-Shot .32 Blanks
$42.50

All Iver Johnson revolvers may be fired single or double action. The .22 caliber models shoot shorts, longs, long rifles, standard or hi-velocity; and have an 8-shot capacity. Features include a flash control cylinder. Each shell rim is recessed preventing blown heads or accidents. Front rim deflects blast and hot gas away from shooter. Equipped with an extra wide loading gate—a thumb flip opens it, closes it.

Hammer-the-Hammer action: Hammer and firing pin are completely separated. Lifter can't impart blow unless trigger holds it up in firing position. Provided on Models 67 and 67S. Other features include a wide hammer spur, and surfaced bores that can't shoot out.

SPECIFICATIONS & PRICES

MODEL 55-A TARGET: **$53.75**
Caliber: .22 Long Rifle (shoots shorts, longs, long rifles; standard or hi-velocity). 8-shots.
Barrel Length: 4¼" and 6".
Sights: Fixed type with blade front.
Length: 10¾" (w/6" barrel).
Weight: 30½ ounces (w/6" barrel).

MODEL 57-A TARGET: **$57.75**
Calibers: .22 Long Rifle (shoots shorts, longs, long rifles; standard or hi-velocity). 8-shots.
Barrel Length: 4¼" and 6".
Sights: Front and rear adjustable sights.
Length: 10¾" (w/6" barrel).
Weight: 30½ ounces (w/6" barrel).

MODEL 55S-A "CADET": **$52.00**
Calibers: .22 Long Rifle, (8-shots);
.22 Magnum, (8-shots);
.32 S&W Short & Long and Colt N.P. (5-shots);
.38 S&W & Colt N.P. (5-shots).
(.38 Special, ... **$59.75**)
Barrel Length: 2½".
Sights: Fixed type with blade front.
Length: 7-inches.
Weight: 24 ounces.

MODEL 56-A "STARTER": **$42.50**
Caliber: .22 Blank ammo. (8-shots)
.32 Blank ammo. (5-shots)
Stock: Tenite.
Length: 6¾".
Weight: 22 ounces.

LLAMA AUTOMATIC PISTOLS

Llama automatic pistols are available in Standard and Deluxe models. Standard models have a high-polished blue finish while the Deluxe models are available in the following finishes: blue engraved, satin, satin engraved and gold damascened. All Deluxe models are equipped with simulated pearl grips. Both Deluxe and Standard models are offered in .32, .380, 9mm, .38 Spl. and .45 Auto. calibers except for the gold damascened which is offered in .380 caliber only. For complete specifications see following page.

"STANDARD"

STANDARD AUTO
Blue Finish
.38 Super, 9mm, .45 Auto.
$159.95

STANDARD AUTO
.22 L.R., .32 Auto., .380 Auto.
$124.95

"DELUXE"

DELUXE SATIN
.22 L.R., .32 Auto., .380 Auto $174.95
.38 Super, 9mm, .45 Auto. $219.95

DELUXE BLUE ENGRAVED
.22 L.R., .32 Auto., .380 Auto. $199.95
.38 Super, 9mm, .45 Auto. $239.95

LLAMA AUTOMATIC PISTOLS

DELUXE GOLD DAMASCENED
.380 Auto. $850.00

DELUXE SATIN ENGRAVED
.22 L.R., .32 Auto., .380 $229.95
.38 Super, 9mm, .45 Auto. $269.95

COMPLETE SPECIFICATIONS FOR LLAMA AUTOMATIC PISTOLS:

CALIBERS:	.22 L.R.	.32 Auto.	.380 Auto.	.38 Super	9 m/m	45 Auto.
FRAME:	Forged high tensile strength steel.					
	Serrated front strap, checkered (curved) back strap.			Plain front strap, checkered (curved) back strap.		
TRIGGER:	Serrated					
HAMMER:	External. Wide spur, serrated.					
OPERATION:	Straight blow-back.			Locked breech.		
LANYARD LOOP:	No			Yes		
SLIDE:	Ventilated-rib with top surface matted to reduce glare.					
LOADED CHAMBER INDICATOR:	No	Yes				
SAFETIES:	Side lever thumb safety, half-cock safety, grip safety. Note: .22 L.R. with additional magazine safety (gun will not fire with magazine removed).					
GRIPS:	Modified thumb-rest plastic grips.			Genuine walnut, hand checkered.		
SIGHTS:	Square notch rear and Partridge-type front:					
	Screw adjustable rear sight for windage.					
SIGHT RADIUS:	4¼ -inches			6¼ -inches		
MAGAZINE CAPICITY:	8-shot		7-shot	9-shot	9-shot	7-shot
WEIGHT WITH EMPTY MAGAZINE:	23-ounces			2 lbs.-8 ozs.		
BARREL LENGTH:	3¹¹⁄₁₆-inches			5-inches		
OVERALL LENGTH:	6½ -inches			8½ -inches		
HEIGHT:	4⅜-inches			5¼ -inches		
FINISH:	Std. models-high polish blue.	Deluxe models—blue engraved, satin, satin engraved & gold damascened with simulated pearl grips.				

LLAMA "MARTIAL" REVOLVERS

The Llama Comanche is a handgun for law enforcement, personal protection and the sportsman as well. Features of the Comanche are checkered walnut target grips, forged steel frame, adjustable rear sight, wide trigger and hammer, float-ing fire pin and raised ventilated rib. The Comanche is available in .357 Magnum caliber with a 4″ barrel and high-polished blue finish.

"STANDARD"

DELUXE MARTIAL
Satin Engraved Finish
.22 L.R. w/ 6″ bbl.
.38 Spl. w/ 4″ & 6″ bbl.
$249.95

COMANCHE
.357 Magnum w/ 4″ bbl.
$169.95

"DELUXE"

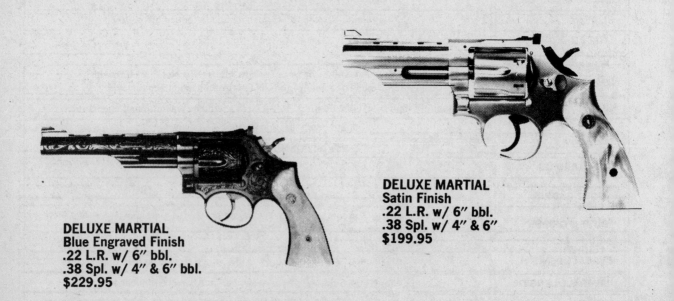

DELUXE MARTIAL
Blue Engraved Finish
.22 L.R. w/ 6″ bbl.
.38 Spl. w/ 4″ & 6″ bbl.
$229.95

DELUXE MARTIAL
Satin Finish
.22 L.R. w/ 6″ bbl.
.38 Spl. w/ 4″ & 6″
$199.95

LLAMA "MARTIAL" REVOLVERS

The Llama Martial revolvers are available in Standard Blue model in .22 L.R. caliber 4″ & 6″ barrel and .38 Spl. caliber with a 6″ barrel. The Martial revolvers are also available in Deluxe models with either a Satin, Satin-Engraved, Blue-Engraved or Gold-Damascened finish. All Deluxe models are offered in .22 L.R. caliber with 4″ & 6″ barrel or .38 Spl. with 6″ barrel with the exception of the Gold Damascened which is offered in .38 Spl. with 4″ barrel only. See following page for specifications.

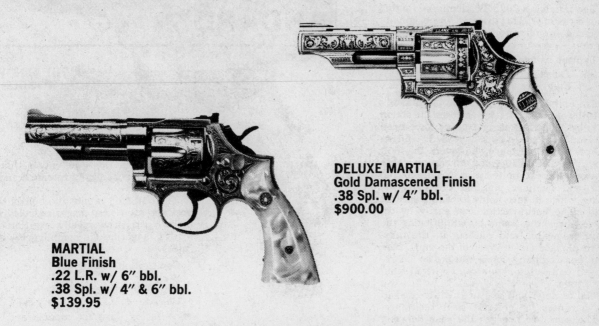

DELUXE MARTIAL
Gold Damascened Finish
.38 Spl. w/ 4″ bbl.
$900.00

MARTIAL
Blue Finish
.22 L.R. w/ 6″ bbl.
.38 Spl. w/ 4″ & 6″ bbl.
$139.95

COMPLETE SPECIFICATIONS FOR LLAMA "MARTIAL" REVOLVERS:

CALIBERS:	.357 Magnum	.38 Special (Hi-speed or Mid-range)	.22 L.R.
BARREL LENGTH:	4-inch	4 and 6 inch	6 inch
	All with raised ventilated-rib and sight-ramp. Top surface matted finish to prevent glare.		
NUMBER OF SHOTS:	6-shots		
FRAME:	Forged high tensile strength steel. Serrated front and back strap.		
ACTION:	Conventional double-action. Floating firing pin.		
TRIGGER:	Wide grooved target trigger. Color case-hardened.		
HAMMER:	Wide spur target hammer with serrated gripping surface. Color case-hardened.		
SIGHTS:	Square notch white outline rear sight with windage and elevation adjustments; serrated quick-draw front sight on ramp.		
SIGHT RADIUS:	With 4-inch barrel—5¾″; with 6-inch barrel—7¾″.		
BUTT & GRIPS:	Square butt. Fitted with magna style genuine walnut checkered grips. Deluxe models fitted with simulated pearl grips. .357 target walnut checkered stocks.		
WEIGHT:	2 lbs. 4 ozs.	w/4″ bbl.—2 lbs. 1 oz. w/6″ bbl.—2 lbs. 4 ozs.	2 lbs. 8 ozs.
OVERALL LENGTH:	With 4-inch barrel—9¼-inches; with 6-inch barrel—11-inches.		
FINISH:	High polish blue. Deluxe models—Blue Engraved, satin, satin engraved and Gold Damascened. with simulated pearl grips.		

LUGER .22 AUTOMATIC PISTOL

DETAILS OF CONSTRUCTION:

The Luger is made with a fixed barrel, solid frame design. The barrel is fastened to the frame with an interference fit; i.e.—an oversize cross pin of novel design is used to lock the barrel to the frame.

The frame is a 7075 T6 aluminum forging (not a casting). This material was originally designed for aircraft fuselages and landing gears.

Typical values are:

Tensile strength, psi: 82,000
Yield strength, psi: 75,000

An uninterrupted band (approximately 2/10ths of an inch thick) encloses the action on all 4 sides. All sharp corners have been avoided and inside cuts have 3/32″ fillets.

For wear resistance, however, the bolt moves on SAE 1050 (medium carbon steel) boltways. These boltways also support the sear and hammer pin and the magazine guide, which in turn holds the hammer strut plate. The entire action can easily be removed from the frame by withdrawing the main frame pin and pushing in the takedown plunger (in the rear of the gun). The sear bar retaining screw must also be removed before the action can be lifted from the frame.

The hammer and sear are heat treated to file hardness for greatest wear resistance.

The sear bar engages the sear *between* its supports, not on one side as in other autoloaders. This results in a smooth, unvarying trigger pull.

The take down plunger hole, in the rear of the frame, is exactly in line with the bore and, after the action has been removed forms an ideal support for any standard size cleaning rod. Thus, it is easy to clean the barrel from the chamber end. By properly guiding the cleaning rod, it is possible to avoid damage to the rifling.

The positioning of the in-line holes (barrel hole and take down plunger hole) permits "piano hinge" fixturing during manufacture. What this means is that the frame can be held by these holes and rotated around them against a stop. All important operations can be performed with the frame in this position, eliminating 75% of normal production tolerances since the width of the frame becomes unimportant as far as fixturing is concerned. A higher quality product is the result.

The most outstanding single feature of the gun is its smooth toggle action, which permits trouble free operation with all .22 L.R. cartridges, standard as well as high velocity.

The combination of the tough lightweight frame and the steel action components gives the gun its unsurpassed balance. The finest materials have been selected for each part. Thirty thousand rounds have been fired without a single malfunction and without a single broken part!

RIGHT SIDE VIEW WITH TOGGLE OPEN

All pins in this gun (other than spring pins) are mechanically retained, and cannot "walk out".

The bolt stop retains the bolt in the open position after the magazine has been removed, permitting speedy insertion of a new loaded magazine (in compliance with NRA rules).

Comparison to original Luger:
Weight:	Within 1 oz.
Grip Dimensions:	Identical
Balance:	Identical

(See facing page for models and prices.)

TOP VIEW SHOWING STATIONARY REAR SIGHT AND FEEDING POSITION OF THE MAGAZINE

TOP VIEW WITH TOGGLE CLOSED AND SAFETY LEVER IN FIRE POSITION

LUGER .22 AUTOMATIC PISTOL

The Luger STLR-4 and STLR-5 pistols, described here, is designed and manufactured in the United States. The STLR-4 and STLR-5 will handle all standard and high velocity .22 Long Rifle cartridges. Grip angle and balance of this model are identical to that of the original German Parabellum pistol. Even in weight the new version differs only by one ounce.

Features, specifications, models and prices are described below:

LUGER
.22 L.R. AUTOMATIC PISTOL

STLR-4 (with 4½″ barrel & safety for R.H. shooter) ...$99.95
STLL-4 (With 4½″ barrel & safety for L.H. shooter) ...$99.95
STLR-5 (With 5½″ barrel & safety for R.H. shooter) ...$99.95
STLL-5 (With 5½″ barrel & safety for L.H. shooter) ...$99.95

FEATURES & SPECIFICATIONS

The Luger .22 caliber pistol is made with a toggle action, stationary sights and a target-quality trigger. It is equipped with an eleven-shot magazine which is housed in the grip portion of the frame. Cartridges feeding from the magazine are positioned in a straight line behind the chamber for smooth loading and trouble free performance.

The barrel is all steel and is hammer rifled for maximum accuracy. Sighting equipment includes a square-bladed front sight in combination with a fixed, square-notch rear sight.

All moving parts result in surfaces that are steel against steel. Cleaning and maintenance is greatly simplified by the simple takedown procedure. A takedown plunger hole, located in the rear of the frame, is aligned with the bore to facilitate cleaning of the barrel from the chamber end.

Available with choice left or right hand safety at no difference in price.

SPECIFICATIONS

Frame: one piece lightweight forged frame, machined to finished dimensions.

Trigger: light, crisp trigger pull of target quality.

Action: Hinged toggle action with fast lock design for instantaneous ignition.

Magazine: Eleven-shot capacity clip type magazine contained in grip area of the frame.

Grips: Genuine smooth wooden grips.

Sights: Square bladed front sight with square-notch, stationary, rear sight.

Safety: Positive side lever safety. (The Luger is generally supplied with the safety on the left side for right handed shooters, however, it may also be had with a right hand safety for left handed shooters at no additional cost).

Barrel: Chambered for all .22 Long Rifle cartridges, standard or high-velocity. With hammer rifled bore the Luger barrel is solidly fixed to the frame. (Though not recommended for use with B-B Caps, C-B Caps, shorts, longs and shot cartridges, these shells may be fired in the Luger IF singly loaded into the chamber.)

MODEL STLR-4 (with 4½″ barrel & safety for R.H. shooter) $99.95

MODEL STLL-4 (with 4½″ barrel & safety for L.H. shooter) $99.95

MODEL STLR-5 (with 5½″ barrel & safety for R.H. shooter) $99.95

MODEL STLL-5 (with 5½″ barrel & safety for L.H. shooter) $99.95

LUGER .22 AUTOMATIC PISTOL

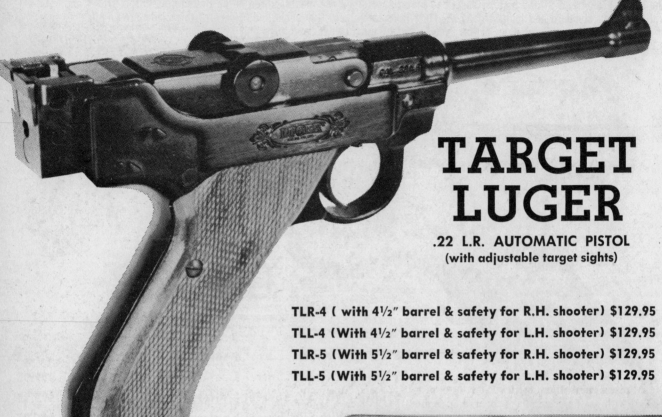

TARGET LUGER

.22 L.R. AUTOMATIC PISTOL
(with adjustable target sights)

TLR-4 (with 4½″ barrel & safety for R.H. shooter) $129.95
TLL-4 (With 4½″ barrel & safety for L.H. shooter) $129.95
TLR-5 (With 5½″ barrel & safety for R.H. shooter) $129.95
TLL-5 (With 5½″ barrel & safety for L.H. shooter) $129.95

LUGER PISTOL KIT

Available in 4½″ or 5½″ barrel lengths, for the right hand or left hand shooter, this kit contains all the equipment required for pistol shooting (except ammo).

The Luger pistol kit contains a genuine top grade cowhide leather holster with snap-equipped retaining strap, a magazine charging device, a extra clip magazine and instruction booklet for the model STLR-4 pistol with warranty card.

STLR-4 KIT (with 4½″ barrel, fixed sights—for right
   or left hand shooter) **$109.95**

STLR-5 KIT (with 5½″ barrel, fixed sights—for right
   or left hand shooter) **$109.95**

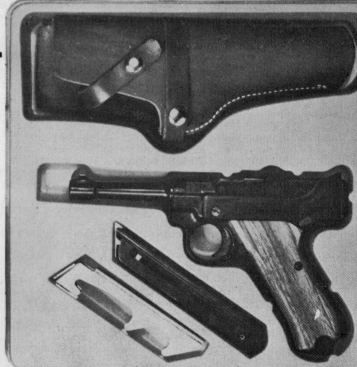

STLR-4 KIT AND STLR-5 KIT

MAUSER PISTOLS

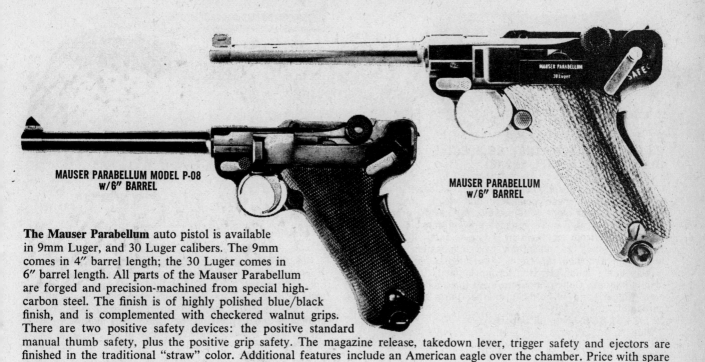

**MAUSER PARABELLUM MODEL P-08
w/6" BARREL**

**MAUSER PARABELLUM
w/6" BARREL**

The Mauser Parabellum auto pistol is available in 9mm Luger, and 30 Luger calibers. The 9mm comes in 4" barrel length; the 30 Luger comes in 6" barrel length. All parts of the Mauser Parabellum are forged and precision-machined from special high-carbon steel. The finish is of highly polished blue/black finish, and is complemented with checkered walnut grips. There are two positive safety devices: the positive standard manual thumb safety, plus the positive grip safety. The magazine release, takedown lever, trigger safety and ejectors are finished in the traditional "straw" color. Additional features include an American eagle over the chamber. Price with spare magazine, cleaning brush and combination tool **$299.00**

The Mauser Parabellum model P-08 auto pistol in 9mm Luger and 30 Luger will be produced in a limited number marked with an American eagle over the chamber and Mauser banner on the toggle. The P-08 incorporates the original frame, design, takedown lever, grip safety, safety bar, and takedown block. Available with a 6" barrel in caliber 30 Luger and with 4" and 6" barrels in the 9mm Luger caliber **$399.00**

MODEL HSc AUTOMATIC PISTOLS

**CALIBERS: .32 ACP,
Std. Blue $199.00
(supplied with extra magazine)**

**Caliber: 380 ACP
Nickel $219.00**

The Mauser Model **HSc** combines the advantages of both the revolver and the automatic pistols through its double-action design which safely permits a cartridge to be carried in the chamber for immediate firing.

The Model **HSc** is built from high-alloy steel. Its special hammer design prevents the intrusion of dirt or dust into the action when the hammer is cocked.

Features:
• Advanced modern design • Exceptionally good custom finish • Simplified takedown • Positive thumb safety • Magazine safety • Exposed hammer for added safety • Matted non-glare sight channel • Checkered, genuine walnut grips • Inertia-type firing pin • Choice of blue or nickel finish.

Each Mauser **HSc** pistol is supplied in a fitted case with extra magazine, cleaning brush and factory test target.

ROSSI REVOLVERS

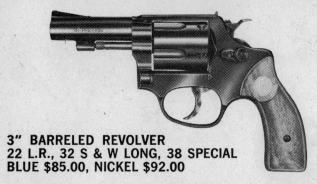

3" BARRELED REVOLVER
22 L.R., 32 S & W LONG, 38 SPECIAL
BLUE $85.00, NICKEL $92.00

Available in three popular calibers and in either blue or nickel finish, these compact guns weigh only 22 ounces. The rear sight is adjustable, yet its low profile design and rounded outer surfaces prevent snagging on clothing. The front sight, which is forged integrally with the barrel, is of the quick-draw type with matted ramp to prevent annoying reflections. The integral barrel rib is also finely sandblasted on its top surface. The hammer is knurled. Coil springs are used throughout. Hammer, trigger, and all critical internal parts are case hardened.

22 L.R., 32 S&W Long, 38 Special
Blue $85.00
Chrome $92.00

6" TARGET REVOLVER
22 L.R. BLUE $92.00

Designed for informal target shooting, this handgun is available only in 22 (Short, Long, and Long Rifle) and only with blued finish. Milled into the frame, the rear sight is fully adjustable for windage and elevation, while the front sight is a modified target type with ramp. The chambers are countersunk, and the gun is fitted with an inertia firing pin and oversized wood grips.

22 L.R. Blue $92.00

STAR AUTOMATIC PISTOLS

STAR PD
45 ACP BLUE $210.00,
CHROME $220.00

Chambered for the sledgehammer 45 ACP, the PD has the same capacity—8 rounds—as the U.S. Government Model, yet it weighs nearly a pound less, as well as being smaller in every dimension. Just a fraction over 7" long, it weighs only 25 ounces.

The Star PD offers a fully adjustable rear sight that's milled into the slide, a ramp front sight, positive thumb safety, grooved non-slip front strap and checkered walnut grips, nylon recoil buffer, inertia firing pin, and the absence of both grip and magazine safeties.

45 ACP Blue $210.00
Chrome $220.00

STAR AS
38 SUPER BLUE $160.00,
CHROME $170.00

The large-frame Star Model AS is based on an improved U.S. Government model design. Made of forged and machined steel, the Model AS is chambered for the extremely powerful, flat-shooting 38 Super. It is blued and polished to perfection, and is a smooth and well-finished gun both inside and out. The hammer, sear, and sear bar are deeply case hardened, and are hand-honed and fitted to maintain a crisp, clean trigger pull. The trigger is grooved, and the wide-spur target-type hammer is checkered. Both the genuine walnut grips and the solid backstrap are checkered for a non-slip grip during rapid fire.

38 Super Blue $160.00
Chrome $170.00

RUGER .22 AUTOMATIC PISTOLS

STANDARD MODEL AUTO PISTOL
(With 4¾″ & 6″ Barrel)

CALIBER: .22 Long Rifle only
BARREL: Length, 4¾″ or 6″ medium weight, 6 groove rifling, 14″ twist.
SPRINGS: Music wire springs.
WEIGHTS: 36 ozs. for 4¾″ barrel; 38 ozs. for 6″ barrel.
OVERALL LENGTH: 8¾″ or 10″ depending on barrel length.
SIGHTS: Front fixed; rear adjustable.
MAGAZINE: Detachable, 9-shot capacity.
TRIGGER: Grooved, curved finger surface, ⅜″ wide. Two stage pull.
SAFETY: Locks sear and bolt. Cannot be put in safe position unless gun is cocked.
GRIPS: Hard rubber; or checkered walnut panels.
RST4—4¾″ Barrel, equipped with hard rubber panels **$69.00**
RST6—6″ Barrel, equipped with hard rubber panels **$69.00**
Checkered walnut panels (available as spare parts) **$6.50**

MARK I
TARGET PISTOL
(With 6⅞″ Barrel)

CALIBER: .22 Long Rifle only.
BARREL: Length, 6⅞″ heavy weight, burnish reamed.
SPRINGS: Music wire springs.
WEIGHT: 42 ounces.
OVERALL LENGTH: 10⅞″.
SIGHTS: Patridge style, front blade, .125″ wide, undercut to prevent glare. Micro rear sight, click adjustment for windage and elevation. Sight radius, 9⅜″.
MAGAZINE: Detachable, 9-shot capacity.
TRIGGER: Light crisp pull, no backlash.
SAFETY: Locks sear and bolt. Cannot be put in safe position unless gun is cocked.
GRIPS: Hard rubber; or checkered walnut with left thumb rest.
T678—6⅞″ Barrel, equipped with hard rubber panels **$86.50**

MARK I
BULL BARREL TARGET PISTOL
(With 5½″ Barrel)

CALIBER: .22 Long Rifle only
BARREL: 5½″ heavyweight bull barrel.
OVERALL LENGTH: 9½″.
SIGHTS: Patridge style, front blade, .125″ wide, undercut Micro rear sight, click adjustments for windage and elevation.
MAGAZINE: Detachable, 9-shot capacity.
TRIGGER: Light crisp pull, no backlash.
GRIPS: Hard rubber; or checkered walnut with left thumb rest.
T-512—5½″ Bull Barrel, with hard rubber panels **$86.50**

RUGER REVOLVERS

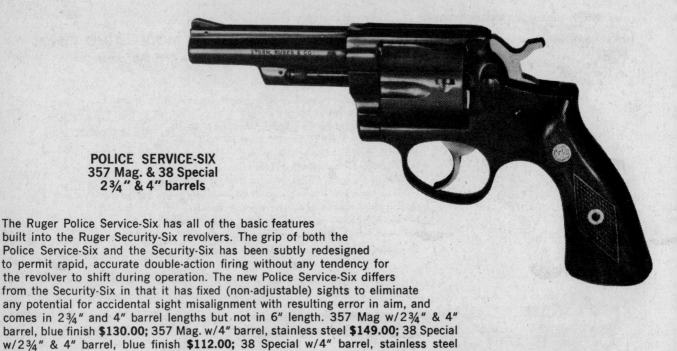

POLICE SERVICE-SIX
357 Mag. & 38 Special
2¾" & 4" barrels

The Ruger Police Service-Six has all of the basic features built into the Ruger Security-Six revolvers. The grip of both the Police Service-Six and the Security-Six has been subtly redesigned to permit rapid, accurate double-action firing without any tendency for the revolver to shift during operation. The new Police Service-Six differs from the Security-Six in that it has fixed (non-adjustable) sights to eliminate any potential for accidental sight misalignment with resulting error in aim, and comes in 2¾" and 4" barrel lengths but not in 6" length. 357 Mag w/2¾" & 4" barrel, blue finish **$130.00;** 357 Mag. w/4" barrel, stainless steel **$149.00;** 38 Special w/2¾" & 4" barrel, blue finish **$112.00;** 38 Special w/4" barrel, stainless steel **$135.00.**

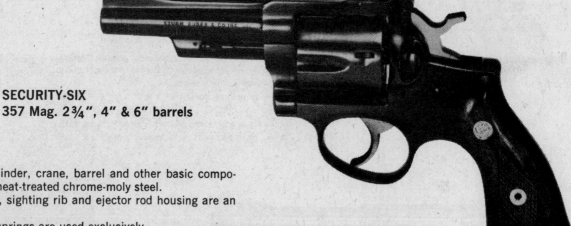

SECURITY-SIX
357 Mag. 2¾", 4" & 6" barrels

Features:
- Frame, cylinder, crane, barrel and other basic components are of heat-treated chrome-moly steel.
- The barrel, sighting rib and ejector rod housing are an integral unit.
- Steel coil springs are used exclusively.
- It is a truly *solid frame* revolver. There is no side plate, thus no screws to work loose.
- Quick and easy takedown and reassembly: With only a coin, the Security-Six can be taken down to its basic components in less than a minute.
- The spring loaded firing pin is in the frame.
- Only when the trigger is in its rear position is the hammer blow transmitted to the firing pin. This is a positive means of internal safety designed to prevent firing should the gun be dropped, or should the hammer be struck.
- When the cylinder is out of the frame the hammer cannot be cocked—and when the hammer is cocked the cylinder cannot be opened.

SPECIFICATIONS: Six Shots. Calibers: 357 Magnum caliber (handles 38 Spec.), 38 Special. **Barrel:** 2¾", 4", 6", five-groove-rifling 18¾" right twist. **Weight:** 33½ ounces (4" barrel). **Overall Length:** 9¼" (4" barrel). **Sights:** Ruger adjustable rear (elevation and windage adjustments). Front sight is ⅛" wide, serrated. **Grips:** Checkered walnut, semi-target style. **Finish:** Polished all over and blued. Stainless steel models have brushed satin finish.
357 Mag. w/ 2¾", 4" & 6" barrel, blue finish . . **$143.50**
357 Mag. w/ 2¾", 4" & 6" barrel, stainless steel **$167.50**

RUGER REVOLVERS

STAINLESS STEEL SECURITY-SIX

Model 717—.357 Magnum Stainless Steel Security-Six with Adjustable Sights

.357 w/2¾″ bbl. $167.50
.357 w/4″ bbl. $167.50
.357 w/6″ bbl. $167.50

The Ruger Security-Six is now offered in an all stainless steel model chambered for .357 Magnum cartridges. Designated Model 717, this stainless steel revolver is available in 2¾″, 4″, and 6″ barrel lengths, and features adjustable sights.

SPEED-SIX

**Double Action, Round Butt
(Checkered Walnut Grip Panels)**

The Speed-Six is a round butt lightened version of the Security-Six, designed for the use by off-duty and plainclothes officers where weight and concealability are essential. The Speed-Six is available on special order with a spurless hammer. The mechanism and construction are identical to the Security-Six. (Models 207 and 208 can be had with a spurless hammer.)

Model 208—.38 Spec. Caliber-Fixed Sights

SS82   2¾″ barrel $112.00
SS84   4″ barrel $112.00

Model 207—.357 Mag. Caliber-Fixed Sights

SS32   2¾″ barrel $130.00
SS34   4″ barrel $130.00

RUGER BLACKHAWK

"BLACKHAWK"
.357 Magnum Caliber

CALIBER: .357 Magnum; .38 Special interchangeably.

BARREL: 4⅝" and 6½", 6 groove rifling, 16" twist.

FRAME: Chrome molybdenum steel with bridge reinforcement and rear sight guard.

SPRINGS: Music wire springs throughout.

WEIGHT: 40 ounces.

SIGHTS: Patridge style, ramp front matted blade ⅛" wide. Rear sight click adjustable for windage and elevation.

GRIPS: Genuine walnut.

FINISH: Polished and blued; or stainless steel.

Also handles .38 Special interchangeably

BN34—4⅝" Barrel, .357 Magnum caliber .... **$119.75** Stainless Steel **$149.75**
BN36—6½" Barrel, .357 Magnum caliber .... **$119.75** Stainless Steel **$149.75**
BN34-X—4⅝" Barrel ⎰ fitted with 9m/m Parabellum extra
BN36-X—6½" Barrel ⎱ cylinder. Walnut panels **$142.80**

Note: (Convertible model not available in Stainless Steel)

RUGER "BLACKHAWK"
.41 Magnum Caliber

CALIBER: .41 Magnum.

BARREL: 4⅝ and 6½", Buttoned rifling 1 turn in 20" twist.

FRAME: Chrome molybdenum steel with bridge reinforcement and rear sight guard.

SPRINGS: Music wire springs throughout.

WEIGHT: 38 ounces (6½ bbl.).

SIGHTS: Patridge style, ramp front matted blade ⅛ wide. Rear sight click adjustment for windage and elevation.

GRIPS: Genuine walnut.

OVERALL LENGTH: 12⅛" (6½" bbl.).

FINISH: Polished and blued.

BN-41—4⅝" Barrel **$119.75**
BN-42—6½" Barrel **$119.75**

RUGER "SUPER BLACKHAWK"
.44 Magnum Caliber

CALIBER: .44 Magnum.

BARREL: 6 groove rifling, 20" twist.

FRAME: Chrome molybdenum steel with bridge reinforcement and rear sight guard.

SPRINGS: Music wire springs throughout.

WEIGHT: 48 ounces.

SIGHTS: Patridge style, ramp front matted blade ⅛" wide. Rear sight click adjustable for windage and elevation.

GRIP FRAME: Chrome molybdenum steel enlarged and contoured to minimize recoil effect.

TRIGGER: Wide spur, low contour, sharply serrated for convenient cocking with minimum disturbance of grip.

Also handles .44 Special interchangeably

OVERALL LENGTH: 13⅜".

FINISH: Polished and blued.

S47N—7½" Barrel only, with Steel grip frame **$157.50**

RUGER BLACKHAWK

.45 Caliber and .45 / .45 ACP Convertible BLACKHAWK

Biackhawk .45 caliber:
4⅝″ & 7½″ barrel **$119.75**

Blackhawk .45 caliber convertible:
(fitted with .45 ACP extra cylinder)
4⅝″ & 7½″ barrel **$142.80**

CALIBER .45 & .45/.45 ACP
For almost a century the caliber .45 Colt cartridge has been a favorite of hunters and outdoorsmen. At 50 yards the 250 grain factory loaded bullet has a velocity of 820 feet per second and remaining energy of 375 foot pounds. The convertible model comes with an extra, interchangeable cylinder chambered for the popular and readily available .45 Automatic (ACP) cartridge.

SPECIFICATIONS: (.45 Colt caliber): **Barrel:** 4⅝″ and 7½″ lengths, 6 groove rifling, 16″ twist. **Weight:** 38 ounces (4⅝″), and 40 ounces (7½″) **Overall Length:** 13⅛″ (with 7½″ barrel). Specifications for **Sights, Grips, Ignition Mechanism, Springs, Screws, Cylinder Frame** the same as for the .44 Magnum Blackhawk. **No. BN-44** (4⅝″ bbl.) **No. BN-45** (7½″ bbl.)—**$119.75.** Convertible model—(includes extra cylinder For .45 ACP cartridge) **No. BN-44X** (4⅝″), **No. BN-45X** (7½″) —**$142.80**

(IN .30 CARBINE CALIBER)

This Ruger Blackhawk provides the many owners of M-1 Carbines with a companion revolver. With the 7½″ barrel, the .30 carbine caliber cartridge develops an energy of over 600 foot-pounds with a muzzle velocity approaching 1600 fps.

"BLACKHAWK" SINGLE-ACTION (IN .30 CARBINE CALIBER) $119.75

SPECIFICATIONS

Caliber: .30 Carbine.
Barrel Length: 7½″ only, 6 groove rifling 20″ twist.
Springs: Unbreakable music wire springs used throughout. No leaf springs.
Screws: For security, Nylok® screws are used at all 5 locations that might be affected by recoil.
Weight: 44 ounces.
Overall Length: 13⅛″.
Sights: Patridge style, ramp front sight with ⅛″ wide blade, matted to eliminate glare. Rear sight adjustable for windage and elevation.
Ignition System: Independent alloy steel firing pin, mounted in frame, transfer-bar.
Frame: Same cylinder frame as .44 mag. Super Blackhawk.
Grips: Genuine walnut.
Finish: Polished, blued and anodized.

RUGER SINGLE-ACTIONS

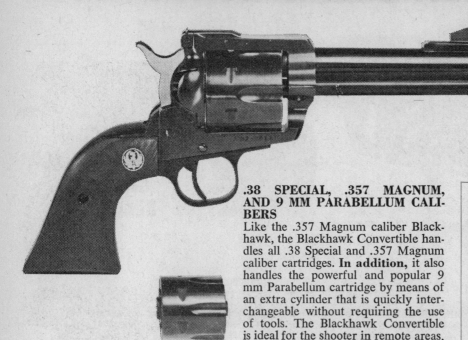

RUGER "BLACKHAWK"
.357 Magnum Caliber
& 9mm Convertible
$142.80

.38 SPECIAL, .357 MAGNUM, AND 9 MM PARABELLUM CALIBERS

Like the .357 Magnum caliber Blackhawk, the Blackhawk Convertible handles all .38 Special and .357 Magnum caliber cartridges. **In addition,** it also handles the powerful and popular 9 mm Parabellum cartridge by means of an extra cylinder that is quickly interchangeable without requiring the use of tools. The Blackhawk Convertible is ideal for the shooter in remote areas, because there's virtually no place in the world where ammunition for this handgun can't be readily obtained.

SPECIFICATIONS: Exclusive (patents pending) "Interlocked" mechanism. Same general specifications as the .357 Magnum Caliber "Blackhawk" with the following exceptions: **Cylinders:** Two interchangeable cylinders: one for .357 Magnum and .38 Special cartridges—and the other for 9 mm Parabellum cartridges. **Price:** $142.80 for revolver with two interchangeable cylinders. In addition, an extra 9 mm cylinder can be fitted to .357 Magnum caliber Blackhawk revolvers now in the field. The cost of the cylinder and its fitting is $16.00.

"SINGLE-SIX" CONVERTIBLE
(With two cylinders—.22 L.R. & .22 WMR)

Features: Ruger single action mechanism. Transfer bar ignition. Interlocked gate, transfer-bar, cylinder latch functions. Gate controlled loading. All stressed components hardened chrome-molybdenum steel. Music wire springs throughout. Improved partridge front sight. **Calibers:** 22 Short, Long, Long Rifle and 22 WMR. **Barrel:** 6 groove, 14" twist. **Cylinders:** 2-interchangeable. **Ignition mechanism:** transfer-bar. Independent-alloy steel firing pin mounted in frame.

Sights: Adjustable rear and ramp front blade sight. **Grips:** Genuine walnut. **Finish:** Polished and blued; or stainless steel.

NR4-4⅝" Barrel (with interchangeable 22WMR cyl.) **$92.25**	stainless steel	......not available
NR5-5½" Barrel (with interchangeable 22WMR cyl.) **$92.25**	stainless steel	.... **$141.75**
NR6-6½" Barrel (with interchangeable 22WMR cyl.).... **$92.25**	stainless steel	.... **$141.75**
NR9-9½" Barrel (with interchangeable 22WMR cyl.).... **$105.45**	stainless steel	.........not available
S4-4⅝" Barrel (single cylinder) **$87.50**;	stainless steel	...........not available
S5-5½" Barrel (single cylinder) **$87.50**;	stainless steel	...........**$123.00**
S6-6½" Barrel (single cylinder) **$87.50**;	stainless steel	...........**$123.00**
S9-9½" Barrel (single cylinder) **$100.50**;	stainless steel	...........not available

SMITH & WESSON AUTO PISTOLS

9MM AUTOMATIC PISTOL
DOUBLE ACTION
(MODEL NO. 39)

CALIBER:	9mm Luger (Parabellum)
MAGAZINE CAPACITY:	8 (2-eight round magazines furnished).
BARREL:	4 inches
LENGTH OVER ALL:	7⁷⁄₁₆ inches
WEIGHT:	26½ ounces without magazine
SIGHTS:	Fixed, ⅛-inch serrated ramp front; Patridge type rear adjustable for windage only.
STOCKS:	Checked walnut with S & W monograms
FINISH:	S & W Blue or Nickel

BLUE
$148.50

NICKEL
$164.50

.22 CAL. AUTOMATIC PISTOL
(MODEL NO. 41)

CALIBER:	.22 Long Rifle
MAGAZINE CAPACITY:	10 rounds
BARREL:	5 or 7⅜ inches
LENGTH OVERALL:	With 7⅜" barrel, 12 inches
SIGHT RADIUS:	With 7⅜" barrel, 9 5/16 inches
WEIGHT:	With 7⅜" barrel, 43½ ounces
SIGHTS:	Front: ⅛-inch Patridge undercut. Rear: S & W Micrometer Click Sight, adjustable for windage and elevation
STOCKS:	Checked walnut with modified thumb rest, equally adaptable to right- or left-handed shooters
FINISH:	S & W Bright Blue
TRIGGER:	⅜-inch width, with S & W grooving and an adjustable trigger stop
MUZZLE BRAKE:	Detachable (7⅜" barrel only)

BLUE ONLY
(5" or 7⅜" BARREL)
WITH MUZZLE BRAKE
$172.00

NOTE: Model 41 is also available in .22 Short caliber for international shooting

.22 AUTOMATIC PISTOL (HEAVY BARREL)
(MODEL NO. 41)

CALIBER:	.22 Long Rifle
MAGAZINE CAPACITY:	10 rounds
BARREL:	5½ inches
LENGTH OVERALL:	9 inches
SIGHT RADIUS:	8 inches
WEIGHT:	44½ oz
SIGHTS:	Front: ⅛" Patridge on ramp base. Rear: New S & W Micrometer Click Sight with wide ⅞" sight slide
STOCKS:	Checked walnut with modified thumb rest, equally adaptable to right- or left-handed shooters
FINISH:	S & W Bright Blue
TRIGGER:	⅜-inch width, with S & W grooving and an adjustable trigger stop

BLUE ONLY
$172.00

SMITH & WESSON AUTO PISTOLS & REVOLVERS

.38 MASTER
(MODEL NO. 52)

CALIBER:	.38 S & W Special for Mid Range Wad Cutter only
MAGAZINE CAPACITY:	5 rounds (2-five round magazines furnished).
BARREL:	5 inches
LENGTH OVERALL:	8⅝ inches
SIGHT RADIUS:	6¹⁵⁄₁₆ inches
WEIGHT:	41 oz. with empty magazine
SIGHTS:	Front: ⅛" Patridge on ramp base. Rear: New S & W Micrometer Click Sight with wide ⅞" sight slide.
STOCKS:	Checked walnut with S & W monograms
FINISH:	S & W Bright Blue with sandblast stippling around sighting area to break up light reflection
TRIGGER:	⅜-inch width with S & W grooving and an adjustable trigger stop

BLUE ONLY
$267.50

9MM AUTOMATIC PISTOL
DOUBLE ACTION
(MODEL NO. 59)

CALIBER:	9mm Luger (Parabellum)
MAGAZINE CAPACITY:	2-14 round magazines furnished
BARREL:	4 inches
LENGTH OVERALL:	7⁷⁄₁₆ inches
WEIGHT:	27 oz. without magazine
SIGHTS:	Front: ⅛-inch serrated ramp. Rear: Square notch with Micrometer Click adjustment for windage only.
STOCKS:	Checked high impact molded nylon
FINISH:	S & W Blue or Nickel

BLUE
$178.50

NICKEL
$194.50

.38 MILITARY & POLICE
(MODEL NO. 10)

CALIBER:	.38 S & W Special.
NUMBER OF SHOTS:	6.
BARREL:	2, 4, 5, 6 inches.
LENGTH OVERALL:	With 4-inch barrel, 9¼ inches.
WEIGHT:	With 4-inch barrel, 30½ oz.
SIGHTS:	Front: Fixed, ¹⁄₁₀-inch serrated ramp. Rear: Square notch.
STOCKS:	Checked walnut Service with S & W monograms, square butt.
FINISH:	S & W Blue or Nickel.

BLUE
$109.00

NICKEL
$119.00

SMITH & WESSON REVOLVERS

.38 MILITARY & POLICE (HEAVY BARREL)
(MODEL NO. 10)

CALIBER:	.38 S & W Special.
NUMBER OF SHOTS:	6.
BARREL:	4 inches.
LENGTH OVERALL:	9¼ inches.
WEIGHT:	34 oz.
SIGHTS:	Front: ⅛-inch serrated ramp. Rear: Square notch
STOCKS:	Checked walnut Service with S & W monograms, square butt.
FINISH:	S & W Blue or Nickel.

**BLUE
$109.00**

**NICKEL
$119.00**

.38 MILITARY & POLICE (AIRWEIGHT)
(MODEL NO. 12)

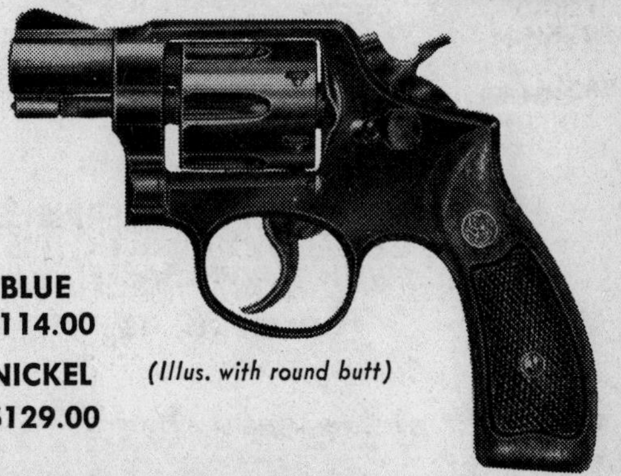

CALIBER:	.38 S & W Special.
NUMBER OF SHOTS:	6.
BARREL:	2 or 4 inches.
LENGTH OVERALL:	With 2-inch barrel and round butt, 6⅞ inches.
WEIGHT:	With 2-inch barrel and round butt, 18 oz.
SIGHTS:	Front: Fixed, ¹⁄₁₀-inch serrated ramp. Rear: Square notch.
STOCKS:	Checked walnut Service with S & W monograms, round or square butt.
FINISH:	S & W Blue or Nickel.

**BLUE
$114.00**

**NICKEL
$129.00**

(Illus. with round butt)

CALIBER:	357 Magnum and 38 S&W Special.
ROUNDS:	6-shot cylinder capacity.
BARREL:	4 inches.
LENGTH OVERALL:	9¼ inches.
WEIGHT:	34 oz.
SIGHTS:	Front: ⅛-inch serrated ramp. Rear: Square notch.
STOCKS:	Checked walnut Service with S&W monograms, square butt.
FINISH:	S&W Blue or Nickel.

**BLUE ONLY

$120.00**

K-38 MASTERPIECE
(MODEL NO. 14)

CALIBER:	.38 S & W Special.
NUMBER OF SHOTS:	6.
BARREL:	6, 8⅜ inches.
LENGTH OVERALL:	With 6-inch barrel, 11⅛ inches.
WEIGHT LOADED:	With 6-inch barrel, 38½ oz.; 8⅜-inch, 42½ oz.
SIGHTS:	Front: ⅛-inch plain Patridge. Rear: S & W Micrometer Click Sight, adjustable for windage and elevation.
STOCKS:	Checked walnut Service with S & W monograms.
FINISH:	S & W Blue.

**BLUE ONLY
6" $135.00
8⅜" $141.50**

SMITH & WESSON REVOLVERS

K-38 MASTERPIECE SINGLE ACTION
(MODEL NO. 14)

CALIBER:	.38 S & W Special.
NUMBER OF SHOTS:	6.
BARREL:	6, 8⅜ inches.
LENGTH OVERALL:	With 6-inch barrel, 11⅛ inches.
WEIGHT LOADED:	With 6-inch barrel, 38½ oz.; 8⅜-inch, 42½ oz.
SIGHTS:	Front: ⅛-inch plain Patridge. Rear: S & W Micrometer Click Sight, adjustable for windage and elevation.
STOCKS:	Checked walnut Service with S & W monograms.
HAMMER:	Checked target type.
TRIGGER:	Grooved target type.
FINISH:	S & W Blue.

BLUE ONLY
6" $155.00
8⅜" $161.50

.38 COMBAT MASTERPIECE
WITH 4-INCH BARREL
(MODEL NO. 15)

CALIBER:	.38 S & W Special
NUMBER OF SHOTS:	6
BARREL:	2 & 4 inches.
LENGTH OVERALL:	9⅛ inches
WEIGHT LOADED:	34 oz.
SIGHTS:	Front: ⅛-inch Baughman Quick Draw on plain ramp. Rear: S & W Micrometer Click Sight, adjustable for windage and elevation
STOCKS:	Checked walnut Service with S & W monograms
FINISH:	S & W Blue or Nickel

BLUE
$125.00
NICKEL
$135.00

K-22 MASTERPIECE
(MODEL NO. 17)

CALIBER:	.22 Long Rifle.
NUMBER OF SHOTS:	6.
BARREL:	6, 8⅜ inches.
LENGTH OVERALL:	With 6-inch barrel, 11⅛ inches.
WEIGHT LOADED:	With 6-inch barrel, 38½ oz.; 8⅜-inch, 42½ oz.
SIGHTS:	Front: ⅛-inch plain Patridge. Rear: S & W Micrometer Click Sight, adjustable for windage and elevation.
STOCKS:	Checked walnut Service with S & W monograms.
FINISH:	S & W Blue.

BLUE ONLY
6" $135.00
8⅜" $141.50

SMITH & WESSON REVOLVERS

.22 COMBAT MASTERPIECE

WITH 4-INCH BARREL

(MODEL NO. 18)

CALIBER:	.22 Long Rifle
NUMBER OF SHOTS:	6
BARREL:	4 inches
LENGTH OVERALL:	9⅛ inches
WEIGHT LOADED:	36½ oz.
SIGHTS:	Front: ⅛-inch Baughman Quick Draw on plain ramp. Rear: S & W Micrometer Click Sight, adjustable for windage and elevation
STOCKS:	Checked walnut Service with S & W monograms
FINISH:	S & W Blue

BLUE ONLY
$135.00

".357" COMBAT MAGNUM

(MODEL NO. 19)

CALIBER:	.357 Magnum (Actual bullet dia. .38 S & W Spec.)
NUMBER OF SHOTS:	6.
BARREL:	2½, 4, 6 inches.
LENGTH OVERALL:	9½ inches with 4" barrel.
WEIGHT:	35 oz. (2½" model weighs 31 oz.)
SIGHTS:	Front: ⅛" Baughman Quick Draw on 4" barrel, ⅛" Patridge on 6" barrel. Rear: S & W Micrometer Click Sight, adjustable for windage and elevation.
STOCKS:	Checked Goncolo Alves Target with S & W monograms. (2½" barrel model comes with round butt; Service type stocks).
FINISH:	S & W Bright Blue or Nickel.

BRIGHT BLUE OR NICKEL
$167.50

1955 .45 TARGET

(MODEL No. 25)

CALIBER:	.45 A. C. P.
NUMBER OF SHOTS:	6
BARREL:	6½ inches
LENGTH OVERALL:	11⅞ inches
WEIGHT:	45 oz.
SIGHTS:	Front: ⅛-inch plain Patridge. Rear: S & W Micrometer Click Sight, adjustable for windage and elevation
STOCKS:	Checked walnut Target with S & W monograms
HAMMER:	Checked target type
TRIGGER:	Grooved target type
FINISH:	S & W Blue

BLUE ONLY
$215.00

SMITH & WESSON REVOLVERS

".357" MAGNUM
(MODEL NO. 27)

CALIBER: .357 Magnum (Actual bullet dia. .38 S & W Spec.)
NUMBER OF SHOTS: 6.
BARREL: 3½, 5, 6, 8⅜ inches.
LENGTH OVERALL: With 6-inch barrel, 11¼ inches.
WEIGHT: With 3½-inch barrel, 41 oz.; 5-inch, 42½ oz.; 6-inch, 44 oz.; 8⅜-inch, 47 oz.
SIGHTS: Front: Choice of any S & W target sight. Rear: S & W Micrometer Click Sight, adjustable for windage and elevation.
STOCKS: Checked walnut Service with S & W monograms.
FRAME: Finely checked top strap and barrel rib.
FINISH: S & W Bright Blue or Nickel.

**BRIGHT BLUE
OR NICKEL
3½", 5", 6" $195.00
8⅜" $201.50**

HIGHWAY PATROLMAN
(MODEL NO. 28)

CALIBER: .357 Magnum (Actual bullet dia. .38 S & W Spec.)
NUMBER OF SHOTS: 6.
BARREL: 4, 6 inches.
LENGTH OVERALL: With 6-inch barrel, 11¼ inches.
WEIGHT: With 4-inch barrel, 41¾ oz.; 6-inch, 44 oz.
SIGHTS: Front: ⅛-inch Baughman Quick Draw on plain ramp. Rear: S & W Micrometer Click Sight, adjustable for windage and elevation.
STOCKS: Checked walnut Service with S & W monograms (Walnut Target stocks at additional cost).
FINISH: S & W Satin Blue with sandblast stippling or barrel rib and frame edging.

**BLUE ONLY
$140.00
with Target stocks (Illus.)
$147.50**

.44 MAGNUM
(MODEL NO. 29)

CALIBER: .44 Magnum.
NUMBER OF SHOTS: 6.
BARREL: 4, 6½, 8⅜ inches.
LENGTH OVERALL: With 6½-inch barrel, 11⅞ inches.
WEIGHT: With 4-inch barrel, 43 oz.; 6½-inch, 47 oz.; 8⅜-inch, 51½ oz.
SIGHTS: Front: ⅛-inch S & W Red Ramp. Rear: S & W Micrometer Click Sight adjustable for windage and elevation. White Outline notch.
STOCKS: Special oversize Target type of checked Goncalo Alves, with S & W monograms.
HAMMER: Checked target type.
TRIGGER: Grooved target type.
FINISH: S & W Bright Blue or Nickel.

**BRIGHT BLUE
OR NICKEL
4", 6½" $235.00
8⅜" $241.50**

SMITH & WESSON REVOLVERS

.32 HAND EJECTOR
(MODEL NO. 30)

CALIBER:	.32 S & W Long.
NUMBER OF SHOTS:	6.
BARREL:	2, 3, or 4 inches.
LENGTH OVERALL:	With 4-inch barrel, 8 inches.
WEIGHT:	With 4-inch barrel, 18 oz.
SIGHTS:	Front: Fixed, 1/10-inch serrated ramp. Rear: Square notch.
STOCKS:	Checked walnut Service with S & W monograms.
FINISH:	S & W Blue or Nickel.

BLUE
$107.00

NICKEL
$117.00

.32 REGULATION POLICE
(MODEL NO. 31)

CALIBER:	.32 S & W Long.
NUMBER OF SHOTS:	6.
BARREL:	2, 3, or 4 inches.
LENGTH OVERALL:	With 4-inch barrel, 8½ inches.
WEIGHT:	With 4-inch barrel, 18¾ oz.
SIGHTS:	Front: Fixed, 1/10-inch serrated ramp. Rear: Square notch.
STOCKS:	Checked walnut Service with S & W monograms.
FINISH:	S & W Blue or Nickel.

BLUE
$107.00
NICKEL
$117.00

1953 .22/32 KIT GUN
(MODEL NO. 34)

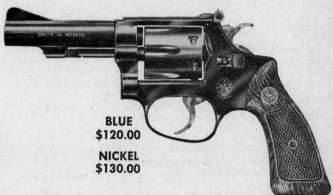

CALIBER:	.22 Long Rifle
NUMBER OF SHOTS:	6
BARREL:	2, 4 inches
LENGTH OVERALL:	With 4-inch barrel and round butt, 8 inches
WEIGHT:	With 4-inch barrel and round butt, 22½ oz.
SIGHTS:	Front: 1/10-inch serrated ramp. Rear: S & W Micrometer Click Sight, adjustable for windage and elevation.
STOCKS:	Checked walnut Service with S & W monograms, round or square butt
FINISH:	S & W Blue or Nickel

BLUE
$120.00

NICKEL
$130.00

SMITH & WESSON REVOLVERS

.38 CHIEFS SPECIAL
(MODEL No. 36)

CALIBER:	.38 S & W Special.
NUMBER OF SHOTS:	5.
BARREL:	2 or 3 inches.
LENGTH OVERALL:	With 2-inch barrel and round butt, 6½ inches.
WEIGHT:	With 2-inch barrel and round butt, 19 oz.
SIGHTS:	Front: Fixed, ⅒-inch serrated ramp. Rear: Square notch.
STOCKS:	Checked walnut Service with S & W monograms, round or square butt.
FINISH:	S & W Blue or Nickel.

BLUE $110.00

NICKEL $121.00

MODEL NO. 37
38 Chief's Special Airweight

Same as Model 36 except: weight 14 oz. **Blue $115.00 Nickel $130.00**

.38 BODYGUARD "AIRWEIGHT"
(MODEL No. 38)

CALIBER:	.38 S & W Special.
NUMBER OF SHOTS:	5.
BARREL:	2 inches.
LENGTH OVERALL:	6⅜ inches.
WEIGHT:	14 oz.
SIGHTS:	Front: Fixed, ⅒-inch serrated ramp. Rear: Square notch.
STOCKS:	Checked walnut Service with S & W monograms,
FINISH:	S & W Blue or Nickel.

NOTE: The Bodyguard also supplied in all-steel construction, Model 49, weighing 20½ oz. Price: Blue, **$106.00**; Nickel, **$116.00**.

BLUE $115.00

NICKEL $130.00

K-22 MASTERPIECE M. R. F.
(MODEL NO. 48)

CALIBER:	.22 Magnum Rim Fire.
NUMBER OF SHOTS:	6.
BARREL:	4, 6, 8⅜ inches.
LENGTH OVERALL:	With 6-inch barrel, 11⅛ inches.
WEIGHT:	With 6-inch barrel, 39 oz.
SIGHTS:	Front: ⅛-inch plain Patridge. Rear: S & W Micrometer Click Sight, adjustable for windage and elevation.
STOCKS:	Checked walnut Service with S & W monograms.
FINISH:	S & W Blue.

BLUE ONLY
4", 6" $140.00
8⅜" $146.50

Auxiliary cylinder available in 22 LR.

MODEL 49
38 Bodyguard
Same as Model 48 except: weight 20½ oz. **Blue $113.00 Nickel $123.00**

SMITH & WESSON REVOLVERS

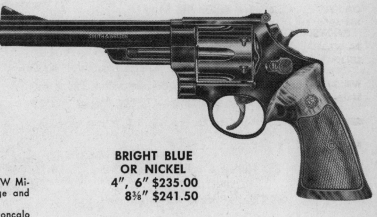

.41 MAGNUM
(MODEL NO. 57)

CALIBER:	.41 Magnum.
NUMBER OF SHOTS:	6.
BARREL:	4, 6, 8⅜ inches.
LENGTH OVERALL:	With 6-inch barrel, 11⅜ inches.
WEIGHT:	With 6-inch barrel, 48 oz.
SIGHTS:	Front: ⅛-inch S & W Red Ramp. Rear: S & W Micrometer Click Sight adjustable for windage and elevation. White Outline notch.
STOCKS:	Special oversize Target type of checked Goncalo Alves, with S & W monograms.
HAMMER:	Checked target type.
TRIGGER:	Grooved target type.
FINISH:	S & W Bright Blue or Nickel.

**BRIGHT BLUE
OR NICKEL**
4", 6" $235.00
8⅜" $241.50

.41 MILITARY & POLICE
(MODEL NO. 58)

CALIBER:	.41 Magnum.
NUMBER OF SHOTS:	6.
BARREL:	4 inches.
LENGTH OVERALL:	9¼ inches.
WEIGHT:	41 oz.
SIGHTS:	Front: Fixed, ⅛-inch serrated ramp. Rear Square notch.
STOCKS:	Checkered walnut Service with S & W monogram.
FINISH:	S & W Blue or Nickel.

**BLUE
$130.00**

**NICKEL
$140.00**

STAINLESS STEEL MODELS

.38 CHIEFS SPECIAL STAINLESS
MODEL NO. 60

SPECIFICATIONS: Caliber: .38 S&W Special. **Number of shots:** 5. **Barrel:** 2 Inch. **Length Overall:** 6½ inches. **Weight:** 19 oz. **Sights:** Front Fixed, 1/10-inch serrated ramp. Rear: Square notch. **Stocks:** Checked walnut Service with S&W monograms. **Finish:** Satin Finish. **Ammunition**—.38 S&W Special, .38 S&W Special Mid Range.

**Stainless
Steel
$135.00**

SMITH & WESSON REVOLVERS

38 MILITARY & POLICE STAINLESS
MODEL NO. 64

SPECIFICATIONS: Caliber: .38 S&W Special. **Number of Shots:** 6. **Barrel:** 4 Inch. **Length Overall:** With 4-inch barrel, 9¼ inches. **Weight:** With 4-inch barrel, 34 ounces. **Sights:** Fixed, ⅛-inch serrated ramp front; square notch rear. **Frame:** Square butt. **Stocks:** Checked walnut Service with S&W monograms. **Finish:** Satin. **Ammunition**—.38 S&W Special, .38 S&W Special Mid Range.

Stainless Steel $135.00

357 Military & Police Stainless
Heavy Barrel
MODEL NO. 65

SPECIFICATIONS: Caliber: 357 Magnum and 38 S&W Special. **Rounds:** 6-shot cylinder capacity. **Barrel:** 4-inch heavy barrel. **Length Overall:** With 4-inch barrel, 9¼ inches. **Weight:** With 4-inch barrel, 34 oz. **Sights:** Fixed, ⅛-inch serrated ramp front; square notch rear. **Stocks:** Checked walnut Service with S&W monograms, square butt. **Finish:** Satin.

Stainless Steel $145.00

357 COMBAT MAGNUM REVOLVER
MODEL NO. 66

SPECIFICATIONS: Caliber: .357 Magnum (Actual bullet diam. .38 S&W Spec.). **Number of shots:** 6. **Barrel:** 4 Inch with square butt. **Length Overall:** 9½″ with 4″ barrel. **Weight:** 35 ounces with 4″ barrel. **Sights:** Front: ⅛″ Baughman Quickdraw on plain ramp. Rear: S&W Micrometer Click Sight, adjustable for windage and elevation. **Stocks:** Checked Goncalo Alves target with square butt with S&W monograms. **Finish:** Satin. **Trigger:** S&W grooving with an adjustable trigger stop. **Ammunition:** .357 S&W Magnum, .38 S&W Special Hi-Speed, .38 S&W Special, .38 S&W Special Mid Range.

Stainless Steel $185.00

K-38 COMBAT MASTERPIECE REVOLVER
MODEL NO. 67

SPECIFICATIONS: Caliber: .38 S&W Special. **Number of shots:** 6. **Barrel:** 4 Inch. **Length Overall:** 9⅛″ with 4″ barrell. **Weight Loaded:** 34 oz. with 4″ barrel. **Sights:** Front: ⅛″ Baughman Quick Draw on plain ramp. Rear: S&W Micrometer Click Sights, adjustable for windage and elevation. **Frame:** Square butt with grooved tangs. **Stocks:** Checked walnut Service with S&W Monograms. **Finish:** Satin. **Trigger:** S&W grooving with an adjustable trigger stop. **Ammunition:** .38 S&W Special, .38 S&W Special Mid Range.

Stainless Steel $152.00

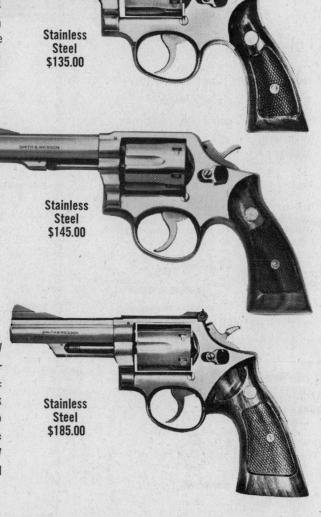

SMITH & WESSON ACCESSORIES

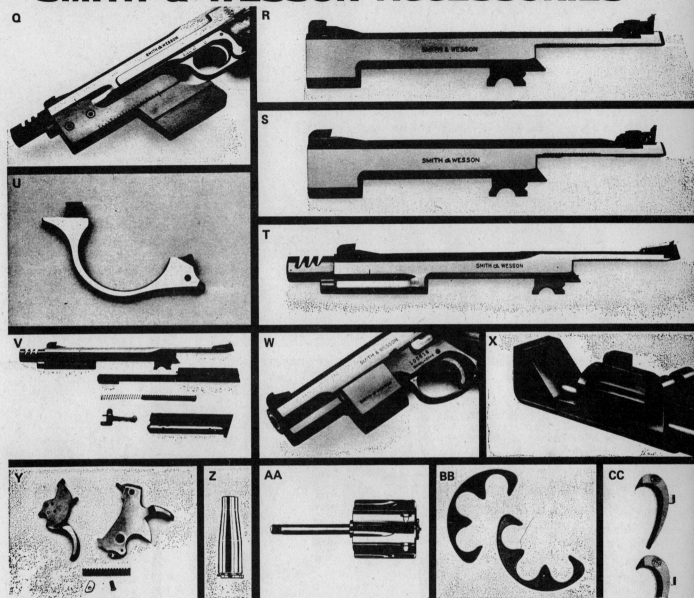

FOR S&W MODEL 41:

Q. Adjustable Olympic Counterweight.

Extra Magazine, Cals. .22 Long Rifle or .22 Short.

5-inch barrel complete with sights, .22 L.R. or .22 Short.

R. 5½-inch heavy barrel with sights.

S. 5½-inch heavy barrel with extendible front sight.

T. 7⅜-inch barrel with sights, muzzle brake.

U. Oversize Trigger Guard.

V. .22 Short or .22 Long Rifle Con- version Kit. Available "parts only," or factory installed and tested (at slightly higher cost) with any of barrels listed.

OTHER ACCESSORIES:

W. Counterweight for Model 52.

Extra Magazine for Model 52

Extra Magazine for Model 39

X. Muzzle Brake for Mod. 1955 Target or K-38.

Y. K-38 Single-Action Kit.

Z. .22 Magnum Chamber Insert, .22 L.R. Rim Fire for Model 53.

AA. .22 L.R. Auxiliary Cylinder for Models 53 and 48, factory installed and tested.

BB. Halfmoon Clip for .45 A.C.P.

CC. Grip Adapter (small, medium or large.)

Smith & Wesson Engraving

Smith & Wesson hand engraving, recognized as among the best in the world, is available to you at extra cost on any S&W handgun. It is produced by skilled artisans in three basic degrees of coverage.

Contact your S&W dealer for further information and prices.

SMITH & WESSON ACCESSORIES

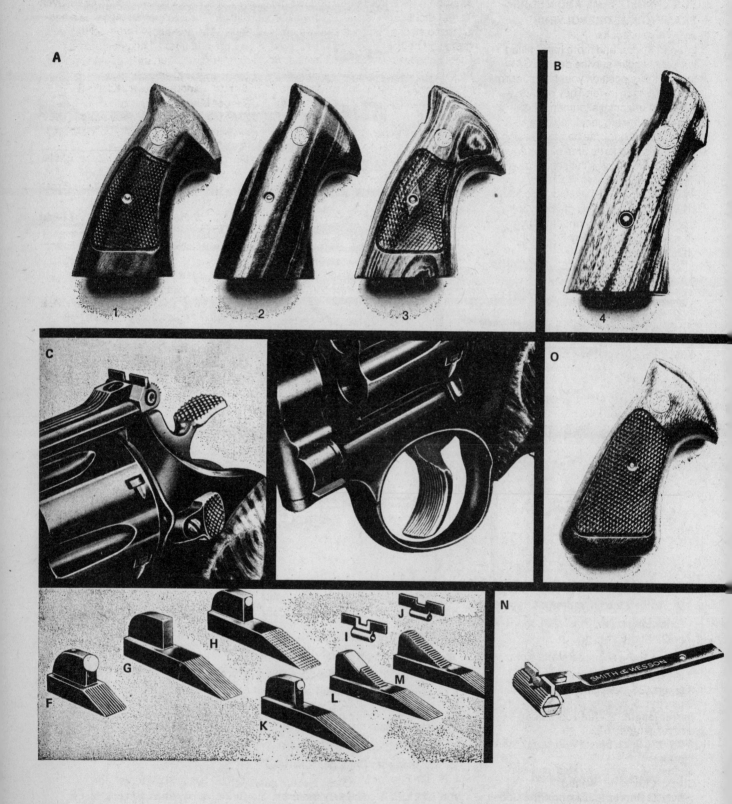

SMITH & WESSON ACCESSORIES

FOR LARGE-FRAME AND MEDIUM-FRAME TARGET REVOLVERS

A. Target Stocks
Longer, thicker and more hand-filling than our regular service design, S&W target stocks position your hand approximately ⅜-inch lower. They provide a precise, horizontal alignment of your finger with the trigger . . . also make it easier to pull back the hammer in single-action fire. The large area of contact with your hand minimizes the sensation of "kick" in recoil.
Available in: selected walnut, checked (1) or smooth colorfully grained, fancy, Goncalo Alves wood, smooth (2) or checked (3) and in fancy Rosewood, checked or smooth.

B. De luxe Service Stocks
The man who likes the size and feel of our regular checked walnut service stocks, but wants an extra touch of distinction in their appearance, will appreciate these. They're available checked or smooth (4) in the same woods as our Target Stocks.
All these stocks come with S&W monograms on both sides.
Due to space limitations we have shown only a few of the stock combinations available, but believe you will have no trouble visualizing what you want from these samples.
Stocks for S&W N-Frame (large-frame) and K-Frame (medium-frame) revolvers *look* almost the same. But the N-Frame stocks *are* slightly larger and different in shape.

C. Target Hammer
If you expect to shoot much single-action timed or rapid fire with your Smith & Wesson revolver, a target hammer will be a valuable addition. Its spur is low and a full half-inch wide, deeply checked to prevent thumb slippage.

D. Target Trigger
This is a feature that makes Smith & Wesson's slick double action seem even slicker. The S&W target trigger is a half-inch wide, and deeply grooved to give a secure and unchanging contact with your trigger finger. Its large area makes the trigger pull seem lighter.

Sights – Adaptable for ALL S&W Target Model revolvers.*
(Those with adjustable rear sights ONLY. NOT adaptable for fixed-sight models.)
- **F.** ⅛" **S&W Red Post**
- **G.** ⅛" **Patridge** on Ramp Base. Blade only also available.
- **H.** ⅛" **Call Gold Bead** on Ramp Base. Blade only also available.
- **I.** ⅛" **White Outline Rear Sight Slide.**
- **J.** ⅛" **Rear Sight Slide**
- **K.** ⅛" **McGivern Gold Bead** on Ramp Base. Blade only also available.
- **L.** ⅛" **S&W Red Ramp**
- **M.** ⅛" **Baughman Quick Draw**
- **N.** **Smith & Wesson Micrometer Click Rear Sight with ⅛" Rear Sight Slide. Above with ⅛" White Outline Rear Sight Slide.**

* These Sights for Small-Frame revolvers measure ⅒" instead of ⅛".

SECURITY INDUSTRIES OF AMERICA

$150.00

.38 POLICE SECURITY SPECIAL
Caliber: .38 Special
Capacity: 5 rounds
Barrel length: 2" full rod shroud
Overall length: 6⅝"
Weight: 19 oz.
Finish: Satin
Sights: ⅛" wide serrated man-sized
Stock: Checkered walnut
Safety features: Inertia firing pin-hammer drop block.

$175.00

.357 MAGNUM SECURITY SPECIAL
Caliber: .357 Magnum
Capacity: 5 rounds
Barrel length: 2½" full shroud
Overall length: 6⅝"
Weight: 19 oz.
Finish: Satin
Sights: ⅛" wide, man-sized
Stock: Walnut gunfighter
Safety features: Inertia firing pin-hammer drop block.

STAR AUTOMATIC PISTOLS

STAR FRS
.22 L.R. Blue $120.00
.22 L.R. Chrome $130.00

STAR FM
.22 L.R. Blue $120.00
.22 L.R. Chrome $130.00

The Star FRS is a totally delightful handgun for plinking or informal target shooting. The FRS is light enough to be comfortably carried, yet it has enough weight for steady holding. The 6-inch barrel, in addition to its longer sighting plane, also gives the FRS a slightly muzzle-heavy balance that further aids accuracy. The sights are fully adjustable for both windage and elevation, and three separate safeties—half-cock, thumb, and magazine—are incorporated. It's a safe, reliable, accurate and pleasant-to-shoot handgun.
22 L.R. Blue $120.00
22 L.R. Chrome $130.00

With its short barrel and heavy frame, the Star FM is designed primarily as a compact field handgun. The additional weight of its heavy-duty all steel frame and the man-sized grip will be found to be a great aid in steady aiming. The Star FM has checkered walnut grips, wide-spur target hammer and grooved trigger, case-hardened hammer, sear and sear bar, simple takedown, windage-adjustable rear sight, 10-round magazine, and half-cock, thumb, and magazine safeties.
22 L.R. Blue $120.00
22 L.R. Chrome $130.00

STAR BKS
9mm LUGER BLUE $160.00
9mm LUGER CHROME $170.00

STAR SUPER SM
.380 ACP Blue $145.00
.380 ACP Chrome $155.00

The BKS utilizes the time-proven U.S. Government short-recoil design, yet weighs nearly a pound less and is an inch shorter. Capable of holding 9 rounds of powerful 9mm Parabellum (Luger), the BKS offers outstanding firepower for such a compact gun. The receiver is of ultra-strong lightweight alloy; the remainder of the gun is of forged and tempered steel. The hammer, sear, and sear bar are color case-hardened. The BKS also has checkered backstrap, checkered walnut grips, wide-spur hammer and positive thumb safety.
9mm Luger Blue $160.00
9mm Luger Chrome $170.00

The Star Super SM is of all steel construction and holds a total of 9 rounds, yet weighs only 22 ounces. Like previous "Super" model Stars, it has a special takedown system that allows the gun to be field stripped in two seconds, and has a loaded-chamber indicator that can be both seen and felt by the shooter. The grips are of checkered walnut, and the rear sight is adjustable for windage. The Super SM has half-cock, thumb, and magazine safeties, plus wide-spur hammer, free falling magazine and grooved trigger.
380 ACP Blue $145.00
380 ACP Chrome $155.00

STERLING AUTOMATIC PISTOLS

STERLING
.25 AUTO
MODEL 300

STERLING ARMS introduces the *dependable* MODEL 300, a personal sized automatic, constructed of ordnance steel, featuring indestructable Cycolac grips.

- **SIZE:** 4½" x 3¾"
- **WEIGHT:** 13 oz.
- **CAPACITY:** 6 shots
- **CALIBER:** .25 A.C.P.
- **CONSTRUCTION:** All steel
- **GRIPS:** Cycolac—Black or White
- **FINISH:** Blue or Satin Nickel

BLUE $69.95
NICKEL $74.95

STERLING
.380 AUTO
MODEL 400
DOUBLE ACTION

BLUE $129.95
NICKEL $134.95

Your *security* is assured with the MODEL 400 featuring both double and single action, combined with the powerful .380 cartridge.

- **SIZE:** 6½" x 4½"
- **WEIGHT:** 24 oz.
- **CAPACITY:** 6 shots
- **CALIBER:** .380
- **CONSTRUCTION:** All ordnance steel
- **GRIPS:** Cycolac—Black
- **FINISH:** Blue or Satin Nickel

STERLING .22 AUTO
MODEL 302

Performance and standards of the potent little MODEL 302, chambered for the .22 LR cartridge, provides companionship above the ordinary.

- **SIZE:** 4½" x 3¾"
- **WEIGHT:** 13 oz.
- **CAPACITY:** 6 shots
- **CALIBER:** .22 Long Rifle
- **CONSTRUCTION:** All steel
- **GRIPS:** Cycolac—Black or White
- **FINISH:** Blue or Satin Nickel

BLUE $69.95
NICKEL $74.95

WALTHER PISTOLS

MODELS PP, PPK/S AND P-38
DOUBLE ACTION AUTOMATIC PISTOLS

The Walther double action system combines the principles of the double action revolver with the advantages of the modern pistol . . . without the disadvantages inherent in either design. Published reports from independent testing laboratories have cited Walther superiority in rugged durability, positive performance and reliability. Special built-in safety design and a simple disassembly procedure combine to make these one of the safest and most easily maintained handguns.

Models PP and PPK/S differ only in the overall length of the barrel and slide. Both models offer the same features, including compact form, light weight, easy handling and absolute safety—both models can be carried with a loaded chamber and closed hammer, but ready to fire either single or double action. Both models in calibers .32 ACP and .380 ACP are provided with a live round indicator pin to signal a loaded chamber. An automatic internal safety blocks the hammer to prevent accidental striking of the firing pin, except with a deliberate pull of the trigger. Sights are provided with white markings for high visibility in poor light. Rich Walther blue/black finish is standard and each pistol is complete with extra magazine with finger rest extension. Available in calibers .22 L.R., .32 ACP and .380 ACP.

The Walther P-38 is a double action, locked breech, semi-automatic pistol with an external hammer. Its compact form, light weight and easy handling is combined with the superb performance of the 9mm Luger Parabellum cartridge.

The P-38 is equipped with both a manual and automatic safety, which allows it to be safely carried while the chamber is loaded.

Available in calibers 9mm Luger Parabellum, .30 Luger and .22 L.R. with either a rugged non-reflective black finish or in a polished blued finish.

Overall length: model PP (6.7″); PPK/S (6.1″); P-38 (8½″). Height: models PP, PPK/S (4.28″); P-38 (5.39″). Weight: model PP (23.5 oz.); PPK/S (23 oz.); P-38 (28 oz.).

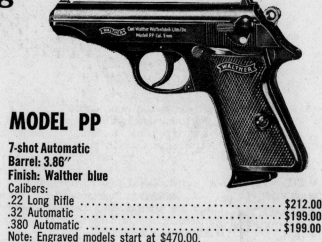

MODEL PP

7-shot Automatic
Barrel: 3.86″
Finish: Walther blue
Calibers:
.22 Long Rifle $212.00
.32 Automatic $199.00
.380 Automatic $199.00
Note: Engraved models start at $470.00.

MODEL PPK/S

7-shot Automatic
Barrel: 3.27″
Finish: Walther blue
Calibers:
.22 Long Rifle $212.00
.32 Automatic $199.00
.380 Automatic $199.00
Note: Engraved models start at $470.00.

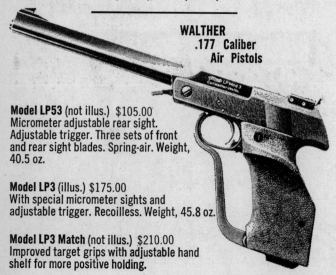

WALTHER
.177 Caliber
Air Pistols

Model LP53 (not illus.) $105.00
Micrometer adjustable rear sight. Adjustable trigger. Three sets of front and rear sight blades. Spring-air. Weight, 40.5 oz.

Model LP3 (illus.) $175.00
With special micrometer sights and adjustable trigger. Recoilless. Weight, 45.8 oz.

Model LP3 Match (not illus.) $210.00
Improved target grips with adjustable hand shelf for more positive holding.

MODEL P-38

8-shot Automatic
Barrel: 4$\frac{15}{16}$″ (9mm & .30 Luger)
      5$\frac{1}{16}$″ (.22 L.R.)
Finish: matte
Calibers:
.22 Long Rifle $285.00
.30 Luger $255.00
9mm Luger $255.00
Note: Engraved models start at $470.00.

VIRGINIAN REVOLVER

VIRGINIAN
SINGLE ACTION

Calibers: .357 Magnum & .45 Colt
Barrel: 4⅝", 5½" & 7½"

$220.00

The Virginian single action revolver by Hammerli, a Swiss firm of master gunmakers, features a unique safety system which prevents the firing pin striking the cartridge accidentally. A special base pin safety arrangement effectively blocks the hammer when in "safe" position. Available in .357 Magnum and .45 Colt calibers, in 4⅝", 5½" and 7½" barrel lengths. The 6-shot Virginian comes with blade front, and fixed notch rear sight, chromed trigger guard and back strap, blue barrel, color case hardened frame, and select walnut, one piece stock. Length overall: with 4⅝" barrel—9⅛"; 5½" barrel—11"; 7½" barrel—13". Weight: 2 lbs. 8 oz. (.357 Magnum with 5½" barrel) **$220.00**

WALTHER PISTOLS

WALTHER GSP
MATCH PISTOL

Calibers: .22 L.R. & .32 S&W wadcutter

WALTHER OSP

.22 Short only
$429.00

Models:
GSP—.22 Long Rifle $429.00
GSP-C—.32 S&W wadcutter $499.00
.22 caliber conversion unit
for GSC-C $279.00

Walther match pistols are built to conform to ISU and NRA match target pistol regulations. The model GSP, caliber .22 L. R. is available with either 2.2 lb. (1000 gm) or 3.0 lb. (1360 gm) trigger, and comes with 4½" barrel and special hand-fitting design walnut stock. Sights consist of fixed front, and adjustable rear sight. The

GSP-C .32 S&W wadcutter center fire pistol is factory tested with a 3.0 lb. trigger. The .22 L. R. conversion unit for the model GSP-C consists of an interchangeable barrel, a slide assembly and two magazines. The .22 caliber model weighs 44.8 oz; .32 S&W weighs 49.4 oz. Overall length is 11.8". Magazine capacity is 5-shot.

DAN WESSON ARMS REVOLVERS

FEATURE INTERCHANGEABLE BARREL CAPABILITY WITHIN CALIBER

The Dan Wesson Arms .38 special and .357 Magnum revolver features interchangeable barrel capability. It may be had with a choice of 2½", 4", 6" & 8" barrel lengths, and comes equipped with Sacramento-, Combat-, Target-, or Michigan-type walnut grips. Extra interchangeable barrel assemblies (includes barrel shroud) are available. To change barrel one simply removes the barrel nut with wrench (supplied), slip off barrel shroud and unscrew barrel from frame. Screw new barrel to clearance gauge (supplied), slip corresponding shroud over barrel, screw on barrel nut and tighten with wrench. Sight adjustment remains constant when changing barrel lengths.

Shown are two handguns designed and developed by Wesson Arms. Each gun can accommodate three different sizes of interchangeable barrels in both .357 Magnum and .38 caliber size. Engraved designs can also be provided and alternate grips in five styles are available—each handcarved in genuine walnut.

Model 8— .38 Special
Model 14— .357 Magnum
(with fixed sights)

SPECIFICATIONS:

Caliber: .357 Magnum (Standard)
.38 Special (Optional)

Ammunition: .357 Magnum, .38 Special, Hi-Speed, .38 Special Mid-Range.

Number of Shots: 6 (Double Action & Single Action)

Barrel Lengths: 2½", 4", 6" & 8" (Optional & Interchangeable)

Weight: 2½", 30 oz.; 4", 34 oz.; 6", 38 oz.; 8", 42 oz.

Dimensions: 4"—9¼" x 5⅜"

Sights: Front — ⅛" Serrated Ramp
Rear — Integral with frame

Trigger: Wide Tang (⅜") with adjustable overtravel stop.

Hammer: Wide Spur (⅜") with short double action travel.

Plate Screws: Socket head high torque.

Grips: Walnut, interchangeable and optional. Traditional style is standard.

Finish: Satin Blue

> Model 8 (38 Special) & Model 14 (357 Magnum):
> 2", 4" & 6" barrel **$130.00**
> 8" barrel **$143.00**

SPECIFICATIONS:

Caliber: .357 Magnum (Standard)
.38 Special (Optional)

Ammunition: .357 Magnum, .38 Special, Hi-Speed, .38 Special Mid-Range.

Number of Shots: 6 (Double Action & Single Action)

Barrel Lengths: 2¼" — 3¾" — 5¾" (Optional & Interchangeable)

Weight: 2½", 32 oz.; 4", 36 oz.; 6", 40 oz.; 8", 44 oz.

Dimensions: 4" — 9¼" x 5½"

Sights: Front — ⅛" Serrated Ramp
Rear — Adjustable for Windage & Elevation Click graduated — 1 click — ⅜" at 25 Yds.

Trigger: Wide Tang (⅜") with adjustable overtravel stop.

Hammer: Wide Spur (⅜") with short double action travel.

Plate Screws: Socket head high torque

Grips: Walnut, interchangeable and optional. Traditional style is standard.

Finish: Brite Blue

Model 9— .38 Special
Model 15— .357 Magnum
(with adjustable rear sights)

> Model 9 (38 Special) & Model 15 (357 Magnum):
> 2", 4" & 6" barrel **$168.00**
> 8" barrel **$185.00**

Rifles

BROWNING RIFLES

Browning 78
SINGLE SHOT RIFLE

BROWNING 78, SINGLE SHOT RIFLE

A superbly accurate rifle, closely resembling the famous Model 1885 High Wall designed by John M. Browning in 1878 (his first invention). Classic falling block action with automatic ejector and exposed hammer. Choose either an Octagon or a Round Sporter barrel. Either is a good, husky barrel without iron sights . . . a nice, clean taper the full 26 inches. Furnished with specially designed scope mounts and rings.
.22/250, 6mm, .25/06, .45/70, and .30/06 calibers $314.50

BROWNING .22 L.R. AUTOMATIC RIFLES

Grade I .22 Long Rifle

Barrels on all models drilled and tapped to accommodate barrel mount base.

Grade III .22 Long Rifle

Grade I Long Rifle	$142.50
Grade II Long Rifle	$214.50
Grade III Long Rifle	$444.50
Grade I Short	$146.50

The Browning .22 automatic rifle is unique in that the barrel and stock separate to a length of 19 inches, by depressing a small latch on the underside of the receiver and giving the barrel section a quarter turn. This facility provides a compact unit for carrying or storage. All moving parts are contained in a solid steel receiver which is completely closed on the top and both sides, and features downward ejection. It is a non-mechanically locked semi-automatic rifle in which the recoil is used to activate the breechblock in such a way that, when the bullet has left the barrel and no harmful gas remains in it, the mechanism ejects the empty shell, cocks the firing pin, and introduces a fresh cartridge into the barrel. The location of the magazine with the loading port on the right face of the stock simplifies loading. Fitted with a new folding leaf rear sight, it folds flush to the barrel when a scope is mounted, and is adjustable for elevation. The front sight is a 1/16 inch gold bead on a slender base.

SPECIFICATIONS

Caliber: .22 Long Rifle ,in Grades I, II, III; .22 Short in Grade I only. **Action:** Semi-automatic, double extractors with bottom ejection. **Barrel length:** .22 LR, 19¼"; .22 Short, 22¼". **Magazine:** Tubular with loading port in stock. **Capacity:** .22 LR, 11 rounds; .22 Short, 16 rounds. **Sights:** Gold bead front. Adjustable, folding leaf rear. **Length of pull:** 13¾". **Overall length:** Long Rifle, 37". Short, 40". **Weight:** 4 lbs., 12 oz.
Grade II—(not illus.) Chrome plated receiver in satin finish with small game scenes engraved on all surfaces. Select walnut and forearm, hand checkered in diamond design.

BROWNING RIFLES

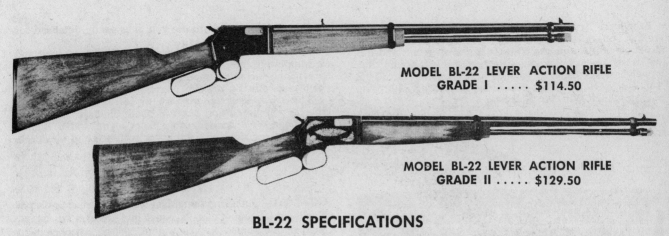

**MODEL BL-22 LEVER ACTION RIFLE
GRADE I $114.50**

**MODEL BL-22 LEVER ACTION RIFLE
GRADE II $129.50**

BL-22 SPECIFICATIONS

ACTION — Short throw lever action. Lever travels through an arc of only 33 degrees and carries the trigger with it, preventing finger pinch between lever and trigger on the upward swing. The lever cycle ejects the fired shell, cocks the hammer, and feeds a fresh round into the chamber.

MAGAZINE — Rifle is designed to handle .22 caliber ammunition *in any combination* from tubular magazine. Magazine capacity is 15 Long Rifles, 17 Longs, and 22 Shorts. The positive magazine latch opens and closes easily from any position.

SAFETY — A unique disconnect system prevents firing until the lever and breech are fully closed and pressure is released from and reapplied to the trigger. An inertia firing pin and an exposed hammer with a half-cock position are other safety features.

RECEIVER — Forged and milled steel. Grooved. All parts are machine finished and hand fitted.

TRIGGER — Clean and crisp without creep. Average pull 5 pounds. Trigger gold-plated on Grade II model.

STOCK AND FOREARM — Forearm and straight grip butt stock are shaped from select, polished walnut. Hand checkered on Grade II model. Stock dimensions:

Length of Pull........................13½"
Drop at Comb....................... 1⅝"
Drop at Heel........................ 2¼"

SIGHTS — Precision, adjustable folding, leaf rear sight. Raised bead front sight.

SCOPES — Grooved receiver will accept the Browning .22 riflescope (Model 1217) and two-piece ring mount (Model 9417) as well as most other groove or tip-off type mounts or receiver sights.

ENGRAVING — Grade II receiver and trigger guard are hand-engraved with tasteful scroll designs.

BARREL — Recessed muzzle. Barrel length: 20 inches.

OVERALL LENGTH — 36¾ inches.

WEIGHT — 5 pounds.

**BLR RIFLE
.243 Winchester & .308 Winchester
$234.50**

BLR SPECIFICATIONS

CALIBERS: .243 Win. and .308 Win.

APPROXIMATE WEIGHT: 6 pounds, 15 ounces.

OVERALL LENGTH: 39¾ inches.

ACTION: Lever action with rotating head, multiple lug breech bolt with recessed bolt face. Side ejection.

BARREL: Individually machined from forged, heat treated chrome-moly steel. Length: 20 inches. Crowned muzzle. Rifling: .243 Win. —one turn in 10 inches. .308 Win.—one turn in 12 inches.

MAGAZINE: Detachable, 4-round capacity.

TRIGGER: Wide, grooved finger piece. Short crisp pull of 4 pounds. Travels with lever.

RECEIVER: Non-glare top. Drilled and tapped to accept most top scope mounts. Forged and milled steel. All parts are machine-finished, and hand-fitted. Surface deeply polished.

SIGHTS: Low profile, square notch, screw adjustable rear sight. Gold bead on a hooded raised ramp front sight. Sight radius: 17¾ inches.

SAFETY: Exposed, 3-position hammer. Trigger disconnect system. Inertia firing pin.

STOCK AND FOREARM: Select walnut with tough oil finish and sure-grip checkering, contoured for use with either open sights or scope. Straight grip stock. Deluxe recoil pad installed.

Length of pull ....13¾ inches
Drop at comb .... 1¾ inches
Drop at heel .... 2⅜ inches

ACCESSORIES: Extra magazines are available as well as sling swivel attachment for forearm bolt and butt-stock eyelet for sling mounting.

BROWNING AUTOMATIC RIFLE

Browning Arms Company has added a center fire (semi) Rifle to their line of sporting arms. Called simply the Browning Automatic Rifle, it is gas operated, and has the strong, precision locking principle of a bolt action rifle. It weighs less than 7½ pounds and is offered in 30-06, .308 Win., .270 Win., .243 Win., 7mm Rem. Mag., .300 Win. Mag., and .338 Win. Mag. calibers.

The Browning Automatic is a magazine-fed rifle with a new "trap door" design, box type magazine that is attached to the hinged floor plate. The magazine may be loaded while attached to the gun or is easily detached for conventional loading.

The receiver is machined from a solid bar of steel and is completely free of exposed screws, pins or holes, except provisions for scope mountings. A multiple head breech bolt locks directly into the barrel, engaging 7 sturdy lugs.

The stock and forearm are of select French walnut, sharply checkered and hand finished. Sights consist of: a gold bead on a hooded ramp front sight, and a folding leaf-type rear sight adjustable for windage and elevation.

GRADE I—Quiet Browning quality. The receiver is deeply blued and left smooth as silk. Stock and forearm are carved from dense-grained French walnut, sharply checkered on the pistol grip and forearm for a good steady hold.
30/06, .270 Win., .308 Win. & .243 Win. $439.50

GRADE IV—The ultimate big-game rifle. The Grade IV's receiver is grayed steel with intricate hand-engraved game scenes. Standard calibers have running deer on one side, running antelope on the other. Magnum calibers have moose on one side, elk on the other. The floor plate and trigger guard are covered with intricate hand engraving too.

The stock on this rifle is the very finest, highly figured French walnut. Flawless hand-checkering covers the pistol grip and forearm, bordered by ornate hand carving. As a final touch, the trigger is gold-plated.
30/06, .270 Win., .308 Win. & .243 Win. $990.00
7mm Rem. Mag., 300 Win. Mag., & 338 Win. Mag.
$1030.00

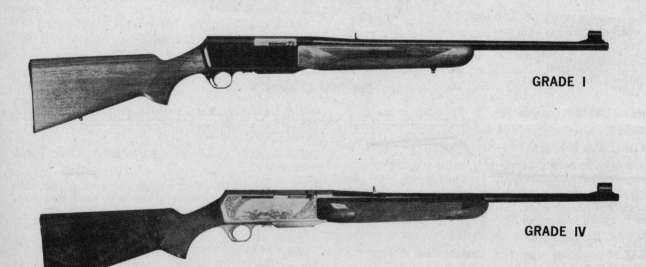

GRADE I

GRADE IV

COLT HIGH-POWER RIFLES

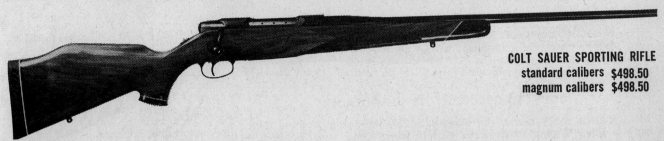

COLT SAUER SPORTING RIFLE
standard calibers $498.50
magnum calibers $498.50

Caliber: .25-06, .270, .30-06, 7mm Rem. Mag., .300 Win. Mag. and Weatherby Mag.
Weight: 8 lbs. (Std.), 8 lbs. 10 oz. (Mag.)
Stock: American walnut, cast-off Monte Carlo design with check piece, forend tip and pistol grip cap are rosewood with white line spacers, hand checkering

Sights: none, specially designed scope mounts for any popular make scope
Features: unique barrel/receiver union, non-rotating bolt with cam-actuated locking lugs, tang-type safety that mechanically locks the sear, detachable magazines of 3 and 4 round capacity

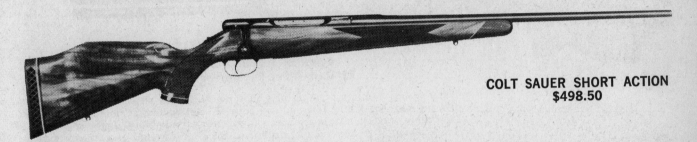

COLT SAUER SHORT ACTION
$498.50

Caliber: 22-250, 243 and 308 (7.62mm NATO)
Barrel Length: 24″
Overall Length: 43″
Barrel Type: Krupp Special Steel, hammer forged
Stock: American walnut, Monte Carlo check-piece with rosewood forend tip and pistol grip cap
Weight (empty): 7 lbs. 8 oz.
Safety: Tang
Sights: Drilled and tapped for scope mounts

Magazine Capacity: 3 rounds in detachable magazine
Finish: Colt Blue

FEATURES:
Now the Colt Sauer Rifle is available in 22-250, 243 and 308. Features the same revolutionary non-rotating bolt with three large locking lugs. American walnut stock with high-gloss finish, 18-line-per-inch checkering, rosewood forend tip and grip cap, black recoil pad. Cocking indicator, loaded chamber indicator, and Safety-on bolt opening capability.

HIGH-POWER RIFLES

COLT SAUER GRAND AFRICAN
$549.00

Caliber: .458 Win. Mag.
Barrel: 24″ round tapered   **Length:** 44½″
Weight: 10½ lbs.
Stock: solid African bubinga wood, cast-off Monte Carlo design with check piece, contrasting rosewood, forend tip and pistol grip cap with white line spacers, and checkering

on forend tip and pistol grip
Sights: front sight-ivory bead hooded ramp, rear sight-sliding, adjustable
Features: unique barrel/receiver union, non-rotating bolt with cam-actuated locking lugs, tang-type safety that mechanically locks the sear, detachable magazine

COLT RIFLES

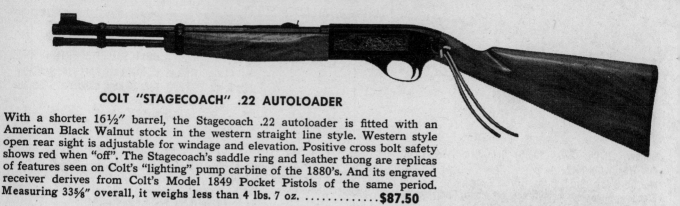

COLT "STAGECOACH" .22 AUTOLOADER

With a shorter 16½" barrel, the Stagecoach .22 autoloader is fitted with an American Black Walnut stock in the western straight line style. Western style open rear sight is adjustable for windage and elevation. Positive cross bolt safety shows red when "off". The Stagecoach's saddle ring and leather thong are replicas of features seen on Colt's "lighting" pump carbine of the 1880's. And its engraved receiver derives from Colt's Model 1849 Pocket Pistols of the same period. Measuring 33⅝" overall, it weighs less than 4 lbs. 7 oz. **$87.50**

COURIER AUTOLOADING RIFLE
.22 Long Rifle, Regular or High Speed

The shooting comfort of a pistol grip type stock and streamlined appearance of a tapered, handfilling fore-end . . . both of solid walnut, combine to deliver a thoroughly modern .22 autoloader of exceptional reliability. Lightweight . . . 4¾ pounds, 15 round tubular magazine. Receiver dovetail grooved for tip-off scope mount. Shoots .22 long rifle, standard or high velocity ammo. **$76.00**

COLT SAUER DRILLING
THREE-BARREL SHOTGUN-RIFLE
$1650.00

The Colt Sauer Drilling is a three-barrel combination side-by-side 12-gauge shotgun available in .30-06 Springfield or .243 calibers. This addition to the Colt Sauer line is 41¾-inches overall. Its 25-inch barrels are mounted on a selected, oil-finish, American walnut stock. The barrels are made from fine Krupp steel, finished in traditional Colt Blue, as are other metal parts, with an engraved rib that reduces glare and a gold-bead front sight. The left shotgun barrel is bored with modified choke and the right barrel with full choke. The barrel has four-groove rifling with a right hand twist. A thumb activated device on the tang raises or lowers the rear sight for firing of the rifle barrel. A system of double triggers fires the two shotgun and one rifle barrels. The safety is located on the left side of the stock for convenient thumb operation. When the safety button is moved, a red dot indicates "fire" position. Checkering on the stock at forend and pistol grip is 16-lines per inch. Each Colt Sauer Drilling is individually engraved at the receiver with game scenes. The recoil pad and pistol grip cap are black composition.

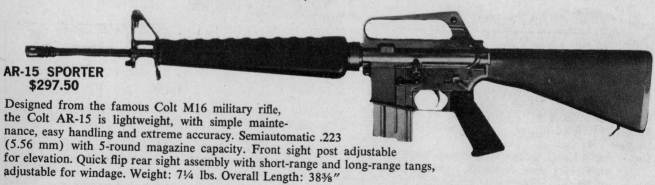

AR-15 SPORTER
$297.50

Designed from the famous Colt M16 military rifle, the Colt AR-15 is lightweight, with simple maintenance, easy handling and extreme accuracy. Semiautomatic .223 (5.56 mm) with 5-round magazine capacity. Front sight post adjustable for elevation. Quick flip rear sight assembly with short-range and long-range tangs, adjustable for windage. Weight: 7¼ lbs. Overall Length: 38⅜"

CARL GUSTAF RIFLES

BOLT-ACTION HIGH-POWER RIFLES

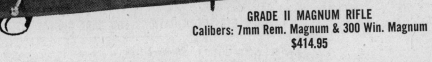

GRADE II RIFLE
Calibers: 22/250, 243, 25/06, 6.5x55,
270, 308 & 30-06
$399.95

GRADE II MAGNUM RIFLE
Calibers: 7mm Rem. Magnum & 300 Win. Magnum
$414.95

Grade II—Oil-finish Monte-Carlo type stock of European walnut with cheekpiece, hand checkered in 18-lines per inch, rosewood forend tip and grip cap with white spacers; iron sights furnished. Left-hand model available in calibers 25/06, 6.5x55, 270 and 30-06.

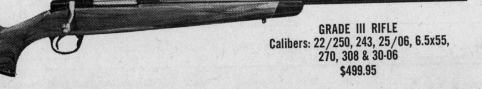

GRADE III RIFLE
Calibers: 22/250, 243, 25/06, 6.5x55,
270, 308 & 30-06
$499.95

GRADE III MAGNUM RIFLE
Calibers: 7mm Rem. Magnum & 300 Win. Magnum
$519.95

Grade III—Same as Grade II except of select French walnut finished in high-gloss urethane; additional amounts of checkering; streamlined barrel without sights; jeweled bolt and engraved floorplate.

Left-hand model is mirror image of right-hand gun with ejection port, bolt handle and safety on the left. Stock is reversed with cheekpiece on right side. Available in calibers: 25/06, 6.5x55, 270 and 30-06.

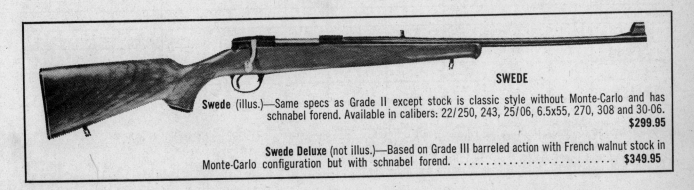

SWEDE

Swede (illus.)—Same specs as Grade II except stock is classic style without Monte-Carlo and has schnabel forend. Available in calibers: 22/250, 243, 25/06, 6.5x55, 270, 308 and 30-06.
$299.95

Swede Deluxe (not illus.)—Based on Grade III barreled action with French walnut stock in Monte-Carlo configuration but with schnabel forend. $349.95

CARL GUSTAF RIFLES

BOLT-ACTION HIGH-POWER RIFLES

VARMINT-TARGET
Calibers: 222, 22/250, 243 & 6.5x55
$449.95

Varmint-Target—Target-type stock with full-floating, heavy barrel; large bolt handle knob, Wundhammer pistol grip and special trigger which adjusts down to 19 ounces.

COMPLETE SPECIFICATIONS FOR CARL GUSTAF RIFLES

	Grade II, III & III LH Swede, Swede DL	Varmint-Target
Receiver	Tubular with integral recoil lug; twin apposed dovetail lugs with anti-bind lip; bolt handle acts as third or safety lug; drilled and tapped for conventional scope mount bases.	
Barrel	Hammer forged, 23.5 inches, .598 inches at muzzle, RH twist.	Hammer forged, 27 inches .850 at muzzle
Sights	Adjustable folding leaf rear (dovetail) hooded ramp front with brass bead (Grade II and Swede only)	none supplied
Trigger	Serrated, externally adjustable down to 3.3 pounds.	Serrated, ext. adj. down to 19 ounces
Magazine	Staggered column holds 5 standard or 3 magnum rounds. Accepts interchangeable accessory clips which accommodate 3 std. or 2 mag. rounds (not available for V-T in .222).	
Weight	Approximately 7.3 pounds depending on wood density and caliber	Approx. 9.5 pounds
Overall length	44 inches	47.5 inches
Stock dimensions	Length of pull—13.5 inches; drop at comb—5/8 inches; drop at heel—1½ inches (drop figures measured from bore line).	Length of pull—14¼ inches; drop at comb—7/16" drop at heel—1⅝ inches.

CALIBERS:	222	22/250	243	25/06	6.5X55	270	7 MM Rem.	308	30-06	300 Win. Mag.
Grade II		X	X	X	X	X	X	X	X	X
Grade III		X	X	X	X	X	X	X	X	X
Grade III LH				X		X	X			X
Varmint-Target	X	X	X		X					
Swede		X	X	X	X	X		X	X	
Swede DeLuxe		X	X	X	X	X		X	X	

Barreled Actions in Grade II, III and III LH are available in those respective chamberings as indicated above. Actions only are available in Grade II and Grade III (jeweled bolt) in standard and magnum bolt face; Left hand actions in standard bolt face only;

Varmint-Target in .222 and standard face only.

Barrel-Action Prices: Grade II, $299.95; Grade II LH, $329.95; Grade III, $349.95; Grade III LH, $369.95; Varmint-Target, $329.95.

H&R COMMEMORATIVE CARBINES

L.B.H. Commemorative Carbine Model 174

SPECIFICATIONS
Caliber: 45-70 GOVT.
Stock: American Walnut with metal grip adapter
Action: Trap door, single shot
Barrel Length: 22"

Sights: Tang mounted aperture sight adjustable for windage and elevation. Blade front sight.
Weight: 7 lbs. 4 oz.
Overall Length: 41"
Metal Finish: Barrel—Blue-Black
Action—Color case hardened

Harrington & Richardson is proud to present another in a series of authentic reproductions of famous firearms . . . the L.B.H. Carbine. A fully functional replica of the 1873 U.S. Springfield Carbine is now offered in a limited, classic model variation designed to commemorate the true story of the 7th Cavalry and the Sioux in the Valley of the Little Big Horn. Total production of this model is limited to 5,000 units. Each of these historic carbines is accompanied with a 128-page, hard cover book entitled "In the Valley of the Little Big Horn" a private printing, fully documented through a six-year study of official U.S. Army records from the National Archives.

"LITTLE BIG HORN" COMMEMORATIVE SPRINGFIELD TRAPDOOR CAR. 45/70 ....$225.00

Cavalry Model Carbine Models 171, 171 DL

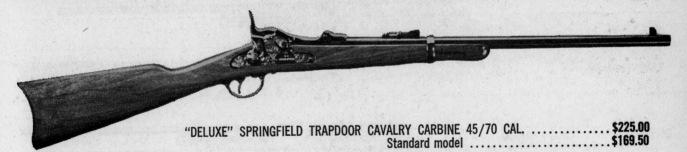

"DELUXE" SPRINGFIELD TRAPDOOR CAVALRY CARBINE 45/70 CAL. $225.00
Standard model $169.50

Another history-making firearm is authentically recreated by Harrington & Richardson in the Cavalry Model Carbine. This collector's gun is a fully functional replica of the 1873 U.S. Springfield Carbine issued to troopers of the U.S. Cavalry from 1873 through 1890. It was the principal service arm during the Indian Wars of the 1870s and 1880s and has been referred to as "the rifle which truly tamed America's Western Frontier."

SPECIFICATIONS
Caliber: 45-70 GOVT.
Stock: American Walnut with saddle ring and bridle
Action: Trap door, single shot
Barrel Length: 22"
Sights: Barrel mounted leaf sight adjustable for elevation. Blade front sight.
Weight: 7 lbs.
Overall Length: 41"
Metal Finish: Blue-Black
NOTE: Deluxe version, as illustrated, available at extra cost. Standard model has open rear sight adjustable for windage and elevation, and is finished in blue-black without engraving.

H&R RIFLES

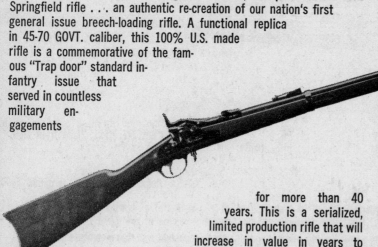
HIGH-POWER RIFLES

H&R RIFLES

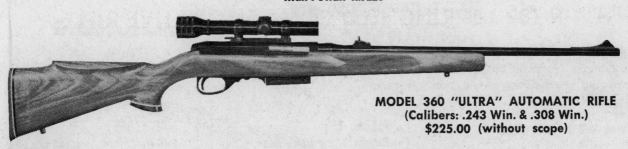

MODEL 360 "ULTRA" AUTOMATIC RIFLE
(Calibers: .243 Win. & .308 Win.)
$225.00 (without scope)

SPECIFICATIONS:
Caliber: 308 Win.
Capacity: 3 rounds in detachable box-type magazine.
Stock: One-piece genuine American walnut Monte Carlo stock with roll-over cheekpiece and contrasting wood pistol grip cap. Hand-checkered. Sling swivel bases. Rifle recoil pad.
Action: Gas operated, semiautomatic. Side ejection. Manually operated bolt stop.

Safety: Sliding safety forward of trigger.
Barrel Length: 22″ tapered.
Sights: Ramp front sight with gold bead. Fully adjustable open rear sight. Drilled and tapped for scope mounts.
Weight: 7½ lbs.
Overall Length: 43½″.
Model 360 Auto. Rifle, w/open sights **$225.00**

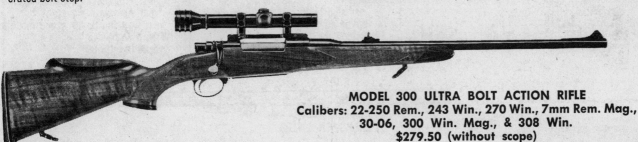

MODEL 300 ULTRA BOLT ACTION RIFLE
Calibers: 22-250 Rem., 243 Win., 270 Win., 7mm Rem. Mag., 30-06, 300 Win. Mag., & 308 Win.
$279.50 (without scope)

SPECIFICATIONS:
Calibers: 22-250 Rem., 243 Win., 270 Win., 30-06 Spfd., 308 Win., 7mm Rem. Mag., 300 Win. Mag.
Capacity: 7mm and 300 calibers have 3-round magazine; all others have 5-round magazine.
Stock: One-piece, genuine American walnut stock with roll-over cheekpiece and pistol grip. Hand-checkered. Contrasting wood on forend tip and pistol grip cap. Sling swivel bases. Rifle recoil pad.
Action: Bolt action with hinged floor plate and adjustable trigger.

Safety: Sliding safety.
Barrel Length: 24″ tapered.
Sights: Fully adjustable rear sight. Drilled and tapped for scope mounts and receiver sights. Gold-bead front sight grooved for hood.
Weight: 7¾ lbs.
Overall Length: 44½″.
Model 300 Ultra Rifle, with or without open sights **$279.50**

MODEL 301 ULTRA BOLT ACTION CARBINE
Calibers: 243 Win., 270 Win., 30-06, 308 Win., 7mm Rem. Mag., & 300 Win. Mag.
$299.50

SPECIFICATIONS:
Calibers: 243 Win., 270 Win., 30-06 Spfd., 308 Win., 7mm Rem. Mag., and 300 Win. Mag.
Capacity: 7mm and 300 calibers have 3-round magazine; all others have 5-round magazine.
Stock: One-piece, genuine American walnut, full-length stock with pistol grip. Hand-checkered. Contrasting wood on pistol grip cap. Rifle recoil pad.
Action: Bold action with hinged floor plate and adjustable trigger.

Safety: Sliding safety.
Barrel Length: 20″ tapered.
Sights: Fully adjustable rear sight. Drilled and tapped for scope mounts and receiver sights. Gold-bead front sight grooved for hood.
Weight: 7¼ lbs.
Overall Length: 40½″.
Model 301 Ultra Carbine, with open sights **$299.50**

H&R RIFLES

H&R RIFLE MODELS 750, 865

Models 750 and 865

A pair of economically priced .22 caliber rifles including single shot Model 750 with "fluid feed" platform for quick, easy loading; double extractors for dependable ejection; "Bulls-Eye" broach rifling for accuracy. Model 865 repeater has double extractors; 5-shot magazine; cocking indicator; side thumb safety. Also available as Model 866 with Mannlicher style stock.

.22 CAL. RIFLES

750	"PIONEER"—Single Shot	$49.50
865	"PLAINSMAN"—5 Shot Clip	$59.50

MODEL 750

Caliber: .22 short, long, and long rifle; standard or high velocity.
Capacity: Single shot.
Stock: Walnut finished American hardwood. Hard rubber butt plate, white liner.
Action: Self-cocking bolt action.
Safety: Side thumb lever.
Barrel Length: 22" tapered.
Sights: Front-dovetail blade. Open rear sight with elevator. Grooved for tip-off scope mounts.
Weight: 5 lbs.
Overall Length: 39".

MODEL 865

Caliber: .22 short, long, and long rifle; standard or high velocity.
Capacity: 5 round magazine.
Stock: Walnut finished American hardwood. Hard rubber butt plate, white liner.
Action: Self-cocking bolt action.
Safety: Side thumb lever.
Barrel Length: 22" tapered.
Sights: Front-dovetail blade. Open rear sight with elevator. Grooved for tip-off scope mounts.
Weight: 5 lbs.
Overall Length: 39".

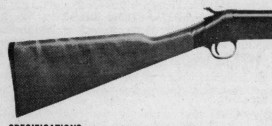

MODEL 155 "SHIKARI" RIFLE
45-70 GOVT. & 44 REM. MAGNUM

SPECIFICATIONS:
Caliber: 45-70 GOVT. and 44 Rem. Magnum.
Stock: Walnut-finished hardwood.
Barrel Length: 45-70 Caliber—24" and 28"; 44 Mag. Caliber—24".
Sights: Blade front sight, adjustable folding leaf rear sight.
Weight: 45-70 Caliber—7 lbs. and 7½ lbs.; 44 Mag. Caliber—7 lbs.

Overall Length: 45-70 Caliber—39" and 43"; 44 Mag. Caliber—39".
Metal Finish: Blue-Black with color case-hardened frame.
Accessories Supplied with Rifle: Solid brass cleaning rod with hardwood handle.
Model 155 "Shikari" $79.50

MODEL 158C TOPPER COMBINATION RIFLE

158C	30/30 Rifle with 20 ga., 26" acc., bbl.	$79.50
158	30/30 Rifle Only	$62.50
158C	22 Hornet Rifle with 20 ga., 26" acc., bbl.	$79.50
158	22 Hornet Rifle Only	$62.50

MODEL 158C

Calibers: Rifle 30-30 Win. Accessory shotgun barrel 20 gauge, chambered for 2¾" and 3" shells.
Capacity: Single shot.
Stock: Walnut finished American hardwood with recoil pad.

Action: Top break, side lever release.
Barrel Length: Rifle—22". Shotgun—26".
Sights: Rifle—ramp front sight. Folding adjustable rear sight. Drilled for Weaver #82 High Ring scope mount. Shotgun—gold bead front sight.
Weight: Rifle—5¼ lbs. Shotgun—6 lbs.
Overall Length: Rifle—37½". Shotgun—41½".

HIGH-STANDARD .22 RIFLES

**SPORT-KING
AUTOMATIC RIFLE**
(.22 Long Rifle Caliber)
$99.95

This model is a .22 automatic loading rifle. It shoots 15 long rifle, 17 longs or 21 hi-speed short cartridges interchangeably or mixed. It has a barrel length of 22¼". The overall length is 42¾" and it weighs 5½" lbs. It is equipped with a tubular magazine with a side loading port. It is dovetailed for telescopic sights. Post front sight and Rocky Mountain Patridge rear sight with stepped blade. Positive thumb-actuated safety is mounted on right side of receiver. Checkered American Walnut Monte Carlo Stock with fluted comb and pistol grip cap. Semi-beavertail forearm and bright trim at butt. **$99.95**

**SPORT-KING
PUMP ACTION RIFLE**
(.22 Long Rifle Caliber)
$99.95

This model is a .22 automatic loading rifle. It handles all three cartridges, 17 long rifle, 19 longs and 24 hi-speed shorts interchangeably or mixed. It has a barrel length of 24". The overall length is 41¾" and weighs 5½" lbs. It is equipped with a tubular magazine with a side loading port. It is dovetailed for telescopic sights. Post front and Rocky Mountain Patridge rear sight with stepped blade. A cross-bolt safety is built into the trigger guard. It has a checkered American Walnut Monte Carlo Stock with a pistol grip cap with semi-beavertail serrated forearm. **$99.95**

CHARTER AR-7 EXPLORER RIFLE

**MODEL AR-7
SEMI-AUTOMATIC RIFLE**
(.22 Long Rifle Caliber)
$75.00

*Stows in
16½ Inches
So Light
it Floats!*

The AR-7 survival weapon is a semiautomatic .22 Long Rifle caliber with a 16" barrel and is fitted with a plastic stock which floats if accidentally dropped in water. For transport, the AR-7 compacts into its own stock, measuring 16½" overall. The rear sight is a hooded peep with the aperature adjustable for elevation changes. Windage may be accomplished by moving the front sight back and forth **$75.00**

SPECIFICATIONS:
CALIBER: .22 Long Rifle. ACTION: Semi-automatic. LOAD: Detachable box, magazine fed. SIGHTS: Adjustable ramp front, adjusting rear peep. CAPACITY: 8 rounds. BARREL: High test alloy with rifled steel liner. STOCK: Full pistol grip, recessed to carry barrel and action. WEIGHT: 2¾ pounds. OVERALL LENGTH: 34½". LENGTH WHEN STOWED: 16½".

ITHACA RIFLES

SINGLE-SHOT .22 CALIBER RIFLES

The Ithaca Model 49 Saddlegun is a single-shot .22 rifle made for the beginning shooter. The gun is chambered for .22 short, long and long rifle cartridges and has a magazine capacity of 15 .22 long rifle cartridges. It also comes in a magnum model chambered for .22 rim fire magnum cartridges only. Its rebounding hammer is hand operated and activated independently from the lever action. This means the gun cannot be fired unless the hammer is fully cocked—by hand. The precision-rifled, solid steel barrel is 18″ long, and overall length is 34½″. Weight is approximately 5½ lbs. Rifle is equipped with adjustable open sights.

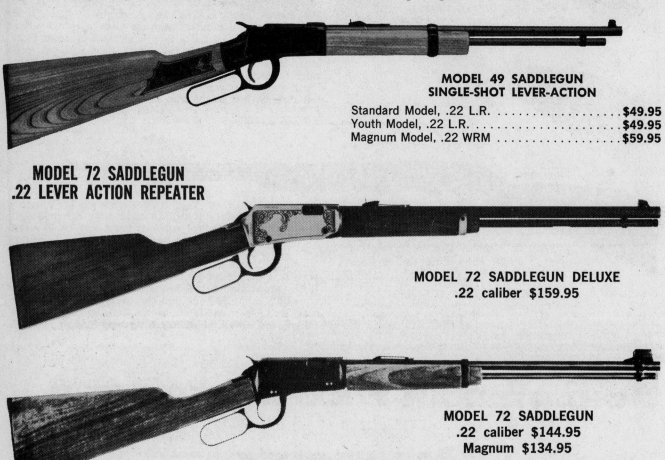

**MODEL 49 SADDLEGUN
SINGLE-SHOT LEVER-ACTION**

Standard Model, .22 L.R. **$49.95**
Youth Model, .22 L.R. **$49.95**
Magnum Model, .22 WRM **$59.95**

MODEL 72 SADDLEGUN .22 LEVER ACTION REPEATER

MODEL 72 SADDLEGUN DELUXE
.22 caliber $159.95

MODEL 72 SADDLEGUN
.22 caliber $144.95
Magnum $134.95

Authentically styled in the Western tradition, the 72 Saddlegun is scaled for .22 long rifle shooting and has a 15-round magazine tube that keeps time-outs for reloading to a minimum. Among its many shooting pluses are its excellent wood-to-metal fit, steel precision rifled barrel, steel-to-steel lockup and receiver which is specially grooved for easy scope mounting. All of the Model 72's action parts are manufactured from solid, high-tensile steel.

With wood of American walnut, the trim 72 Saddlegun features a big-game-style hooded front-sight and a half-cock safety. Equally suitable for either a left- or right-handed shooter, this gun must be fully cocked by hand and the trigger released in order to fire. Model 72 Saddlegun **$114.95**, Model 72 Saddlegun w/4X scope **$129.95**.

Model 72 Magnum. Same features as Standard Model 72 except it is chambered for eleven .22 Magnum cartridges for extra power and accuracy **$134.95**.

Model 72 available in deluxe model (not illustrated) intended as a presentation model for young or adult shooters committed to small game hunting or plinking. This .22 lever action repeater is scaled for .22 long rifle shooting and has a 15-round magazine tube that keeps time-outs for reloading to a minimum.

Authentically styled in the time-honored Western tradition, the 72 Deluxe is distinguished by its steel precision-rifled 18½″ octagonal barrel, handsomely engraved silver frame, Western-style sights, "semifancy" European walnut oilfinished stock and steel butt plate.

Smooth feeding with positive ejection, the 72 deluxe is noted for its deeply blued barrel and action. Other features include, a crisp trigger pull and steel-to-steel lockup; the receiver is specially grooved for easy scope mounting. All moving parts are made of high-grade steel. . . .

Price for the Model 72 deluxe is **$134.95**. An easy-to-follow cleaning and instruction manual is supplied with each rifle.

ITHACA RIFLES

TURKEY GUN

Ithaca's Turkey Gun, designed to reduce the odds between the dedicated hunter and the elusive turkey, is also intended for any time either a close or long shot is possible. Because of its special sights and positive barrel selection, the Turkey Gun is also ideal for fox, coyote and other varmint hunting.
Available in 12 gauge

only, this 7½ lb. over/under with a .222 Remington rifle barrel is made of Bofors ordnance steel and has a skip-line hand-checkered European, oil-finished walnut stock, cheekpiece and forend with white spacer accents. This shotgun/rifle combination, noted for its easy takedown and adjustable trigger pull, carries a solid barrel rib with a folding rear leaf sight and ramp front sight for accuracy and quick-pointing shotgun option.
Among the other outstanding features of the Turkey Gun are its completely separated barrels; the wide serrated hammer which must be fully cocked to fire; the easy-to-use selector button for positive barrel selection and shooting flexibility; and the muzzle brake on the rifle barrel for maximum accuracy, minimum recoil.
The gun, which is grooved for scope mounting, has a detachable choke tube (full) with modified and improved cylinder tubes available as options. Sling swivels are included. Price $259.95

ITHACA HIGH-POWER BOLT-ACTION RIFLES

STANDARD MODEL
Calibers: 222 Rem., 22-250, 6mm Rem.,
243 Win., 308 Win., 25-06 Rem.,
270 Win. & 30-06 $249.95

DELUXE MODEL
Calibers: 222 Rem., 22-250, 6mm Rem.,
243 Win., 308 Win., 25-06 Rem.,
270 Win. & 30-06 $279.95
222 & 22-250 (heavy barrel) $329.95

Ithaca is broadening its line of rifles by extending the calibers in the LSA-65, a high-powered centerfire rifle. Weighing approximately 6½ lbs. with a 22½" barrel, the gun is currently available in .222 Rem., 22-250, 6mm Rem., 243 Win., 308 Win., 25-06 Rem., 270 Win. & 30-06 calibers to accommodate the shooter's largest game needs.
Proportioned for easy handling with a slimline receiver and furnished with a hand-checkered European Walnut stock, the LSA-65 features an improved Mauser-type bolt action, built-in palm swell, fully adjustable trigger pull, four locking lugs and a recessed bolt face with gas escape ports for added safety. Unique is a four shot detachable clip which can also be loaded from the top.
Made of Bofors Ordnance steel, the LSA-65 is equipped with a freefloating barrel and special receiver guide rails that prevent bolt binding and jamming. The receiver is drilled and tapped for mounting scope rings; sling swivels are installed.
The standard LSA-65 has an open-notched rear sight and a hooded ramp front sight. Scope rings are supplied with the deluxe model which also features a rollover cheekpiece, deluxe skip-line checkering and a contrasting rosewood forend tip and pistol-grip cap.

MARLIN LEVER ACTION CARBINES

IN .22 LONG RIFLE CALIBER

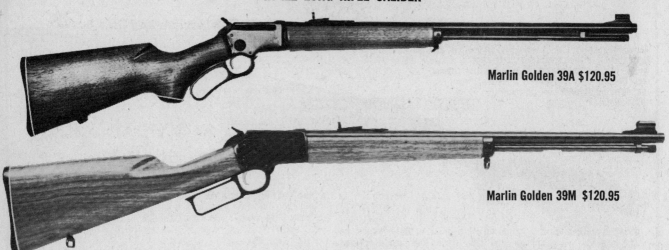

Marlin Golden 39A $120.95

Marlin Golden 39M $120.95

Marlin Golden
39A

The Marlin lever action .22 is the oldest (since 1891) shoulder gun still being manufactured. In fact, the only older gun design still being manufactured is Colt's 1873 Single Action Army revolver.

Solid Receiver Top. You can easily mount a scope on your Marlin 39 by screwing on the machined scope adapter base provided. The screw-on base is a neater, more versatile method of mounting a scope on a .22 sporting rifle. The solid top receiver and scope adapter base provide a maximum in eye relief adjustment. If you prefer iron sights, you'll find the 39 receiver clean, flat and sand-blasted to prevent glare.

Exclusive Brass Magazine Tube. A small point perhaps, but not if you've ever had a steel tube rust.

Micro-Groove® Barrel. Marlin's famous rifling system of multi-grooving has consistently produced fine accuracy because the system grips the bullet more securely, minimizes distortion, and provides a better gas seal.

And the Model 39 maximizes accuracy with the heaviest barrels available on any lever action .22.

Marlin Golden 39A Specifications

Caliber .22 Short, Long and Long Rifle

Capacity: Tubular magazine holds 26 Short, 21 Long and 19 Long Rifle Cartridges

Action: Lever action; solid top receiver; side ejection; gold plated steel trigger; one-step take-down; deeply blued metal surfaces; receiver top sand-blasted to prevent glare.

Stock: Two-piece genuine American black walnut with fluted comb; full pistol grip and forend. Blued-steel forend cap; sling swivels. grip cap; white butt plate and pistol-grip spacers; tough Mar-Shield™ finish.

Barrel: 24″ with Micro-Groove® rifling (16 grooves)

Sights: Adjustable folding semi-buckhorn rear, ramp front sight with new Wide-Scan™ hood. Solid top receiver tapped for scope mount or receiver sight; scope adapter base; offset hammer spur for scope use—works right or left.

Overall Length: 40″

Weight: About 6¾ lbs.

Marlin Golden 39M Specifications

Caliber: .22 Short, Long and Long Rifle.

Capacity: Tubular magazine holds 21 Short, 16 Long or 15 Long Rifle Cartridges.

Action: Lever action with square finger lever; solid top receiver; side ejection; gold-plated steel trigger; one-step take-down; deeply blued-metal surfaces; receiver top sandblasted to prevent glare.

Stock: Two-piece straight-grip genuine American walnut with fluted comb and full fore-end. Blued steel fore-end cap; sling swivels; white butt plate spacer; tough Mar-Shield™ finish.

Barrel: 20″ with Micro-Groove rifling (16 grooves).

Sights: Adjustable folding semi-buckhorn rear, ramp front sight and new Wide-Scan™ hood. Solid top receiver tapped for scope mount or receiver sight; scope adapter base; offset hammer spur for scope use—works right or left.

Overall Length: 36″

Weight: About 6 lbs.

MARLIN BOLT ACTION RIFLES

Marlin 780 $57.95
(less scope)

Marlin 781 $57.95
(less scope)

700 SERIES IN .22 LONG RIFLE CALIBER

Marlin 780 Specifications
Caliber: .22 Short, Long or Long Rifle
Capacity: Clip magazine holds 7 Short, Long or Long Rifle Cartridges.

Action: Bolt action; serrated, anti-glare receiver top; gold-plated steel trigger; positive thumb safety.
Stock: Monte Carlo genuine American black walnut with full pistol grip; checkering on pistol grip and underside of fore-end; white butt plate spacer; tough Mar-Shield™ finish.
Barrel: 22″ with Micro-Groove® rifling (16 grooves)
Sights: Adjustable folding semi-buckhorn rear, ramp front, Wide-Scan™ front sight hood; receiver grooved for tip-off scope mount.

Overall Length: 41″
Weight: About 5½ lbs.
Marlin 781. Specifications same as Marlin 780, except with tubular magazine that holds 25 Short, 19 Long or 17 Long Rifle Cartridges. Weight: About 6 lbs.

700 SERIES IN .22 MAGNUM

Marlin 783 Magnum $66.95 (less scope)

Marlin 783 Magnum Specifications
Caliber: .22 Win. Magnum Rimfire (Not interchangeable with any other .22 cartridge)

Capacity: 12-shot tubular magazine

Action: Bolt action; serrated, anti-glare receiver top; gold-plated steel trigger; positive thumb safety.
Stock: Monte Carlo genuine American black walnut with full pistol grip; checkering on pistol grip and underside of fore-end; white butt plate spacer; sling swivels and handsome leather carrying strap; tough Mar-Shield™ finish.
Barrel: 22″ with Micro-Groove rifling (20 grooves)
Sights: Adjustable folding semi-buckhorn rear, ramp front with new Wide-Scan™ hood; receiver grooved for tip-off scopt mount.
Overall Length: 41″
Weight: About 6 lbs.

Marlin 782 Magnum $64.95 (less scope)

Marlin 782 Magnum Specifications
Same as 783 Magnum, except with 7-shot clip magazine.

MARLIN LEVER ACTION CARBINES

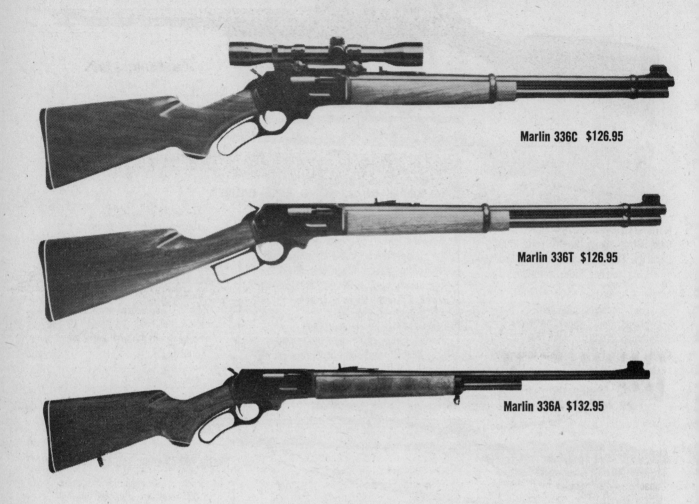

Marlin 336C $126.95

Marlin 336T $126.95

Marlin 336A $132.95

Now you have three models to choose from. The 336C with full pistol grip, the 336T saddle gun, or the 336A, a rifle model with 24″ barrel and half magazine. All three models feature side-ejecting, solid top receivers, heat-treated machined steel forgings, American black-walnut stock with Mar-shield™ finish, Micro-Groove® rifling, and folding semi-buckhorn rear sights.

Marlin 336C Specifications
Caliber: .30/30 Win., or .35 Rem.
Capacity: 6-shot tubular magazine
Action: Lever action; solid top receiver; side ejection; gold plated steel trigger; deeply blued metal surfaces; receiver top sand-blasted to prevent glare
Stock: Two-piece genuine American black walnut with fluted comb and full pistol grip. Grip cap, white butt plate and pistol-grip spacers; tough Mar-Shield™ finish
Barrel: 20″ with Micro-Groove® rifling (12 grooves)
Sights: Adjustable semi-buckhorn folding rear, ramp front sights. Wide-Scan™ front sight hood. Solid top receiver tapped for scope mount or receiver sight; offset hammer spur for scope use —works right or left.
Overall Length: 38½″
Weight: About 7 lbs.

Marlin 336T Specifications
Same action as 336C, available in .30/30 Win. only, with straight-grip stock and squared finger lever.

Marlin 336A Specifications
Same action as 336C, with 24″ barrel, ½ magazine tube with 5-shot capacity, blued steel fore-end cap and sling swivels. Approx. 7 lbs.
Available in .30/30 Win. only.

Forgings. Marlin uses six forged parts in the manufacture of all 336 high-power rifles: receiver, lever, trigger plate, carrier, hammer, and locking bolt.

MARLIN LEVER ACTION CARBINES

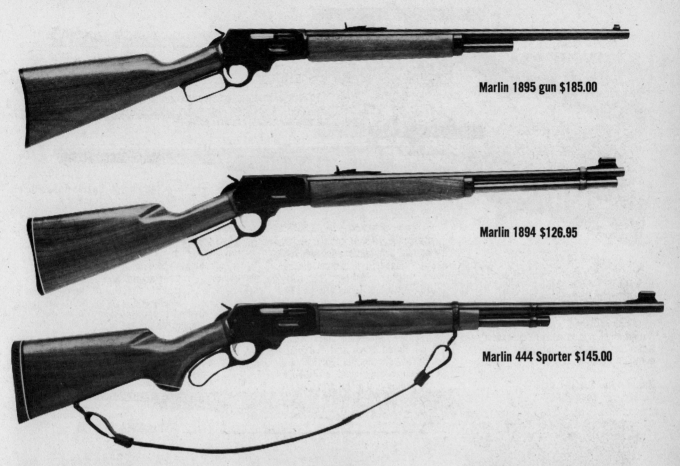

Marlin 1895 gun $185.00

Marlin 1894 $126.95

Marlin 444 Sporter $145.00

Marlin 1895 Specifications
Caliber: .45/70 Government
Capacity: 4-shot tubular magazine
Action: Lever action; solid top receiver; side ejection; blued steel trigger; deeply blued metal surfaces; receiver top sand-blasted to prevent glare.
Stock: Two-piece straight-grip genuine American black walnut; traditional hard-rubber rifle butt plate, blued-steel forend cap; tough Mar-Shield™ finish.
Barrel: 22″, with rifling designed to give maximum performance with both lead and jacketed bullets (12 grooves.)
Sights: Adjustable semi-buckhorn folding rear, bead front sights; solid top receiver tapped for scope mount or receiver sight; offset hammer spur for scope use —works right or left.
Overall Length: 40½″
Weight: About 7 lbs.

Marlin 1894 Specifications
Caliber: .44 Rem. Magnum
Capacity: 10-shot tubular magazine
Action: Lever action with traditional squared finger lever; solid top receiver side ejection; blued steel trigger; deeply blued metal surfaces; receiver top sand-blasted to prevent glare.
Stock: Two-piece straight-grip genuine American black-walnut traditional hard-rubber rifle butt plate; blued-steel forend cap; tough Mar-Shield™ finish.
Barrel: 20″ with Micro-Groove® rifling (12 grooves).
Sights: Adjustable semi-buckhorn folding rear, hooded-ramp front sights; solid top receiver tapped for scope mount or receiver sight; offset hammer spur for scope use—works right or left.
Overall Length: 37½″
Weight: About 6 lbs.

Marlin 444 Sporter Specifications
Caliber: .444 Marlin
Capacity: 4-shot tubular magazine
Action: Lever-action; solid top receiver; side ejection; gold plated steel trigger; deeply blued metal surfaces; receiver top sand-blasted to prevent glare.
Stock: Two-piece genuine American walnut with fluted comb; recoil pad; full pistol grip; white butt plate and pistol grip spacers; tough Mar-Shield™ finish. Detachable sling swivels and handsome leather carrying strap.
Barrel: 22″ with Micro-Groove® rifling (12 grooves)
Sights: Adjustable folding semi-buckhorn rear, hooded-ramp front sights. Solid top receiver tapped for scope mount or receiver sight; offset hammer spur for scope use —works right or left.
Overall Length: 40½″
Weight: About 7½ lbs.

MARLIN .22 AUTOLOADERS

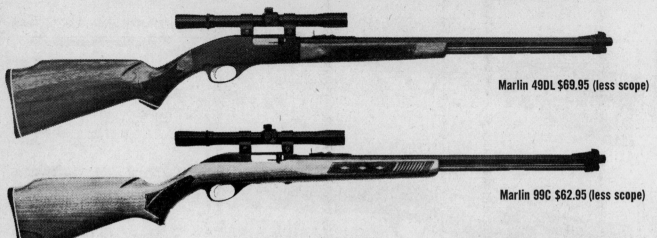

Marlin 49DL $69.95 (less scope)

Marlin 99C $62.95 (less scope)

Marlin 49 Deluxe. Handsome scrollwork adorns both sides of the receiver; the bolt is damascened; and the American black-walnut stock and forend are checkered. White line spacers on butt plate and pistol-grip cap.

Marlin 49DL Specifications
Caliber: .22 Long Rifle

Capacity: 18-shot tubular magazine
Action: Semi-automatic; side ejection; bolt hold-open device; damascened bolt; receiver top has serrated, non-glare finish; gold-plated trigger; cross-bolt safety.
Stock: Two-piece Monte Carlo genuine American black walnut with fluted comb and full pistol grip; checkering on pistol grip and forend; grip cap; white butt plate and pistol-grip spacers; tough Mar-Shield™ finish.

Barrel: 22" with Micro-Groove® rifling (16 grooves)
Sights: Adjustable open rear, ramp front sights. Scroll-engraved receiver grooved for tip-off scope mount and receiver sight.
Overall Length: 40½"
Weight: About 5½ lbs.

Marlin 99C Specifications
Same as Model 49DL, except with one-piece American black-walnut stock, polished bolt, conventional receiver and pistol grip.

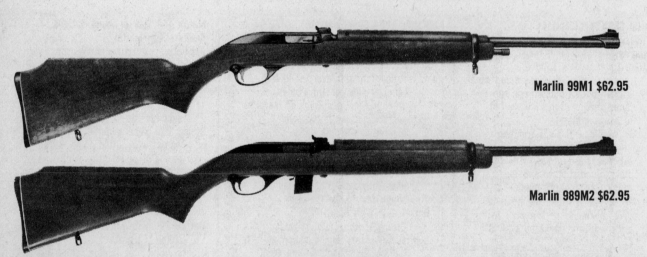

Marlin 99M1 $62.95

Marlin 989M2 $62.95

Marlin 99M1 Specifications

Caliber: .22 Long Rifle
Capacity: 9-shot tubular magazine
Action: Semi-automatic; side ejection; bolt hold-open device; receiver top has serrated, non-glare finish; gold-plated trigger; cross-bolt safety.

Stock: Monte Carlo genuine American black walnut with hand guard; full pistol grip; white butt plate spacer; sling swivels; tough Mar-Shield™ finish.
Barrel: 18" with Micro-Groove® rifling (16 grooves)
Sights: Adjustable and removable

open rear, ramp front sights; receiver grooved for tip-off scope mount.
Weight: About 4½ lbs.
Overall Length: 37"
Marlin 989M2 Specifications
Same as 99M1 except with 7-shot clip magazine.

MOSSBERG HIGH POWER RIFLES

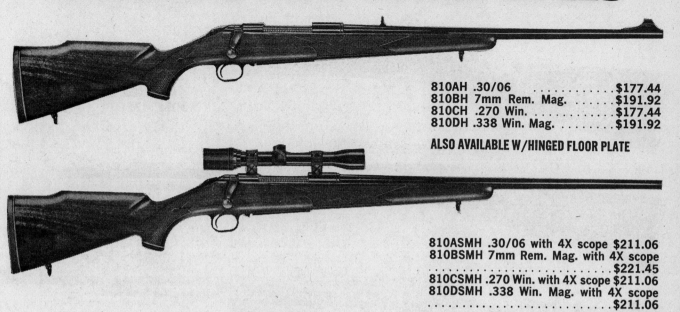

810AH .30/06 . . . . $177.44
810BH 7mm Rem. Mag. $191.92
810CH .270 Win. $177.44
810DH .338 Win. Mag. $191.92

ALSO AVAILABLE W/HINGED FLOOR PLATE

810ASMH .30/06 with 4X scope $211.06
810BSMH 7mm Rem. Mag. with 4X scope
. . . . $221.45
810CSMH .270 Win. with 4X scope $211.06
810DSMH .338 Win. Mag. with 4X scope
. . . . $211.06

model 810 center fire rifles

The Mossberg Model 810 bolt action repeater is a big game rifle built for accuracy and rugged use. This year we are offering the popular 7 m/m Rem. Magnum caliber as well as the world's most versatile cartridge, the 30/06. Our exclusive AC-KRO-GRUV, 8 groove rifled barrel, receiver and bolt are all heat treated Chrom Moly steel of high tensile stength. The stock with Monte Carlo and cheek piece, is of genuine American walnut. Here are the specifications:

MODEL 810AH Bolt-Action Center-Fire Rifle   Price **$177.44**

Caliber—30/06, to handle all factory loaded bullet weights. **Action**—Damascened bolt with deep blue shaped bolt handle has four in-line locking lugs, for smooth operation and increased strength; action cocks on opening of bolt. Bolt has recessed head, covering cartridge base and rim, for added safety to the shooter. Positive extraction and ejection. **Trigger**—Internal adjustments for both sear let-off and weight of trigger pull. Standard trigger pull approximately 5½ lbs. with crisp let-off. **Safety**—Jar proof shotgun type, right under shooter's thumb, simple no mistake safety. **Magazine**—Detachable 4-shot (makes 5-shot rifle) inserted into solid, one piece trigger guard-magazine assembly. Part #3469. Price $4.75. **Stock**—Modern marksman style made of genuine American walnut with waterproof high gloss finish. Custom checkered stock has Monte Carlo comb and cheek piece with pistol grip cap and rifle style recoil pad with white liners. Sling swivels provided. **Barrel**—22 inch with Crowned muzzle, highly polished and deep blue finished to match receiver. **Sights**—Ramp front with gold bead and folding leaf middle sight adjustable for both elevation and windage. Receiver drilled and tapped for receiver peep sights and telescope sight mounts. **Weight**—Depending on density of wood 7½ to 8 lbs. Length overall 42 inches.

7 m/m   **30/06**

MODEL 810BH Bolt-Action Center-Fire Rifle
Price $191.92

Caliber—7 m/m Rem. Magnum, to handle all factory loaded bullet weights. **Action**—Damascened bolt with deep blue shaped bolt handle has four in-line locking lugs, for smooth operation and increased strength; action cocks on opening of bolt. Bolt has recessed head, covering cartridge base and rim, for added safety to the shooter. Positive extraction and ejection. **Trigger**—Internal adjustments for both sear let-off and weight of trigger pull. Standard trigger pull approximately 5½ lbs. with crisp let-off. **Safety**—Jar proof shotgun type, right under shooter's thumb, simple no mistake safety. **Magazine**—Detachable 4-shot (makes 5-shot rifle) inserted into solid, one piece trigger guard-magazine assembly. **Stock**—Modern marksman style made of genuine American walnut with waterproof high-gloss finish. Custom-checkered stock has Monte Carlo comb and cheekpiece with pistol-grip cap and rifle-style recoil pad with white liners. Sling swivels provided. **Barrel**—24 inch with crowned muzzle, highly polished and deep blue finished to match receiver. **Sights**—Ramp front with gold bead and folding leaf middle sight adjustable for elevation and windage. Receiver drilled and tapped for receiver peep sights and telescope sight mounts. **Weight**—depending on density of wood 7½ to 8 lbs. Length overall 44 inches.

MODEL 810ASMH .30/06 caliber Scooped Rifle   Price **$211.06**
MODEL 810BSMH 7mm Rem. Mag. Scooped Rifle   Price **$211.45**

Made to the exact same specifications as our other Model 810 rifles, furnished without sights and fitted with our own Mossberg 4 power riflescope. A scope equipped rifle ready to shoot. These rifles with Mossberg Model 84 4X scope mounted are targeted in our own shooting range using all bullet weights and brands of factory loaded cartridges. Weight—Model 810ASMH with scope about 8 lbs. Length overall 42 inches. Model 810BSMH with scope about 8 lbs. Length overall 44 inches.

MOSSBERG CENTER-FIRE RIFLES

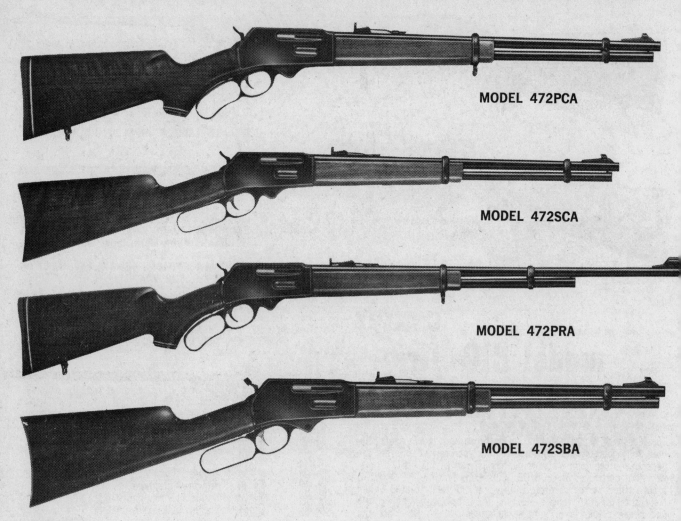

MODEL 472PCA

MODEL 472SCA

MODEL 472PRA

MODEL 472SBA

FEATURES:

Trigger: The trigger is pinned to the operating lever and disconnects completely when the lever is operated. This allows your finger to remain in the guard on the trigger, for smooth, rapid working of the lever action.

Safety: The hammer-block safety on the side of the receiver prevents accidental firing when the hammer is cocked. When the thumbpiece is in the "safe" position, hammer travel is limited to prevent the hammer from striking the firing pin.

Receiver: Model 472 Series receivers are drilled and tapped for top-mounting.
The receiver top is serrated to prevent glare.

Side Ejection: Fired-cartridge cases are ejected to the side, away from your line of sight.

Hammer Spur: Offset hammer spur lets you easily cock the hammer by hand when using a scope—works left or right.

Sling Swivels: Pistol-grip-stock models come equipped with front and rear sling swivels.

Saddle Ring: Straight-grip-stock models have a removable saddle ring on the side of the receiver.

"Hammer Rebound", an exclusive safety feature: This additional safety mechanism automatically places hammer in safe "half-cock" position immediately upon firing. Also, when hammer is manually moved from "full-cock," it cannot, in its final forward position, rest directly on firing pin, but rebounds and resets hammer to safe "half-cock" position.

Other Features: American walnut fluted stock wtih rubber butt pad; white-line spacers; pistol-grip cap (pistol-grip models only); blued trigger; adjustable buckhorn rear sight, ramp front sight with gold bead; barrel tapped for top-mounting scope; offset hammer spur; serrated receiver top; 6-shot tubular magazine (rifle and brush gun models have 5-shot capacity.); AC-KRO-GRUV barrel; deeply blued-metal surfaces. Straight-grip models have blued-steel buttplate.

472PCA	.30/30 Win.	$143.21
472PCB	.35 Rem.	$143.21
472SCA	.30/30 Win.	$143.21
472SCB	.35 Rem.	$143.21
472PRA	.30/30 Win.	$143.21
472PRB	.35 Rem.	$143.21
472SBA	.30/30 Win.	$143.21

MOSSBERG HIGH POWER RIFLES

800A
.308 Win.

800 V/T
.243 & .22/250

800SM
.308, .243 & .22/250
w/ 4X scope

The Mossberg 800 series includes scope-mounted, varmint-barreled, as well as the standard field rifle. A variety of calibers are available, including .308, .243, and .22/250.

SPECIFICATIONS

Action: Bolt is damascened for good looks and smooth action. Sure-grip bolt handle and short throw for fast shooting. Six locking lugs on bolt and recessed head for extra strength. Receiver made of special alloy steel, heat-treated and blued for long-lasting finish. Drilled and tapped for scope mounts.

Trigger: Specially designed short trigger take-up for safety, with crisp let-off. Positive slide-type safety on top of bolt.

Magazine: A 5-shot rifle, 4-shot hinged-floor plate magazine, plus one in chamber. (.22/250 has 3-shot capacity magazine.) Easily loaded for single-shot use. Heavy-spring magazine with staggered feed for sure, smooth operation. Hinged floor plate for quick, safe unloading with safety on.

Stock: American walnut with Monte Carlo comb and cheekpiece. High-gloss waterproof filled finish. Sling swivels factory installed. Checkered at pistol grip and forend. Attractive white-line spacers at buttplate and capped pistol grip. Stock dimensions —drop at comb 1⅞″; at Monte Carlo, 1⅝″; at heel, 2⅛″; length of pull, 14″; and pitchdown, 2⅝″.

Barrel: 22″, crowned at muzzle. Highly polished, with long-lasting blue finish to match receiver. AC-KRO-GRUV 8-groove rifling. Special-analysis chrome-moly gun steel.

Sights: Gold-bead front sight on ramp. Folding-leaf adjustable rear sight.

Weight: About 6½ lbs. (depending upon density of wood and caliber). Overall length, 42″.

MODEL 800V/T: For the long-range varmint or target shooter. Heavy, straight-tapered 24-inch barrel, dovetail receiver scope mounts. Marksman-style stock, low-vibration barrel and crisp let-off trigger, with solid bolting. Comes complete with scope mounting blocks installed. Weight 9½ lbs.; 44″ length. Offered in .243 cal., .22/250 cal. **$178.87**

MODEL 800SM: A rifle equipped with Model 84 Mossberg 4X scope without iron sights. Deluxe split-ring detachable mounts. Other specifications similar to Model 800 without scope. **$195.51**

MOSSBERG RIFLES

22 caliber rim fire rifles

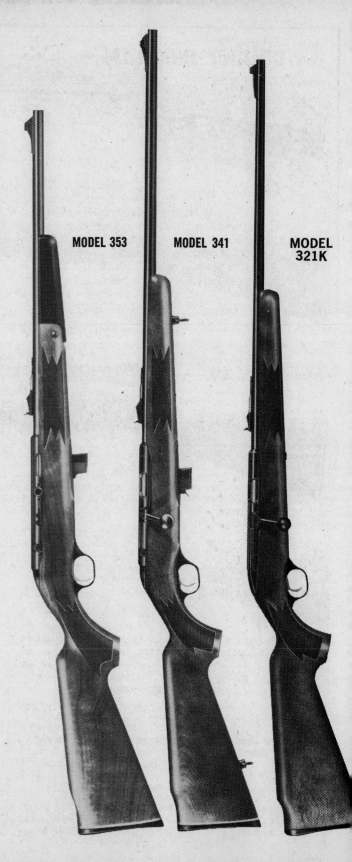

MODEL 353   **MODEL 341**   **MODEL 321K**

MODEL 321 .22 cal. single-shot. Price **$56.84**
Action—Hammerless single-shot bolt-action with drop-in loading platform and automatic safety. The safety goes on when the action is open. Won't fire until the action is locked and safety moved to "off" position. **Stock**—Walnut-finish stock with cheekpiece; checkered pistol grip and forend; black buttplate and sling swivels. **Barrel** —24″ barrel. Shoots all short, long, and long-rifle cartridges. **Sights** —Ramp front sight and adjustable rear sight. **Weight**—About 6½ lbs. Length overall, 43½″.

MODEL 353 .22 cal. "Auto" Carbine. Price **$73.55**
With exclusive two-position, extension forend of black Tenite for steady firing from the prone position, up to 7 shots in less than 2 seconds. **Action**—Shoots .22 cal. Long Rifle, regular or High Speed cartridges. Automatic self loading action from 7 shot clip. Receiver grooved for scope mounting.

Stock—Genuine American walnut with Monte Carlo. Checkered at forend and pistol grip. Sling swivels and web strap on left of stock. Butt plate with white liner. **Barrel** —18″ AC-KRO-GRUV® 8-groove rifled barrel. **Sights**— Open rear with "U" notch, adjustable for windage and elevation; ramp front with bead. **Weight**—About 5 lbs. Length overall 38″.

MODEL 341 .22 cal. Bolt-Action Sporter. Price **$64.58**
Action—Hammerless bolt rifle action with Mossberg's "Magic 3-Way" 7 shot clip magazine which adjusts instantly to load, Short, Long or Long Rifle cartridges. Positive safety at side of receiver. Receiver grooved for scope mounting, tapped and drilled for peep sights. (Mossberg No. S330 receiver peep sight.) **Stock**—Genuine American walnut with Monte Carlo and cheek piece. Custom checkering on pistol grip and forend. Sling swivels. Butt plate with white line spacer. **Barrel**— 24″ AC-KRO-GRUV® 8-groove rifled barrel. **Sights**—Open rear with "U" notch, adjustable for windage and elevation; ramp front with bead. **Weight**— About 6½ lbs. Length overall 43½″.

MOSSBERG RIFLES

22 caliber magnum

MODEL 640K

MODEL 640K .22 cal. Magnum. **Price $74.12** Especially designed for the powerful and accurate .22 WMRF Magnum cartridge. Our exclusive Mossberg AC-KRO-GRUV® rifling assures your long range shots. **Action**—Hammerless, bolt action, with extra-heavy receiver and bolt. (Caution: Do not use any other .22 RF cartridge.) Double shell extractors, grooved trigger and 5-shot detachable clip. Thumb operated safety on right hand side of receiver. Receiver grooved for scope mounting, tapped and drilled for Mossberg S330 peep sight. **Stock**—Genuine American walnut with Monte Carlo and cheek piece. Sling swivels. Custom checkered at pistol grip and forend. Butt plate and pistol grip cap with white line spacers. **Barrel**—24" special gun quality steel. **Sights**—Fully adjustable, folding leaf rear sight. Ramp front with bead. **Weight**—About 6 lbs. Length overall 44¾".

Magnum   22LR

APPROXIMATE MUZZLE VELOCITIES

Magnum — 2,000 ft./sec.
22LR — 1,335 ft./sec.

target rifles

MODEL 340B

MODEL 144

MODEL 340B .22 cal. Target Sporter. **Price $69.84 Action**—Hammerless bolt action rifle with Mossberg's "Magic 3-Way" 7 shot clip magazine that adjusts instantly to load Short, Long, or Long Rifle cartridges. Positive safety at side of receiver. Receiver grooved for scope mounting. **Stock**—Walnut finish with pistol grip. Monte Carlo and cheek piece. Sling swivels. **Barrel**—24" AC-KRO-GRUV® 8-groove rifled barrel. **Sights**—Furnished Mossberg S331 receiver peep sight has ¼-minute adjustments for windage and elevation. S320 Mossberg hooded ramp front sight. **Weight**—About 6 lbs. Length overall 43½".

MODEL 144 .22 cal. Super Target Rifle. **Price $100.28. Action**—Hammerless bolt action with 7 shot clip magazine; also loads as single shot. Features adjustable trigger pull, grooved trigger and thumb safety with red and green safety buttons inlaid in stock. Receiver grooved for scope mounting. Furnished with Mossberg S331 receiver peep sight. **Stock**—Genuine American walnut, target type with beavertail forend, cheek piece, high thick comb, adjustable hand stop, pistol grip and special 1¼" target sling swivels. Butt plate, with white liner. **Barrel**—26" heavy target barrel, 15/16" round. Chambered for .22 Long Rifle, regular or High Speed cartridges. **Sights**—Lyman 17A hooded front sight with 7 interchangeable inserts. **Weight**—About 8 lbs. Length overall 43".

S330. Receiver Peep Sight has ¼-minute click adjustments. No backlash. Bracket removable for scope mounting. On Models 320B, 340B and 346B. Same features on S331 Sight for Model 144.

S320. Hooded Ramp Front Sight offers instant choice of post or aperture, both contained within the sight. On Models 320B, 340B and 346B. Lyman Hooded Sight 17A with 7 interchangeable inserts on Model 144

PEDERSON RIFLES

**MODEL 3000
Grade I
$880.00**

3000 Series Grade I
Receiver and bolt are heat-treated chrome-moly steel with four in-line bolt locking lugs. The stock is American black walnut with high-cheekpiece roll over and Monte Carlo drop with 22-line borderless wraparound hand-checkering. Equipped with Pachmayr recoil pad or optional hinged metal buttplate, rosewood grip cap and forend tip, and detachable sling swivels. Available in four calibers: .30-06, .270 Win. 7mm Rem. Mag., .338 Win. Mag. $880.00

Grade II
Same action as all the Pederson Model 3000 Series. Has 20-line borderless wraparound hand-checkered fancy American black-walnut stock. Pachmayr recoil pad, detachable sling swivels, damascened bolt, and knurled bolt handle. Available in the same calibers as Grade I. $715.00

**MODEL 3500
$284.50**

MODEL 3500
Rich deep blue and a damascened bolt make this a beautiful functioning rifle. The stock is American black walnut and features a 20-line pattern of hand-checkering. Available in both high-comb and low-comb styles, the Monte Carlo stock sports a roll over cheekpiece, rosewood grip cap and forend accents. The Pachmayr recoil pad and detachable sling swivels complete this elegantly finished rifle. All Model 3500/3500A rifles are available in these calibers: .270 Win., .30/06 Springfield and 7mm Rem. Mag. $284.50

MODEL 3500A
This rifle offers all the superb high-quality finish of the 3500, but with a select grade of American black walnut in the stock. $352.00

**MODEL 4700
$200.00**

MODEL 4700
The safety of the 4700 uses a solid bar to prevent the hammer from striking the firing pin, the hammer-block safety completely prevents accidental firing, making unloading easier and safer.

The 4700's polished and blued chrome-moly receiver is drilled and tapped for scope mounting, and houses a richly damascened bolt. Side ejection makes low-scope mounting possible. In addition, a Williams Guide rear sight and hooded-ramp front sight are included.

Stocked in select American black walnut, the rifle features a unique "hand-filling" beavertail forearm and cheekpiece butt stock contoured for scope sighting. Detachable sling swivels are also provided. The Model 4700 action is available in .30/30 Win. and .35 Rem. $200.00

REMINGTON BOLT ACTION RIFLES

MODEL 788 CLIP REPEATER

Calibers: 222 Remington, 233 Rem. 22-250
Remington, 6mm Rem., 243 Win., 308 Win.
$124.95

MODEL 788 LEFT HAND
Calibers: 6mm Rem. & 308 Win.
$129.95

The Model 788 bolt action rifle is also available in a left hand version chambered for 6mm Rem. and 308 Win. calibers only. Has all the features of the regular Model 788 but left hand bolt handle is tailored for the left handed shooter. The artillery type bolt has nine extra heavy locking lugs that engage grooves in the solid steel receiver. Rear bolt cover provides extra protection and streamlining. The clip magazine slips in or out of the receiver with one hand. Tapered barrel is of ordnance steel and is crowned at muzzle. Elevated barrel provides a solid, positive scope back-up. Round receiver permits accurate wood-to-metal bedding. Receiver is also drilled and tapped for 'scope mounts and receiver sight at left rear. Blade front sight on serrated ramp is detachable and U notch rear sight is lock-screw adjustable for windage and elevation. Rear sight barrel holes are correct for target scope block. Serrated safety is positioned at rear of receiver. The American walnut Monte Carlo type stock is designed for use with 'scope or open sights. Stock dimensions are: 13⅝" length of pull; 2⅝" drop at heel; 1⅞" drop at comb (from open sight line).

Calibers	Clip Mag. Cap.	Barrel Length	Overall Length	Av. Wt. Lbs.
Model 788				
222 Remington	4	24"	43⅝"	7½
223 Remington	4	24"	43⅝"	7½
22-250 Remington	3	24"	43⅝"	7½
6mm Rem.	3	22"	42"	7¼
243 Win.	3	22"	42"	7¼
308 Win.	3	22"	42"	7¼

MODEL 700 BDL
HEAVY BARREL "VARMINT SPECIAL"

Calibers: 222 Rem., 223 Rem., 22-250 Rem.,
25-06 Rem., 6mm Rem. & 243 Winchester
$234.95

The Model 700 BDL heavy barrel "Varmint Special" version comes equipped with a 24" heavy target-type barrel with target-rifle (Remington 40XB) scope bases. The "Varmint Special" is available in a wide range of popular high velocity, varmint calibers which include the 222 Rem., 223 Rem., 22-250 Rem., 25-06 Rem., 6mm Rem. and 243 Winchester calibers. The "Varmint Special" was designed for minimum-target, maximum-range precision shooting—suitable for chucks, 'cats, foxes and other pests. Features include hinged floor plate; quick release swivels and strap; crisp trigger pull; American walnut stock, Monte Carlo style with cheek piece, custom fleur-de-lis checkering on grip and all three sides of fore end, grip cap with white line spacer and butt plate; DuPont developed RK-W wood finish. Stock dimensions are as follows: 13⅜" length of pull; 2-5/16" drop at heel;

1-11/16" drop at comb (from open sight line). The safety is a thumb-lever type and is serrated. The bolt knob is oval shaped, serrated top and bottom. As in the Model 700 BDL the cartridge head is completely encased by the bolt face and is supported by three rings of steel when the action is closed.

SPECIFICATIONS

Calibers	Clip Mag. Cap.	Barrel Length	Overall Length	Av. Wt. Lbs.
22-250 Rem.	5	24"	43½"	9
222 Rem.	6	24"	43½"	9
223 Rem.	6	24"	43½"	9
25-06 Rem.	5	24"	44½"	9
6 mm Rem.	5	24"	43½"	9
243 Win.	5	24"	43½"	9

REMINGTON AUTOMATIC RIFLES

The Model 742 "Woodsmaster" is a gas-operated automatic rifle available in .30-06, .280 Rem., .308 Win., .243 Win., and 6mm Rem. calibers. The "Woodsmaster" automatic comes in both rifle and carbine models with fleur-de-lis checkering and all-purpose stock (for use with either scope or open sights). The rifle model is also available with basket-weave checkering, Monte-Carlo stock with cheekpiece, RK-W wood finish, and step receiver, in .30-06 and .308 Winchester calibers only. The rifle models are equipped with 22-inch barrels, come in all five calibers, and measure 42-inches overall in length. The carbine

model comes with an 18½-inch barrel, and is made in .30-06 and .308 Winchester calibers only. The overall length for the carbine model—38½ inches. The solid-steel receiver houses a rotary multiple-lug breech bolt, which locks bolt and barrel together when action is closed, ensuring strength and constant headspace. The bolt face is recessed which completely encases the cartridge. The receiver is drilled and tapped for scope mounts. Comes with one 4-shot detachable clip magazine (extra 4-shot clip costs $6.00).

MODEL 742 "WOODSMASTER"
Calibers: 30-06, .280 Rem., .308 Win., 243 Win., & 6mm Rem.
$214.95

MODEL 742 CARBINE
Calibers: 30-06 & .308 Winchester
$214.95

MODEL 742 BDL CUSTOM DELUXE RIFLE
Calibers: 30-06 & .308 Winchester
$234.95

Special basket weave checkering, Monte Carlo stock with full cheekpiece. Left hand version built with reversed cheekpiece and safety at no extra cost.

MODEL 742F

The Model 742 F "Premier" grade, with gold inlay, priced at $2,400.00, has figured American-walnut stock, cheekpiece, and is hand-checkered. Available with Monte Carlo or offset stock. The receiver and barrel are engraved. (Also available in D "Peerless" grade—not illus., priced at $800.00.) F "Premier" Grade with Gold Inlay $1,550.00.

MODEL 742 SPECIFICATIONS

CALIBERS: Regular Model: 6mm Rem., 243 Win., .280 Rem., 30/06, .308 Win. Carbine: 30/06 and .308 Win. Deluxe: 30/06, .308 Win.

CAPACITY: 4 in clip magazine plus one in chamber.

BARREL LENGTH: 22"—Carbine 18½".

OVER-ALL LENGTH: 42"—Carbine 38½".

STANDARD STOCK DIMENSIONS: Stock and fore-end: rich American

Walnut. 13¼" length of pull, 2¼" drop at heel, 1¾" drop at comb.

Deluxe Model: 13⁵⁄₁₆" length of pull, 2½" drop at heel, 1⅝" drop at comb, ¹³⁄₁₆" drop at Monte Carlo.

RECEIVER: Drilled and tapped for 'scope mounts. Removable clip magazine.

SIGHTS: Flat faced gold bead with ramp front sight. Step adjustable rear sight with windage adjustment screw.

AVERAGE WEIGHT: 7½ lbs.—Carbine 6¾ lbs.

REMINGTON BOLT ACTION RIFLES

MODELS 580, 581 & 582 IN .22 L. R. CALIBER

The 580 series .22 Long Rifle rimfire bolt-action rifles feature the look, feel and balance of big-game center-fire rifles. They are available in three styles—a single shot; a clip repeater; and a tubular-magazine repeater. The single shot also comes in a smoothbore model. The bolt is an artillery type with rear lock-up and has six extra-heavy, rotary locking lugs at the back that engage grooves in the solid-steel receiver. A bolt cover at rear keeps dirt and bad weather outside. Two extractors are standard on this new series of .22 rifles. Hunting-type trigger is wide and the trigger guard is roomy enough to accommodate a gloved finger. The stock is Monte Carlo style with pistol grip suitable for use with or without a scope. Sights consist of a bead front sight and U-notch lock-screw adjustable rear. Precise bedding into the stock is achieved by a new round receiver. The receiver is also grooved for tip-off scope mounts. There are no slots or notches cut into the receiver and the bolt handle isn't used as lock-up lugs. The barrel is of ordnance steel, crowned at the muzzle, polished and blued. The non-slip thumb safety is located at the right rear of the receiver. With positive safety.

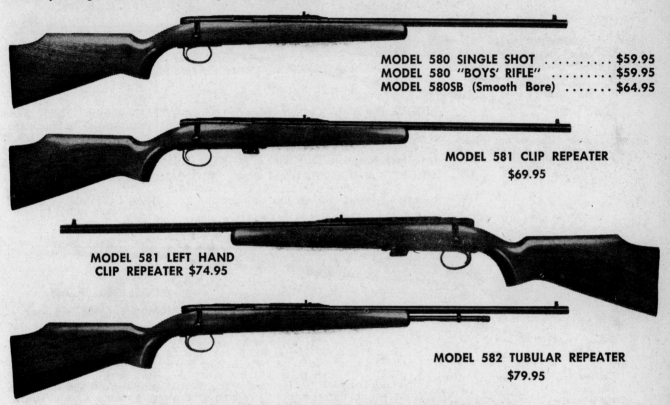

MODEL 580 SINGLE SHOT $59.95
MODEL 580 "BOYS' RIFLE" $59.95
MODEL 580SB (Smooth Bore) $64.95

MODEL 581 CLIP REPEATER
$69.95

MODEL 581 LEFT HAND CLIP REPEATER $74.95

MODEL 582 TUBULAR REPEATER
$79.95

MODEL 580 & 580 "BOYS' RIFLE"   MODEL 581 & MODEL 582

	MODEL 580 & 580 "BOYS' RIFLE"	MODEL 581 & MODEL 582
Action	Bolt Action Single Shot.	Bolt Action Repeater.
Caliber	22 short, long, long rifle rim fire.	22 short, long, long rifle rim fire.
Capacity	Single Shot.	581 5-shot, 582 20 short, 15 long or 14 long rifle.
Barrel	24 inch ordnance steel, precision rifled, crowned at muzzle.	24 inch ordnance steel, precision rifled, crowned at muzzle.
Stock	Monte Carlo type, full size, black butt plate. Single screw take-down.	Monte Carlo type, full size, black butt plate. Single screw take-down.
Sights	Front: bead, dovetail adjustable. Rear: U Notch type, lock-screw adjustable.	Front: bead, dovetail adjustable. Rear: U Notch type, lock-screw adjustable.
Bolt	Artillery style, lock-up at rear. 6 locking lugs, double extractors.	Artillery style, lock-up at rear. 6 locking lugs, double extractors.
Receiver	Round, ordnance steel, grooved for scope mounts.	Round, ordnance steel, grooved for scope mounts.
Safety	Positive, serrated thumb type, Forward for fire, Rearward for safe.	Positive, serrated thumb type, Forward for fire, Rearward for safe.
Over-All Length	42⅜"; Boys Rifle—41⅜".	42⅜".
Weight	5 lbs.—Average wt. per case of ten—56 lbs.	5¼ lbs.—Average wt. per case of 10—58 lbs.

REMINGTON BOLT ACTION RIFLES

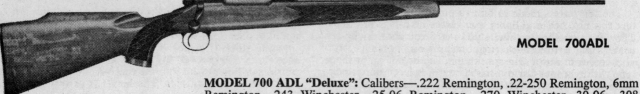

MODEL 700ADL

MODEL 700 ADL "Deluxe": Calibers—.222 Remington, .22-250 Remington, 6mm Remington, .243 Winchester, .25-06 Remington, .270 Winchester, 30-06, .308 Winchester **$189.95**
MODEL 700 ADL "Deluxe" MAGNUM: Caliber—7mm Rem. Mag. . . . **$204.95**

MODEL 700BDL

Note: Model 700 BDL Custom Deluxe also available in Left-Hand model.

MODEL 700 BDL "Custom Deluxe": Calibers—.222 Remington, .22-250 Remington, 6mm Remington, .243 Winchester, .25-06 Remington, .270 Winchester, 30-06, .308 Winchester **$219.95**
17 Remington caliber **$234.95**
Left-Hand Model in .270 Win. & 30-06 . . . . **$224.95**
MODEL 700 BDL "Custom Deluxe" MAGNUM: Calibers—7mm Remington Mag., .264 Winchester Mag., .300 Winchester Mag. **$234.95**
Left-Hand Model in 7mm Rem. Magnum **$239.95**

MODEL 700 SAFARI

375 H&H Magnum, 458 Win. Mag.

$410.00

Calibers	Lands or Grooves	Twist Right Hand
375 H&H Mag.	8	1 in 12"
458 Win. Mag.	8	1 in 14"

The Remington Model 700 is available in two safari grades—the .375 H&H Magnum and .458 Winchester Magnum (with the big 500-grain bullet) built to stop and drop dangerous game such as rhino, elephant and buffalo. It has all the features of the 700BDL plus a recoil pad and hand-checkering. Barrel length, 24". Cartridge capacity, 4 rounds. Overall length, 44½" (includes pad). Weight, 9 lbs.

MODEL 700 C • "Custom"

CALIBERS: Same as Model 700 BDL except 17 Remington, .375 H&H Mag. and .458 Win. Mag. **CAPACITY:** Same as Model 700 BDL. **BARREL:** Choice of 20", 22", or 24" length in Remington high-proof ordnance steel. With or without sights. Not available with stainless-steel barrel. **BOLT:** Jeweled with shrouded firing pin. **RECEIVER:** Drilled and tapped for scope mounts. Fixed magazine with or without hinged floor plate. **STOCK:** Hand-checkered selected American walnut with quick detachable sling swivels installed. Recoil pad standard equipment on Magnum rifles. Installed at extra charge on others.

Model 700 C "Custom"	$425.00
Recoil Pad — extra	15.00
Model 700 C "Custom" Magnum	440.00
Oil finish — extra	13.75

REMINGTON PUMP ACTION RIFLES

The Model 760 "Gamemaster" pump action rifle is available in both rifle and carbine models. The regular rifle model 760 is made in 6mm Rem., 243 Win., 270 Win., 30-06 and 308 Win. calibers and come with a 22-inch barrel. The rifle model is also available in a custom deluxe version with basket weave checkering, black fore-end tip and pistol grip cap with white line spacer, full cheek-piece (right or left), with Monte-Carlo, RK-W wood finish, and step receiver, in 30-06, .270 Win. and .308 Win. calibers only.

The carbine model comes with an 18½-inch barrel, in 30-06, and .308 Win. calibers only. Overall length for the carbine model—38½ inches.

The trigger must be released and squeezed for each shot—can't fire unless action is completely closed. With positive cross-bolt safety, free floating barrel, double action slide handle bars, rotary multiple-lug breech bolt, recessed bolt face and detachable 4-shot clip magazine.

MODEL 760 "GAMEMASTER" RIFLE
Calibers: 6mm Rem., 243 Win., 270 Win., 30-06 & 308 Win.
$184.95

MODEL 760 CARBINE
Calibers: 30-06 & .308 Win.
$184.95

MODEL 760 BDL • CUSTOM DELUXE
Calibers: 30-06, .308 Win. & .270 Win.
$204.95

This deluxe model has as additional features: Beautiful basket weave checkering, black fore-end tip with tasteful white line spacer, full cheek-piece (right or left) with Monte Carlo stock.

MODEL 760F

The Model 760F "Premier" grade, priced at $2,400.00, has engraved game scenes and fine scroll with gold inlay, hand-checkered figured American walnut stock and forend and may be had in any stock dimensions. (Also available in D "Peerless" grade—not illus., priced at $880.00.) "Premier" Grade without gold inlay $1,500.00.

MODEL 760 SPECIFICATIONS

CALIBERS: Regular Model: 6mm Rem., 243 Win., 270 Win., 30/06, 308 Win. Carbine: 30/06, 308 Win. Deluxe: 30/06, 270 Win., 308 Win.

CAPACITY: 4 in clip magazine plus one in chamber

BARREL LENGTH: 22"—760 Carbine 18½".

OVER-ALL LENGTH: 42"—760 Carbine 38½".

STANDARD STOCK DIMENSIONS: Stock and fore-end; American Walnut. 13¼" length of pull, 2¼" drop at heel, 1¾" drop at comb.
Deluxe Model: 13⁵⁄₁₆" length of pull, 2½" drop at heel, 1⅝" drop at comb, 1¹³⁄₁₆" drop at Monte Carlo.

RECEIVER: Drilled and tapped for 'scope mounts. Removable clip magazine.

SIGHTS: Flat faced gold bead with ramp front sight. Step adjustable rear sight with windage adjustment screw.

AVERAGE WEIGHT: 7½ lbs.—760 Carbine 6¾ lbs.

REMINGTON PUMP ACTION RIFLES

MODEL 572 A FIELDMASTER • .22 Short, Long, Long Rifle

Exclusive cartridge-feeding design prevents jamming, permits easy single loading. By simply removing the inner magazine tube, parent or instructor can convert the Model 572 into a single-shot rifle for the beginning shooter; when shooter is experienced, magazine tube can be put back again to make the Model 572 a repeater. $94.95
Model 572 A $84.95

MODEL 572 BDL Deluxe • .22 Short, Long, Long Rifle
Features of this rifle with big-game feel and appearance are: Du Pont beautiful but tough RK-W finish, center-fire-rifle-type rear sight fully adjustable for both vertical and horizontal sight alignment, big-game style ramp front sight, beautiful Remington impressed checkering on both stock and forend.
Model 572 BDL DELUXE $104.95
Model 572 SB Smooth Bore (for use with pellet-loaded shot cartridges) $104.95
Sling Strap & Swivels installed ....$ 8.75

SPECIFICATIONS • MODELS 572A & 572 BDL DELUXE

ACTION:	Pump repeater.	**SIGHTS:**	A—Adjustable rear, bead front. BDL—Fully adjustable rear, ramp front. Screw removable.
CALIBER:	22 Short, Long and Long Rifle rim fire.	**SAFETY:**	Positive cross bolt.
CAPACITY:	Tubular magazine holds 20 Short, 17 Long, 14 Long Rifle cartridges.	**RECEIVER:**	Grooved for "tip-off" scope mounts.
		OVER-ALL LENGTH:	42".
STOCK AND FORE-END:	A—American Walnut. BDL—American Walnut with DuPont RK-W tough lustrous finish and fine line custom checkering.	**BARREL LENGTH:**	24".
		AVERAGE WEIGHT:	5½ lbs.

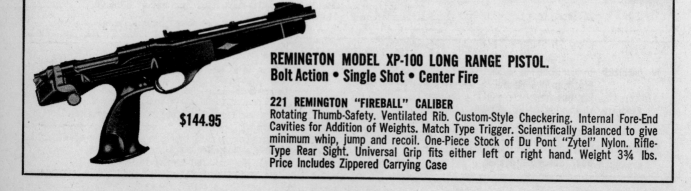

$144.95

REMINGTON MODEL XP-100 LONG RANGE PISTOL.
Bolt Action • Single Shot • Center Fire

221 REMINGTON "FIREBALL" CALIBER
Rotating Thumb-Safety. Ventilated Rib. Custom-Style Checkering. Internal Fore-End Cavities for Addition of Weights. Match Type Trigger. Scientifically Balanced to give minimum whip, jump and recoil. One-Piece Stock of Du Pont "Zytel" Nylon. Rifle-Type Rear Sight. Universal Grip fits either left or right hand. Weight 3¾ lbs. Price Includes Zippered Carrying Case

REMINGTON AUTOMATIC .22 RIFLES

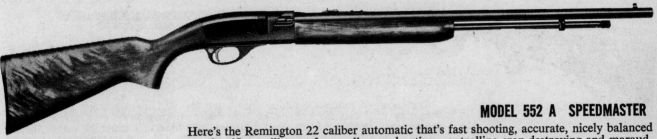

MODEL 552 A SPEEDMASTER

Here's the Remington 22 caliber automatic that's fast shooting, accurate, nicely balanced . . . the rifle you'll want for small game hunting, controlling crop-destroying and marauding pests, or for just plain fun-shooting. The Model 552 has every feature the shooter wants, such as: twenty shots as fast as you can squeeze the trigger, rich walnut stock, cross bolt safety, receiver grooved for "tip-off" 'scope mounts. $89.95

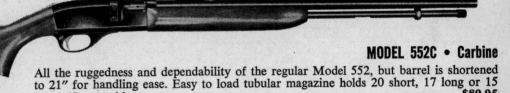

MODEL 552 BDL DeLuxe

A deluxe model with all the tried and proven dependable mechanical features on the inside, plus special design and appearance extras on the outside. The 552 BDL includes new tasteful Remington custom impressed checkering on both stock and fore-end, the new DuPont RK-W tough lifetime finish that brings out the lustrous beauty of the walnut while protecting it, and rugged big-game type fully adjustable rear sight with ramp front sight. $99.95
Remington 552 GS Gallery Special (Shorts only) $101.95

MODEL 552C • Carbine

All the ruggedness and dependability of the regular Model 552, but barrel is shortened to 21″ for handling ease. Easy to load tubular magazine holds 20 short, 17 long or 15 long rifle cartridges. $89.95

SPECIFICATIONS FOR MODELS 552A, 552BDL, 552C CARBINE

ACTION:	Automatic. Tubular Magazine.		**SAFETY:**	Positive cross bolt.
CALIBER:	22 Short, Long and Long Rifle rim fire.		**RECEIVER:**	Grooved for "tip-off" scope mounts.
CAPACITY:	Holds 20 Short, 17 Long, 15 Long Rifle cartridges.		**OVER-ALL LENGTH:**	42″—Carbine 40″. Carbine not available in BDL grade.
STOCK:	American Walnut. DuPont RK-W tough lustrous finish and fine-line custom checkering on BDL Model.		**BARREL LENGTH:**	23″—Carbine 21″.
SIGHTS:	552 A and C—Adjustable rear, bead front. 552 BDL—Fully adjustable rear, ramp front. Screw removable.		**AVERAGE WEIGHT:**	5¾ lbs.

REMINGTON AUTOMATIC .22 RIFLES

(IN MOHAWK BROWN)

NYLON 66 • AUTOLOADING RIFLE
$74.95

The Nylon 66 Automatic rifle is chambered for .22 Long Rifle cartridges. Tubular magazine thru butt stock holds 14 long rifle cartridges. Remington's Nylon 66 receiver parts, stock and barrel are interlocked with steel and structural nylon. There's no need for lubrication because friction-free parts glide on greaseless bearings of nylon. Barrel made of Remington proof steel. Stock is made of DuPont "Zetel" nylon, a new gunstock material. Resembles wood, weighs less than wood, outwears, outlasts wood. Stock features fine-line non-slip checkering, white diamond inlays and white line spacers at grip cap, butt plate and fore-end tip. Receiver is grooved for "tip-off" scope mounts. The Nylon 66 is also available in a "Gallery Special" (22 Shorts only) as Model 66-GS priced at $84.95

(IN APACHE BLACK)

NYLON 66 • AUTOMATIC RIFLE
$79.95

The Nylon 66 is also made in an Apache Black deluxe model. The stock is jet black nylon and both the barrel and the receiver cover are chrome plated.

	NYLON 66 "MOHAWK BROWN"	NYLON 66 "APACHE BLACK"
ACTION	Automatic.	Automatic.
CALIBER	22 Long Rifle Rim Fire.	22 Long Rifle Rim Fire.
CAPACITY	Tubular magazine thru butt stock. Holds 14 long rifle cartridges.	Tubular magazine thru butt stock. Holds 14 long rifle cartridges.
STOCK	DuPont "ZYTEL" nylon, checkered grip & fore-end with white diamond inlays, white line spacers on butt plate, grip cap & fore-end. Black fore-end tip.	DuPont "ZYTEL" nylon, checkered grip & fore-end with white diamond inlays, white line spacers on butt plate, grip & fore-end.
SIGHTS	Rear sight adjustable for windage and range, blade front, common sight line for iron sights and 'scope.	Rear sight adjustable for windage and range, blade front, common sight line for iron sights and 'scope.
SAFETY	Top-of-grip, Positive.	Top-of-grip, Positive.
RECEIVER	Grooved for "tip-off" 'scope mounts. Double extractors.	Grooved for "tip-off" 'scope mounts. Double extractors. Chrome Plated Receiver and Barrel.
OVER-ALL LENGTH	38½".	38½".
WEIGHT	4 lbs.	4 lbs.

MODEL 541-S "CUSTOM" SPORTER • Clip Repeater

Remington Model 541-S "Custom" Sporter $159.95
Extra 5 Shot Clip Magazine 3.25
Extra 10 Shot Clip Magazine 4.00
Sling Strap and Quick Release Swivels Installed 10.50

A customized .22 rim fire rifle. Combines the match rifle accuracy of the Model 540-X with the features of a custom rifle. American walnut Monte Carlo stock with fine-line cut checkering in an attractive, raised diamond pattern, and protected by DuPont's rugged RK-W finish. Receiver and bowed trigger guard handsomely scroll engraved. Matching rosewood-colored fore-end tip, pistol grip cap and checkered butt plate

fitted with white line spacers.
Hand polished exterior metal surfaces richly blued to a tasteful, medium high lustre. Receiver is drilled and tapped for regular scope mounts or receiver sights as well as grooved for "tip-off" type mounts. Barrel also drilled and tapped for open sights. Supplied with a 5 shot clip magazine. 5 and 10 shot extra magazines are available.

REMINGTON TARGET RIFLES

MODEL 540-XR
Rim Fire Position Rifle

An extremely accurate 22 caliber single shot match rifle. Extra fast lock time contributes to this fine accuracy. Specially designed stock has deep fore-end and 5 way adjustable butt plate for added comfort and better scores in all positions.

Pistol grip designed to eliminate wrist-twisting and assures straight-back trigger pull. Adjustable match trigger. Match style sling strap with adjustable front swivel block and set sight available as accessories at extra charge. $134.95

MODEL 540-XRJR • Junior Rim Fire Position Rifle

A match rifle with all the features of the Model 540-XR but fitted with 1¾" shorter stock to fit the junior shooter. $134.95

MODEL 540-XR, 540-XRJR
Redfield Match Sight Set (Optional Accessory at Extra Charge). $34.50
Front Swivel Block and Sling Strap Assembly (Optional Accessory at Extra Charge). .... $ 8.00

MODEL 40-XR
"RANGEMASTER"
Rim Fire Position Rifle

Stock designed with deep fore-end for more comfortable shooting in all positions. Butt plate vertically adjustable. Exclusive loading platform provides straight line feeding with no shaved bullets. Crisp, wide, adjustable match trigger. Meets all International Shooting Union standard rifle specifications. $250.00

MODEL 40-XC National Match Course Rifle

MODEL 40-XR
Redfield Match Sight Set (Optional Accessory at Extra Charge). ... $55.25

Chambered for the 7.62mm NATO cartridge solely, this match rifle was designed to meet the needs of competitive shooters firing the national match courses. Position style stock, five shot repeater with top loading magazine, anti-bind bolt and receiver and in the bright stainless steel barrel. Meets all International Shooting Union Army Rifle specifications. $415.00

	MODEL 540-XR, 540-XRJR RIM FIRE POSITION RIFLE	MODEL 40-XR RIM FIRE POSITION RIFLE
ACTION	Bolt action single shot.	Bolt action single shot.
CALIBER	22 Long Rifle rim fire.	22 Long Rifle rim fire.
CAPACITY	Single loading.	Single loading.
SIGHTS	Redfield #75 rear sight with ¼ minute clicks. #63 Globe front sight with 7 inserts. Optional accessory at extra charge.	Redfield Olympic front & rear sights with 10 inserts. Optional accessory at extra charge.
SAFETY	Positive thumb safety.	Positive thumb safety.
LENGTH OF PULL	540-XR—Adjustable from 12¾" to 16". 540-XRJR—Adjustable from 11" to 14¼".	13½".
RECEIVER	Drilled and tapped for receiver sight.	Drilled and tapped for receiver sight or target 'scope blocks.
BARREL	26" medium weight target barrel countersunk at muzzle. Drilled and tapped for target 'scope blocks. Fitted with front sight base.	24" heavy barrel.
BOLT	Artillery style with lock-up at rear. 6 locking lugs, double extractors.	Heavy, oversized locking lugs and double extractors.
TRIGGER	Adjustable from 1 to 5 lbs.	Adjustable from 2 to 4 lbs.
STOCK	Position style with Monte Carlo, cheekpiece and thumb groove. 5-way adjustable butt plate and full length guide rail.	Position style with front swivel block on fore-end guide rail.
OVER-ALL LENGTH	540-XR—Adjustable from 43½" to 46¾". 540-XRJR—Adjustable from 41¾" to 45".	43".
AVERAGE WEIGHT	8 lbs. 13 oz. without sights. Add 9 oz. for sights.	10 lbs. Add 12 oz. for sights. Case wt. 1 rifle—14 lbs.

REMINGTON TARGET RIFLES

MODEL 40-XB "RANGEMASTER"
Center Fire

MODEL 40-XB "RANGEMASTER" • Center Fire Rifle

The Remington 40-XB Center Fire rifle continues to be the favorite of many top shooters throughout the world because of its sensational accuracy. Barrels are unblued stainless steel. Choice of either standard weight or heavy barrel. Comb grooved for easy bolt removal. Mershon White Line non-slip rubber butt plate supplied. See below for complete specifications and prices.

MODEL 40XB-BR • Bench Rest Center Fire Rifle

Built with all the features of the extremely accurate Model 40-XB-CF but modified to give the competitive bench rest shooter a standardized rifle that provides the inherent accuracy advantages of a short, heavy, extremely stiff barrel. Wider, squared off fore-end gives a more stable rest on sandbags or other supports and meets weight limitations for the sporter and light-varmint classes of National Bench Rest Shooters Association competition.

	MODEL 40-XB CENTER FIRE	MODEL 40XB-BR CENTER FIRE
ACTION	Bolt—Single shot in either standard or heavy barrel versions. Repeater in heavy barrel only. Receiver bedded to stock. Barrel is free floating.	Bolt, single shot only.
CALIBERS	See listing below.	222 Rem., 222 Rem. Mag., 223 Rem., 6mm x 47, 7.62 NATO (308 Win.)
SIGHTS	No sights supplied. Target 'scope blocks installed.	Supplied with target 'scope blocks.
SAFETY	Positive thumb operated.	Positive thumb operated.
RECEIVER	Drilled and tapped for 'scope block and receiver sights.	Drilled and tapped for target 'scope blocks.
BARREL	Drilled and tapped for scope block and front target iron sight. Muzzle diameter S2—approx. ¾", H2—approx. ⅞". Length: 27¼". Unblued stainless steel only.	Unblued stainless steel only. 20" barrel for Light Varmint Class. 26" barrel for Heavy Varmint Class.
TRIGGER	Adjustable from 2 to 4 lbs. pull. Special 2 oz. trigger available at extra cost. Single shot models only.	Adjustable from 1½ to 3½ lbs. Special 2 oz. trigger available at extra cost.
STOCK	American Walnut. Adjustable front swivel block on rail. Rubber non-slip butt plate.	Selected American Walnut. Length of pull—12".
OVER-ALL LENGTH	Approx. 47".	38" with 20" barrel. 44" with 26" barrel.
AVERAGE WEIGHT	S2—9¼ lbs. H2—11¼ lbs.	Light Varmint Class (20" barrel) 9¼ lbs. Heavy Varmint Class (26" barrel) 12 lbs.

MODEL 40-XB CENTER FIRE	NUMBERS	PRICES
40XB-CF-S2 Stainless steel, standard weight barrel.	Special	} $325.00
40XB-CF-H2 Stainless steel, heavy barrel.	Special	

CALIBERS: 222 Rem., 222 Rem. Mag., 22-250 Rem., 223 Rem., 6mm Rem., 6mm x 47, 6mm International, 243 Win., 25-06 Rem., 7mm Rem. Mag., 30-06, 7.62 NATO (308 Win.), 30-338, 300 Win. Mag.

MODEL 40-XB CENTER FIRE	NUMBERS	PRICES
Extra for repeating models. Heavy barrel version only.	Special	$25.00
CALIBERS: 222 Rem., 222 Rem. Mag., 22-250 Rem., 223 Rem., 6mm Rem., 6 mm x 47, 6mm International, 243 Win., 7.62 NATO (308 Win.) only.		
Extra for two ounce trigger. Single shot version only.	Special	$45.00

MODEL 40XB-BR CENTER FIRE	NUMBERS	PRICES
40XB-BR Heavy barrel without sights.	Special	$345.00
Extra for two-ounce trigger.	Special	$45.00

RUGER No. 1 SINGLE-SHOT RIFLES

GENERAL DESCRIPTION & SPECIFICATIONS

RUGER NUMBER ONE STANDARD RIFLE

General Description

The RUGER No. 1 SINGLE-SHOT action belongs in the under-lever, falling-block category and follows in many characteristics the Farquharson design. In all mechanical details, however, the RUGER No. 1 action is completely new and is in no sense a replica of any older action. The action has been engineered to use the most powerful of the modern magnum cartridges with safety and reliability.

Receiver Design.

The heart of the design is the massive receiver which forms a rigid connection between the barrel and butt stock. The butt stock is mortised into the receiver in such a way as to reinforce the grip section against splitting or cracking. A longitudinal bolt which passes through the butt stock binds the butt stock and receiver together into a solid, rigid structure. Projecting forward from the main part of the receiver and lying directly below the barrel is a heavy steel extension formed integrally with the receiver to facilitate forearm attachment. Because of this forearm hanger, it is possible to arrange the forearm to be completely clear of the barrel or to have any desired pressure on the barrel. The side walls of the receiver are .218″ thick; these side walls are joined behind the breech block by a massive solid section. It is in this area that the RUGER No. 1 receiver represents the major improvement over the Farquharson type. In these older actions, there is only a thin web of steel effectively joining the side walls behind the breech block.

Firing Pin Hammer Design.

The advantages of the No. 1 hammer-firing pin design are:

1. The mainspring located in the forearm, is in an area where ample space is available for a large, lightly stressed spring.
2. Mounting of the hammer on the lever pivot simplifies the mechanism.
3. Hammer notch located on the periphery of the hammer greatly reduces the pressure on the sear.
4. The swinging transfer block, located in the upper interior of the breech block, functions to virtually lock the firing pin in its forward position against gas pressure during firing.
5. The ignition mechanism requires no openings in the rear of the breech block and, accordingly, no gas can issue in the direction of the shooter's face as it might in some older designs where some leakage can pass along the sides of the firing pin and exit at the rear surface of the breech block.
6. The hammer is retracted upon the first opening motion of the lever and can never actuate the firing pin unless the breech block is fully elevated into firing position.

Ejector Design.

The provisions for removal of fired cartridge cases from the chamber are particularly complete. The action readily handles any type of cartridge case i.e., rimmed, semi-rimmed, belted, rimless, etc. The extractor-ejector mechanism is designed to provide great leverage between the hand-lever and the point where the ejector actually engages the rim or groove of the cartridge case. It is so powerful, in fact, that if the case does not come out, the extractor will usually pull through the rim by use of a moderate force on the lever. With this mechanism, the shells will be thrown clear of the gun when the action is opened and the mechanism is in effect, a powerful spring-actuated automatic ejector. However, if the auto ejector feature is not desired, the ejector spring may be removed.

Trigger and Safety.

The trigger mechanism is adjustable for sear engagement, over travel, and weight of pull. The minimum pull at the present time is slightly under three pounds. The mechanism is free of take-up motion and trigger release is notably crisp. The crispness of this pull is attained by simply establishing leverages which greatly multiply, at the point of sear engagement, the movement of the trigger finger. The safety engages both the sear and the hammer directly to provide an absolute maximum of real security. The safety cannot be put on if the hammer is not cocked, but the action may be opened and closed whether the safety is on or off. The safety is of the sliding shotgun type.

Sights.

The mounting of telescopic sights has been carefully studied in connection with the RUGER No. 1 Single Shot. The rifle is sold complete with scope mounts of RUGER design, made particularly for this rifle. These mounts are split horizontally and fit 1″ diameter scope tubes. They are the tip-off type, made entirely of steel. RUGER No. 1 rifles are equipped with ¼ rib scope mount only unless open sights are also ordered. This ¼ rib functions primarily as a base for the RUGER scope mounts and may also be used for mounting open sights which are optional.

Two forearms are available: a semi beaver-tail modern type of forearm and a short slender design patterned after the typical designs of Alexander Henry.

When the short Henry type forearm is used, the front sling swivel is mounted on a barrel band and a sling in this event would be regarded as primarily a carrying sling. The front swivel is mounted in the forearm.

Both pistol grip and forearm are hand-checkered in an ample area to a borderless design. The finish completely reveals the character and grain of the carefully selected American walnut from which the stocks and forearms are made.

RUGER No. 1 SINGLE-SHOT RIFLES

These five illustrations show the variations which are currently offered in the Ruger No. 1 Single-Shot Rifle. Orders for variations or calibers other than those listed are not available from Ruger. The Ruger No. 1 rifles come fitted with selected American walnut stocks. Pistol grip and forearm are hand-checkered to a borderless design. Price for any listed model is $265.00.

RUGER Number One Light Sporter
Calibers: 243 Win., 30/06, 270 Win.
Barrel: 22 inches.
Sights: Open.
Weight: 7¼ pounds.
(Catalog Number 1A)

RUGER Number One Medium Sporter
Calibers: 7mm Rem. Mag., 300 Win. Mag.
Barrel: 26 inches.
Sights: Open.
Weight: 8 pounds.
Also available in caliber 45/70, but with 22 inch barrel. Weight: 7¼ lbs.
(Catalog Number 1S)

RUGER Number One Standard Rifle
Calibers: 22/250, 243 Win., 6mm Rem., 25/06, 270 Win., 30/06, 7mm Rem. Mag., 300 Win. Mag.
Barrel: 26 inches.
Sights: Ruger steel tip-off scope rings, 1″.
Weight: 8 pounds.
(Catalog Number 1B)

RUGER Number One Special Varminter
Caliber: 22/250, 25/06
Barrel: 24 inches.
Sights: Standard target scope blocks for target scope rings with external adjustments.
Weight: 9 pounds.
(Catalog Number 1V)

RUGER Number One Tropical Rifle
Calibers: 375 H & H Mag., 458 Win., Mag.
Barrel: 24 inches.
Sights: Open.
Weight: 8¼ pounds for 375, 9 pounds for 458.
(Catalog Number 1H)

General information on specifications:
Sights: Catalog Numbers 1A, 1S, and 1H have adjustable folding leaf rear sight mounted on quarter rib and ramp front sight base with caterpillar type gold bead sight. All quarter ribs are machined to accommodate Ruger steel tip-off rings. Scope rings are $15. additional for all models except 1B.

Woodwork: Carefully selected American Walnut. Pistol grip and forearm hand-checkered to a borderless design.
Price: Suggested retail price is $265 for any of the models listed above.
How to order: Place an order with your Ruger dealer by Catalog Number and caliber. (No variations from the above specifications are possible).

RUGER No. 3 CARBINE

The Same Strong, Rugged Action as the Ruger No. 1 Rifle, with an American Style Lever

A mechanism of power and precision. Receiver and all action parts are made of heat treated alloy steel.

No. 3 CARBINE SINGLE-SHOT
Calibers: .45/70 Gov't.
30/40 Krag & .22 Hornet
$165.00

SPECIFICATIONS

Caliber—45/70, 30/40 Krag, .22 Hornet. Single-shot.
Barrel—22 inches.
Weight—6 pounds.
Overall Length—38½ inches.
Rear Sight—Folding leaf adjustable.
Front Sight—Gold bead.
Safety—Sliding tang.
Stock and Forearm—Solid American Walnut.

RUGER MINI-14 .223 CARBINE

RUGER MINI-14
.223 (5.56mm)
$200.00

General:

MATERIALS—Heat treated Chrome-molybdenum and other alloy steels, as well as music wire coil springs, are used throughout the mechanism to ensure reliability under field operating conditions.

SAFETY—The safety blocks both the hammer and sear. The slide can be cycled when the safety is on. The safety is mounted in the front of the trigger guard so that it may be set to Fire position without removing finger from trigger guard.

FIRING PIN—The firing pin is retracted mechanically during the first part of the unlocking of the bolt. The rifle can only be fired when the bolt is safely locked.

STOCK—One-piece American hardwood reinforced with steel liner at stressed areas. Handguard and forearm separated by air space from barrel to promote cooling under rapid-fire conditions.

FIELD STRIPPING—The Carbine can be field stripped to its eight (8) basic subassemblies in a matter of seconds and without the use of tools. All of these subassemblies are significant in size and not subject to loss. Further disassembly can be accomplished, if desired, without the use of special tools. This should, however, not be necessary for cleaning or field maintenance.

SPECIFICATIONS—CALIBER: .223 (5.56mm). **LENGTH:** 37¼". **WEIGHT:** 6 lbs. 6 oz. **MAGAZINE:** 5 or 20 round, detachable box magazine. **BARREL LENGTH:** 18½".

RUGER M-77 BOLT-ACTION RIFLE

**MODEL No. M77R (TELESCOPE NOT INCLUDED)
COMPLETE WITH 1" STEEL RUGER RINGS (NO SIGHTS)**

**MODEL No. M77RS COMPLETE WITH 1"
STEEL RUGER RINGS AND OPEN SIGHTS**

Calibers: .22-250 Remington, .243 Winchester, 6mm Remington, .25-06 Remington, .220 Swift, .257 Roberts 250-3000, 7x57mm, .270 Winchester, .30-06, 7mm Remington Magnum, 300 Winchester Mag., .338 Winchester Mag., and .458 Win. Magnum.

Action. The M-77 is available in two action lengths—the Short Stroke and the Magnum.

The Short Stroke action is designed to take advantage of the accuracy and ballistic efficiency of the modern short series of cartridges. (Magazine box length: 2.920")

The Magnum action—about ½" longer than the Short Stroke—assures smooth and faultless feeding of the versatile long series of cartridges. (Magazine box length: 3.340")

The M-77 short stroke is available in calibers .22-250, .243, 6mm, .220 Swift, and .250-3000. The M-77 Magnum is chambered for .270, .25-06, .257 Roberts, 7x57mm 30-06, 7mm Rem. Magnum, .300 Win. Mag., .338 Win. Mag. and .458 Win. Magnum. Also available in calibers .22-250, .220 Swift, .243 Win., 6mm Remington and .25-06 with a heavy 24" barrel, drilled and tapped for target-scope blocks, and supplied with 1" Ruger steel rings. 26" barrel in .220 Swift.

The M-77 Round top (Magnum Action only) is equipped with open sights. The receiver is shaped and tapped to accommodate standard commercial scope mount bases. The Round top is not milled for Ruger scope rings. Available only in 25/06, .270, 30-06, 7mm Rem. Mag., .300 Win. Mag., and .338 Win. Magnum.

In the rare event of a cartridge case failure, the mechanism of the Model 77 has been provided with numerous vents to minimize the effect of escaping gas. A vent of the usual type is provided on the right side of the receiver. Gas which flows along the locking lug channel is largely diverted by the rugged bolt stop and vented through a special opening. In addition, the substantial flange on the bolt sleeve is designed to deflect gas away from the shooter. The one-piece bolt of the Model 77 avoids the brazed joints which are now commonly used as an economy measure. Two massive front locking lugs and a positive long extractor, combined with one-piece construction, result in extraordinary strength and reliability.

The external bolt stop, held in position by a strong hidden spring, is conveniently located on the left rear of the receiver. No tools are needed to open the bolt stop and remove the bolt.

The serrated steel-trigger is adjustable to a minimum pull of 3½ pounds. Trigger action is smooth, crisp and free from creep at all adjustments.

The safety, which is securely mounted in the heavy metal of the tang, is of the desired shotgun type; positive and readily accessible.

For added safety and convenience, the magazine floor plate is hinged to allow emptying of the magazine without having to work the cartridges through the action. The floor plate can be easily opened by pressing the release lever located at the inside front of the trigger guard.

Specifications:

ACTION: Short-stroke or magnum lengths. **BOLT:** One-piece construction, with two massive locking lugs. **EXTRACTOR:** Long external type. **BOLT STOP:** Left side of receiver, coil spring action. **TRIGGER:** Serrated steel, adjustable for weight of pull. **SPRINGS:** Music wire coil springs throughout (except for special magazine follower spring). **MAGAZINE:** Staggered box type with stainless steel follower and quick release hinged floor plate. Capacity: five rounds (plus one in chamber), three rounds in Magnum calibers. **BARREL:** 22", Chrome-molybdenum alloy steel. Except calibers 25/06, .300 Win. Mag., .338 Win. Mag., .458 Win. Magnum and 7mm Remington Magnum and all M77V which are 24". **SAFETY:** Sliding shotgun-type, mounted on receiver tang. **STOCK:** Genuine American Walnut, thoroughly seasoned, hand-checkered, and hand rubbed. Pistol grip cap with Ruger medallion. Swivel studs. Live rubber recoil pad. **STOCK DIMENSIONS:** Drop at heel: 2⅛". Drop at comb: 1⅝". **LENGTH OF PULL:** 13¾". **STOCK BEDDING:** Ruger diagonal-front-mounting-screw system (Patented) insures consistent bedding of receiver barrel assembly in stock. **LENGTH OVERALL:** 42 inches. **WEIGHT:** Approximately 6½ pounds without scope. (M77V 9 lbs.)

MODELS AND PRICES

M77R—with scope rings only	**$215.00**
M77ST—(Round Top) with open sights	**$215.00**
M77R or M77ST— .338 Mag.	**$230.00**
M77RS—with rings and sights	**$190.00**
M77RS—.458 Win. Mag., .338 Win. Mag.	**$298.00**
M77V—with 24" heavy barrel	**$215.00**
M77B/A—Barreled actions	**$167.50 to $232.50**
D-71—Ruger 1" Steel Extra Rings (pr.)	**$15.00**

RUGER AUTOLOADING CARBINES
IN .22 LONG RIFLE AND .44 MAGNUM CALIBERS

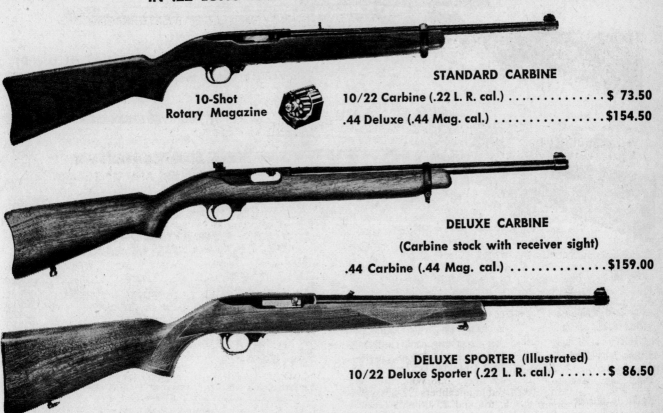

10-Shot Rotary Magazine

STANDARD CARBINE

10/22 Carbine (.22 L. R. cal.) . . . . $ 73.50

.44 Deluxe (.44 Mag. cal.) $154.50

DELUXE CARBINE

(Carbine stock with receiver sight)

.44 Carbine (.44 Mag. cal.) $159.00

DELUXE SPORTER (Illustrated)

10/22 Deluxe Sporter (.22 L. R. cal.) . . . .$ 86.50

Model 10/22 Carbine
.22 LONG RIFLE CALIBER

Identical in size, balance and style to the Ruger .44 Magnum Carbine and nearly the same in weight, the 10/22 is a companion to its high-power counterpart. Construction of the 10/22 Carbine is rugged and follows the Ruger design practice of building a firearm from integrated sub-assemblies. For example, the trigger housing assembly contains the entire ignition system, which employs a high-speed, swinging hammer to insure the shortest possible lock time. The barrel is assembled to the receiver by a unique dual-screw dove-tail system that provides unusual rigidity and strength—and accounts, in part, for the exceptional accuracy of the 10/22.

Specifications: Caliber: .22 long rifle, high-speed or standard velocity loads. **Barrel:** 18½" length. Barrel is assembled to the receiver by unique dual-screw dove-tail mounting for added strength and rigidity. **Weight:** 5 pounds. **Overall Length:** 37". **Sights:** 1/16" gold bead front sight. Single folding leaf rear sight, adjustable for elevation. Receiver drilled and tapped for scope blocks or tip-off mount adapter. **Magazine:** 10-shot capacity, exclusive Ruger rotary design. Fits flush into stock. **Trigger:** Curved finger surface, 3/8" wide. **Safety:** Sliding cross-button type. Safety locks both sear and hammer and cannot be put in safe position unless gun is cocked. **Stocks:** Solid American walnut, oil finished. Available in 2 styles. The Standard Carbine and The Sporter. **Finish:** Polished all over and blued or anodized.

Model 44 Carbine
.44 MAGNUM CALIBER

The carbine is gas-operated, with the slide energized by a short-stroke piston driven by a very small quantity of gas tapped from the barrel during firing. The mechanism is exceptionally smooth in operation, strong, reliable and safe; the breech remains locked until it is opened automatically *after* the bullet has left the barrel. The receiver is machined from a solid block of hot-rolled chrome molybdenum steel. The tubular magazine is located in the fore-end, capacity is 4 shots, with an additional shot in the chamber. When the last shot has been fired, the breech remains open until it is released by operating the latch located just ahead of the trigger guard.

Specifications: Caliber: .44 Magnum only, using all factory loads. The use of jacketed bullets is recommended to insure optimum accuracy and maximum stopping power. **Barrel:** 18½" long, 12 groove rifling, 38" twist. Barrel is permanently assembled to the receiver by 20 pitch screw threads. **Weight:** 5 pounds, 12 ounces. **Overall Length:** 36¾". **Sights:** 1/16" gold bead front sight. Single folding leaf rear sight, adjustable for elevation. Receiver drilled and tapped. **Magazine:** Fixed, tubular type located in fore-end. **Capacity:** 4 rounds plus 1 round in chamber. **Trigger:** Two stage pull. Curved finger surface 3/8" wide. **Safety:** Sliding cross-button type. Safety locks both sear and hammer and cannot be put in safe position unless gun is cocked. **Stock:** Genuine American walnut, oil finished.

SAKO RIFLES
MODEL 74 SUPER BOLT ACTION RIFLES

SAKO M74 SPORTER
(in short, medium & long action)

SAKO M74 HEAVY BARREL
(in short, & medium action)

SAKO MODEL 74 SPORTER

Caliber	Action Length	Magazine Capacity	Barrel Length	Approx. Weight	Price
.222	Short	5	23½"	6½	$325.00
.223	Short	5	23½"	6½	325.00
.243	Medium	5	23"	6¾	325.00
.270	Long	5	24"	8	325.00
.30-06	Long	5	24"	8	325.00
7mm Rem. Mag.	Long	4	24"	8	325.00
.300 Win. Mag.	Long	4	24"	8	325.00
.338 Win. Mag.	Long	4	24"	8	325.00
.375 H & H Mag.	Long	4	24"	8	325.00

The Sako Model 74, a super-grade Sako of richness and quality. The stock is classic Sako . . . European walnut with Monte Carlo cheekpiece, beautifully finished and generously hand checkered. A fitted recoil pad is supplied on all magnum calibers, and the Heavy Barrel rifles have a hand-filling beavertail forend.

The actions of the Sako Model 74 rifles are made in three action lengths to provide maximum strength without unnecessary bulk. The result is a bolt throw that's short and quick, with no lost motion. The light, crisp trigger is adjustable, and the floorplate is hinged to allow the removal of live rounds without working them through the action.

As with all Sakos, the barrels are bored, honed, lapped and hammer-forged to perfection. Both the Sporter and Heavy Barrel are superbly accurate rifles.

SAKO MODEL 74 HEAVY BARREL

Caliber	Action Length	Magazine Capacity	Barrel Length	Approx. Weight	Price
.222	Short	5	23½"	8¼	$325.00
.223	Short	5	23½"	8¼	325.00
.22-250	Medium	5	23"	8½	325.00
.243	Medium	5	23"	8½	325.00

SAKO DELUXE SPORTER
(in short, long & medium action)

All exposed metal surfaces are perfectly polished to a virtual mirror finish. The top surfaces of the integral dovetail bases, the bolt sleeve, and bolt-handle root are finely checkered to eliminate unwanted reflection, and a ring of checkering encircles the bolt handle for a better grip.

The stocks are of European walnut with fitted recoil pad, contrasting forend and pistol grip cap set off by white-line spacers, and generous skip-line hand checkering.

Action Length	Caliber	Weight	Barrel Length	Mag. Cap.	Price
Short	.222	6½	23½"	5	$470.00
Short	.223	6½	23½"	5	470.00
Medium	.22-250	6¾	23"	5	470.00
Medium	.243	6¾	23"	5	470.00
Long	.270	8	24"	5	470.00
Long	7mm Mag.	8	24"	4	470.00
Long	.30-06	8	24"	5	470.00
Long	.375 H&H	8	24"	4	470.00

SAKO RIFLES

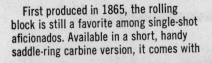

First produced in 1865, the rolling block is still a favorite among single-shot aficionados. Available in a short, handy saddle-ring carbine version, it comes with

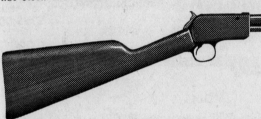

STAR ROLLING BLOCK
Calibers: 30-30 Win., .357 Magnum & .44 Magnum
$160.00

a stubby 20-inch barrel giving it an overall length of 35 inches. It's chambered for .30-30, .357 Magnum and .44 Magnum calibers. The sights consist of a folding-leaf rear and ramp front with square blade. And with its forged steel receiver and crescent butt plate, both color-case-hardened. Fitted with walnut stock and forend.

Caliber	Approx. Weight	Barrel
.30-30	6 lbs.	20"
.357 Magnum	6 lbs.	20"
.44 Magnum	6 lbs.	20"

ROSSI SLIDE-ACTION GALLERY MODEL
.22 Long Rifle model $115.00
.22 Magnum model $125.00

The tubular magazine holds 20 short, 16 long, and 13 long rifle .22 rimfire cartridges interchangeably, (.22 Mag. holds 10 rounds).

Model	Caliber	Weight	Barrel
Standard	.22 S., L., L.R.	5¼ lbs.	23"
Magnum	.22 Mag.	5¼ lbs.	23"

BRONCO
.22 Short, Long, L.R. $39.00
.410 $49.00
.410/.22 O/U

The weight of the Bronco is only 3 lbs. in the .22 and 3½ lbs. in the .410 and O/U calibers. There is a rust-free crackle finish one-piece stock and receiver, and can be loaded with 3-inch slugs in the .410 gauge. Barrel lengths in all calibers are 18½".

SPRINGFIELD ARMORY

SPRINGFIELD ARMORY 7.62MM M1A
Standard Rifle $330.00
Target Rifle $440.00

Specifications: Mechanism Type: Gas-operated, semi-automatic, clip-loaded, detachable box magazine. **Grade:** Standard "Issue-Grade" w/walnut stock. **Caliber:** 7.62 mm. NATO (.308 Winchester). **Weight:** 8 lbs. 15 ozs. **Barrel Length:** 25-1/16" w/flash suppressor. **Over-All Length:** 44¼".

Magazine Capacity: 20 rounds. **Stock Dimensions:** Length of pull, 13¼"; drop at comb, 2⅜"; drop at heel, 2¾". **Sights:** Military. Square blade front; full click-adjustable aperture rear. **Sight Radius:** 26-1/16". **Rifling:** Four grooves, right twist, one turn in 12". **Accessories:** 2 magazines.

SAVAGE CENTER-FIRE RIFLES

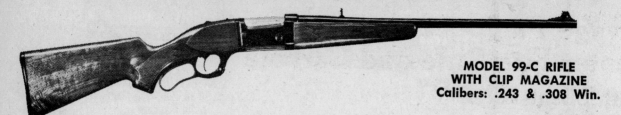

MODEL 99-C RIFLE
WITH CLIP MAGAZINE
Calibers: .243 & .308 Win.

Caliber: .243 & .308 Win. **Barrel:** Tapered, lightweight, chrome-moly steel, proof-tested. Length, 22″. **Action:** Hammerless, solid breech, lever action. Damascened bolt, case-hardened lever, blued steel receiver. Gold plated trigger, improved sear mechanism for crisp pull. Indicator on top tang shows when action is cocked. Safety on top tang locks trigger and lever. **Magazine:** Staggered clip magazine. Handy release and ejection push-button recessed in receiver. Holds 4 cartridges plus one in chamber.

Extra clip magazines available at $4.00 each. **Stock:** Selected walnut, checkered. Capped pistol grip; fluted comb. Checkered fore-end. Dimensions: length 13½″; drop 1½″ at comb, 2½″ at heel. Corrugated steel butt plate. **Sights:** Front, gold bead on raised ramp; rear, semi-buckhorn with step elevator, folds flat for scope use, returns to same elevation setting. Tapped for top-mount scopes. **Weight:** About 7¼ pounds. Length overall, 41¾″. **$199.50**

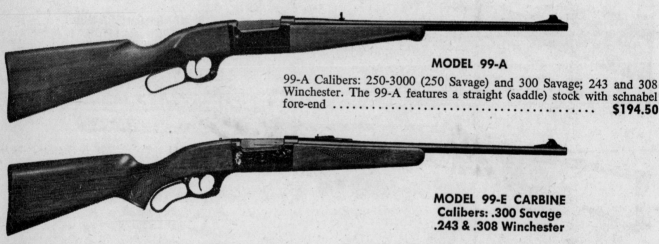

MODEL 99-A

99-A Calibers: 250-3000 (250 Savage) and 300 Savage; 243 and 308 Winchester. The 99-A features a straight (saddle) stock with schnabel fore-end **$194.50**

MODEL 99-E CARBINE
Calibers: .300 Savage
.243 & .308 Winchester

The 99-E lever-action carbine comes with a 20″ barrel and is made in 300 Savage, 243 and 308 Winchester calibers. The fully enclosed box type magazine with rotary carrier has a 5-shot capacity; plus one in chamber. With

99-CD The North American Classic (not illustrated)—Calibers: 250-3000 Savage and 308.
Features: Select walnut stock designed with a high Monte Carlo, cheekpiece and deeply fluted comb. Stock and grooved forend hand-checkered (20 lines to the inch).

blued steel lever, grooved trigger and corrugated butt plate. Walnut finished stock has tapered fore-end. Finger tip safety on right side of trigger locks trigger and lever. **$168.50**

Stock is fitted with white-line recoil pad and pistol-grip cap. Quick adjustable sling with swivels. Detachable hooded ramp front sight, rear sight adjustable for elevation and windage. **$219.95**

SPECIFICATIONS—FEATURES

MODEL	Barrel Length	Barrel Steel	Steel Receiver	Tapped For Top Mount Scope	Sights Front	Sights Rear	Cocking Indicator	Magazine Type	Cartridge Counter	Capacity	Safety	Stock and Fore-end	Checkered	Flut. Comb.	Capped Grip	Butt Plate	Avg. Wgt. (Lbs.)
99-CD	22″	Chrome Moly	Blued	X	Removable Hooded Ramp	Removable -Adjustable	X	Clip		5	Top Tang	Select Walnut	X	X	X	White-Line Recoil Pad	7
99-C	22″	Chrome Moly	Blued	X	Removable Ramp	Folding Leaf	X	Clip		5	Top Tang	Select Walnut	X	X	X	Hard Rubber	7¼
99-A	20″	Chrome Moly	Blued	X	Removable Ramp	Folding Leaf	X	Rotary	X	6	Top Tang	Select Walnut		X		Steel	7
99-E	20″	Chrome Moly	Blued	X	Removable Ramp	Folding Leaf	X	Rotary		6	Slide Safety	Wal. Fin. Hardwood	X	X		Hard Rubber	7

MODELS 99-CD Stock: Length 13½″; drop 1⅝″ at comb, at Monte Carlo 1½″, at heel 2½″.
99-C, A and E Stock: Length 13½″; drop 1½″ at comb, 2½″ at heel.
Length over-all: 41¾″. 99-A and E, 39¾″.

RATE OF TWIST (R.H.) 1 turn in 10″ 250 Savage, 243 and 12″ 300 Savage, 308.

Savage Pump Action
Center Fire Rifle and Carbine
With Silent-Lok Slide Handle.

The Model 170 pump-action rifle was designed to handle the 30-30 Winchester cartridge. The 170 pump stroke is 3-¾". Savage claims to have reduced friction in the action by an automatic vibrating process. It's Savage's answer to what hand-honing is meant to do. It includes the slide, bolt and sear. All locking surfaces between receiver and bolt are heat hardened. The receiver is machined from 8.9 pounds of solid tempered steel. The receiver is drilled and tapped for scope mounts.

170

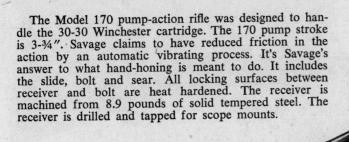

170-C

MODEL 170 PUMP ACTION RIFLE

.30-30 Winchester

$119.95

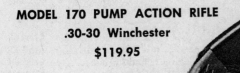

MODEL 170-C PUMP ACTION CARBINE
.30-30 WINCHESTER
$119.95

Features include a top tang safety (under the shooter's thumb). The 170 comes with a selected walnut Monte Carlo style stock with checkered pistol grip and slide handle. Savage designed the slide handle of the 170 to slightly overlap the receiver while in the forward position. The action is hammerless, and the trigger must be released and squeezed for each shot. With 22" barrel, the 170 weighs 6¾ lbs.

170-C (Carbine) 30-30.

The 170 is offered in a carbine variation. Shorter barrel (18½"). Sporter stock and Silent-Lok feature.

SPECIFICATIONS — FEATURES

MODEL	Barrel Length	Tapped For Top Mount Scope	Sights Front	Sights Rear	Safety Fire Control	Maga-zine Type	Ca-pacity	Top Tang Safety	Stock and Slide Handle	Silent -Lok	Check-ered	Monte Carlo	Sling Studs	Stock Finish	Butt Plate	Avg. Wgt. (Lbs.)
170	22"	X	Removable Ramp	Folding Leaf	X	Tubular	4	X	Select Walnut	X	X	X	X	Electro -Cote	Hard Rubber	6¾
170-C	18½"	X	Removable Ramp	Sport-ing	X	Tubular	4	X	Select Walnut	X	X		X	Electro -Cote	Hard Rubber	6

MODEL 170   Stock: Length 14"; drop 1½" at comb, 1½" at Monte Carlo, 2½" at heel.
Length over-all 41½".

170-C   Stock: Length 14"; drop at comb 1½", 2½" at heel.
Length over-all 38". Models proof-tested.

RATE OF TWIST (R.H.) 1 turn in 12" for 30-30.

SAVAGE CENTER-FIRE RIFLES

MODEL 110 BOLT ACTION CENTER FIRE RIFLES (Right & Left-Hand)

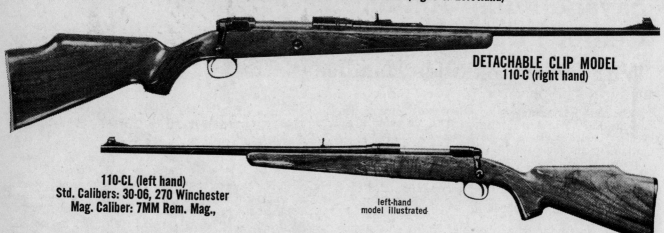

DETACHABLE CLIP MODEL
110-C (right hand)

110-CL (left hand)
Std. Calibers: 30-06, 270 Winchester
Mag. Caliber: 7MM Rem. Mag.,

left-hand
model illustrated

110-C (right hand) 110-CL (left hand) Calibers: Standard—30-06 and 270 Win. & 243 (110-C only). Magnum—7mm Rem. Mag. The solid features of the 110 plus the ejector clip magazine for convenient loading and unloading. To unload, press the recessed button and out pops the clip with the shells neatly held and tips protected. An extra loaded clip in a jacket pocket provides additional fire power.

Exclusive twin gas ports in receiver, gas baffle lugs on bolt and bolt end cap give most complete protection.

Standard calibers: . . . . right-hand $180.50
    " . . . . left-hand $185.75
Magnum calibers: . . . . right-hand $195.00
extra clip, $5.50 (specify caliber) left-hand $199.50

MODEL 110-D (right hand)
MODEL 110-DL (Lefthand)
Std. calibers: 30-06, & 270 Win.
Mag. Caliber: 7mm. Rem. Mag.,

110-D (right-hand) 110-DL (left-hand) Calibers: Standard—30-06 and 270 Win. Magnum—7mm Rem. Mag. The new 110-D and DL has all the 110 features, but with a hinged floor plate instead of the ejector clip. By pressing the release in front of the trigger guard, the cartridges are conveniently emptied. A safety and convenience feature, it also eliminates unloading shells through the action. Features include Satinslide bolt and new electro-cote stock finish.

New electrostatic stock finishing process is like electroplating, but on wood. In electro-cote—the finish is attracted to the wood, penetrating and sealing all surfaces. It is then baked to give a beautiful and durable finish.

Standard calibers: . . . . right-hand $180.50
    " . . . . left-hand $185.75
Magnum calibers: . . . . right-hand $195.00
    " . . . . left-hand $199.50

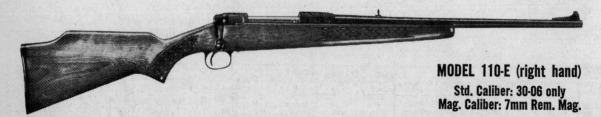

MODEL 110-E (right hand)
Std. Caliber: 30-06 only
Mag. Caliber: 7mm Rem. Mag.

110-E (right-hand) Calibers: Standard—30-06. Magnum—7mm Rem. Mag. Has all the 110 features described but stock is walnut finished hardwood instead of walnut. Magazine is internal, and is unloaded by working shells through the action.

Recessed bolt face completely covers and supports cartridge head. Two massive, heat-hardened steel locking lugs fit intimately to steel receiver.

Standard calibers: . . . . right-hand $145.00
Magnum calibers: . . . . right-hand $159.85

SAVAGE CENTER-FIRE RIFLES

MODEL 112-V
Calibers: 222, 22-250, 220 Swift, 25-06 and 243
$219.00

Features: Solid, single-shot action (no magazine cuts in receiver) for rugged strength. A 26″ tapered barrel (¹³⁄₁₆″ diameter at muzzle) for greater accuracy. Receiver is drilled and tapped for scope mounting. Blocks are also provided for target-type scopes. Free-floating special var-mint stock of select walnut has high, deeply fluted comb, Wundhammer swell pistol grip for right- or left-hand use, and is hand-checkered (20 lines to the inch). Stock is fitted with white-line recoil pad and 1¼″ quick detachable swivel loops.

MODEL 111 CHIEFTAIN
(with clip magazine)

Std. calibers: 30-06 & .270 Win. $212.00
Mag. caliber: 7mm Rem. Magnum $222.00

111 Chieftain (right hand only)-Calibers: 30-06, 270, 7mm Rem. Mag.
Features: Select walnut stock designed with a high Monte Carlo, cheekpiece and hand-checkered pistol grip and forend (20 lines to the inch) for improved grip and sighting. A deep gloss finish protects its natural walnut beauty. The buttplate and pistol-grip cap accented by white-line spacers. Quick adjustable sling strap with swivels. Detachable hooded ramp front sight and rear sight adjustable for elevation and windage. A teardrop-design bolt handle accents the beauty of this addition to the Savage center-fire rifle line.

Std. calibers $212.00
Magnum calibers $222.00

SPECIFICATIONS—FEATURES

MODEL	Free Floating Barrel — Barrel Length	Free Floating Barrel — Barrel Steel	Gas Ports	Tapped For Top Mount Scope	Sights — Front	Sights — Rear	Satin Slide Bolt	Recessed Bolt Face	Safety Gas Baffles	Magazine	Capacity	Top Tang Safety	Hand Checkered Stock	Check-piece	Swivels-Adj. Sling	Grip Cap Butt Plate	Avg. Wgt. (Lbs.)
111 (Stand. Cal.)	22″	Chrome Moly	2	X	Removable Hooded Ramp	Removable —Adjustable	X	X	3	Clip	5	X	Select Walnut	X	X	White-Line Hard Rubber	7½
111 (Mag.)	24″	Chrome Moly	2	X	Removable Hooded Ramp	Removable —Adjustable	X	X	3	Clip	4	X	Select Walnut	X	X	White-Line Recoil Pad	8¼
112-V	26″	Chrome Moly	2	X Plus Blocks			X	X	3		1 In Chamber	X	Select Walnut		Swivels Only	White-Line Recoil Pad	9¼

MODEL 111 Stock: Length 13½″; drop 1⅝″ at comb, 1½″ at Monte Carlo, 2¼″ at heel.
Length over-all: 43½″-45″.
112-V Stock: Length 13½″; drop at comb and heel ⁹⁄₁₆″ (measured from barrel center line).
Length over-all: 47″.

RATE OF TWIST (R.H.): 1 turn in 10″ for 25-06, 243, 30-06, 270 and 14″ for 222, 22-25, 220 Swift; 9½″ for 7mm Rem. Mag.

SAVAGE & STEVENS RIFLES
MODEL 340 BOLT ACTION RIFLES

MODEL 340
Calibers: 30-30, 22 Hornet, & 222 Re
$111.65

The Savage 340 bolt-action center-fire rifle comes in calibers 30-30, 22 Hornet, and 222 Remington. The bolt locks up in front, assuring strength and accuracy. The barrel is precision-rifled and the muzzle is crowned. Barrel length is 24" for all calibers. The bolt handle is curved.

Features include a Monte Carlo style stock of American walnut; checkering; pistol-grip cap and white-line spacers. Other features include detachable clip magazine (the clip pops out when the release lever is pushed) and metal open sights. Weight, 6½ lbs.

SPECIFICATIONS — FEATURES

MODEL	Barrel Length	Barrel Steel	Steel Receiver	Tapped For Side Mount Scope	Sights Front	Sights Rear	Savage Head Spacing	Thumb Safety	Maga-zine Type	Ca-pacity	Checkered Stock Select Walnut	Checkered Stock Fluted Comb.	White Line Butt Plate	White Line Grip Cap	Monte Carlo Stock	Electro-Cote Finish	Butt Plate	Avg. Wgt. (Lbs.)
340	222 Rem 24"	Special Alloy	Blued	X	Removable Ramp	Folding Leaf	X	X	Clip	5	X	X	X	X	X	X	Hard Rubber	7½
	30-30 22"	Special Alloy	Blued	X	Removable Ramp	Folding Leaf	X	X	Clip	4	X	X	X	X	X	X	Hard Rubber	7¼

MODEL   Stock: Length 13½"; drop 1¾" at comb, 1¾" at Monte Carlo, 2½" at heel. Length over-all 40"–42". Model proof-tested.   RATE OF TWIST (R.H.) 1 turn in 12" for 30-30 and 14" for 222.

FALLING BLOCK MODEL SINGLE SHOT IN .22 LONG RIFLE CALIBER

$66.50

Stevens 72 Crackshot. This unique falling block action is a pleasure to handle, shoot or simply admire. It has balance, smooth functioning and safety. This popular 22 rifle is truly in the great Stevens traditon. It features an octagonal barrel, case hardened frame, walnut stock and fore-end with oil finish.

BOLT-ACTION RIFLES IN .22 LONG RIFLE & .22 MAGNUM CALIBERS

65-M, Clip
22 Magnum

65-M (extra clips): 5 shot $3.50

65-M 22 magnum. The Savage 65M, with select walnut, Monte Carlo stock, is patterned after a high power rifle. The solid steel receiver houses a smooth, fast action with a crisp trigger pull. Action is safe and dependable, with bolt encased in the receiver, a recessed bolt face, and double extractors. The free-floating barrel means accuracy.
The 65-M offers accurate shooting at ranges up to 100-125 yards for the varmint and small game hunter. Exceptionally strong lock-up and free-floating barrel make the 65-M a good choice for the magnum cartridge.   **$62.90**

STEVENS .22 RIFLES

34, clip
.22 Long Rifle

34 (extra clips): 5 shot **$3.50**
10 shot **$4.40**

Stevens 34 22 long rifle. This Stevens bolt action 22 has a free-floating tapered barrel for remarkable accuracy. Convenient thumb safety at rear of receiver. Walnut finish hardwood stock has fluted comb. Receiver is grooved for scope mount.
34 $51.00

73, single shot
.22 Long Rifle

Stevens 73 22 long rifle. For the man or boy choosing his first gun—for anyone who wants a safe, dependable rifle. The safety goes on automatically when the bolt is operated—an ideal design for a first-rifle. Dependable—the bolt action is sturdy. Accurate—the free floating barrel is precision rifled. With a handsome stock and a streamlined receiver that has a satin finish.
$36.50

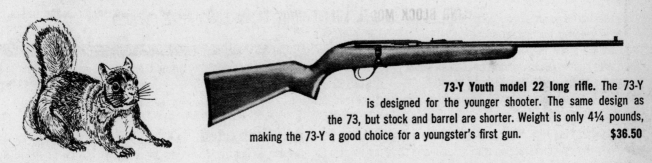

73-Y Youth model 22 long rifle. The 73-Y is designed for the younger shooter. The same design as the 73, but stock and barrel are shorter. Weight is only 4¼ pounds, making the 73-Y a good choice for a youngster's first gun.
$36.50

SPECIFICATIONS — FEATURES

MODELS	Barrel Length	Steel Barrel	Steel Receiver	Grvd. For Scope	Sights Front	Rear	Bolt Action Repeater	Single Shot	Magazine Type	Capacity	Side Safety	Checkered	Monte Carlo	Sporter	Select Walnut	Walnut Fin. Hardwood	Fluted Comb.	White Line Butt Plate	Stock Finish	Butt Plate	Length Overall	Avg. Wgt. (Lbs.)
34	20″	X	X	X	Sporting	Open	X		Clip	6*	X	X	X			X	X		Electro-Cote	Hard Rubber	39″	5½
65-M	20″	X	X	X	Removeable Ramp	Open	X		Clip	6	X	X	X		X		X	X	Electro-Cote	Hard Rubber	39″	5½
73	20″	X	Alloy	X	Sporting	Open		X	Automatic	1*				X		X				Hard Rubber	38½″	4¼
73-Y	18″	X	Alloy	X	Sporting	Open		X	Automatic	1*				X		X				Hard Rubber	35″	4½

Note: 65-M chambered for 22 WMR ONLY.
*Chambered for 22 long rifle, long or short cartridges. Table includes one in chamber.
MODELS 65M and 34 Stock: Length 14″; drop 1½″ at comb, 1⅜″ at Monte Carlo, 2½″ at heel.
73 and 73-Y Stock: Length 14″ (73-Y12½″); drop 1½″ at comb, 2½″ at heel.

RATE OF TWIST (R.H.) 1 turn in 16″ for 22 L.R. and 22 Mag.

MODEL	Barrel Length	Barrel Type	Action Falling Block	Single Shot	Frame Finish	Visible Hammer	Manually Cocking	Positive Extraction	Sights Front	Rear	Select Walnut	Stock Finish	Butt Plate	Length Overall	Avg. Wgt. (Lbs.)
72	22″	Octagonal	X	X	Case Hardened	X	X	X	Sporting	Open	X	Oil Finish	Hard Rubber	37″	4½

Note: Chambered for 22 long rifle, long or short cartridges.
Stock: Length 14″; drop 1¾″ at comb, 2¾″ at heel.

RATE OF TWIST (R.H.) 1 turn in 16″ for 22 L.R.

164

54 SPORTER (.22 L.R. or .22 Mag.)

184
Model 1432 (.22 Hornet)

CUSTOM GRADE 22 SPORTERS

164 22 long rifle, 164-M 22 magnum. The action of the 164—is the same one used on the Savage/Anschutz model 64 target rifle. The barrel is precision bored for pinpoint accuracy. Receiver is grooved for instant scope mounting. The select European walnut stock has all the custom grade features,—Monte Carlo with cheek-piece, Wundhammer swell pistol grip, schnabel fore-end and hand checkering. **$189.50**
The 164-M is chambered for the 22 magnum cartridge for those longer range shots. **$204.50**

54 Sporter 22 long rifle, 54-M 22 Magnum. The model 54 Sporter combines the smallbore action with a handsome sporting Monte Carlo stock of fine French walnut. Strictly custom grade from the hand-carved roll-over cheek-piece and contoured pistol grip to the graceful schnabel fore-end. Both fore-end and pistol grip are hand checkered in a skip-line pattern.

The action is the Anschutz Match 54 that has dominated smallbore rifle shooting in recent years. Receiver is grooved for scope mount and drilled and tapped for scope bases. 54 Sporter, .22 L. R. **$330.00**

The 54-M magnum offers Anschutz - accurate shooting up to 100-125 yards for the varmint and small game hunter. 54-M, 22 Magnum. **$345.00**

Anschutz 1432 Caliber: 22 Hornet. Anschutz has introduced this handsome sporter featuring a custom Monte Carlo stock with roll over cheekpiece, contoured pistol grip and schnable for-end. Grip and forend are lavishly hand-checkered in a skip-line pattern. The stock is of fine French walnut. Receiver is grooved for scope mount and drilled and tapped for scope bases. **$360.00**

SPECIFICATIONS — FEATURES

MODEL	Barrel Length	Grooved for Scope	Tapped For Scope Mount	Sights Front	Sights Rear	Trigger Factory set for crisp trigger pull.	Clip Mag-azine	Capa-city	Safety	Checkered Stock Cheek-piece	Checkered Stock Monte Carlo	Checkered Stock Wal-nut	Fluted Comb.	White Liner	Butt Plate	Length Overall	Average Weight (Lbs.)
164, 164-M	24″	X		Hooded Ramp	Folding Leaf	X	X	6*	Slide	X	X	X	X	X	Hard Rubber	40¾″	6
54, 54-M	23″	X	X	Hooded Ramp	Folding Leaf	X	X	6*	Wing	X	X	X	X	X	Hard Rubber	42″	6¼
1432	24″	X	X	Hooded Ramp	Folding Leaf	X	X	5	Wing	X	X	X	X	X	Hard Rubber	43⅝″	6¼
184	21½″	X		Hooded Ramp	Folding Leaf	X	X	6*	Slide	X	X	X	X	X	Hard Rubber	39½″	4½

*Chambered for 22 long rifle ONLY.
MODEL 164 Stock: Length 14″; drop 1½″ at comb, 1½″ at Monte Carlo, 2¼″ at heel.
184 Stock: Length 14″; drop 1¾″ at comb, 2″ at Monte Carlo, 2⅛″ at heel.
54 and 1432 Stock: Length 14″; drop 1¼″ at comb, 1¼″ at Monte Carlo, 1¼″ at heel.
Note: 164-M and 54-M chambered for 22 W.M.R. ONLY. Clip capacity 4.
1432 chambered for 22 Hornet ONLY. Clip capacity 5.
RATE OF TWIST (R.H.) 1 turn in 16″ for 22 L.R., 22 Mag. and 22 Hornet.

Anschutz and Savage/Anschutz Target Rifles

With Adjustable Cheek Piece, Combination Hand Stop / Sling Swivel and Variable Angle Hook Butt Plate

1413 Super Match 54.

You can have the Super Match 54 in three models (1413, 1407, 1411). All have the same satin smooth action, fully adjustable trigger and hand lapped barrel. Stock design is the chief difference. The model 64 is an intermediate target rifle.

Shooters starting with the Model 64 can progress up to the 1413 as ability improves. The value here lies in the fact that stock feel and sighting is similar to what the shooter is accustomed to. Scores do not temporarily suffer as the shooter upgrades his equipment. Most accessories are interchangeable among Anschutz models.

1413 Super Match 54. The Free-style International target rifle that dominates international competition. For these very telling reasons:

The superb Super Match 54 action is satin smooth, with a large loading platform and a single stage trigger—adjusts from 15.9 oz. to 4 lbs. (See specifications.) There's a new combination hand stop/sling swivel, hook butt plate for right and left-hand use. Also new adjustable cheek-piece.

Other features of the 1413 are an adjustable butt plate with lateral and cant adjustments, plus horizontal and vertical. There's the yoke-style palm rest, adjustable pistol grip base and hand-filling beavertail fore-end. The 1413—a winner in the true international tradition. **1413 $585.00** left-hand stock **1413-L $605.00** (sights extra).

1407 Match 54. Meets all International Shooting Union requirements and is suitable for all N.R.A. matches. The straight stock allows the shooter to position his head in the same location each and every time.

"Anatomically shaped pistol grip . . . is especially helpful. The aluminum rail permits adjustment . . . so that a wide choice of swivel positions is available." Hand stop/sling swivel included. "The large and sweeping thumbrest of the stock is amply wide and proved to be very comfortable." And the 1407 has the same trigger mechanism as the 1413. There's also a blackline butt plate spacer—allows you to adjust length. **1407 $340.00** left-hand stock **1407-L $357.50** (sights extra).

SPECIFICATIONS — FEATURES

	1413 1413-L	1411 1411-L	1407 1407-L	64
BARREL	Precision rifled, hand-lapped. 22 long rifle only.			
Length	27½". Extra heavy, ¹⁵⁄₁₆" diameter.		26". ⅞" diameter.	26". Medium heavy ¹¹⁄₁₆" diameter.
ACTION	Bolt action, single shot. Double locking lugs. Large loading platform.			Single shot. Large loading platform.
TRIGGER	Single stage. Adjustable from 15.9 oz. to 21.2 oz. Two additional springs. One, adjusts pull from 21.2 oz. to 28.2 oz. Second, adjusts from 1½ lbs. to 4 lbs.			3 lbs. Single stage, adjustable for weight of pull, take-up, over-travel.
SAFETY	Wing type safety locks firing pin and bolt.			Slide safety locks sear and bolt.
STOCK	European walnut, adjustable cheek-piece. Cast-off. Long swivel rail.		European walnut, cheek-piece. Cast-off. Long swivel rail.	Walnut finished hardwood. Cheek-piece. Swivel rail.
	International type, cheek-piece.	Monte Carlo, cheek-piece.		
Butt Plate	Variable angle hook for right or left-hand use.	Non-slip rubber, spacer and vertical adjustment.		
SIGHTS	Receiver grooved for Anschutz sights. Scope blocks. (Sights extra).			Receiver grooved for Anschutz sights. Scope blocks. Front sight base. 64-S models are equipped with Anschutz 6723 match sight set.
LENGTH	50"	46"	44½"	44"
WEIGHT (avg.)	15½ lbs.	11 lbs.	10 lbs.	7¾ lbs.

Left-hand rifles built to same specifications, except with left-hand stock, cast-off.   RATE OF TWIST (R.H.) 1 turn in 16" for 22 L.R.

ANSCHUTZ & SAVAGE/ANSCHUTZ TARGET RIFLES

1407 Match 54

1411 Match 54.

Savage/Anschutz 64

1408ED "Super" Running Boar Rifle

1411 Match 54. Here's the Match 54 action (with all its international traditions) in a prone stock model designed especially for American matches. With adjustable cheek-piece stock and hand stop/sling swivel. Other features include heavy barrel and blackline butt plate spacer—allows you to adjust length of trigger pull to your own specifications.

The words written by the experts about the 1407 are equally true of the 1411: straight pistol grip for better trigger control, superbly designed prone straight stock, anatomically shaped pistol grip, hand-filling fore-end with a wide choice of swivel positions, comfortable thumbrest and the same trigger mechanism as the 1407 and 1413. During the recent National Matches at Camp Perry, more shooters in the prone events used Anschutz rifles.

1411 **$326.00** left-hand stock **1411-L $350.00** (sights extra).
1408ED "Super" Running Boar Rifle. Available on special order only.
SAVAGE/ANSCHUTZ 64. The 64 offers shooters a superior but moderately priced, medium weight entry into the world of international champions. Target stock has checkered pistol grip, contoured thumb groove, Wundhammer swell, beavertail fore-end and adjustable butt plate with new blackline spacer—allows you to adjust length of trigger pull to your own specifications. Three-pound single stage trigger is adjustable for weight of pull, take-up and over-travel. 64-S models are equipped with the Anschutz 6723 Match Sight Set. 64 right-hand **$138.50** 64-L left-hand **$151.50** 64-S right-hand (with sights) **$179.50** 64-SL (left-hand) (with sights) **$192.50.**

WEATHERBY RIFLES

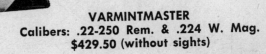

VARMINTMASTER
Calibers: .22-250 Rem. & .224 W. Mag.
$429.50 (without sights)

Mark V VARMINTMASTER—Calibers: .22-250 Rem. and .224 Weatherby Magnum. **Action:** Mark V bolt action scaled down, six locking lugs, enclosed cartridge case head, three gas ports. **Sights:** shown with 2X to 7X Weatherby Variable Scope on Buehler Mount. **Stock:** Monte Carlo with cheek piece and hand checkering. Fore-end tip, pistol grip and rubber butt pad. $429.50 without sights.

CALIBERS: .240 W.M., .257 W.M., .270 W.M.
7 M/M W.M., .300 W.M., .340 W.M.,
.378 W.M., .460 WEATHERBY MAGNUM & 30-06

MARK V DELUXE RIFLE—Calibers: .257, .270, 7m/m, .300, .340, .378 and .460 Weatherby Magnum and 30-06 calibers. **Action:** Weatherby Mark V with recessed bolt face, nine locking lugs, three gas escape ports. 54° bolt lift. **Sights:** shown with hooded ramp front sight and receiver peep sight. **Stock:** Monte Carlo with cheek piece and checkering, fore-end tip, pistol grip cap, fitted rubber recoil pad.

Mark V Deluxe Rifle, less sights, in .240, .257, .270, 7m/m, 300 W.M. and 30-06 calibers $449.50. In .340 W.M., less sights $459.50; .378 W.M. less sights $549.50; and in .460 W.M. caliber less sights $649.50. Rifles with factory-mounted scopes at extra cost. (Left hand deluxe model, $10.00 additional without sights)

MARK V DELUXE RIFLE

MARK V CUSTOM RIFLE
(Priced from $745.00 to $2,500.00)

MARK V CUSTOM RIFLE—Specifications same as Deluxe rifle except with fancy grade walnut stock and full metal engraving. Prices range from $745.00 to $2,500.00 depending upon degree of decoration and sights desired by the shooter. Mark V Custom rifle shown is equipped with 2X to 7X Weatherby Variable scope on Buehler mount.

SPECIFICATIONS

CALIBER	.224	.22/250	.240	.257	.270	7mm	.30-06	.300	.340	.378	.460
Weight w/o sights	6½ lbs.		7¼ lbs.						8½ lbs.		10½ lbs.
Overall length	43¼" or 45¼" dependent on barrel length		44½" or 46½" dependent on barrel length						46½"		
Capacity	5 shots: 4 in magazine; 1 in chamber	4 shots: 3 in mag.; 1 in chamber	6 shots: 5 in mag.; 1 in chamber	4 shots: 3 in magazine 1 in chamber			5 shots: 4 in mag.; 1 in chamber	4 shots: 3 in magazine; 1 in chamber	3 shots: 2 in magazine; 1 in chamber		
Barrel	24" standard or 26" semi-target		24" standard or 26" #2 contour						26" #2 contour	26" #3 contour	26" #4* contour
Rifling	1-14" twist		1-10" twist		1-10" twist		1-10" twist	1-12" twist	1-10" twist	1-12" twist	1-16" twist
Sights	Scope or iron sights extra										
Stock	American walnut, individually hand-bedded to assure precision accuracy. High lustre, durable stock finish. Quick detachable sling swivels. Basket weave checkering. Monte Carlo style with cheek piece, especially designed for both scope and iron sighted rifles. Length of pull 13½". Length of pull of .460-13⅞".										European Walnut
Action	A scaled-down version of the popular Mark V action, with 6 precision locking lugs in place of 9.		Featuring the Mark V, world's strongest and safest action. The nine locking lugs have almost double the shear area of the lugs found on conventional bolt rifles. The cartridge case head is completely enclosed in the bolt and barrel. .460: action includes hand honing, bolt knob fully checkered, bolt and follower damascened, custom engraved floor plate.								
Safety	Forward moving release accessible and positive										

*Pendleton Streamline muzzle brake is an integral part of the barrel.

WEATHERBY RIFLES

"VANGUARD" RIFLE BY WEATHERBY, EQUIPPED WITH WEATHERBY PREMIER 3X TO 9X VARIABLE SCOPE ON BUEHLER MOUNT.

The Vanguard by Weatherby is now available in the following calibers: .243 Win., .25-06, .270 WCF 7mm Rem. Mag., .30-06, and .300 Win. Mag.

The "hammer-forging" method of barrel manufacture, guarantees a glass-smooth bore with optimum dimensional stability from breech to muzzle. It is this "hammer-forging" technique which gives the Vanguard rifle its accuracy and long life.

The Vanguard action is based on one of the most highly acclaimed designs in the gun industry, yet sports many of the modern safety advancements. The bolt face is recessed and it in turn is recessed into the barrel forming 3 concentric bands of steel around the cartridge case head. In addition to this case support, the Vanguard also features a completely enclosed bolt sleeve to prevent escaping gasses from flowing back through the bolt into the shooter's face. Other safety features include a gas ejection port, two massive bolt lugs, and side operated safety lever. The action

has a knurled bolt knob for a better grip, a hinged floor plate for easy removal of loaded cartridges from the magazine, and a drilled and tapped receiver for simplified scope installation. The action is forged out of high strength chrome moly steel, polished and blued to a rich deep hue. The trigger guard and floor plate are black chromed for maximum durability.

The Vanguard has a fully adjustable trigger mechanism providing a crisp and clean pull down to 3 pounds.

The Vanguard stock is made of select American walnut and bedded for accuracy, it sports a Weatherby butt pad, 45° rosewood fore-end tip and pistol grip cap, white line spacers, and the traditional Weatherby diamond inlay. The finish of the Vanguard stock is the same high luster type found on the Mark V . . . scratch resistant and impervious to water, perspiration, or solvents. The Vanguard stock has a 13½" pull and just the right amount of cast-off and drop for the average shooter.

SPECIFICATIONS
Vanguard Rifles available in right-hand models only

Calibers	.243 Win.	.25-06 Rem.	.270 WCF	7mm Rem. Mag.	.30-06	.300 Win. Mag.
Price	$269.50	$269.50	$269.50	$269.50	$269.50	$269.50
Weight (approximate)	7 lb. 14 oz.	7 lb. 14 oz.	7 lb. 14 oz.	7 lb. 14 oz.	7 lb. 14 oz.	7 lb. 14 oz.
Overall Length	44½"	44½"	44½"	44½"	44½"	44½"
Magazine Capacity	5 rds.	5 rds.	5 rds.	3 rds.	5 rds.	3 rds.
Barrel Length	24"	24"	24"	24"	24"	24"
Rifling	1-10"	1-10"	1-10"	1-10"	1-10"	1-10"
Sights	Scope or iron sights at extra cost.					
Stocks	American Walnut, 13½" pull, fore-end tip & pistol grip cap					
Action	Vanguard action of the improved Mauser type					
Safety	Side operated, forward moving release, accessible & positive					
Scope Mounts	The Vanguard accepts any Mark V scope mount					

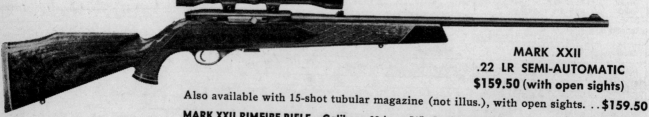

MARK XXII
.22 LR SEMI-AUTOMATIC
$159.50 (with open sights)

Also available with 15-shot tubular magazine (not illus.), with open sights. . .$159.50

MARK XXII RIMFIRE RIFLE—Caliber: .22 Long Rifle Rimfire. **Action:** semi-automatic, clip magazine (5 and 10 shot). Single shot selector. Bolt stays open after last shot. Shotgun type tang safety. Receiver grooves for scope mounting. **Sights:** folding rear leaf and ramp front sight. **Stock:** Monte Carlo with cheek piece and hand checkering. Rosewood pistol grip cap and fore-end tip, and a "non-skid" rubber butt plate. Sling swivels. **Overall length:** 42¾". **Weight:** approximately 6 lbs.

WINCHESTER MODEL 70s

- Classic stock design and finish • Real, cut checkering • Pistol grip contour
- Machined chrome molybdenum steel barrel and action • Hinged floor plate

Model 70
$235.00

Calibers: 22-250, 243 Win., 270 Win.,
30-06, 308 Win., 222 Rem. & 25-06 Rem.

Magnum calibers:
7mm Rem. Mag.
300 Win. Mag.

Model 70A
Bolt Action Rifle
Standard calibers $200.00
Magnum calibers $215.00

Model 70

Plus hinged Super-Grade floor plate and non-slip rubber butt pad with white spacers. Knurled bolt handle. Three-position safety. Special matted finish on receiver bridge. White triangle on rear leaf sight. Detachable sling swivels. In four calibers: 243†, 270 Winchester†, 30-06 Springfield, and 300 Winchester Magnum† (with black rubber recoil pad).

The Winchester Proof-Steel barrel is made from chrome molybdenum steel, the barrel is cold-forged to give the ultimate in uniformity and precision.

The new stock on the Winchester Model 70s is American walnut, kiln dried, sized, and turned. Real, cut checkering and an all-weather and wear-resistant finish add to its impressive appearance . . . highlighted by an improved cheek piece, undercut pistol grip, satin finish, new fore-end tip, and pistol grip cap . . . a recessed bolt-face for 50% better cartridge head support . . . a bolt that's engine-turned steel with anti-bind device . . . new spring and plunger-style ejector. Stainless steel magazine follower. Plus a hinged floor plate and exclusive three-position safety. Rear sight and machined steel front sight ramp and hood are detachable. Choice of four big game stoppers and big bore competition models in 13 calibers.

1. Model 70. Classic stock design with distinctive forearm, pistol grip, undercut cheek piece, new fore-end tip and pistol grip cap. Detachable sling swivels and real, deep-cut checkering complete the custom-like features. New pistol grip cap. Wide, serrated trigger. Knurled bolt handle. In 243, 270, 308 Winchester, 30-06 Springfield, 22-250, and 222 and 25-06 Rem. calibers.

Model 70A

Features include chrome molybdenum steel barrel and action, deep-cut real checkering, and a totally redesigned stock. There's no sacrifice in versatility. The model 70As come in ten popular calibers, including three magnums, and give you capability for everything from varmints to the heaviest big game.

The stock is solid American walnut, richly finished, and has a high comb Monte Carlo and cheek piece for quick alignment with either iron or telescopic sights.

2. Model 70A Bolt Action Rifle. Includes such features as adjustable rear sights and front sight ramp and hood, exclusive three-position safety, engine-turned bolt and a wide serrated trigger. In 22-250, 222 Rem., 243, 270, and 308 Winchester, 25-06 Rem., and 30-06 Springfield calibers. Model 70A Bolt Action Magnum (not shown). Black rubber recoil pad. In 264 and 300 Winchester Magnums, plus 7mm Rem. Magnum.

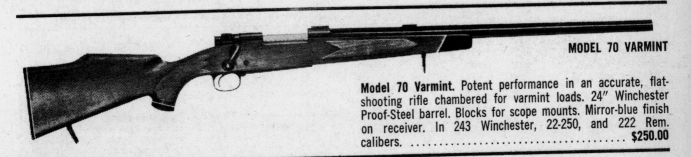

MODEL 70 VARMINT

Model 70 Varmint. Potent performance in an accurate, flat-shooting rifle chambered for varmint loads. 24″ Winchester Proof-Steel barrel. Blocks for scope mounts. Mirror-blue finish on receiver. In 243 Winchester, 22-250, and 222 Rem. calibers. **$250.00**

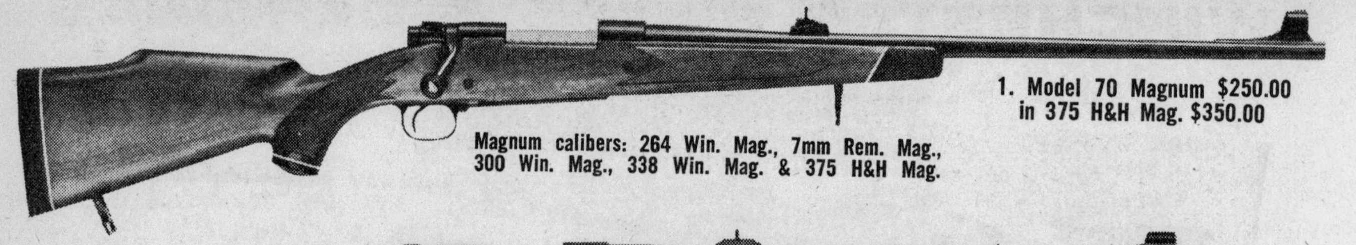

1. Model 70 Magnum $250.00
in 375 H&H Mag. $350.00

Magnum calibers: 264 Win. Mag., 7mm Rem. Mag., 300 Win. Mag., 338 Win. Mag. & 375 H&H Mag.

2. Model 70 African
.458 Win. Magnum
$415.00

Known the world over as "The Rifleman's Rifle", today's Winchester Model 70s are quality sporting arms perfectly suited to the needs and desires of the shooter. The Model 70, and the 70A improvements and modifications—from all-weather stock finish and cut checkering to steel barrel and action—give every sportsman all he's ever looked for in a bolt action big game rifle.

1. Model 70 Magnum. Knock-down punch for the biggest North American game . . . and then some. Black rubber recoil pad with white spacer. Twin stock reinforcing bolts. In 264, 300, and 338 Winchester Magnums, 7mm Rem. 375 H & H Magnum.

2. Model 70 African—458 Winchester Magnum. More than five thousand foot-pounds of crushing muzzle energy placed on target with superb Model 70 accuracy. Special African open rear sight. Rubber recoil pad. Hand checkering. Detachable sling swivels. Carrying strap. Twin steel stock reinforcing bolts. Ebony fore-end tip.

Model 70 Specifications

Caliber	222 Rem.	222 Rem. Varmint	22-250	22-250 Varmint	243 Win.	243 Win. Varmint	25-06 Rem.	264 Win. Mag.	270 Win.	7mm Rem. Mag.	30-06 Springfield	30-06 Springfield Target	308 Win.	308 Target	308 Int'l. Army Match	300 Win. Mag.	338 Win. Mag.	375 H & H Mag.	458 Win. Mag. African
Mag. Capacity (a)	5	5	5	5	5	5	5	3	5	3	5	5	5	5	5	3	3	3	3
Overall Length	42½"	44½"	42½"	44½"	42½"	44½"	44½"	44½"	42½"	44½"	42½"	44¼"	42½"	44¼"	43¼"	44½"	44½"	44½"	42½"
Barrel Length	22"	24"	22"	24"	22"	24"	24"	24"	22"	24"	22"	26"	22"	26"	24"	24"	24"	24"	22"
Length of Pull	13½"	13½"	13½"	13½"	13½"	13½"	13½"	13½"	13½"	13½"	13½"	13½"	13½"	13¼"	12"	13¼"	13½"	13½"	13½"
Drop at Comb	1¾"	*9/16"	1¾"	*9/16"	1¾"	*9/16"	1¾"	1¾"	1¾"	1¾"	1¾"	*½"	1¾"	*½"	1¼"	1¾"	1¾"	1¾"	1⅜"
Drop at Heel	2⅛"	*15/16"	2⅛"	*15/16"	2⅛"	*15/16"	2⅛"	2⅛"	2⅛"	2⅛"	2⅛"	*⅞"	2⅛"	*⅞"	1¼"	2⅛"	2⅛"	2⅛"	2⅜"
Drop at Monte Carlo	1½"	*⅜"	1½"	*⅜"	1½"	*⅜"	1½"	1½"	1½"	1½"	1½"	—	1½"	—	—	1½"	1½"	1½"	1¾"
Weight (lbs.)	7½	9¾	7½	9¾	7½	9¾	7½	7¾	7½	7¾	7½	11	7½	11	11	7¾	7¾	8½	8½
Rate of Twist (R.H.) 1 turn in	14"	14"	14"	14"	10"	10"	10"	9"	10"	9½"	10"	10"	12"	12"	12"	10"	10"	12"	14"

(a) Add one round for cartridge in chamber *From center line of bore. All others from line of sight.

Model 70A Specifications

Caliber	222 Rem.	22-250	243 Win.	25-06 Rem.	264 Win. Magnum	270 Win.	7mm Rem. Magnum	30-06 Springfield	308 Win.	300 Win. Magnum
Magazine capacity (a)	4	4	4	4	3	4	3	4	4	3
Overall Length	42½"	42½"	42½"	44½"	44½"	42½"	44½"	42½"	42½"	44½"
Barrel Length	22"	22"	22"	24"	24"	22"	24"	22"	22"	24"
Length of Pull	13½"	13½"	13½"	13½"	13½"	13½"	13½"	13½"	13½"	13½"
Drop at Comb	1¾"	1¾"	1¾"	1¾"	1¾"	1¾"	1¾"	1¾"	1¾"	1¾"
Drop at Heel	2⅛"	2⅛"	2⅛"	2⅛"	2⅛"	2⅛"	2⅛"	2⅛"	2⅛"	2⅛"
Drop at Monte Carlo	1½"	1½"	1½"	1½"	1½"	1½"	1½"	1½"	1½"	1½"
Weight (lbs.)	7⅛	7⅛	7⅛	7½	7¼	7⅛	7¼	7⅛	7⅛	7¼
Rate of Twist (R.H.) 1 turn in	14"	14"	10"	10"	9"	10"	9½"	10"	12"	10"

(a) Add one round for cartridge in chamber.

WINCHESTER RIFLES & CARBINES

MODEL 70 TARGET
CALIBERS: 30-06, 308 Winchester

The Model 70 Target rifle is available in 30-06 and 308 Win. calibers and equipped with a 26" free-floating target weight barrel; twist: 1 turn in 10", right hand. Furnished with a high comb Marksman stock for both iron and telescopic sights, full pistol grip, and wide checkered steel butt plate. Stock dimensions are listed at right. Drop dimensions are taken from center line of bore. It's also drilled and tapped for standard micrometer sights. Fitted with telescope blocks for target type mounts. Slotted for clip loading. Over-all length, 44½". Weight, 10¼ lbs. . . . . Special Order

SPECIFICATIONS
Caliber: 30-06 Springfield, 308 Winchester.
Capacity: 6 cartridges, magazine holds 5.
Sights: None; telescope blocks attached for target type mounts. Barrel tapped for front sight base.
Receiver: Tapped for popular scope mounts and receiver sights; clip slot.
Safety: 3-position type—located at rear of bolt.
Barrel: 26" Free-Floating heavyweight; twist: 1 turn in 10", right hand.
Overall Length: 46½".
Stock Dimensions: Pull—13¾"; drop at comb—½"*; heel—⅞"*.
Weight: 10½ lbs.
*From center line of bore.

1. Model 94 Regular $129.00
30-30 Winchester

2. Model 94 Antique $139.00
30-30 Winchester

Model 94 Lever-Action

A steel carrier of sturdy machined design provides smoother feeding of cartridges from magazine to chamber. Improved linkage, from a redesigned lever camming slot, results in easier, faster lever action.

There's a 20" cold-forged Winchester Proof-Steel barrel.

A loading port with improved cover makes filling the magazine a snap, even in cold weather. And with time-tested top ejection, the Model 94 performs equally well for both right- and left-handed shooters. The 94 is chambered for the traditional 30-30 Winchester. Features include a solid American walnut stock and forearm.

1. Model 94 Lever Action Carbine. Straight tang-to-toe lines

of the American West. Hooded front sight. Sporting rear sight. Barrel band. Half-cock safety. In 30-30 Winchester, 32 Winchester Special.

2. Model 94 Antique Lever Action Carbine. Handsome scrollwork on marbled, case-hardened receiver. Brass-plated loading gate. Saddle ring. 30-30 Winchester.

Model 94 Specifications

	Model 94 Carbine 30-30 Win.	Model 94 Antique Carbine 30-30 Win.
Mag. Capacity (a)	6	6
Overall Length	37¾"	37¾"
Barrel Length	20"	20"
Length of Pull	13"	13"
Drop at Comb	1¾"	1¾"
Drop at Heel	2½"	2½"
Weight (lbs.)	6½	7
Rate of Twist (R.H.) 1 turn in	12"	12"

(a) Add one round for cartridge in chamber

WINCHESTER Model 9422 & 9422M

LEVER-ACTION RIM FIRE
1. Model 9422 Standard $149.95
2. Model 9422M Magnum $154.95

The Model 9422s have been designed with a lever action that operates quickly and smoothly, with superior control during cartridge feeding. Both the Standard and Magnum rifles are grooved for scope mounting and include these most-wanted features: a front ramp sight with dovetail bead and hood. An adjustable semi-buckhorn rear sight. Simplified takedown. Scalloped tangs. And a solid American walnut stock and forearm. All important features when you buy a sporting arm.

The Model 9422M Magnum already has become a favorite sporting arm for those who shoot 22 Magnum cartridges and want to load up with this ammunition at an economical price. It has become an instant favorite as a turkey and varmint rifle. The 9422s combine the accuracy and traditional styling of the great Winchester Model 94 with the economy of a rim fire.

1. Model 9422 Standard. Magazine tube holds 21 Shorts, 17 Longs, or 15 Long Rifles interchangeably.
2. Model 9422M Magnum. Magazine tube holds 11 22 W.M.R. cartridges. Get real center fire power and accuracy at an economical rim fire price.

A choice of 22 rim fire Standard or Magnum cartridge capability.

- **Coldformed Winchester Proof-Steel Barrel**
- **Forged steel receiver, frame, and finger lever**
- **Solid American walnut stock and forearm**
- **Side ejection**
- **Receiver grooved for scope mounting**

Specifications

	9422	9422M Magnum
Caliber	22 Rim Fire	22 Win. Mag.
Magazine Capacity	21 Shorts, or 17 Longs, or 15 Long Rifles	11 W.M.R.
Overall Length	37⅛"	37⅛"
Barrel Length	20½"	20½"
Length of Pull	13½"	13½"
Drop at Comb	1¾"	1¾"
Drop at Heel	2½"	2½"
Weight (lbs.)	6¼	6¼
Rate of Twist (R.H.) 1 turn in	16	16

WINCHESTER MODEL 70 INTERNATIONAL ARMY MATCH RIFLE

Model 70 performance and dependability in a big-bore match rifle that's accepted in International Army Match competition. Built with the same quality-engineered precision as the famed Model 70 Target. Heavy contour 24 in. barrel bedded to special stock for ultimate stability and accuracy. Receiver drilled and tapped for all standard target sights. Clip slot in receiver bridge. Counterbore protects muzzle crown. External trigger adjustment. Special stock conforms to International Shooting Union dimensions. Military oil finish on stock. Serrations on sides and bottom. Forearm rail fits all standard accessories. "Standard Rifle" type butt plate with 3 centimeters vertical adjustment. Special non-glare finish on barrel and receiver.

Bolt Action Rifle, 6 Shot†

24 in. barrel; twist 1 turn in 12 in., right hand. Stock dimensions: length of pull 12 in., drop at comb 1¼ in., drop at heel 1¼ in. Magazine holds 5 cartridges plus 1 in chamber. Weight, 11 lbs.

G7041 .308 Winchester .... Special Order

(7-62 mm Nato)

WINCHESTER MODEL 70 ULTRA MATCH
Bolt Action, 6 Shot

(not illustrated) Externally adjustable trigger provides quick, positive trigger adjustments without removing action from the stock. New glass bedding to insure perfect fit and rigidity for greater accuracy. In .308 Win. and .30-06 Springfield.

26 in. barrel. Overall length 46½ in. Magazine holds 5 cartridges plus 1 in chamber. Stock dimensions: length of pull 13¼ in., drop at comb ½ in., drop at heel ⅞ in. Rate of twist: one R.H. turn in 12 in. Weight, 12 lbs.

.308 Win. .... Special Order
.30-06 Springfield .... Special Order

WINCHESTER RIM-FIRE RIFLES

.22 LONG RIFLE CALIBER SEMI-AUTOMATIC

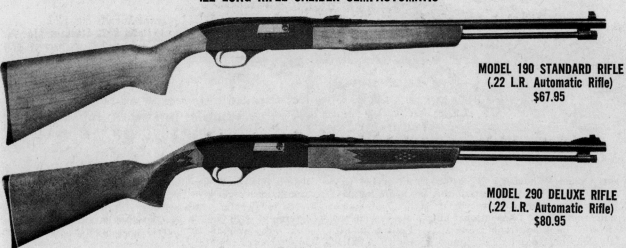

MODEL 190 STANDARD RIFLE
(.22 L.R. Automatic Rifle)
$67.95

MODEL 290 DELUXE RIFLE
(.22 L.R. Automatic Rifle)
$80.95

MODEL 190 STANDARD RIFLE

The Model 190 is available in a .22 Rimfire Long or Long Rifle and offers traditional features such as bead-post front-sight, cross-bolt safety and open-elevator rear sight. It holds 17 Longs or 15 Long Rifles and has a barrel length of 20½".

MODEL 290 SEMI-AUTOMATIC

The Model 290 is available in .22 Rimfire Long or Long Rifle and has a richly checkered pistol grip and forearm.

Model 190, 290 Specifications

Action Type	Model	Caliber	Magazine Capacity	Overall Length	Barrel Length	Length of Pull	Drop at Comb	Drop at Heel	Drop at M.C.	Weight (lbs.)	Rate of Twist
Auto	190* 290	22 Rimfire Long Long Rifle	17 Longs, or 15 Long Rifles	39"	20½"	13⅝"	1¾"	2¾"	2¼"	5	16"

MODEL 490 RIFLE
(.22 L.R. Automatic Rifle)
$110.00

The Model 490 .22 autoloader combines center-fire styling with rimfire action. The one-piece stock is solid walnut with a satin finish. The tapered 22-inch barrel, comes equipped with a folding-leaf sporting rear sight, plus a hooded front sight with ramp. The all-steel receiver is grooved for tip-off scope mount, and the detachable clip magazine holds five rounds (ten-shot clip available). The blued-steel cocking handle has a serrated front surface and acts as an open-action lock. Safety is a positive cross-bolt type. Weight, 6 lbs.

Model 490 Automatic Specifications

Caliber	22 Long Rifle Only
Magazine Capacity	5 (a)
Overall Length	42"
Barrel Length	22"
Length of Pull	13⅝"
Drop at Comb	1⅜"
Drop at Heel	2½"
Weight (lbs.)	6
Rate of Twist	14½"

(a) Add one round for cartridge in chamber.

WINCHESTER .22 TARGET RIFLES

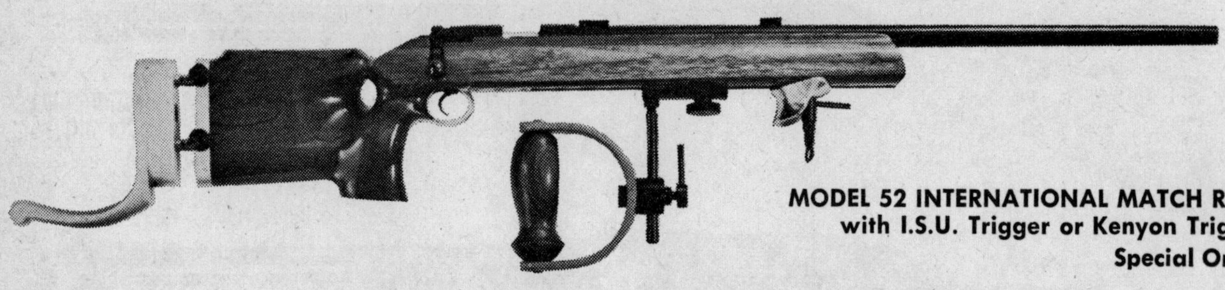

MODEL 52 INTERNATIONAL MATCH RIFLE
with I.S.U. Trigger or Kenyon Trigger
Special Order

This entry from Winchester is designed and styled to offer serious competitive shooters the finest in match rifles. Features include international style laminated stock with thumbhole. International butt plate assembly complete with hook and rubber butt plate. Fully adjustable for cant, horizontal and vertical movement. Full length, black modified aluminum accessory track. Polished aluminum trigger guard with trigger adjustment holes. International palm rest assembly. Aluminum fore-end stop assembly with felt base, detachable swivel, clamping bar. Heavyweight 28″ barrel with special Winchester counterbore. Supplied with steel telescopic blocks.

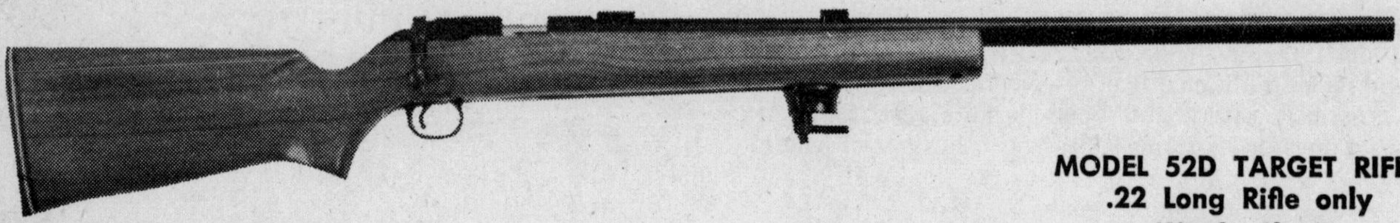

MODEL 52D TARGET RIFLE
.22 Long Rifle only
(Single Shot)

The Model 52D single-shot target rifle is made in 22 Long Rifle only. Available with 28″ heavy weight barrel; comes without sights. With free-floating barrel, adjustable bedding device and squared bright finished muzzle. Receiver, bolt and firing pin are carburized. American Walnut stock with non-slip rubber butt pad and adjustable hand-stop in full length channel.

G5225 Target Rifle (Heavy Wt. Barrel) . . Special Order

Capacity—Single shot.
Sights—None.
Receiver—Tapped for popular receiver sights.
Barrel—28″, tapped for front sight base; twist 1 turn in 16″. Right hand.
Overall Length—46″.
Stock Dimensions—
Standard Weight—Pull—13⅝″; drop at comb—¼″; drop at heel—¾″. Heavy Weight—Pull—13⅝″; drop at comb—¼″; drop at heel—none (drop dimensions taken from center line of bore.)
Weight—Heavy Weight barrel—11 lbs.

Rim Fire Rifle Specifications

	Model	Caliber	Magazine Capacity	Over-all Length	Barrel Length	Length of Pull	Drop at Comb	Drop at Heel	Drop at M.C.	Weight (lbs.)	Rate of Twist
Lever	9422	22 Rim Fire Short, Long, Long Rifle	21 Shorts, or 17 Longs, or 15 Long Rifles	37⅛″	20½″	13½″	1¾″	2½″	—	6¼	16″
	9422M	22 Win. Mag.	11 W.M.R.	37⅛″	20½″	13½″	1¾″	2½″	—	6¼	16″
Bolt	310	22 Rim Fire Short, Long, Long Rifle	Single Shot	39½″	22″	13½″	1⅝″	2 7/16″	1 13/16″	5⅝	16″
Target	52D Hvy. Wt.	22 Long Rifle Only	Single Shot	46″	28″	13⅝″	¼″††	None	—	11	16″
	52 Int'l Match	22 Long Rifle Only	Single Shot	44½″	28″	12 1/16″ 14 1/16″ ◆	1/16″††	9/16″	1/16″	13½	16″

◆ Spread of Adjustment ††Drop dimensions taken from center line of bore

Shotguns

BERETTA SHOTGUNS

SINGLE BARREL TRAP GUN BERETTA Mark II
$410.00

The Mark II is created for trapshooting. The gun opens smoothly on a massive, full-width hinge. The automatic ejector, special sear and trigger—all internal parts—are hand-fitted.

The wood on the Mark II is hand-picked for density of grain and beauty of figure. The forend is extra-long, with a tapered full-beavertail shape. All checkering is done by hand. Stock dimensions are:

Length of Pull, 14⅜"; Drop at Comb, 1⅜"; Drop at Heel, 1¾".

The hand-fitted, tapered vent rib is extra-wide and extra-high for better sighting and more efficient reduction of heat waves. Weight is approximately 8½ lbs.

12 gauge, 32" barrel, full choke
12 gauge, 34" barrel, full choke

AL-3
12 & 20 ga. Field $310.00
12 ga. Trap $360.00
12 & 20 ga. Skeet, 12 ga. Mag. $345.00

AL-3

The AL-3 has recoil-reducing gas-operated action, stainless-steel operating parts, chrome-lined bores, lightweight, hand-fitted vent. rib, beautifully engraved receiver, and instantly interchangeable barrels.

Stock dimensions on Field and Skeet models: Length of Pull, 14⅛"; Drop at Comb, 1½"; Drop at Heel, 2½". Trap gun dimensions (with Monte Carlo and recoil pad) are 14⅜", 1⅜", 1¾".

AL-3 DELUXE TRAP

In addition to the features found in the standard AL-3—recoil-absorbing gas-operated action, stainless-steel operating parts for easy maintenance, hard-chromed bore and hand-fitted Beretta Wide Rib—the AL-3 Deluxe has a stock and forend of premium-grade European walnut, hand-selected for its outstanding grain and coloration, plus gold-plated trigger and safety, gold monogram escutcheon inlaid in the buttstock, and full engraving coverage of the receiver.

Model	Barrel Length	Choke	Approx. Weight	
12 Ga. Field	30"	Full	7⅛	$310.00
12 Ga. Field	28"	Full	7	310.00
12 Ga. Field	28"	Mod.	7	310.00
12 Ga. Field	26"	Imp. Cyl.	7	310.00
20 Ga. Field	28"	Full	6½	310.00
20 Ga. Field	28"	Mod.	6½	310.00
20 Ga. Field	26"	Imp. Cyl.	6½	310.00
12 Ga. Trap	30"	Full	7½	360.00
12 Ga. Trap	30"	Imp. Mod.	7½	360.00
12 Ga. Skeet	26"	Skeet	7	345.00
20 Ga. Skeet	26"	Skeet	6½	345.00
12 Ga. 3" Mag.	30"	Full	7¾	345.00
12 Ga. 3" Mag.	28"	Mod.	7¾	345.00
DELUXE				
12 Ga. Trap	30"	Full	7¾	$575.00
12 Ga. Trap	30"	Imp. Mod.	7¾	575.00
12 Ga. Trap	30"	Mod.	7¾	575.00

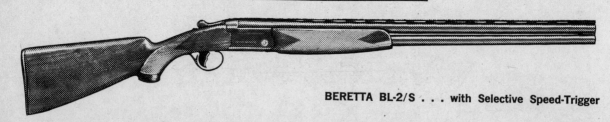

BERETTA BL-2/S . . . with Selective Speed-Trigger

It's the first trigger of its kind ever seen on any gun; it's fully and instantly selective, and it's all in the trigger.

There's no fiddling with your thumb to manipulate a selector. Just pull the trigger . . . top half for the open-choke barrel, bottom half for the tighter-choked barrel. Or reverse the order, if that's what the shot calls for. **Not only is the first shot fast, but so is the second. Your finger moves naturally into position for an instant second shot. There's no delay, no hesitation. Your second shot is as fast as you could want.**

The Beretta BL-2/S, comes with a hand-fitted ventilated rib, hand-checkered stock.

Stock dimensions: Length of Pull, 14⅛"; Drop at Comb, 1½"; Drop at Heel, 2½".

Gauge	Chamber	Barrel Length	Chokes	Approx. Wt.	Price
12 Mag.	3"	30"	M/F	7½ lbs.	$410.00
12	2¾"	28"	M/F	7¼ lbs.	$410.00
12	2¾"	26"	IC/M	7 lbs.	$410.00

BERETTA OVER & UNDER SHOTGUNS

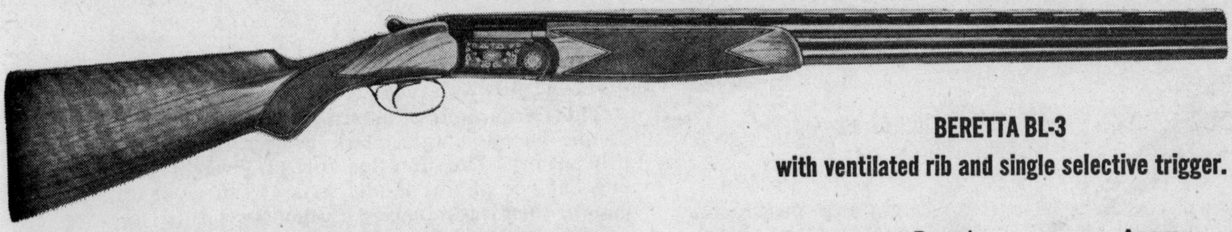

BERETTA BL-3

with ventilated rib and single selective trigger.

The beautifully slim receiver is handsomely set off by Deluxe walnut hand-engraving and hand-checkered European walnut stock and forearm. The gold-plated single-selective trigger offers a rich contrast to the carefully polished and richly blued metal surfaces.

The ventilated rib of the BL-3 is fitted by hand, for a perfectly flat, distortion-free sighting plane.

The BL-3 features the famous Beretta 'all-position' barrel selector, that lets you select your barrel with the safety in either the 'on' or 'off' position. It is equipped with extractors.

Gauge	Chamber	Barrel Length	Chokes	Approx. Weight	
12 Mag.	3″	30″	M/F	7½	**$490.00**
12	2¾″	30″	M/F	7½	**475.00**
12	2¾″	28″	M/F	7¼	**475.00**
12	2¾″	26″	IC/M	7¼	**475.00**
20	3″	28″	M/F	6¼	**475.00**
20	3″	26″	IC/M	6	**475.00**
12 Skeet	2¾″	26″	S/S	7¼	**515.00**
20 Skeet	3″	26″	S/S	6	**515.00**

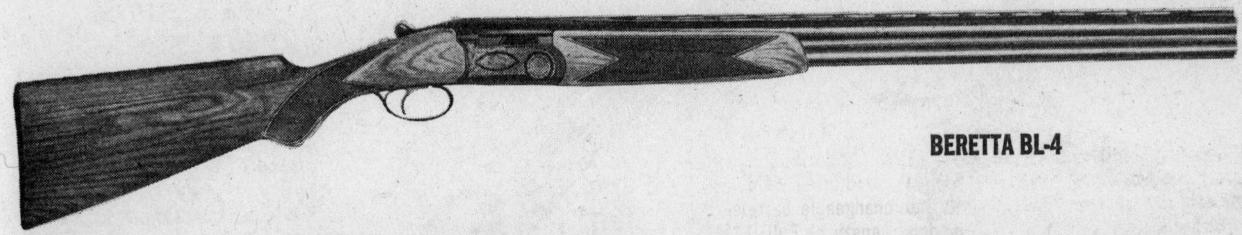

BERETTA BL-4

Automatic ejectors, that selectively toss out the empties, but hold the live shells for easy removal. Hand-fitted ventilated rib, with a special matte finish for a non-glare, distortion-free sighting plane. Gold-plated single selective trigger, with the exclusive Beretta 'all-position' selector. Chromium Molybdenum barrels with mirror-lapped bores. Windsor grade hand engraving, finely and cleanly executed by old-world artisans. Dense, close-grained European walnut, perfectly inletted and hand-rubbed to a beautiful satin finish. Deluxe hand-checkering that completely encircles the forearm.

Stock dimensions: Length of Pull, 14⅛″; Drop at Comb, 1½″; Drop at Heel, 2½″.

Gauge	Chamber	Barrel Length	Chokes	Approx. Weight	
12 Mag.	3″	30″	M/F	7½	**$580.00**
12	2¾″	30″	M/F	7½	**565.00**
12	2¾″	28″	M/F	7½	**565.00**
12	2¾″	26″	IC/M	7¼	**565.00**
20	3″	28″	M/F	6	**565.00**
20	3″	26″	IC/M	6	**565.00**
12 Skeet	2¾″	26″	S/S	7¼	**600.00**
20 Skeet	3″	26″	S/S	6	**600.00**

BL-4 WITH EXTRA SET OF BARRELS

12 Ga. Field/Skeet	28″ M/F & 26″ S/S	**$885.00**
12 Ga. Field	28″ M/F & 26″ IC/M	**865.00**
20 Ga. Field/Skeet	28″ M/F & 26″ S/S	**885.00**
20 Ga. Field	28″ M/F & 26″ IC/M	**865.00**

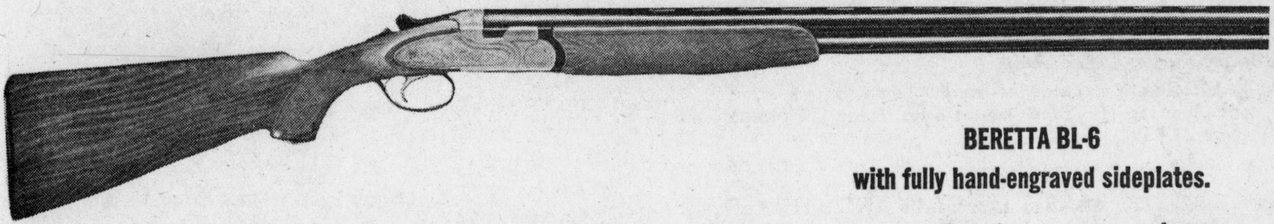

BERETTA BL-6

with fully hand-engraved sideplates.

Combining the ruggedness and strength inherent in the Beretta box-lock action with superlatively hand-engraved sideplates, specially selected European walnut, and deluxe hand checkering, the BL-6 is truly a consummate example of the gunmaker's art. The BL-6 is equipped with hand-fitted ventilated rib, selective automatic ejectors, and single selective trigger.

Gauge	Chamber	Barrel Length	Chokes	Approx. Weight	
12 Mag	3″	30″	M/F	7½	**$885.00**
12	2¾″	28″	M/F	7½	**875.00**
12	2¾″	26″	IC/M	7¼	**875.00**
20	3″	28″	M/F	6	**875.00**
20	3″	26″	IC/M	6	**875.00**
12 Skeet	2¾″	26″	S/S	7¼	**910.00**
20 Skeet	3″	26″	S/S	6	**910.00**

BERNARDELLI STANDARD GAMECOCK

DOUBLE BARREL SHOTGUNS

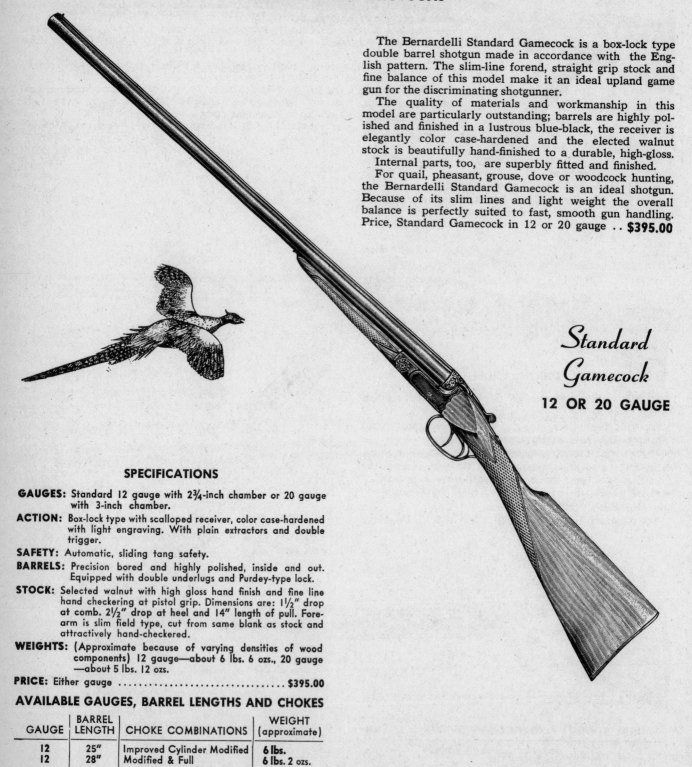

The Bernardelli Standard Gamecock is a box-lock type double barrel shotgun made in accordance with the English pattern. The slim-line forend, straight grip stock and fine balance of this model make it an ideal upland game gun for the discriminating shotgunner.

The quality of materials and workmanship in this model are particularly outstanding; barrels are highly polished and finished in a lustrous blue-black, the receiver is elegantly color case-hardened and the elected walnut stock is beautifully hand-finished to a durable, high-gloss.

Internal parts, too, are superbly fitted and finished.

For quail, pheasant, grouse, dove or woodcock hunting, the Bernardelli Standard Gamecock is an ideal shotgun. Because of its slim lines and light weight the overall balance is perfectly suited to fast, smooth gun handling. Price, Standard Gamecock in 12 or 20 gauge .. **$395.00**

Standard Gamecock

12 OR 20 GAUGE

SPECIFICATIONS

GAUGES: Standard 12 gauge with 2¾-inch chamber or 20 gauge with 3-inch chamber.

ACTION: Box-lock type with scalloped receiver, color case-hardened with light engraving. With plain extractors and double trigger.

SAFETY: Automatic, sliding tang safety.

BARRELS: Precision bored and highly polished, inside and out. Equipped with double underlugs and Purdey-type lock.

STOCK: Selected walnut with high gloss hand finish and fine line hand checkering at pistol grip. Dimensions are: 1½" drop at comb. 2½" drop at heel and 14" length of pull. Forearm is slim field type, cut from same blank as stock and attractively hand-checkered.

WEIGHTS: (Approximate because of varying densities of wood components) 12 gauge—about 6 lbs. 6 ozs., 20 gauge —about 5 lbs. 12 ozs.

PRICE: Either gauge $395.00

AVAILABLE GAUGES, BARREL LENGTHS AND CHOKES

GAUGE	BARREL LENGTH	CHOKE COMBINATIONS	WEIGHT (approximate)
12	25"	Improved Cylinder Modified	6 lbs.
12	28"	Modified & Full	6 lbs. 2 ozs.
20	25"	Improved Cylinder Modified	5 lbs. 8 ozs.
20	28"	Modified & Full	5 lbs. 10 ozs.

BERNARDELLI PREMIER GAMECOCK

Fine side-by-side double guns are still, today, almost entirely hand made.

Bernardelli's Premier Gamecock, is patterned along distinctively English lines with a gracefully slim straight grip stock and narrow field forend. This gun also has the famous Greener-type cross-bolt, double underlugs, non-selective single trigger, automatic ejectors, box lock with dummy side plates and automatic safety.

Wood components are of finely grained Italian Walnut, exactingly hand checkered and finished in a double high-gloss epoxy.

In 12 or 20 gauge, the Premier Gamecock is a very smooth, aristocratic upland game gun. Quail, pheasant, partridge and dove hunters will thrill to its light weight, exquisite balance and smooth handling qualities.

For the shooter who wants a truly outstanding side-by-side—a gun that he can one day pass on to his son, the Bernardelli Premier Gamecock is the ideal choice. **$500.00**

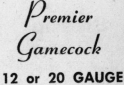

Premier Gamecock

12 or 20 GAUGE

SPECIFICATIONS

GAUGES: 12 or 20 (all 20 gauge models with 3 inch chambers).

ACTION: Box lock with dummy side plates, with light scroll engraving and beautiful color case-hardened finish. Automatic ejectors. Automatic safety. Greener-type cross bolt. Double underlugs.

TRIGGER: Non-selective single trigger.

STOCK: English style with straight grip. 1⅝" drop at comb, 2½" drop at heel and 14" length of pull. Hand checkered.

BARRELS: Hard chrome lined with matted rib. (See chokes and weights below).

AVAILABLE GAUGES, BARREL LENGTHS & CHOKES

GAUGE	BARREL LENGTH	CHOKE COMBINATIONS	(Approximate) Weight
12	25"	Improved Cylinder & Modified	6 lbs.
12	28"	Modified & Full	6 lbs. 2 ozs.
20	25"	Improved Cylinder & Modified	5 lbs. 8 ozs.
20	28"	Modified & Full	5 lbs. 10 ozs.

BERNARDELLI HAMMER SHOTGUNS

Italia
PIGEON GUN
Double Barrel
HAMMER MODEL

**With
Half-Cock Safety**

The Italia Pigeon Gun is a hammer-type shotgun made from modern steels and designed for use with either standard or high-velocity 2¾ inch shells.

This model is exceptionally finished and is unusually attractive. Mechanical features include: Greener-type cross bolt, double triggers, purdy-type forend catch, slim, English style forend and stock of extra fancy walnut, elaborately hand-engraved side plates, side-wings, double underlugs, fine-line hand checkering, half-cock safety, and hard chrome lined barrels.

Available in the following choices of gauges and barrel lengths:

12 gauge, 30-inch, modified & full chokes
12 gauge, 28-inch, modified & full chokes

Price, Italia Model, all variations, each **$450.00**

Brescia
Double Barrel
HAMMER MODEL

**With
Half-Cock Safety**

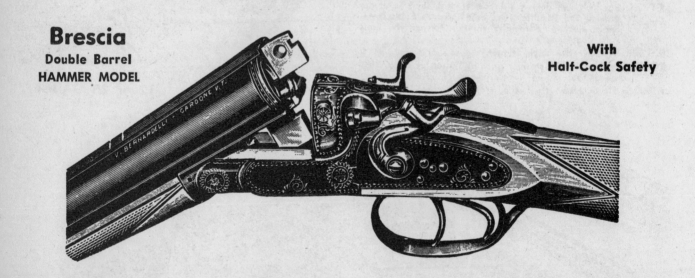

The hammer shotgun has enjoyed a revival of interest in recent years and the Bernardelli firm, in acknowledging this renewed interest, has released a new line of hammer models constructed of modern steels for modern high-velocity shells.

The Brescia Model, shown here, has Greener-type locks, cross bolt, case-hardened action, English-style select walnut stock and forend, and light engraving.

In 12 gauge this model may be had in choice of 30-inch (M & F), or 28-inch (M & F) barrels and chokes.

In 20 gauge this model is made only with 25-inch barrels bored improved cylinder and modified. The Brescia Model cannot be had in any other gauges or with any other barrel lengths or chokes **$395.00**

BERNARDELLI SHOTGUNS

ELIO
12 ga. with 25" Imp. Cylinder & Modified barrel **$525.00**
12 ga. with 28" Modified & Full barrel **$525.00**

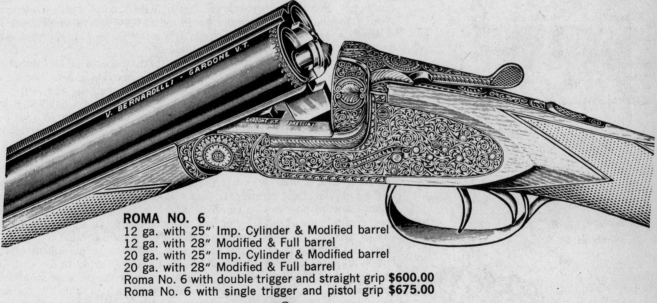

ROMA NO. 6
12 ga. with 25" Imp. Cylinder & Modified barrel
12 ga. with 28" Modified & Full barrel
20 ga. with 25" Imp. Cylinder & Modified barrel
20 ga. with 28" Modified & Full barrel
Roma No. 6 with double trigger and straight grip **$600.00**
Roma No. 6 with single trigger and pistol grip **$675.00**

HOLLAND
12 ga. with 28" Modified and Full barrel **$3000.00**

BROWNING SUPERPOSED SHOTGUNS

Diana Grade

SINGLE SELECTIVE TRIGGER—The Superposed has only one trigger which fires both barrels in the sequence of your preference. You may fire either the *over* barrel or the *under* barrel first by the quick and easy movement of the "barrel selector button" to the right or to the left.

This selector button is appropriately located on the top tang of the Superposed just behind the receiver where the thumb naturally rests when the hand is in shooting position. It is equally convenient for the right or left hand shooter.

After the first shot, is is not necessary to use the barrel selector button again in order to fire the remaining barrel. The gun's mechanism automatically readies the second barrel for firing, and does it so swiftly it is completed before the trigger can be pulled the second time. This "barrel selector" need not be reset with each loading. If, for instance, you are pheasant hunting under conditions which would advocate that the *under* barrel generally be fired first, the "barrel selector button" need only be set once to that position. Thereafter the *under* barrel will always fire first, followed by the *over* barrel on the second pull of the trigger, for any period of time you might wish.

It should also be noted that the shifting mechanism of this single trigger completely disconnects between the first and the second shot, thereby preventing "doubling" which means the firing of both barrels simultaneously.

Another safety feature of this trigger is the fact that it is positively locked whenever the action is not completely closed.

Though it is infrequent, a misfire can occur because of a faulty shell. In such event, there is no alternative in a single barreled gun to ejecting or removing the problem shell and chambering a new shell, usually at the expense of losing the chance at the target. In the Superposed a quick shot can still be delivered merely by flipping the selector button rearward and then back to its original position. It is not necessary to shift the selector button to the position for the other barrel.

SAFETY—The manual safety, for added convenience, operates off the "barrel selector button" described above, located just behind the opening lever at the top rear of the receiver. In its forward position the gun is "off-safe." In its rearward position the complete action is "on safe." One can readily see the advantages of this selector button also actuating the safety mechanism. Let us assume you have positioned the selector mechanism (on the right side) to shoot the *under* barrel first. A straight forward movement of this button takes the gun "off safe" and readies the under barrel to fire first. On the other hand, if the game or target of the moment should more wisely call for using the *over* barrel, a slight pressure to the left first, then a forward movement of the button (to its "off-safe" position) simultaneously selects the *over* barrel in the same simple maneuver.

AUTOMATIC EJECTORS—Fired shells are automatically ejected or flipped from their respective chambers by a dependable ejection system upon each opening of the breech. Unfired shells remain in the chamber or chambers upon opening but are conveniently lifted above the level of the chamber so that, on occasions for unloading, they can be lifted out easily by hand. Spent shells can be ejected in almost any direction desired by the shooter or can be caught by the hand as the breech is opened should he wish to keep them for reuse. Hand loaders especially like the empty cases from a Superposed. Rarely is resizing necessary and of course there is no damage to the ends of the cases.

TAKEDOWN SYSTEM—For ease of carrying or cleaning, the barrels and forearm portion of the gun may be separated from the receiver and stock portion very simply. A latch in the forearm unlocks the two sections after which they need only be unhinged. The forearm does not separate from the barrels in this maneuver; it is securely attached for finer fit and to eliminate the possibility of becoming lost or inadvertently damaged.

BROWNING SUPERPOSED SHOTGUNS

IN 12, 20, 28 & .410 GAUGE (Complete specifications and prices on following page)

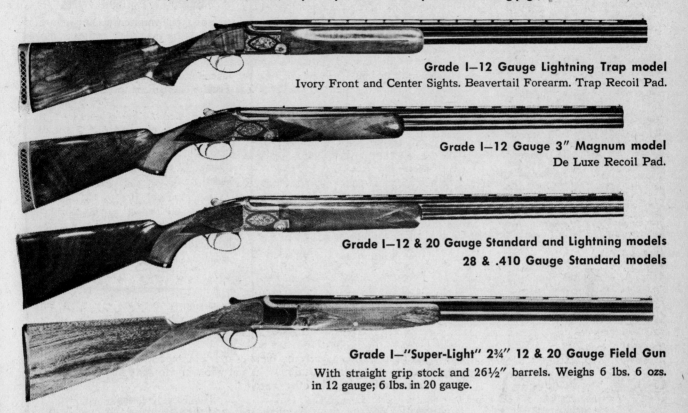

Grade I—12 Gauge Lightning Trap model
Ivory Front and Center Sights. Beavertail Forearm. Trap Recoil Pad.

Grade I—12 Gauge 3" Magnum model
De Luxe Recoil Pad.

Grade I—12 & 20 Gauge Standard and Lightning models
28 & .410 Gauge Standard models

Grade I—"Super-Light" 2¾" 12 & 20 Gauge Field Gun
With straight grip stock and 26½" barrels. Weighs 6 lbs. 6 ozs. in 12 gauge; 6 lbs. in 20 gauge.

Lightning Superposed: Weighing approximately 6-pounds in the 20 gauge and 7-pounds in the 12 gauge. These models are identical in appearance to the Standard line of superposed shotguns but average about one half-pound less in weight in both gauges.

Unlike 12 and 20 gauge models, the 28 and 410 gauge Superposed are available only in one weight deemed most suitable to the use requirements of these gauges.

Superlight Superposed: Ultra light field gun with straight grip stock. Weight is approximately 6 pounds, 6 ounces. Made in 12 and 20 gauge only with 26½" barrels. Features raised ventilated rib and tapered forearm. Chambered for all 2¾" factory loads. Available in four ascending grades.

20 Gauge Superposed: Accepts all 20 gauge loads up to and including the 3-inch Magnum (except Super Light model).

Superposed Magnum 12: This model is chambered for the 3-inch, 12 gauge shell, however, it will also shoot 2¾" shells. It features 30" barrels with a ventilated rib. All Magnum models are fitted with recoil pads.

Superposed Skeet Models: (not illustrated) Available in the following models: 12 and 20 gauge Standard and Lightning models; 28 and .410 gauge Standard models. Made with 26½ or 28-inch barrels; all have special Skeet choke.

Skeet Superposed available in 12, 20, 28 and .410 gauges. Twelve and 20 gauges available in Standard or Lightning models and all gauges offered in four grades. Each features a beavertail forearm, pistol grip, ivory front and center sights and contoured recoil pad. Made with 26½" or 28" barrels.

Superposed Trap Models: Two distinct models are available, the Lightning and Broadway model. Stock and forearm dimensions are the same on either model. Any combination of chokes is available; Full and Full, Improved-Modified and Full, or Modified and Full. The Lightning model carries 30-inch barrels and a 5/16 inch wide full ventilated rib. The Broadway rib (⅝") is available only in 12 gauges, 32" and 30" barrels.

Diana Grade

Midas Grade

BROWNING O&U SPECIFICATIONS

STANDARD 12 and 20 Gauge
Average Weights

12 Gauge Magnum—28"	7 lbs. 15 oz.
12 Gauge—26½"	7 lbs. 11 oz.
20 Gauge—28"	6 lbs. 12 oz.
20 Gauge—26½"	6 lbs. 8 oz.
12 Gauge Magnum—30"	8 lbs. 1 oz.
12 Gauge SKEET 28"	7 lbs. 14 oz.
12 Gauge SKEET 26½"	7 lbs. 12 oz.
20 Gauge SKEET 28"	6 lbs. 15 oz.
20 Gauge SKEET 26½"	6 lbs. 13 oz.

SUPER-LIGHT
12 and 20 Gauge Field

12 Gauge—26½"
6 lbs. 8 oz.
20 Gauge—26½"
6 lbs.

BROADway
Trap

12 Gauge—32"
8 lbs.
12 Gauge—30"
7 lbs. 12 oz.

LIGHTNING 12 and 20 Gauge
Average Weights

12 Gauge—28"	7 lbs. 8 oz.
12 Gauge—26½"	7 lbs. 6 oz.
20 Gauge—28"	6 lbs. 6 oz.
20 Gauge—26½"	6 lbs. 4 oz.
12 Gauge Trap—30"	7 lbs. 13 oz.
12 Gauge SKEET 28"	7 lbs. 11 oz.
12 Gauge SKEET 26½"	7 lbs. 9 oz.
20 Gauge SKEET 28"	6 lbs. 12 oz.
20 Gauge SKEET 26½"	6 lbs. 8 oz.

LIGHTNING 28 and .410 GAUGE

28 Gauge—28"	6 lbs. 10 oz.
28 Gauge—26½"	6 lbs. 7 oz.
28 Gauge SKEET 28"	6 lbs. 14 oz.
28 Gauge SKEET 26½"	6 lbs. 11 oz.
.410 Gauge—28"	6 lbs. 14 oz.
.410 Gauge—26½"	6 lbs. 10 oz.
.410 Gauge SKEET 28"	7 lbs.
.410 Gauge SKEET 26½"	6 lbs. 13 oz.

The stock and forearms fitted to Diana and Midas grades are made from more highly figured walnut which is generally denser in texture and somewhat heavier. The weights shown above are for Grade I models. Other grades usually weigh slightly more.

GRADES AVAILABLE	Grade I	Diana	Midas
Standard 12 & 20 gauge Hunting & Skeet	X	----	----
Lightning 12 & 20 gauge Hunting & Skeet	X	X	X
Super-Light 12 & 20 Gauge Field	X	----	----
3" Magnum 12 Gauge	X	X	X
28 and .410 gauge Hunting and Skeet	X	X	X
Lightning Trap	X	X	X
BROADway Trap	X	X	X

RECEIVER —

Grade I — Blued steel with hand-engraved graceful scroll and rosette designs.

Diana Grades — Steel in silver gray tone with hand-engraved game scenes ascending in artistic design.

Midas Grade — Specially blued steel with deeply hand-carved background and hand-engraved 18 carat gold inlaid pheasant and ducks on the 12 gauge — smaller game birds on the 20 gauge.

EXTRA SETS OF BARRELS — Any of the specifications listed above in gauge combinations of 12 & 12, 12 & 20, 20 & 20, 20 & 28 and/or .410, 28 & .410.

CHOKE — On all models any combination of Full — Improved-Modified — Modified — Improved-Cylinder — Skeet — Cylinder.

STOCK AND FOREARM — Finest select walnut — hand-rubbed finish — skillfully checkered. Grade I; fine 20-line checkering. The Deluxe Engraved models have correspondingly more intricate patterns with finer checkering.

	12 Gauge Hunting	12 Gauge Trap (Pistol Grip)	12 Gauge Skeet (Pistol Grip)	20, 28 and .410 Gauge Hunting	20, 28 and .410 Gauge Skeet (Pistol Grip)
Stock — Length of Pull	14¼"	14⅜"	14⅜"	14¼"	14⅜"
Drop at Comb	1⅝"	1 7/16"	1½"	1½"	1½"
Drop at Heel	2½"	1⅝"	2"	2⅜"	2"

Forearm — Hunting — Full grip contour.
Super-Light — Slim contour, ultra light.
Trap and Skeet — Beavertail with full grip.

TRIGGER — Gold plated all models. Fast, crisp, positive — Doubling impossible.

SAFETY — Manual; combined in thumb piece with automatic barrel selector mechanism.

SIGHTS — Medium raised steel bead. Trap and Skeet models: Ivory Front and Center sights.

RIB — Ventilated on all models

On all 12 gauge except BROADway trap and Super-Light 5/16" wide. On all 20, 28 and .410 gauge ¼" wide. On BROADWAY Trap Model ⅝" wide. Broadway ribs for 12 gauge 28" or 26½" barrels may be acquired on special order for an additional charge.

A regular dimension solid raised rib is available on all other models on special order at the same price as the ventilated rib.

RECOIL PADS — Deluxe recoil pads are provided in hunting type on the 3" Magnum 12 gauge, contoured type on all Trap models and special skeet type on Skeet models.

SUPERPOSED SHOTGUN PRICES

All Models With Ventilated Rib

Lightning 12 and 20 Gauge
3" Magnum 12 Gauge

Grade I	$1,100.00
Diana	1,950.00
Midas	2,650.00

Super-Light 12 and 20 Gauge

Grade I	$1,170.00
Diana	2,000.00
Midas	2,700.00

Lightning 28 and .410 Gauge

Grade I	$1,300.00
Diana	2,150.00
Midas	2,850.00

TRAP MODELS

Lightning 12 Gauge

Grade I	$1,120.00
Diana	1,970.00
Midas	2,670.00

BROADway 12 Gauge

Grade I	$1,160.00
Diana	2,010.00
Midas	2,720.00

SKEET MODELS

Lightning 12 and 20 Gauge

Grade I	$1,120.00
Diana	1,970.00
Midas	2,670.00

Lightning 28 and .410 Gauge

Grade I	$1,300.00
Diana	2,150.00
Midas	2,850.00

CHAMBERING—Indicated below is the factory loads for which each model is chambered: 12 ga. Hunting, Trap & Skeet—2¾", 2¾" Mag.; 12 ga. 3" Magnum—2¾", 2¾" Mag., 3" or 30" Mag.; 20 ga. Hunting (including those with skeet chokes)—2¾", 2¾" Mag., 3" or 3" Mag.; 20 ga. Super-Light—2¾", 2¾" Mag.; 20 ga. Skeet—2¾", 2¾" Mag.; 28 ga. Hunting & Skeet—2¾"; .410 ga. Hunting (including those with skeet chokes)—2½", 3" or 3" Mag.; .410 ga. Skeet—2½".

BROWNING SHOTGUNS

CITORI OVER-UNDER SHOTGUN

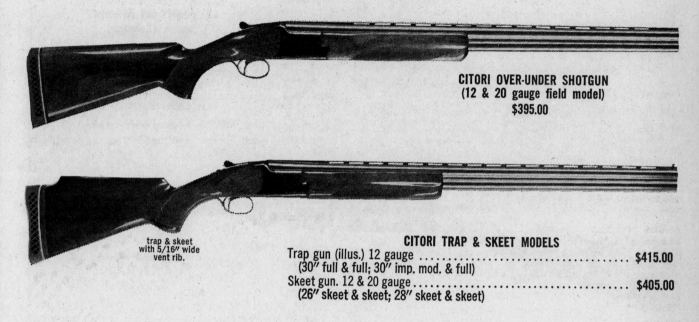

CITORI OVER-UNDER SHOTGUN
(12 & 20 gauge field model)
$395.00

trap & skeet
with 5/16″ wide
vent rib.

CITORI TRAP & SKEET MODELS
Trap gun (illus.) 12 gauge $415.00
   (30″ full & full; 30″ imp. mod. & full)
Skeet gun. 12 & 20 gauge $405.00
   (26″ skeet & skeet; 28″ skeet & skeet)

FIELD GRADE CITORI SPECIFICATIONS

Gauge—12 and 20 gauge.
Barrels—Choice of 30″, 28″ or 26″ in 12 gauge. 28″ or 26″ in 20 gauge. Ventilated rib with matted sighting plane. Medium raised German nickel silver sight bead.

Overall Length—12 or 20 gauge.
   With 26″ barrels—43″
   With 28″ barrels—45″
   With 30″ barrels—47″

Chokes—Choice of Full-Full or Mod-Full in 30″ barrels; choice of Mod-Full or Imp Cyl-Mod in 28″ and 26″ barrels.

Trigger—Single selective. Gold plated. Fast and crisp.

Chamber—All 20 gauge Field models and all 12 gauge Field models accept all 3″ magnum loads, as well as 2¾″ loads.

Safety—Manual thumb safety. Combined with barrel selector mechanism.

Automatic Ejectors—Fired shells thrown out of gun; unfired shells are elevated for easy removal.

APPROXIMATE WEIGHT—

	12 gauge	20 gauge
With 26″ barrels —	7 lbs. 9 oz.	6 lbs. 11 oz.
With 28″ barrels —	7 lbs. 11 oz.	6 lbs. 13 oz.
With 30″ barrels —	7 lbs. 13 oz.	

Stock and Forearm—Dense walnut. Skillfully checkered. Full pistol grip. Hunting Beavertail forearm. Field type recoil pad installed on 12 gauge models.

	12 gauge	20 gauge
Length of pull—	14¼″	14¼″
Drop at comb—	1⅝″	1½″
Drop at heel—	2½″	2⅜″

BT-99 BROWNING TRAP SPECIAL

Available in full, improved-modified, and modified choke, with choice of 32″ or 34″ barrel **$399.50**
   Drop at Heel: 1⅝″
   Forearm: Full beavertail.

SAFETY—No manual safety, a feature preferred by trap shooters.
SIGHTS—Ivory front and center sight beads.
RIB—High post, ventilated, full floating, matted, 11/32 inch wide.
RECOIL PAD—Deluxe, contoured trap style.
WEIGHT—32 inch barrel 8 lbs., 34 inch barrel 8 lbs. 2 oz.
AUTOMATIC EJECTION—Fired shell ejected automatically on opening action, unfired shell elevated from chamber for convenient removal.

BT-99 SPECIFICATIONS: RECEIVER—Machined steel, tastefully hand-engraved and richly blued. **BARREL**—Choice of 32 inch or 34 inch. **CHOKE**—Choice of Full, Improved Modified or Modified. **CHAMBER**—for 12 gauge, 2¾″ shells only. **TRIGGER**—Gold plated, crisp, positive, pull approximately 3½ pounds.

STOCK AND FOREARM—Select French walnut, hand-rubbed finish, sharp 20-line hand-checkering.
   Stock: Full pistol grip.
      Length of Pull: 14⅜″
      Drop at Comb: 1 7/16″

BROWNING SHOTGUNS

BUCK-SPECIAL
12, 16 & 20 GAUGES
AND 12 & 20 3" MAGNUM

Gauges, Barrel Lengths & Weights

Light 12	24"	7 lbs.
3" Mag. 12	24"	8 lbs. 4 oz.
Sweet 16	24"	6 lbs. 6 oz.
Light 20	24"	6 lbs. 2 oz.
3" Mag. 20	24"	6 lbs. 15 oz.

Plain barrel with special sights. Rear adjustable for windage and elevation. Gold bead front on contoured ramp. Specially choked and bored for rifled slug and buckshot loads. Carrying sling and swivel attachments also available.

The Buck Special is available in Lightweight 12, 16 and 20 gauge, plus the 3" Magnum 12 and 20 gauge. For use with rifles slug, or buckshot loads. Comes with open sights and 24" barrel.

Lightweight Buck Special, without accessories .. **$434.50**
Lightweight Buck Special, with accessories **$434.50**

SIDE-BY-SIDE SHOTGUN

BROWNING "B-SS"
12 & 20 GAUGE
$319.50

12 GAUGE
B-SS SPECIFICATIONS:

GAUGE: 12 gauge.

BARRELS: Choice of 26" or 28" barrels. Solid rib with matted top. Sight bead is German nickel silver.

CHOKE: 28" barrel model choked modified and full. 26" barrels choked modified and full, or improved cylinder and modified.

TRIGGER: Single mechanical trigger fires right barrel first (the more open choke).

CHAMBER: All 12 gauge 2¾" and 2¾" magnum shells.

AUTOMATIC SAFETY: Goes on safe when breech is opened and remains there until manually moved to off safe.

AUTOMATIC EJECTORS: Fired shells are thrown out of gun. Unfired shells are elevated for easy removal.

WEIGHT: With 26" barrels approx. 7 lbs. 3 oz., with 28" barrels approx. 7 lbs. 5 oz., 30" bbls. approx. 7 lbs. 7 oz.

OVERALL LENTH: 26" barrels 43". 28" barrels 45".

STOCK AND FOREARM: Select walnut, hand-rubbed finish, sharp 20-line hand checkering. Full pistol grip. Full grip beavertail forearm.
  Length of pull: 14¼".
  Drop at comb: 1⅝".
  Drop at heel: 2½".

The Browning Side by Side has a "mechanical" trigger which differs from the "inertia" trigger found on many two barreled guns in that the recoil of the first shot is not used to set up the mechanism for the second shot. The first pull of the trigger fires the right barrel. The next pull fires the left barrel. The positive linkage of the B-SS mechanical trigger prevents doubling (both barrels firing at the same instant) or balking. The chromed trigger lets off crisply at about 4½ pounds.

B-SS SIDE BY SIDE SHOTGUN
BARREL LENGTH & CHOKE COMBINATIONS

Modified/Full Imp.-Cylinder Modified

Grade 1 26" Barrel	$319.50
Grade 1 28" Barrel	$319.50
Grade 1 30" Barrel	$319.50

20 GAUGE
B-SS SPECIFICATIONS:

GAUGE: 20 gauge, chambered for all 2¾" and 3" loads.

BARRELS: choice of 26" or 28" with solid matted rib, German nickel sight bead.

CHOKES: 26" barrel—modified and full or improved cylinder and modified.
  28" barrel—modified and full.

TRIGGER: single mechanical, fires right barrel first. (the more open the choke)

AUTOMATIC SAFETY: goes on safe when breech is opened and remains there until manually moved to safe.

AUTOMATIC EJECTORS: fired shells are ejected. Unfired shells elevated for easy removal.

WEIGHT: 26" barrel—6 lbs. 14 oz.
  28" barrel—7 lbs.

OVERALL LENGTH: 26" barrel—43"
  28" barrel—45"

STOCK AND FOREARM: Select walnut, hand-rubbed finish, sharp 20-line hand-checkering.

FULL PISTOL GRIP: Length of pull—14¼"
  Drop at comb—1⅝"
  Drop at heel—2½"

BROWNING AUTOMATIC SHOTGUNS

**Light 12, Sweet-16 and
Light 20 Gauge**
Ventilated Rib $434.50

AUTOMATIC-5 MODELS—The Browning Automatic-5 Shotgun is offered in an unusually wide variety of models and specifications. The Browning 12-gauge 3-inch Magnum accepts up to and including the 3-inch, 1⅞ ounce, 12-gauge Magnum load, which contains only ⅛ ounces of shot less than the maximum 3½-inch 10-gauge load. The 2¾-inch Magnums and 2¾-inch high-velocity shells may be used with equal pattern efficiency. Standard features include a special shock absorber and a hunting-style recoil pad. The kick is not unpleasant with even the heaviest 3-inch loads.

Browning also offers the 20 gauge in a 3-inch Magnum model. This powerful, light heavyweight offers maximum versatility to 20-gauge advocates. It handles the 20-gauge, 2¾-inch high velocity and Magnums, but it literally thrives on the 3-inch, 1¼ ounce load which delivers real 12-gauge performance in a 20-gauge package.

The 12-gauge Automatic-5, chambered for regular 2¾-inch shells handles all 12-gauge, 2¾-inch shells, from the very lightest 1 ounce field load to the heavy 1½ ounce Magnums. Browning 16-gauge and 20-gauge Automatics are lightweight guns and each is a top performer for the upland hunter. Yet, with 2¾-inch high velocity or 2¾-inch Magnums, either does a fine job in the duck blind.

All models and gauges of the Automatic-5 are available in the Buck Special version, which is designed to accurately fire the rifled slug or buckshot loads. In addition, its specially bored 24-inch barrel will deliver nice open patterns with standard field loads.

SKEET MODELS—Special 26-inch skeet barrels fit all Browning Automatic-5's of like gauge and model so an owner may easily convert his favorite hunting gun to a skeet gun by a quick change of barrels.

2000 GAS OPERATED AUTOMATIC SHOTGUN

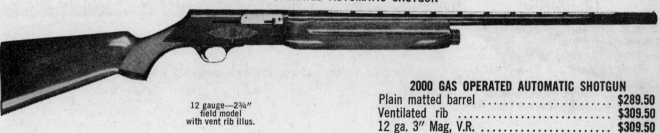

12 gauge—2¾"
field model
with vent rib illus.

2000 GAS OPERATED AUTOMATIC SHOTGUN
Plain matted barrel $289.50
Ventilated rib $309.50
12 ga. 3" Mag, V.R. $309.50

2000 Specifications
Gauge—12 gauge.
Barrel—Choice of 26", 28" or 30" barrel in 2¾" Field models. 28", 30" or 32" in 3" Magnum models. Plain or ventilated rib. Plain barrels have matted sighting surface. All barrels are completely interchangeable within the same gauge.
Chamber—All 2¾" standard and 2¾" Magnum loads with 2¾" chambered barrel. 3" Magnum loads with Magnum barrel.
Choke—Choice of Full, Modified, Improved Cylinder or Cylinder in 2¾" models. Full of Modified in 3" Magnum models.

Capacity—Five 2¾" loads; Four 3" Magnum loads. Reduced to three 2¾" or 3" Magnum loads with magazine plug.
Trigger—Crisp. Positive.
Safety—Cross bolt. Red warning band visible when in "fire" position. Easily reversible by gunsmith for left hand shooter.
Receiver—Engraved with handsome scroll designs. Machined and forged from high grade steel.
Sight—Medium raised bead. German nickel silver.
Stock and Forearm—French walnut, skillfully checkered. Full pistol grip. No recoil pad.

Length of pull—14¼"
Drop at comb—1⅝"
Drop at heel—2½"

Overall Length—
26" Barrel—45⅜"
28" Barrel—47⅜"
30" Barrel—49⅜"
32" Barrel—51⅜"

Approximate Weight—Ventilated Rib Models. (Plain barrel models weigh 3 oz. less.)

26" Barrel—7 lbs. 8 oz.
28" Barrel—7 lbs. 9 oz.
30" Barrel—7 lbs. 10 oz.
32" Barrel—7 lbs. 11 oz.

2000 20 Gauge Specifications
Barrel—Ventilated Rib only. Front and center ivory sight beads on skeet barrel. Available in 26" & 28" lengths.
Chamber—All 2¾" standard and 2¾" Magnum loads with 2¾" chambered barrel. 3" Magnum loads only with Magnum barrel.
Capacity—Five 2¾" loads; four 3" loads. Reduced to three 2¾"

or 3" Magnum loads with magazine plug provided.
Trigger—Crisp, positive.
Safety—Cross bolt. Red warning band. Easily reversible.
Receiver—Engraved with scroll designs. Cold forged and machined from high-grade steel.

CHARLES DALY SHOTGUNS

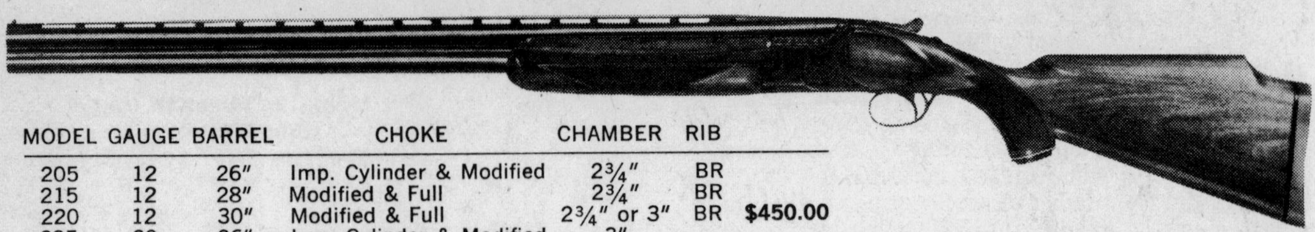

MODEL	GAUGE	BARREL	CHOKE	CHAMBER	RIB	
205	12	26″	Imp. Cylinder & Modified	2¾″	BR	
215	12	28″	Modified & Full	2¾″	BR	
220	12	30″	Modified & Full	2¾″ or 3″	BR	$450.00
235	20	26″	Imp. Cylinder & Modified	3″		
245	20	28″	Modified & Full	3″		
200	12	26″	Skeet & Skeet	2¾″	BR	
230	20	26″	Skeet & Skeet	3″		$415.00
240	20	28″	Skeet & Skeet	3″		

Superior Grade
Field and Skeet Models

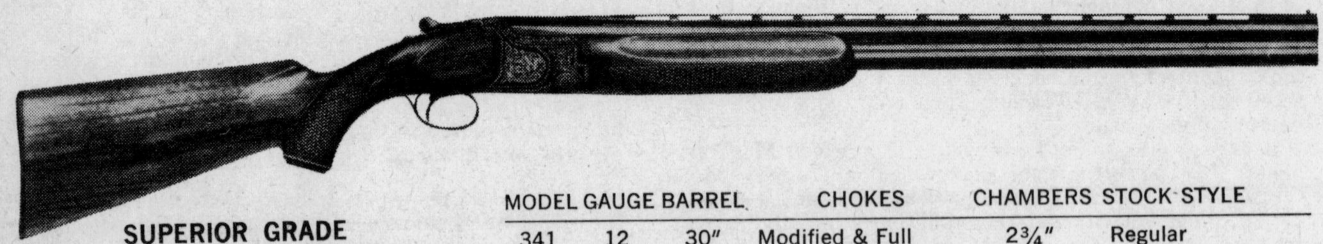

SUPERIOR GRADE
Trap Gun
BROADENED RIB

MODEL	GAUGE	BARREL	CHOKES	CHAMBERS	STOCK STYLE	
341	12	30″	Modified & Full	2¾″	Regular	
343	12	30″	Imp. Modified & Full	2¾″	Regular	
349	12	32″	Imp. Modified & Full	2¾″	Regular	$500.00
363	12	30″	Imp. Modified & Full	2¾″	Monte Carlo	
369	12	30″	Imp. Modified & Full	2¾″	Monte Carlo	

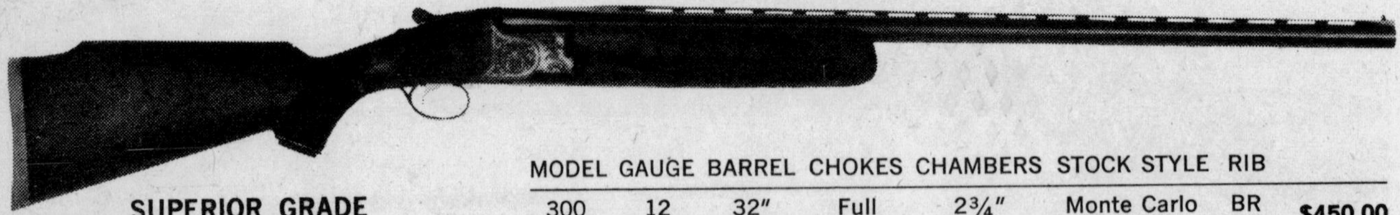

SUPERIOR GRADE
Single Barrel Trap Gun

MODEL	GAUGE	BARREL	CHOKES	CHAMBERS	STOCK STYLE	RIB	
300	12	32″	Full	2¾″	Monte Carlo	BR	
304	12	34″	Full	2¾″	Monte Carlo	BR	$450.00

DIAMOND GRADE
& DIAMOND GRADE INTERNATIONAL TRAP
Stock Dimensions:
Field and Skeet—14″ x 1½″ x 2½″.
Monte Carlo Trap—14⅜″ x 1½″ x 2½″ x 1½″.

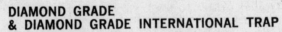

MODEL	GAUGE	BARREL	CHOKES	CHAMBERS	STOCK STYLE	RIB	
505	12	26″	Imp. Cylinder & Modified	2¾″	Field	BR	
500	12	26″	Skeet & Skeet	2¾″	Field	BR	
515	12	28″	Modified & Full	2¾″	Field	BR	
571	12	30″	Modified & Full	2¾″	Monte Carlo	BR	$600.00
572	12	30″	Full & Full	2¾″	Monte Carlo	BR	
573	12	30″	Imp. Modified & Full	2¾″	Monte Carlo	BR	
579	12	32″	Imp. Modified & Full	2¾″	Monte Carlo	BR	

FLAT-TOP TRAP MODELS

563	12	30″	Imp. Modified & Full	2¾″	Monte Carlo	FT	
569	12	32″	Imp. Modified & Full	2¾″	Monte Carlo	FT	$650.00

FRANCHI SHOTGUNS

Luigi Franchi, S.P.A. of Brescia, Italy, founded in 1868, has become one of the outstanding manufacturers of firearms in Europe. This success and recognition is due to their policy of constant improvement, the perfection of production techniques, and to utilization of the newest and most modern machinery and equipment.

However, the same quality craftsmanship . . . the skills passed from father to son . . . the patient care for detail, however minute, the fine honing and finish to parts the average shooter never even sees . . . these vital details are still performed and supervised by the best-trained gunsmiths, as they were over a hundred years ago.

At Franchi, machines aid the artisan —they do not take his place. A shotgun is the most difficult of all firearms to produce; in order to reach the highest expec-

PEREGRINE
451

tation . . . the epitome of consummate quality . . . demands and gets—constant supervision throughout every step of planning, construction, and finishing by master gunsmiths.

This year, Franchi continues their perpetual program of refinement and improvement in order to produce the finest examples of superbly accurate, precision-made, hand-crafted, field and target shotguns ever offered to shooters at a fair price.

The ejection system has been completely revised after much study and evaluation by Franchi engineers. The new ejectors will always stay synchronized, and will retain their strength and timing over the years. Both upper and lower barrels will throw the empty hulls within a foot of each other.

Receivers are also completely redesigned this year. Falconet Field models feature a special lightweight alloy,

scientifically hardened for maximum strength and wear; yet light enough to allow the gun to be carried in comfort all day by the hunter.

In Skeet and Trap models, where more weight is desireable, a solid steel billet is forged, meticulously machined, and multihardened to stand up to the many hundred thousands of shells target guns are subjected to.

Both receivers share a massive low hinge which guarantee a micro-fit over the entire frame surface. The receiver opens sufficiently to allow easy insertion of a shell into the lower barrel.

Choice walnut stocks, discriminately chosen for their density and figure are hand fitted to

such minute tolerance that removed or replacement can be accomplished easily, without need of any fitting.

All models are meticulously hand checkered *after* a durable, lasting epoxy finish is applied. Target guns are also available in a traditional, dull, oil finish.

Franchi Peregrine Series share a very fast lock-time as a result of the employment of the very finest coil springs attached to *the bottoms* of the sears; thus creating a much shorter "throw," or travel time.

The safety (automatic on field models, non-automatic on target guns) is conveniently located on the tang, completely separated from the barrel selector button on the trigger.

The advantages of this arrangement are obvious for fast, safe, gun handling; particularly so in the field, because the two separate functions cannot be confused.

The trigger itself will prove a joy to both field and target shooter alike. It is a very short pull, selective trigger, shaped perfectly; with neither creep or play. In short, it is *the* perfect shotgun trigger.

The 3003, a target gun, is available in Skeet and Trap form. It features a broad 10mm, *concave,* tapered rib. Each shot barrel is patterned before it leaves the factory to ensure even, well distributed shot patterns.

The extra-choice walnut is hand chosen for these guns, hand checkered faultlessly, and completely finished and rubbed by hand.

FRANCHI

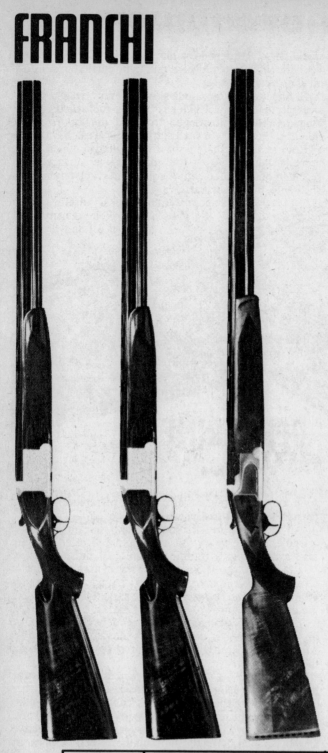

FRANCHI PEREGRINE SHOTGUNS

MODEL 451

12 Gauge $595.00

Features: lightweight receiver; hand-cut checkering; European walnut stock and forend; a tang safety independent of any other function, a trigger mechanism that is a unified assembly independent of floor plate, assuring consistency of pull; total surface contact between barrel walls and frame for extreme rigidity; a firing sequence selector button on the trigger; full length one piece rib from muzzle to breech face; coil spring powered extractors; chrome-moly blued steel bbls.; chrome bores; and side walls that extend to center line of top bbl. Chambered for 2¾" shells.

MODEL 400

12 Gauge $695.00

Features: steel receiver; hand-cut checkering; European walnut stock and forend; a tang safety, independent of any other function; a trigger mechanism that is a unified assembly, independent of floor plate, assuring consistency of pull; total surface contact between barrel walls and frame; a firing sequence selector button on the trigger; full length one piece rib from muzzle to breech face; coil spring powered extractors; chrome-moly blued steel bbls.; chrome bores; and side walls that extend to center line of top bbl. Chambered for 2¾" shells.

MODEL 3003

12 Gauge Trap & Skeet $2000.00

Features: steel receiver, real hand-cut checkering; European walnut stock and forend; a tang safety independent of any other function; a trigger mechanism that is a unified assembly independent of floor plate, assuring consistency of pull; total surface contact between barrel walls and frame for extreme rigidity; a firing sequence selector button on the trigger; full length one piece rib from muzzle to breech face; coil spring powered extractors; chrome-moly blued steel bbls.; chrome bores; and side walls that extend to center line of top bbl. Chambered for 2¾" shells.

BARREL LENGTH AND CHOKE COMBINATION IN 400 AND 451		
	26½"	28"
Cyl. & Imp. Cyl.	X	
Imp. Cyl. & Mod.	X	
Mod. & Full	X	X

BARREL LENGTH AND CHOKE COMBINATION IN 3003 TRAP AND SKEET:				
	26½"	28"	29"	30"
Skeet 1 & Skeet 2	X			
Mod. & Full		X	X	X

MODELS		451	400	Trap 3003	Skeet 3003
GAUGES		12	12	12	12
STOCK DIMENSIONS	Length of pull	14½	14½	14⅜	14⅜
	Drop at comb	1½	1½	1¼	1½
	Drop at heel	2¼	2¼	1½	1½
WEIGHTS	26½" Bbl.	6 lbs. 1 oz.	6 lbs. 15 ozs.	7 lbs. 11 ozs.	7 lbs. 8 ozs.
	28" Bbl.	6 lbs. 3½ ozs.	7 lbs. 2 ozs.		
	29" Bbl.				

FRANCHI O&U SHOTGUNS

STANDARD FALCONET FIELD MODELS IN 12 & 20 GAUGE

The Falconet shotgun is a *lightwight* over & under equipped with selective single trigger, automatic ejectors, chrome-lined barrels, high ventilated rib, automatic safety and epoxy-finished, checkered, walnut stock and forend. These custom features, combined with Franchi's overhead trigger mechanism, have propelled this model to the top of the over & under market.

For quail, pheasant, dove, grouse, turkey, rabbit or ducks, it's the lightest and fastest twin-tubed shotgun that a hunter could ever hope to handle. Yet, in spite of its light-weight, it is ruggedly built with chrome-molybdenum steel barrels, and an exclusive, rugged, light alloy receiver. Entirely forged and machined first quality components are used throughout.

The beautiful engraving of the receiver surfaces is particularly attractive in Buckskin and Ebony models.

One of the most important features of all Falconet shotguns is the unique design of the selective trigger and sear mechanism which provides for a light, uniform and crisp trigger pull. This design is exceptionally reliable; it has virtually eliminated faults such as mis-firing or doubling.

WEIGHT

20 Gauge . . . 6 lbs.
Overall weight may vary slightly, depending upon barrel length and density of wood components.

FALCONET

12 & 20 Gauge Buckskin $499.95
12 & 20 Gauge Ebony $499.95

CHOICE OF MODELS, BARRELS & CHOKES

24-inch Barrels, Cylinder & Imp. Cylinder Chokes
26-inch Barrels, Imp. Cyl. & Modified Chokes
28-inch Barrels, Modified & Full Chokes
30-inch Barrels, Modified & Full Chokes (12 ga. only)

Detailed view of Ebony model

SPECIFICATIONS

BARRELS: Made from chrome-molybdenum steel with cold-forged chokes and chrome lined bores. Regularly equipped with high, ventilated rib, 12 gauge models are chambered for all 12 gauge 2¾-inch shells. 20 gauge models are chambered for all 2¾ and 3 inch shells. **TRIGGERS:** Selective single trigger with overhead sears. Selector is operated by safety button on tang; triggers are adjusted for a light, crisp pull. **SAFETY:** All models equipped with automatic ejector. **RECEIVER:** Forged and machined from a special lightweight gun-making alloy and hardened for maximum strength and wear. Side surfaces attractively engraved with wild bird scenes. **STOCK & FOREND:** Genuine Italian Walnut with checkered grip surfaces, epoxy finished. 14½" length of pull, 1½" drop at comb and 2¼" drop at heel. Pitch down is 2¾".

FRANCHI FALCONET O&U SHOTGUN

"SILVER" MODEL IN 12 GAUGE ONLY

The Franchi Falconet-Silver Over and Under Shotgun, described on this page, has attained world-wide recognition for its exceptional design and flawless quality.

With new, positive, overhead sears, the single trigger mechanism is foolproof and the possibility of doubling is prevented. Light in weight and with chrome lined barrels, this model is a fast pointing, easy-handling over and under. Don't be confused by "chrome-vanadium steel" barrels. These are still just basically steel. There is no substitute for Franchi's high quality *chrome-molybdenum* steel barrel with hard chrome lining!

Exterior finish is extra smooth and "custom" in appearance.

STANDARD 12 GAUGE WITH PICKLED-SILVER RECEIVER & CHROME-LINED BARRELS $599.95

WEIGHT

12 Gauge . . . . 7 lbs.

Overall weight may vary slightly, depending upon barrel length and density of wood components.

SPECIFICATIONS

BARRELS: Hard chrome lined and equipped with ventilated rib. In 12 gauge only, choice of following lengths and chokes:
- 24-inch Cylinder & Improved Cylinder
- 26-inch Improved Cylinder & Modified
- 28-inch Modified & Full
- 30-inch Modified & Full

TRIGGER: Selective single trigger. Easy cocking design of hammers, with short travel, provide lightning-like ignition. Simple, fool-proof, selector system made in combination with the sliding tang safety. Overhead sears.

EJECTOR: Selective automatic ejectors.

SAFETY: Automatic safety. Safety button on tang also serves as trigger selector.

STOCK & FOREARM: Italian walnut, hand finished and fully checkered. Dimensions: length of pull—14¼ inches; drop at comb—1½ inches; drop at heel—2¼ inches; pitch down—2¾ inches. Stock designed with full pistol grip, fitted with cap.

WEIGHTS:
Standard 12 gauge with 24 or 26-inch barrels . . . . .7 lbs.
Standard 12 gauge with 28-inch barrels. . . . . .7 lbs. 2 ozs.
Standard 12 gauge with 30-inch barrels. . . . . .7 lbs. 4 ozs.

FINISH: Standard 12 gauge field model with pickled-silver colored receiver and bright-blue barrels.

ENGRAVING: English scroll engraving on receiver.

FRANCHI AUTOMATIC SHOTGUNS
STANDARD MODELS IN 12, 20 & 28 GAUGES

The Franchi Automatic Shotgun is made in 12, 20 and 28 gauges chambered for all 2¾-inch shells.

All models are made with chrome-lined barrels, automatic cut-off, five-shot capacity, genuine walnut stock and forend with fully checkered pistol grip and fore-grip.

In a wide selection of barrel lengths and chokes, the Franchi is the world's lightest automatic shotgun: the 12 gauge model weighs only 6 lbs. 4 ozs. and the 20 and 28 gauges weigh about 5 lbs. 2 ozs.

Adjustable friction piece controls recoil action, permitting specific settings for standard or high velocity loads. Effects of recoil are therefore greatly minimized.

All barrels for each gauge are fully interchangeable without factory fitting; this is a particularly desirable feature because a gun purchased with both a 30-inch full choke barrel and a 26-inch improved cylinder barrel could be used for anything from quail to ducks, (and skeet and trap, too, if the shooter is so inclined.)

In addition to its extreme light weight, the Franchi automatic shotgun has two exclusive and unique features: hard chrome-lined barrels and simplified take-down.

The smooth chrome lining not only adds greatly to the life of the barrel by preventing rust and corrosion, but improves patterning at all ranges by reducing pellet deformation. Removal of two lateral pins, located through the receiver immediately above the trigger guard, permits the trigger-safety-lifter mechanism to be removed as a single unit. For cleaning purposes this can then be rinsed in a kerosene bath, oiled lightly and re-installed simply and easily. Note: 28 gauge models are available only with ventilated rib barrels in the standard grade.

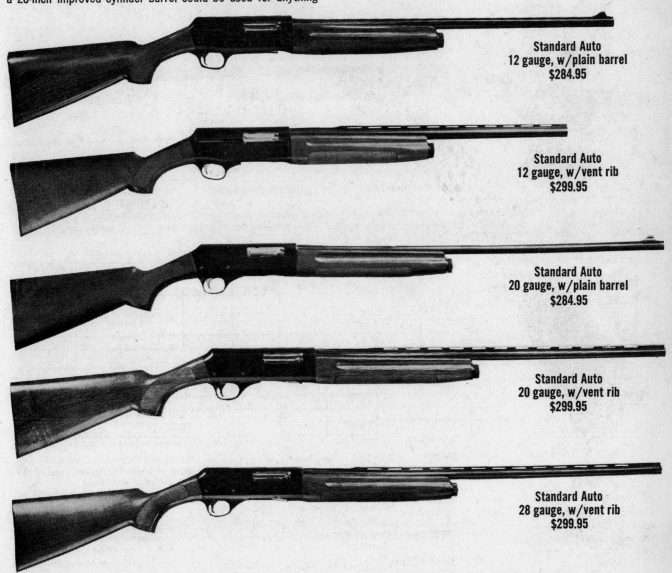

**Standard Auto
12 gauge, w/plain barrel
$284.95**

**Standard Auto
12 gauge, w/vent rib
$299.95**

**Standard Auto
20 gauge, w/plain barrel
$284.95**

**Standard Auto
20 gauge, w/vent rib
$299.95**

**Standard Auto
28 gauge, w/vent rib
$299.95**

FRANCHI AUTOMATIC SHOTGUNS

12 & 20 GAUGE 3-INCH MAGNUM

The Franchi Magnum Automatic in 12 or 20 gauge, is a shotgun designed specifically for 3-inch Magnum shells. With factory-fitted recoil pad, automatic cut-off and long, full-choke barrels, these Magnum models are considerably heavier than the standard field guns; 12 gauge Magnum weighs 8 lbs. 4 ozs. and the 20 gauge Magnum weighs 6 lbs. These weights, coupled with the recoil-operated design common to all Franchis, greatly reduces the effects of recoil felt by the shooter.

All models are regularly furnished with 3-shot plug to conform with Federal Migratory Bird Laws. Normal capacity is four in the magazine and one in the chamber for a total of five shots.

Barrel lengths: 12 gauge—32-inch with full choke and 20 gauge—28-inch with full choke. Hard-chrome lining—an exclusive Franchi feature—greatly reduces deformation of pellets and facilitates smooth, even patterns at all ranges. Furthermore, this chrome lining resists rust and corrosion and lengthens barrel life.

Standard 12 gauge 3-inch Magnum w/plain barrel
$329.95

Standard 20 gauge 3-inch Magnum w/vent rib barrel
$349.95

(12 gauge models furnished only with 32-inch full choke barrels and 20 gauge models furnished only with 28-inch full choke barrel.)

SPECIFICATIONS FOR FRANCHI AUTOMATIC SHOTGUNS:

STYLE: 5-shot automatic shotgun.
GAUGES: 12, 20 & 28 gauges (chambered for all 2¾″ shells). 12 & 20 gauge Magnum (chambered for 3″ Magnum shells).
BARREL: Hard chrome-lined barrel. Extra barrel is interchangeable within gauge except Magnum. Slug-gun barrel comes equipped with fully adjustable rifle-type sights.

BARREL LENGTHS & CHOKES AVAILABLE FOR FRANCHI AUTOMATICS:

Plain Barrel	22″ (cyl.) Slug	24″ **** I.C.	24″ *** Mod.	26″ **** I.C.	26″ *** Mod.	26″ (sk) Skeet	28″ *** Mod.	28″ * Full	30″ * Full	32″ * Full
Std. 12*	X	X	X	X	X		X	X	X	
Std. 20	X		X	X	X		X	X		
Mag. 12										X
Mag. 20								X		
Vent Rib Barrel										
Std. 12*		X	X	X	X	X	X	X	X	
Std. 20		X		X	X	X	X	X		
Std. 28				X				X		
Mag. 12										X
Mag. 20								X		

OVER-ALL LENGTH: 47½″ with 28-inch barrel.
SAFETY: Convenient lateral push button safety. Removal of two lateral pins, located through the receiver, permits the trigger-safety-lifter mechanism to be removed as a single unit.
STOCK: Genuine walnut stock and forend with fully machine cut checkered pistol grip and fore-grip. Magnum models come equipped with factory fitted recoil pad. Optional on other 12 gauge models.
STANDARD STOCK DIMENSIONS: 14″ length of pull, 1½″ drop at comb; 2¼″ drop at heel.
AVERAGE WEIGHT: 12 gauge—6 lbs., 4 ozs.; 20 & 28 gauge—5 lbs., 2 ozs.; 12 gauge Magnum—8 lbs., 4 ozs.; 20 gauge Magnum—6 lbs. Overall weight may vary slightly depending on density of wood.
Note: All Franchi automatic shotguns are supplied with 3-shot plug to conform with migratory bird laws, where applicable.
*Deluxe Grades use same barrels as Standard Grade although former usually with ventilated rib. (Star count stamped in barrel denotes choke.)

FRANCHI AUTOMATIC SHOTGUNS

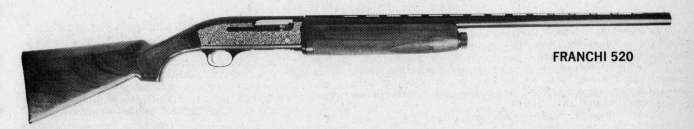

FRANCHI 520

FRANCHI 520

There are four main units in the Franchi 520: Stock-receiver, barrel, breachbolt-cocking rod, and forend. The gun can be easily disassembled into these four units without any tools, in less than 15 minutes.

Fixed barrel: the reloading operation is entirely carried out by the gas-piston-breech bolt system.

Fast cycling time: it fires, ejects and reloads in less than 120 thousandths of a second!

The only shotgun with its magazine completely isolated from the gas, thus preventing carbon deposits which could affect functioning.

Can accommodate five 2¾ inch shotshells when not in conflict with State or area regulations.

Easy ejection and extremely smooth cocking. Removable plug converts four-round magazine capacity to two to comply with Federal regulations on the hunting of waterfowl. **$349.95**

FEATURES: Finish: semi-gloss. **Stock and forend:** selected walnut-checkered pistol grip. **Drop at heel:** 2" - 2⅛" - 2¼". **Barrels:** 26 inches and 28 inches with ventilated rib. **Gauge:** 12. **Chamber:** 2¾". **Weight:** Approx. 7 pounds. **Chokes:** 26 inch. vent. rib. barrel Imp., Cyl., Mod. 28 inch. vent. rib. barrel. Mod., Imp/Mod., Full.

SLUG GUNS 12 & 20 GAUGES WITH ADJUSTABLE RIFLE SIGHTS

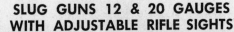

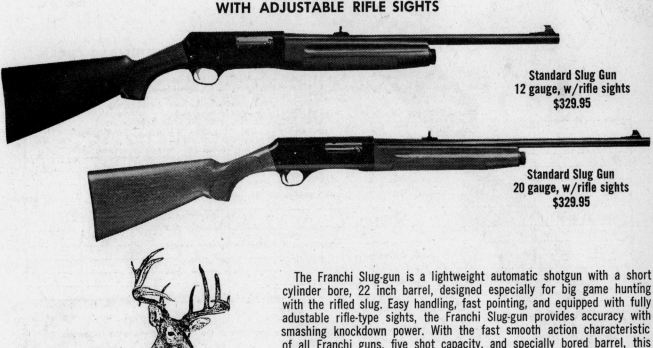

**Standard Slug Gun
12 gauge, w/rifle sights
$329.95**

**Standard Slug Gun
20 gauge, w/rifle sights
$329.95**

Slug-gun barrel only (can be used interchangeably on any Standard Franchi Auto.) **$159.95**

The Franchi Slug-gun is a lightweight automatic shotgun with a short cylinder bore, 22 inch barrel, designed especially for big game hunting with the rifled slug. Easy handling, fast pointing, and equipped with fully adustable rifle-type sights, the Franchi Slug-gun provides accuracy with smashing knockdown power. With the fast smooth action characteristic of all Franchi guns, five shot capacity, and specially bored barrel, this model is an ideal brush gun for the big game hunter and is particularly effective when used with the deadly Brenneke slug.

Except for the special slug-barrel and adjustable sights, all other mechanical specifications of this model are the same as those described for the standard Franchi auto shotgun. Sights are raised gold-bead front and Lyman folding leaf open rear.

FRANCHI AUTOMATIC SHOTGUNS

ELDORADO MODEL

The Franchi Eldorado Model is a superbly finished firearm with elaborate ornamentation for the shooter who wants something out of the ordinary.

This model is made with exceptionally fine Italian scroll engraving covering 75% of the receiver surfaces. In deep relief against highly polished background surfaces, the silver-like result is unusually attractive.

Other deluxe features include gold-plated trigger and chrome-plated breech bolt.

Stock and forend are of selected walnut with meticulously checkered pistol and fore grips.

In 12 or 20 gauges, the Eldorado Model is furnished only with ventilated rib barrel and—like all standard Franchi's—chrome lined bore. Extra, interchangeable, plain or ventilated rib barrels may be purchased separately.

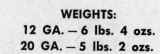

WEIGHTS:
12 GA. — 6 lbs. 4 ozs.
20 GA. — 5 lbs. 2 ozs.

CHOICE OF BARREL LENGTHS AND CHOKES

ELDORADO 12 GAUGE MODELS WITH VENTILATED-RIB BARREL:
EVR1224C: 12 ga. with 24-inch cylinder-bore vent-rib barrel
EVR1226I: 12 ga. with 26-inch improved-cylinder vent-rib barrel
EVR1226M: 12 ga. with 26-inch modified choke vent-rib barrel
EVR1228M: 12 ga. with 28-inch modified choke vent-rib barrel
EVR1228F: 12 ga. with 28-inch full choke vent-rib barrel
EVR1230F: 12 ga. with 30-inch full choke vent-rib barrel

ELDORADO 20 GAUGE MODELS WITH VENTILATED-RIB BARREL:
EVR2024C: 20 ga. with 24-inch cylinder-bore vent-rib barrel
EVR2026I: 20 ga. with 26-inch improved-cylinder vent-rib barrel
EVR2026M: 20 ga. with 26-inch modified choke vent-rib barrel
EVR2028M: 20 ga. with 28-inch modified choke vent-rib barrel
EVR2028F: 20 ga. with 28-inch full choke vent-rib barrel

ELDORADO MODEL WITH VENTILATED RIB $429.95

EXTRA INTERCHANGEABLE BARRELS
(No Fitting Necessary for Installation)

PLAIN ROUND BARREL $119.95
LIGHTWEIGHT VENTILATED RIB BARREL $144.95

22-INCH CYLINDER BORE, WITH SIGHTS $159.95

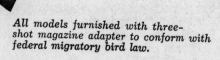

All models furnished with three-shot magazine adapter to conform with federal migratory bird law.

Illustration shows details of elaborate scroll engraving.

FRANCHI AUTOMATIC SHOTGUNS

HUNTER MODELS

Specifications for the Franchi Hunter Grade are the same as those of the Standard Models except for details of finish. The Hunter Model is furnished only with a ventilated rib barrel, fully engraved receiver and selected walnut stock.

Handsome scenes adorn both sides of the receiver. To further enhance the appearance, the trigger has been highly polished and chrome plated.

In choice of 12 or 20 gauge (chambered for all 2¾-inch shells); full length illustration shows 20 gauge Model, close-up view at bottom illustrates 12 gauge model.

Hard-chrome lined barrels—an exclusive Franchi feature, common to all Franchi guns—resists rust and corrosion and reduces deformation of pellets. Barrel life is therefore greatly enhanced.

Takedown is unusually fast and easy.

WEIGHTS:
12 GAUGE—6 LBS 4 OZS.
20 GAUGE—5 LBS 2 OZS.

CHOICE OF BARREL LENGTHS AND CHOKES

HUNTER 12 GAUGE MODELS WITH VENTILATED-RIB BARREL:
HVR1224C: 12 ga. with 24-inch cylinder-bore vent-rib barrel
HVR1226I: 12 ga. with 26-inch improved-cylinder vent-rib barrel
HVR1226M: 12 ga. with 26-inch modified choke vent-rib barrel
HVR1228M: 12 ga. with 28-inch modified choke vent-rib barrel
HVR1228F: 12 ga. with 28-inch full choke vent-rib barrel
HVR1230F: 12 ga. with 30-inch full choke vent-rib barrel

HUNTER 20 GAUGE MODELS WITH VENTILATED-RIB BARREL:
HVR2024C: 20 ga. with 24-inch cylinder-bore vent-rib barrel
HVR2026I: 20 ga. with 26-inch improved-cylinder vent-rib barrel
HVR2026M: 20 ga. with 26-inch modified choke vent-rib barrel
HVR2028M: 20 ga. with 28-inch modified choke vent-rib barrel
HVR2028F: 20 ga. with 28-inch full choke vent-rib barrel

FRANCHI HUNTER MODEL SHOTGUN, WITH VENTILATED RIB BARREL, CHOICE OF 12 OR 20 GAUGE $349.95

EXTRA INTERCHANGEABLE BARRELS
(No Fitting Necessary for Installation)

PLAIN ROUND BARREL $119.95
LIGHTWEIGHT VENTILATED RIB BARREL $144.95

22-INCH CYLINDER BORE, WITH SIGHTS $159.95

All models furnished with three-shot magazine adapter to conform with federal migratory bird law.

View of 12 gauge receiver, at right, shows details of engraving; both sides are similarly decorated.

GALEF SHOTGUNS

GALEF

Silver Snipe and Golden Snipe Shotguns with Single Trigger

Specifications:

Gauge: 12 and 20 gauge chambered for 3" magnum shells, and, therefore, suitable for 2¾" shells as well.

Breech Assembly: (Barrels) Barrels and chambers individually bored from one piece of hi-pressure resistant nickel-chrome alloy steel. Chrome lined bores. Ventilated Rib.*

Receiver: Purdey type double box lock with cross bolt. Machined from solid stock and handsomely engraved in satin chrome.

Safety: Automatic, except on Trap and Skeet models.

Extractors: Silver Snipe—Plain
Golden Snipe—Selective Automatic Ejectors

Trigger: Selective Single Trigger

Standard Stock Dimensions:		12 Gauge	20 Gauge
	Drop at Comb .	1⅜"	1⅝"
	Drop at Heel ..	2⁷⁄₁₆"	2⁷⁄₁₆"
	Length of Pull .	14⅜"	14⁵⁄₁₆"
	Pitch	1⅝"	2⅛"

Stock and Forearm: Selected European Walnut, hand checkered two point panel design. Full pistol grip with hard plastic butt plate.

Sights: Gold bead on field models. Ivory bead on Trap and Skeet models.

Approximate Weights: 12 gauge 28" barrels ....6 lbs. 8 ounces
20 gauge 28" barrels ....6 lbs. 4 ounces

Silver Snipe—Ventilated Rib

Gauge:	Barrel-Chokes:	
12	30"	Modified & Full
12	28"	Modified & Full
12	26"	IC-Modified
20	28"	Modified & Full
20	26"	IC-Modified

$369.55

Golden Snipe—Ventilated Rib with Automatic Ejectors

Gauge:	Barrel-Chokes:	
12	30"	Modified & Full
12	28"	Modified & Full
12	26"	IC-Modified
20	28"	Modified & Full
20	26"	IC-Modified

$409.95

**SILVER SNIPE
OVER & UNDER SHOTGUN
WITH SELECTIVE SINGLE TRIGGER
(12 & 20 Gauge)**

GALEF SHOTGUNS

Monte Carlo — Single Barrel Trap Shotgun

MONTE CARLO SINGLE BARREL TRAP GUN $195.00

Barrel Assembly: Monobloc. Barrel tubes of superior quality hi-tensil chromoly steel with extra heavy walls. Chambered for 2¾" shells.

Rib: 5/16" tapered wide track Ventilated Rib with front and rear bead sights.

Action: Monte Carlo design with release forward of trigger guard. Handsomely engraved and finished in a non-glare blue. Automatic type extractor. Gold plated trigger and forend screw.

Safety: Slide type mounted on upper tang.

Stock Dimensions: Drop at Comb: 1⅛", Drop at Heel: 1⅝", Length of Pull: 14½", Pitch: ½". Straight without cast-off or cast-on. Monte Carlo comb. Full pistol grip with cap. Trap style recoil pad.

Forearm Dimensions: Length: 12½", Width: 2⅝". Beavertail semi-pear shaped.

Stock And Forearm: Selected European Walnut. Custom finished and fitted. Generously hand checkered in two point panel design.

Weight: Approximately 8¼ pounds.

Specifications of the "Monte Carlo" single barrel trap shotgun

Gauge: 12 gauge only

Barrel Length: 32 inches

Choke: Trap

COMPANION FOLDING SINGLE BARREL SHOTGUNS
(12, 16, 20, 28 & 410 Gauges)

COMPANION, w/plain barrel $71.00

COMPANION w/vent rib barrel $78.00

Specifications:

Gauge: 12, 16, 20, 28, and 410 gauge, 12 and 20 gauge chambered for 3" magnum shells. 16 and 28 gauge are chambered for 2¾" shells. 410 with 3 inch chamber.

Style: Single barrel, folding shotgun.

Breech Assembly: (Barrel) Monobloc. Special alloy steel drawn from a single block including the rib extension and locking lug. Greatest elasticity and strength are thus obtained, especially as the barrel tubes are completely inserted to coincide with the breech face. Also available in Ventilated Rib Barrel with specifications same throughout.

Receiver: Machined from solid stock and handsomely engraved in satin chrome.

Safety: Non-automatic shotgun type, positioned at upper tang.

Standard Stock Dimensions: Drop at Comb ..... 1½" / Drop at Heel ...... 2⅝" / Length of Pull ......14" / Pitch .... 3" } Approximate for all gauges and lengths

Sights: Gold bead front. Receiver notched for alignment in pointing.

Stock and Forearm: Selected European Walnut, hand checkered two point panel design. Full pistol grip with cap and hard plastic butt plate.

Approximate Weights: 12 gauge 30" barrel ....5 lbs. 9 ounces / 410 gauge 28" barrel ....4 lbs. 8 ounces

Barrel Length & Choke Combinations:

Gauge:		Barrel-Chokes:
12	30"	Full—Magnum
12	28"	Full—Magnum
16	28"	Full
20	28"	Full—Magnum
28	28"	Full
410	26"	Full

H&R SHOTGUNS

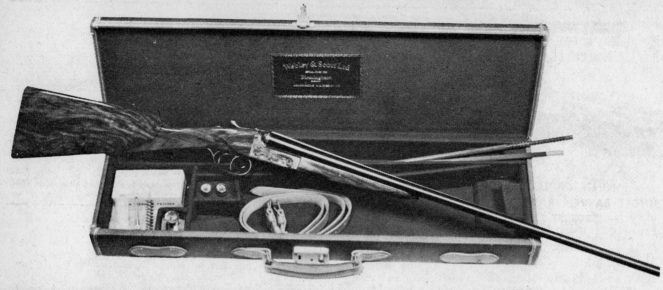

WEBLEY & SCOTT DOUBLE BARREL SHOTGUNS
MODELS 720 AND 728

Superb Webley craftsmanship is evident in every detail of these classic double barrel shotguns. Model 728 (shown) is a traditional 28 gauge quail gun chambered for 2¾-inch shells, choked one-quarter and three-quarters. It features 25-inch barrels with smooth concave rib, figured walnut stock with and checkering on forend and grip. The shotgun comes in a handsomely fitted, felt lined case with lock. The leather-trimmed case also contains cleaning rod, polishing cloth, wire loop, phosphor bronze brush, wool mop, cleaning patches, nickel plated snap caps and oiler. Also available in 20 gauge as Model 720, chambered for 3-inch shells, with turned flat rib. Frame and barrels for each shotgun are individually scaled to size and properly proportioned.

SPECIFICATIONS

Gauges: 20 ga.—3" chambers
28 ga.—2¾" chambers
Barrel Lengths: 20 ga.—26" with engine turned flat rib
28 ga.—25" with smooth concave rib
Chokes: ¼ and ¾.
Action: Engraved, Grade II, box lock, hammerless, top lever, non-extension, solid tumblers, automatic safety.
Stock: Selected figured walnut in Grade II with gold oval and drop points.
Forend: Splinter type with forend diamond.
Checkering: Grade I
Dimensions: Pull—14⅝"
Drop at Comb—1½"
Drop at Heel—2¼"
Weight: 20 ga.—6 lbs.
28 ga.—5½ lbs.

720 (1)	SHOTGUN — WEBLEY & SCOTT - DOUBLE BARREL - 20 ga. - cased with accessories		$1,950.00
728 (1)	SHOTGUN — WEBLEY & SCOTT - DOUBLE BARREL - 28 ga. - cased with accessories		$1,950.00
018	CLEANNG SET—WEBLEY & SCOTT — AVAILABLE in 12, 20 28, 410 gauge		$14.95
019	ADAPTORS - Webley & Scott - To convert 12 ga. guns to handle 410 ga., 2½" or 3" shells		$16.00
020	SNAPCAPS — WEBLEY & SCOTT — available in 12, 20, 28, 410 ga. per pair		$9.95
021	OILER — WEBLEY & SCOTT "Classic" Square Oiler — chromed brass		$14.95

H&R HARRICH NO. 1
The single barrel shotgun created by Austrian craftsmen for American trap shooting competition.

Anson & Deeley type locking system with Kersten top locks and double under-locking lugs. Finest European walnut Monte Carlo stock

FEATURES AND SPECIFICATIONS

Gauge: 12, chambered for 2¾" shells.
Choke: Full choke.
Stock: Select grade walnut with trap recoil pad.
Drop at Comb: 1¼" x 1¼" x 2".
Length of Pull: 14¾".
Barrel Length: 32" or 34". **Weight:** 8½ pounds.
Features: Precision machined Bohler Rassant steel barrel with massive wall and chamber to minimize heat expansion effect. High line ventilated rib with full length, two dimensional taper overcomes sighting plane distortion.

PRICE
$1,850.00

H&R SINGLE BARREL SHOTGUNS

H&R MODEL 162 TOPPER BUCK

Model 162, 12-gauge, single shot shotgun with cylinder bore barrel, fires rifled slugs for deer hunting. Also can be used for birds and small game.

Model 162
TOPPER BUCK 12/24″ Cyl. Bore
$62.50

MODEL 162
Gauge: 12, chambered for 2¾″ and 3″ shells.
Capacity: Single shot
Stock: Walnut finished American hardwood.

Overall Length: 40″
Weight: 5½ lbs.
Barrel Length: 24″ with fully adjustable rear sight and dovetail front sight.

H&R SHOTGUN MODELS 58, 490, 98

From the H&R Topper series of shotguns comes these three single shot models.
Model 58 has self-adjusting barrel lock, positive shell ejection, rebounding hammer.
Model 490, with identical features, is designed for young shooters and overall length is 3″ shorter. **Model 98,** available in .410 and 20 gauge, features a rich ebony-finished stock and distinctive chrome frame.

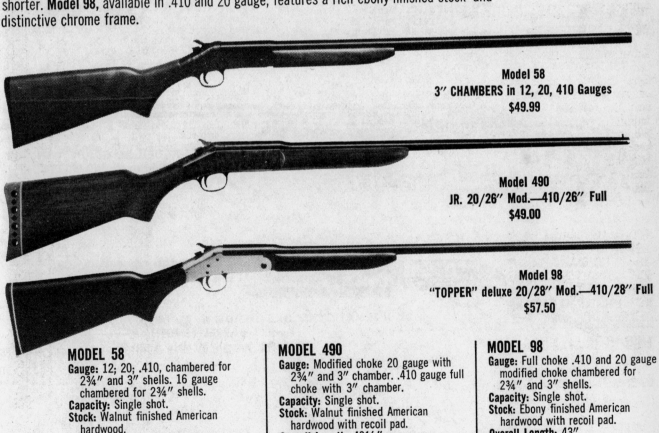

Model 58
3″ CHAMBERS in 12, 20, 410 Gauges
$49.99

Model 490
JR. 20/26″ Mod.—410/26″ Full
$49.00

Model 98
"TOPPER" deluxe 20/28″ Mod.—410/28″ Full
$57.50

MODEL 58
Gauge: 12; 20; .410, chambered for 2¾″ and 3″ shells. 16 gauge chambered for 2¾″ shells.
Capacity: Single shot.
Stock: Walnut finished American hardwood.
Overall Length: 43½″.
Weight: 5½ lbs.

Available in these gauges, barrel length, choke combinations: 12/36″ Full; 12/32″ Full; 12/30″ Full; 12/28″ Full; 12/28″ Mod.; 20/28″ Full; 20/28″ Mod.; 16/28″ Mod.; .410/28″ Full.

MODEL 490
Gauge: Modified choke 20 gauge with 2¾″ and 3″ chamber. .410 gauge full choke with 3″ chamber.
Capacity: Single shot.
Stock: Walnut finished American hardwood with recoil pad.
Overall Length: 40½″.
Weight: 5 lbs.
Barrel Length: 26″ barrel in both gauges.

MODEL 98
Gauge: Full choke .410 and 20 gauge modified choke chambered for 2¾″ and 3″ shells.
Capacity: Single shot.
Stock: Ebony finished American hardwood with recoil pad.
Overall Length: 43″.
Weight: 5¼ lbs.
Barrel Length: 28″ with brass bead front sight.

HIGH-STANDARD SHOTGUNS

AUTOLOADING SHOTGUNS IN 12 AND 20 GAUGE

The High-Standard "Supermatic" is a gas-operated auto-loading shotgun made in 12 and 20 gauges. The single piece receiver houses a damascene finished bolt which is actuated by double action bars. Models equipped with adjustable chokes, enables the shooter to click from full choke to cylinder bore. All 12 gauge autoloaders adjust for high and low pressure loads. 20 gauge Supermatic has manually operated selector.

12 Gauge Supermatic specifications are as follows: Chamber—all 2¾" shells. Capacity—five 2¾" shells, including one in chamber. Four 3" Magnums. Removable plug cuts capacity to three. Stock & Forearm—American walnut; checkered. Safety—Cross bolt with red indicator. Drop at Comb—1½"; drop at heel, 2½"; pull, 14". Sights —Bead type, except Deer Gun, which has rifle sights, front and rear.

20 Gauge Supermatic specifications are as follows: Chamber—chambered for 2¾" or 3" shells. Capacity— three 3" or 2¾" shells, including one in chamber. Stock and Forearm—checkered American walnut. Safety—cross bolt with red indicator. Drop at Comb—1½". Drop at Heel—2½". Pull—14".

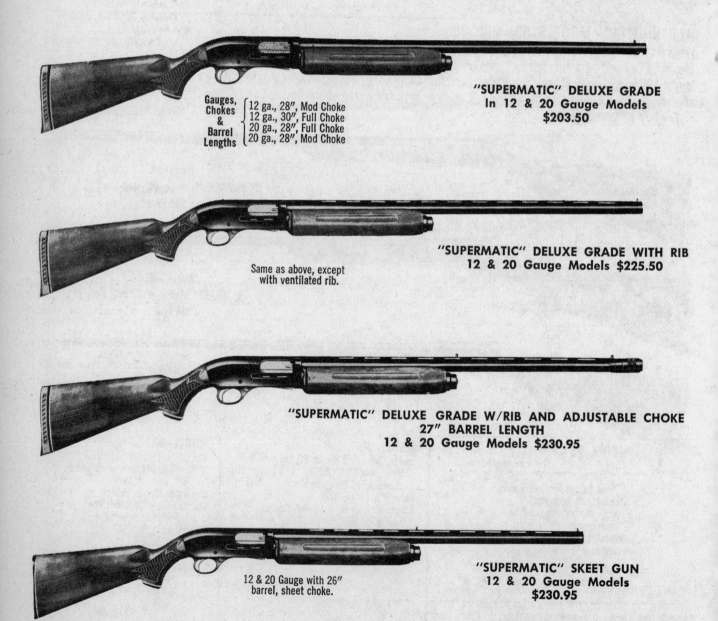

Gauges, Chokes & Barrel Lengths {
12 ga., 28", Mod Choke
12 ga., 30", Full Choke
20 ga., 28", Full Choke
20 ga., 28", Mod Choke

"SUPERMATIC" DELUXE GRADE
In 12 & 20 Gauge Models
$203.50

Same as above, except with ventilated rib.

"SUPERMATIC" DELUXE GRADE WITH RIB
12 & 20 Gauge Models $225.50

"SUPERMATIC" DELUXE GRADE W/RIB AND ADJUSTABLE CHOKE
27" BARREL LENGTH
12 & 20 Gauge Models $230.95

12 & 20 Gauge with 26" barrel, sheet choke.

"SUPERMATIC" SKEET GUN
12 & 20 Gauge Models
$230.95

HIGH-STANDARD SHOTGUNS

(AUTOLOADING SHOTGUNS IN 12 AND 20 GAUGE)

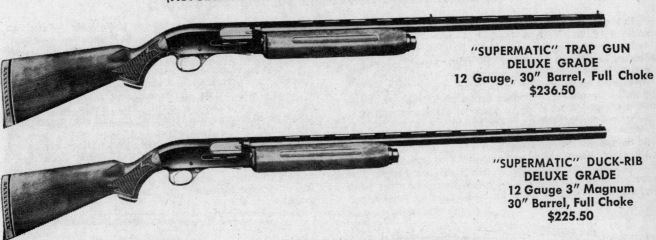

**"SUPERMATIC" TRAP GUN
DELUXE GRADE**
12 Gauge, 30" Barrel, Full Choke
$236.50

**"SUPERMATIC" DUCK-RIB
DELUXE GRADE**
12 Gauge 3" Magnum
30" Barrel, Full Choke
$225.50

Auto Loading Shotguns

12 Gauge Deluxe Auto Loading Supermatic Shotguns (fixed barrel)

NAME	BBL. TYPE	BBL. LGTH.	CHOKE	FINISH
Supermatic	Vent Rib	28"	Full	Trophy Blue
Supermatic	Vent Rib	28"	Mod.	Trophy Blue
Supermatic	Vent Rib	27"	Adj.	Trophy Blue
3" mag.				
Supermatic	Vent Rib	30"	Full	Trophy Blue
Supermatic	Vent Rib	30"	Full	Trophy Blue
Supermatic	Plain	28"	Mod.	Trophy Blue
Supermatic	Plain	30"	Full	Trophy Blue

20 Gauge Deluxe Auto Loading Supermatic Shotguns (fixed barrel)

NAME	BBL. TYPE	BBL. LGTH.	CHOKE	FINISH
Supermatic	Plain	26"	Imp. Cyl	Trophy Blue
Supermatic	Vent Rib	28"	Full	Trophy Blue
Supermatic	Vent Rib	28"	Mod.	Trophy Blue
Supermatic	Vent Rib	27"	Adj.	Trophy Blue
Supermatic	Plain	28"	Full	Trophy Blue
Supermatic	Plain	28"	Mod.	Trophy Blue

Skeet and Trap Shotguns—all with vent rib

NAME	BBL. TYPE	BBL. LGTH.	CHOKE	FINISH
Flite-King	12 Ga Pump	26"	Skeet	Trophy Blue
Flite-King	20 Ga Pump	26"	Skeet	Trophy Blue
Flite-King	410 Ga Pump	26"	Skeet	Trophy Blue
Supermatic	12 Ga Auto	26"	Skeet	Trophy Blue
Supermatic	20 Ga Auto	26"	Skeet	Trophy Blue
Flite-King	12 Ga Pump	30"	Trap	Trophy Blue
Supermatic	12 Ga Auto	30"	Trap	Trophy Blue

**HIGH STANDARD IDENTIFIES
CHOKE THIS WAY:** *Full **Modified ***Improved Cylinder ****Skeet Bore No Mark—Cylinder Bore

Specifications
12 Gauge:

Action: Supermatic gas operated.
Chamber: Functions all 2¾" shells, including Magnum loads. **Exception:** DUCK-MODELS shoot 3" Magnum or 2¾" Magnum only.
Capacity: Five 2¾" shells, including one in chamber. Four 3" Magnums. Removable plug cuts capacity to three on all models. All models fire rifled slugs.
Stock and Forearm: American Walnut, checkered.
Safety: Cross bolt with red indicator.
Drop at Comb: 1½". **Drop at Heel:** 2½".
Exceptions: Deer Gun and Trap Model. **Drop at Heel:** 1⅞".

20 Gauge:

Action: Supermatic gas operated, with twin action bars.
Chamber: Functions 2¾" and 3" shells including Magnum loads. All models fire rifled slugs.
Capacity: Three 3" or 2¾" shells, including one in chamber.
Stock and Forearm: American Walnut, checkered.
Safety: Cross bolt with red indicator.
Drop at Comb: 1½". **Drop at Heel:** 2½".

HIGH-STANDARD SHOTGUNS

(PUMP ACTION SHOTGUNS IN 12, 20, 28 & .410 GAUGES)

High Standard "Flite-King" pump action shotguns are made in 12, 20 and .410 gauges. Loading, ejection and reloading is accomplished by sliding forearm backward and forward about the length of the shell. Flite-King pumps feature lock-aligned barrel, assuring positive alignment of barrel and receiver. The bolt is damascene finished, and operates by means of double action bars. Ventilated ribs are machined from a single piece of steel and united to the barrel throughout its entire length.

The "Flite-King" brush models are offered in standard and deluxe grades; the Brush Deluxe has Williams receiver peep sight, leather sling and swivels. The Standard Brush model comes with adjustable rifle sights on barrel. The receiver is drilled and tapped for Williams receiver peep sight and provision is made for attachment of swivels and sling strap.

Flite-King 12 gauge specifications are as follows: Chamber—all 2¾" shells. Capacity—six shells (five in magazine, one in chamber). Removable plug limits to three. Stock and Forearm—American walnut; checkered; with pistol grip cap. Safety—cross bolt with red indicator. Drop at Comb—1½". Drop at Heel—2½". Pull—14". Sights—brass bead, except for brush which has rifle sights front and rear.

Flite-King 20 and .410 gauge specifications are as follows: Chamber—all shoot 2¾" or 3" shells. Capacity—5—2¾" shells, including one in chamber. 4–3", including one in chamber. Removable plug cuts capacity to three. All other specifications are the same as the 12 gauge model.

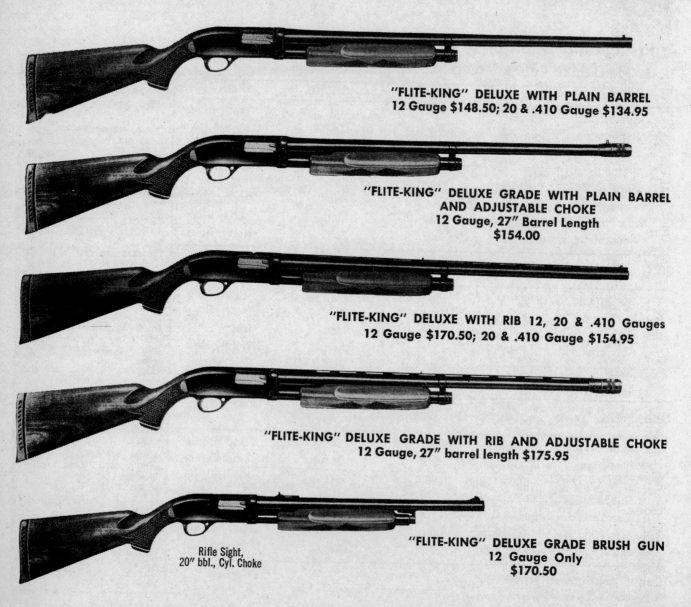

"FLITE-KING" DELUXE WITH PLAIN BARREL
12 Gauge $148.50; 20 & .410 Gauge $134.95

"FLITE-KING" DELUXE GRADE WITH PLAIN BARREL AND ADJUSTABLE CHOKE
12 Gauge, 27" Barrel Length
$154.00

"FLITE-KING" DELUXE WITH RIB 12, 20 & .410 Gauges
12 Gauge $170.50; 20 & .410 Gauge $154.95

"FLITE-KING" DELUXE GRADE WITH RIB AND ADJUSTABLE CHOKE
12 Gauge, 27" barrel length $175.95

Rifle Sight,
20" bbl., Cyl. Choke

"FLITE-KING" DELUXE GRADE BRUSH GUN
12 Gauge Only
$170.50

HIGH-STANDARD SHOTGUNS

(PUMP ACTION SHOTGUNS IN 12, 20, 28 & .410 GAUGES)

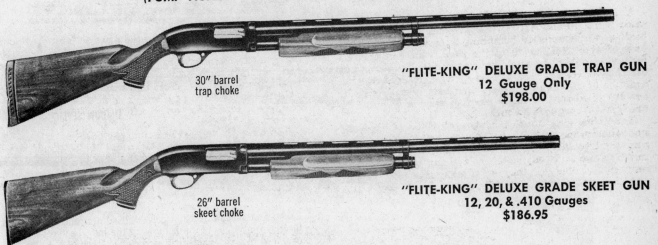

30" barrel
trap choke

"FLITE-KING" DELUXE GRADE TRAP GUN
12 Gauge Only
$198.00

26" barrel
skeet choke

"FLITE-KING" DELUXE GRADE SKEET GUN
12, 20, & .410 Gauges
$186.95

SPECIFICATIONS

MODEL	GAUGE	NO.	RIB	CHOKE	RECOIL PAD	PULL	BBL. LGTH.	FULL LGTH.	WT. LBS.	PRICE
PLAIN BBL.	12	8132	No	Full	Yes	14"	28"	47¾"	7¼	$ 99.95
	12	8133	No	Mod.	Yes	14"	28"	47¾"	7¼	99.95
	12	8134	No	Imp. Cyl.	Yes	14"	26"	45¾"	7¼	99.95
	12	8135	No	Full	Yes	14"	30"	49¾"	7¼	99.95
	12	8115	No	Adjust.	Yes	14"	27"	46¾"	7¼	109.95
PLAIN BBL.	20	8403	No	Full	Yes	14"	28"	47¾"	6	99.95
	20	8404	No	Mod.	Yes	14"	28"	47¾"	6	99.95
	20	8405	No	I.C.	Yes	14"	26"	45¾"	6	99.95
	20	8411*	No	Mod.	Yes	14"	28"	46¾"	6	104.95
	28	8332	No	Full	No	14"	26"	45¾"	6	104.95
	28	8333	No	Mod.	No	14"	26"	45¾"	6	99.95
	.410	8453	No	Full	No	14"	26"	45¾"	6	122.95
VENT RIB BBL.	12	8136	Yes	Full	Yes	14"	30"	49¾"	7½	122.95
	12	8137	Yes	Full	Yes	14"	28"	47¾"	7½	122.95
	12	8138	Yes	Mod.	Yes	14"	28"	47¾"	7½	122.95
	12	8142	Yes	Adjust.	Yes	14"	27"	46¾"	7½	129.95
VENT RIB BBL.	20	8429	Yes	Full	Yes	14"	28"	47¾"	6¼	122.95
	20	8430	Yes	Mod.	Yes	14"	28"	47¾"	6¼	122.95
	20	8442	Yes	Adj.	Yes	14"	27"	46¾"	6¼	129.95
	28	8334	Yes	Full	No	14"	26"	45¾"	6	129.95
	28	8335	Yes	Mod.	No	14"	26"	45¾"	6	129.95
	.410	8454	Yes	Full	No	14"	26"	45¾"	6	122.95
BRUSH	12	8116**	No	Cyl. Bore	Yes	14⅜"	20"	39¾"	7	112.95
BRUSH	12	8117***	No	Cyl. Bore	Yes	14⅜"	20"	39¾"	7	132.95

* New Boys model with two stocks.

**Adjustable rifle sights on barrel. Drilled and tapped for Williams receiver peep sight.
Provision made for quick attachment of swivels and strap.

*** Has Williams receiver peep sight for accuracy with slugs. Leather sling and swivels.

SPECIFICATIONS

MODEL	GAUGE	NO.	RIB	CHOKE	RECOIL PAD	PULL	BBL. LGTH.	FULL LGTH.	WT. LBS.	PRICE
SKEET	12	8164	Yes	Skeet	No	14"	26"	45¾"	7½	$132.95
SKEET	20	8431	Yes	Skeet	No	14"	26"	45¾"	6¼	132.95
	28	8336	Yes	Skeet	No	14"	26"	45¾"	6	139.95
	410	8455	Yes	Skeet	No	14"	26"	45¾"	6	132.95
TRAP	12	8165	Yes	Full	Yes	14⅜"	30"	49⅝"	7¾	144.95
TRAP	12	8166*	Yes	Full	Yes	14⅜"	30"	49⅝"	7	229.95

*Executive trap with Fajen Monte Carlo stock.

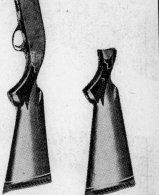

20-GAUGE CONVERTIBLE PUMP FOR BOYS/WOMEN

Equipped with two interchangeable stocks — one size for boys and small women and one for men. The convertible Pump comes with a 28 inch, modified choke plain barrel. Full length of the short stock version is 46¼ inches. Equipped with a standard stock, it is a full 47¾ inches.

Cost of the complete two-stock "Convertible Pump" package is **$144.95** including recoil pads. Comes in 20 ga. only.

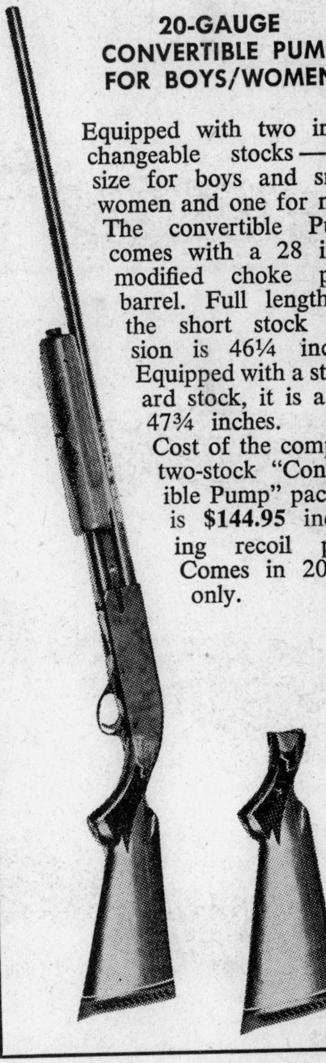

HIGH-STANDARD SHOTGUNS
THE SUPERMATIC SHADOW

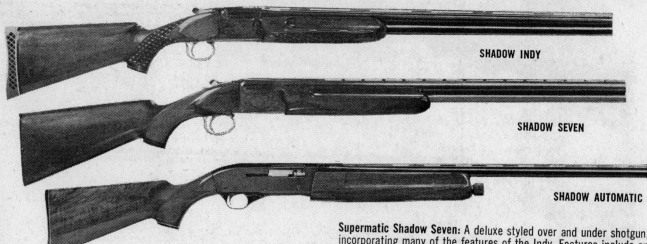

SHADOW INDY

SHADOW SEVEN

SHADOW AUTOMATIC

Supermatic Shadow Indy: A fine over and under shotgun featuring a unique full size airflow rib, solidly affixed to the barrel, with full vented forearm, for lower barrel heat dissipation. The receiver is fully engraved, and the stock is of fine American walnut, with skipp line hand checkering on butt and forearm. Its highly polished and damascened action is equipped with a single, selective trigger, and a selective auto ejection system permitting only the fired case to eject, while automatically extracting unfired shells. Other features include a deluxe recoil pad, with white line spacer, and pistol grip cap. The action is highly polished and damascened $595.00

Supermatic Shadow Seven: A deluxe styled over and under shotgun, incorporating many of the features of the Indy. Features include an engraved receiver, vented rib, and comes fitted with a fine American walnut stock, hand checkered butt and forearm. Equipped with the same selective auto ejection and extraction system found in the Indy, with single, selective trigger $499.95

Supermatic Shadow Automatic: A gas operated shotgun, with a gas system that cleans itself with each round. Features include a unique full airflow vented rib, for quick heat dissipation. The hand checkered stock is of American walnut, with checkered butt stock and forearm. Other features include a highly polished octagonal bolt; barrel interchangeability; pistol grip cap; and recoil pad on 3" Magnum model. Available in 12 or 20 gauge in all popular barrel lengths and chokes $269.00

IVER JOHNSON'S SHOTGUNS

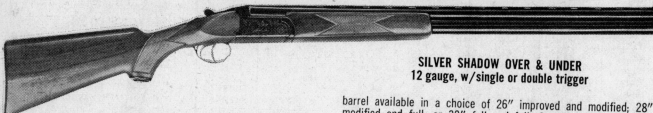

The Iver Johnson Silver Shadow over-and-under shotgun features a fine grain walnut stock, with point-to-point checkering, while the action is delicately engraved. Made in 12 gauge only, with

SILVER SHADOW OVER & UNDER
12 gauge, w/single or double trigger

barrel available in a choice of 26" improved and modified; 28" modified and full; or 30" full and full. Overall length with 26" barrel, 43-inches. Length of pull, 14¼". Approximate weight (depending on density of the wood) 7¼ to 7½ pounds.
Silver Shadow, w/double trigger, 12 gauge $252.95
Silver Shadow, w/single trigger, 12 gauge $272.95

**IVER JOHNSON'S "CHAMPION"
SINGLE BARREL SHOTGUN
12, 20 &
.410 GAUGES**

3-piece take-down; Walnut finish stock and trap style forend. Heat treated frame. Top lever compensating bolt keeps gun always tight. Auto ejection. Full choke.
No. 312 12 ga. 28 in. or 30 in. bbl $48.00
No. 320 20 ga. 28 in. bbl $48.00
No. 341 .410 Bore 26 in. bbl $48.00
(all chambered for 3" shell)

ITHACA OVER & UNDER SHOTGUNS

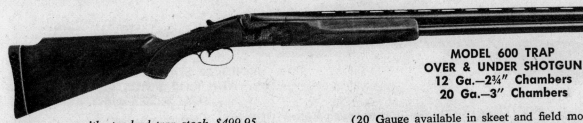

MODEL 600 TRAP
OVER & UNDER SHOTGUN
12 Ga.—2¾″ Chambers
20 Ga.—3″ Chambers

with standard trap stock $499.95
with Monte Carlo trap stock $499.95
Double Gun, 12 Gauge $499.95

(20 Gauge available in skeet and field models.) Equipped with chrome-lined barrels, automatic selective ejectors, non-automatic safety, double locking lugs, Monte Carlo stock, gold-plated oval nameplate, gold-plated trigger, ventilated rib, bead middle sight, white spacer at pistol-grip cap, curved trap pad.

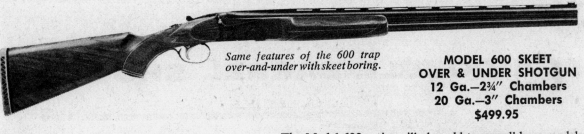

Same features of the 600 trap over-and-under with skeet boring.

MODEL 600 SKEET
OVER & UNDER SHOTGUN
12 Ga.—2¾″ Chambers
20 Ga.—3″ Chambers
$499.95

The Model 600 series will also add two small bore models to round out its skeet line. Both the 28 gauge and .410-2½″ Model 600's will have a 28″ barrel length and be choked skeet and skeet. Priced at **$509.95** Also available in 20, 28 & .410 Skeet Combo Set **$1200.00**

MODEL 600 FIELD GRADE
OVER & UNDER SHOTGUN
12 Ga.—2¾″ Chambers
20 Ga.—3″ Chambers
$489.95

All the features of the 600 line in a field model. With standard butt plate and white spacer. Available in wide choice of chokes and barrel lengths as listed in specifications table.

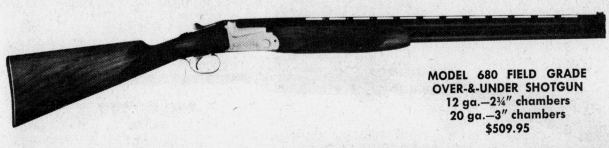

MODEL 680 FIELD GRADE
OVER-&-UNDER SHOTGUN
12 ga.—2¾″ chambers
20 ga.—3″ chambers
$509.95

All the features of the Model 600 plus classic, straight-grip, English stock with wraparound hand checkering. Gold-plated nameplate. White spacer on butt. Middle bead sight.

ITHACA SLIDE-ACTION SHOTGUNS

MODEL 37 STANDARD DEERSLAYER
WITH RIFLE SIGHTS $189.95
(12, & 20 Gauges)

Model 37 Standard Deerslayer: With checkered walnut stock; checkered walnut beavertail forearm; roto-forged barrel; standard model supplied less scope or mount but with factory grooved rear-sight base. Rubber recoil pad.

Model 37 Super Deluxe Deerslayer: Same as Model 37 Deluxe plus "full fancy" American walnut stock and forearm $184.95

SPECIFICATIONS—ITHACA DEERSLAYER MODEL 37 SERIES. Approximate Weight: 12 ga.—6 lbs; 20 ga.—5¾ lbs. **Barrels:** Choice of 26-inch standard barrel or 20-inch carbine barrel on all models. **Bore:** Specially bored factory-loaded rifle slugs. **Chamber Length:** 2¾", all gauges. **Stocks:** For all models—drop at comb of 1⅝"; drop at heel of 2⅝"; stock length, 14".

ITHACA DOUBLE-BARREL SHOTGUNS

MODEL 100 FIELD GRADE
SIDE-BY-SIDE
$299.95

12 Ga.—2¾" Chambers
20 Ga.—3" Chambers

A light, quick, perfectly balanced double field gun. Deep black-chrome finish, chrome-lined barrels, single selective trigger, hand-checkered stock and etched scrollwork frame. Double locking lugs automatic safety.

MODEL 200-E DELUXE GRADE
SIDE-BY-SIDE
$424.95

12 Ga.—2¾" Chambers
20 Ga.—3" Chambers

A deluxe-grade field gun with pure silver-plated frame and black-chrome barrels. Single selective trigger, double locking lugs, automatic selective ejectors, deluxe etched frame, chrome-lined barrels, beavertail forearm, gold-plated oval nameplate and trigger. Hand-finished walnut stock with white spacers.

MODEL 200-E SKEET
$439.95

12 ga.—2¾" chambers
20 ga.—3" chambers

The model 200-E is also available in a skeet model with recoil pad and non-automatic safety in 12 gauge with 2¾" chambers, and 20 gauge with 3" chambers.

ITHACA SHOTGUNS

GAS-OPERATED SEMI-AUTOMATIC 10 GAUGE MAGNUM

The Ithaca gas-operated semiautomatic 10 gauge magnum, is intended for anyone who can handle a 12 gauge shotgun with field loads comfortably, the full-choked Ithaca Mag 10 features a unique reverse gas system—in which the cylinder moves, not the piston—that not only minimizes recoil sensation but which facilitates cleaning as well.

Made of a combination of high-tensile and stainless steel to withstand punishment and prevent corrosion, this 3-shot, 3-1/2" magnum was designed from scratch rather than adapted from an existing field design; consequently, the weight

(11-1/4 lb.) and balance are in the right place for the shooter's magnum needs. In addition, the top of the magnum's 3/8" free-floating vent rib is milled to match the milled portion of the hand-polished receiver to give an uninterrupted 39" sighting plane.

Featuring fine-line handcheckering and semi-fancy American walnut with a semi-gloss finish, the Ithaca Mag 10 measures 1-1/2" x 2-3/8" x 14-1/8" and comes with a 32" barrel only. Extra features include a reversible cross-bolt safety and a punch within the forend nut that can be used like the Model 51 firing pin to take the trigger housing unit down with ease.
.... **$499.95**

Specifications: Choke: full only. **Chamber length:** 3½" Magnum. **Shell capacity:** 3-shot. **Stock dimensions:** 1½"x2⅜"x14⅛". **Weight:** 11¼ lbs. **Safety:** easily reversible cross bolt. **Barrel:** 32". **Receiver:** hand polished, milled and raised top made from a solid block of high tensile 4130 steel. **Action:** gas-operated semiautomatic with tube type of operating rod reverse gas system—cylinder moves, not the piston; cylinder, bolt, charging lever, action release and carrier all made of stainless steel. **Rib:** free-floating straight ⅜" vent rib; top milled to match milled portion of receiver to give uninterrupted 39" sighting plane. **Wood:** semi-fancy American walnut stock and forearm; semi-gloss finish; hand checkered 18-lines to the inch.

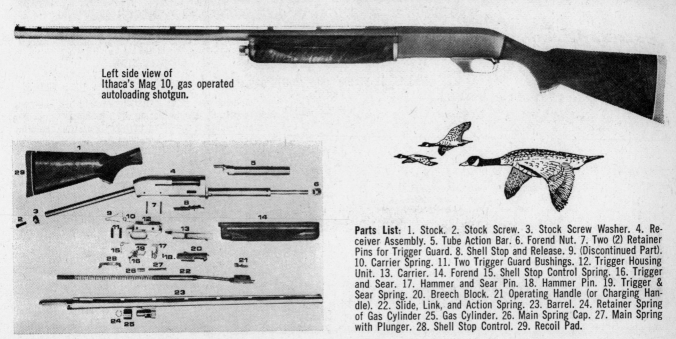

Left side view of Ithaca's Mag 10, gas operated autoloading shotgun.

Parts List: 1. Stock. 2. Stock Screw. 3. Stock Screw Washer. 4. Receiver Assembly. 5. Tube Action Bar. 6. Forend Nut. 7. Two (2) Retainer Pins for Trigger Guard. 8. Shell Stop and Release. 9. (Discontinued Part). 10. Carrier Spring. 11. Two Trigger Guard Bushings. 12. Trigger Housing Unit. 13. Carrier. 14. Forend 15. Shell Stop Control Spring. 16. Trigger and Sear. 17. Hammer and Sear Pin. 18. Hammer Pin. 19. Trigger & Sear Spring. 20. Breech Block. 21 Operating Handle (or Charging Handle). 22. Slide, Link, and Action Spring. 23. Barrel. 24. Retainer Spring of Gas Cylinder 25. Gas Cylinder. 26. Main Spring Cap. 27. Main Spring with Plunger. 28. Shell Stop Control. 29. Recoil Pad.

ITHACA AUTOMATIC SHOTGUNS

ITHACA MODEL 51 FEATHERLIGHT AUTOMATIC GAS-OPERATED. 12 & 20 GAUGE

MODEL 51 STANDARD, 12- & 20-GAUGE $239.95

MODEL 51 STANDARD, VENTILATED RIB, 12- & 20-GAUGE $269.95

MODEL 51 MAGNUM STANDARD, 3″ 12- & 20-GAUGE MAGNUM $264.95
MODEL 51 MAGNUM VENTILATED RIB, 3″ 12- & 20-GAUGE MAGNUM $294.95

MODEL 51 DELUXE SKEET GRADE, 12- & 20-GAUGE $299.95

MODEL 51 DELUXE TRAP GRADE, 12-GAUGE ONLY $339.95

MODEL 51 DELUXE TRAP MONTE CARLO, 12-GAUGE ONLY $354.95

AMERICAN WALNUT STOCK AND FOREARM

Only select American walnut is used —hand finished and hand fitted for perfect joining of wood and steel. The fluted comb and pistol grip fit the hand naturally, and the forearm is shaped for a firm, comfortable grip.

Deluxe target models feature "full fancy" American walnut stock and forearm. This beautifully patterned wood is superbly hand checkered and hand finished to impart an elegant, custom appearance.

SPECIFICATIONS MODEL 51 FEATHERLIGHT

Approximate weight: 7½ pounds. Model 51 field grades feature the Ithaca Raybar® front sight. Target grades have Bradley-type front sight. Ventilated-rib models have middle bead sight. All models feature easy hand-takedown. No tools required.

MODEL 51 FEATHERLIGHT 12 Gauge, Capacity—3-shot

Chamber 2¾″, (Magnum—3″*)			
Barrel Length	30″	28″	26″
Choke	Full	Full, Modified	Imp. Cylinder or Skeet

Stock Dimensions Field gun: 1½″ x 2½″ x 14″

Deluxe Skeet: 1½″ x 2¼″ x 14″

Deluxe Trap: Standard, 1½″ x 1⅞″ x 14⅛″; Monte Carlo, 1½″ x 1½″ x 2¼″ x 14⅜″

(Trap guns furnished with Ithaca trap pads.) (Magnum furnished with Ithaca std. recoil pad.) *Designed for 3″ and 2¾″ MAGNUM SHELLS ONLY. Additional interchangeable barrels are available. See page 46 for details.

ITHACA AUTOMATIC SHOTGUNS

**ITHACA MODEL 51
"DEER SLAYER"
In 12 Gauge Only $264.95**

The Model 51 Deerslayer which borrows from its Model 37 counterpart in both its barrel and sights. Specially bored for factory-loaded rifle slugs, the 51's barrel is rotoforged for maximum strength: The gun also features the Ithaca Raybar blade front sight; the open rear sight is adjustable and the sight base is grooved for easy scope mount installation.

The model, weighing approximately 7½ lbs: with a 24" barrel and 2¾" chamber, has an engraved receiver, recoil pad, and pistol-grip cap. The stock and forend are checkered American walnut with a fine, semigloss lacquer finish. Left-handers can reverse the safety easily.

NEW XL GAS-OPERATED AUTOMATIC SERIES

XL 900

A deluxe semiautomatic shotgun with a standard-grade price tag. The XL 900 has the appearance and performance features you normally expect to get only at a much higher price. These features include Roto-Forged barrel with black-chrome finish; black anodized receiver with silver-colored game scene; ventilated rib with Raybar front sight on field-grade gun, Bradley-type front sight and middle bead on target grades; exclusive hand-applied highlight finish on stock and forearm; handy action-release button on receiver; five-shot capacity. Reversible safety. 12- and 20-gauge. Trap grade, 12-gauge only.

XL 900 VENT RIB	**$244.95**
XL 900 TRAP GRADE	**$269.95**
XL 900 TRAP GRADE, WITH MONTE CARLO STOCK.....	**$269.95**
XL 900 SKEET GRADE	**$269.95**
XL 900 SLUG GUN	**$244.95**

XL 300

A well-balanced, reliable semiautomatic. Its fast action, flawless performance and easy handling qualities make it an all-around utility field gun. Roto-Forged barrel, brass front sight (Raybar on vent. rib), self-compensating gas system, action-release button and reversible safety are features to give you dependable performance. Anodized finish on receiver and black-chrome barrel, hand-finished stock and forearm, etched scrollwork on receiver and smooth lines are value-added appearance features.

XL 300 STANDARD	**$219.95**
XL 300 VENT RIB	**$234.95**

ITHACA-SKB XL 300 and XL 900 SPECIFICATIONS

	12 ga.	20 ga.
Chamber	2¾"	3", Skeet 2¾"
Weight	7½ lbs.	6¾ lbs.
Stock dimensions		
Field Grade	1½" x 2½" x 14"	1½" x 2½" x 14"
XL 900 Skeet Grade	1½" x 2¼" x 14"	1½" x 2¼" x 14"
XL 900 Trap Grade	1½" x 1⅞" x 14½"	
XL 900 Trap, M/C	1½" x 1½" x 2" x 14½"	
Barrel lengths/chokes		
Field Grade	30"/Full 28"/Full or Mod. 26"/Imp. Cyl.	28"/Full or Mod. 26"/Imp. Cyl.
Trap Grade	30"/Full or Imp. Mod.	
Skeet Grade	26"/Skeet	26"/Skeet

XL 900 available with 24" barrel with RS choke. 20-gauge chamber will handle either 2¾" or 3" shells.

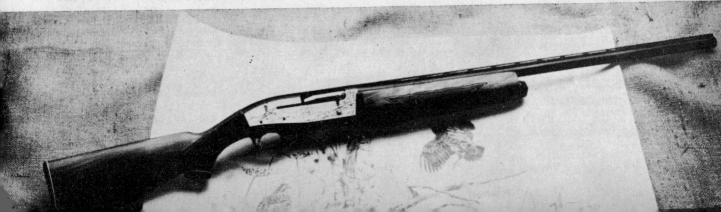

ITHACA SLIDE-ACTION SHOTGUNS

ALL MODELS AVAILABLE IN 12, 16 & 20 GAUGES

MODEL 37 STANDARD GRADE WITH PLAIN BARREL $169.95

Model 37: Slide-action shotguns feature bottom ejection and come equipped with Ithaca's raybar front sight. Approximate weight—12 ga. 6½ lbs., 20 ga. 5¾ lbs. Walnut forearm and stock with fluted comb. Also available with Monte Carlo, cheek-piece, offset or unusual stock at extra cost.

MODEL 37-V STANDARD GRADE WITH VENTILATED-RIB BARREL $194.95

Model 37-V: Approximate weight—12 ga. 6½ lbs., 16 ga. 6 lbs., 20 ga. 5¾ lbs. Standad specifications plus ventilated rib barrel. Stock dimensions: Pull—14"; drop at comb—1½"; drop at heel 1½". Plus choice of 24-inch barrel length wth imp. cylinder choke.

MODEL 37-D DELUXE GRADE WITH PLAIN BARREL $174.95

Model 37-D: Approximate weight—12 ga. 6¾ lbs.; 16 ga. 6½ lbs., 20 ga. 6 lbs. Standard specifications and stock dimensions plus checkered beavertail forearm, checkered stock with fluted comb and anti-recoil pad set off by a white spacer.

MODEL 37-DV DELUXE GRADE WITH VENTILATED-RIB BARREL $199.95

Model 37-DV: Approximate weight—12 ga. 7 lbs., 16 ga. 6¾ lbs., 20 ga. 6½ lbs. Same specifications as Model 37-D Deluxe. Stock dimensions: Pull—14"; drop at comb—1½"; drop at heel—2½". Plus the choice of a 24-inch barrel length with imp. cyl. choke.

MODEL 37 SUPREME GRADE WITH VENTILATED-RIB BARREL $319.95

Model 37 Supreme: Approximate weight—12 ga. 7 lbs., 16 ga. 6¾ lbs., 20 ga. 6½ lbs. Standard Grade specifications plus ventilated rib barrel, hand-checkered "full fancy" American walnut stock and forearm; fluted comb. Anti-recoil pad with white spacer. Available in either Trap or Skeet stock.

SPECIFICATIONS—ITHACA FEATHERLIGHT MODEL 37 SERIES

Barrel length, inches: 12 ga.—26", 28", 30"; 16 ga.—26", 28"; 20 ga.—26", 28". **Choke:** Full, modified or improved cylinder choke. **Chamber length:** 2¾" for all gauges. **Stock Measurements:** Drop at comb, 1⅝"; drop at heel, 2⅝"; stock length, 14".

Choice of Stocks: Standard trap-stock dimensions—14½" x 1½" x 1⅞" with anti-recoil pad. Standard skeet-stock dimensions—14" x 1⅝" x 2½" with anti-recoil pad. (no extra charge on Supreme model).

ITHACA SHOTGUNS

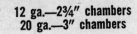

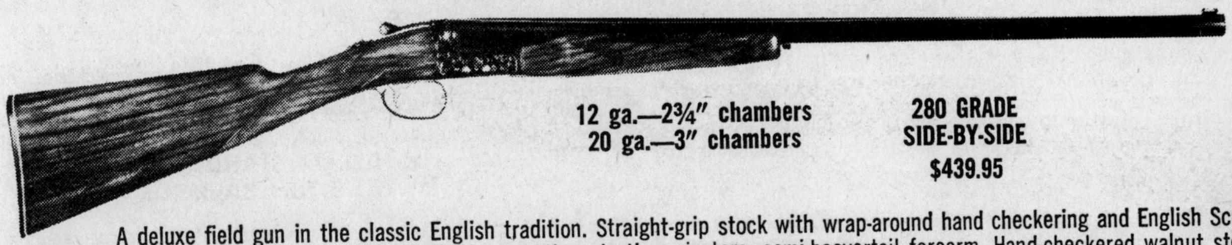

12 ga.—2¾" chambers
20 ga.—3" chambers

280 GRADE
SIDE-BY-SIDE
$439.95

A deluxe field gun in the classic English tradition. Straight-grip stock with wrap-around hand checkering and English Scroll engraved frame. Single selective trigger, automatic selective ejectors, semi-beavertail forearm. Hand-checkered walnut stock with inset gold-plated nameplate. **MODEL 280 QUAIL.** Ithaca Gun is expanding its Model side-by-side line to include a new model designed specifically for quail shooting but also adaptable for similarly fast, close, upland game action. The 20 gauge Model 280 Quail Gun is choked i.c./i.c., has a 25" barrel, and is offered at the price of **$439.95**

ITHACA-SKB DOUBLE-GUN SPECIFICATIONS

SIDE-BY-SIDE DOUBLE GUNS

Chambers: 12-ga.—2¾"; 20-ga.—3" (20-ga. skeet —2¾"). Selective single trigger; matted-rib barrels —deep black-chrome finish resists weather, won't rust, bleed or pit. Hand-checkered pistol-grip stock and forend of beautifully finished walnut. Ithaca Raybar® front sight on field grades, Bradley front sight on target grades. Mirror-finish chrome-lined barrels wipe clean with a dry patch. Box-lock action.

Grade	Model	Gauge	Barrel Length	Available Chokes	Length	Stock Comb	Heel	Approx. Wt.
100	Field	12	30"	Full and Modified	14"	1½"	2⅝"	7 lbs.
			28"	Full and Modified				
			26"	Modified and Imp. Cylinder				
200E		20	28"	Full and Modified	14"	1½"	2⅝"	6 lbs.
			25"	Modified and Imp. Cylinder				
200E	Skeet	12	26"	Skeet and Skeet	14"	1½"	2½"	7¼ lbs.
		20	25"	Skeet and Skeet	14"	1½"	2½"	6¼ lbs.
280	English Field	12	28"	Full and Modified	14"	1½"	2⅝"	7⅛ lbs.
			26"	Modified and Imp. Cylinder				
		20	28"	Full and Modified	14"	1½"	2⅝"	6½ lbs.
			25"	Modified and Imp. Cylinder				

100 FIELD GRADE. Nonautomatic extractor. Perfect double locking. Safety: automatic.

200 E FIELD GRADE. Specifications the same as Model 100 but has gold-plated trigger and nameplate, silver-finish, scrolled frame. Automatic selective ejectors. White spacers at pistol-grip cap and stock butt. Beavertail forend.

280 ENGLISH FIELD. Automatic selective ejectors, straight-grip stock with wraparound hand-checkering; semi-beavertail forearm. Engraving: extra-fine quail and English Scroll.

200E SKEET GRADE. Same specifications as 200E Field Grade, plus nonautomatic safety and Ithaca Recoil Pad.

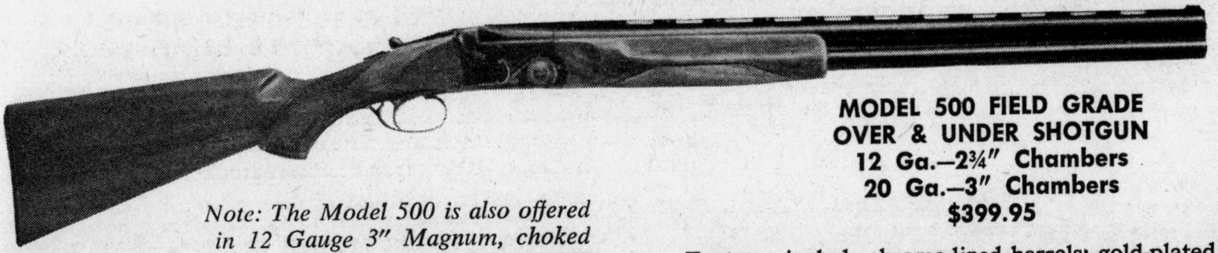

Note: The Model 500 is also offered in 12 Gauge 3" Magnum, choked full/imp. mod. with a 30" barrel, priced at $314.95.

MODEL 500 FIELD GRADE
OVER & UNDER SHOTGUN
12 Ga.—2¾" Chambers
20 Ga.—3" Chambers
$399.95

Features include chrome-lined barrels; gold-plated trigger; automatic selective ejectors, ventilated rib and non-automatic safety.

ITHACA OVER & UNDER SHOTGUNS

TRAP DOUBLES GUNS Ithaca-SKB Model 600 and Model 700 target series. Built expressly for shooting doubles, this new trap gun is choked to give the most efficient pattern for breaking the first target at 21 yards and the second at 30 yards. The Model 700 Trap Doubles Gun is essentially the deluxe version of the Model 600 Doubles Gun and is distinguished by its fancier wood, additional hand checkering, extra-wide rib and more intricate scrollwork. Both models are noted for their hand fitted, hand checkered and hand finished stock; double-locking lugs; non-automatic safety; curved trap pad; and Bradley-type sights.

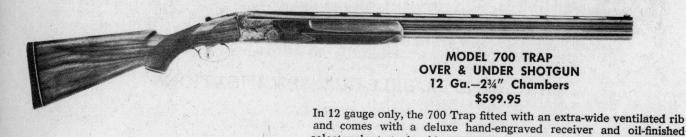

MODEL 700 TRAP
OVER & UNDER SHOTGUN
12 Ga.—2¾" Chambers
$599.95

In 12 gauge only, the 700 Trap fitted with an extra-wide ventilated rib and comes with a deluxe hand-engraved receiver and oil-finished select walnut stocks. Also available in 12 gauge doubles gun **$599.95**

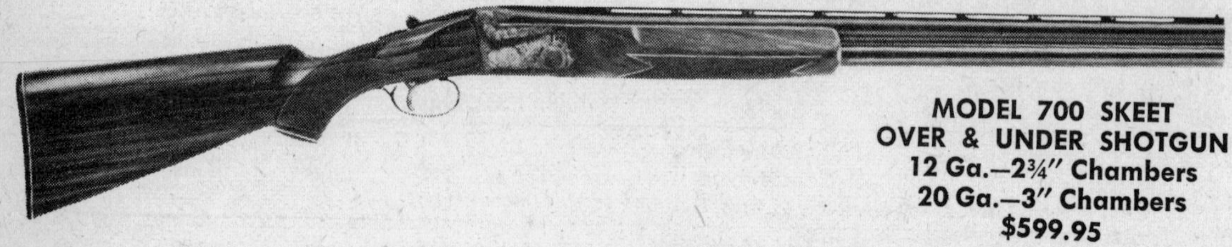

MODEL 700 SKEET
OVER & UNDER SHOTGUN
12 Ga.—2¾" Chambers
20 Ga.—3" Chambers
$599.95

Identical to the 700 trap gun but presented in a skeet model.

OVER-AND-UNDER DOUBLE-GUNS: All guns in 12 gauge with 2¾" chambers or the new 20 gauge with 3" chambers. Selective trigger, ventilated-rib barrels, hand-checkered walnut stock and forend, Ithaca Raybar® front sight.

GRADE	MODEL	GAUGE	BARREL LENGTH	AVAILABLE CHOKES	STOCK				OVERALL WT. (Approx.)
					LENGTH	COMB	MONTE CARLO	HEEL	
500	Field	12	30"	Full and Modified	14"	1½"		2⅝"	7½ lb.
			28"	Full and Modified					
			26"	Modified and Imp. Cylinder					
		20	28"	Full and Modified	14"	1½"		2⅝"	6½ lb.
			26"	Modified and Imp. Cylinder					
600	Trap	12	30" or 32"	Imp. Modified and Full	14½"	1½"	1½"	2"	7¾ lb.
			30" or 32"	Imp. Modified and Full	14½"	1½"		1⅞"	7¾ lb.
600	Skeet	12	26" or 28"	Skeet and Skeet	14"	1½"		2½"	7¾ lb.
		20	26" or 28"	Skeet and Skeet	14"	1½"		2½"	7 lb.
		28	28"	Skeet and Skeet	14"	1½"		2½"	7¼ lb.
		.410	28"	Skeet and Skeet	14"	1½"		2½"	7¼ lb.
600	Field	20	28" or 30"	Full and Modified					
			26"	Modified and Imp. Cylinder					
			28"	Full and Modified	14"	1½"		2⅝"	6½ lb.
600	Magnum	12	30"	Full and Full	14"	1½"		2⅝"	8½ lb.
700	Skeet	12	26" or 28"	Skeet and Skeet	14"	1½"		2⅝"	7½ lb.
		20	26" or 28"	Skeet and Skeet	14"	1½"		2⅝"	6½ lb.
700	Trap	12	30" or 32"	Full and Full	14½"	1½"	1½"	2"	7¾ lb.
					14½"	1½"		1⅞"	7¾ lb.

500 FIELD GRADE: Action: box-lock type. Ejectors: automatic selective. Inside of barrels and action are hard chrome-lined. Engraving: border scroll hand engraving on receiver. Safety: nonautomatic.

600 TRAP GRADE: Action box-lock type. Ejectors: automatic selective. Locking: double locking lugs. Safety: nonautomatic. Inside of barrels and action are hard chrome-lined. Bead middle sight. Engraving: extra-fine scroll hand engraving on receiver. Ithaca Anti-Recoil Pad.

700 GRADE—SKEET AND TRAP: Action: box-lock type. Ejectors: automatic selective. Locking: double locking lugs. Safety: nonautomatic. Inside of barrels and action are hard chrome-lined. Engraving: Deluxe hand engraving adds maximum beauty and distinction. Stocks: select walnut with oil finish.

ITHACA SHOTGUNS

(MODEL 66 "SUPERSINGLE" IN 12, 20 & .410 GAUGES)

MODEL 66 SUPERSINGLE
SINGLE SHOT LEVER ACTION SHOTGUN
(20 & .410 Gauges)

The model 66 Supersingle is a lever-action, single-shot shotgun made with 3-inch chamber—takes either 2¾" (2½" in .410) or 3" Magnum shells. Available in 20 or .410 gauge, standard and youth models. Youth models come with shorter American stock and anti-recoil pad. Rebounding hammer-type safety operates independently of lever action. To fire, gun must be fully cocked by hand before the trigger is released. The gun will not fire if the hammer should accidently slip during cocking. Barrel length and choke combinations: 20 ga—(Standard) 28" full or modified; 20 ga—(Youth) 26" modified; .410 ga—(Standard & Youth) 26" full choke.

66 Supersingle (Standard) 20 or .410 gauge **$59.95**
66 Supersingle (Youth) 20 or .410 gauge **$65.95**

NO. 4E GRADE SINGLE-BARREL TRAP GUN

No. 4E GRADE SINGLE-BARREL TRAP GUN. **Stock and forearm:** Hand-finished and carefully fitted from beautifully figured American walnut. **Engraving:** Frame, top lever, guard and trigger plate are hand-engraved with a trap-shooting scene on one side and an American Indian shooting scene on the opposite side. Hardened, polished trigger, and gold nameplate in the stock. **$2,500.00**

NO. 5E GRADE SINGLE-BARREL TRAP GUN

No. 5E GRADE SINGLE-BARREL TRAP GUN. **Stock and forearm:** Extra-fine, carefully selected walnut of outstandingly beautiful grain and coloring is hand-checkered. **Engraving:** Frame, top lever, forearm iron, guard and trigger plate are elaborately engraved with specially selected designs. Woodcock is inlaid with gold on the right side of the frame, and a pheasant is on the left side. American eagle design on trigger plate and gold nameplate in the stock. **$3,500.00**

$5,000 Grade (not illustrated). Specifications the same as models 4E & 5E with highly figured walnut and precious-metal inlays. **$5,000.00**

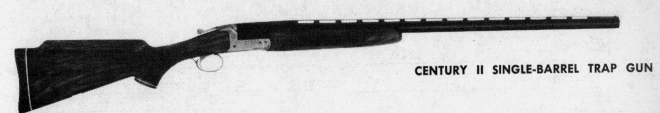

CENTURY II SINGLE-BARREL TRAP GUN

CENTURY II SINGLE-BARREL TRAP GUN. **Stock and forearm:** Straight stock: drop at comb 1⅜", drop at heel 1⅜", weight 8 lbs.; Monte Carlo stock: drop at comb 1⅜", drop at Monte Carlo 1⅜", drop at heel 2", weight 8 lbs. **Engraving:** The silvered frame and trigger plate are engraved, as is the breech of the black-chrome barrel. Century II **$599.95**

ITHACA-PERAZZI SHOTGUNS

MIRAGE

Unique choke arrangement makes the Mirage a superb trap doubles gun. Bottom barrel has extra-full choke—top barrel has modified choke. Tapered rib creates perfect sighting plane. Ventilated middle rib dissipates heat. Hand-checkered walnut stock and schnabel forearm are beautifully hand finished. Skeet and Live Bird models also available.

MX-8

The gun that won both the men's and women's International World Championships in 1969. High-concave rib with 5-inch ramp for maximum ease in aligning the shooter's eye with the center of the rib. Vented middle rib for maximum heat dissipation and smoother, faster swings for dependable performance on even the windiest days.

SINGLE-BARREL TRAP

Perfect balance and handling qualities assure fast swinging and excellent pointing ability.

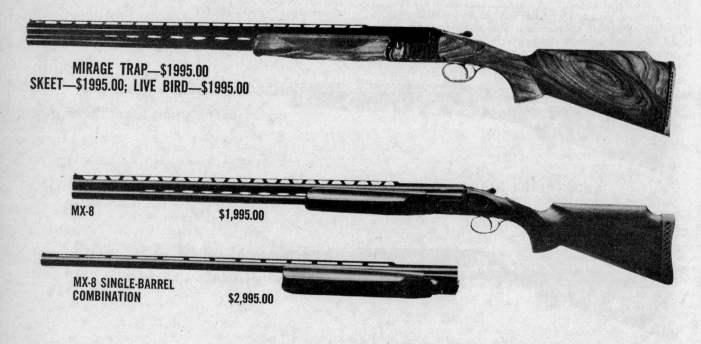

**MIRAGE TRAP—$1995.00
SKEET—$1995.00; LIVE BIRD—$1995.00**

MX-8   **$1,995.00**

**MX-8 SINGLE-BARREL
COMBINATION**   **$2,995.00**

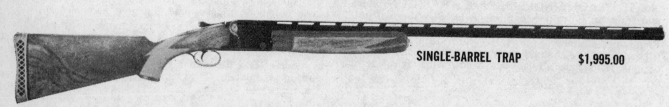

SINGLE-BARREL TRAP   **$1,995.00**

PERAZZI SPECIFICATIONS

Model	Ga.	Chamber	Appx. Wght.	Bbl. Lgth.	Chokes
Lusso Grade Competition	12	2¾"	8½ lbs.	30"	Custom
Mirage	12	2¾"	8¼ lbs.	28", 30" or 32"	Skeet and Skeet or Extra-full and Modified

Model	Ga.	Chamber	Appx. Wght.	Bbl. Lgth.	Chokes
MX-8	12	2¾"	8¼ lbs.	30", 32"	Special bore for international trapshooting
Single-Barrel Trap	12	2¾"	8½ lbs.	32", 34"	Custom

KRIEGHOFF O&U SHOTGUNS

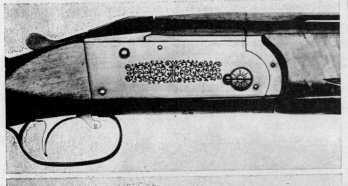

Standard

Features unique Krieghoff split barrel design, simplified construction. Internal parts are specially hardened, heat-treated steel. Single trigger is mechanical, dependable. Selected European stocks and forends.

Standard:	
28" skeet	$ 1,795.00
4 bbl. skeet	$ 4,795.00
all reg. trap	$ 1,595.00
all Vandalia	$ 1,995.00
Extra barrels:	
all skeet	$ 895.00
all trap	$ 695.00
all hunting	$ 895.00
all Vandalia	$ 895.00

San Remo (Vandalia Grade only)

Fine American walnut wood. Relief engraving meticulously insculpted. Polished mechanism. Krieghoff weight is between the hands for perfect balance, fast pointing. All Krieghoffs have special short hammer fall for instant response.

San Remo:	
28" skeet	$ 3,250.00
4 bbl. skeet	$ 6,995.00
all Vandalia	$ 3,795.00
Extra barrels:	
all skeet	$ 995.00
all trap	$ 795.00
all Vandalia	$ 995.00

Monte Carlo

Superb relief engraving, silver inlaid figurines. Fancy grade walnut. All Krieghoffs have light recoil, straight back, no barrel whip, better position for second shot. In Monte Carlo grade.

Monte Carlo:	
4 bbl. skeet	$11,995.00
all reg. trap	$ 6,495.00

Crown

The finest Krieghoff. Gold inlaid figurines. Superbly grained, polished, epoxy-finished woods. Polished mechanism. Double and triple checking of every Krieghoff assures matchless quality.

Crown:	
4 bbl. skeet	$12,995.00
all reg. trap	$ 7,995.00

Super Crown

The ultimate version of the Crown Krieghoff. Relief engraving with gold and silver inlaid figurines. Polished mechanism. Epoxy-finished woods, superbly grained and polished. Peerless performance.

Super Crown:	
4 bbl. skeet	$14,995.00
all reg. trap	$ 6,795.00
all Vandalia	$ 6,995.00

MARLIN SHOTGUNS

MARLIN MODEL 120 12-GAUGE MAGNUM PUMP-ACTION SHOTGUN

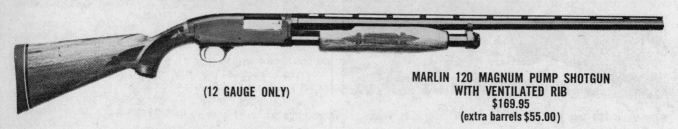

(12 GAUGE ONLY)

**MARLIN 120 MAGNUM PUMP SHOTGUN
WITH VENTILATED RIB
$169.95
(extra barrels $55.00)**

After years of design study, Marlin has introduced a pump action shotgun that is designed to fill the demand for a solid, reliable, all-steel pump action gun. An all-steel action, the entire receiver is made from a solid block of high tensile steel—and all parts, both operating and non operating, are made from tough steel alloys. New-design, exclusive slide lock release lets you open the action to remove unfired sheel even with gloved hands. All-steel floating concave ventilated rib, serrated on top, provides clean sighting, reduces mirage when trap and skeet shooting. Front and middle sights help the eye align barrel and target. Handsomely engine turned bolt, shell carrier and bolt slide add elegance and double action bars provide smoothest possible operation with no binding or twisting. Matte finish, grooved receiver top eliminates glare, aids natural gun pointing and sighting. Big safety button—serrated and located where it belongs, in front of the trigger—operates the cross-bolt safety that positively blocks the trigger. Choice of five barrels—26″ improved cylinder choke, 28″ modified choke, 30″ full choke, 26″ slug barrel (with rifle sights), and 40″ full choke barrel. Select the length and boring of your choice. Extra barrels are completely interchangeable. 5-shot magazine capacity (4 with 3″ shells) 3-shot plug furnished. Stainless steel, non-jamming shell follower. Like all Marlins, the 120 Magnum has a genuine American walnut stock and fore-end. The buttstock design is made to fit American shooters with its full dimensions. Semi-beavertail fore-end is full and fits a full range of hands. Both stock and fore-end are checkered with a handsome pattern and feature Mar-Shield (TM) finish. Deluxe recoil pad is standard.

MARLIN 120 MAGNUM SPECIFICATIONS: 12 gauge, 2¾″ or 3″ Magnum or regular shells interchangeably; 5 shots in magazine (4 with 3″ shells), 3-shot plug furnished; approx. 7¾ #; 26″, 28″ or 30″ barrels with steel ventilated ribs, front and middle sights; recoil pad; grip cap; white butt and grip spacers; stock dimensions: 14″ long including recoil pad, 1½″ drop at comb, 2⅜″ drop at heel; genuine American walnut stock and fore-end are finely checkered and Mar-Shield(TM) finished; all-steel action and parts; cross bolt safety.

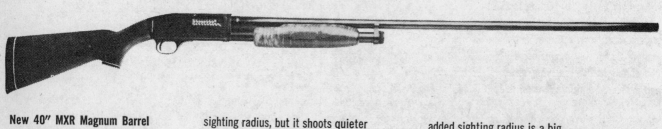

New 40″ MXR Magnum Barrel
Not only does it offer increased sighting radius, but it shoots quieter and balances surprisingly well. The added sighting radius is a big advantage for extra long range shooting.

New Slug Barrel
Now you can convert your 120 to an accurate deer gun in seconds. This new specially choked 26″ slug barrel comes with rifle sights. The rear sight is adjustable, and its base is drilled and tapped for scope mounting.

MARLIN SHOTGUNS

Marlin 120 Trap Gun $234.95

New Marlin 120 Trap Gun
Features a handsome American black-walnut Monte Carlo stock and full forearm with hand-cut checkering. Stock dimensions: length of pull 14¼"; drop at comb 1¼"; drop at heel 1¾"; drop at Monte Carlo 1¼".

Available with 30" full choke barrel with steel floating ventilated rib.

---

12 GAUGE 3" MAGNUM BOLT-ACTION SHOTGUN

**ORIGINAL GOOSE GUN
12 GAUGE 3" MAGNUM—36" BARREL
(FULL CHOKE ONLY)
$74.95**

High-flying ducks and geese are the Goose Gun's specialty. The Marlin Goose Gun has an extra-long 36" full-choked barrel and Magnum capability, making it the perfect choice for tough shots at wary waterfowl. It also features a quick-loading 2-shot clip magazine, a convenient leather carrying strap and a quality ventilated recoil pad.

Marlin Goose Gun Specifications
Gauge: 12 gauge; 3" Magnum or 2¾" Regular shells
Choke: Full
Capacity: 2-shot clip magazine (with the exception of some No. 2 and 00 Buck shells, which are too long for the clip magazine and must be single loaded).
Action: Bolt action; gold-plated steel trigger.

Stock: Genuine American walnut with pistol grip and ventilated recoil pad; white butt spacer; swivels and leather carrying strap; tough Mar-Shield™ finish.
Barrel: 36" with bead front sight.
Overall Length: 57"
Weight: About 7¼ lbs.

**Marlin Slug Gun Model 55S
$79.95 (less scope)**

New Marlin Slug Gun
Based on the Goose Gun bolt action system, the Model 55S is a heavy cover deer gun. Its short 24" barrel gets into action fast. It comes with iron sights—rear sight is adjustable—and is drilled and tapped for scope mounting. Chambered for 2¾" and 3" shells, the 55S is also equipped with swivels, a handy leather carrying strap and a quality recoil pad. 2-shot clip magazine. About 7 lbs. Overall length 45".

MOSSBERG SHOTGUNS

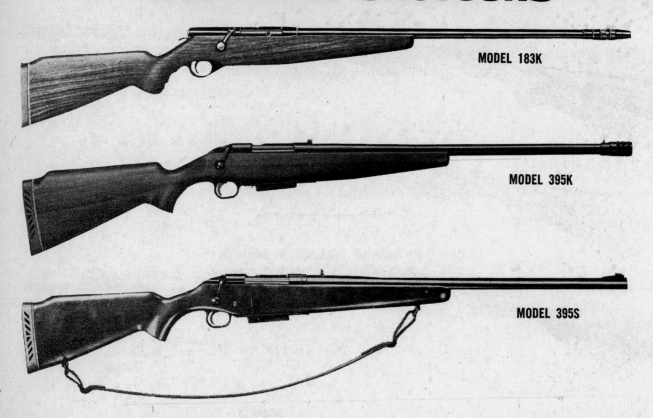

MODEL 183K

MODEL 395K

MODEL 395S

bolt action shotguns

The most popular bolt action shotguns are those made by Mossberg, in 12, 16 and 20 gauge and 410 bore. Proof tested in our factory and chambered for all standard and Magnum factory loads. A modern streamline designed self-cocking action with **positive safety on top—right under your thumb**. The design and dimensions of these guns make them ideal for fast shooting. All Mossberg shotguns shoot rifled slugs accurately for deer or other big game.

MODEL 183K 410 bore Bolt Action. Price **$69.40**
The only 410 bore shotgun that gives you the advantage of finger-operated adjustable choke. **Action**—Fixed-type top loading magazine holds two shells, plus one in chamber. Chambered for all 2½" and 3" factory loaded shells. Convenient thumb-operated safety with red and green button inlaid in stock. **Stock**—Walnut finish Monte Carlo design. Rubber recoil pad with white liner. Molded trigger guard. **Barrel**—25" tapered blued steel barrel, including C-LECT-CHOKE. Mossberg's exclusive factory installed adjustable choke lets you instantly choose Full Choke, Modified Choke, Improved Cylinder Bore or points in between Gold bead front sight. **Weight**—About 6¾ lbs. Length overall 43½".

MODEL 395K 12 gauge Bolt Action. Price **$80.70**
With 3" Magnum shells and number 2 shot this becomes a great goose gun. **Action**—Strong bolt action chambered for 3" Magnum as well as 2¾" factory loaded shells.

Double locking lugs for added strength. Quick removable bolt with double extractors. Detachable clip magazine. Magazine holds two shells plus one in chamber. Positive Safety on Top—"Right Under Your Thumb". **Stock**—Walnut finish, modern Monte Carlo design, pistol grip and cushion rubber recoil pad. **Barrel**—28" including C-LECT-CHOKE. **Sights**—Grooved rear sight for accurate alignment. Shotgun bead front. **Weight**—About 6¾ lbs. Length overall 47½".

MODEL 385K 20 gauge Bolt Action. Price **$74.88**
Identical to Model 395K except that it is a 20 gauge shotgun with 26" barrel, including C-LECT-CHOKE. Chambered for 3" Magnum as well as 2¾" factory loaded shells. **Weight**—About 6¼ lbs. Length overall 45½".

MODEL 395S 12 gauge Slugster. Price **$82.17**
Same specifications as Model 395K, but equipped with 24" Slugster barrel with sights for running shots. Front sight is Partridge type on ramp and rear sight is adjustable folding leaf. Gun is equipped with web sling.

MOSSBERG SHOTGUNS

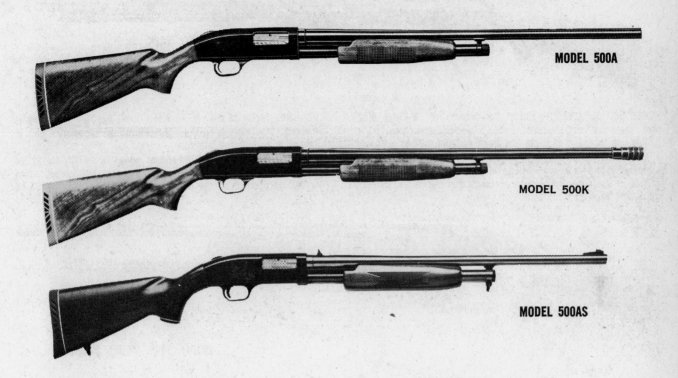

MODEL 500A

MODEL 500K

MODEL 500AS

MODEL 500 SERIES
Slide-Action Shotguns, Field Grade, 12 and 20 gauges; .410 bore

All Mossberg 500 12-gauge and 20-gauge shotguns are designed to operate with both 2¾" and 3" Magnum shotshells. The .410 will shoot 2½" and 3" shells.

SPECIFICATIONS:
Fast slide action feeds shells into chamber quickly. All 12-gauge models have double slide bars for smoother operation. Straight-line feeding aligns shell with chamber before chambering for better functioning. Bolt locks into barrel extension, and action must be locked before gun will fire. Extra-large double extractors for positive ejection; double shell releases assure smooth feeding into carrier and chamber. Action is easily disassembled without special tools.

Positive slide-safety on top of receiver is "right under your thumb." Disconnecting trigger is an added safety feature. Trigger must be released after each shot before the next round will fire. This prevents accidental doubling.

Bolt and carrier have chrome-damascened finish. All other metal parts are deep-blue finished.

Stock—Walnut with filled finish; fluted comb and pistol grip with white-line spacer and cap. Cushion-rubber recoil pad with white-line spacer. Checkered on both beavertail forend and pistol grip.

Barrel—All Model 500 barrels are made of selected gun-quality steel machined from solid-bar stock with deep-blue finish. All Model 500 field guns are available with a variety of barrel lengths and chokes. All barrels are easily interchangeable within gauge.

Shell capacity—All Model 500's have six-shot capacity (2¾")—five in the magazine and one in the chamber. Hold five magnum shells **(3")**.

12-ga.—500A; 30" Full Choke,
  28" Modified,
  26" Improved Cylinder.
  500AK; 26" C-LECT-CHOKE
  500AS; 24" Slugster® barrel with adjustable rear sight
20-ga.—500C; 28" Full Choke,
  28" Modified,
  26" Improved Cylinder
  500CK; 26" C-LECT-CHOKE
.410-bore—500E; 26" Full Choke
All Model 500 barrels are easily interchangeable within their gauge, including 12-gauge Magnum with 3" chamber and extra-heavy barrel.

MODEL 500-AK C-LECT-CHOKE—This version of our Model 500 features the 26" barrel with exclusive C-LECT-CHOKE adjustable choke. Each C-LECT-CHOKE is factory installed and individually fitted on each gun. Clearly marked with graduated lines for full choke, modified choke, improved cylinder bore and points in between. Choke is easily adjusted to desired setting by hand—no adjusting tool is needed.

MODEL 500AS Slugster—The Mossberg 500 action is coupled with a barrel designed to handle rifled slugs for deer and other large game. The etched receiver features a running-deer scene on the side. Ramp front sight and adjustable folding-leaf rear sight. Receiver drilled and tapped for scope sights, fitted with sling swivels and web sling strap.

500A	12-ga. Field-Grade	$137.06
500C	20-ga. Field-Grade	$137.06
500E	.410-bore Field-Grade	$137.06
500AK	12-ga. Field-Grade C-LECT-CHOKE	$142.71
500CK	20-ga. Field-Grade C-LECT-CHOKE	$142.71
500AS	12-ga. Field-Grade Slugster	$142.71

MOSSBERG SHOTGUNS

MODEL 500 DSPR

MODEL 500 DSPR Limited-Edition Commemorative 12-gauge Magnum, steel-shot barrel, pigeon-grade slide-action shotgun.

Only one thousand of these Mossberg shotguns will be produced to commemorate the Migratory Bird Hunting Stamp Program. Each hunter who purchases one will receive a handsome plaque as a symbol of his contribution to waterfowl conservation. A 1974-75 stamp is affixed to the plaque.

The illustration of the pair of Wood Ducks used on the stamp is depicted as an etching on the right side of the receiver. A pair in flight is etched on the left side.

Each shotgun in this limited-edition series is serially numbered and registered as a commemorative sporting arm. The corresponding number is recorded on the plaque. **$232.75**

MODEL 500R, MODEL 500AMR

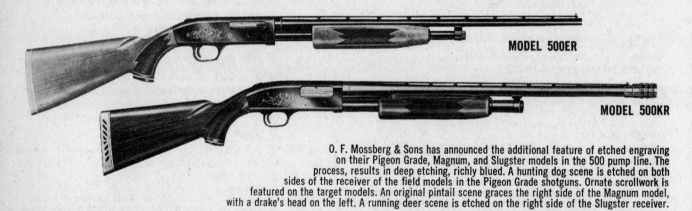

MODEL 500ER

MODEL 500KR

O. F. Mossberg & Sons has announced the additional feature of etched engraving on their Pigeon Grade, Magnum, and Slugster models in the 500 pump line. The process, results in deep etching, richly blued. A hunting dog scene is etched on both sides of the receiver of the field models in the Pigeon Grade shotguns. Ornate scrollwork is featured on the target models. An original pintail scene graces the right side of the Magnum model, with a drake's head on the left. A running deer scene is etched on the right side of the Slugster receiver.

MODEL 500R. Super Grade. Price **$153.28**
Model 500AR, 12 gauge, Model 500CR, 20 gauge and Model 500ER, 410 bore. In 12 or 20 gauge or 410 bore chambered for all 2¾" (2½" in 410) and 3" factory loaded shells, with our own Mossberg ventilated rib roll engraved receiver and custom checkered genuine American walnut, with fluted comb and pistol grip. All the same fine features as in our standard 500 including your choice of interchangeable barrels, our "Safety-on-Top" and the double slide bars on 12 gauge. Model 500AR available with 30" Full Choke, 28" Modified Choke and 26" Improved Cylinder (SKEET). Model 500CR 28" Full Choke, 28" Modified Choke and 26" Improved Cylinder (SKEET). Model 500ER, 26" Full Choke.

MODEL 500KR. C-LECT-CHOKE. Price **$161.79**
Model 500AKR, 12 gauge, Model 500CKR, 20 gauge. Same specifications as our Model 500 Super Grade but with 26" C-LECT-CHOKE our factory installed adjustable choke with individual settings for Full Choke, Modified Choke, Improved Cylinder Bore and points in between. Like our standard 500 Field Grade all barrels are instantly and easily interchangeable within their gauge. See page 78 for a complete listing of the regular and special barrels available.

MODEL 500AMR. MAGNUM. Price **$161.79**
Identical to our standard Super Grade 500 but with 30" Full Choke heavy weight Magnum barrel with 3" chamber.

MOSSBERG SHOTGUNS
model 500 pigeon grade slide action shotguns

MODEL 500APTR

MODEL 500APR

EXTRA BARRELS for MODEL 500 SERIES		
Model No.		**Price**
30F12	12 ga. Regular 2¾" & 3" 30" Full Choke	$32.45
30FR12	12 ga. Ventilated Rib 2¾" & 3" 30" Full Choke	60.50
30FRP12	12 ga. Pigeon Grade 2¾" & 3" 30" Full Choke	69.40
30FTRP12	12 ga. Pigeon Grade 2¾" & 3" 30" Full Choke TRAP	69.40
28F12	12 ga. Regular 2¾" & 3" 28" Full Choke	32.45
28FR12	12 ga. Ventilated Rib 2¾' & 3" 28" Full Choke	60.50
28M12	12 ga. Regular 2¾" & 3" 28" Modified Choke	32.45
28MR12	12 ga. Ventilated Rib 2¾" & 3" 28" Modified Choke	60.50
28MRP12	12 ga. Pigeon Grade 2¾" & 3" 28" Modified Choke	69.40
26I12	12 ga. Regular 2¾" & 3" 26" Improved Cylinder Bore	32.45
26SKR12	12 ga. Ventilated Rib 2¾" & 3" 26" Skeet Bore	69.40
26SKRP12	12 ga. Pigeon Grade 2¾" & 3" 26" Skeet Bore	69.40
26K12	12 ga. Special 2¾" & 3" 26" with C-LECT-CHOKE	40.90
26KR12	12 ga. Ventilated Rib 2¾" & 3" 26" C-LECT-CHOKE	69.40
24S12	12 ga. Special 2¾" & 3" 24" "SLUGSTER"	40.90
30MG12	12 ga. Special 3" Magnum 30" Full Choke	40.90
30MGR12	12 ga. Special Ventilated Rib 3" Magnum 30" Full Choke	69.40
28F16	16 ga. Regular 2¾" 28" Full Choke	32.45
28M16	16 ga. Regular 2¾" 28" Modified Choke	32.45
26I16	16 ga. Regular 2¾" 26" Improved Cylinder Bore	32.45
26K16	16 ga. Special 2¾" 26" with C-LECT-CHOKE	40.90
24S16	16 ga. Special 2¾" 24" "SLUGSTER"	40.90
28F20	20 ga. Regular 2¾" & 3" 28" Full Choke	32.45
28FR20	20 ga. Ventilated Rib 2¾" & 3" 28" Full Choke	60.50
28M20	20 ga. Regular 2¾" & 3" 28" Modified Choke	32.45
28MR20	20 ga. Ventilated Rib 2¾" & 3" 28" Modified Choke	60.50
26I20	20 ga. Regular 2¾" & 3" 26" Improved Cylinder Bore	32.45
26SKR20	20 ga. Ventilated Rib 2¾" & 3" 26" Skeet Bore	69.40
26K20	20 ga. Regular 2¾" & 3" 26" C-LECT-CHOKE	40.90
26KR20	20 ga. Ventilated Rib 2¾" & 3" 26" with C-LECT-CHOKE	69.40
24S20	20 ga. Special 2¾" & 3" 24" "SLUGSTER"	40.90
26F410	410 bore Regular 2½" & 3" 26" Full Choke	32.45
26FR410	410 bore Ventilated Rib 2½" & 3" 26" Full Choke	60.50
26M410	410 bore Regular 2½" & 3" 26" Modified Choke	32.45
26MR410	410 bore Ventilated Rib 2½" & 3" 26" Modified Choke	60.50
26I410	410 bore Regular 2½" & 3" 26" Improved Cylinder Bore	32.45
26SKR410	410 bore Ventilated Rib 2½" & 3" 26" Skeet Bore	69.40
26K410	410 bore Special 2½" & 3" 26" with C-LECT-CHOKE	40.90
26KR410	410 bore Ventilated Rib 2½" & 3" with C-LECT-CHOKE	69.40

MODEL 500APR. Pigeon Grade. **$192.44**
The popularity of the Mossberg Model 500 slide action repeating shotgun has created a demand for the highest grade gun in this line, for the sportsman who enjoys owning and shooting a gun to carry with pride. **Action—** Same modern slide action design as our standard Model 500 Field Grade. Light weight, high-tensile alloy forged receivers have gold filled roll engraving on both sides of receiver. Double slide bars for faster repeating action. **Stock—**Semi-fancy American walnut, hand checkered stocks and forends. Gold "M" emblem in pistol grip cap. White liners at rubber recoil pad and pistol grip cap. Stock dimensions are: Length of pull 14", drop at comb 1½", drop at heel 2½". **Barrel—** Special high polished deep gun blue ventilated rib barrels. Available in 30" Full Choke, 28" Modified Choke and 26" Improved Cylinder (SKEET). Red bead front and middle sights. Like all our Model 500's these Pigeon Grade barrels are interchangeable. See chart at left for a complete listing of the 12 gauge barrels that will fit this shotgun.

MODEL 500APTR. Pigeon Grade "Trap" **$199.98**
Identical to our Mossberg Model 500APR this is a Pigeon Grade 30" Full Choke Ventilated Rib TRAP GUN supplied with Monte Carlo style stock with the ideal trap gun dimensions: Length of pull 14½", drop at Monte Carlo 1½", drop at heel 2", pitch down 1". With several interchangeable barrels available, the Model 500APTR is a most versatile trap and game gun.

PEDERSEN SHOTGUNS

1000 Series Over & Under Shotguns

The Pedersen 1000 Series over-and-under shotguns bring all of the gun crafts to a new degree of excellence. Hand checkering, flawlessly executed in distinctive patterns, is tastefully achieved by top American craftsmen in the 1000 Series. These crafted features are combined with the stock-maker's talents to provide suitable trappings for the Pedersen Model 1000 actions. They are strong frames, forged from alloy steel, with desirable features such as single-selective trigger in the 1000 Series, plus automatic ejectors which are standard. Add the superlative engraving, silver-inlaid in the Grade I, for the supreme expression of handcraftsmanship.

The type of hand checkering used throughout the 1000 Series is known as "borderless hand checkering." Undoubtedly the most difficult technique to employ, this method requires special attention and infinite care by the craftsman. We feel that only the best possible checkering could complement the wood used in Pedersen Custom Guns. These American black-walnut blanks are personally chosen by highly skilled stock-makers for the 1000 Series.

They then hand work each piece, both butt—stock and forend, to bring out the hidden beauty only a piece of wood of this grade can show.

The action used in all the Pedersen Model 1000 Series has two hardened-steel bolts located on the breech face which correspond to holes located in the Monobloc barrel. These tapered bolts ensure positive locking with an absolute minimum of wear. It gives the Pedersen a simple, durable and exceptionally strong lockup. The Pedersen Monoblock barrels are drilled from a solid, forged billet of chrome-moly steel. The Monoblock system is much stronger than normal breeching methods. Drilling, boring, then reaming, choking and turning are all essential steps in the manufacturing process. Each barrel is tested with an air gauge (normally used only for precision benchrest rifle barrels) to guarantee perfection in each bore. The barrels are constantly inspected during the entire production phase. Each tube is finally lapped and polished.

Only quality parts are used throughout the action. Spring-loaded firing pins retract into the breech face, preventing wear by the opening of the breech. The mainsprings of the 1000 Series action are coiled-spring steel—not flat, as used in some shotgun actions.

Every part of the action is crafted to give the shooter years of trouble-free service.

Grade I **$1,980.00**
Grade II **$1,540.00**

MODEL 1000 GRADE II, 12 GAUGE

GRADE I TARGET
Handcraftsmanship is evident in the rich silver-inlaid engraving and flawless 22-line borderless hand-checkering on full-fancy American black-walnut stock and forend. A selection of target chokes and barrel lengths are available. All Pedersen target guns are equipped with front and middle white Bradley sights, ventilated rib, and Pachmayr "Presentation" pad. Trap gun is equipped with Monte Carlo stock.
Model 1000, Grade I Trap, 12 gauge **$1980.00**
Model 1000, Grade I Skeet, 12 gauge, 20 gauge .**$1980.00**

GRADE II TARGET
The Grade II target guns are built to standard trap- and skeet-stock dimensions and configurations. The braised-steel ventilated rib assures a perfect sighting plane regardless of the number of shots fired. Features include Monte Carlo stock on the trap model, 20-line borderless hand-checkering on fancy American black-walnut stock and forend, front and middle white Bradley sights and Pachmayr "Presentation" pad.
Model 1000, Grade II Trap, 12 gauge **$1570.00**
Model 1000, Grade II Skeet, 12 gauge, 20 gauge .**$1555.00**

PEDERSEN SHOTGUNS

4000/4500 SERIES
Slide Action Shotguns

The 4000 and 4500 series shotguns in 12, 20 gauge and .410 bore offer all the features the slide-action shooter demands, while sporting ornately engraved receivers and richly finished, hand-checkered walnut stocks. The series offer deep-luster blued receivers in two distinct engraving styles. The 4000 has a full-coverage floral-engraved receiver, while the 4500 offers a pattern of tasteful scroll work.

Stocked in select American walnut, both guns feature hand-checkering, a rosewood pistol-grip cap and a Pachmayr "Old English" recoil pad. Model 4000 and 4500 series trap guns come with Monte Carlo stock.

Interchangeable barrels, within the same gauge, are available in 26", 28" and 30" lengths, choked in full, modified, improved cylinder and skeet. Also available is a "Slugster" 12-gauge interchangeable barrel.

Model 4000 .... $275.00
Model 4000 Trap $283.00
Model 4500 .... $225.00
Model 4500 Trap $233.00

SPECIFICATIONS

M/4000 12 Gauge 30″ Full	M/4500 20 Gauge 28″ Full
M/4500 12 Gauge 30″ Full	M/4000 20 Gauge 28″ Modified
M/4000 12 Gauge 28″ Modified	M/4500 20 Gauge 28″ Modified
M/4500 12 Gauge 28″ Modified	M/4000 20 Gauge 26″ Improved Cylinder
M/4000 12 Gauge 26″ Improved Cylinder	M/4500 20 Gauge 26″ Improved Cylinder
M/4500 12 Gauge 26″ Improved Cylinder	M/4000 20 Gauge 26″ SKEET
M/4000 12 Gauge 30″ Full—TRAP	M/4500 20 Gauge 26″ SKEET
M/4500 12 Gauge 30″ Full—TRAP	M/4000 .410 Bore 26″ Full
M/4000 12 Gauge 26″ SKEET	M/4500 .410 Bore 26″ Full
M/4500 12 Gauge 26″ SKEET	M/4000 .410 Bore 26″ SKEET
M/4000 20 Gauge 28″ Full	M/4500 .410 Bore 26″ SKEET

THE CONNECTICUT STATE COMMEMORATIVE SHOTGUN

This firearm, one of only three to be created, is a superb example of our presentation-grade firearms. It contains such significant features as a gold- and silver-inlaid engraving of the state's symbol—The Charter Oak—on one side of the receiver backed by the state's seal on the opposite side. In addition, an ivory scrimshaw depicting another of the state's symbols—the whale—is set into the receiver bottom. All are symbolic of the state's history. Flawlessly finished and securely protected in a custom-fitted case, this shotgun will be the envy of historians—shooters and nonshooters —in the years to come. $3,000.00

REMINGTON AUTOMATIC SHOTGUNS

The Remington Model 1100 is a 5-shot gas operated automatic shotgun with a gas metering system designed to operate with all types of shotgun shells. This design enables the shooter to use all 2¾" standard velocity, "Express," and 2¾" magnum loads without any gun adjustments. Barrels, within gauge and similar chamber lengths, are interchangeable. The 1100 is made in 12, 16, 20, 28 and .410 gauge, with a choice of different chokes, barrel lengths, and gauge combinations. The solid-steel receiver features decorative

scroll work. Stocks come with fine-line checkering in a fleur-de-lis design combined with American walnut (Mahogany supplied in some lightweight 20-gauge models) and a scratch-resistant finish developed by Du Pont called RK-W. Features include decorative receiver scrolls, white-diamond inlay in pistol-grip cap, white-line spacers, full beavertail forend, fluted-comb cuts and chrome-plated bolt.

MODEL 1100 FIELD GUN
(12, 16 & 20 Gauges)
with plain barrel $219.95
with ventilated rib $244.95

REMINGTON MODEL 1100 TB AUTOLOADING TRAP GUN
LEFT HAND ACTION — 12 GAUGE
(SHOWN WITH OPTIONAL MONTE CARLO STOCK)

MODEL 1100 LEFT HAND

A complete mirror image of the regular Model 1100, these left hand shotguns put an end to the bothersome flying hulls that left-handed shooters had to face. Ejection is on the left side—all other specifications are the same as the regular Model 1100, 12 and 20 gauge. Left hand Monte Carlo stock available on trap model.

Model	Barrel length, in.	Choke	
1100LH with Vent. Rib Barrel	30	Full	$249.95
	28	Full	249.95
	28	Mod.	249.95
	26	I.C.	249.95
1100LH Mag. with Vent. Rib Barrel	30	Full	$269.95
1100LH SA Skeet with Vent. Rib Barrel	26	Skeet	$259.95

Model	Barrel length, in.	Choke	
1100LH TB Trap with Vent. Rib Barrel	30	Full	$294.95
1100LH TB Trap with Vent. Rib Barrel, Monte Carlo Stock	30	Full	$304.95

(12 & 20 Gauges)
For 3" & 2¾" Magnum Shells Only

MODEL 1100 MAGNUM
with plain barrel $239.95
with ventilated rib $264.95

Designed for 3" and 2¾" Magnum shells only. Available in 30" plain and 30" ventilated-rib full or modified choke in 12 gauge, and 28" full or modified choke in 20 gauge, plain or ventilated-rib barrels. Stock dimensions: 14" long including pad, 2½" drop at comb. Furnished with recoil pad. Weight: about 7¾ lbs.

MODEL 1100 DEER GUN
(12 & 20 Gauges)

22" barrel, improved cylinder choke. Rifle sights adjustable for windage and elevation. Recoil pad. Weight. about 7¾ lbs. Choked for both rifled slugs and buck shot. $239.95

REMINGTON TRAP & SKEET GUNS

MODEL 1100 AUTOMATIC SHOTGUNS—SKEET & TRAP MODELS

MODEL 1100SA SKEET GUN
WITH VENTILATED RIB BARREL
(12 & 20 GAUGES)

Model 1100SA Skeet Gun: is made in 12 and 20 gauges, and comes with 26" barrel, skeet boring, ventilated rib, ivory bead front sight and white metal rear sight. Stock dimensions are 14" long, 2½" drop at heel, 1½" drop at comb. Weight, about 7½ lbs. This model is also available in SB grade with better walnut stock. Both models may be had with factory fitted Cutts Compensator choke devices. 20 gauge model available with lightweight mahogany stock.

Model 1100 SA Skeet, with ventilated rib barrel **$254.95**
Model 1100 SA Skeet, w/vent rib & cutts compensator **$279.95**
Model 1100 SB Skeet, w/vent rib (better wood) **$279.95**

BARREL LENGTH & CHOKE COMBINATIONS

26"	Rem. Skeet
26"	Cutts Comp.

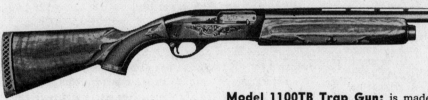

MODEL 1100TB TRAP GUN
WITH VENTILATED RIB BARREL
(12 GAUGE ONLY)

Model 1100TB Trap Gun: is made in 12 gauge only and is equipped with rubber recoil pad and ventilated rib barrel. Stock is of selected grade wood and features fine-line fleur-de-lis design checkering and white spacers on butt plate and grip cap. Fore-end has swept back design and fluting to give secure gripping area. Trap stock dimensions: 14⅜" long including recoil pad, 1¾" drop at heel, 1⅜" drop at comb. Weight: about 8½ lbs. Available in 30" full choke and 30" modified choke only. Ivory bead front sight, white metal rear sight. Also available with Monte Carlo stock $10.00 extra.
Model 1100 TB Trap, with ventilated rib barrel **$289.95**
Model 1100 TB Trap, w/vent rib & Monte Carlo stock **$299.95**

BARREL LENGTH & CHOKE COMBINATIONS

30"	Full Choke
30"	Modified Trap

(Shown with Monte Carlo stock)
12 GAUGE ONLY

MODEL 1100 TB • Left Hand Trap Gun
The Model 1100 TB is the first automatic shotgun to achieve serious acceptance by the trap shooting fraternity. Now this famous trap gun is offered in a true "mirror-image" left hand version featuring left hand feeding and ejection. Produced in 30" full choke ventilated rib barrels with either regular or Monte Carlo stocks. Other specifications same as above. With regular stock **$294.95** with Monte Carlo stock **$304.95**

SPECIFICATIONS: Model 1100 (12, 16 & 20 Gauges):

SPECIFICATIONS: STYLE —5 shot gas operated shotgun. 3 shot plug furnished. **GAUGE** —Made in 12, 16 and 20 gauge. **BARREL** —Special Remington ordnance steel. Extra barrel is interchangeable within gauge. **OVER-ALL LENGTH** —48" (with 28" Barrel). **SAFETY** —Convenient cross-bolt type. **RECEIVER** —Made from solid steel, top matted, scroll work on bolt and both sides of receiver. **STANDARD STOCK DIMENSIONS** —Stock and fore-end: Rich American walnut. 14" long, 2½" drop at heel, 1½" drop at comb. Trap reg., 14⅜" long, 1¾" drop at heel, 1⅜" drop at comb. Monte Carlo, 14⅜" long, 1¾" drop at heel, 1¼" drop at comb, 1¼" drop at M.C. **AVERAGE WEIGHT** —12 ga.-7½ lbs., 16 ga.-7¼ lbs., 20 ga.-7 lbs.

MODEL 1100
12, 16 & 20 GAUGES
BARREL LENGTH & CHOKE COMBINATIONS

30"	Full Choke
28"	Full Choke
28"	Modified Choke
26"	Imp. Cyl. Choke

Note: (16 & 20 gauge models are not available in 30" barrel length).

REMINGTON AUTOMATIC SHOTGUNS

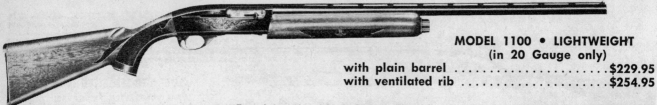

MODEL 1100 • LIGHTWEIGHT
(in 20 Gauge only)

with plain barrel $229.95
with ventilated rib $254.95

Barrel length and choke combinations for the Model 1100 lightweight in 20 gauge: 28" full; 28" modified; and 26" improved Cylinder. Weight, 6½ pounds.

MODEL 1100 • SMALL GAUGES
(28 & 410 Gauges)

with plain barrel $229.95
with ventilated rib $254.95
SA Skeet Ventilated Rib,
   28 & .410 ga., 25" skeet bbl. $264.95

The Remington Model 1100 Automatic shotguns in 28 and 410 gauges are an exact copy of the 12, 16, and 20 gauge versions. Built on its own receiver and frame, these small gauge shotguns are available in a wide selection of chokes with either plain or ventilated rib barrels. The 410 gauge field grade will handle 2½" and 3" shotgun shells, while the 410 Skeet gun is supplied with a 2½" chambered barrel.

Extra barrels are interchangeable within gauge regardless of chamber length of original barrel. 410 gauge guns are designed for the exclusive use of plastic shells. The model 1100 field grade 28 and 410 gauge guns are equipped with mahogany stocks and fore-ends (for extra light weight), and feature a scratch resistant RK-W wood finish.

MODEL 1100
28 & 410 GAUGES
BARREL LENGTH
& CHOKE COMBINATIONS

25" Full Choke
25" Modified Choke
25" Imp. Cyl. Choke

SPECIFICATIONS: STYLE — Gas operated. 5 shot capacity with 28 ga. shells — 4 shot capacity with 3" - 410 ga. shells. 3 shot plug furnished. **BARREL** — Special Remington ordnance steel. Extra barrels interchangeable within gauge. **CHAMBER** — 2½" in 410 ga. skeet; 3" shells only in field grades; 2¾" in 28 ga. field and skeet models. **OVER-ALL LENGTH** — 45½". **SAFETY** — Convenient cross-bolt type. **RECEIVER** — Made from solid steel, top matted, scroll work on bolt and both sides of receiver. **STOCK DIMENSIONS,** mahogany in field grades, walnut in skeet grades — 14" long, 2½" drop at heel, 1½" drop at comb. **AVERAGE WEIGHT**—28 ga. skeet-6¾ lbs.; .410 ga. skeet - 7¼ lbs. (adjustable weight will add up to 12 oz. in skeet guns, $11.50 extra); 28 ga. plain barrel-6¼ lbs.; .410 ga. plain barrel-6¾ lbs.; 28 ga. vent. rib - 6½ lbs.; .410 ga. vent. rib - 7 lbs.

MODEL 1100 20 GAUGE MAGNUM LIGHTWEIGHT

with plain barrel $249.95
with vent rib barrel $274.95

The Model 1100 20 Gauge Lightweight Magnum is chambered for 20 gauge Magnum loads only (either 2¾" or 3"), and comes furnished with rubber recoil pad. Designed for the "all-day" hunter, this new Lightweight Magnum will shoot 2¾" and 3" Magnum shells giving the hunter the power of the standard 12 gauge load. Weight is only 6¾ lbs. Operation and appearance is the same as the standard Model 1100.

SPECIFICATIONS: Style—Gas operated automatic shotgun. **Barrel**—28" barrel, full choke, chambered for 3" 20 gauge Magnum shells. **Capacity**—4 shot with 3" shells. **Overall Length**—48½". **Safety**—Convenient positive cross-bolt type. **Receiver**—Made from solid steel, top matted, decorative scroll work on bolt and both sides of receiver. **Standard Stock Dimensions**—Lightweight Mahagony stocks & fore-ends. 1½" drop at comb, 2½" drop at heel, 13⅞" length of pull. **Weight**—6¾ lbs.

REMINGTON O&U SHOTGUNS

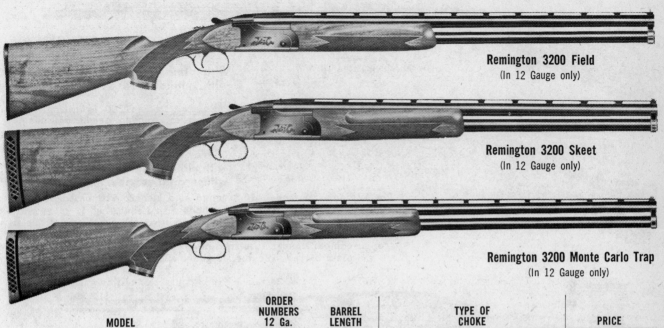

Remington 3200 Field
(In 12 Gauge only)

Remington 3200 Skeet
(In 12 Gauge only)

Remington 3200 Monte Carlo Trap
(In 12 Gauge only)

MODEL	ORDER NUMBERS 12 Ga.	BARREL LENGTH	TYPE OF CHOKE	PRICE
3200 Field with Ventilated Rib Barrel	3201	30"	Modified & Full	$595.95
	3203	28"	Modified & Full	
	3205	26"	Improved Cylinder & Modified	
3200 Skeet with Ventilated Rib Barrel	3209	28"	Skeet & Skeet	$650.00
	3211	26"	Skeet & Skeet	
3200 3" Magnum with Ventilated Rib Barrel	3241	30"	Full & Full	
	3243	30"	Modified & Full	
3200 Trap with Ventilated Rib Barrel	3215	30"	Full & Full	
	3217	30"	Improved Modified & Full	
	3213	32"	Improved Modified & Full	
3200 Trap with Ventilated Rib Barrel and Monte Carlo Stock	3221	30"	Full & Full	$675.00
	3223	30"	Improved Modified & Full	
	3219	32"	Improved Modified & Full	
3200 Special Trap with Ventilated Rib Barrel	3227	30"	Full & Full	$740.00
	3229	30"	Improved Modified & Full	
	3225	32"	Improved Modified & Full	
3200 Special Trap with Ventilated Rib Barrel and Monte Carlo Stock	3233	30"	Full & Full	
	3235	30"	Improved Modified & Full	
	3231	32"	Improved Modified & Full	

SPECIFICATIONS

GAUGE	12 with 2¾" chambers
FRAME	Machined steel with sliding top lock. Sides embellished with pointing dogs.
OVER-ALL LENGTH	43" with 26" barrels.
SAFETY SELECTOR	Mounted on tang. "Safe" in middle position. Move to left for bottom barrel; right for top. Trap and skeet models can be "locked off" on desired barrel selection.
TRIGGER	Single selective, 5/16" wide. Crisp with extra fast lock time.
EJECTORS	Automatic. Fired shells eject on opening. Unfired shells remain in chamber but are raised above chamber level for easy manual extraction.

STOCK & FORE-END American Walnut with cut checkering running 20 lines to inch. RK-W wood finish. Rosewood toned grip cap and butt plate. Trap and Skeet guns fitted with recoil pad. Field guns fitted with semi-beavertail fore-end; trap and skeet guns with full beavertail fore-end.

STANDARD STOCK DIMENSIONS	Field and Skeet	Trap	Trap with Monte Carlo
Length of pull	14"	14⅜"	14⅜"
Drop at comb	1½"	1½"	1½"
Drop at Monte Carlo	—	—	1½"
Drop at heel	2⅛"	1¾"	2"

AVERAGE WEIGHT Field and Skeet—7¾ lbs. with 26" barrels. Trap—8¼ lbs. with 30" barrels.

REMINGTON PUMP SHOTGUNS

shown with ventilated rib

STANDARD MODEL 870
(12, 16 & 20 Gauges)
with plain barrel $159.95
with ventilated rib $184.95

*shown with
ventilated rib*

MODEL 870 MAGNUM
(12 & 20 Gauges)
with plain barrel $179.95
with ventilated rib $204.95

The Wingmaster model 870 Magnum is a 5 shot; chambered for 3" Magnum shells—will also handle 2¾" shells with 3-shot plug. 12 gauge with 28" and 30" full choke, plain or ventilated rib barrel. Steel-bead front sight, rubber recoil pad. Stock: 14" long including pad, 2½" drop at heel, 1⅝" drop at comb. 20 gauge furnished in 28" full and modified choke ventilated rib and plain barrels. Weight: 12 gauge about 8 lbs., 20 gauge about 7 lbs.

*deluxe "Brushmaster" shown
with rifle sight barrel*

MODEL 870 R DEER GUN
(12 & 20 Gauges)
Brushmaster Deluxe (illus.) .. $179.95
Standard Deer Gun $154.95

The Model 870 Brushmaster is made to handle rifled slugs and buck shot. With 20" barrel and fully adjustable rifle-type sights. Stock fitted with rubber recoil pad and white line spacer. Other specifications same as standard 870. Also available in standard model. Same as Deluxe Brushmaster above, but with lacquer finish; no checkering, recoil pad, grip cap; special handy short fore-end.

MODEL 870 SA SKEET GUN
WITH VENTILATED RIB BARREL
(12 & 20 Gauges)

The "Wingmaster" Model 870SA skeet gun comes with 26" barrel, special skeet boring, ventilated rib with ivory-bead front and white-metal middle sight.
12 ga. about 7 lbs., 20 ga. about 6½ lbs. Also available in SC grade with selected wood and hand checkering.
870 SA Skeet gun, with ventilated rib, Rem. Skeet choke $189.95
870 SA Skeet gun, with ventilated rib, cutts compensator $214.95
870 SC Skeet gun, with vent rib, Rem Skeet choke (select wood) . $264.95

MODEL 870
12, 16 & 20 GAUGE
BARREL LENGTH
& CHOKE COMBINATIONS

30"	Full Choke
28"	Full Choke
28"	Modified Choke
26"	Imp. Cyl. Choke
Deer Gun 20" Imp. Cyl.	

SPECIFICATIONS: STYLE — 5 shot pump action shotgun. Take down. 3 shot plug furnished. **GAUGES** — 12, 16 and 20. **BARREL** — Special Remington ordnance steel. Extra barrel is interchangeable within gauge. **OVER-ALL LENGTH** — 48½" with 28" barrel. **SAFETY** — Convenient cross-bolt type, positive. **RECEIVER** — Made from solid steel, top matted. **STANDARD STOCK DIMENSIONS** — Stock and fore-end: Rich American walnut. Beautiful checkering. 14" long, 2½" drop at heel, 1⅝" drop at comb. Trap reg., 14⅜" long, 1⅞" drop at heel, 1½" drop at comb. Monte Carlo; 14⅜" long, 1⅞" drop at heel, 1⅜" drop at comb, 1⅜" drop at M.C. **AVERAGE WEIGHT** — 12 ga. - 7 lbs.; 16 ga. - 6¾ lbs.; 20 ga. - 6½ lbs.

REMINGTON PUMP SHOTGUNS
MODEL 870 PUMP ACTION SHOTGUNS—TRAP MODELS

12 GAUGE ONLY

REMINGTON MODEL 870 ALL AMERICAN TRAP GUN
SHOWN WITH OPTIONAL MONTE CARLO STOCK
(Gun comes with hard, foam-lined carrying case)

MODEL 870 • ALL AMERICAN • Trap Gun

A customized trap gun sure to warm the pride of every shooter who owns one. Both sides of the receiver, as well as the trigger guard and barrel's breech end fully engraved in a delicately cut scroll pattern. Specially designed All American shield fitted to left side of receiver. Selected American walnut stock and fore-end cut checkered with attractive raised diamond pattern, and finished with DuPont's rugged RK-W finish. Pistol grip cap fitted with gold plate for personalized initialing. Supplied with a deluxe luggage type, foam lined case at no extra charge. The All American trap gun is produced in 30″ full choke ventilated rib barrels with either regular or Monte Carlo stocks. Dimensions same as TB and TC grade Model 870 guns.

Model	Barrel length, in.	Choke	
870 "All American" Trap with Vent. Rib	30	Full	$575.00
870 "All American" Trap with Vent. Rib Monte Carlo Stock	30	Full	$575.00

Monte Carlo stock shown

12 GAUGE ONLY

MODEL 870 TB • Trap Gun

SPECIFICATIONS: Available with 30″ full or modified trap, ventilated rib barrel. Ivory bead front and white metal rear sight. Recoil pad. Special target grade hammer, sear and trigger assembly. Beautiful "B" grade walnut stock with lustrous DuPont RK-W finish, fleur-de-lis checkering, special small pistol grip with cap. Regular stock dimensions: drop at comb 1½″, drop at heel 1⅞″, length of pull 14⅜″. Monte Carlo stock dimensions: drop at comb 1½″, drop at Monte Carlo 1½″, drop at heel 1⅞″, length of pull 14⅜″. . . . . Extra 34″ full choke trap gun barrels.

Model	Barrel length, in.	Choke	
870TB with Vent. Rib Barrel	30 / 30	Mod. / Full	$224.95 / 224.95
870TB with Vent. Rib Barrel & Monte Carlo Stock	30 / 30	Mod. / Full	$234.95 / 234.95
870TBLH with Vent. Rib Barrel	30	Full	$229.95
870LH with Monte Carlo Stock	30	Full	$239.95

MODEL 870 TB • Left Hand Trap Gun

The only pump action trap gun built specifically for the left handed shooter. True "mirror image" design offers left hand feeding and ejection. Produced in 30″ full choke ventilated rib barrels with either regular or Monte Carlo stocks. Other specifications same as above.

12 GAUGE ONLY

MODEL 870 TC • Trap Gun

SPECIFICATIONS: Same as 870 TB except: Rich, highly figured, hand-rubbed walnut stock with beautiful hand-checkering. Special hand-polished parts.

Model	Barrel length, in	Choke	
870TC with Vent. Rib Barrel	30″ / 30″	Mod. . . . . . / Full	$299.95 / $299.95

Model	Barrel length, in.	Choke	
870TC with Vent. Rib Barrel & Monte Carlo Stock	30″ / 30″	Mod. . . . . . / Full	$309.95 / $309.95

REMINGTON MODEL 870
PUMP ACTION SHOTGUNS

12 and 20 Gauges

MODEL 870 LEFT HAND • Field Gun "WINGMASTER"

A complete mirror image of the regular Model 870, these left hand shotguns put an end to the bothersome flying hulls that left-handed shooters had to face. Ejection is on the left side—all other specifications are the same as the regular Model 870, 12 and 20 gauge. Left hand Monte Carlo stock available on trap model.

Model	Barrel length, in.	Choke	12 Gauge Order No.	20 Gauge Order No.	
870LH	30	Full	5510	....	$189.95
With Vent.	28	Full	....	5528	189.95
Rib Barrel	28	Mod.	5514	5530	189.95
	26	I.C.	5516	5566	189.95
870LH Mag. with Vent. Rib Barrel	30	Full	5496	....	$209.95
870TBLH with Vent. Rib Barrel	30	Full	5518	....	$229.95
870LH with Monte Carlo Stock	30	Full	5520	....	$239.95

SPECIFICATIONS

STYLE	5 shot pump action shotgun.
GAUGES	Right hand versions: 12, 16 and 20. Left hand versions: 12 and 20.
BARREL	Special Remington proof steel. Extra barrels are interchangeable within version (reg. or left hand), gauge and chamber length without fitting.
OVER-ALL LENGTH	48½" with 28" barrel.
SAFETY	Convenient positive cross-bolt type. Reversed on left hand models.
RECEIVER	Made from solid steel, top matted.
STANDARD STOCK DIMENSIONS	Stock and fore-end: Rich American walnut. Beautiful checkering. 14" long including recoil pad, 2½" drop at heel, 1⅝" drop at comb.
AVERAGE WEIGHT	20 ga.-6½ lbs.; 16 ga.-6¾ lbs.; 12 ga.-7 lbs.

20 GAUGE LIGHTWEIGHT SHOWN

MODEL 870 • 20 Gauge Lightweight
MODEL 870 • 20 Gauge Lightweight Magnum

20 Gauge Lightweight
20 Gauge Lightweight 3 Inch Magnum

This is the pump action designed for the upland game hunter who wants enough power to stop fast flying game birds but light enough to be comfortable on all day hunting. The 20 gauge Lightweight handles all 20 gauge 2¾ in. shells. The magnum version handles all 20 gauge shells including the powerful 3 in. shells.

Model	Barrel length, in.	Choke	Order No.	
870L.W.	28	Full	5176	$169.95
With Plain	28	Mod.	5178	169.95
Barrel	26	I.C.	5180	169.95
870L.W.	28	Full	5182	$194.95
With Vent.	28	Mod.	5184	194.95
Rib Barrel	26	I.C.	5186	194.95
870L.W. Mag. With Plain Barrel	28	Full	5188	$189.95
870L.W. Mag. With Vent. Rib Barrel	28	Full	5190	$214.95

MODEL 870 • 28 & .410 Gauges

These small gauges are exact copies of the famous Model 870 "Wingmaster" in the larger gauges. Built on their own receiver and frame, they give the shooter unique handling and pointing characteristics. Beautiful fleur-de-lis fine line checkering, white line spacers at butt plate and grip cap, chrome plated bolt, and steel bead front sight are bonus features.

Model	Barrel length, in.	Choke	28 ga.	410 ga.	
870 with Plain Barrel	25	Full	4868	4948	$169.95
	25	Mod.	4904	4950	169.95
	25	I.C.	4916	4978	169.95
870 with Vent. Rib Barrel	25	Full	4918	4986	$194.95
	25	Mod.	4920	5086	194.95
	25	I.C.	4932	4990	194.95

SAVAGE PUMP-ACTION SHOTGUNS

With Solid Steel Receiver, Interchangeable Barrels and 3" Magnum Chambering

MODEL 30-D DELUXE
(12, 20 & .410 Gauges)
$148.50

30-D Deluxe Gauges: 12, 20 & 410. Has all the deluxe features including the ventilated rib, rubber recoil pad and an elaborate game scene on the receiver. 12 and 20 gauge chambered for 2¾" and 3" magnum shells. (410 for 2½" and 3" shells). Any barrel of the same gauge in the model 30 line can be interchanged.

MODEL 30 FIELD GRADE
(12, 20 & .410 Gauges)
$127.50

30 Field Grade Gauges: 12, 20 & 410. The Field Grade offers the same basic quality as the more deluxe model 30's. Trim solid steel receiver houses a fast, dependable action. From the handfilling walnut slide handle to the checkered walnut stock with fluted comb.. Interchangeable barrels available.

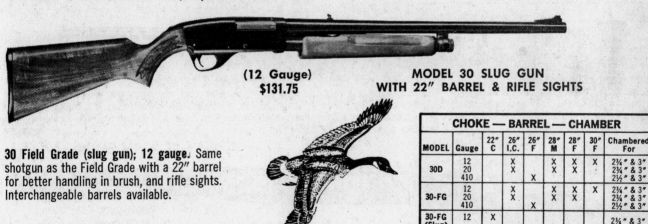

(12 Gauge)
$131.75

MODEL 30 SLUG GUN
WITH 22" BARREL & RIFLE SIGHTS

30 Field Grade (slug gun); 12 gauge. Same shotgun as the Field Grade with a 22" barrel for better handling in brush, and rifle sights. Interchangeable barrels available.

MODEL	Gauge	22" C	26" I.C.	26" F	28" M	28" F	30" F	Chambered For
CHOKE — BARREL — CHAMBER								
30D	12		X		X	X	X	2¾" & 3"
	20		X		X	X		2¾" & 3"
	410			X				2½" & 3"
30-FG	12		X		X	X	X	2¾" & 3"
	20		X		X	X		2¾" & 3"
	410			X				2½" & 3"
30-FG (Slug)	12	X						2¾" & 3"

C—Cyl. (Slug Bore)   M—Mod.
I.C.—Imp. Cyl.   F—Full

SPECIFICATIONS — FEATURES

MODEL	Vent Rib	Plain Barrel	Bead Sights	Rifle Sights	Take-down	Inter-chang-able Barrels	Safety Fire Control	Top Tang Safety	Tu-bular Maga-zine	Ca-pacity	Mag-num Cham-ber	Receiver Steel	Receiver Deco-rated	Select Walnut	Recoil Pad	Stock Finish	Butt Plate	Average Weight (Lbs.)
30-D	X		2		X	X	X	X	X	5*	X	Blued	X	X	X	Electro -Cote		7–7¾
30-F.G.		X	1		X	X	X	X	X	5*	X	Blued		X		Electro -Cote	Hard Rubber	7–7½
30-F.G. (Slug Gun)		X		X	X	X	X	X	X	5*	X	Blued		X		Electro -Cote	Hard Rubber	7¼

MODELS   30-D, 30-F.G. and 30-FG (Slug) Stock: Length 14"; drop 1½" at comb, 2½" at heel.
   Model 30-D and 30-F.G. Length over-all 45½"–49½"; taken down 26"–30". 30-F.G. (Slug) Length over-all 41½"; taken down 22". All Models proof-tested.
   *5 2¾" shells (3" one less) 3 shot plug provided.

SAVAGE OVER & UNDER SHOTGUNS

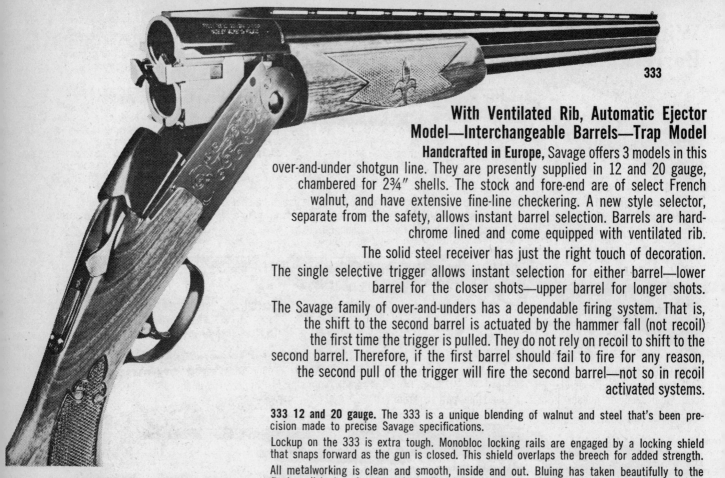

333

With Ventilated Rib, Automatic Ejector Model—Interchangeable Barrels—Trap Model

Handcrafted in Europe, Savage offers 3 models in this over-and-under shotgun line. They are presently supplied in 12 and 20 gauge, chambered for 2¾" shells. The stock and fore-end are of select French walnut, and have extensive fine-line checkering. A new style selector, separate from the safety, allows instant barrel selection. Barrels are hard-chrome lined and come equipped with ventilated rib.

The solid steel receiver has just the right touch of decoration. The single selective trigger allows instant selection for either barrel—lower barrel for the closer shots—upper barrel for longer shots.

The Savage family of over-and-unders has a dependable firing system. That is, the shift to the second barrel is actuated by the hammer fall (not recoil) the first time the trigger is pulled. They do not rely on recoil to shift to the second barrel. Therefore, if the first barrel should fail to fire for any reason, the second pull of the trigger will fire the second barrel—not so in recoil activated systems.

Savage Model 333 Breech View
The two bright pins just below the safety are cocking indicators. They project about 1/32" when gun is cocked.

333 12 and 20 gauge. The 333 is a unique blending of walnut and steel that's been precision made to precise Savage specifications.

Lockup on the 333 is extra tough. Monobloc locking rails are engaged by a locking shield that snaps forward as the gun is closed. This shield overlaps the breech for added strength.

All metalworking is clean and smooth, inside and out. Bluing has taken beautifully to the finely polished surfaces to give a deep, rich lustre.

The 333 features a selective single trigger, wide vent rib, automatic ejectors and cocking indicators. Top tang safety is right under the thumb for instant use. The two bead sights get you quickly on target. The French walnut stock has a high-lustre finish. Custom grade features also include fleur-de-lis checkering...................................$381.50

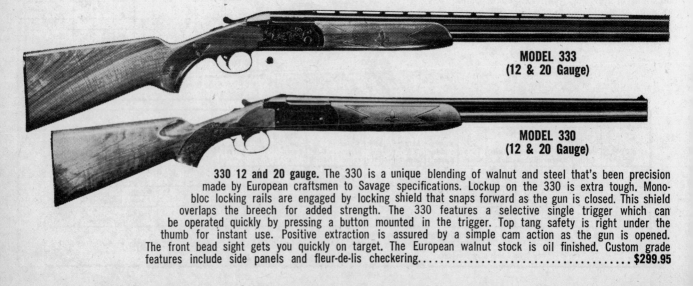

**MODEL 333
(12 & 20 Gauge)**

**MODEL 330
(12 & 20 Gauge)**

330 12 and 20 gauge. The 330 is a unique blending of walnut and steel that's been precision made by European craftsmen to Savage specifications. Lockup on the 330 is extra tough. Monobloc locking rails are engaged by locking shield that snaps forward as the gun is closed. This shield overlaps the breech for added strength. The 330 features a selective single trigger which can be operated quickly by pressing a button mounted in the trigger. Top tang safety is right under the thumb for instant use. Positive extraction is assured by a simple cam action as the gun is opened. The front bead sight gets you quickly on target. The European walnut stock is oil finished. Custom grade features include side panels and fleur-de-lis checkering.......................................$299.95

SAVAGE OVER & UNDER SHOTGUNS

333-T

333-T 12 Gauge Trap Gun. When a shotgun is fired as much as most trap guns, dimensions, balance and dependability are paramount. The 333-T excells in these areas. It has a rugged top breech lockup, similar to that of guns selling for much more. The finely polished surfaces, both inside and out, assure smooth operation. Other features include an extra wide ventilated rib, selective single trigger, extractors, manual top tang safety, recoil pad and Monte Carlo stock. Wood is European walnut, and checkered. $381.50

SPECIFICATIONS — FEATURES

MODEL	Vent Rib	Plain Barrel	Mono-block Const.	Inter-chang. Barrels	Bead Sights	Auto-matic Top Tang Safety	Extrac-tors	Ejectors	Cocking Indi-cators	Barrel Selector	Frame Steel	Frame Deco-rated	Frame Top Lockup	Coil Springs	Checkered Stock Select Walnut	Checkered Stock Monte Carlo	Butt Plate	Avg. Wgt. (Lbs.)
333	X		X		2	X		X	X	X	Blued	X	X	X	X		Hard Rubber	6¼ — 7¼
330		X	X	X	1	X	X			X	Blued	X	X	X	X		Hard Rubber	6¼ — 7¼
333T	X		X		2	Manual Safety	X			X	Blued	X	X	X	X	X	Recoil Pad	7¾

MODELS 333 and 330 Stock: Length 14"; drop 1½" at comb, 2½" at heel.
333-T Stock: Length 14½"; drop 1½" at comb, 1½" at Monte Carlo, 2½" at heel.
Length over-all 42½"–46½"; taken down 26"–30", 333-T, 47"; taken down 30" All Models proof-tested.

CHOKE — BARREL — CHAMBER

MODEL	Gauge	26" SK & SK	26" I.C. & M	28" M & F	30" M & F	30" I.M. & F	Chamberd For
333	12	X	X	X	X		2¾"
	20	X	X	X			2¾" & 3"
330	12		X	X	X		2¾"
	20		X	X			2¾" & 3"
333-T	12					X	2¾"

SK—Skeet
I.C.—Imp. Cyl.
M—Mod.
I.M.—Imp. Mod.
F—Full

330 Set. Now you can match your gauge to your game with just one over-and-under. Any Model 330 12 gauge gun listed is available with an interchangeable 20 gauge barrel, 28" choked Mod. and Full, or 26" Imp. Cyl. and Mod. barrel. Same fore-end fits both barrel sets. Comes with a beautiful black, soft gun case with pocket for extra barrel. $415.00

SAVAGE 330 BARREL SET

STEVENS .410 GAUGE BOLT-ACTION SHOTGUN

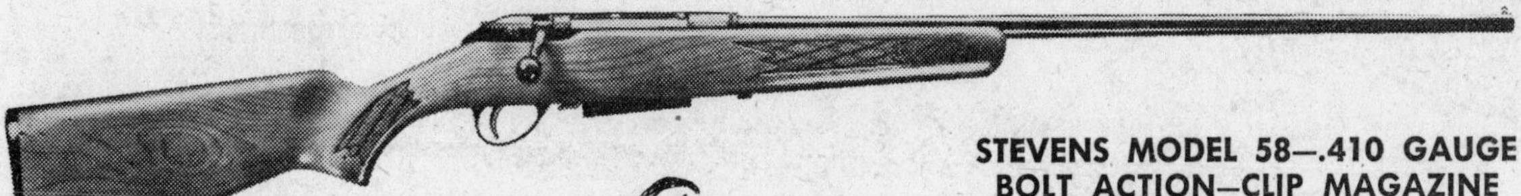

STEVENS MODEL 58—.410 GAUGE BOLT ACTION—CLIP MAGAZINE
(.410 Gauge, $59.95)

Stevens 58 410 gauge. The 58 in 410 gauge has a three-shot detachable clip magazine. A shell in the chamber makes it a four-shot repeater. The electro-cote stock finish seals the stock for longer protection. It comes equipped with a 24" full choke barrel, chambered for 2½" and 3" shells. Length overall, 43". Weight, 5½ lbs.

FOX AND STEVENS SHOTGUNS

(DOUBLE BARREL SHOTGUNS IN 12, 20 & .410 Gauges)

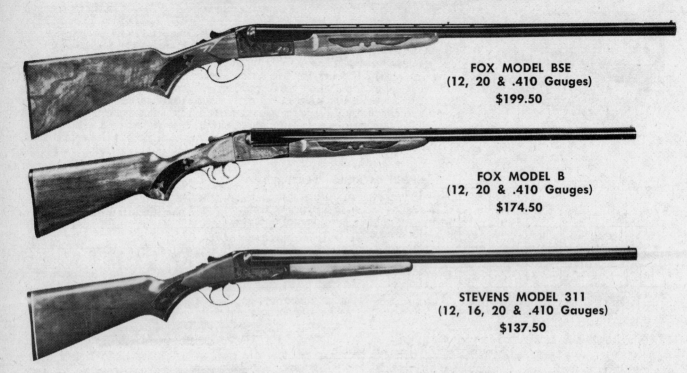

FOX MODEL BSE
(12, 20 & .410 Gauges)
$199.50

FOX MODEL B
(12, 20 & .410 Gauges)
$174.50

STEVENS MODEL 311
(12, 16, 20 & .410 Gauges)
$137.50

Fox B-SE Gauges 12, 20 and 410. Automatic ejectors are standard equipment on the Fox B-SE. Other fine gun features are the single trigger and ventilated rib. The B-SE has the lines found only in a double gun, enriched with materials and finishes typical of expensive custom guns. Its selected walnut stock has a deeply fluted comb and checkering on pistol grip. The gracefully tapered beavertail fore-end is also attractively checkered. The frame has color case hardened finish with decoration on bottom. Convenient top tang safety.

24" Fox B 12 and 20 Gauge. With 24" barrels this Fox B is ideal for grouse, woodcock, quail—any game bird at closer range or in thick cover. Impossible shots made possible with this short, light-barreled, fast-swing Fox shotgun. Other specifications are the same as Fox-B above.

Fox-B Gauges: 12, 20 & 410.

(12 and 20 gauge now in 3" magnum.) For sheer beauty of design, fine balance and fast handling, nothing equals a double—the traditional sporting gun. The Fox B standard equipment includes ventilated rib, select walnut stock with fluted comb, beavertail fore-end and checkering. Two triggers give the shooter instant command of two shots—the split second choice of two chokes.

The Stevens 311 Gauges: 12, 16, 20 & 410.

(12 and 20 gauge now in 3" magnum.) This double barrel shotgun has many refinements usually found only in higher priced guns. It offers sturdy construction, solid lockup, excellent balance and superior shooting qualities.

SPECIFICATIONS — FEATURES

MODEL	Vent Rib	Solid Rib	Bead Sights	Automatic Top Tang Safety	Extractors	Selective Ejectors	Trigger		Frame		Coil Springs	Checkered Stock		White Line Butt Plate	Average Weight (Lbs.)
							Single	Double	Case Hardened	Decorated		Select Walnut	Walnut Finished Hardwood		
B-SE	X		2	X		X	X		X	X	X	X			7—8
B	X		2	X	X			X	X	X	X	X			7—8
311		X	1	X	X			X	X		X		X	X	7¼—8
ALL MODELS	Stock: Length 14"; drop 1½" at comb, 2½" at heel. Length over-all 41¾"–45¾"; take down 24"–30". All Models proof-tested.														

SAVAGE RIFLE/SHOTGUNS

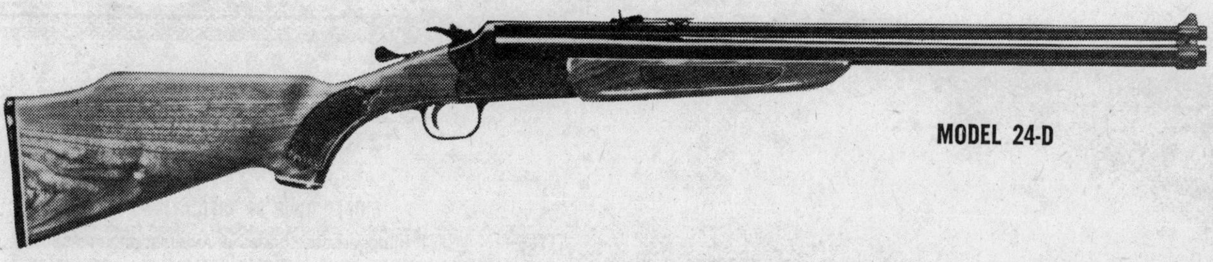

MODEL 24-D

MODEL 24 FIELD GRADE

24-C Campers Companion Combination: 22 long rifle/20 gauge. At 5¾ pounds, it's a pound lighter and five inches shorter than other 24's. When stored in special case, it measures just 5″ x 22″. The case has handles for carrying, thongs for tieing to pack or saddle. Recess in stock holds extra shells. **$92.60**

24-D Deluxe Combinations: 22 long rifle/20 or 410 gauge; 22 magnum/20 gauge. A breech and separated barrels on this handsome deluxe model means lighter weight and better balance. Two-way top opening lever swings either way for right- or left-hand use. The checkered walnut stock and fore-end are protected for lasting beauty with our new electro-cote finish. The decorated receiver adds a final deluxe touch. This combination gun is ideal for small game, pests and varmints as well as plinking. A 20 gauge slug can be used for larger game; the 22 magnum adds extra power and range for bobcat, fox, turkey **$97.65**

24 Field Grade Combinations: 22 long rifle/20 or 410 gauge; 22 magnum/20 or 410 gauge. A combination gun at a field grade price makes this model an ideal first gun—combines the ever popular 22 cartridge with either of two popular shotgun gauges. New top lever opening. Walnut finished hardwood stock and fore-end receives our new electro-cote finish. **$82.50**

CHOKE—BARREL—CHAMBER

MODEL	Caliber Gauge	23½″ I.M.	24″ F	20″ C	Chambered For
2400	308, 12 222, 12	X X			2¾″ 2¾″
24-V	30-30, 20 222, 20		X X		2¾″ & 3″ 2¾″ & 3″
24-D	22 L.R., 20 22 L.R., 410 22 Mag., 20		X X X		2¾″ & 3″ 2½″ & 3″ 2¾″ & 3″
24-F.G.	22 L.R., 20 22 L.R., 410 22 Mag., 20		X X X		2¾″ & 3″ 2½″ & 3″ 2¾″ & 3″
24-C	22 L.R., 20			X	2¾″

F—Full C—Cylinder I.M.—Improved Modified

SPECIFICATIONS—FEATURES

MODELS	Barrels Length	Tapped For Scope	Grooved For Scope	Sights		Color Case Hardened Frame	Rebounding Hammer	Hammer Selector	Top Lever Opening	Takedown	Stock		Checkered Stock	Monte Carlo	White Line Butt Plate	White Line Grip Cap	Length Over-all	Avg. Wgt. (Lbs.)
				Front	Rear						Select Walnut	Walnut Finished Hardwood						
2400	23½″	X		Blade	Folding Leaf	Blued		Trigger Selector	X	X	X		Cut Checked	X	X		40½″	7½
24-V	24″	X		Ramp	Folding Leaf	X	X	X	X	X	X		X	X	X	X	40″	6¾–7½
24-D	24″		X	Ramp	Sporting	X	X	X	X	X	X		X	X	X	X	40″	7½
24-F.G.	24″		X	Ramp	Sporting	X	X	X	X	X		X					40″	6½
24-C	20″		X	Ramp	Sporting	X	X	X	X	X		X					36″	5¾

MODELS 2400 Stock: Length 14″; drop 1½″ at comb, 1¾″ at Monte Carlo, 2½″ at heel; taken down 23½″.
24-V, 24-D Stock: Length 14″; drop 2″ at comb, 1¾″ at Monte Carlo, 2⅝″ at heel; taken down 24″.
24-C Stock: Length 13½″; drop 1¾″ at comb, 2¾″ at heel; taken down 20″.
24-F.G. Stock: Length 14″; drop 1¾″ at comb, 2¾″ at heel; taken down 24″.

RATE OF TWIST (R.H.) 1 turn in 12″ for 30-30, 308; 14″ for 222; 16″ for 22 Mag., for 22 L.R.

SMITH & WESSON SHOTGUNS

AUTOLOADING SHOTGUN MODEL 1000

The S&W Model 1000 auto shotgun comes in 12 gauge only. Features includes high luster blue steel finish; genuine American Walnut, specially selected for superior grain, lustrously finished and sure grip hand checkered; cross hatched, smooth flowing ventilated sighting rib; double sighting beads; broad comfort-contoured hard chromed trigger handsomely designed and executed scroll engraving on both sides of the receiver and the unique inset Smith & Wesson logo in the pistol grip cap.

Additional features include right or left handed safety; cold hammer-forged chrome molybdenum steel barrel hard chromed bolt, bolt carrier, pressure compensator valve and piston; and an all new patent pending gas operating system which features a unique gas pressure compensator valve (to stabilize variations in gas port pressures) and an oversized gas expansion chamber with a piston actuated gas port cutoff. Virtual self-cleaning of the gas cylinder wall is achieved by the sharp edge of the piston which expels carbon residue with every stroke. The S & W Model 1000 will shoot thousands of rounds without cleaning.

MODEL 1000 AUTO SHOTGUN
12 Gauge, w/vent. rib
$249.95

MODEL 1000 SPECIFICATIONS

STYLE: 4-Shot (Plugged for 2 Shots) Autoloading gas-operated shotgun with pressure compensator and floating piston for light recoil.

GAUGE: 12 (2¾" Chamber).

BARREL: Smith & Wesson Proof-Tested Chrome Molybdenum Steel.

RECEIVER: Light Weight High Tensile Strength Alloy, Scroll Engraved both sides.

LENGTH: 48" Over-all (with 28" Barrel).

SAFETY: Positive Cross-Bolt Type, Interchangeable left or right hand.

STOCK: Selected American Walnut: Length of Pull 14", Drop at Comb 1½", Drop at Heel 2⅜".

WEIGHT: 7⅛ Lbs. (28" Barrel).

BARREL LENGTH & CHOKE COMBINATIONS

26"	Skeet	
26"	Improved Cylinder	with
28"	Modified	Vent.
30"	Full	Rib

"EASTFIELD" PUMP SHOTGUN MODEL 916

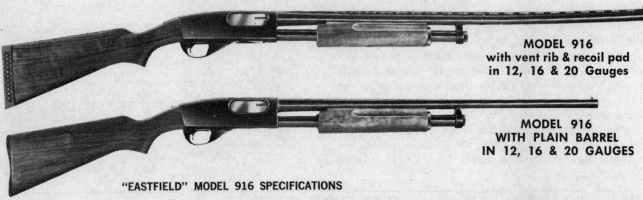

MODEL 916
with vent rib & recoil pad
in 12, 16 & 20 Gauges

MODEL 916
WITH PLAIN BARREL
IN 12, 16 & 20 GAUGES

"EASTFIELD" MODEL 916 SPECIFICATIONS

STYLE: 6 Shot Pump Action Shotgun, Plugged for 3 shots.

GAUGES: 12 (3" Chamber), 20 (3" Chamber).

BARREL: Smith & Wesson Proof-Tested Steel.

RECEIVER: From Solid Chrome Molybdenum Steel with Hardened Lock Areas, Satin, Non-Glare Top.

LENGTH: 48" Over-All with 28" Barrel.

SAFETY: Convenient Top Tang Type.

STOCK: Genuine American Walnut with Fluted Comb and Finger Grooved Walnut Fore-End. 14" Length of Pull, 2½" Drop at Heel, 1⅝" Drop at Comb.

WEIGHT: 7¼ lbs. (12 Gauge with a 28" Plain Barrel).

MODEL	GAUGE	BARREL LENGTH	CHOKE	
MODEL 916 PLAIN BARREL	12	30"	Full	
	12, 16, 20	28"	Modified	$110.50
	12, 16, 20	26"	Imp. Cylinder	
	12	20"	Cylinder Bore	
MODEL 916 PLAIN BARREL WITH VENTILATED RECOIL PAD	12	30"	Full	
	12, 16, 20	28"	Modified	$115.00
	12, 16, 20	26"	Imp. Cylinder	
MODEL 916 VENTILATED RIB AND VENTILATED RECOIL PAD	12	30"	Full	
	12, 16, 20	28"	Modified	$131.75
	12, 16, 20	26"	Imp. Cylinder	

WEATHERBY SHOTGUNS

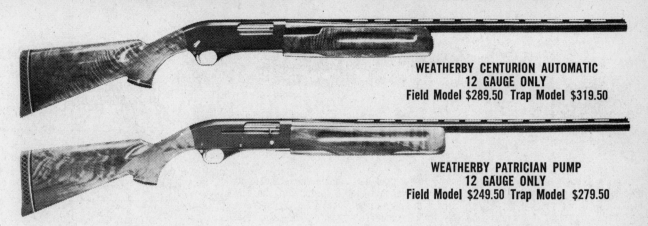

WEATHERBY CENTURION AUTOMATIC
12 GAUGE ONLY
Field Model $289.50   Trap Model $319.50

WEATHERBY PATRICIAN PUMP
12 GAUGE ONLY
Field Model $249.50   Trap Model $279.50

WEATHERBY CENTURION AUTOMATIC

Gas operated means no friction rings and collars to adjust for different loads. The barrel holds stationary instead of plunging backward with every shot.

To these natural advantages of the gas-operated automatic, Weatherby has added revolutionary "Floating Piston" action. In the Weatherby Centurion, the piston "floats" freely on the magazine tube completely independent of every other part of the action. Nothing to get out of alignment. Nothing to cause drag or friction.

WEATHERBY PATRICIAN PUMP

The super-fast slide action operates on double rails for precision and reliability. No twists, no binds, no hang-ups.

To remove a loaded round, push the gold-plated forearm release lever to its forward position. Now the forearm is unlocked and the action can be opened.

SPECIFICATIONS for PATRICIAN and CENTURION SHOTGUNS

Gauges:	12 ga. only
Chamber length:	2¾" chamber
Barrel lengths & chokes:	30" Full 28" Mod 26" Imp Cyl
	28" Full 26" Mod 26" Skeet

Stock dimensions	Field	Trap
Length of pull:	14¼"	14¾"
Drop at comb:	1⅜"	1⅜"
Drop at heel:	2¼"	1¾"

Approx. weight:	
Patrician pump shotguns:	30" bbl — 7 lb. 9 oz.
	28" bbl — 7 lb. 7 oz.
	26" bbl — 7 lb. 5¼ oz.
Centurion auto shotguns:	30" bbl — 7 lb. 11¾ oz.
	28" bbl — 7 lb. 10½ oz.
	26" bbl — 7 lb. 9¼ oz.

Safety:	Cross bolt type, right or left hand
Stock:	Figured American walnut, fine line hand checkering.
Interchangeable barrels:	Available in above lengths and chokes.
Price of extra barrels:	Patrician pump — $89.95
	Centurion auto — $99.95

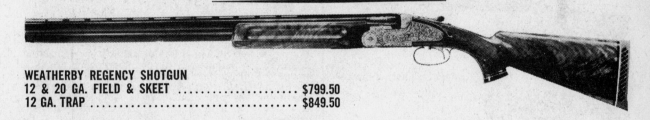

WEATHERBY REGENCY SHOTGUN
12 & 20 GA. FIELD & SKEET $799.50
12 GA. TRAP $849.50

RECEIVER . . . The Regency receiver houses a strong, reliable box lock action, yet it features side lock type plates to carry through the fine floral engraving. The hinge pivots, are made of a special high strength steel alloy. The locking system employs the time-tested Greener cross bolt design.

SINGLE SELECTIVE TRIGGER . . . It is mechanically rather than recoil operated. This provides a fully automatic switch-over, allowing the second barrel to be fired on a subsequent trigger pull, even in the event of a misfire.

The Regency trigger is selective, as well. A flick of the trigger finger and the selector lever, located just in front of the trigger, is all the way to the left enabling you to fire the lower barrel first, or to the right for the upper barrel.

SELECTIVE AUTOMATIC EJECTORS . . . The Regency contains ejectors that are fully automatic both in selection and action. **SLIDE SAFETY** . . . The safety is the traditional slide type located conveniently on the upper tang on top of the pistol grip **BARRELS** . . . The breech block is hand fitted to the receiver, providing closest possible tolerances Every Regency is equipped with a matted, ventilated rib and bead front sight.

REGENCY SHOTGUN SPECIFICATIONS

	Field and Skeet Models		Trap Models
Gauges	12 ga.	20 ga.	12 ga. (20 ga. not avail.)
Chamber Length	2¾" chamber	3" chamber	2¾" chamber
Barrel Lengths & Chokes	26" M/IC. S/S	26" F/M M/IC. S/S	30" F/F. F/IM.
	28" F/M. M/IC. S/S	28" F/M M/IC. S/S	32" F/F. F/IM. F/M
	30" F/M		
Stock Dimensions			
Length of pull	14¼"	14¼"	14⅜"
Drop at comb	1½"	1½"	1⅜"
Drop at heel	2½"	2½"	1⅞"
Approx. Weight	26" 7 lbs. 3 oz.	26" 6 lbs. 11 oz.	30" 7 lbs. 12 oz.
	28" 7 lbs. 6 oz.	28" 6 lbs. 14 oz.	32" 8 lbs.
	30" 7 lbs. 9 oz.		

Safety on all models — Slide operated rear tang
Stock on all models — Select American Walnut

WINCHESTER CUSTOM SHOTGUNS

MODEL 12 SLIDE-ACTION SHOTGUNS IN 12 GAUGE ONLY

Literally brought back by popular demand, the Model 12 remains the standard of the slide action shotgun world. Many years ago we said that a lifetime of shooting wouldn't wear out a Model 12. It is still true with today's new Model 12 . . . a sporting arm made the same uncompromising way from machined chrome molybdenum steel and choice walnut by craftsmen in Connecticut who enthusiastically welcome a chance to turn this old favorite out again.

Standard Trap Model With ventilated rib and recoil pad. Hand checkered. Full-fancy walnut stock and slide handle. Engine-turned bolt and carrier. Length of pull 14¾", drop at comb 1⅜", drop at heel 1⅞". Overall length 49¾" with 30" full choke barrel **$460.00**

Trap Model With Monte Carlo Same specifications as Standard model with drop at comb 1½ in., drop at heel 2⅛ in., drop at Monte Carlo 1½ in. with 30" full-choke-barrel **$470.00**

Model 12 Specifications

Type	Trap Standard	Trap Monte Carlo
Gauge	12	12
Magazine Capacity	6 (a)	6 (a)
Barrel Length	30"	30"
Overall Length	49¾"	49¾"
Length of Pull	14¾"	14¾"
Drop at Comb	1⅜"	1½"
Drop at Heel	1⅞"	2⅛"
Drop at M.C.	—	1½"
Weight (lbs.)	8¼	8¼

(a) Add one round for shell in chamber. Model 12s have factory-installed plug, which, when removed, increases magazine capacity to six shells.

DOUBLE BARREL SHOTGUNS
WINCHESTER MODEL No. 21

Custom Grade

Choice of gauge—12, 16 or 20 gauge; choice of barrel lengths—

> 12 gauge—32, 30, 28 and 26 in.
> 16 gauge—30, 28 and 26 in.
> 20 gauge—30, 28 and 26 in.

Choice of choke combination; matted rib barrel, 2¾ in. chamber, rounded frame. Stock and beavertail forearm of Grade AA full-fancy American walnut. Stock built to individual specifications (within manufacturing limits). Straight or pistol grip—includes cheek piece, Monte Carlo and/or offset. Choice of forearm—field, skeet or trap; black insert in forearm tip. Fancy checkering on stock and forearm; steel pistol grip cap. Choice of composition butt plate, recoil pad or checkered butt. Panel in top rib inscribed "Custom built by Winchester for (Customer's Name)." Automatic or non-automatic safety (optional). Choice of front and middle bead sights.

Engine turned standing breech, frame, barrel flats, barrel lug, extractors, barrel breech, forearm retainer and inside upper surfaces of forearm shoe. Custom style ornamentation. Gold plated trigger. Gold oval name plate (optional). Choice of three initials engraved on name plate or trigger guard.

Custom Grade .... Special Order

Pigeon Grade

Carries all features of the Custom Grade plus the following added refinements: Matted rib or ventilated rib. 2¾ or 3 in. chamber (3 in. chamber not available in 16 gauge). Full leather covering on recoil pad (optional). Style "A" carving on stock and beavertail forearm. No. 6 engraving on frame and barrels. Gold inlaid pistol grip cap. Gold oval name plate or three initials gold inlaid on trigger guard.

Pigeon Grade .... Special Order

Grand American

Carries all features of the Custom and Pigeon Grades plus the following: Style "B" carving on stock and beavertail forearm. No. 6 engraving with all figures gold inlaid. Set of interchangeable barrels complete with extra beavertail forearm suitably engraved and carved to match balance of gun. Leather trunk gun case with canvas cover—both case and cover embossed with three initials in gold or black.

Grand American .... Special Order

WINCHESTER AUTOMATIC SHOTGUNS

Winchoke 1400s

The Winchester Model 1400 with the Winchoke feature. It offers fully interchangeable precision-machined steel choke units to make three guns out of one.

Winchester Model 1400 automatic shotguns with Winchoke feature are offered in 12 and 20 gauges, featuring a push-button carrier release for loading ease. There's a unique, self-compensating gas system that automatically adjusts for standard and 2-¾" magnum loads. Plus frontlocking, rotating steel bolthead that locks into a steel barrel breech. Rustproof aluminum receiver. Engine-turned bolt. Crossbolt safety.

Winchester Winchokes are actually three, 2-inch interchangeable shotgun barrels, precision-bored to a specific choke. The lightweight tubes are machined from chrome molybdenum steel. One is an Improved Cylinder; the second is a Modified choke and the third is a Full choke. Together, they amount to three guns in one.

Shotgunners know that most shotgun barrels are slightly constricted or "choked" at the muzzle to achieve a particular type of shot pattern. For close-in shooting you want an open-bored gun with little or no choke. You have to pick up another gun for best performance in moderate range hunting. You'd want another with a full-choked barrel for long range shooting of larger game or high-flying wildfowl.

Winchoke lets you change chokes freely and quickly without altering either the gun's point of impact or the shooter's sight picture. Winchokes are lightweight, 2"-long, threaded choke tubes that simply screw into the muzzle of the specially adapted gun barrel . . . without changing the streamlined appearance of the shotgun. There's no bulge and the tube of your choice fits snugly and won't shoot loose. In effect, the Winchoke is a two-inch interchangeable barrel . . . without changing the entire barrel.

For Winchester Model 1200 and 1400 field guns, three Winchoke tubes are offered, including Improved Cylinder for close-in shooting, Modified choke for medium-range patterns, and Full choke for long-range hunting. All three are packed with each gun, with the Modified choke tube installed and a handy spanner wrench included. Together, they amount to a cabinet-full of shotguns you can carry in your pocket, allowing you to change your pattern to suit your changing sport . . . with the same gun.

Winchoke available in 12 or 20 gauge 2¾" chamber only, ventilated rib or plain **barrel.**

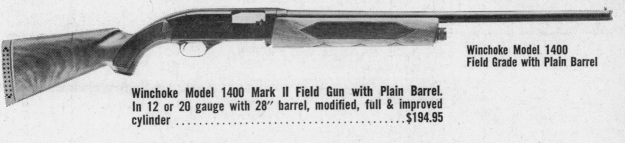

**Winchoke Model 1400
Field Grade with Plain Barrel**

Winchoke Model 1400 Mark II Field Gun with Plain Barrel.
In 12 or 20 gauge with 28" barrel, modified, full & improved cylinder $194.95

**Winchoke Model 1400
Field Grade with Ventilated Rib**

Winchoke Model 1400 Mark II Field Gun with Ventilated Rib.
In 12 or 20 gauge with 28" barrel, modified, full & improved cylinder $214.95

WINCHESTER AUTOMATIC SHOTGUNS
SUPER-X MODEL 1 GAS-OPERATED AUTOMATIC SHOTGUN

SUPER-X MODEL 1

Receiver and all other metal parts machined steel.

All Ventilated Rib models have a mid-rib sight.

1. Super-X Model 1 Field Gun. With ventilated rib barrel and bead front sight. 12 gauge chambering 2¾" shells available in 26" improved cylinder, 28" with modified or full choke, and 30" full choke.

3" Magnum with 30" ventilated rib barrel, modified or full choke.

2. Super-X Model 1 Trap Gun. 12 gauge. 30" ventilated rib barrel, modified choke. Selected walnut regular or Monte Carlo stock and wide forearm. Engraved receiver. Black-rubber recoil pad with white spacer. Red-bead front sight.

3. Super-X Model 1 Skeet Gun. 12 gauge with 26" ventilated rib barrel. Skeet choke. Selected walnut stock with wide forearm. Engraved receiver.

Super-X Model 1 Prices:

Field Gun, w/vent rib $330.00
Trap Gun, w/reg. trap stock
  & vent rib $395.00
Trap Gun, w/Monte Carlo trap stock
  & vent rib $395.00
Skeet Gun, w/vent rib $385.00

Extra Barrels:

Field, plain .... $ 62.95
Field, vent rib .... $ 92.95
Trap or Skeet .... $ 94.95

Super-X Model 1 Specifications

Model	Gauge	Chamber	Mag. Cap*	Choke	Length Barrel	Length Overall	Length Pull	Drop at Comb	Drop at Heel/Monte Carlo	Sights
Field Plain	12	2¾"	4	IC, M, F	26"- 28"-30"	46"-50"	14"	1⅜" 1½"	2⅜" 2½"	MBF
Field V.R.	12	2¾"	4	IC, M, F	26"- 28"-30"	46"-50"	14"	1½"	2½"	MB, F & M
Deer	12	2¾"	4	—	22"	42"	14"	1⅝"	2⅝"	RTFR
Trap V.R.	12	2¾"	4	M, F	30"	50⅜"	14⅜"	1⅜"	1⅞"	MB, F & M
Trap V.R. MC	12	2¾"	4	M, F	30"	50⅜"	14⅜"	1⁵/₁₆"	2⅛"- 1⅜"	MB, F & M
Skeet V.R.	12	2¾"	4	S	26"	46¼"	14¼"	1½"	2"	MB, F & M

*Add one round for shell in chamber. Super X Model 1 has a five-round capacity with factory-installed plug removed and one round in chamber.
MBF — Metal Bead Front; MB, F & M — Metal Bead, Front & Middle; RTFR — Rifle Type, Front & Rear; IC — Improved Cylinder; M — Modified; F — Full; S — Skeet.

MODEL 37A SINGLE SHOT SHOTGUN

Model 37A Standard

The Model 37A single shot shotgun is styled with a full-size butt stock and a large hand-fitting forearm. The stock and forearm are of hardwood with a dark finish. Checkering on the bottom of the forearm and on the pistol grip.

Features include a gold-plated trigger and engraved receiver; a concave hammer spur for non-slip cocking; a pistol grip cap with white spacer and a white spacer between the buttplate and stock.

There's a Winchester Proof-Steel barrel. Positive lock forearm. Automatic ejector. Top level that opens either right or left and a brass bead front sight.

Model 37A Standard Shotgun. In 12, 16, 20 and 28 gauge, 410 bore. Chambers 3" or 2¾" shells. 410 fires 3" or 2½" shells. Full choke only $59.95
12 gauge available with extra-long 36" barrel $64.95

Model 37A Youth Shotgun. (not illus.) Shorter 26" barrel and youth-size stock. 20 gauge with Improved Modified choke. 410 bore with Full choke. Rubber recoil pad $64.95

WINCHESTER PUMP SHOTGUNS
MODEL 1200 IN 12 & 20 GAUGES

Hunters and shooters know that they've got to have a reliable shotgun that practically points by itself. They want a gun light enough to carry through a long day but just heavy enough to swing smoothly and surely when the chance comes. That's why more and more sportsmen are turning to a Model 1200—a shotgun that's lightweight, versatile, and troublefree.

The Winchester Model 1200 slide action shotguns blend fit, feel and performance with advanced engineering. Twin action slide bars give the Model 1200s a self-starting action designed to move back in a quick, effortless motion. Exclusive front-locking, rotating bolthead locks the steel bolt securely into the steel breech for superb strength and safety. High-strength rustproof forged aluminum receiver. Crossbolt safety. Extended beavertail fore-end. Positive checkering. Weather-resistant stock finish. Engine turned steel bolt. American walnut stock and forearm. Fluted comb.

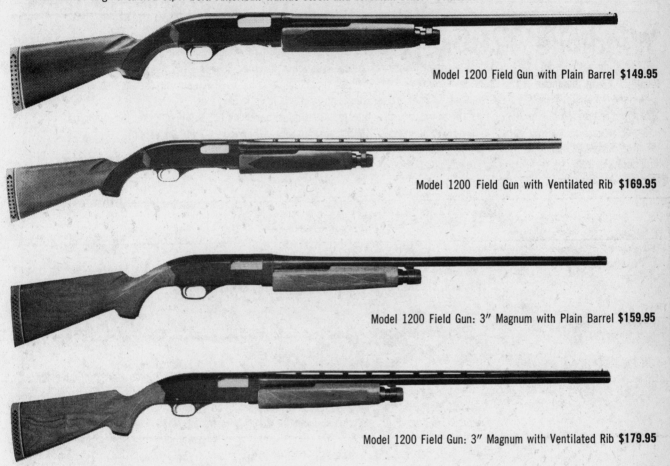

Model 1200 Field Gun with Plain Barrel **$149.95**

Model 1200 Field Gun with Ventilated Rib **$169.95**

Model 1200 Field Gun: 3" Magnum with Plain Barrel **$159.95**

Model 1200 Field Gun: 3" Magnum with Ventilated Rib **$179.95**

Model 1200 Specifications

Type	Field Plain Barrel	Field V.R.	Magnum Field Available only in Model 1200 with 3" chamber Plain Barrel 12	20	V.R. 12	20
Gauge	12-20	12-20	12	20	12	20
Magazine Capacity*	5	5	5	5	5	5
Barrel Length	26"	26"	30"	28"	30"	28"
Overall Length	46⅝"	46⅝"	50⅝"	48⅝"	50⅝"	48⅝"
Length of Pull	14"	14"	14"	14"	14"	14"
Drop at Comb	1⅜"	1½"	1⅜"	1⅜"	1½"	1½"
Drop at Heel	2⅜"	2½"	2⅜"	2⅜"	2½"	2½"
Weight (lbs.)	6½-7	6½-7¼	7¾	7⅜	7⅞	7⅝
Sights	MBF	MBF	MBF	MBF	MBF	MBF

*Includes one round in chamber. Model 1200s have factory installed plug which limits total capacity to three shells.
V.R. — Ventilated Rib   MBF — Metal Bead Front

WINCHESTER PUMP SHOTGUNS

Model 1200 Extra barrels:	
1200—Field	$47.95
1200—Field, w/winchoke (full, mod., & imp. cyl.)	$47.95
1200—Field, w/vent rib	$67.95
1200—Field, vent rib, w/winchoke (full, mod. & imp. cyl.)	$67.95
Winchoke:	
Extra tube	$ 5.95
Tube wrench	$ 1.50

Model 1200	12 Ga.	20 Ga.	Barrel Length	Type of Choke
Field Grade	x	—	30"	Full
Plain or Ventilated	—	x	28"	Full
Rib	x	x	28"	Modified
	x	x	26"	Imp. Cyl.
3" Magnum Plain or Ventilated	x	—	30"	Full
Rib	—	x	28"	Full

Winchoke 1200s

To change shot patterns to suit your sport, just unscrew the Winchoke in your slide action shotgun. Replace it with the Winchoke tube of your choice, screw it in snugly and you're ready to swing . . . with the same gun. If quail is your game . . . bobwhite, mountain or valley quail . . . pick up the Improved Cylinder Winchoke. With this tube, you get an open pattern that's most effective up to 30 yards.

When you're hunting one of America's favorite game birds—the pheasant—Just screw on the Modified choke tube with the spanner wrench. Here you get a pattern-tightening effect that's best on ranges between 25 and 45 yards.

When it comes to duck and goose hunting, you can change to a Winchoke.

Full choke unit. For waterfowl long shots a Full choke can do the job.

Winchoke Model 1200
Field Grade with Plain Barrel

Winchoke Model 1200 Field Gun with Plain Barrel. In 12 or 20 gauge. Chambers 2¾" shells. Available in 28" barrel $154.95

Winchoke Model 1200
Field Grade with Ventilated Rib

Winchoke Model 1200 Field Gun with Ventilated Rib. In 12 or 20 gauge. Chambers 2¾" shotshells. Available in 28" barrel. $174.95

Chokes:
12 ga., 28", mod., full & imp. cyl.
20 ga., 28", mod., full & imp. cyl.

Winchoke Model Specifications

Type	Field Plain Barrel	Field V.R.
Gauge	12-20●	12-20●
Magazine Capacity M/1200 ★	5	5
Magazine Capacity M/1400 ★★	3	3
Barrel Length	28"	28"
Overall Length	48⅝"	48⅝"
Length of Pull	14"	14"
Drop at Comb	1⅜"	1½"
Drop at Heel	2⅜"	2½"
Weight (lbs.)	6½-7	6½-7¼
Sights	MBF	MBF

WINCHOKE TUBES & WRENCH

●Winchoke in 12 or 20 gauge Models; supplied with Full and Improved Cylinder Winchoke tubes, with Modified unit installed.
★Includes one round in chamber. Model 1200s have factory installed plug which limits total capacity to three shells.
V.R. — Ventilated Rib   MBF — Metal Bead Front
★★ Includes one round in chamber.

WINCHESTER O&U SHOTGUNS

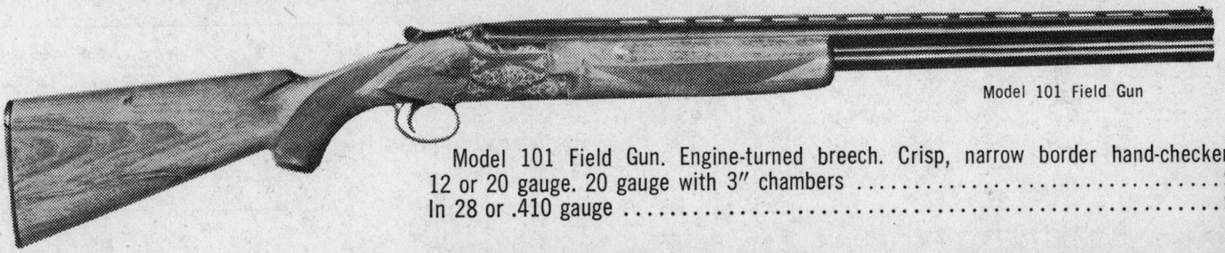

Model 101 Field Gun

Model 101 Field Gun. Engine-turned breech. Crisp, narrow border hand-checkering. In 12 or 20 gauge. 20 gauge with 3″ chambers **$580.00**
In 28 or .410 gauge **$610.00**

Model 101 Magnum Field Gun

Model 101 Magnum Field Gun. Mixes 3″ Magnum and all 2¾″ loads. In 12 gauge. **$590.00**
Model 101 Magnum Field Gun with 3″ chamber (not shown). 12 gauge. 30″ Modified and Full **$590.00**

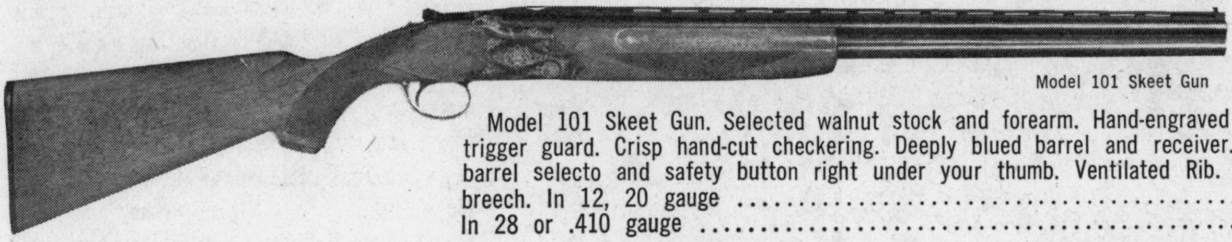

Model 101 Skeet Gun

Model 101 Skeet Gun. Selected walnut stock and forearm. Hand-engraved receiver and trigger guard. Crisp hand-cut checkering. Deeply blued barrel and receiver. Combination barrel selecto and safety button right under your thumb. Ventilated Rib. Engine-turned breech. In 12, 20 gauge **$620.00**
In 28 or .410 gauge **$650.00**

Model 101 Pigeon Grade Trap Gun.

Trap Gun, w/std. trap stock **$695.00**
Trap Gun, w/Monte Carlo trap stock .. **$700.00**

Model 101 Pigeon Grade Trap Gun. Ventilated Rib with white bead front sight and middle sight. In 12 gauge. With regular or Monte Carlo stock. 30″ and 32″ barrels with Improved Modified and Full chokes.

Model 101 Field Gun. Engine-tuned breech. Crisp, narrow border hand-checkering. In 12, 20, 28 gauge and 410 bore. 20 gauge and 410 bore have 3″ chambers.

Model 101 Magnum Field Gun. Mixes 3″ Magnum and all 2¾″ loads. In 12 gauge.

Model 101 Skeet Gun. Selected walnut stock and forearm hand-engraved receiver and trigger guard. Crisp hand-cut checkering. Ventilated Rib engine-turned breech. In 12, 20 and 28 gauge and 410 bore.

101 Pigeon Grade Trap
Model 101 Specifications

Model	Gauge	Chamber	Choke	Length Barrel (in inches)	Length Overall (in inches)	Nominal Length of Pull	Comb	Heel/ Monte Carlo	Pitch Down	Sights	Nominal Weight (lbs.)
101 Pigeon Grade Trap	12	2¾″	IM & F	30″, 32″	47⅛″, 49⅛″	14⅜″	1⅜″	1⅞″	—	WB, F & M	8¼
Field	12	2¾″	IC & M	26″	42¾″	14″	1½″	2½″	—	MBF	7¼
Field	12	2¾″	M & F	28″	44¾″	14″	1½″	2½″	—	MBF	7½
Field	12	2¾″	M & F	30″	46¾″	14″	1½″	2½″	—	MBF	7¾
Field	20	3″	IC & M	26½″	43¼″	14″	1½″	2½″	—	MBF	6½
Field	20	3″	M & F	28″	44¾″	14″	1½″	2½″	—	MBF	6½
Field	28	2¾″	IC & M	26½″	43¼″	14″	1½″	2½″	—	MBF	6¼
Field	28	2¾″	M & F	28″	44¾″	14″	1½″	2½″	—	MBF	6⅜
Field	410	3″	IC & M	26½″	43¼″	14″	1½″	2½″	—	MBF	6¼
Field	410	3″	M & F	28″	44¾″	14″	1½″	2½″	—	MBF	6⅜
Field Magnum	12	3″	M & F, F & F	30″	46¾″	14″	1½″	2½″	—	MBF	7¾
Skeet	12	2¾″	S & S	26″	42¾″	14″	1½″	2½″	2″	MB, F & M	7¼
Skeet	20	3″	S-& S	26½″	43¼″	14″	1½″	2½″	2″	MB, F & M	6½
Skeet	28	2¾″	S & S	28″	42¾″	14″	1½″	2½″	2″	MB, F & M	6⅜
Skeet	410	2½″	S & S	28″	42¾″	14″	1½″	2½″	2″	MB, F & M	6⅜
Skeet Set	20	2¾″	S & S	28″	42¾″	14″	1½″	2½″	2″	MB, F & M	6½
Interchangeable	28	2¾″	S & S	28″	42¾″	14″	1½″	2½″	2″	MB, F & M	6½
Double Barrels	410	2½″	S & S	28″	42¾″	14″	1½″	2½″	2″	MB, F & M	6½

MBF — Metal Bead Front; WB — White Bead; MB, F & M — Metal Bead Front and Middle; F & F — Full and Full; IC & M — Improved Cylinder and Modified; IM & F — Improved Modified and Full; M & F — Modified and Full; F — Full; S & S — Skeet and Skeet.

Model	Gauge	Chamber	Mag. Cap*	Choke	Length Barrel (in inches)	Length Overall (in inches)	Nominal Length of Pull	Nominal Drop at Comb	Nominal Drop at Heel/Monte Carlo	Pitch Down	Sights	Nominal Weight (lbs.)
37A	12	3″	—	F	30″-32″-36″‡	46¼″ to 52¼″	14″	1⅜″	2⅜″	—	MBF	5¾-6¼
37A	16	2¾″	—	F	30″	46¼″ to 48¼″	14″	1⅜″	2⅜″	—	MBF	6¼
37A	20†	3″	—	F	28″	44¼″	14″	1⅜″	2⅜″	—	MBF	6
37A	28	2¾″	—	F	28″	44¼″	14″	1⅜″	2⅜″	—	MBF	6¼
37A	410†	3″	—	F	26″	42¼″	14″	1⅜″	2⅜″	—	MBF	5½
101 Field	12	2¾″	—	IC & M	26″	42¾″	14″	1½″	2½″	—	MBF	7¼
Field	12	2¾″	—	M & F	28″	44¾″	14″	1½″	2½″	—	MBF	7½
Field	12	2¾″	—	M & F	30″	46¾″	14″	1½″	2½″	—	MBF	7¾
Field	20	3″	—	IC & M	26½″	43¼″	14″	1½″	2½″	—	MBF	6½
Field	20	3″	—	M & F	28″	44¾″	14″	1½″	2½″	—	MBF	6½
Field	28	2¾″	—	IC & M	26½″	43¼″	14″	1½″	2½″	—	MBF	6¼
Field	28	2¾″	—	M & F	28″	44¾″	14″	1½″	2½″	—	MBF	6⅜
Field	410	3″	—	IC & M	26½″	43¼″	14″	1½″	2½″	—	MBF	6¼
Field	410	3″	—	M & F	28″	44¾″	14″	1½″	2½″	—	MBF	6⅜
Field Magnum	12	3″	—	M & F, F & F	30″	46¾″	14″	1½″	2½″	—	MBF	7¾
Field Magnum	20	3″	—	F & F	30″	46¾″	14″	1½″	2½″	—	MBF	6½
101 Trap	12	2¾″	—	F & F	30″	47⅛″	14⅜″	1⅜″	1⅞″	1¼″	MB,F & M	8
Trap M.C.	12	2¾″	—	IM & F**	30″	47⅛″	14⅜″	1⅜″	2⅛″-1⅜″	1¼″	MB,F & M	8
Trap M.C.	12	2¾″	—	IM & F	32″	47⅛″	14⅜″	1⅜″	2⅛″-1⅜″	1¼″	MB,F & M	8¼
Skeet	12	2¾″	—	S & S	26″	42¾″	14″	1½″	2½″	2″	MB,F & M	7¼
Skeet	20	3″	—	S & S	26½″	43¼″	14″	1½″	2½″	2″	MB,F & M	6½
Skeet	28	2¾″	—	S & S	28″	42¾″	14″	1½″	2½″	2″	MB,F & M	6⅜
Skeet	410	2½″	—	S & S	28″	42¾″	14″	1½″	2½″	2″	MB,F & M	6⅜
Skeet Set	20	2¼″	—	S & S	28″	42¾″	14″	1½″	2½″	2″	MB,F & M	6½
Interchangeable	28	2¾″	—	S & S	28″	42¾″	14″	1½″	2½″	2″	MB,F & M	6½
Double Barrels	410	2½″	—	S & S	28″	42¾″	14″	1½″	2½″	2″	MB,F & M	6½
1200 Field Plain Barrel	12-20	2¾″	4	IC, M, F	26″-28″-30″	46⅝″ to 50⅝″	14″	1⅜″	2⅜″	—	MBF	6½-7
Field Plain Barrel	12-20	2¾″	4	W	26″-28″	46⅝″ to 50⅝″	14″	1⅜″	2⅜″	—	MBF	6½-7
Field V.R.	12-20	2¾″	4	IC, M, F	26″-28″-30″	46⅝″ to 50⅝″	14″	1½″	2½″	—	MBF	6½-7¼
Field V.R.	12-20	2¾″	4	W	26″-28″	46⅝″ to 50⅝″	14″	1½″	2½″	—	MBF	6½-7¼
Field Magnum Plain Barrel	12	3″	4	F	30″	50⅝″	14″	1⅜″	2⅜″	—	MBF	7¾
Field Magnum Plain Barrel	20	3″	4	F	28″	48⅝″	14″	1⅜″	2⅜″	—	MBF	7⅜
Field Magnum V.R.	12	3″	4	F	30″	50⅝″	14″	1½″	2½″	—	MBF	7⅞
Field Magnum V.R.	20	3″	4	F	28″	48⅝″	14″	1½″	2½″	—	MBF	7⅝
Deer	12	2¾″	4	—	22″	42⅝″	14″	1½″	2⅜″	—	RTFR	6½
Trap	12	2¾″	2	F	30″	51″	14⅜″	1⅜″	1⅞″	—	MM, RF	8¼
Trap M.C.	12	2¾″	2	F	30″	51″	14⅜″	1⁷⁄₁₆″	2⅛″	—	MM, RF	8¼
1400 Field Plain Barrel	12-20	2¾″	2	IC, M, F	26″-28″-30″	46⅝″ to 50⅝″	14″	1⅜″	2⅜″	—	MBF	6½-7
Field Plain Barrel	12-20	2¾″	2	W	26″-28″	46⅝″ to 50⅝″	14″	1⅜″	2⅜″	—	MBF	6½-7
Field V.R.	12-20	2¾″	2	IC, M, F	26″-28″-30″	46⅝″ to 50⅝″	14″	1½″	2½″	—	MBF	6½-7¼
Field V.R.	12-20	2¾″	2	W	26″-28″	46⅝″ to 50⅝″	14″	1½″	2½″	—	MBF	6½-7¼
Deer	12	2¾″	2	—	22″	42⅝″	14″	1½″	2⅜″	—	RTFR	6½
Trap	12	2¾″	2	F	30″	51″	14⅜″	1⅜″	1⅞″	—	MM, RF	8¼
Trap M.C.	12	2¾″	2	F	30″	51″	14⅜″	1⁷⁄₁₆″	2⅛″	—	MM, RF	8¼
Skeet	12-20	2¾″	2	S	26″	46⅝″	14″	1½″	2½″	—	MM, RF	7¼-7½

* Add one round for shell in chamber. Model 1200 has factory installed magazine plug which when removed increases capacity to four shells. V.R. — Ventilated Rib; M.C. — Monte Carlo Stock; MBF — Metal Bead Front; MB, F & M — Metal Bead Front and Middle; MM, RF — Metal Middle, Red Front; RTFR — Rifle Type Front and Rear; F & F — Full and Full; IC & M — Improved Cylinder and Modified; IM & F — Improved Modified and Full; F, SB — Full, Single Barrel; IM, SB — Improved Modified, Single Barrel; M & F — Modified and Full; F — Full; S — Skeet; S & S — Skeet and Skeet; W — Winchoke — Comes with Winchoke set including Full, Modified and Improved Cylinder tubes with wrench.

** Also available in Full & Full.   † 37A Youth Model available with 26″ barrel, 12½″ pull, 40¾″ overall length. 20 gauge has Improved Modified Choke.   ‡ 36″ barrel.

Black Powder Guns

AMERICAN HERITAGE

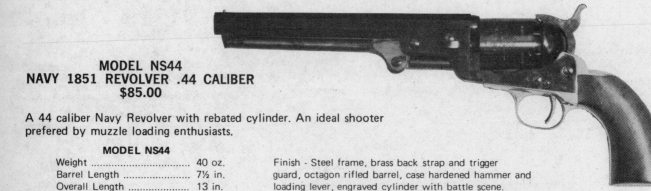

MODEL CB36
CONFEDERATE REVOLVER .36 CALIBER
$57.95

A modern replica of a Confederate Percussion
Army Revolver. Polished brass frame, rifled
high luster blued round barrel and polished
walnut grips.

MODEL CB36

Weight .... 41 oz.
Barrel Length .... 7½ in.
Overall Length .... 13 in.

Finish - Brass frame, back strap and trigger guard,
blued round rifled barrel, case hardened hammer
and loading lever, engraved cylinder with battle
scene.

Confederate Revolver Now Available
In 44 Caliber

MODEL CB44

Weight .... 39 oz.
Barrel Length .... 7½ in.
Overall Length .... 13 in.

MODEL NS44
NAVY 1851 REVOLVER .44 CALIBER
$85.00

A 44 caliber Navy Revolver with rebated cylinder. An ideal shooter
prefered by muzzle loading enthusiasts.

MODEL NS44

Weight .... 40 oz.
Barrel Length .... 7½ in.
Overall Length .... 13 in.

Finish - Steel frame, brass back strap and trigger
guard, octagon rifled barrel, case hardened hammer and
loading lever, engraved cylinder with battle scene.

MODEL SS36
$85.00

Police, 36 caliber, fluted cylinder, steel frame, 5 in.
octagonal barrel.

Weight .... 38 oz.
Barrel Length .... 5 in.
Overall Length .... 10½ in.

Finish - Deep luster blue rifled octagon barrel.

MODEL RA36
NAVY MODEL REVOLVER
$90.45

The Navy Model Remington Revolver in 36 caliber
with a 6½ inch barrel. Always a popular companion
to the Remington Army Model.

MODEL RA36

Weight: .... 40 oz.
Barrel Length .... 6½ in.
Overall Length .... 13¼ in.

Finish - Deep luster blue rifled barrel, polished walnut stock, brass trigger guard.

AMERICAN HERITAGE

MODEL P130

Corsair Double-Barrel Pistol. .36 caliber. A beautifully designed double-barrel pistol with rifled barrels, an ideal pistol for the collector as well as the black-powder shooter. Weight: 34 oz.; barrel length: 8¼"; overall length: 13¾". Blued rifle barrels, brass trigger guard and buttcap, tastefully engraved.
Model P130 .... $78.75

MODEL P125

Kentucky Pistol Original 1850 Deluxe Model. Length: 15½"; weight: 35 oz.; .45 caliber. Case-hardened lock, slim-contoured polished walnut stock, deep octagon rifled-barrel, dovetailed rear and front brass-blade sight, brass-tipped ramrod, percussion nipple in original flash-shield bolster.
Model P125 .... $72.00

MODEL P127

Kentucky Pistol Original 1830 Deluxe Model. Length 15½ in., weight 35 oz., caliber 45. Case hardened flintlock with original gooseneck hammer, slim contoured polished walnut stock, deep rifled octagon barrel, dovetailed rear and front brass blade sight, brass tipped ramrod.

Model P127 .... $72.00

MODEL PM25D

Kentucky Belt Pistol Deluxe. Length: 13"; weight: 30 oz.; .45 caliber. Full-engraved lock and barrel, walnut full-stock, octagon barrel, brass-tipped ramrod.
Model PM25D $51.25

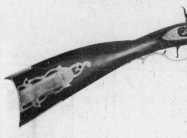

MODEL R120
$182.55

SPECIFICATIONS:

Caliber: .45 (actual bore size .453) Deep rifling.
Barrel: Octagonal 13/16" across flats, length of barrel 36".
Lock Plate: Flint or Percussion. Case-hardened with flash shield on percussion-guns.
Stock: Full-length one-piece walnut stock.
Ramrod: Made in a single piece, brass tipped at both ends and threaded at bottom end.
Mountings: Polished brass, including a large original-type patch box. Light-engraving on lock plate.
Length Overall: 50".
Weight: 6½ to 7 lbs., depending on density of walnut stock.

MODEL R150
$87.10

SPECIFICATIONS:

Caliber: .45.
Ignition: Case-hardened percussion lock with bridle.
Barrel: 36", fully rifled.
Overall Length: 50".
Weight: 8½ lbs.
Finish: Polished blued octagon barrel, polished brass mountings.
Sights: Blade front, open-type rear, dovetailed.
Stock: Two-piece dark-walnut stock.
Ramrod: Wood, brass tipped at both ends.
Patch Box: Large brass patch box.

AMERICAN HERITAGE

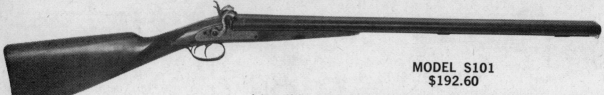

MODEL S101
$192.60

A beautifully designed 12-gauge percussion muzzle-loading shotgun with modified and full choke. Tastefully engraved side locks and English-browned barrels. A wooden ramrod, brass tipped, capable of taking a brush or worm (worm is included with each shotgun). The weight is approximately 6 lbs. making it an easy-to-handle lightweight field gun.

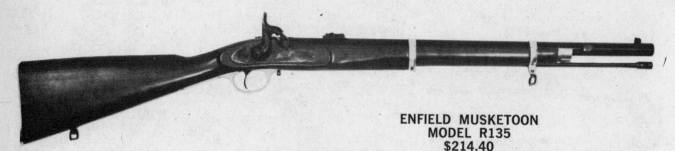

ENFIELD MUSKETOON
MODEL R135
$214.40

SPECIFICATIONS:

Caliber: 58. (575213) minie ball. **Barrel Length:** 24". **Overall Length:** 40¼". **Weight:** 7 to 7½ lbs., depending on density of wood. **Barrel:** Round high-luster blue barrel. **Stock:** Seasoned walnut stock, with sling swivels. **Ignition:** Heavy-duty percussion lock. **Sights:** Graduated military-leaf sight. **Furniture:** Brass furniture.

BROWN BESS MUSKET
$201.00

The Brown Bess made famous during the American Revolution, is now offered to the muzzle-loading shooter. It has a barrel length of 42", overall length of 59", and is in .75 caliber. The barrel and lock are polished bright as were the originals and makes an excellent replica for those who would plan to use it in the forthcoming American Revolution Bicentennial.

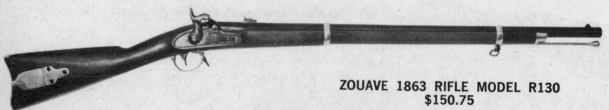

ZOUAVE 1863 RIFLE MODEL R130
$150.75

SPECIFICATONS:

Caliber: 58. **Ignition:** Case-hardened percussion lock. **Barrel:** Rifled 32½" in length. **Overall Length:** 48½" **Weight:** 9½ lbs. **Finish:** High-polished round barrel, polished brass mountings and cap box. **Sights:** Original 3-leaf rear sight, blade front sight. **Ramrod:** Heavy one-piece steel.

COLT PERCUSSION REVOLVERS

Colt 1851 Navy

.36 Caliber
$136.00

OPTIONAL ACCESSORIES

LARGE POWDER FLASK: Antique-finished copper with polished brass fittings and original Dixon design. Measuring spout throws a charge of 20 grains. $37.00

BAG FLASK: Similar to large size but without design. Adjustable measuring spout throws ½, ⅝, and ¾ dram (20 grains). $40.00

TWO-CAVITY BULLET MOLD: Casts round ball and conical bullet simultaneously. Polished brass with color case-hardened sprue cutter. $17.50

NIPPLE WRENCH: An essential part of any complete accessory set—invaluable to the serious black powder shooter. $6.00

MODEL 1851 NAVY SPECIFICATIONS:

Caliber—.36. **Barrel Length**—7½".
Overall Length—13⅛". **Weight**—40 Ounces.
Sights—Bead Type Front Sight. **Trigger**—Smooth.
Hammer Spur—Knurled. **Stock**—American, Black, Walnut.
Finish—Frame Color Case-hardened. Barrel & Cylinder Blue.
Silver-plated Trigger guard and Backstrap.

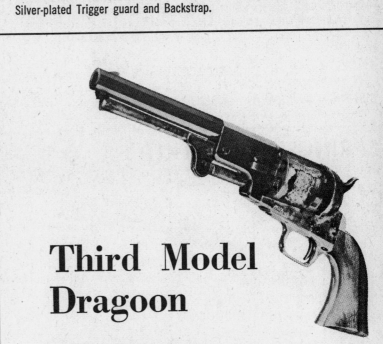

Third Model Dragoon

.44 Percussion Revolver $204.00

Brass backstrap and trigger guard. Color case hardened frame, hammer and loading lever. Colt Blue barrel and cylinder engraved with the original "Ranger and Indian" scene. Six-shot .44 caliber with 7½" barrel. One piece American Walnut oiled stocks. Serial numbers resume at 20,901 where production stopped in 1860. Weight: 4 lb. 2 oz. Overall length: 14". Accurately duplicated Colt Dragoon accessories: Brass Stand-of-Flags powder flask, brass two-cavity bullet mold, nipple wrench, percussion cap can, wooden presentation case partitioned in the American style.

H&R MUZZLE LOADERS

THE HUNTSMAN

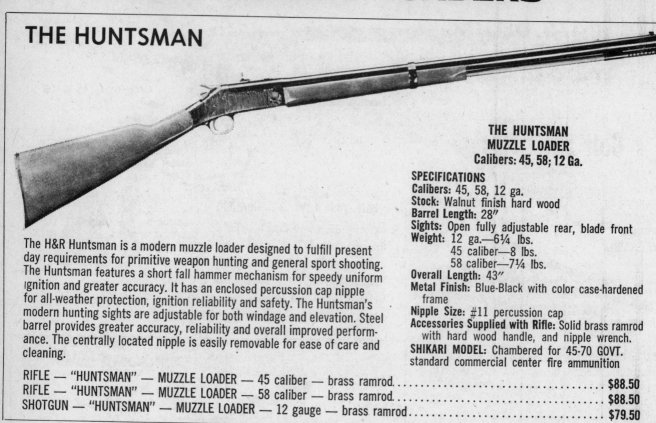

**THE HUNTSMAN
MUZZLE LOADER
Calibers: 45, 58; 12 Ga.**

SPECIFICATIONS
Calibers: 45, 58, 12 ga.
Stock: Walnut finish hard wood
Barrel Length: 28″
Sights: Open fully adjustable rear, blade front
Weight: 12 ga.—6¼ lbs.
        45 caliber—8 lbs.
        58 caliber—7¼ lbs.
Overall Length: 43″
Metal Finish: Blue-Black with color case-hardened
    frame
Nipple Size: #11 percussion cap
Accessories Supplied with Rifle: Solid brass ramrod
    with hard wood handle, and nipple wrench.
SHIKARI MODEL: Chambered for 45-70 GOVT.
standard commercial center fire ammunition

The H&R Huntsman is a modern muzzle loader designed to fulfill present day requirements for primitive weapon hunting and general sport shooting. The Huntsman features a short fall hammer mechanism for speedy uniform ignition and greater accuracy. It has an enclosed percussion cap nipple for all-weather protection, ignition reliability and safety. The Huntsman's modern hunting sights are adjustable for both windage and elevation. Steel barrel provides greater accuracy, reliability and overall improved performance. The centrally located nipple is easily removable for ease of care and cleaning.

RIFLE — "HUNTSMAN" — MUZZLE LOADER — 45 caliber — brass ramrod **$88.50**
RIFLE — "HUNTSMAN" — MUZZLE LOADER — 58 caliber — brass ramrod **$88.50**
SHOTGUN — "HUNTSMAN" — MUZZLE LOADER — 12 gauge — brass ramrod **$79.50**

SPRINGFIELD STALKER

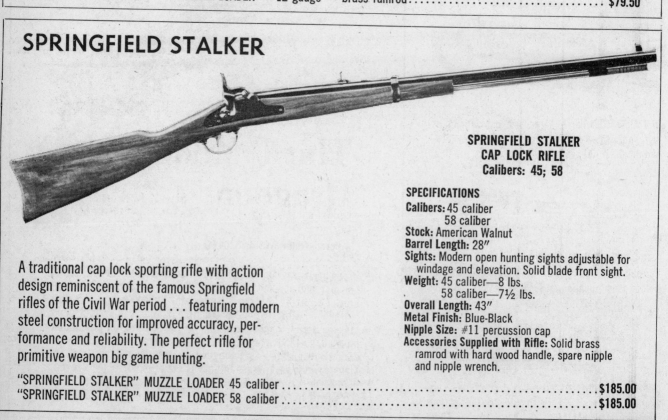

**SPRINGFIELD STALKER
CAP LOCK RIFLE
Calibers: 45; 58**

SPECIFICATIONS
Calibers: 45 caliber
        58 caliber
Stock: American Walnut
Barrel Length: 28″
Sights: Modern open hunting sights adjustable for
    windage and elevation. Solid blade front sight.
Weight: 45 caliber—8 lbs.
        58 caliber—7½ lbs.
Overall Length: 43″
Metal Finish: Blue-Black
Nipple Size: #11 percussion cap
Accessories Supplied with Rifle: Solid brass
    ramrod with hard wood handle, spare nipple
    and nipple wrench.

A traditional cap lock sporting rifle with action design reminiscent of the famous Springfield rifles of the Civil War period . . . featuring modern steel construction for improved accuracy, performance and reliability. The perfect rifle for primitive weapon big game hunting.

"SPRINGFIELD STALKER" MUZZLE LOADER 45 caliber **$185.00**
"SPRINGFIELD STALKER" MUZZLE LOADER 58 caliber **$185.00**

H&R MUZZLE LOADER

MODEL 175 DELUXE SPRINGFIELD STALKER CAP LOCK RIFLE

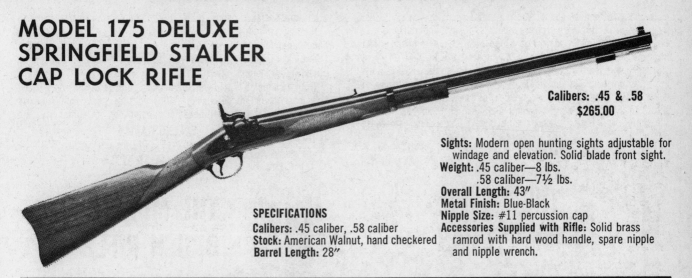

Calibers: .45 & .58
$265.00

Sights: Modern open hunting sights adjustable for windage and elevation. Solid blade front sight.
Weight: .45 caliber—8 lbs.
         .58 caliber—7½ lbs.
Overall Length: 43″
Metal Finish: Blue-Black
Nipple Size: #11 percussion cap
Accessories Supplied with Rifle: Solid brass ramrod with hard wood handle, spare nipple and nipple wrench.

SPECIFICATIONS
Calibers: .45 caliber, .58 caliber
Stock: American Walnut, hand checkered
Barrel Length: 28″

HOPKINS & ALLEN

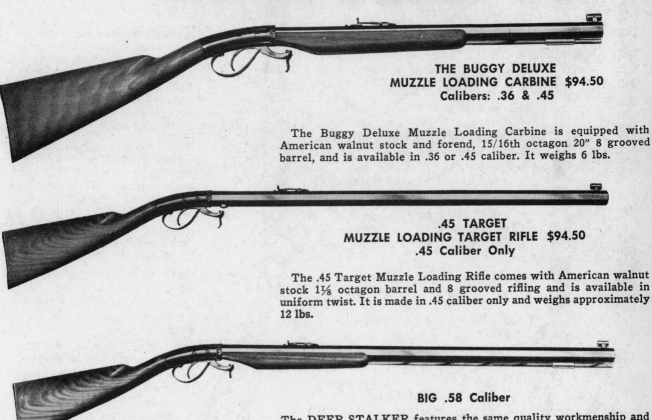

THE BUGGY DELUXE MUZZLE LOADING CARBINE $94.50
Calibers: .36 & .45

The Buggy Deluxe Muzzle Loading Carbine is equipped with American walnut stock and forend, 15/16th octagon 20″ 8 grooved barrel, and is available in .36 or .45 caliber. It weighs 6 lbs.

.45 TARGET MUZZLE LOADING TARGET RIFLE $94.50
.45 Caliber Only

The .45 Target Muzzle Loading Rifle comes with American walnut stock 1⅛ octagon barrel and 8 grooved rifling and is available in uniform twist. It is made in .45 caliber only and weighs approximately 12 lbs.

BIG .58 Caliber

THE DEER STALKER
$99.50

The DEER STALKER features the same quality workmenship and generous amount of hand fitting common to all Hopkins & Allen Muzzleloaders. The receiver and octagonal barrel are finished in a high luster custom blue complimented by handsome genuine American walnut stocks. The loading barrel has one turn in 72″ and is 32″ long. The bore is 5.75 shooting a .580 grain slug. Total weight of the firearm is approximately 9½″ lbs.

HOPKINS & ALLEN

The muzzle loading gun blazed a great era in the pages of history. It is the turning point of weapons design and perhaps the very apex of basic fundamentals which started the renaissance of firearms design and improvement in which we are living. "Charcoal burning" as it is affectionately called by its advocates, is a rapidly-growing sport and its devotees are increasing in number daily. It is truly a rewarding pastime and one of the finest new shooting sports in existence. Muzzle loading clubs are springing up all over the nation and their very existence have caused some states to open up special seasons for hunting game with muzzle loaders.

Hopkins and Allen offers the black powder shooter an **entirely American-made,** black powder rifle, featuring both the traditional "Kentucky Type" Minuteman rifle and the American Hopkins & Allen "underhammer" guns.

The Hopkins & Allen underhammer guns are the only truly American designed percussion rifles, dating back to the early 1830's when the design became popular for its simplicity and well known reliability.

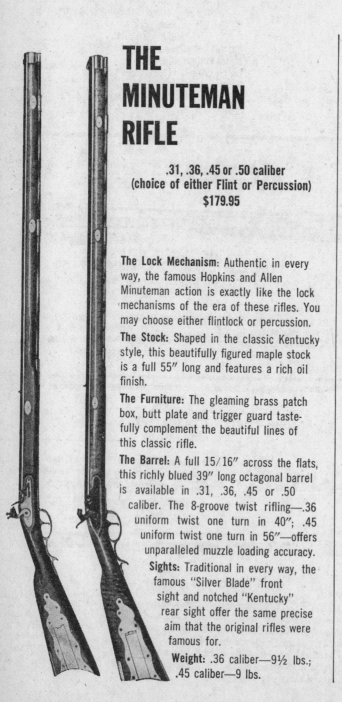

THE MINUTEMAN RIFLE

.31, .36, .45 or .50 caliber
(choice of either Flint or Percussion)
$179.95

The Lock Mechanism: Authentic in every way, the famous Hopkins and Allen Minuteman action is exactly like the lock mechanisms of the era of these rifles. You may choose either flintlock or percussion.

The Stock: Shaped in the classic Kentucky style, this beautifully figured maple stock is a full 55" long and features a rich oil finish.

The Furniture: The gleaming brass patch box, butt plate and trigger guard tastefully complement the beautiful lines of this classic rifle.

The Barrel: A full 15/16" across the flats, this richly blued 39" long octagonal barrel is available in .31, .36, .45 or .50 caliber. The 8-groove twist rifling—.36 uniform twist one turn in 40"; .45 uniform twist one turn in 56"—offers unparalleled muzzle loading accuracy.

Sights: Traditional in every way, the famous "Silver Blade" front sight and notched "Kentucky" rear sight offer the same precise aim that the original rifles were famous for.

Weight: .36 caliber—9½ lbs.; .45 caliber—9 lbs.

THE MINUTEMAN BRUSH RIFLE

.31, .36, .45 or .50 caliber
$179.95

The Minuteman Brush Rifle sports the clean, classic lines of the Minuteman Rifle, yet is shortened into an ideal brush gun for the whitetail hunter to use in thickly wooded terrain. It is crafted by American gunsmiths with the same fine maple stock and richly blued metal as the big Minuteman.

SPECIFICATIONS

The Lock Mechanism: As in the Minuteman Rifle, the famous Hopkins & Allen action is just like the lock mechanisms as found in the early Kentucky rifles. You may choose either flint lock or percussion.

The Stock: The beautifully finished maple stock is shaped in the classic Kentucky style.

The Furniture: This rifle features the same gleaming brass patch box, butt plate and trigger guard that enhance the Minuteman Rifle.

The Barrel: Shortened to 24" for easy handling in heavy brush country, the precision rifled or smooth bore octagonal barrel in .31, .36, .45 or .50 caliber offers you Hopkins & Allen renowned accuracy and authentic design.

Sights: The famous "Silver Blade" front sight and notched "Kentucky" rear sight offer the same precise aim and traditional design as the Minuteman Rifle.

Weight: 8 lbs.

HOPKINS & ALLEN

**THE HERITAGE MODEL
MUZZLE LOADING RIFLE $99.95
Calibers: .36 & .45**

The Heritage Model is exactly like the Hopkins & Allen underhammer guns of the 1830's. The underhammer is the one truly American muzzle loading design. Its unique simplicity and clean lines make it very popular with knowledgeable black powder shooters.

This underhammer gun, features a beautifully finished American walnut stock, complemented by a special trigger guard and brass patch box.

A lifetime of precision shooting is assured by the famous Hopkins & Allen richly blued octagonal barrel.

SPECIFICATIONS

Lock Mechanism: Dependability and long life are assured by the supremely simple lock mechanism. With only two moving parts, the underhammer provides fast, sure ignition, and allows the shooter to aim without visual distraction. **The Stock:** Authentic in design, the traditional American walnut stock is finely finished by skillful American craftsmen. **The Furniture:** Faithful to the details of the early New England underhammers, Hopkins & Allen enhances the clean lines of the rifle with a gleaming brass cap box, crescent-shaped butt-plate, and trigger guard extension. **The Barrel:** To their 32″ long octagonal barrel, a full

$^{15}/_{16}$″ across the flats, Hopkins & Allen has added a non-reflecting matted top flat and decorative gold inlay signature. Available in .36 or .45 caliber. **Sights:** The utmost in accuracy is assured by the combination of hooded, standard dovetail front sight with ring aperture, the Kentucky open rear sight, and the Hopkins & Allen aperture long range rear target sight. **Weight:** .36 caliber: 8¼ lbs.; .45 caliber: 8 lbs.

**THE OFFHAND DELUXE
MUZZLE LOADING RIFLE $94.50
Calibers: .36 & .45**

SPECIFICATIONS

The Lock Mechanism: The supremely simple Hopkins & Allen underhammer assures the shooter the same fast, sure ignition, dependability, and long life as in the Heritage Model. **The Stock:** A skillfully finished

American walnut stock and fore-end give this rifle classic beauty. **The Barrel:** The Hopkins & Allen octagonal barrel, famous for precision and finished in a high blue luster, is a full 32″ long, $^{15}/_{16}$″ across the flats, and available in .36 or .45 caliber

uniform twist. **Sights:** A hooded front sight with ring aperture combines with the Kentucky type rear sight for accurate aiming. **Weight:** .36 caliber—8¼ lbs.; .45 caliber —8 lbs.

**PENNSYLVANIA
HALF-STOCK RIFLE $179.95
Calibers: .31, .36, .45 & .50**

SPECIFICATIONS

Here's an exact reproduction of the famous Pennsylvania Half-Stock Rifle. The half-stock's design, fine handling characteristics, and superb accuracy made it popular with early frontiersmen who came to rely heavily on these guns for food and protection.

The Lock Mechanism: The famous Hopkins & Allen lock mechanism is just like the favorite Pennsylvania Half-Stock Rifle action. You may choose either flintlock or percussion. **The Stock:** The traditional stock is of fine maple, hand rubbed and finished to a rich lustre just like they were originally. **The Furniture:** The traditional beauty

of this rifle is high-lighted by highly polished brass funiture. **The Barrel:** The beautifully blued barrel is 32″ long and is available in .31, .36, .45 or .50 caliber: either smoothbore or with the famous Hopkins & Allen precision rifling. **Sights:** With sights like the originals, these guns are authentic in every way. **Weight:** 10 lbs.

HOPKINS & ALLEN

HOPKINS & ALLEN SWIVEL BREECH RIFLE

.45 caliber only $139.95

Now the black powder muzzle loader can have a 2-shot capability. The special swivel breech allows the second shot to be fired in only seconds by merely rotating the barrels. Positive and precise sighting for each barrel is assured by a complete set of sights on each barrel, making this rifle a true hunting gun.

The Lock Mechanism: The lock is specially designed to accommodate a swivel breech and still provide long-lasting, dependable ignition.

The Stock: Fine American gunsmiths crafted this rich American walnut stock with pride.

The Furniture: A classic Crescent butt plate in gleaming brass highlights the traditional stock.

The Barrels: Two famous Hopkins & Allen precision rifled barrels mounted to a rugged swivel breech.

Sights: Each barrel carries its own set of quick-aligning rifle sights.

Weight: 8½ lbs.

LIGHTWEIGHT MUZZLE LOADING SHOTGUN

12 Gauge only $129.50

Like the fine early English fowling pieces, this lightweight muzzle loader is a well-balanced and fast-handling.

It's the ideal choice for either clay targets or wing shooting. In addition, it will double as a great gun in the National Forests that allow hunting only with a smooth bore muzzle-loading rifle.

Just under 6 lbs., this 12-gauge shotgun has a 28" smoothbore barrel with modified choking, set in a rich honey-tone maple stock. The gleaming brass furniture adds the final touch to this beautiful fowling piece.

SPECIFICATIONS

The Lock Mechanism: This rifle has the same dependable percussion lock mechanism as the Minuteman Rifle.

The Stock: The traditional maple stock reproduces the fine hand finishing of the original English fowling pieces.

The Furniture: Skillful American gunsmiths have made the brass furnishings like the original rifle to give you a gun authentic down to the smallest detail.

The Barrel: The 28" smooth bore barrel is finished in a rich custom blue.

The Sights: The standard front bead offers all the quick pointing of a good bird gun.

Weight: Under 6 lbs.

BOOT PISTOL

The "Boot Pistol" is available in .36 and .45 calibers and comes with a sculptured walnut pistol grip and a full 6" octagonal barrel. It measures 13" over-all in length. The 15/16" octagon barrel is fitted with open sights—post type front sight and open rear sight with step elevator. The H&A "Boot Pistol" features a rich blueblack finish and is equipped with a match trigger.

Calibers: .36 & .45
$39.95

HIGH-STANDARD
BLACK POWDER REVOLVERS

Arms of the Confederacy . . .
High Standard's "Arms of the Confederacy," a series of black powder revolvers commemorating Confederate firearms manufacturers that existed in the South during the Civil War.
Features include a trophy blue finish, highly polished brass frame and trigger guard, with a hand-rubbed one piece walnut stock.

Griswold & Gunnison
.36 Cal. Revolver
$145.00

The first two issues, the Griswold and Gunnison and the Leech and Rigdon, are 6 shot, 36 Caliber, Single Action "Colt type" revolvers. The G&G has a brass frame, while its counterpart, the L&R has a steel frame.

Leech & Rigdon
.36 Cal. Revolver
$145.00

High Standard's second issue of its "Arms of the Confederacy" the Leech and Rigdon, is also available in a production model. Like the Griswold & Gunnison, it's a six shot .36 Cal. Single Action revolver, with 7½" barrel length. It differs in that it is a steel framed version of the "Colt type" revolver. (not shown)

Black Powder Pistols

	Type	Finish	Caliber	Barrel Length
Griswold & Gunnison	Percussion	Trophy Blue Brass Frame	.36 Cal.	7½"
Leech & Rigdon	Percussion	Trophy Blue Steel Frame	.36 Cal.	7½"

LYMAN RIFLES

PLAINS RIFLE
.45 and .50 caliber

The Lyman Plains Rifle is patterned after the reliable and accurate guns used by the early plainsmen who opened the West and Northwest. Traditionally styled, this black-powder firearm features a double-set trigger and fully adjustable sight. In addition, its hooked breech makes takedown and cleaning a breeze. The handsome European walnut stock is highlighted by a gleaming brass trigger guard, buttplate, and a distinctive, easy-to-open patch box. Available in .45 or .50 caliber; barrel length: 28"; overall length: 45"; weight: 8¾ lbs.

The Lyman Plains Rifle .45 or .50 cal. $225.00
The Lyman Plains Rifle Accessory Kit (alone) . .   26.00
The Lyman Plains Rifle and Accessory Kit 240.00

BROWN BESS
.75 caliber

At the beginning of the Revolutionary War, America had few facilities for manufacturing guns. Luckily there were many British muskets available which had seen service in earlier colonial wars against the French and Indians. The Brown Bess musket was the mainstay of U.S. forces during the early stages of the American Revolution.

Lyman's Brown Bess is a replica of the "New Land Pattern" in .75 caliber. The 42" barrel and lock are brightly polished as are the originals while the walnut-finished stock and rich polished-brass trigger guard combine to produce a classic American flintlock. The Brown Bess fires either the .715 round ball and patch or bird shot in all sizes. Overall Length: 59". Weight: 10½ lbs.
Brown Bess $275.00

1863 Zouave
.58 caliber

The 1863 Zouave is one of the most popular reproduction rifles used today. The Lyman Zouave is truly authentic and features a beautifully color case-hardened lock and gleaming brass fixtures.
The Zouave kit includes a .58 Mini-ball mould and handles, a spare nipple, a nipple wrench, Hodgdon's "Minnie Lube," and Lyman's "Black Powder Basics." Available in .58 caliber; overall length: 48½"; barrel length: 32½"; weight: 9½ lbs.

The Lyman Zouave (alone) $175.00
The Lyman Zouave with Accessory Kit 190.00

1851 SQUAREBACK NAVY .36

This .36 caliber replica is patterned after what may be the most famous percussion revolver ever made. Its classic lines and historic appeal make it as popular today as it was when Sam Colt was turning out the originals. Like the Remingtons, this replica of the second model 1851 (about 5,000 made) is made of quality material. The revolver features a color case-hardened steel frame, hammer and loading lever. The blued cylinder is engraved with the same naval battle scene as were the originals. The nickle-plated backstrap, squareback trigger guard and one-piece walnut grips combine to make Lyman's 1851 a real classic. Available in .36 caliber; barrel length: 7½"; overall length: 13"; weight: 2 lbs. 9 oz. 1851 Navy (alone) **$115.95** 1851 Navy with Kit **$124.95**

LYMAN REVOLVERS

1860 ARMY .44

This revolver was the most widely used sidearm during the Civil War. Both sides prized the 1860 for its reliability and advanced features such as the "creeping" loading lever system. This, the last U.S. military percussion revolver, was the most advanced of the open-top revolvers. After the War, this gun went West and helped the pioneers survive and settle in the new Lyman's 1860 Army .44 is patterned exactly after the original and features one-piece walnut grips, color case-hardened frame, hammer and loading lever. The barrel and rebated engraved cylinder are polished blued steel while the backstrap and trigger guard are nickle-plated brass. The four-screw frame is cut for a shoulder stock.

Available in .44 caliber; barrel length: 8"; overall length: 13⅝"; weight: 2 lbs. 9 oz.

1860 Army (alone) $119.95
1860 Army with Kit $129.95

NEW MODEL ARMY .44

This rugged replica of Remington's 1858 New Model Army .44 has been the favorite of target shooters and other experienced muzzle loaders. The sturdy top strap, besides strengthening the basic frame design, provides an excellent platform for installation of an adjustable rear sight. Features include a deep-blue finish on the machined steel frame, barrel, cylinder and loading lever. The trigger and hammer are color case-hardened. The trigger guard is polished brass and the two-piece grips are well-finished European walnut. Available in .44 caliber; barrel length: 8"; overall length: 13½"; weight: 2 lbs. 9 oz. **Note:** Single cavity .451 round-ball mould included at no additional charge.

New Model Army .44 ....$115.95

NEW MODEL NAVY .36

The same features found in the New Model Army .44 replica can be found in its smaller naval version. Many of these revolvers are fitted with target sights and provide years of reliable service. The reduced length of this pistol makes it a handy belt gun which, when properly loaded, performs comparably to the .38 Special. Features include a deep-blue finish on the machined steel frame, barrel, cylinder and loading lever. The trigger and hammer are color case-hardened while the trigger guard is of polished brass. Grips are well-finished European walnut. Available in .36 caliber; barrel length: 6½"; overall length: 12¼"; weight: 2 lbs. 10 oz. **Note:** Single cavity .375 round-ball mould included at no additional charge.

New Model Navy .36 ....$115.95

NAVY ARMS REPLICAS

1862 POLICE MODEL

4½", 5½", 6½" barrel—This is the last gun manufactured by the Colt Plant in the percussion era. It encompassed all the modifications of each gun starting from the early Paterson to the 1861 Navy. It was favored by the New York Police Dept. for many years. One-half fluted and rebated cylinder, .36 cal., 5 shot, .380 dia. ball, 18 grains of black powder, brass trigger guard and backstrap. Case hardened frame, loading lever and hammer—balance blue.

1862 POLICE
.36 Caliber
$95.00

SPILLER & BURR REVOLVER

A brass-frame copy of the Whitney revolvers made in the Confederacy. Available in .36 caliber only with 7" full-octagon barrel. Weight 2½ lbs., overall length 12½". $75.00

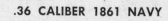

.36 CALIBER 1861 NAVY

The Officer model 1861 Navy Replica comes in .36 caliber with a 7½" barrel and may be had with a 6-shot round or fluted cylinder and choice of brass or iron straps. The model with iron straps is also available with a square back guard. Features include: case hardened frame, lever, and hammer; balance of gun is blued. The 1861 Navy comes cut for a shoulder stock.

.36 Caliber
$100.00

COLT WALKER 1847

The 1847 Walker replica comes in .44 caliber with a 9½" barrel. The full size Walker .44 weighs 4 lbs. 9 oz. and is well suited for the collector as well as the black powder shooter. Features include: rolled cylinder scene; blue and case hardened finish; and brass guard. Proof tested.

COLT WALKER 1847
$125.00

NAVY ARMS REPLICAS

"YANK" REVOLVER .36 CAL.

One of the most famous guns in all American history. During the Civil War it served both the North and South. Later, when the rush to open the west began, it became "standard equipment" for every man who ventured on a horse or rode a covered wagon to the virgin lands of wheat, cattle and gold. Due to its light recoil, and lightning-fast action, it is still selected by many quick draw artists as the fastest single-action revolver in the world.

Cylinder roll engraved with classic naval battle scene. Back Strap and trigger guard are polished brass **Price $100.00**

ENGRAVED "YANK"

Just for that special spot in a collection. Hand-engraved to your specifications with gold inlay and special grips of pearl, ivory and ebony plastic available.

Engraving type "A"	$ 95.00
type "B"	$140.00
type "C"	$275.00
Grips (per pair)	$ 6.00
Gold Inlay	$75.00 extra
Gold bands	$ 50.00

SPECIFICATIONS:

Weight:	2 lbs. 9 oz.
Barrel Length:	7½"
Over-all length:	13"
Caliber:	.36

Finish: Polished Brass back strap and trigger guard. Engraved cylinder, Navy scene. Case hardened frame hammer and loading lever.

NEW MODEL NAVY REVOLVER
CIVILIAN MODEL "YANK" NAVY .36 CAL. (not shown)
Cylinder roll engraved with classic naval battle scene. Backstrap and trigger guard silverplated. ....**Price $100.00**

TARGET MODEL REMINGTON REVOLVER

Based on the most advanced design of its time, the Remington Percussion Revolver was considered the most accurate and dependable of all the cap and ball of its era. With its top strap and frame these guns are considered the magnum of Civil War revolvers and are ideally suited for the heavy .44 caliber charges. We are now offering our popular Army Model as a Target gun with target sights for the serious target shooter who desires to control the accuracy of his shooting with a more definite set of sights. Ruggedly built from modern steel and proof tested. **$125.00**

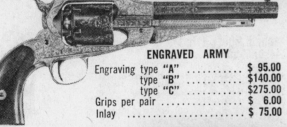

ENGRAVED ARMY

Engraving type "A"	$ 95.00
type "B"	$140.00
type "C"	$275.00
Grips per pair	$ 6.00
Inlay	$ 75.00

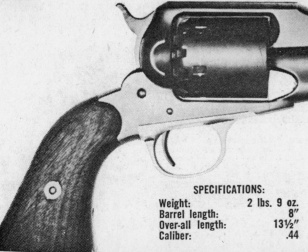

SPECIFICATIONS:

Weight:	2 lbs. 9 oz.
Barrel length:	8"
Over-all length:	13½"
Caliber:	.44

NEW MODEL ARMY REVOLVER—.44 CAL.

The most advanced design of the time, the Remington was considered the most accurate cap & ball revolver. A rugged, dependable, battle-proven Civil War veteran. With its top strap and rugged frame these guns are considered the magnum of C. W. revolvers and are ideally suited for the heavy .44 charges. Favored by many a gallant frontiersman as the most reliable heavy duty .44 cal percussion revolver made. Faithfully reproduced by NAVY ARMS...................**Price $95.00**
BELT REVOLVER .36 CAL.
A shortened and lightened version of the "44" Remington Army Revolver which was desired by many officers during the C. W. because it still featured rugged top strap & frame. ....**Price $100.00**

NAVY ARMS REPLICAS

ARMY MODEL 60

SPECIFICATIONS: .36 caliber—Weight: 2 lbs. 11 oz. Barrel Length: 7¼". Over-all Length: 13". .44 caliber—Weight: 2 lbs. 10 oz. **Barrel Length:** 7¼". **Over-all Length:** 13". **Finish:** Brass Frame, back strap & trigger guard, round barrel hinged rammer and on the .44 cal. rebated cylinder.

A modern replica of the confederate Griswold & Grier percussion Army revolver. In .36 or .44 caliber, rendered with a polished brass frame and a rifled steel barrel finished in a high luster blue with genuine walnut grips. All **Army Model 60's** are completely proof-tested by the Italian Government to the most exacting standards. ......**Price $60.00**

LEECH & RIGDON

SPECIFICATIONS—Weight: 2 lbs. 10 oz. **Barrel Length:** 7¼". **Over-all Length:** 13". **Caliber:** .36. **Finish:** Steel Case hardened frame. Round barrel, hinged rammer.

A modern version of the famous Leech & Rigdon Army Revolver. Manufactured during the Civil War in Augusta, Georgia and furnished to many of the Georgia Cavalry units. It is basically a copy of the Colt Navy Revolver, but with a round Dragoon type barrel. ....**Price $100.00**

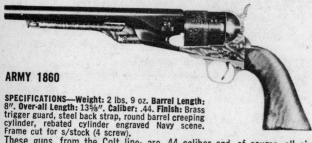

ARMY 1860

SPECIFICATIONS—Weight: 2 lbs. 9 oz. **Barrel Length:** 8". **Over-all Length:** 13⅝". **Caliber:** .44. **Finish:** Brass trigger guard, steel back strap, round barrel creeping cylinder, rebated cylinder engraved Navy scene. Frame cut for s/stock (4 screw).

These guns, from the Colt line; are .44 caliber and, of course, all six shot. The cylinder was authentically roll engraved with a polished brass trigger guard and steel strap cut for shoulder stock. The frame, loading lever and hammer are finished in high luster color case hardening. Walnut grips complement the high quality craftsmanship metal work. ....**Price $100.00**

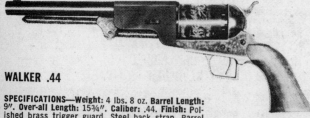

WALKER .44

SPECIFICATIONS—Weight: 4 lbs. 8 oz. **Barrel Length:** 9". **Over-all Length:** 15¾". **Caliber:** .44. **Finish:** Polished brass trigger guard. Steel back strap. Barrel marked "U.S. 1847". Round barrel, engraved cylinder scene.

A big powerful .44 caliber six-shot revolver weighing 4 lbs. 8 oz. The largest of all the Colt revolvers. Authentically reproduced. This is the famous gun developed with the help of Captain Sam Walker of the United States Mounted Rifles and saw extensive service in the Mexican War. ....**Price $125.00**
Engraved with gold bands at muzzle— **$250.00**

NAVY CALIBER POCKET MODEL
MODEL #1853

SPECIFICATIONS: Weight, 1 lb. 9 oz.; Barrel Length, 4½"; Overall Length, 9½"; Caliber, .36; Number of Shots, 5.
One of the rarer colt firearms, the Navy Caliber Pocket Model, made in .36 caliber so that they could employ the same conical balls used in the standard Navy Pistol. ....**Price $95.00**

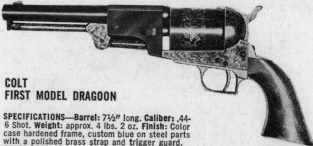

COLT FIRST MODEL DRAGOON

SPECIFICATIONS—Barrel: 7½" long. **Caliber:** .44- 6 Shot. **Weight:** approx. 4 lbs. 2 oz. **Finish:** Color case hardened frame, custom blue on steel parts with a polished brass strap and trigger guard.
First of the really big Colts, made basically as a military side arm for the Government with a cylinder engraving of a soldier and Indian fight scene. It retained the old cylinder locking slots and square back guard housing of its predecessors. The grip abuts the frame and guard squarely. ....**Price $100.00**
Engraved with gold bands at muzzle— **$250.00**

SECOND MODEL .44 DRAGOON

SPECIFICATIONS—Weight: 4 lbs. **Barrel Length:** 7½". **Over-all Length:** 14". **Caliber:** .44. **Finish:** Steel case hardened frame, Round barrel, hinged Navy type rammer.
The cylinder is fully roll engraved and finished in a deep, blue with contrasting color hardened frame and loading lever. The barrel is manufactured from precision rifled modern ordnance steel and each gun is proof fired and tested. ....**Price $100.00**
Engraved with gold bands at muzzle— **$250.00**

THIRD MODEL DRAGOON

SPECIFICATIONS—Barrel: 7½" long. **Caliber:** .44- 6 Shot. **Weight:** 4 lbs. 2 oz. **Finish:** Color case hardened frame and loading lever with contrasting custom blue on the remaining steel parts. Polished brass trigger guard.
Sam Colt's favorite, of the Dragoon models. The third model Dragoon varied from its predecessors by having provisions for a shoulder stock, and a three leaf sight. First Dragoon model that had a rounded trigger guard. ....**Price $125.00**
Engraved with gold bands at muzzle— **$250.00**
Matching Shoulder Stock— $50.00

NAVY ARMS REPLICAS

1848 WELLS FARGO
.31 Caliber
$95.00

The 1848 Wells Fargo replica is a 5-shot .31 caliber percussion pistol made in 3", 4", 5" and 6" barrel lengths. This model comes without a loading lever. Features include: etched cylinder scene; blue and case hardened finish.

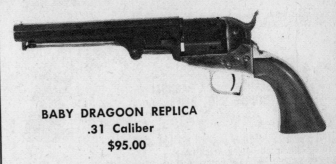

BABY DRAGOON REPLICA
.31 Caliber
$95.00

The 1848 Baby Dragoon Replica percussion pistol is made in .31 caliber with a choice of 4", 5" and 6" barrel lengths. The Baby Dragoon may be had with or without the loading lever. Features include etched cylinder scene, blue and case hardened finish.

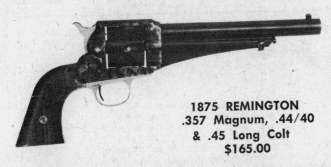

1875 REMINGTON
.357 Magnum, .44/40
& .45 Long Colt
$165.00

Replica Arms first cartridge gun—copy of the 1875 Remington that was used by the James boys and Butch Cassidy. Available in .357 Magnum, .44/40 and .45 Long Colt. Two-piece walnut, all blue, frame-case hardened, 7½" barrel.

SECOND MODEL DRAGOON REPLICA
.44 Caliber
$125.00

The .44 Dragoon is a 6-shot percussion pistol equipped with a 7½" barrel, and is a detailed replica of the second model Dragoon. It comes with a blue and case hardened finish.

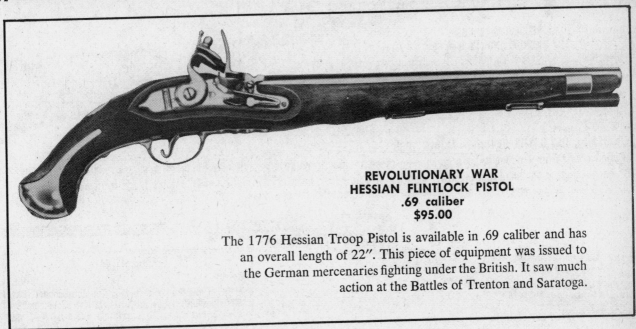

REVOLUTIONARY WAR
HESSIAN FLINTLOCK PISTOL
.69 caliber
$95.00

The 1776 Hessian Troop Pistol is available in .69 caliber and has an overall length of 22". This piece of equipment was issued to the German mercenaries fighting under the British. It saw much action at the Battles of Trenton and Saratoga.

NAVY ARMS REPLICAS

ROLLING BLOCK MAGNUM SINGLE SHOT PISTOL

This pistol is an exact copy of the famous Number Three Remington Rolling Block Pistol.
It has a precision rifled ordnance steel barrel in the traditional half round, half octagonal pattern, finished in a high luster custom blue. The authentically reproduced action is finished in a rich color-case hardening. The stocks are genuine walnut with a deep oil finish. Available in the popular .357 magnum caliber, each gun is handsomely cased with cleaning accessories. **Price $135.00.** Additional calibers available: .22LR, .22 magnum and Remington 5mm magnum.

SHERIFF'S MODEL

SPECIFICATIONS—Weight: 2 lbs. 7 oz. Barrel length: 5". Over-all length: 10½". Caliber: .36. Finish: Polished brass back strap and trigger guard. Engraved Navy scene. Case hardened frame, hammer and loading lever.

These shortened versions of the Navy Revolvers were favored by both sides of the law in the old west. With their reduced barrel length they are ideal for quick draw and as a personal protection weapon. .... **Price $100.00**

THIRD MODEL DRAGOON SHOULDER STOCKS

An interesting, practical accessory to enhance the value of your favorite Dragoon. Third Model Dragoon Shoulder Stocks are so authentically reproduced that they will fit all original, as well as replica Colts. Colt was the first to patent the detachable stock. An adjustable folding leaf sight also became standard equipment on this type of revolver. This beautifully rendered Shoulder Stock will enhance the value of any Dragoon replica or original. A revolver fitted with a Shoulder Stock automatically becomes the highlight of a collection. **Price $50.00**

REVOLVING CARBINES

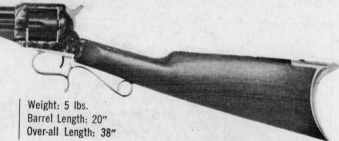

REVOLVING CARBINE
.357 MAGNUM AND .45 Long Colt

A Revolving Carbine Rifle based on the famous and popular Remington pattern. It features a precision rifled ordnance steel barrel complemented by color case hardened frame and a high polished brass trigger guard and butt plate complementing the richly grained walnut stock. This is an ideal lightweight brush gun for the average whitetail deer fan. It is available in .38 special and the popular .45 Long Colt $190.00

Weight: 5 lbs.
Barrel Length: 20"
Over-all Length: 38"

PERCUSSION REVOLVING CARBINE—MODEL 1865

An additional carbine model to be a companion piece to the Army Revolver. In matching .44 caliber available in 18" and 20" barrel lengths. Finished in a beautiful high luster blue with buckhorn rear sight and adjustable blade front sight. A beautiful, light, handy six-shot repeating carbine which affected the design stimulus of the automatic weapon. **Price $165.00**

SPECIFICATIONS:
Weight ....5 lbs.
Barrel length ....18 and 20"
Over-all length ....38"
Caliber 44
Finish: Walnut Stock, Brass Mounts, Solid Frame with Top Strap.

NAVY ARMS REPLICAS

Brown Bess Rifle

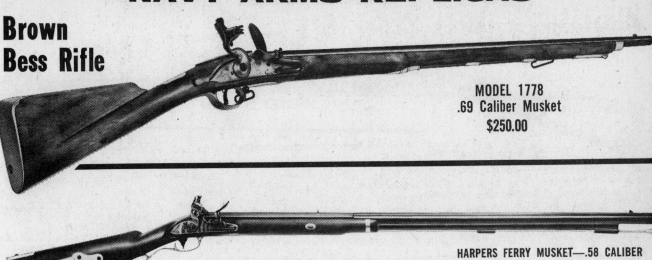

MODEL 1778
.69 Caliber Musket
$250.00

HARPERS FERRY MUSKET—.58 CALIBER

Navy Arms is now proud to offer the ever popular and most sought Harpers Ferry Musket. The most authentic replica rendition ever offered to the American shooter. Available in limited quantities. A historically significant weapon complete with precision rifled .58 caliber browned barrel with attractive highly polished brass furniture. $200.00

KENTUCKY PISTOLS

PERCUSSION

FLINTLOCK

The Kentucky Pistol is truly a historical American gun ... carried during the Revolution by the Minutemen ... the sidearm of "Andy" Jackson in the Battle of New Orleans. Now Navy Arms Company has gone through great research to manufacture a pistol truly representative of its kind and with the balance and handle of the original for which it became famous. Both models **$90.00**

Brass-barrel models ....**$25.00 extra**

SPECIFICATIONS—Weight: 2 lbs. **Barrel length:** 10⅛". **Over-all length:** 15½". **Caliber:** .44. **Finish:** Walnut stock, brass mounted, case hardened lock, blued barrel.

HARPER'S FERRY PISTOLS

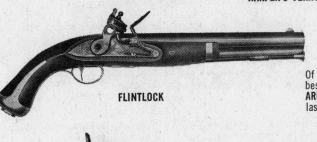

FLINTLOCK

HARPER'S FERRY

Weight: 2 lb. 9 oz. **Barrel length:** 10". **Over-all length:** 16". **Caliber:** 54 smoothbore. **Finish:** Walnut stock, case hardened lock, brass mounted browned barrel.

Of all the early American martial pistols, Harper's Ferry is one of the best known. They were carried by both the Army and the Navy. **NAVY ARMS COMPANY** has authentically reproduced the Harper's Ferry to the last minute detail. Well balanced and well made. $100.00

PERCUSSION

HARPER'S FERRY MODEL 1855 DRAGON PISTOL

Developed at Harpers Ferry Arsenal as a holster pistol for the U.S. mounted rifles, this pistol was later fitted with a shoulder stock and designated the Springfield Pistol Carbine Model 1855. In .58 cal., this pistol fires the standard 500 gr. minnie ball and is the most powerful pistol ever made. Issued in pairs and designed to be carried in saddle holsters ... a true horse pistol $100.00

Shoulder stock (not illus.) $25.00

NAVY ARMS REPLICAS
MISSISSIPPI—RIFLE Model 1841

NEW FROM NAVY ARMS—Model 1841 Mississippi Rifle —The historic percussion lock weapon that gained its name as a result of its performance in the hands of Jefferson Davis' Mississippi Regiment during the heroic stand at the Battle of Buena Vista. Also known as the "Yager" (a misspelling of the German **Jaeger**) this was the last rifle adopted by Army Ordnance to fire the traditional round ball. In .58 caliber, the Mississippi is handsomely furnished in brass including patch box for tools and spare parts. This rifle is an authentic addition to Navy Arms' growing line of historic replica arms. **Price $160.00**

SPECIFICATIONS:
Weight ....9½ lbs.
Barrel length ....32½"
Over-all length ....48½"
Caliber 58
Finish: Walnut Finish stock, Brass mounted,

DOUBLE BARREL MUZZLE LOADING SHOTGUNS

The gun is classic in design with the styling reminiscent of the early English & French doubles. It is a Rabbit Ear sidelock configuration with a forward locking pin holding the barrels. A lightweight, fast handling beauty with traditionally hand checkered wooden stock walnut in color, and browned barrels.

Careful attention has been paid to the most minute detail including a limited covering of delicate scroll graving. Weight of the gun is just about 6 lbs. and the barrels are choked in IC and MOD. **Price $150.00**

SPECIFICATIONS: Weight approx. 6¼ lbs. Length of barrels 30". Choking, Improved cylinder and modified. Length of pull, 14" Over-all-length, 45". Finish: Oil-finished, hand-rubbed walnut stock tastefully hand checkered. Barrels are browned with the remaining metal parts engraved with delicate scroll and polished.

Note: Above double also available in 12 ga. Magnum, Model 100 Mag. Fowler (not illus.) **$175.00**

BROWN BESS CARBINE: weighs 7¾ lbs. with a 30½" barrel. The overall length of the gun is 45-inches and is made in the original 70 caliber. (dia. .700) Standard Cherry stock **$325.00**
Walnut stock **$350.00**

BROWN BESS MUSKET: reproduced in the 42-inch New Land pattern. Each gun is hand-fitted and assembled; the locks are hand-engraved.
Standard Cherry stock **$325.00**
Walnut stock **$350.00**

THE ZOUAVE RIFLE, .58 Caliber: A .58 Caliber muzzle-loading rifle featuring a walnut colored stock, highly polished brass fittings, color case-hardened lock and blued full 33-inch rifled ordnance steel barrel. Weight, about 9½ lbs. **$150.00**

.58 CALIBER BUFFALO HUNTER: a percussion rifle designed to handle a .58 caliber 500 grain slug, it comes with a walnut colored wood stock, and features a color case-hardened lock and hammer. The barrel is precision rifled of ordnance steel **$160.00**

NAVY ARMS REPLICAS

HAWKEN

A Hawken Rifle designed for the hunter and serious target shooter. In the past, all Hawken-type rifles have relied on the round ball projectile . . . but now Navy Arms offers a Hawken designed to handle hollow base mini-type bullets. This is the most advanced muzzle loading rifle ever offered to the sportsman with match accuracy and a new positive magnum ignition system.

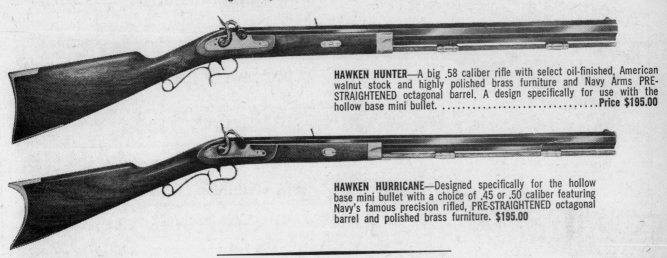

HAWKEN HUNTER—A big .58 caliber rifle with select oil-finished, American walnut stock and highly polished brass furniture and Navy Arms PRE-STRAIGHTENED octagonal barrel. A design specifically for use with the hollow base mini bullet. . . . . **Price $195.00**

HAWKEN HURRICANE—Designed specifically for the hollow base mini bullet with a choice of .45 or .50 caliber featuring Navy's famous precision rifled, PRE-STRAIGHTENED octagonal barrel and polished brass furniture. **$195.00**

BLUNDERBUSS

Model 1802

The history of the Blunderbuss started in Holland where the name came from the Dutch word for "thunder box." It spread to England where it was a popular defensive weapon carried by coachmen to protect against daring highwaymen. The Blunderbuss was also carried aboard ships of the British Navy exclusively for repelling boarders and was brought to America by early Colonial settlers. The Navy Arms Flintlock Blunderbuss, reminiscent of the Queen Anne period, has a beautifully turned barrel with a cannon motif and is made of highly polished brass. The trigger guard, side plate and butt plate are engraved. **Priced at $125.00**

SPECIFICATIONS:
Solid brass, smooth bore.
Barrel . . . . 15¼" long
Weight . . . . . . approx. 6 lbs. 3½ oz.
Finish: Polished brass barrel, trigger guard and butt plate. Hand-rubbed stock with all remaining metal parts polished to a high luster.
Over-all Length . . . . .30"

REMINGTON ROLLING BLOCK
BUFFALO RIFLE & CARBINE
.45/70 AND .444 MARLIN CALIBER

Navy Arms is proud to introduce the creation of the famous Remington Rolling Block Action. Authentically reproduced in modern steels to the very finest detail. Each rifle is barreled with a famous octagonal Numrich Arms Corp. barrel featuring the famous hook rifling which is a process that every groove is singularly cut. The actions are case hardened complemented by a solid highly polished brass trigger guard and walnut colored stock. There are four models available. A Standard model with a full-length octagonal barrel for both rifle and carbine, a Creedmoor model which features half-round, half-octagonal barrel in both rifle and carbine model. All four models are available in .45/70 or a new heavy .444/Marlin caliber . . . . $160.00 Creedmoor Model (not illus.) $185.00

MORSE

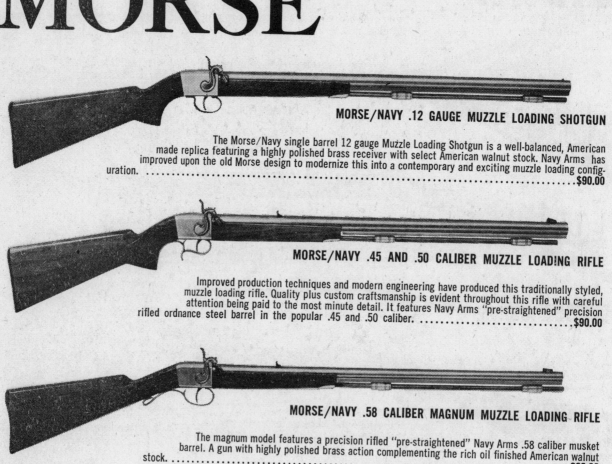

MORSE/NAVY .12 GAUGE MUZZLE LOADING SHOTGUN

The Morse/Navy single barrel 12 gauge Muzzle Loading Shotgun is a well-balanced, American made replica featuring a highly polished brass receiver with select American walnut stock. Navy Arms has improved upon the old Morse design to modernize this into a contemporary and exciting muzzle loading configuration. $90.00

MORSE/NAVY .45 AND .50 CALIBER MUZZLE LOADING RIFLE

Improved production techniques and modern engineering have produced this traditionally styled, muzzle loading rifle. Quality plus custom craftsmanship is evident throughout this rifle with careful attention being paid to the most minute detail. It features Navy Arms "pre-straightened" precision rifled ordnance steel barrel in the popular .45 and .50 caliber. $90.00

MORSE/NAVY .58 CALIBER MAGNUM MUZZLE LOADING RIFLE

The magnum model features a precision rifled "pre-straightened" Navy Arms .58 caliber musket barrel. A gun with highly polished brass action complementing the rich oil finished American walnut stock. $90.00

1863 SPRINGFIELD

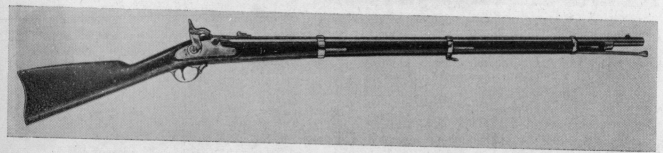

Navy Arms addition of this authentically reproduced replica of one of America's most historical firearms. The 1863 Springfield Rifle was the last muzzle loading rifle issued to the U.S. Army . . . although a great controversey arose as to whether the Rifle .58 Caliber was more efficient than the earlier smooth bores, it soon became a favorite as the stabilizer of the dreaded minnie ball. Navy Arms has carefully reproduced this famous historical rifle down to the last minute detail. A full size three-band musket with a precision rifled barrel in .58 caliber, identical to the original in every way. $200.00

RUGER BLACKPOWDER REVOLVER

OLD ARMY

Ruger Old Army cap and ball revolver. .44 caliber, 7½ in. barrel, 46 ounces, American Walnut grips, adjustable rear sight, stainless steel nipples. Made to same best quality standard as the Ruger cartridge revolvers.
Note: Use with lead ball or conical bullet of .457 diameter.

—Old Army **$125.00**
—Old Army with solid brass, Dragon style, grip frame and wide trigger **$140.00**

SPECIFICATIONS of the OLD ARMY

Frame, Cylinder, and other **Working Components** are of heat treated chromemoly steel.
Caliber: .44. Bore .443 in., groove .451 in.
Weight: 2 pounds 14 ounces (46 ounces).
Barrel: 7½ in. Six grooves, right twist, 1 in 16 in.
Sights: Target rear (adjustable for elevation and windage) and ramp front.
Nipples: Stainless steel for standard caps.
Grips: American Walnut.
Finish: Polished all over and blued and anodized.
The Lockwork is the same as that in the original Ruger Super Blackhawk. All
  Springs are coil, made from the highest quality steel music wire.

10-RING PRECISION PISTOLS

DUELLER
.45 caliber flintlock
$175.00

RIVAL
.45 caliber percussion
$144.50

Flintlock and percussion models equipped with custom barrels with one-in-twenty twist. Equipped with fully adjustable target sights. Caliber .45 (.440 ball). Trigger is adjustable for length and weight of pull and engagement. Each pistol is supplied with a Lee precision bullet mould, complete with handles ramrod, tools, patches and lube.
.45 Dueller (flintlock) $175.00
.45 Rival (percussion) $144.50

THOMPSON/CENTER

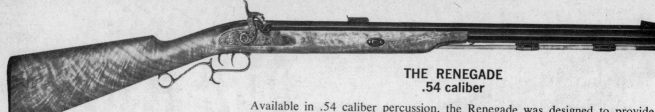

THE RENEGADE
.54 caliber

Available in .54 caliber percussion, the Renegade was designed to provide maximum accuracy and maximum shocking power. Constructed from superior modern steel with investment cast parts carefully fitted to an American walnut stock, the rifle features a precision-rifled (26″ carbine-type) octagon barrel, hooked-breech system, coil spring lock, double-set triggers, adjustable hunting sights and steel trim.
Renegade .54 caliber Caplock $165.00

THE HAWKEN
.45 & .50 caliber

Similar to the famous Rocky Mountain rifles made during the early eighteen hundreds, the Hawken is intended for serious shooting. Button-rifled for ultimate precision, the Hawken is available in .45 or .50 caliber, flint or percussion. Featuring a hooked breech, double-set triggers, first-grade American walnut, adjustable hunting sights, solid-brass trim, beautifully decorated and color case-hardened lock.
Hawken .45 or .50 caliber Caplock $205.00
Hawken .45 or .50 caliber Flintlock $215.00

THE SENECA
.36 & .45 caliber

Available in either .36 or .45 caliber percussion, the Seneca rifle is patterned on the style of an early New England hunting rifle. Six pounds light, this graceful little half-stock features a hooked breech, double-set triggers, first-grade American walnut, adjustable hunting sights, solid-brass trim, coil mainspring and finely patterned color case-hardened lock.
Seneca .36 or .45 caliber Caplock $205.00

THE PATRIOT
.45 caliber

Featuring a hooked breech, double-set triggers, first-grade American walnut stock, adjustable (patridge-type) target sights, solid-brass trim, beautifully decorated and color case-hardened lock with a small dolphin-shaped hammer, the Patriot weighs approximately 36 ounces. Inspired by traditional gallery and dueling-type pistols, its carefully selected features retain the full flavor of antiquity, yet modern metals and manufacturing methods have been used to ensure its shooting qualities.
Patriot Pistol .45 caliber $125.00

Air Guns

BENJAMIN AIR & GAS GUNS

MODELS 3100-3120: Benjamin Super Repeater Air Rifles with Monte Carlo stock. Cal. BB or .22 . . **$56.00**

MODELS NO. 340, 342, 347: Benjamin Super Single Shot Air Rifle with Monte Carlo stock. Cal BB or .177 or .22 has new rugged square top ramp-type front sight **$54.80**

MODEL 3030: BB Carbine Repeater CO_2 Gas Operated with regular stock.
Price **$31.15**

No. 273 Detachable Rear Peep
Sight. Adjustable. For Models 340 - 342 - 347 - 310 - 312 - 317 - 720 - BENJAMIN AIR RIFLES. Advise Model.
Each $3.90
Extra Discs. Small, Medium, Large. Each. $1.95

BAR-O Detachable Rear Peep
Sight. Adjustable. For all Models Benjamin Rifles with BAR-V Sight. Advise Model.
Each $1.70

Extra Discs. Small, Medium, Large. Each. . . . . $ .85

Benjamin BAR-V Rear
Sight. It Rotates! Provides Quick, Sensitive Adjustment of Elevation and Windage. Each. $1.70

BENJAMIN H-C LEAD PELLETS
"Sized and Lubricated"

	Per Can
Benjamin H-C Lead Pellets Cal. .177 (250)	**$1.10**
Benjamin H-C Lead Pellets Cal. .177 (500)	**$2.00**
Benjamin H-C Lead Pellets Cal. .22 (250)	**$1.35**
Benjamin H-C Lead Pellets Cal. .22 (500)	**$2.50**

BENJAMIN ROUND BALL SHOT

Benjamin Steel Air Rifle Shot—BB 500	**$ .75**
Benjamin Steel Air Rifle Shot—BB 1 lb.	**$1.55**
Benjamin Lead Air Rifle Shot—BB 500	**$1.95**
Benjamin Lead Air Rifle Shot—BB—4.5 mm	
1 lb.	**$3.00**
Benjamin Round Lead Shot—Cal. .22—5.5 mm.	
1 lb.	**$3.00**

MODELS 130, 132, 137 Single Shot Air Pistol Cal. BB or .177 or .22 $48.05

STANDARD SIZE JET KING CO_2 CARTRIDGE

For use in Benjamin Super Gas Rifles and Pistols. 10 in a box. . $2.13
Size 2⅝" x 47/64". 8.5 Gram.

BSA AIR RIFLE

BSA METEOR
Calibers: .177 & .22
$44.95

Designed for small game hunting and indoor plinking, the Ithaca-BSA Air rifles are offered in .177 or .22 calibers with a dovetail receiver to accommodate any standard scope.

The two models available are the Meteor (illustrated above) and the Mercury (not illustrated). Both models carry an adjustable single stage trigger, fully adjustable sights for windage and elevation and cold-formed carbon steel barrels. The Mercury comes with a Monte Carlo cheekpiece and rubber recoil pad. It is intended for use up to 50-60 yards. It weighs 7 lb. and comes complete with pellets, targets, target holders and lubricant.

The Meteor is smaller, weighing 6 lb. and has a normal effective range up to 40-50 yards. Both models feature handsanded stocks and a durable melamine acrylic lacquer finish.

Meteor $49.95
Mercury $89.95

CROSMAN AIR & GAS PISTOLS

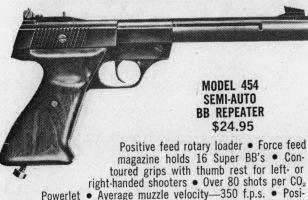

MODEL 454
SEMI-AUTO
BB REPEATER
$24.95

Positive feed rotary loader • Force feed magazine holds 16 Super BB's • Contoured grips with thumb rest for left- or right-handed shooters • Over 80 shots per CO_2 Powerlet • Average muzzle velocity—350 f.p.s. • Positive slide-action safety • Rear sights adjustable for windage and elevation • Barrel length—7¾" • Overall length—11"; • Weight —30 Oz.

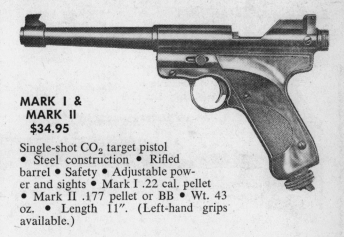

MARK I &
MARK II
$34.95

Single-shot CO_2 target pistol • Steel construction • Rifled barrel • Safety • Adjustable power and sights • Mark I .22 cal. pellet • Mark II .177 pellet or BB • Wt. 43 oz. • Length 11". (Left-hand grips available.)

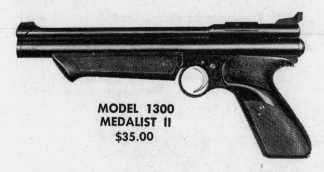

MODEL 1300
MEDALIST II
$35.00

A .22 cal. pump pistol • Heavy-duty pump link with sure-grip checkered forearm • Fully adjustable sights • Brass-plated trigger • Cross-bolt safety • Selective pump power • Button-rifled steel barrel • Gun-blued steel parts • Matching barrel spacer • Weight 32 oz., length 11¾".

MODEL 38-T
ILLUSTRATED
$44.95

MODEL 38-C: Combat. CO_2 .22 Pellet Revolver. Holds six .22 caliber Pells. Single and Double action and revolving cylinder. Length 8½". Weight 3½ ozs. 10 lands R.H. twist. 4" barrel. **$44.95**

MODEL 38-T: CO_2 .22 Pellet Revolver. For Target shooting. Length 11". Weight 42 ozs. Rifling: 10 lands R.H. twist, 1 turn in 16", button rifled. 6" barrel. **$44.95**

CROSMAN AIR & GAS RIFLES

the 761 Powermaster XL

The 761 XL . . . the great Features
of the Powermaster, plus a Flair of elegance and ruggedness

- Full-size, hand-rubbed walnut-finished, contoured hard-wood stock and forearm
- Gold-finished receiver for added elegance and greater durability
- Button-rifled, heavy duty solid steel barrel
- Improved, adjustable rear sight for pinpoint accuracy
- Hooded front sight
- Receiver grooved for scope

- Solid steel trigger
- Reservoir holds over 180 Super BB's
- Also shoots .177 cal. Super Pells®
- Cross-bolt safety
- Butt-plate
- Improved bolt for better action
- Barrel length 19" O/A length 36" Weight 4¾#
- Price without scope $39.95

MODEL M-1: BB Air Repeater Carbine. Length 35½". Weight 4 lbs., 4 oz. Magazine holds 22 BB's. Clip Stores 180 BB's $26.95

Scope & Mount optional

MODEL 622 Pump Action: Removable pell clip holds 6 .22 caliber Super Pells. Grooved receiver for scope. Wood stock and forearm. Adjustable rear sight for windage and elevation. Positive cross-bolt safety. Barrel length 23"; overall length 40"; 6½ lbs. $44.95

Scope & Mount optional

MODEL 760: 180 shot BB repeater, pump action. Shoots .177 or BB Caliber. BB's from storage chamber are metered into visual loading magazine. **$30.95**

Scope & Mount optional

MODEL 1400: Air Powered Pellgun Rifle, Single Shot. .22 Caliber pump gun. Tru-Flyte button rifled barrel, self cocking mechanism. Length 35". Weight 5 lbs., 2 ozs. $45.95

CROSMAN RIFLES & ACCESSORIES

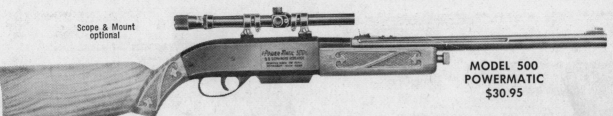

Scope & Mount optional

MODEL 500
POWERMATIC
$30.95

50 shot semi-auto BB repeater. Positive continuous feed. Quick positive safety. Grooved receiver for scope and peep sight. Adjustable sights. Solid zinc receiver and steel construction. "0" ring-free valve design. Over 100 uniform shots per Powerlet. Weight 4 lbs., length 37¾". No. 410 scope & mount optional.

MODEL 70
BOLT-ACTION
$49.95

The Model 70 features a rifled steel barrel and hand-rubbed hardwood stock. .177 caliber pellet, CO_2 powered. Velocity 600 ft. per sec. 40 shots per CO_2 Powerlet. Length 41". Weight 5¾ lb. Open sights, fully adjustable. Cross-bolt safety. Cam action piercing assembly.

CROSMAN SUPER BB's

- Perfect-round, copper-plated steel shot.
- Top accuracy.

Model 225—5 oz. pack; over 350 BB's ...... $ .50
Model 727-10 oz. pack; over 750 BB's .... .75
Model 737-20 oz. pack; over 1500 BB's $1.20
Model 747-6 lbs. 4 oz. pack; over 8,000 BB's ..$4.55

CROSMAN POWERLETS

CO_2 cartridges with Perma-Lok caps assure positive seal, and are clean piercing. Zinc-chromium plating, no rust, scale or grease. Box of 5-Model 321/5. 8.5 grams; box of 5 (for all other guns other than Crosman) Model 238/5.

DAISY AIR GUNS

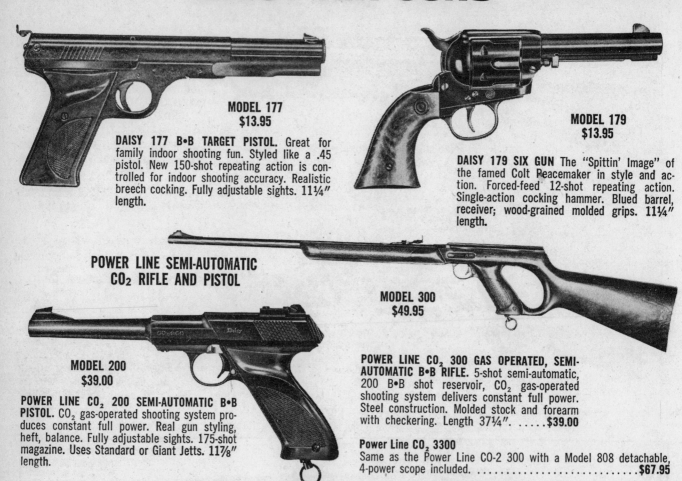

MODEL 177
$13.95

DAISY 177 B•B TARGET PISTOL. Great for family indoor shooting fun. Styled like a .45 pistol. New 150-shot repeating action is controlled for indoor shooting accuracy. Realistic breech cocking. Fully adjustable sights. 11¼" length.

MODEL 179
$13.95

DAISY 179 SIX GUN The "Spittin' Image" of the famed Colt Peacemaker in style and action. Forced-feed 12-shot repeating action. Single-action cocking hammer. Blued barrel, receiver; wood-grained molded grips. 11¼" length.

POWER LINE SEMI-AUTOMATIC CO₂ RIFLE AND PISTOL

MODEL 300
$49.95

MODEL 200
$39.00

POWER LINE CO₂ 200 SEMI-AUTOMATIC B•B PISTOL. CO₂ gas-operated shooting system produces constant full power. Real gun styling, heft, balance. Fully adjustable sights. 175-shot magazine. Uses Standard or Giant Jetts. 11⅞" length.

POWER LINE CO₂ 300 GAS OPERATED, SEMI-AUTOMATIC B•B RIFLE. 5-shot semi-automatic, 200 B•B shot reservoir, CO₂ gas-operated shooting system delivers constant full power. Steel construction. Molded stock and forearm with checkering. Length 37¼". **$39.00**

Power Line CO₂ 3300
Same as the Power Line CO-2 300 with a Model 808 detachable, 4-power scope included. **$67.95**

POWER LINE MODEL 62
TARGET AIR PISTOL
$59.95

POWER LINE TARGET AIR PISTOL
• **MODEL 62:** right-hand grips. • **MODEL 162:** left-hand grips. Latest entry in a high velocity, advanced design target pistol. Long under lever makes cocking easy. Fixed barrel for accuracy. Boxed. **GRIPS:** Contoured, articulated, adjustable to any shooting position. **BARREL:** Rifled, 12 grooves, right-hand twist; fixed for highest accuracy. **ACTION:** Under lever. **SIGHTS:** Hooded ramp front; 2-way adjustable rear. **CALIBER:** .177, pellet, single shot, hinged side-breech loading. **VELOCITY:** 390 feet per second. **WEIGHT:** 2 pounds, 14 ounces. **OVERALL LENGTH:** 14⅞ inches. **$59.95**

DAISY AIR GUNS

DAISY MODEL 104 GOLDEN EAGLE
$16.00

DAISY MODEL 104 GOLDEN EAGLE. Perfect for B●B shooting indoors or out. Detachable, sturdy steel, peep sight "scope." Automatic safety. 350-shot repeating action. Molded stock and forearm. Sturdy steel, lever, receiver section and barrel with simulated gold finish: Length: 30½".

DAISY MODEL 102
$13.75

DAISY 102 CUB. Full sturdy seasoned wood stock. "Big gun" features include lever cocking, gravity-feed 350-shot repeating action, controlled velocity and realistic styling. Sturdy steel construction. Length, 30¼".

DAISY MODEL 98 MONTE CARLO
$27.00

DAISY MODEL 98 MONTE CARLO. New, sporter-style B●B rifle, with unique, extra-strength, structural molded stock and forearm. With true, solid-gun feel. Fully contoured, Monte Carlo stock with cheek piece, checkered beavertail forearm. Lever cocking; gravity feed, 700-shot repeating action. Automatic trigger-block safety. Length: 36".

DAISY MODEL 453
$33.95

DAISY MODEL 453 PELLET RIFLE. Selected as an official competition pellet rifle by NRA. With rifled barrel, .177 caliber. Specially designed removable Rota-Clip pellet cylinder. Lever action. Monte Carlo hardwood stock and forearm. Rear peep sight and hooded front sight with four inserts. Length. 37".

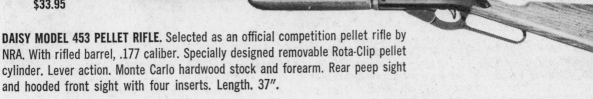

POWER LINE MODEL 770

$34.95

POWER LINE 770. A high velocity, spring-action B●B gun for exceedingly low-cost sport shooting. It has a single-stroke cocking system that takes the effort out of shooting, an automatic trigger-block safety which engages during cocking, a smoothbore steel barrel, and a 200-shot gravity feed reservoir. The stock and forearm are fully contoured, super-strength molded plastic with Monte Carlo styling and checkered forearm and grip. Overall length: 39⅛ inches; Weight: 4 pounds.
$34.95

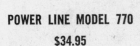

DAISY AIR GUNS

POWER LINE MODEL 1770
$56.95

POWER LINE MODEL 1770.
Same as the Power Line Model 770 with a Model 808 detachable, 4-power scope included. $56.95

POWER LINE MODEL 880 PUMP-UP
B·B REPEATER & SINGLE SHOT PELLET

$43.95

POWER LINE MODEL 880 PUMP-UP B·B REPEATER AND SINGLE SHOT PELLET GUN IN ONE. Great for shooters 14 and over. Pneumatic pump-up for variable power (velocity and range) increasing with pump strokes. Only 10 strokes required for maximum power. 100-shot capacity B·B magazine. Single-shot .177 caliber pellets. Ramp front and open rear sights. Scope mount. Monte Carlo design, molded stock with cheek piece and molded fore-arm. Cross bolt safety with red indicator and positive cocking valve safety prevents hang-fires. Length: 37¾".

POWER LINE MODEL 1880 PUMP-UP
B·B REPEATER & SINGLE SHOT PELLET
$61.00

Power Line Model 1880 Pump-Up B·B Repeater and Single Shot Pellet Gun in One.
Same as Model 880 with Daisy Model 808 4x scope which is adjustable for windage and elevation. Cross hair reticle. Sure and easy pump action rapidly achieves maximum velocity and range limits with 10 quick strokes. Custom gun design loaded with quality extras sport shooters want: pump handle is easy to grasp and operate; man-size; perfectly weighted and balanced for shooting comfort; constant trigger pull through entire pumping range; longer sights radius makes for greater accuracy.

POWER-LINE
MODEL 881
$57.95

POWER LINE MODEL 881 PNEUMATIC PUMP-UP AIR GUN. Burnished receiver. Molded Monte Carlo stock with cheek piece and white spacer before the butt plate and grip cap. Checkered, molded forearm. It's a B·B repeater and a single-shot pellet gun in one. With pneumatic pump-up for variable power (velocity and range) increasing with pump strokes. Only 10 strokes for maximum power. Shoots .177 caliber pellets. 100 B·B shot capacity magazine. Ramp front sight and open rear sight. Cross bolt trigger safety with red indicator and positive cocking valve. Length: 37¾".

DAISY AIR GUNS

POWER LINE MODEL 1881
$68.95

POWER LINE MODEL 1881 PNEUMATIC PUMP-UP AIR GUN CRAFTED BY DAISY. Same as Power Line Model 881 with Model 808 detachable, 4-power scope. **$68.95**

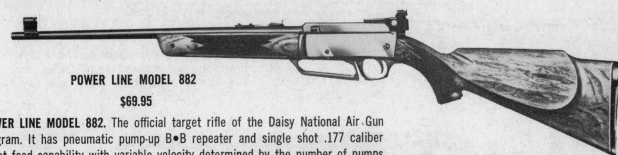

POWER LINE MODEL 882
$69.95

POWER LINE MODEL 882. The official target rifle of the Daisy National Air Gun Program. It has pneumatic pump-up B•B repeater and single shot .177 caliber pellet feed capability with variable velocity determined by the number of pumps from 1 to 10. The decagon-rifled barrel and super-strength molded stock and forearm with checkering give the Model 882 real gun looks, feel, and performance. An exclusively designed Power Line receiver sight by Williams has positive locking internal micrometer adjustments for maximum shooting accuracy. Overall length: 37¾ inches, Weight: 4½ pounds. $69.95

DAISY—FWB PRECISION AIR GUNS

DAISY/FWB MODEL 4301
$350.00

Air rifle of the champions, with improved, shorter side-cocking lever requires less cocking effort; new, improved line of sight has become lower and longer; new, improved trigger design with 4 adjustments. Single shot, .177 caliber; patented recoil eliminator. Length, 45"; weight, 14 pounds. Choice walnut stock.

DAISY/FWB MODEL 65
$250.00

DAISY/FWB MODEL 65 MATCH AIR PISTOL. Single shot, .177 caliber, with patented recoil eliminator. Shroud front sight, with blade; rear open iron sight. Side lever cocking action. 16" length.

Both DAISY/FWB 4301 and 65 Available in Right- and Left-Hand Models

DAISY AIR GUNS

DAISY MODEL 99
$30.95

DAISY 99 TARGET SPECIAL. Approved for NRA, Jaycee, Scout, 4-H training programs. **Full seasoned wood Monte Carlo stock, modified forearm.** Target features include controlled velocity, forced-feed 50-shot action, hooded front sight with 4 inserts, deluxe rear peep sight. New army sling. Special stock medallion. Length 36¼".

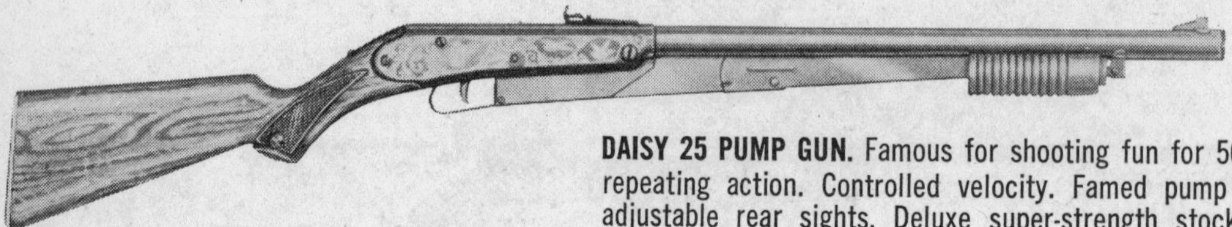

DAISY MODEL 25
$25.95

DAISY 25 PUMP GUN. Famous for shooting fun for 50 years. Forced-feed 50-shot repeating action. Controlled velocity. Famed pump cocking. Ramp front, fully adjustable rear sights. Deluxe super-strength stock. Takes down for storage, carrying. Length 37¼".

DAISY MODEL 95
$19.95

DAISY 95 WOODSTOCK. Modern sporter style with real gun heft and feel. **Full Seasoned wood stock,** sporter forearm. Gravity-feed 700-shot repeating action. Controlled velocity. Ramp front, adjustable "V" slot rear sights. Length 35".

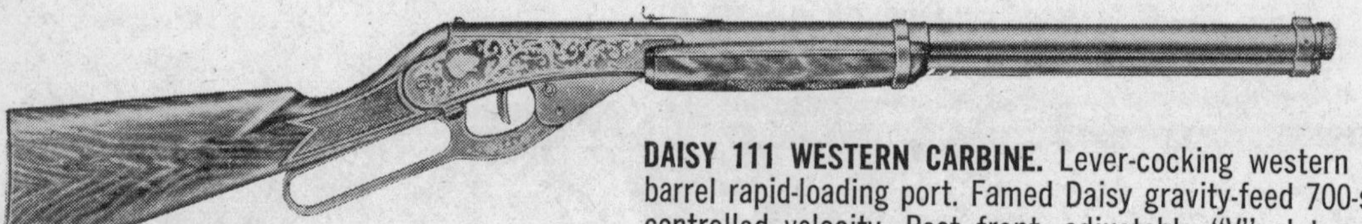

DAISY MODEL 111
$18.95

DAISY 111 WESTERN CARBINE. Lever-cocking western carbine style with under-barrel rapid-loading port. Famed Daisy gravity-feed 700-shot repeating action with controlled velocity. Post front, adjustable "V" slot rear sights. Simulated gold receiver engraving. Length 35".

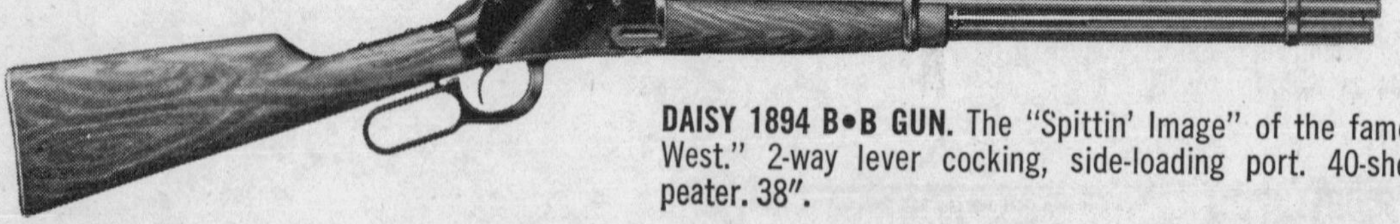

DAISY MODEL 1894
$30.00

DAISY 1894 B•B GUN. The "Spittin' Image" of the famed "carbine that won the West." 2-way lever cocking, side-loading port. 40-shot controlled-velocity repeater. 38".

DAISY MODEL 5994
$34.00

DAISY MODEL 5994 WELLS FARGO COMMEMORATIVE B•B CARBINE. Another successful entry in Daisy's commemorative gun series. With antiqued gun metal receiver with bold, Wells Fargo design and metallic-look agent's star on stock. Two-way cocking lever, side loading port, 40-B•B shot repeater. Post ramp front sight; adjustable open rear sight. Length: 38⅜".

DAISY AIR GUNS

Daisy 86/70
SAFARI MARK I B•B RIFLE . . . $19.95

This Daisy Safari Mark I B•B gun captures the look and feel of the classic big-game rifle, with **trigger guard** cocking, a cross-bolt safety, plus "high-powered" features like a tapered barrel and ramp front sight. It's 34½" long, with a 240-shot magazine, and thanks to Daisy controlled velocity, you can even shoot indoors. All you need are 15 feet of space, a box filled with wadded newspaper to hold the target and an old blanket as a backstop.

DAISY MODEL 7938
RED RYDER COMMEMORATIVE
$24.95

DAISY MODEL 7938 RED RYDER COMMEMORATIVE. The B•B gun Dads remember. Wood stock burned with Red Ryder lariat signature, wood forearm, saddle ring with leather thong. Lever cocking, 700-shot repeating action. Post front, adjustable V-slot, rear sights. Length: 35".

DAISY MODEL 7454
PELLET RIFLE
$34.95

DAISY MODEL 7454 PELLET RIFLE. Gutsy, sport-rated model with a rifled barrel and a true, solid-gun feel. Shoots .177 caliber pellets. Five-shot repeater with specially designed, removable Rota-Clip pellet cylinder. Structural molded, checkered Monte Carlo stock and checkered beaver-tail forearm.

Lever action. Post ramp front sight; adjustable open rear sight. Automatic trigger-block safety. Length: 37".

DAISY MODEL 7404
PELLET RIFLE
$23.00

DAISY MODEL 7404 PELLET RIFLE. Featherweight version with a smooth-bore. Shoots .177 caliber pellets. Five-shot repeater with specially designed, removable Rota-Clip pellet cylinder. Monte Carlo hardwood stock and forearm. Lever

action. Post ramp front sight; step-adjusting rear sight. Automatic trigger block safety. Length: 35½".

HY-SCORE

TARGET AIR PISTOL—MODEL 815T . . .
standard recoil model . . . .177 or .22 caliber

This pistol features unusual target grip design which will help even the beginning shooter improve his accuracy. Its penetrating power comes from simple one-break loading. Match trigger is fully adjustable. The 4-way rear sight has micro-click adjustment for windage and elevation combined with hooded target front sight. **Barrel length 7″; overall length 15¾″; muzzle velocity—.177 caliber: 405 f.p.s.; weight 48 oz.** **$49.95**

TARGET AIR PISTOL—MODEL 816M . . . recoilless match model . . . accurized . . . .177 caliber
Fully recoilless target air pistol designed for the most discriminating pistol shooter. It has the balance and feel of a real precision target firearm. The match trigger is fully adjustable to satisfy the shooter's personal requirements. The accurizing greatly increases the weapon's capability to shoot with pinpoint accuracy. Rear sight has 4 adjustable click sights. The shooter is urged to use HY-SCORE No. 215 wadcutter pellets. Barrel length 7″; overall length 16″; muzzle velocity 400 f.p.s.; weight 50 oz.
Price **$79.95**

HY-SCORE

TARGET AIR PISTOL—MODEL 822T . . . standard .177 or .22 caliber

Features real, gun type, checkered target grip with thumb rest for perfect balance. Power comes from instantaneous spring action. Adjustable match type trigger. Front and rear sights are fully adjustable for accurate shooting. **Precision rifled barrel—length 5⅞″; overall length 12⅜″; weight 43 ozs.** **$34.95**

HY-SCORE

BOYS PELLET PISTOL—MODEL 814 . . .
shoots .177 caliber pellets and darts

A genuine air pistol with a real gun look. Ideal for training the beginning shooter. Simple to operate, it features a unique firing system. Beautifully gift boxed with instructions. **Overall length 10″; weight 13 oz.** **$7.95**

HY-SCORE

POWERFUL MATCH AIR PISTOL—MODEL 817M . . .
Western genuine walnut handle . . . .177 caliber

The grip of this air pistol is correctly shaped for the American target shooter. It has excellent balance and the feel of a genuine match target pistol. The high muzzle velocity of 472 f.p.s. with No. 215 HY-SCORE match wadcutter pellets gives superior accuracy. Model 817M is the hardest hitting of all HY-SCORE air pistols. Furnished with 100 wadcutter pellets and cleaning rod in gift storage box. **Barrel length 7 ″; overall length 15″; sighting radius 14″; weight 50 oz.** **$49.95**

HY-SCORE

HAMMERLI—HY-SCORE MODEL 824M . . . CO2 . . .
Master model . . . .177 caliber

HAMMERLI of Switzerland—a name well-known among the world's leading target pistol shooters. Engineers of this famous factory have designed the Master model—a gun capable of shooting high scores and real tight groups. The weight of the barrel and the lead insert in the handle can be increased. The sights may be changed to suit the individual shooter's need. The regulation match hair trigger has 3-way adjustment. The CO_2 gas is retained by a diamond polished steel ball-bearing. 60 to 70 excellent shots can be obtained from a CO_2 cartridge. When the pressure drops to minimum level, an automatic valve opens thus preventing the loss of accuracy. This weapon comes complete in a handsome, fitted carrying case containing 100 No. 215 wadcutter pellets, CO_2 cartridge, brass cleaning rod, illustrated data booklet and test target. **Barrel length 6″; overall length 13-3/32″; sighting radius adjustable from 11-3/32″ to 13-1/32″; weight 43 oz.** **$74.95**

HY-SCORE

HAMMERLI—HY-SCORE MODEL 823M . . . CO2 . . .
Single model . . . .177 caliber

Same as Model 824M—Master model—but shorter barrel, and without automatic gas release mechanism. In fitted carrying case, with accesories same as for Master model. **Barrel length 4½″; overall length 12″; sighting radius 6″; weight 36 oz.** **$69.95**

HY-SCORE

CARBINE MODEL 808 . . . for .177 caliber pellets, darts and BB. "THREE GUNS IN ONE"

Shoots pellets, darts and BB's. By employing modern jet-age production techniques, HY-SCORE can now offer this "triple threat" quality air gun with power and accuracy. **Barrel length 12"; overall length 33"; weight 3 lbs.; .177 caliber; muzzle velocity 385 f.p.s. $17.95**

HY-SCORE

STANDARD MODEL 805 . . . for .177 caliber pellets, darts and BB. "THREE GUNS IN ONE"

This handsome junior model is furnished with full stock—see illustration. It has the same shooting capabilities, length, weight and velocity as Model 808, above. **$26.95**

HY-SCORE

LONG RANGE MODEL 806 . . . .177 caliber

Built with all the famous HY-SCORE power and quality features. A powerful, accurate, man-sized rifle with handsome walnut-finished wood stock of classic lines. Will transmit pride of ownership. **Barrel rifled; length 14½"; overall length 36½"; weight 3¾ lbs.; .177 caliber; range 110 ft.; muzzle velocity 496 f.p.s.**
Price **$34.95**

HY-SCORE

MARK I—MODEL 813 . . . .177 or .22 caliber

Increased velocity combines with rifled steel barrel and ramp front sight to bring to the shooter pleasure and fun. Handsome walnut-finished wood stock . . . a deluxe custom feature exclusive with HY-SCORE. **Barrel rifled; length 14½; overall length 36½"; weight 4 lbs.; muzzle velocity—.177 caliber models: 425 f.p.s.; range 125 ft. with genuine HY-SCORE pellets. $39.95**

HY-SCORE

CHAMPION MODEL 801 . . . .177 or .22 caliber

A big, powerful, handsomely stocked airgun with true rifle feel. The precision rifled barrel has hooded front sight. Powerful and accurate enough to command respect. Will accept riflescopes. **Barrel rifled; length 15¾"; overall length 39"; weight 5½ lbs.; muzzle velocity— .177 caliber model: 572 f.p.s.; range 175 ft. with genuine HY-SCORE pellets. $59.95**

HY-SCORE

MARK III—MODEL 870 . . . .177 caliber

This model, with a longer barrel, is designed for target training. It is a break-loading system with a locking device, coupling the barrel and housing solidly together. Walnut colored stock with checkered pistol grip. Advanced trigger mechanism is locked when barrel is opened. Not illustrated. **Barrel rifled; length 18"; overall length 42½"; weight 5½ lbs.; .177 caliber; muzzle velocity 525 f.p.s.**
Price. **$37.95**

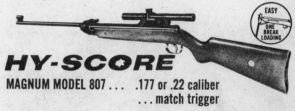

HY-SCORE

MAGNUM MODEL 807 . . . .177 or .22 caliber . . . match trigger

In caliber .177, suitable for target work; in caliber .22, for pest control. Built-in super-silent power is instantly yours. Maximum power obtained with trouble-free, one break loading. Simply break barrel, load, and fire like expensive over and under shotguns. Accepts any standard riflescope. **Barrel rifled; length 17⅜"; overall length 42"; weight 6 lbs.; muzzle velocity—.177 caliber model: 690 f.p.s.; range 185 ft. $69.95**

HY-SCORE

MARK V—MODEL 809 . . . .177 or .22 caliber . . . the most powerful

Ideal choice for target work or pest control. Regular firearm-size stock has rubber butt and checkered pistol grip. Match trigger and hooded 4 aperture front sight. Accepts riflescopes. Model 809 is also available as a target gun, with added target sight . . . see description of Model 809M. **Barrel rifled; length 19"; overall length 44"; weight 7 lbs.; muzzle velocity—.177 caliber model: 725 f.p.s.; range 200 ft. with genuine HY-SCORE Pellets. $79.95**

HY-SCORE
LEVER ACTION AIR RIFLE—MODEL 821 . . .
standard . . . .177 or .22 caliber

HY-SCORE'S lowest-priced, high power, lever action model. Easy lever action, with one movement, delivers 775 f.p.s. with HY-SCORE lowest-priced, high power, lever action model. Easy lever action, with one movement, delivers 775 f.p.s. with HY-SCORE .177 caliber penetrating pellets.   Walnut-colored Monte Carlo stock has cheek piece. Furnished with WILLIAMS detachable swivel and HUNTER military sling. **Barrel length 18½"; overall length 43¾"; weight 7½ lbs.** **$74.95**

HY-SCORE
LEVER ACTION AIR RIFE—MODEL 894 . . .
with barrel weight . . . .177 or .22 caliber

Combination target and pest control air rifle with easy-handling side lever. The removable barrel weight stabilizer provides greater accuracy. Receiver is grooved for standard riflescope mount. Furnished with WILLIAMS detachable swivel and HUNTER military sling. The .177 caliber model delivers smashing 775 f.p.s. with HY-SCORE penetrating pellets. **Barrel length 18½; overall length 43¾"; weight 8½ lbs.** **$84.95**

HY-SCORE
LEVER ACTION AIR RIFLE—MODEL 833SM . . .
super match model . . . .177 or .22 caliber

A genuine match target air rifle with easy side lever action. Automatic safety prevents discharge when lever is open. Has genuine Olympic front and rear target sight adjustment, with inter-changeable blades for various sight pictures.

Furnished with WILLIAMS detachable swivel and HUNTER military sling. Delivers 775 f.p.s. with pinpoint accuracy using HY-SCORE No. 215 .177 caliber wadcutter pellets. **Barrel length 18½; overall length 44¾"; weight 9½ lbs.** **$164.95**

HY-SCORE
TARGET MODEL 810M . . . match . . . recoilless . . .
.177 caliber

4 way adjustable hair match trigger. Walnut stock with cheekpiece and rubber butt. Olympic target sight equipment furnished, same as used by U.S. team at the International air rifle competition. **Barrel—polished rifled bore—12 grooves; length 19¼"; overall length 44"; muzzle velocity 605 f.p.s.; weight 9½ lbs.** . .**$199.95**

HY-SCORE
PENETRATING OVAL NOSE PELLETS . . . .177 caliber . . .
96% lead—4% antimony

INDEX No. 8851. Low weight 7 grain pellet for increased velocity and higher penetration. Packed in attractive, re-usable plastic boxes, with lock, of 250. Packed 6 counter displays per case, each containing 12 boxes..........................**$1.20 per box**

PENETRATING OVAL NOSE PELLETS . . . .22 caliber . . .
96% lead—4% antimony

INDEX No. 8852. Pellet weight 14¾ grains. Same packing and specifications as for Index #8851. ....**$1.20 per box**

HY-SCORE
WADCUTTER MATCH FLAT NOSE PELLETS . . .
.177 caliber . . . 100% pure lead

ITEM No. 215. Flat nose for accurate shooting. Low pellet weight only 8 grains. Pellets are packed individually to prevent rattling in boxes of 100. 6 counter displays per case, each containing 12 boxes. **Price per box** **$1.35**

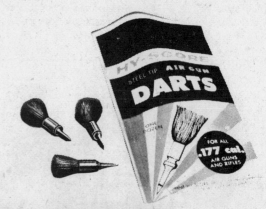

HY-SCORE
STEEL DARTS—ASSORTED COLORS . . . .177 caliber

ITEM No. 221. Darts, packed in envelopes containing one dozen, may be re-used. 6 displays, containing 12 envelopes each, per case. **Price per box** ....**$.90**

MARKSMAN AIR GUNS

MODEL 746
.22 or .177 calibers

The Model 746 is available in .22 or .177 pellet calibers. Effective range is 70 yards. Weight: 6 lbs. 10 oz. Rifle bore: .177 (4.5mm.), .22 (5.5mm.) Velocity: 580 f.p.s. Trigger pull: 3½ lbs. Cocking: 22 lbs. Checkered grips and polished aluminum trigger with two-pull action. Rear adj. sight and grooved cylinder to accept std. scope sight. Positive safety catch and Monte Carlo stock. Price **$79.95**

MODEL 740
.177 caliber

The 740, 100 plus BB repeater requires only one "break" for full-shooting force because of its "Break-Action" cocking. It has an adj. rear sight and one-piece walnut finished stock. Barrel length: 15½". Overall length: 36½". Also available in .177 caliber pellet. Price **$24.95**

MARKSMAN AIR PISTOL 1010

1010 Repeater Air Pistol: 20-shot, .177 caliber BB or .177 caliber pellet. Black finish. Also available, Model 1020 Air Pistol, shoots BB's only
Price **$12.95**

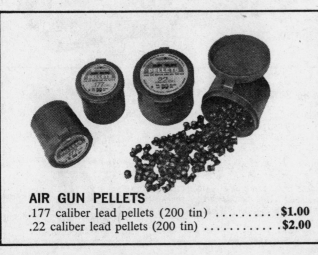

AIR GUN PELLETS
.177 caliber lead pellets (200 tin) **$1.00**
.22 caliber lead pellets (200 tin) **$2.00**

.177 caliber Darts **$1.50**
.22 caliber Darts **$2.00**

MARKSMAN ACCESSORIES

MARKSMAN SHOOTING GALLERY

For indoor or outdoor shooting. For use with most .177 and .22 cal. air pistols and air rifles. Improve skill by shooting at moving ducks, spinning targets, and Ring-the-Bell Bull's-Eye. Electrically operated. Set includes Shooting Gallery with a supply of replacement paper Moving Duck Targets—Spinning Targets—Ring-the-Bell Bulls-Eye Targets and assembly instructions. $21.95

REPLACEMENT TARGETS FOR HOME SHOOTING GALLERY
Includes 24 Duck Targets, 6 Bulls-Eye Targets, 4 Spinning targets. **$1.00**

MARKSMAN FIRING RANGE

No batteries or electric power required. Automatic descending and rotating targets. Improves marksmanship safely. For use with most .177 and .22 cal. air pistols and air rifles. $17.95
FIRING RANGE REPLACEMENT PAPER TARGET SET
Includes supply of colorful replacement paper duck targets, plus scenic sunrise background panel in full color. $1.00

MARKSMAN BIG GAME TARGET

Safe for indoor or outdoor shooting. For use with .177 and .22 caliber air pistols and air rifles. Action packed target permits user to improve skill by safely shooting at moving animals, flying ducks and "Grizzly Bear" Ring-the-Bell Bulls-Eye $21.95
BIG GAME REPLACEMENT TARGET SET
Includes supply of colorful replacement animal targets and game birds, mountain lions, timberwolves, deer, moose, grizzly bears, flying ducks plus background scenic panel. ....$ 1.15

30/30 Wrist-Lock Slingshot No. 3030

Comes equipped with adjustable and removable support arm which features a quick-positioning, uni-grip wrist support for amazing accuracy and power shot after shot. Equipped with genuine leather pouch and high-tension tubular thrust bands.

Repeater Slingshot No. 3020

Molded from formula high-impact styrene in dramatic wood-grain finish. High-tension pure gum-rubber thrust bands designed for stronger, longer, life. Features genuine leather firing pouch.

SHERIDAN AIR GUNS

BLUE OR SILVER STREAK
5m/m (.20) Caliber

Sheridan Pneumatic Rifle
Shown with Intermount and Weaver D4 Scope
Blue $83.95; Silver $86.95

The Sheridan INTERMOUNT will accept any scope and mount made to fit the ⅜" standard dove tail.

Sheridan Pneumatic Rifle
Shown with Standard Open Sight
Blue $59.75; Silver $62.75

Sheridan Pneumatic Rifle
(Left Hand Model)
Shown with Standard Open Sight
Blue $59.75; Silver $62.75

For the convenience of the many left-handed and left master-eyed shooters Sheridan is now offered in a left hand model in Silver and Blue Streak.

It is the same world-famous Sheridan Pneumatic but designed, engineered and built for the Southpaw—or right handers with left master-eyes, who want to switch over—a quite common situation.

- Weight 5 lbs.; compact overall length 37"
- Full length Mannlicher-type walnut stock.
- "Over and Under" construction with rigid-mount barrel and adjustable open sights. (Excellent Receiver Sight or Scope Sight available at extra cost.)
- Precision-rifled, rust-proof barrel

and piston tube.
- 5m/m (.20) caliber solid nosed bullet that really packs a wallop.
- Bolt action. Single shot.
- "Fire-Proof" Safety. On or off positions most convenient and in a position that can't be overlooked.
- Sturdy valving mechanism with "Locked-in" charge.
- Durable silver-satin or blued finish.

SHERIDAN BANTAM 5m/m AMMUNITION

This is a 5m/m (.20 cal.) ogive nosed, straight sided, solid bullet of correct sectional density for best pneumatic ballistics. It is super penetrating and its shoulder and driving band cut a wad-cutter hole in a target and produce maximum shock on small game. Packed in sturdy metal containers holding 500 rounds.

Ammunition (Per 500 rounds) **$3.00**

Sheridan 5m/m Cleaning Rod **$3.00**

MODELS & PRICES

Sheridan Blue Streak . .(Right and Left handed models) **$59.75**
Sheridan Silver Streak . .(Right and Left handed models) 62.75
Sheridan Blue Streak With Sheridan-Williams 5D-SH 70.00
Sheridan Silver Streak With Sheridan-Williams 5D-SH 73.00
Sheridan Blue Streak W/Intermount & Weaver D4 Scope 83.95
Sheridan Silver Streak W/Intermount & Weaver D4 Scope 86.95
Sheridan Intermount 7.75
Sheridan Intermount W/Weaver D4 Scope 21.70
5D-SH Receiver Sight 7.75

SMITH & WESSON AIR GUNS

MODEL 80 BB RIFLE
$37.50

Features . . . • Top Tang Safety • Rich Walnut colored, checkered stock with a wood grain finish • S & W imprinted and contoured recoil butt plate • Ramp style front sight • Fully adjustable rear sight • Grooved receiver for scope mounting • Fast CO_2 cartridge loading—just cycle the S & W CO_2 loading cam lever • Simplified BB loading—through the contoured loading funnel built into the stock • Conserve gas—an automatic gas cut-off is actuated when the last shot in the 50 shot tubular magazine is fired • Have a safe rifle—empty the magazine when you've finished shooting. The Model 80 magazine can be emptied with a charged CO_2 cartridge in place.

SPECIFICATIONS—ACTION: Autoloading. **FEED SYSTEM:** Tubular, 50 shot spring forced. **CALIBER:** .177 BB **SAFETY:** Manual, top tang type. **FRONT SIGHT:** Ramp style with fixed post. **REAR SIGHT:** Fully adjustable. **SIGHT RADIUS:** 18¾″. **BARREL:** 22″ Smooth Bore, steel. **POWER SYSTEM:** S & W 12.5 Gram CO_2 cartridge. **STOCK:** Monte Carlo style, walnut finished, checkered with contoured butt plate. **RECEIVER:** Gun blued, grooved for scope mounting. **OVER-ALL LENGTH:** 39″. **WEIGHT:** 3.25 lbs.

MODEL 77A AIR RIFLE
$46.50

FEATURES—an automatic safety which engages everytime a pellet is loaded, adjustable rear sight, rifled steel barrel, walnut finished Monte Carlo stock and forearm (both made of choice hardwood), and a durable gun blue finish. The pump handle can't droop either because it locks securely into place.

SPECIFICATIONS—ACTION. Lever action, single shot. **CALIBER:** .22 cal. Pellet. **SAFETY:** Automatic Safety. **SIGHTS:** Fixed front post; Adjustable rear notch. **BARREL:** 22″ long. Rifled steel (10 lands-right hand twist). **POWER:** Variable Pump Action. **STOCK:** Monte Carlo Style—walnut finish. **FINISH:** Gun Blue. **WEIGHT:** 6 lbs., 8 oz. **OVERALL LENGTH:** 40″.

MODEL 78G CO_2 PISTOL .22 CAL.
MODEL 79G CO_2 PISTOL .177 CAL.
$41.00

Features include a rifled steel barrel, and fully adjustable rear sight. It's a natural for target practice or handgun training.

You don't have to pump this one up. It uses economical **S&W** CO_2 cartridges. Set it for high power and you get 65 shots from each cartridge, or change to low power for up to 125 shots. Adjustable power means that you can use this pellet gun anywhere—indoors or out.

Each pistol features a cross-bolt safety. If you are left handed, you won't need special stocks like you do with other pistols. These checkered target stocks comfortably fit both left and right hands.

Each CO_2 Pistol is packed with a can of **Smith & Wesson Pellets** and **Smith & Wesson** CO_2 cartridges.

SPECIFICATIONS—AC-TION: Pull Bolt—single shot. **CALIBER:** .22 cal. Pellet (78G) or .177 cal. Pellet (79G). **SIGHTS:** Partridge Front; Fully Adjustable Rear with Micrometer Click Windage Adjustment. **SIGHT RADIUS:** 10″. **SAFETY:** Cross-bolt safety. **BARREL:** 8½″ long. Rifled Steel (10 lands, right hand twist). **POWER:** Smith & Wesson 12.5 gram CO_2 cartridge, High-Low Power Adjustment. **STOCKS:** Simulated walnut. Checkered. Fits left and right hands. **FINISH:** Gun Blue. **WEIGHT:** 42 oz.

SMITH & WESSON PELLETS AND CO_2 CARTRIDGES

Smith & Wesson CO_2 Cartridges are made for use in any CO_2 gun calling for a 12.5 gram cartridge. With the **Smith & Wesson Model 78G** or **Model 79G Pistol** you can get up to 125 shots from each bottle. **Smith & Wesson's** extra-tight top keeps the cartridge full until you are ready to use it. Packet in boxes of 5 .... **$2.00**

Smith & Wesson Pellets are precision-made. Available in .22 caliber and .177 caliber, they complement the quality of **Smith & Wesson Pellet Guns.** In fact they'll help bring out the best in you no matter what kind of pellet gun you shoot. Packed 250 to a can. .22 cal. .... **$1.40** per can, .177 cal. .... **$1.20** per can.

Sights, Scopes & Mounts

BAUSCH & LOMB "TROPHY" SCOPES

2½X BALTUR B

For the hunter just making the transition from iron sights. For wooded areas and all medium-range shooting. Wide field of view for running game and non-critical eye position due to large exit pupil. Can be used with any standard-type mount. Prices do not include mount.

Baltur B Scope, with Cross-Hair Reticle, or 3½ Minute Dot Reticle. Price **$68.50**

4X BALFOR B

For the Western hunter and the experienced Eastern hunter, as well as abroad. The higher magnification sometimes will reveal game in foliage or shadow which cannot be seen at 2½X. Allows high accuracy for long-range shooting with a wide field of view and large exit pupil. Can be used with any standard mount. Prices do not include mount.

Balfor B Scope, with Cross-Hair Reticle, Tapered Cross-Hair, Dualine with Thick or Thin Line Reticle. Price **$118.50**

2½X TO 8X BALVAR 8B

A zoom power scope that provides a continuous range of magnification from 2½X to 8X with a partial turn of the eyepiece. Adapts to any hunting situation and can be used for varmints. Reticle size decreases as power increases. No change in zero, focus or eye relief with power change. Uses standard mounts. Prices do not include mount.

Balvar 8B Scope, with Cross-Hair Reticle, Tapered Cross-Hair, Dualine with Thick or Thin Line Reticle. Price **$114.50**

TROPHY SCOPE SPECIFICATIONS (All scopes have internal adjustments with ½ minutes click).

	Baltur B	Balfor B	Balvar 8 B	
Magnification	2½ X	4 X	2.5 X	8 X
Entrance Pupil (mm)	32	32	36	36
Exit Pupil (mm)	12.8	8	14.4	4.5
Relative Brightness	164	64	207	20
Real Field (ft. at 100 yards)	42	30	40	12.5
Eye Distance (inches)	3	3	3½	3½
Length (inches)	12⅛	11⅞	11⅞	
Weight (ounces)	11	11	12½	
Diameter of Main Tube (inches)	1	1	1	
Diameter of Objective Cell (inches)	1⅝	1⅝	1¾	
Diameter of Eyepiece Cell (inches)	1½	1½	1½	
Reticles Available				
Cross-Hair (minutes)	1¼	¾	1³⁄₁₆	⅜
Tapered Cross-Hair (minutes at center)	—	⅜	⁹⁄₁₆	³⁄₁₆
Dualine Thick Lines (minutes)	—	1½	2²⁄₅	¾
Thin Lines (minutes)	—	½	⁴⁄₅	¼

BAUSCH & LOMB TELESCOPES

A variable-power telescope with a range from 15X to 60X. Rolling a finger across a knob changes power but does not affect focus. Power change is continuous and not in steps. Low power is used when light is poor or heat waves (mirage) are heavy. Also, field of view is greater at lower power.

Objective lens is 60mm diameter and all optics are coated. Body is die-cast aluminum with a sage green crinkled enamel finish that is virtually mar-proof. Body has integral lug for tripod attachment. Length with protective caps supplied, 16 11/16", weight 48 ounces.

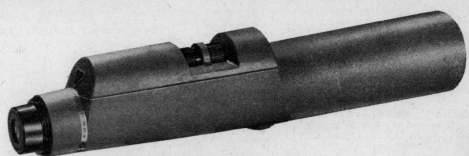

BALSCOPE ZOOM 60
with straight eyepiece, **$224.50**
with 45 degree eyepiece, **$269.50**

BALSCOPE SR.
$164.50

with choice of
15X, 20X, 25X, 40X or 60X
(Extra eyepieces, **$29.50** each)

The Balscope Sr. can be used with six interchangeable eyepieces—15x, 20x, 20x Wide Angle, 25x, 40x, and 60x. Changing eyepieces is simply a matter of screwing out the eyepiece and putting another in its place. (The scope comes equipped with the eyepiece of your choice.)

Protective lens caps are provided for the objective and eyepiece. The Balscope Sr. can follow a bird in flight keeping a bird in focus all the time. Focusing is done by merely rolling a finger across the control knob. The adjustment is internal and the eyepiece remains fixed.

The body is aluminum die casting finished with tough crinkled enamel. It has an integral tripod lug. Length, 16 7/16", Weight, 48 oz., Minimum Focus, 30 feet.

SPECIFICATIONS

	Balscope Zoom 60				Balscope Sr.					
	15X	20X	30X	60X	15X	20X	20X W.A.	25X	40X	60X
Field in ft. at 1000 yds.	150	112.5	75	37.5	166	130	184	110	64	28.6
Relative Brightness	16	9	4	1	16	9	9	2.4	2.25	1

BALSCOPE TWENTY

A twenty-power telescope designed for both general observation and as a spotting scope for the handgun shooter (it fits standard pistol cases). Will serve as a spotting scope for rifle target shooting in good light conditions. A single turn of the eyepiece focuses for all ranges (no drawtube).

The die-cast aluminum body has an integral threaded lug for attaching to either a shooter's tripod or any camera tripod. All lenses are anti-reflection coated. The objective is 40mm diameter and the field of view is 75 feet at 1000 yards. Length, 15 3/8"; weight, 22 ounces.
Balscope Twenty Telescope **$45.50**

BALSCOPE TEN

This ten-power telescope was designed as a hand-held, general-use instrument. It serves the same purposes as a binocular for seeing distant detail. The optical system consists of six lenses which give excellent definition. The body tube is a tough melamine-phenolic plastic that will resist considerable abuse.

Focusing is done within a single turn of the eyepiece, eliminating the usual clumsy drawtube. Length, 10 1/4"; weight, 9 ounces.
Balscope Ten Telescope **$19.95**
Carrying Case ....**.98**
Tripod Adapter ....**.98**

BUEHLER SCOPE MOUNTS

BUEHLER TELESCOPIC SIGHT MOUNTS: By using one of the five basic styles of mount bases, you may position the scope of your choice in the best possible location. The best location is the one that positions the scope in such a way as to give a full field of view when the shooter's face is nestled in a comfortable, natural position against the stock. Scopes vary in eye relief from 3 to 5 inches. Sight adjustment turrets are in different locations. The amount of space available on the scope for the mount varies, Most important of all is the difference in shooters and in the way each one holds a rifle. One of the five styles of mounts will locate your scope in the best position for you. A good gunsmith or experienced sporting goods dealer is a great help in making this choice. All Buehler mount rings fit and are interchangeable with all Buehler bases.

4 AND 5-INCH BASES

SHORT ONE-PIECE BASES

The short one-piece base locates the front ring over the top of the receiver ring about 1 inch aft of the long one-piece base. The rear ring is in about the same location. Thus, ring spacing averages 4 inches. The short base is recommended for shorter scopes, scopes with large and long objective bells, and scopes with turrets near the center of the tube.

LONG ONE-PIECE BASES

This base is made to fit most of the rifles in common use. In most models it has the rings spaced about 5 inches apart with the front ring located *ahead* of the receiver on all bolt action rifles. The long base gives the greatest possible support to the scope and the longest amount of eye relief. It is recommended for long scopes, and scopes with adjustment turrets located ahead of center.

One Piece Scope Mount base, 4" or 5" $13.75

TWO-PIECE BASES

Two-piece bases locate the front ring over the receiver ring in the same place as the short one-piece base. The rear ring, however, is over the bridge on bolt action rifles, not ahead of it as is the case with the one-piece bases. The ring spacing averages 4½ inches. Will accommodate scopes described under the *short* one-piece bases. The eye relief is shorter than either one-piece base but adequate for the average installation.

Two-Piece Scope Mount Base. $13.75

BUEHLER RINGS FOR BOTH ONE- AND TWO-PIECE MOUNTS

SOLID RINGS   **SPLIT RINGS**

A double split type ring with the added beauty of a smoothly rounded "ball turret top." The steel spacer at the top of each ring not only fills up an unsightly gap, but is made of 16 laminations .002 thick which may be peeled off one or more at a time, thus accurately fitting all scopes up to .010 smaller in size than the normal dimension of the ring.

BUEHLER RINGS AND HEIGHTS:

CODE	SOLID RINGS	Height
1	1" Solid	.040
2	7/8" Solid	.040
3	3/4" Solid	.040
5	7/8" Split	.075
6	1" Split (Standard)	.075
7	1" High Split	.136
8	1" Extra High Split	2.12
10	26 mm. (Standard)	.125
11	26 mm. High	.200
13	26½ mm.	.110
14	26½ mm. High	.188
15	27 mm.	.181
16	28 mm.	.181

SOLID & DOUBLE RING

Solid rings, per set $12.75
Double split rings, codes 6, 7, & 8 . . . . $18.75
Double split rings, codes 5, 10 thru 16 . . . . $24.00

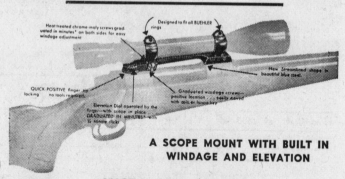

A SCOPE MOUNT WITH BUILT IN WINDAGE AND ELEVATION

MICRO DIAL MOUNT

Both windage and elevation features are built in. A twist of the fingers dials the elevation desired on a dial clearly marked in minutes (one inch at 100 yards). With ¼ minute clicks. Another twist on the lock wheel directly below the dial securely locks the setting. The windage screws also are calibrated in minutes on both sides. The Micro Dial is designed primarily for all scopes with internal adjustments, such as the Balvar 2½ to 8 (use Code 7 Rings for Balvar), but can be used to advantage with many other scopes—the reticule can always be perfectly centered. The Micro Dial also makes it possible to switch scopes between rifles. The ring spacing is 4 inches.

Micro-Dial Base Only $21.50
Solid Rings Only, per set $12.75
Split Rings Only, per set, codes 6, 7, & 8 . . . . $18.75
Split Rings Only, per set, codes 5, 10 thru 16 . . . . $24.00

BUEHLER SAFETY & GUN SCREWS

BUEHLER LOW-SCOPE SAFETY

The Buehler Safety operates on the same mechanical principles as the manufacturer's original safety. In the "ON" position, pressure of the striker spring locks it securely. It will not cam over into firing position. Safety holds BOTH BOLT and STRIKER in locked position.

This safety operates on the right side of the action, rotating through an arc of 70 degrees with definite stops in the OFF and ON positions. It can be used equally well with or without a scope, and will be found to be faster and more convenient than the original safety. Complete with instructions for installation.

FILLISTER HEAD & PLUG SCREWS

	Prices
6x48 SCREWS (⅛, ¼, 5/16, ½" Mixed)	12-$1.00
6x48 PLUG SCREWS 3/32"	12-$1.00
8x40 SCREWS (¼ & ⅜" Mixed)	12-$1.00
8x40 PLUG SCREWS 3/32"	12-$1.00
10x32 PLUG SCREWS 3/32"	12-$1.00

GUARD SCREWS:
	Prices
UNIVERSAL	75¢ Ea.
ENFIELD GUARD SCREW	
SCREWS UNIVERSAL	75¢ Ea.
SPRINGFIELD (KRAG) GD.	
MAUSER GUARD SCREWS	75¢

For following models:
MAUSER (M98, F.N.), KRAG, SPRINGFIELD WINCHESTER M54, 1891 ARGENTINE MAUSER

M93 (Fits most small ring Mauser actions which cock on closing such as M93, M95 and M96 Spanish, Mexican, Swedish) Price each $9.75

RIFLE ACTION CHART—TOP MOUNT BASES

(Mount bases listed by our Code. Use this code in ordering.)

Catalog No. 30 1975	Micro Dial	Long 1-Piece Base	Short 1-Piece Base	2-Piece Base
MAUSER				
M98 Military. Com. (1.4-1.42 dia.)	FI-U ④	FM	FI-S	98
Small Ring (1.3 dia.) M91-M98 etc.	HV-U ④		SR-S	95
1891 Argentine	HV-U ④		91-S	
F.N. & Mark X Actions	FI-U	FM	FI-S	F
Mauser 3000 R.H., L.H. Models				M3
BRNO Mauser Commercial				
Flat Top	BLU-WCC ②	5/16 BBWCC ②		B2 ②
Round Rec. Ring	HV-U ④		SR-S	H2 ①
BROWNING				
F.N. Action .264 thru .458	FI-U	FM	FI-S	F
Sako L461 Short Action .222, .222 Mag.				BL-4 ⑦
Sako L579 Med. Act. .22/250, .243, .284, .308				BL-5 ⑦
Automatic Rifle (All Grades)				BA-2
Lever Action High Power				BL-2
B.S.A. Monarch Round Receiver				U9
COLT SAUER				CS
ENFIELD Remington 30 Conversion		E	E-S	
Bridge flat up to .075 low	E-U		E7-S	
Bridge shaped like M70	70-U			W ③
Bridge shaped like R721	21-U ③	21 ③	21-S ③	R ③
HARRINGTON & RICHARDSON, 22s				S2 ②
H&R 300 Ultra Bolt F.N. Action	FI-U	FM	FI-S	F
H&R 300 Sako				HS
HERTERS J9				F
HIGGINS — SEARS ROEBUCK				
50 & 51 ½" Bridge Hole Spacing	FI-U	FM	FI-S	F
51L, 51C, 52C	HV-U			H2
53C	70-U	70	70-S	W
237C, 238C			36	
29, 31, 33			60	
HUSQVARNA				
HVA crown grade rifles	HV-U		SR-S	H2
8000 & 9000 Series				8-9
HVA-Carl Gustaf				8-9
JAPANESE ARISAKA		E ④	E-S ④	
MARLIN				
336			36	
455	FI-U	FM	FI-S	F
39A, 56, 57, 62			36 ⑥	
80, 81, 88, 89, 98				S2
MOSSBERGS — Most Models .22 Cal.				S2 ②
M800				M8
M810 & 812				81
PARKER-HALE Super 1200 Series ⑥	FI-U	FM	FI-S	F
RANGER "TEXAS MAGNUM"				TM-2

	Micro Dial	Long 1-Piece Base	Short 1-Piece Base	2-Piece Base
REMINGTON				
M600 & XP-100, M660			6XP	
M700, 721, 725 long actions	21-U	21	21-S	R
M700, 722, 725 short actions			6XP	R
M700 L.H. short or long action				R
760, 740, 742			60	
M788				78
37				T2
510, 511, 512, 513, 514, 521, 550, 560				S2
12, 121, 552, 572, 24, 241			60 ②	
40X, 40XB				R
RUGER 44 CARBINE AND				RC2
M77 Round Receiver	21-U	21	21-S	R
No. 3 Carbine Single Shot				R3
10/22 Carbine				R1
SAKO MAGNUM F.N. Action	FI-U	FM	FI-S	F
FINNWOLF		FW		
SAVAGE				
99 — All Models		99		V2
110 R.H., L.H. short or long				V2
110 R.H. long action only	10-U			S2
4, 5, 6				
170			60	
SPRINGFIELD				
1906-03, A1	S-U	S	S-S	
A3	A-U		A3-S	
M22's		S (Undrilled)		
SCHULTZ & LARSEN 54, 60, 64, 65, 68				L2
WEATHERBY F.N. Actions	FI-U	FM	FI-S	F
Mark V R.H., L.H. long action				R
Mark V R.H., long action only	21-U	21	21-S	R
Mark V Varmintmaster .224, .22/250				MV
Vanguard (all calibers)	21-U	21	21-S	R
WINCHESTER				
M70 Std. ⑤ M670, 770	70-U	70	70-S	W
M70 Prewar, M54	54-U			W4
M70 Mag. H&H .300, .375 & N.M.	70-U			W
M70 Mag. .375 (Ser. No. 700,000 UP)	70-U			
M88, M100			88	
69, 72, 75, 74				S2
M52				T2
07, 61, 63, 77			60 ②	
BLANK BASES, flat on bottom for special installations	BL-U / BL-UWCC	5/16, ⅜, 7/16, ½ Full Blanks		B-2 ⑨

FOOTNOTES (indicated by circled numbers above)
① If clip lips and hump are removed.
② Mounted with screws.
③ Rear screw hole matches hole in bridge.
④ File small flat at top of clip lips.
⑤ Serial numbers above 66,350, incl. Win. Magnums.
⑥ May be adapted with minor changes.
⑦ Final Model with ¾" hole spacing in Rec. Ring.
⑨ 2 piece available flat on the bottom ⅜" thick.

BUSHNELL RIFLE SCOPES

Dawn & dusk or normal lighting conditions

SCOPECHIEF V

Equipped with "Lite-Site" lighted aiming point, powered by a compact long life battery. Clicks on for dawn or dusk light conditions and instantly there appears a steady lighted aiming point projected onto the center of the crosshairs. Clicked off for normal light conditions, only the crosshairs remain in view.

The eyepiece is ringed in neoprene. Lenses have wide distortion-free field of view. All optical surfaces are covered with anti-reflection coating. Both red and green filters are included to obtain desired intensity. The scope finish is mar-resistant—glossy black, Rhino-coated. Scopechief V is nitrogen purged, fog free and sealed against dust and moisture.

1.5X-4X VARIABLE
$96.50

3X-9X VARIABLE
$114.50

4X FIXED POWER
$75.50

.22 RIFLESCOPES

SCOPECHIEF® .22

ScopeChief 3x-8x .22 Variable

Magnifications:	3x	4x	5x	6x	7x	8x
Field at 100 yards (ft.):	30	24	18	16	14	12
Exit pupil (mm):	7.4	5	4	3.4	2.9	2.5

Overall length: 10¼"; overall weight: 7½ oz.; clear aperture of objective lens: 20mm; outside diameter, eyepiece end: 1 3/16"; outside diameter, objective end: ⅞"; eye relief: 2¼"-3"; adjustment scale graduations equal: 1" at 100 yds.

ScopeChief 4x .22

Field at 100 yards (ft.): 30; exit pupil: 5mm; overall length: 11"; overall weight: 7½ oz.; clear aperture of objective lens: 20mm; outside diameter, eyepiece end: 1 1/16"; outside diameter, objective end: ⅞"; eye relief: 2½"; adjustment scale graduations equal: 1" at 100 yds.

3X - 8X Variable . . . $39.95

4X All Purpose . . . $29.95

CUSTOM .22

Custom 3x-7x .22 Variable

Magnifications:	3x	4x	5x	6x	7x
Field at 100 yards (ft.):	29	23	17	15	13
Exit pupil (mm):	5.3	4	3.2	2.7	2.3

Overall length: 10"; overall weight: 6½ oz.; clear aperture of objective lens: 18mm; outside diameter, eyepiece end: 1½"; outside diameter, objective end: ⅞"; eye relief: 2¼"-2½"; adjustment scale graduations equal: 1" at 100 yds.

Custom 4x .22

Field at 100 yards (ft.): 28.4; exit pupil: 4mm; overall length: 10 5/16"; overall weight: 5¼ oz.; clear aperture of objective lens: 18mm; outside diameter, eyepiece end: 1"; outside diameter, objective end: ⅞"; eye relief: 2½"; adjustment scale graduations equals: 1" at 100 yds.

3X - 7X Variable . . . $24.95

4X All Purpose . . . $19.95

BUSHNELL RIFLE SCOPES

SCOPECHIEF IV

The ScopeChief riflescope is the product of optical engineers who shoot and hunt . . . who know the tough requirements of performance in the field. Long, safe eye-relief . . . large eyepiece . . . wide, distortion-free field . . . anti-reflection, coated optics . . . extra strength tube . . . all add up to fast, easy sighting. It's rugged and light . with handsome, mar-resistant, Rhino-coat finish. Nitrogen filled . . . fog-free and completely sealed against dust or moisture. Retractable post standard for dawn to dusk lighting conditions.

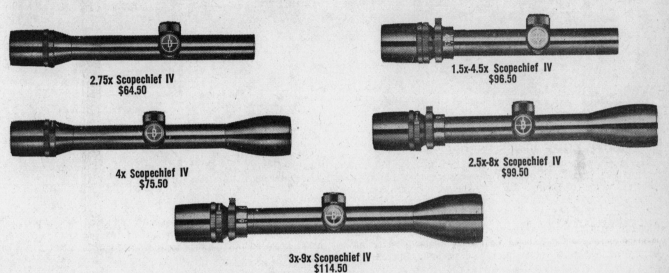

2.75x Scopechief IV
$64.50

4x Scopechief IV
$75.50

1.5x-4.5x Scopechief IV
$96.50

2.5x-8x Scopechief IV
$99.50

3x-9x Scopechief IV
$114.50

SCOPECHIEF RIFLESCOPE SPECIFICATION CHART

Nitrogen filled and sealed against moisture. Hard, anodized, scratch-resistant finish. Click adjustment equals ½ inch at 100 yards. Scale equals ½ inch at 100 yards. Tube diameter: 1 inch.

MODEL	FIXED POWERS		VARIABLE POWERS at principle settings								
	2.75x	4x	1.5x–4.5x		2.5x–8x			3x–9x			
	2.75	4	1.5	4.5	2.5	4	8	3	4	6	9
Actual magnification	2.75	4	1.5	4.5	2.5	4	8	38	38	38	38
Clear aperture of objective lens (mm)	21	32	21	21	32	32	32	38	38	38	38
Exit Pupil (mm)	7.6	8	14	4.7	12.4	8	4	12.7	9.5	6.4	4.2
Relative Brightness	87	96	294	33	226	96	24	241	135	61	27
Field of view at 100 yards (ft.)	43	30	78	26	46	30	15	39	31.5	21.5	13
Eye-relief (in.)	3.5	3.5	4.38	3.25	4	3.5	3.25	4	3.5	3.25	3.25
Crosshair width at 100 yards (in.)	1.3	.9	3	1	1.22	.72	.38	.96	.72	.48	.32
Post width at 100 yards (in.)	5	3	9	3	5	3	1.5	4	3	2	1.3
Total weight (oz.). Add 1.75 oz. for models with built-in mounts	9	10.7	7.75		11.4			12			
Outside diameter-objective end (in.)	1	1.6	1		1.6			1.8			
Overall length focused to infinity (in.)	9.9	11.6	9.3		11.1			11.4			
Outside diameter-eyepiece end (in.)	1.5		1.5		1.5			1.5			
Corrected for parallax at (yds.)	100		100		150			150			

1.3X BUSHNELL MAGNUM PHANTOM (complete with mount)

The Phantom increases clarity of sight picture and permits accurate holding on the target because the crosshair and target are on the same plane. The scope has micrometer reticle adjustments, and is made in crosshair reticle only.

This scope was designed specifically for handguns, and has an eye-relief of 6" thru 17" which takes the shooter easily from "two hand" varmint to "arms length," target position. All optics are hard coated. No drilling or tapping is required to mount the scope on most guns, and there is no need to remove iron sights when clip mount is used.

1.3x all purpose game & target $39.50
2.5x varmint & long range $49.50

BUSHNELL RIFLE SCOPES

SCOPE CHIEF VI RIFLESCOPE

The Scope Chief VI Riflescope with Rangemaster and Mult-X Reticle (MX) features extra-wide, distortion-free field, anti-reflection coated optics; extra-strength tube, rugged mar-resistent, Rhino-coated finish; nitrogen-filled, fog free and completely sealed against dust and moisture.

3X-9X, 40mm Variable **$118.50**
4X, 32mm Fixed **79.50**

SCOPECHIEF VI SPECIFICATION CHART			
Click adjustment equals ⅓ inch at 100 yards. Scale equals 1 inch at 100 yards. Tube diameter: 1 inch.			
MODEL	**FIXED POWER** 4x	**VARIABLE POWERS** 3x—9x	
Actual magnification	4	3	9
Clear aperture of objective lens (mm)	32	40	40
Exit Pupil (mm)	8	13.3	4.4
Relative Brightness	96	265	29
Field of view at 100 yards (ft.)	30	39	13
Eye-relief (in.)	3.5	3.75	3
Crosshair width at 100 yards (in.)	.9	.93	.31
Post width at 100 yards (in.)	3	4	1.3
Total weight (oz.). Add 1.75 oz.	10.7	12	
Outside diameter-objective end (in.)	1.6	1.8	
Overall length focused to infinity (in.)	11.6	11.4	
Outside diameter-eyepiece end (in.)	1.5	1.5	
Corrected for parallax at (yds.)	100	100	

The Banner Riflescope line is equipped with neoprene protective eyeguard fastened to the end of the eyepiece. Lenses are locked in place and hermetically sealed. Completely weatherproof tested. Scopes are finished in glossy black hard anodizing. Offered in a choice of reticles including the Multi-X. All styles of reticles are shock mounted and remain centered. The 10X and 4x-12x variable come equipped with parallax focus adjustments.

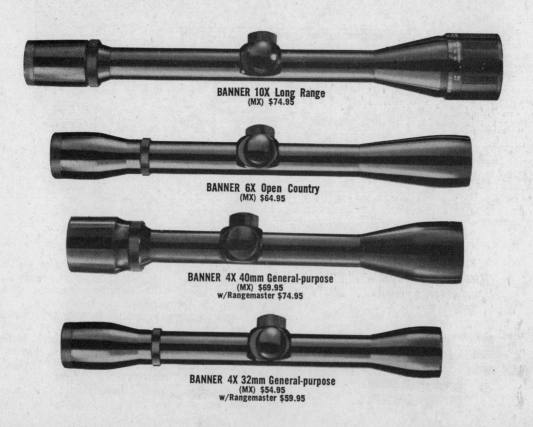

BANNER 10X Long Range
(MX) $74.95

BANNER 6X Open Country
(MX) $64.95

BANNER 4X 40mm General-purpose
(MX) $69.95
w/Rangemaster $74.95

BANNER 4X 32mm General-purpose
(MX) $54.95
w/Rangemaster $59.95

BUSHNELL RIFLE SCOPES

BANNER 2.5X Short Range
(MX) $43.95

BANNER 4X-12X Medium to Long Range
(MX) $94.95

BANNER 3X-9X 40mm All-purpose
(MX) $84.95
w/Rangemaster $89.95

BANNER 3X-9X 38mm All-purpose
(MX) $94.95
w/Rangemaster $99.95

BANNER 3X-9X 32mm All-purpose
(MX) $74.95
w/Rangemaster $79.95

BANNER 1.75X-4.5X Close Medium Range
(MX) $79.95

BANNER 1.5X-4X Close-in Medium Range
(MX) $67.95

BUSHNELL RIFLE SCOPES

BANNER RIFLESCOPE SPECIFICATION CHART

Magnification	RANGE-MASTER	Field of view at 100 yds. (ft.)	Weight (oz.)	Length (inches)	Eye distance (inches)	Entrance pupil (mm)	Exit pupil (mm)	Relative Brightness Light Efficiency	MX center CH width at 100 yds. (mm)	MX distance post tip to post tip (mm)	Graduation at 100 yds. (inches)
4x-12x 40mm		29 at 4x / 10 at 12x	15.5	13.5	3.2	40	10 at 4x / 3.3 at 12x	150 / 16	0.5 / .167	20 / 6.7	.5
3x-9x 40mm	RANGE-MASTER	39 at 3x / 13 at 9x	13	13	3.5	40	13.3 at 3x / 4.4 at 9x	265 / 29	.66 / .22	26.6 / 8.9	.5
3x-9x 38mm	RANGE-MASTER	43 at 3x WIDE ANGLE / 14.6 at 9x	14	12	3	38	12.7 at 3x / 4.2 at 9x	242 / 26.5	.66 / .22	26.6 / 8.9	.6
3x-9x 32mm	RANGE-MASTER	39 at 3x / 13 at 9x	11	11.5	3.5	32	10.7 at 3x / 3.6 at 9x	172 / 19	.66 / .22	26.6 / 8.9	.5
1.75x-4.5x 21mm		71 at 1.75x WIDE ANGLE / 27 at 4.5x	11.5	10.2	2.9	21	12 at 1.75x / 4.7 at 4.5x	216 / 33	1.18 / .44	45.7 / 17.8	1.0
1.5x-4x 21mm		63 at 1.5x / 28 at 4x	10.3	10.5	3.5	21	14 at 1.5x / 5 at 4x	294 / 37.5	1.3 / 0.5	53.3 / 20	.9
10x 40mm		12	14.6	14.5	3	40	4	24	0.2	8.0	.5
6x 32mm		19.5	10.5	13.5	3	32	5.3	42	0.3	13.3	.75
4x 40mm	RANGE-MASTER	37.3 WIDE ANGLE	12	12.3	3	40	10	150	0.5	20	1.5
4x 32mm	RANGE-MASTER	29	10	12.0	3.5	32	8	144	0.5	20	1.0
2.5x 20mm		45	8	10.9	3.5	20	8	144	0.8	32	1.5

TRU SCOPE POCKET BORE SIGHTER

This pocket-size bore sighter gives you the flexibility to carry it in your shirt or hunting jacket pocket. Rugged plastic case; comes complete with weatherproof cap and adjustable arbor. Fits any bore from .243 to .308 caliber.

Tru Scope will work on all scopes and most rifles, excluding rifles with magazines, full stocks or extra wide barrels (bull barrels). **Color**—Gray; Weight 4 oz.; Size 3½" x 2¾" x 1⅛" **$24.95**

FEATHERLIGHT

7 power, 50mm with INSTA-FOCUS Traditional Navy style, ideal when image brightness is more important than size or weight.
Field at 1000 yards: 375′
Exit pupil: 7.1mm
Height: 7⅜″
Weight: 39 oz.
Deluxe case and straps included **$114.50**

FREELAND'S ACCESSORIES

FREELAND INTERNATIONAL SHOOTING STAND

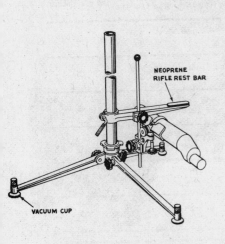

NEOPRENE RIFLE REST BAR

VACUUM CUP

International Stand — Prone Position

In 1964, Al Freeland attended the Olympics in Tokyo and in 1966 was present at the famous Wiesbaden ranges in Germany. As many as 92 countries were represented and in both competitions the need for a suitable stand for position shooting in both 22 and 300 meter calibers was very evident; many make-shift stands were in use, but still no International Shooting Stand. Now, Al has made this all possible . . . from prone to standing . . . all in one serviceable, compact but rugged unit.

The International Base is fitted with spikes for earth penetration giving added stability. By reversing the unit on each leg a triple action suction cup gives definite stability on both black top or concrete. The main upright shaft is 2" in diameter and is of Hi Tensile aluminum alloy, anodized black for hardness of surface — all this gives definite stability.

Other great features are apparent. The neoprene bar support of the rifle cuts fatigue which is very important in a long Olympic match. The position master simply attaches to the main extension of the regal head and either the 22 cal. Dewar block or the 300 meter ammo block gives the shooter quick access to ammunition in the kneeling or off-hand position. It can be quickly changed to be used in the prone position.

The INTERNATIONAL STAND is finished in grey wrinkle with blued and anodized appointments . . . Approximately 16 lbs.

Freeland INTERNATIONAL SHOOTING STAND W/Carrying Case $102.50
Freeland INTERNATIONAL SHOOTING STAND **LESS** Regal Head Assy. . . . .$ 87.50
Carrying Case . . . .$ 19.50

FREELAND *REGAL* BIPOD

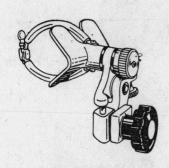

REGAL "SADDLE HEAD" ASSEMBLY

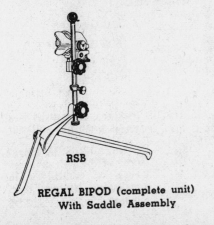

RSB

REGAL BIPOD (complete unit)
With Saddle Assembly

The FREELAND REGAL BIPOD is similar to the Freeland Olympic Bipod. The REGAL BIPOD is available with either the ZOOM HEAD, for scopes with the "boss," or the regular SADDLE HEAD, which is adaptable to spotting scopes with various diameters. The REGAL BIPOD comes with the Freeland "ball" carrying "handle" and one 12" extension. Finish is the B&L Sage, Forest Green or gray. The REGAL BIPOD features the quick adjustment for elevation to any position up or down with the same accurate adjustment for positioning scope on target, and also panoramic movement. These are SPECIAL REFINEMENTS to the Freeland Olympic Bipod. The FREELAND REGAL BIPOD IS THE ALL POSITION BIPOD by the addition of our 12", 18" or 24" extensions to desired heights. **Gray or green.** F.O.B. Rock Island.

#RSB-12 FREELAND **REGAL** BIPOD W/Saddle Head & 12" Extension **$33.25**
#RZB-12 FREELAND **REGAL** BIPOD W/ZOOM HEAD & 12" Extension **$33.25**
#RHA **REGAL HEAD ASSEMBLY ONLY** (less extension and ball)
　Mention if ZOOM or SADDLE Head & make of Scope, gray or green **$20.00**

Freeland 12" EXTENSION . . . . **$ 4.50**
Freeland 18" EXTENSION . . . . **$ 6.00**
Freeland 24" EXTENSION . . . . **$ 7.50**
Freeland **Carrying Ball** . . . . **$ 2.25**

Freeland REGAL TRIPOD **RZTW-12 (Zoom) RSTW 12 (Saddle)** with
STABILITY WEIGHT, gray or green **$48.75**
　(Stability weight recommended for REGAL TRIPOD)

JAEGER MOUNTS & ACCESSORIES

JAEGER QUICK DETACHABLE SIDE MOUNT

The Jaeger mount permits removing and attaching scope within a few seconds without the use of any coins or tools. The construction combines light weight with great rigidity. The unique clamping device locks the slide to the base securely, and insures return to zero. All mounts have windage adjustment at the rear ring.

Made for most bolt action rifles as well as Remington 740 & 760, Savage 99, Winchester 88 and other lever action rifles.

Especially well suited for Mannlicher Schoenauer rifles. **$45.00**

All mounts have split rings and are made in the following ring sizes and heights:

Mod. 10—22 mm (⅞") low
Mod. 11—22 mm high
Mod. 20—1" low
Mod. 21—1" medium
Mod. 22—1" high
Mod. 30—26 mm low
Mod. 31—26 mm high

Low rings for most scopes in low position, medium height rings for large objective scopes in low position, high rings for use of iron sights below scope.

JAEGER M2 SAFETY

For low mounted scope. Available in two models: For Springfield and Mauser.
$10.00

JAEGER MODEL 69 TRIGGER WITH SAFETY

Basically like the Mod. 50 trigger with an attached positive safety. The safety cam lifts the sear away from the trigger, and locks it. The trigger adjustments are not connected with, nor affected by the safety. Bolt locks in safe position.
Price $31.00

Mod. 69 FN Supreme action.
Mod. 69 H.......for Husqvarna, S&W, rifles w/H.V.Z. action.
Mod. 69 MA, no bolt lock . . . for 98 & Mauser actions.
Mod. 69 MB, same as 69 MA, but w/ bolt lock.
Mod. 69 MX . . . for Mark X Mauser actions.

JAEGER MODEL 50 ADJUSTABLE TRIGGER

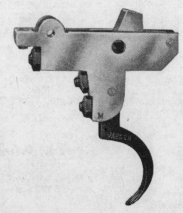

50 MAUSER
50S SPRINGFIELD
50E ENFIELD

An improved trigger mechanism which can be safely adjusted to a light, clean pull without backlash.

Not affected by looseness of the bolt or pressure of cartridges in magazine against bolt.
Price **$20.00**

LEUPOLD RIFLE SCOPES

M8-2X (2-Power)

This scope is specially designed for a non-critical (8″ to 18″) eye relief, permitting mounting ahead of the receiver opening. It is primarily intended for the Winchester 94, and other rifles where a rear-mounted scope would interfere with top ejection. Also used on handguns, such as the popular Thomas/Center single-shot pistol. **$58.50**

M8-3X (3-Power)

This light, compact scope combines an extra-wide field-of-view for getting on game quickly in heavy cover, with adequate magnification to make it usable up to normal hunting ranges for big game. A good choice for timbered country. Widely used on .375's and .458's for hunting dangerous African game. **$75.50**

M8-4X (4-Power)

Light, compact and modestly priced, this scope has what many big-game hunters consider to be the optimum combination of a generous field-of-view and magnification. In fact, the M8-4X is by far the most popular of all Leupold fixed-power scopes. **$81.50**

M8-6X (6-Power)

Only slightly larger than our 4X, and very close to the same external dimensions of many other 4-powers, if offers a little better resolution (because of the extra magnification) and therefore can be considered an improved long-range, big-game scope. Also excellent for light varmint rifles. **$94.50**

M8-7.5X AO (7½-Power)

The scope has both the magnification and excellent resolution needed for hunting mountain sheep and goats. It could be excellent for antelope, as well as a fine varmint scope, too. The AO (Adjustable Objective) provides precise focusing and eliminates parallax error at any distance from less than 50 yards to infinity. **$112.50**

M8-10X AO (10-Power) **and**
M8-12X AO (12-Power)

Both of these scopes offer superb resolution for precision shooting at extended ranges, thus are naturals for long-range varmint hunting. The M8-10X is 1½″ shorter than the M8-12X, for those who prefer a more compact scope. The AO (Adjustable Objective) provides precise focusing and eliminates parallax error at any distance from less than 50 yards to infinity.
10xAO ...**$114.50**, 12xAO ...**$118.50**

Leupold Target Scope

Improvements in Bench Rest equipment and shooter ability have advanced to the point where 5-shot-group measurements in the area of .100″ (at 100 yards) are no longer uncommon. The Leupold target scope was designed to be lightweight, compact and to provide the resolution needed to not only clearly see the aiming point, but also the bullet imprint at 100 and 200 yards. Changing conditions, such as wind and mirage movement readily can be seen. The scope weight of less than a pound allows for maximum rifle weight. Since it is only about 15″ long and has a generous eye relief, the M8-24X can be mounted on the receiver like a hunting scope.

M8-24X AO (24-Power)

A 2¼″ screw-on sunshade of the same diameter as the objective is furnished and packaged with the scope. The M8-24X AO is available only with Crosshair or conventional Dot reticles. **$181.50**
Crosshair **$169.50**

LEUPOLD RIFLE SCOPES

The "GOLD-MEDALLION" Vari-X III Series

The introduction of Leupold's newest series, the Vari-X III scopes, advances the state-of-the-art of scope technology another step. In scientific terms, these scopes feature a new "Anastigmat" power-changing system that is similar to the sophisticated lens systems in today's finest cameras. Some of the improvements are subtle, such as the extremely accurate internal control system which is the result of both design and time-consuming hand matching of critical mating parts. Others —the sharp, superb-contrast sight picture and the "flatness" of field—are obvious. The total result is a series of tough, dependable scopes that are superior in optical and mechanical quality . . . particularly pleasing to the discriminating sportsman who really appreciates the true value of such quality. Reticles are same apparent size throughout power range, stay centered during elevation and windage adjustments. Fog free, of course.

Note: Vari-X III scopes available with Duplex reticle only.

VARI-X III 1.5x5 (1½ to 5-Power)

This scope's 1.5X-power setting is particularly helpful for hunting whitetail deer, since they often are taken in fairly heavy cover. Also, because a large field-of-view makes it easier to get on target fast, this magnification is often used when hunting dangerous game. $131.50

VARI-X III 2.5x8 (2½ to 8-Power)

This scope is excellent for all types of big game and varmint hunting. It offers a versatile range of magnifications—in a compact package (approximately the same size as a Leupold M8-6X). $142.50

VARI-X III 3.5x10 AO (3½ to 10-Power)

The extra power and Adjustable Objective feature makes this scope the optimum choice for the year-round shooter who enjoys every phase of shooting, from big game and varmint hunting to target shooting. $153.50

The PERFORMANCE-PROVED Vari-X II Series

VARI-X II 1x4 (1 to 4-Power)

This is a good magnification range for a variety of hunting. At the low end, the larger field-of-view makes it easier to make close-in shots on fast-moving game. At the high end, many hunters feel the 4X power is the optimum magnification for big-game hunting. $104.50

VARI-X II 2x7 (2 to 7-Power)

A compact scope, no larger than the Leupold M8-4X offering a wide range of power. It can be set at 2X for close ranges in heavy cover, or zoomed to maximum power for shooting or identifying game at longer ranges. $112.50

VARI-X II 3x9 and VARI-X II 3x9 AO
(3 to 9-Power)

A wide selection of powers lets you choose the right combination of field-of-view and magnification to fit the particular conditions you are hunting at the time. Many hunters use the 3x9 at the 3X or 4X setting most of the time, cranking up to 9X for positive identification of game or for extremely long shots. The AO (Adjustable Objective) eliminates parallax and permits precise focusing on any object from less than 50 yards to infinity, for extra-sharp definition. 3x9 . . . $124.50, 3x9 AO . . . $136.50

	Scope	Magnification	Field @ 100 yds. (Feet)	Optimum Eye Relief (inches)	Length (inches)	Weight (ounces)	Adjustment Scale Div. Equal (Min. of angle)	Max. Adj. Elev. & Wind. @ 100 Yds. (inches)	Duplex	CPC	Post & Dupl.	Cross-hair	Dot
M8	2X	1.80	25.0	8 to 18	8.6	6.9	1	100	✓	✓	✓	✓	—
	3X	2.70	43.0	3.9	10.3	8.7	1	100	✓	✓	✓	✓	✓
	4X	4.00	30.0	3.9	11.8	9.3	1	80	✓	✓	✓	✓	✓
	6X	6.00	18.0	3.9	11.6	10.4	1	70	✓	✓	✓	✓	✓
	7.5X AO	7.30	14.0	3.6	12.6	13.5	1	70	✓	✓	—	✓	✓
	10X AO	10.20	10.0	3.5	13.0	14.1	½	60	✓	✓	—	✓	✓
	12X AO	12.20	9.0	3.5	14.3	14.3	½	60	✓	✓	—	✓	✓
	24X AO	23.80	4.5	3.5	15.2	15.5	1*	60	—	—	—	✓	✓
Vari-X II	1x4	1.48 / 4.10	70.5 / 28.5	4.3 / 3.4	9.6	9.5	1	50	✓	✓	✓	✓	✓
	2x7	2.30 / 6.70	42.0 / 18.0	4.1 / 3.7	11.0	10.9	1	36	✓	✓	✓	✓	✓
	3x9 & 3x9 AO	3.20 / 9.00	30.5 / 13.0	4.1 / 3.5	12.5 / 12.6	13.3 / 14.6	½	26	✓	✓	✓	✓	✓
Vari-X III	1.5x5	1.50 / 4.75	64.0 / 23.0	4.7 / 3.5	9.8	9.8	1	80	✓	—	—	—	—
	2.5x8	2.60 / 8.00	36.0 / 12.7	4.2 / 3.4	11.7	11.5	1	60	✓	—	—	—	—
	3.5x10 AO	3.50 / 10.00	29.5 / 10.5	3.9 / 3.4	12.8	12.8	½	44	✓	—	—	—	—

NOTES:

1. All Leupold Scopes have self-centered, non-magnifying reticles.

2. Windage and Elevation adjustments are internal.

3. Diameter of all scope tubes is 1".

4. We reserve the right to make design modifications and other improvements without prior notice.

5. Leupold Scopes are manufactured under one or more of the following patents: No. 3,058,391; No. 3,161,716; No. 3,286,352; No. 3,297,389.

M8-24X AO has 1-minute scale divisions, with ¼-minute "clicks"

Leupold Reticles

Note: Be sure to check Specification Chart to find out what reticles are available in the Leupold scope of your choice.

DUPLEX

Other reticles available on some Leupold scopes (See Specification Chart).

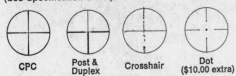

CPC   Post & Duplex   Crosshair   Dot ($10.00 extra)

Leupold "STD" Standard Mount

. . . the perfect companion to your Leupold "Golden Ring®" Scope

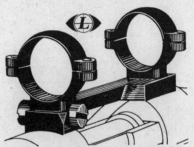

The new Leupold "STD" Mount is carefully machined from cold-rolled bar-stock steel to provide the ultimate in strength and rugged dependability. Featuring generous windage adjustments, precision-fitted dovetail and handsome, streamlined rings, the "STD" offers a firm, slip-free mount for any 1"-tube-diameter scope. Permits quick removal and return of scope. Available for the majority of popular rifles. *Note: "STD" Mount Bases and Rings interchange with Redfield "JR" and "SR" components.*

Bases $10.50
Rings (per set) $16.70

CHOICE OF 3 RING HEIGHTS

Leupold "STD" Mounts fit these rifles:	
STD FN	FN Mauser and other rifles using this basic long action
STD BA	Browning Automatic Rifle, all calibers
STD BLA	Browning Lever Action
STD 336R	Marlin 36 and 336 Models and Western Field M/740
STD 700RH-LA	Remington 700, 721, 725 (long actions); Ruger M/77 (round receiver); and Weatherby Mark V
STD 700LH-LA	Remington 700 (left hand—long action)
STD 700RH-SA	Remington 700, 722, 725 & 40X (short actions)
STD 760	Remington 740, 742, 760
STD 99R	Savage 99 Lever Action
STD 70A	All Winchester Model 70's above #66,350, not including .300 H&H & .375 H&H Magnums
STD 88	Winchester 88 and 100
STD HC	Husqvarna Crown Grade, J. C. Higgins (after 1955), Smith & Wesson and HVA-Carl Gustaf
STD M	Mauser 95 and 98
STD S	Springfield 1903
STD S-Spec.	Springfield 1903A3

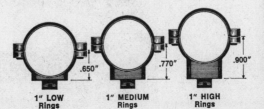

.650"   .770"   .900"

1" LOW Rings   1" MEDIUM Rings   1" HIGH Rings

SCOPE REMOVED EASILY

LYMAN RIFLE SCOPES

Lyman rifle scopes are made in 2½, 3, 4, 6, 8 and 10 power; all models are equipped with their new Perma-center reticule.

Specifications are shown below; descriptions and prices may be found on the following page.

SPECIFICATIONS OF LYMAN TELESCOPIC SIGHTS

Power	Length (Inches)	Weight (Ounces)	Tube Diameter (Inches)	Windage and Elevation Adjustment Click Values In Inches at 100 Yds.	Field of View in Feet at 100 Yards	Eye Distance or Relief Optimum (Inches)	Factory Pre-Set Parallax Corrected Range Optimum
2½ x	10½"	8¾ oz.	1 Inch	1 Inch or Minute of Angle	43 Feet	3¼" - 5"	100 Yds. To Infinity
3 x	11"	9 oz.	1 Inch	⅞ Inch	35 Feet	3¼" - 5"	100 Yds. To Infinity
4 x	12"	10 oz.	1 Inch	¾ Inch	30 Feet	3¼" - 5"	100 Yds. To Infinity
6 x	13⅞"	12¼ oz.	1 Inch	½ Inch	20 Feet	3¼" - 5"	150 Yds. To Infinity
8 x	14⅜"	13 oz.	1 Inch	⅓ Inch	14 Feet	3¼" - 5"	Adjustable for Parallax Correction
10 x	15½"	13½ oz.	1 Inch	3/10 Inch	12 Feet	3¼" - 5"	Adjustable for Parallax Correction

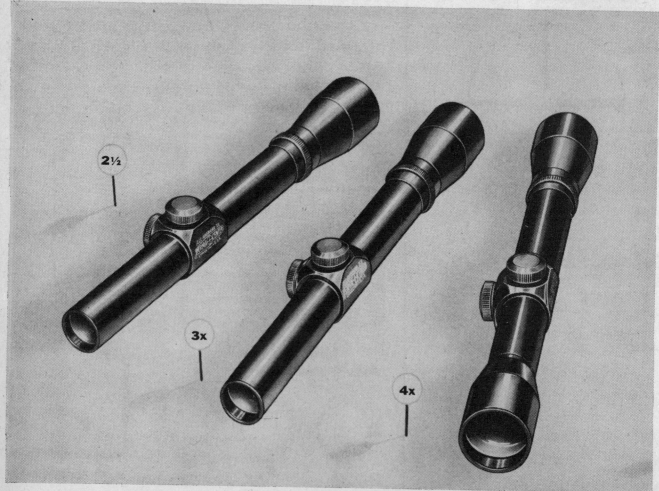

LYMAN RIFLE SCOPES

A scope should be selected on the basis of power, or magnification. The lower powers will give the widest fields of view, excellent for snapshots of running game, or deer-stalking in dense woods. The higher powers with their narrow fields come into their own for long-range big-game hunting, and varmint shooting in particular.

There is no hard-and-fast rule when it comes to scope power. Four power scopes are generally considered best for all-around hunting, but many shooters prefer the panoramic view and easier holding of the lower powers. And other shooters will swear by the superb accuracy they derive from the high magnification of their scopes—even though the range is moderate anad the game fair-sized.

All Lyman scopes are made in standard crosshair, tapered post & crosshair, and tapered post reticles.

Various sizes of dot reticles are also availabale (at $10.00 additional) as follows:

½ MINUTE DOT in 8X and 10X model;
1 MINUTE DOT in 6X, 8X and 10X models;
2 MINUTE DOT in all models;
3 MINUTE DOT in 2½, 3, 4, and 6X models;
4 MINUTE DOT in 2½, 3 and 4X models.

Lyman All-American 2½X . . . for big game, close-in brush country where wide field-of-view (43') at 100 yards permits easy "off-hand" shots at fast-moving targets. **$74.95**

Lyman All-American 3X . . . steps-up magnification from 2½X, still offers 35' field-of-view at 100 yards, fast sighting for running game. **$74.95**

Lyman All-American 4X . . . preferred for forest-and-plains shooting at big game. Ideal for distances of 75 - 300 yards and beyond, most often selected as "all-round" sight. **$74.95**

Lyman All-American 6X . . . perfect for big game at long range, small game and varmints to 300 yds., and where most shooting is done from rest or prone. **$89.95**

Lyman All-American 8 and 10X . . . strictly long-range shooting, finest for varmints like crows, woodchucks, predator and other small animals where extremely accurate, pinpoint shooting is an absolute requirement.
8X **$114.95**
10X **$114.95**

Lyman Haze Filter

Available in sizes for most popular model scopes **$3.55**

6x

8x

10x

LYMAN SUPER-TARGETSPOT

AVAILABLE IN 10X, 12X, 15X, 20X, 25X AND 30X

This model is made in a wide selection of magnifications to cover virtually every specialized target need: (10, 12, 15, 25 and 30 power).

The Super-Targetspot is furnished with calibrated head permitting parallax-corrected range settings from 50' to infinity. It is also equipped with focussing device, crosshaircant adjustment, and micrometer target mounts.

All adjustments for windage and elevation are contained in the mount. Prices: Super-Targetspot, less case—$194.95, case only—$29.95; dot reticle (extra)—$12.50; sun shade—$4.95.

3-Point Rear Mount

The Lyman 3-point suspension ¼ minute click rear mount provides markings on the windage and elevation bosses that read the same as a micrometer. Both front and rear mounts are the 3-point suspension type. The rear mount has non-rotating nylon rocker bearings which hold tube without marring.

REAR $30.00
FRONT $15.00
BASE NOT INCLUDED
BASE $5.00

SUPER-TARGETSPOT SPECIFICATIONS

Power	Length (Inches)	Weight (Ounces)	Eye Lens Diameter	Objective Lens Diameter	Windage and Elevation Adjustment Values At 100 Yds.	Field of View in Feet At 100 Yds.	Eye Distance or Relief Optimum	Parallax Corrected Range Optimum
10 X	24"	24¼ oz.	.8650"	34 MM	¼" With 7³⁄₁₆" Mount Spacing	12 Feet	2 Inches	Adjustable 50 Feet to Infinity
12 X	24"	24¼ oz.	.8650"	34 MM	¼" With 7³⁄₁₆" Mount Spacing	9' 3"	2 Inches	Adjustable 50 Feet to Infinity
15 X	24⅜"	25 oz.	.8650"	34 MM	¼" With 7³⁄₁₆" Mount Spacing	8' 9"	2 Inches	Adjustable 50 Feet to Infinity
20 X	24⅜"	25 oz.	.8650"	34 MM	¼" With 7³⁄₁₆" Mount Spacing	5' 6"	2 Inches	Adjustable 50 Feet to Infinity
25 X	24⅜"	25 oz.	.8650"	34 MM	¼" With 7³⁄₁₆" Mount Spacing	4' 3"	2 Inches	Adjustable 50 Feet to Infinity
30 X	24⅜"	25 oz.	.8650"	34 MM	¼" With 7³⁄₁₆" Mount Spacing	4 Feet	1⅞ Inches	Adjustable 50 Feet to Infinity

LYMAN 3-9 VARIABLE SCOPE

$114.95

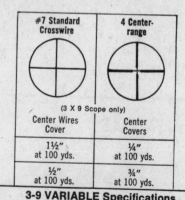

#7 Standard Crosswire	4 Center-range
(3 X 9 Scope only)	
Center Wires Cover	Center Covers
1½" at 100 yds.	¼" at 100 yds.
½" at 100 yds.	¾" at 100 yds.

3-9 VARIABLE Specifications

Length	12"
Weight	14 oz.
Tube Dia.	1"
Click Values	½" at 100 yds.
Field of View (3x)	39' at 100 yds.
Field of View (9x)	13' at 100 yds.
Eye Relief (3x)	3¾"
Eye Relief (9x)	3¼"

FEATURES

• Full magnification at all power settings. • Full field of view.

• Non-magnifying, constantly centered reticle • Finest quality, fully coated optical system to provide top light transmission.

• Ultra durable anodized exterior surface. • Matted interior surfaces to reduce stray light reflection. • Smooth control power ring, free of projections which could snag on clothing or straps.

LYMAN RIFLE SCOPES

20 POWER L·W·B·R*

SPECIFICATIONS:
Length: ....12¼"
Weight: ....12¼ oz.
Tube Diameter: ....1 inch
Click Value: ....¼" at 100 yards
Field of View(1.75X): ....47½' at 100 yards
Field of View(5X): ....18' at 100 yards
Eye Relief: ....3"
Price with standard reticle: $174.95

The Lyman 20 power L.W.B.R.* scope is a high powered bench rest scope that is small bored for the varmint shooter. Features include • internally adusted with the Lyman Perma-Center System • light weight, compact • fits all standard mounts • available with all popular reticles • available with two different click values-⅛" and ¼".

*Light weight bench rest

6X-P ALL-AMERICAN

SPECIFICATIONS:
Length: ....17⅛"
Weight: ....15¼ oz.
Tube Diameter: ....1"
Click Values: ....⅛" at 100 yards
or ¼" at 100 yards
Field of View: ....5'6" at 100 yards
Eye Relief: ....2¼"
Price with standard reticle: $109.95

The 6X-P is parallax-adjustable from 50 yards to infinity just as the 8X and 10X All American Scopes. Now you can eliminate parallax with a simple twist of the wrist and tighten groups a bit more. The 6X-P, along with the standard 6X, is a suitable choice for the open hunt country hunter who needs more magnification than the 4X but not the extremes of the 10X and above. A feature of the 6X-P All American, inherited from the 6X, is the precise adustment mechanism which permits a variety of sight changes but can always be returned to zero.

1.75-5X VARIABLE

SPECIFICATIONS:
Length: ....14"
Weight: ....14 oz.
Tube Diameter: ....1"
Click Values: ....½" at 100 yards
Field of View: ....20' at 100 yards
Eye Relief: ....3¼"
Price with standard reticle: $109.95

The 1.75-5X Variable was designed for hunting dense dark cover where deer could make two jumps and disappear. Use the low power for the maximum light-gathering and the widest-possible field of view for those jump shots; increase magnification with a flick of the wrist when time allows a more deliberate shot.

LYMAN RECEIVER SIGHTS

NO. 57 SIGHTS

LYMAN 57 RECEIVER SIGHT: An unobtrusive micrometer receiver sight for hunting or target shooting with sporter, target or military rifle.

This sight is equipped with a push-button quick-release slide that makes it ideal for alternating use on a scope-equipped rifle.

Fully adjustable with audible ¼-minute clicks for windage and elevation. Choice of coin-slotted stayset knobs for hunting or finger operated target knobs.

Slide adjustments are equipped with precision scales to aid in pre-setting sights for specific ranges or wind conditions. Slide furnished with elevation stop screw that facilitates return to "zero" if removed and re-attached.

Slide operates in dovetail channel.

No. 57 Receiver Sight, complete **$21.00**

LYMAN 66 RECEIVER SIGHT: Similar in design and construction to the No. 57 receiver sight, the model 66 was designed specifically for autoloading, pump-action and lever-action rifles. Ideally suited for use on the new Ruger .44 Carbine.

Features include ¼-minute click adjustments for windage and elevation, quick release slide, and elevation stop screw for return to "zero" if detached.

Push button release features of slide facilitates speedy removal and re-attachment.

May be had with choice of coin-slotted stayset hunting knobs or target knobs.

Like the model 48 and 57 this sight is furnished with settings scales for easy reference.

No. 66 Receiver Sight, complete **$21.00**

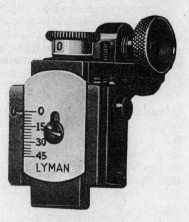

NO. 66 SIGHTS

SERIES 53 CS SHOTGUN SIGHT

When you use your shotgun for slug shooting, you need a rear sight that provides quick, accurate shooting. The Series 53 shotgun slug sight turns your birdgun into a deadly deer rifle at 100 yards. Series 53 sights can be fitted to most slug-shooting shotguns.

Here's a 50 yard group shot with a 12 gauge pump shotgun equipped with a Series 53 shotgun slug sight.

- Simple, precise windage and elevation adjustments.
- Mounts low on the receiver.
- Detaches quickly for wing shooting.

Price: Series 53 CS Receiver Sight **$7.00**

TARGET FRONT SIGHTS

SIGHT HEIGHT*

17AHB	.360"	17AMI	.445"	17AUG	.532"
17AHI	.360"	17ASF	.500"		

*From bottom of dovetail to center of aperture.

INSERTS FOR USE WITH SERIES 17A SIGHTS

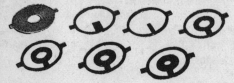

SERIES 17A TARGET FRONTS

Teamed with a Lyman receiver sight, these low silhouette front sights provide precise, X-ring accuracy on the range. Designed for use with dovetail slot mounting, they are supplied with seven interchangeable inserts (see descriptions below) that are locked into place with a threaded cap.

Price:
Series 17A Target Front Sight Complete with Inserts..... **$7.50**

Set includes: two post type inserts (.100" and .050" wide), five aperture type inserts (1 plastic .120" hole insert and four steel inserts with .070", .093", .110", and .120" holes).

Price: Complete Set of Inserts for Series 17A or 77 Sights.............. **$2.50**

LYMAN HUNTING FRONT SIGHTS

Despite the exceptionally sharp definition provided by a fine aperture receiver sight, an equally fine front sight is necessary for consistently accurate shooting—particularly in extreme glare and overcast in the field. Lyman ivory bead front sights are the ideal field front sights. They present a flat optical surface that's equally illuminated by bright or dull light, and they keep their "color" under all light conditions. The Lyman ivory bead front sight is the perfect teammate for your favorite Lyman receiver sight, and will give you a reliable, sharply defined, glareless aiming surface, even under the worst conditions. You can fit a readily adaptable Lyman bead front sight to your rifle in minutes.

A—WIDTH   F—WIDTH

These illustrations show the size and appearance difference between the two standard base widths. In general, the outside diameter of the barrel determines the width of the base to be used. "A" width is used with most ramps.

DOVETAIL TYPE FRONT SIGHTS (first letter following number of sight gives the height, the second letter the width)

DOVETAIL FRONTS

No. 31

○ 1/16" BEAD

No. 37

○ 3/32" BEAD

NO. 31 AND NO. 37 FRONT SIGHTS . . . Identical except for bead size, these sights are designed to be used on ramps. Standard 3/8" dovetail. Choice of ivory or gold bead. See Sight Selection Chart.

Price: No. 31 or No. 37 Front Sight... **$4.00**

No. 3

○ 1/16" BEAD

No. 28

○ 3/32" BEAD

NO. 3 AND NO. 28 FRONT SIGHTS . . . Identical except for bead size, these sights are mounted directly in the barrel dovetail. 3/8" dovetail is standard but the sights are also available for narrow Mauser, Enfield, or Mannlicher-Schoenauer dovetail. Choice of ivory, silver, gold, or red bead. See Sight Selection Chart.

Price: No. 3 or No. 28 Front Sight. **$4.00**

MODELS SUPPLIED		Height Inches	Width Inches
1/16" bead	3/32" bead		
31BA	37BA	.240	11/32
31CA	37CA	.290	11/32
3CF	28CF	.290	17/32
31FA	37FA	.330	11/32
		.330	7/16
3FF	28FF	.330	17/32
31GA	37GA	.345	11/32
		.345	7/16
3GF	28GF	.345	17/32
31HA	37HA	.360	11/32
		.360	7/16
3HF	28HF	.360	17/32
31JA	37JA	.390	11/32
		.390	7/16
3JF	28JF	.390	17/32
31KA	37KA	.410	11/32
		.410	7/16
3KF	28KF	.410	17/32
31MA	37MA	.445	11/32
		.445	7/16
3MF	28MF	.445	17/32
31SA	37SA	.500	11/32
		.500	7/16
3SF	28SF	.500	17/32
31VA	37A	.560	11/32
		.560	7/16
3VF	28VF	.560	17/32

LYMAN TRU-LOCK MOUNTS

Lyman Tru-Lock Mounts are made from a durable lightweight alloy in a wide range of sizes to accommodate most any rifle-scope combination. With one-piece or two-piece base (depending on rifle) Lyman Mounts are easily detachable and leave but a small, flat base on the rifle when removed.

RAMP FRONT SIGHTS

18E

18A   18C

NO. 18 SCREW-ON TYPE RAMP . . . The screw-on ramp is designed to be secured with a heavy 8-40 screw (it may be brazed on if desired). Screw-on ramps are ruggedly built and extremely versatile. They use A width front sights, and are available in the following heights:

18A — Low Ramp: .100" from top of barrel to bottom of dovetail.

18C — Medium Ramp: .250" from top of barrel to bottom of dovetail.

18E — High Ramp: .350" from top of barrel to bottom of dovetail.

Price:
No. 18 Screw-On Ramp Complete With Sight **$9.50**
No. 18 Screw-On Ramp Less Sight **$5.50**

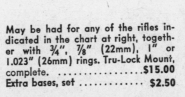 

May be had for any of the rifles indicated in the chart at right, together with 3/4", 7/8" (22mm), 1" or 1.023" (26mm) rings. Tru-Lock Mount, complete. **$15.00**
Extra bases, set **$2.50**

LYMAN SIGHTS

LEAF SIGHTS

NO. 16 FOLDING LEAF SIGHT... Designed primarily as open rear sights with adjustable elevation, leaf sights make excellent auxiliary sights for scope-mounted rifles. They fold close to the barrel when not in use, and they can be installed and left on the rifle without interfering with scope or mount. Two lock screws hold the elevation blade adjustments firmly in place. A sight of this type could save the day if the scope becomes damaged through rough handling. Leaf sights are available in the following heights:

16A —.400" high; elevates to .500".
16B —.345" high; elevates to .445".
16C —.500" high; elevates to .600".
For installation on rifles without a dovetail slot, use Lyman No. 25 Base.

SIGHT FOLDS TO CLEAR SCOPE

GRADUATED BLADE ELEVATES BY SLIDING IN ELONGATED SCREW HOLES

A "Partridge" type blade for the No. 16A Folding Leaf Sight is offered as an auxiliary blade.

Price:
No. 16 Folding Leaf Sight,..... **$4.00**

BASES

NO. 25 BASES
Permit the installation of dovetail rear sights such as Lyman 16 leaf sight on rifles that do not have dovetail cut in barrel. They also supply a higher line of sight when needed. The No. 25 Base is mounted by drilling and tapping the barrel for two 6-48 screws. Screws are supplied with base.

Price: No. 25 Base **$3.00**

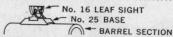

No. 16 LEAF SIGHT
No. 25 BASE
BARREL SECTION

STANDARD BASES	HEIGHT FROM TOP OF BARREL to BOTTOM of DOVETAIL	BARREL RADIUS
25A-Base (Low)	.025—	.875 or larger
25C-Base (High)	.125—	.875 or larger
SPECIAL BASES		
25B-Base Fits factory screw holes on Remington 740, 742, 760, 725 & replaces factory rear	.125—	.875 or larger
25D-Base For small diameter barrels, Note Radius	.025—	For Barrels under .875 dia.

NOTE: For gunsmith use — 25A, C and D bases are also available in the white (unblued), and without screw holes. Heights and radii as above. **Price: $1.25**

NO. 12 SLOT BLANKS

These Blanks fill the standard ⅜" rear barrel dovetail when a receiver sight is installed. They are also available for front sight dovetails and ramps when a scope is being used. Three lengths are available, all fit standard ⅜" dovetails.
No. 12S (⅜" x ⅝" long) for standard rear barrel slots.
No. 12SS (⅜" x ¾₁₆" long) for standard front sight slots and some rear slots in narrow barrels.
No. 12SF (¾" x ¹¹⁄₃₂" long) this blank has square ends and is intended for use in ramps.

Price: (all sizes) **$1.50**

SHOTGUN SIGHTS

SHOTGUN SIGHTS . . . . . . Lyman shotgun sights are available for all shotguns. Equipped with oversized ivory beads that give perfect definition on either bright, or dull days, they are easy to see under any light conditions. They quickly catch your eye on fast upland targets, and point out the lead on long passing shots. Lyman shotgun sights are available with WHITE or RED bead, and can be fitted to your gun in minutes.

NO. **10 FRONT SIGHT** (Press Fit) for use on double barrel, or ribbed single barrel guns.
Sight **$1.50**

NO. **10D FRONT SIGHT** (Screw Fit) for use on non-ribbed single barrel guns. These sights are supplied with a wrench. Sight & Wrench **$1.75**

NO. **11 MIDDLE SIGHT** (Press Fit) This small middle sight is intended for use on double barrel and ribbed single barrel guns. Sight **$1.25**

NO. **9 SET** — This set consists of both the No. 10 and No. 11 sight listed above.
Set **$2.50**

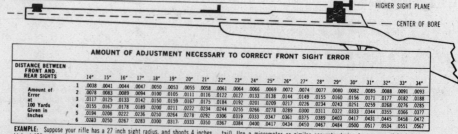

HIGHER SIGHT PLANE
CENTER OF BORE

When you replace an open rear sight with a receiver sight, it is usually necessary to install a higher front sight, to compensate for the higher plane of the new receiver sight. The table below shows the increase in front sight height that's required to compensate for a given error at 100 yards.

AMOUNT OF ADJUSTMENT NECESSARY TO CORRECT FRONT SIGHT ERROR																					
DISTANCE BETWEEN FRONT AND REAR SIGHTS		14"	15"	16"	17"	18"	19"	20"	21"	22"	23"	24"	25"	26"	27"	28"	29"	30"	31"	32"	33"	34"
Amount of Error at 100 Yards Given in Inches	1	.0038	.0041	.0044	.0047	.0050	.0053	.0055	.0058	.0061	.0064	.0066	.0069	.0072	.0074	.0077	.0080	.0082	.0085	.0088	.0091	.0093
	2	.0078	.0083	.0089	.0094	.0100	.0105	.0111	.0116	.0122	.0127	.0133	.0138	.0144	.0149	.0155	.0160	.0165	.0171	.0177	.0182	.0188
	3	.0117	.0125	.0133	.0142	.0150	.0159	.0167	.0175	.0184	.0192	.0201	.0209	.0217	.0226	.0234	.0243	.0251	.0259	.0268	.0276	.0285
	4	.0155	.0167	.0178	.0189	.0200	.0211	.0222	.0234	.0244	.0255	.0266	.0278	.0289	.0300	.0311	.0322	.0333	.0344	.0355	.0366	.0377
	5	.0194	.0208	.0222	.0236	.0250	.0264	.0278	.0292	.0306	.0319	.0333	.0347	.0361	.0375	.0389	.0403	.0417	.0431	.0445	.0458	.0472
	6	.0243	.0250	.0267	.0283	.0300	.0317	.0333	.0350	.0367	.0384	.0400	.0417	.0434	.0450	.0467	.0484	.0500	.0517	.0534	.0551	.0567

EXAMPLE: Suppose your rifle has a 27 inch sight radius, and shoots 4 inches high at 100 yards, with the receiver sight adjusted as low as possible. The 27 inch column shows that the correction for a 4 inch error is .0300 inch. This correction is added to the over-all height of the front sight (including dovetail. Use a micrometer or similar accurate device to measure sight height. Thus, if your original sight measured .360 inch, it should be replaced with a sight .390 inch high, such as a J height sight.

MARLIN SCOPES FOR .22 RIFLES

500
Zoom

$21.95

3-7X20 millimeter. With big ⅞" tube. This zoom variable. 22 Marlin scope is built ruggedly and offers "camera optics", double coated lenses and a larger field of view. Precise ½-minute click stops. Fits all .22's grooved for tipoff scopes. Complete with mounts.

300 B

$19.95

4X 20 millimeter with big ⅞" tube. The fixed power .22 Marlin scope scoops in light with big 20 millimeter double coated objective lens. Precise ½-minute click stops. Fits any .22 rifle grooved for tipoff scope. Complete with two piece mounts.

HIGH-POWERED SCOPES

825
Zoom Variable

$49.95

3-9X, 32mm. Weatherproof, nitrogen-filled, hermetically sealed, and fog-proof/scratch-resistant 1" tube. 32 mm. double hard-coated lens scoops in light. Optically centered, non-magnifying 1-MR hunting reticle helps you hold closely even in fading light. Dialable magnification is at your fingertips; ¼-minute windage and elevation click stops. Eye relief — 2¾" to 3¼". Field at 100 yards — up to 35'. Designed especially for marlin 444 and 1895 high power rifles.

Marlin 425: 4X 32mm. (not shown) Precision fixed-power scope. Parallax-corrected hard-coated optical system has exceptional light-gathering power. Smaller diameter objective enables lowest possible mounting. Features an optically centered 1-MR reticle in which cross-hairs are extended from Tri-post to insure pin-point aiming even in weak light. Reticle remains centered throughout full range of windage and elevation adjustment. ¼-minute click stops. Tough scratch-resistant 1" tube. Eye relief—3½". Field at 100 yards—approx. 28'. Fog-proof and moisture resistant. Lens caps included. **$31.95**

Marlin 750 (not shown) Specially designed for use on shotguns designed for rifled slugs. 1.5X, 20mm, weatherproof, nitrogen-filled, hermetically sealed. 1" tube is fog-proof and scratch-resistant. Optically centered 1-MR reticle. ¼-minute windage and elevation click stops. Eye relief—9-15". Field at 100 yards—approx. 25'. Especially designed for use on Marlin 120 with slug barrel and Marlin 55S. **$29.95**

MARLIN —— HIGH-POWER MOUNT

$7.95

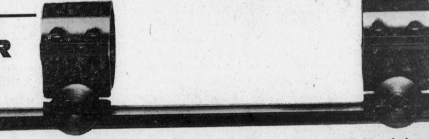

Carefully engineered and handcrafted, machined mount fits all popular high powered rifles designed for scope equipment. Rings and bases packaged together.

MERIT SHOOTING AIDS

MERIT IRIS SHUTTER MASTER TARGET DISC

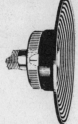

PATENT PENDING

WITH

FLEXIBLE NEOPRENE LIGHT SHIELD

May be cut to size

Particularly adapted for use with extension, telescope height and tang sights . . .

- The 1½" in diameter flexible neoprene light shield is permanently attached to the eye cup which is replacable by removing three screws. The shield is concentrically ribbed on its concave face for cutting to suitable size. It is more advantageous than a large metal disc since it protects the sighting equipment in case the disc is accidentally bumped.

- The Master Target Disc may be used on all sights having clearance for a disc 7/16" thick and 3/4" or larger in diameter.

Master Disc . . .	**$17.00**
MERIT DELUX Master Disc . . .	**$21.00**
Replacement Shield	**$ 2.00**
Delux Replacement Shield and Steel Cup	**$ 3.00**

THE MERIT LENS DISC is made with any of the No. 3 Series shanks. The body of the Standard Lens Disc is 7/16" thick . . . the Master Target Lens Disc is ¾" thick . . . Outside diameters are the same as shown for No. 3 Series and Master Target Discs. The Merit Lens Disc is properly cushioned to absorb recoil shock.

MERIT DELUX No. 3 Lens Disc	**$21.00**
MERIT DELUX Master Lens Disc	**$25.00**

MERIT No. 4SS—Outside diameter of disc ½". Shank 5/16" long. Disc thickness ¼".	**$14.00**
MERIT No. 4LS—Outside diameter of disc ½". Shank 11/32" long. Disc thickness ¼".	**$14.00**
MERIT No. 4ELS—Outside diameter of disc ½". Shank ½" long. Disc thickness ¼".	**$14.00**

SIGHT CHART

Popular Peep Sights and the proper Merit Discs to fit them. The Merit Master Target Disc may be had with any of the No. 3 series shanks. All of the sights marked ★ will take the Master Disc depending on the front sight used. See chart below:

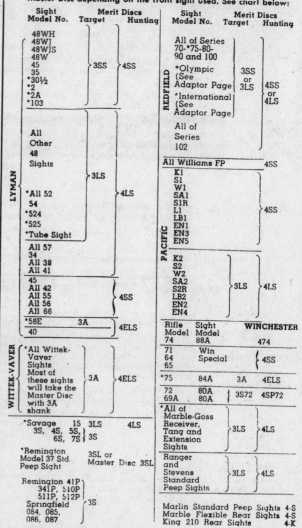

	Sight Model No.	Merit Discs Target	Merit Discs Hunting
LYMAN	48WH 48WJ 48WJS 48W 45 35 *30½ *2 *2A *103	3SS	4SS
	All Other 48 Sights	3LS	
	*All 52 54 *524 *525 *Tube Sight		4LS
	All 57 34 All 38 All 41 45 All 42 All 55 All 56 All 66		4SS
	*58E	3A	4ELS
	40		
WITTEK-VAVER	*All Wittek-Vaver Sights Most of these sights will take the Master Disc with 3A shank	3A	4ELS
	*Savage 3S, 4S, 5S, 6S, 7S	15 3LS 3S	4LS
	*Remington Model 37 Std. Peep Sight	3SL or Master Disc 3SL	
	Remington 41P 341P, 510P 511P, 512P Springfield 084, 085, 086, 087	3S	

	Sight Model No.	Merit Discs Target	Merit Discs Hunting
REDFIELD	All of Series 70-*75-80-90 and 100	3SS or 3LS	4SS or 4LS
	*Olympic (See Adaptor Page)		
	*International (See Adaptor Page)		
	All of Series 102		
	All Williams FP		4SS
PACIFIC	K1 S1 W1 SA1 S1R L1 LB1 EN1 EN3 EN5		4SS
	K2 S2 W2 SA2 S2R LB2 EN2 EN4	3LS	4LS

Rifle Model	Sight Model	WINCHESTER
74	88A	474
71 64 65	Win Special	4SS
*75	84A	3A 4ELS
72 69A	80A 80A	3S72 4SP72
*All of Marble-Goss Receiver, Tang and Extension Sights		3LS 4LS
Ranger and Stevens Standard Peep Sights		3LS 4LS

Marlin Standard Peep Sights	4-S
Marble Flexible Rear Sights	4-S
King 210 Rear Sights	4-K

THE MERIT OPTICAL ATTACHMENT WITH APERTURE IS THE ANSWER TO A SHOOTER'S PROBLEM WHEN THE EYESIGHT IS IMPAIRED.

(1) concentrates and sharpens the vision by increasing the focal depth of the eye, making pistol or rifle sights stand out sharp and clear; (2) Cuts out objectionable side lights; (3) Helps the shooter to take the same position for each shot. (This is a very vital factor in accurate shooting;) (4) Gives instant and easy choice of just the right aperture

suiting your own eye and particular conditions at time of shooting.

Standard Optical Attachment Price:	**$14.00**
Delux Optical Attachment Price:	**$16.00**

The Delux model has swinging arm feature so that the shooter can swing the aperture from the line of vision when not shooting.

Re-placement suction cup—Price . . . . **$ 2.50**

MICRO SIGHTS FOR HANDGUNS

The Micro Sight is small and compact. The sight is attached to models with dovetail slot for rear and removable front sights in the same manner as the factory sight. The rear sight has positive self-locking click adjustments in both windage and elevation. Each click changes point of impact ½" at twenty-five yards. Once set—the sight is constant and will not move from recoil. The sighting radius is raised, allowing for a deep notch in the rear aperture. This added depth gives the shooter sharper definition and eliminates glare. It is necessary to install a higher front sight to conform with the rear.

Front sight blades are available in three widths: 1/10", 1/8" or 5/32". The styles are plain post, undercut or quick-draw.

ADJUSTABLE REAR SIGHTS with BLADE FRONT SIGHTS for the following:

1P Standard Adj. sights for Colt .45 ACP & .45 Commander; and Star Model "B" 9m/m	$ 20.00
2P Standard Adj. sights for Colt .38 Super, 9 MM & .38 Commander	20.00
3P Low Mount Adj. sights for Colt .45 ACP and .45 Commander	20.00
4P Low Mount Adj. sights for Colt .38 Super, 9 MM & .38 Commander	20.00
5P Low Mount Adj. sights for Colt .22 Service Ace & .22/.45 Conversion unit	20.00
15P Colt M. T. Woodsman, Postwar	20.00
16P Colt Target Woodsman, Postwar	20.00
17P Colt M. T. Woodsman, Prewar	20.00
19P Colt .22 Officers Model Match & Officers Model Special	20.00
20P Colt .38 Officers Model Match & Officers Model Special	20.00
23P Ruger .22 Standard Sport Model	20.00
25P High Standard Sport King, 102 Series	20.00
26P Browning 9m/m Hi-Power	20.00
27P Browning 9MM Hi-Power LOW MT	20.00
28P Llama 38 Super w/rib	20.00
29P Llama 45 Auto w/rib	20.00
Adjustable Micro Rear only	17.00
Micro Front Blade only	4.00
MICRO front ramp only—less blade	5.00
MICRO blade only for front ramp	4.00
MICRO-TITE barrel bushing for Colt 45 Govt Model	7.50
MICRO barrel bushing wrench	1.25
MICRO insert only for rear sight	1.25

TYPES OF MICRO FRONT BLADE SIGHTS

Undercut   Plain Post   Quick Draw

DIFFERENT WIDTHS OF FRONT BLADES

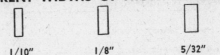

1/10"   1/8"   5/32"

ADJUSTABLE REAR SIGHTS with RAMP FRONT SIGHTS for the following:

AR Ruger Single Six	$ 23.50
BR Smith & Wesson .38 Military & Police	23.50
CR Colt .38 Official Police	23.50
DR Colt .22 Official Police	23.50
ER Smith & Wesson 1917 .45 Revolver	23.50
FR Smith & Wesson .38/.44	23.50
GR Smith & Wesson .44 Special	23.50
HR Smith & Wesson 1950 .45	23.50
IR Colt Single Action .22	23.50
JR Colt Single Action .38	23.50
KR Colt Single Action .45	23.50
LR Great Western .22	23.50
MR Great Western .38	23.50
NR Great Western .45	23.50
OR Colt New Service .38	23.50
PR Colt New Service .45	23.50
QR Colt Challenger .22	23.50
RR Colt Sport Model Woodsman (Prewar)	23.50
VR Supermatic Trophy & Citation	23.50
WR Supermatic Tournament	23.50
XR 102 Series Sport King & Duramatic	23.50
ZR Colt Scout 22	23.50
2R Browning 9MM Hi-Power	23.50
3R Colt Huntsman	23.50
4R Colt Targetsman	23.50
5R Colt Navy Cap & Ball	23.50
6R Hawes 44 Rem Cap & Ball	23.50
7R Navy Arms 44 Rem Cap & Ball	23.50
8R Hy Hunter Six Shooter 357	23.50

(RAMP STYLE NOT MADE FOR 45 GOVT)

INTERCHANGEABILITY OF MICRO ADJUSTABLE REAR SIGHTS

Group #1—1P 2P QR RR 28P 3R 4R 5R 7R 29P
Group #2—3P 4P 5P 16P 17P 19P 20P 27P 25P
Group #3—6P 13P 14P SR
Group #4—7P 18P TR
Group #5—8P 21P
Group #6—BR CR DR ER FR GR HR IR JR KR LR MR NR OR PR ZR 8R 9R
Group #7—VR WR
Group #8—UR YR 6R
Group #9—XR 25P

INTERCHANGEABILITY OF MICRO FRONT SIGHTS

Group #1—7P 14P
Group #3—UR WR
Group #4—15P 20P
Group #5—8P 13P 25P
Group #6—BR FR
Group #7—ER HR
Group #8—JR MR
Group #9—KR NR OR PR
Group #10—LR QR 3R
Group #11—XR YR
Group #12—ZR 9R

FREELAND'S ALL ANGLE TRIPOD

Freeland AAT All-Angle Tripod

Made of aluminum, light weight, strong and rigid.

Wide spread legs. Saddle is both manually controlled, or by the micro screw adjustment for elevating or lowering the saddle. Takes all scopes from the Draw tube size to the 63mm. Clamping ring with worm drive, assures holding scope to saddle firmly, no leather or web straps to contend with. Scope is easily and quickly removed from the saddle. The offset is either right or left hand, and thereby accommodates the right or left hand shooter. Can be folded up with scope attached and placed in your shooting kit, and easily and quickly set up on 30 seconds notice. 8" minimum height, 12" extreme height without extensions.

NOTE: Specify Scope to be used. Weight, approximately 3 pounds.

AAT—ALL ANGLE TRIPOD, green or gray, mention scope	$29.50
18" Extension	6.00
24" Extension	7.50
ZT—Freeland tripod for zoom scope, gray or green	29.50
Freeland Standard "OB" bipod	31.50

PACHMAYR SCOPE MOUNTS

(FOR 1-INCH & 26 M/M SCOPES)

PACHMAYR LO-SWING® SCOPE MOUNT

Combines two important advantages in one mount. Provides instant use of open sights and a scope mounted as low as possible on your rifle. Don't let fogged lenses or a damaged scope spoil your chance for a kill. Guaranteed to maintain zero alignment no matter how many times removed or swung to the side. Side mount $30.00 top mount $35.00

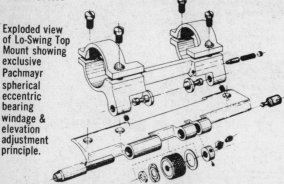

Exploded view of Lo-Swing Top Mount showing exclusive Pachmayr spherical eccentric bearing windage & elevation adjustment principle.

TOP MOUNTS   Available for:

MAKE OF GUN	GUN MODELS	MOUNT NO.
Remington	700, 721, 725 (long actions)	R700 RT
	700, 722, 725 (short actions)	R700 RT
	700 L.H. (long action)	R700 L.H.RT
	700 L.H. (short action)	R700 L.H. ST
	720, 30	R30T
	600	R600T
	(**660)	R600T
	740	
	742 Ser. 184, 499 & below	R7 40T
	742 Ser. 184, 500 & up	R742BDLT
	760 Ser. 443, 499 & below	R740T
	760 Ser. 443, 500 & up	R742 BDLT
	788 short action	R788S-T
	788 long action	R788L-T
	788 extra long action	R788X-T
	141	R141-T
Winchester	Win. 70 - 670, 770 All calibers, except .300 & .375 H&H Mag., above Serial No. 66,350	W 70T
	Win. 70 .300 / .375 H&H Mag., above Serial No. 700,000	W70MT
	Win. 70 Target	W70 TGT
	Win. 70 .300 & .375 H&H Mag., between Serial Nos. 66,350 and 700,000	W70 TGT
	Win. 70 All Cals. except .300 & .375 H&H Mag., below Serial No. 66,350	W70 T
	Win. 70 .300 & .375 H&H Mag., below Serial No. 66,350	W70 TGT
	88 & 100	W-88T
Savage	99	S-99T
	110 R.H. Long Action	S-110 RHT
	110 L.H. Long Action	S-110 LHT
	110 short action R.H.	S-110 RHST
	110 short action L.H.	S-110 LHST
	**24V	S-24VT
Sako	Finnbear	SK-FIT
	Forester	SK-FOT
	Vixen	SK-VT
Marlin	**336, 1895, 44	M-336T
	**1894	M-1894T
Mauser	98 (large ring long action)	MR-T
	Yugoslav 1924 (lrg. Rg. sht. act.)	YU-T
	Kar 98 (sm. ring, long action)	KA-T
	Mexican (sm. ring, short action)	Mex-T
	FN (std. FN action)	FN-T
	Santa Fe (FN action spec. hole spacing)	MSF-T
	66 (dovetail receiver)	MR66T
	2000	MR2000T
	4000	M-4000T

**Due to special stop pin lengths, these bases should be ordered only with matching loops

MAKE OF GUN	GUN MODELS	MOUNT NO.
Mossberg	800	MO-800T
	810	MO-810T
	472	MO-472T
Krico	Varmint	KRICO-T
Husqvarna	Short action (small ring)	HV-SRT
	Long action (large ring)	HV-T
Springfield	03-06	SPR-03T
	03/A3	SPR-A3T
Enfield	Eddystone	EN-T
Schultz & Larsen	Regular	SLR-T
	Magnum	SLM-T
Ruger	44	R-44T
	10/22	R-22T
	M-77 RS long (dovetail)	R77-RS-LT
	M-77 RS short (dovetail)	R77-RS-ST
	M-77 ST long (round)	R77-ST-LT
	No. 1	R No. 1T
Browning Sako	222, 222 Magnum	B469-T
	243. 308, 22-250	B479-T
Browning	Safari	FN-T
	Short Action	BRO-S-T
	Semi-auto. rifle	BRO-SAT
	Lever action	BRO-LAT
BSA Monarch	Dovetail rec. long action	BSA-TR
	Dovetail rec. short action	BSA-TS
	Round Receiver Long Action	R 700 RT
	Round Receiver Short Action	R 700 ST
Weatherby	Mark V, left hand Vangard, LH	WLH-T
	Mark V, Vangard, RH	R700 RT
Parker Hale Harrington	1200 & P1200	FN-T
Richardson	300 & 301	FN-T
Smith & Wesson	A, B, C, D, E	HV-SRT
Ranger Arms	Texas Maverick	RA-TMV
	Texas Magnum 458	RA-458-T
	Texas Magnum 375	RA-375-T
Interarms	Mark X	FN-T
Voere Shikar		VST

SIDE MOUNTS   Available for:

MAKE OF GUN	GUN MODELS	MOUNT NO.
Winchester	54, 70	W-70
	64, 94, Rem. 121, 241	W-94
	Model 12 shotgun	W-12
	88, 100	W-88
Remington	Enfield 30S, R720	Enf
	8, 81	R-81
	141, 14	R-14
	721, 722, 725 and 700 series	R-721
	740, 760, 742	R-740
	Shotgun 1100	R-1100
	870	R-1100
Savage	40, 45 and Ariska, Husqvarna Cr., Swedish Mauser	S-40
	20, Japanese 25	S-20
	99	S-99
	340, 342, Sako .222	S-340
	24 DL	S-24 DL
Springfield	1903, A3, 1922, Sedley-Newton	Spr.
Stevens	325C, 322 Sako L 46	S-325C
Marlin	36A, 336	M-36
	39A	M-39
Mauser	93	S-40
	98	MR
	FN 1949 Auto	FN 49A
	All FN Bolt Actions	MR
Mauser Carbine	Carbine Brno	MC
Mannlicher-Schoenauer	1950 or later	MS
Krag..		K
Garand	Military auto 30/06, 308	M-1
Brng. Std. Rem. 11	Shotguns	B-R
Military	*Carbine 30M1	M-1 Carbine
Lee Enfield	SMLE No. 1, Mk. 1, 2, 3	L-Enf A
	SMLE No. 4 Mk.1	L-Enf B
Ithaca	37	W-12

*Due to near vertical shell ejection, it is recommended that these bases be used with a left hand loop and a crosshair reticle scope.

REDFIELD SCOPES

Traditional

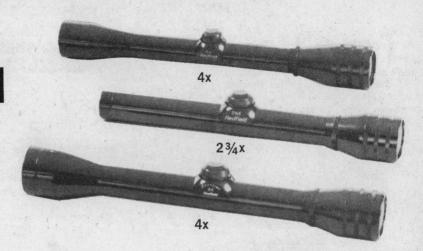

4x

2 3/4 x

4x

4x Traditional
The Traditional's ¾" tube, at 6¼ ozs. and a compact 9½" long, is the perfect complement to a .22 or other small caliber rifle. This scope is hermetically sealed to prevent fogging. The Traditional features precision-ground coated glass lenses throughout for precise resolution. This tough scope is designed and tested to withstand the recoil of magnum caliber rifles.

4x Traditional
¾" Tube Diameter

Reticle	Item No.	Price
4-Plex	138006	**$36.50**

Lens Covers	Item No.	Price
Storm Queen	150011	**$3.80**

2½ x Traditional
Provides a 43' field of view for close-in type brush hunting. Complements any "slug gun package" for use on shotguns where slugs are used for deer hunting. All the features of the 4x.

2½ x Traditional
1" Tube Diameter

Reticle	Item No.	Price
4-Plex	132106	$59.70
PCH	132103	$57.70

4x Traditional
Efficient performance at a moderate price for hunters who prefer a medium power scope. All the quality Redfield features: unscratchable, hard anodized finish. Magnum proof. Streamlined Redfield look. Coated glass lenses for increased light transmission. Brilliant distortion-free resolution. Hermetically sealed with O-rings to prevent fogging.

4x
1" Tube Diameter

Reticle	Item No.	Price
4-Plex	135006	**$70.40**

Lens Covers	Item No.	Price
Storm Queen	150021	**$3.80**
Storm King	150024	**$4.40**

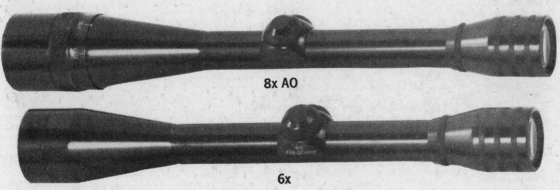

8x AO

6x

8x AO (Adjustable Objective) For game and varmint hunting. Offers external parallax adjustment sleeve on scope objective bell. Adjustment from fifty yards to infinity may be made with one hand. Positive stops prevent over-turning of the adjustment sleeve. 1" tube diameter.

Reticle	Item No.	Price
4-Plex	137106	**$99.80**

10x AO (Adjustable Objective) (not illustrated) This varmint bench-rest scope also has an external adjustment sleeve (50 yards to infinity) similar to the 8x AO and the popular Redfield 4x-12x and 6x-18x variable power scopes. 1" tube diameter.

Reticle	Item No.	Price
4-Plex	133106	**$110.00**

6x This traditional 6x eyepiece gives extra magnification for longer ranges. Has all the famous Redfield features including tough aluminum alloy construction, coated lenses. Hermetically sealed. 1" tube diameter.

Reticle	Item No.	Price
4-Plex	136106	**$81.00**

REDFIELD SCOPES

Traditional

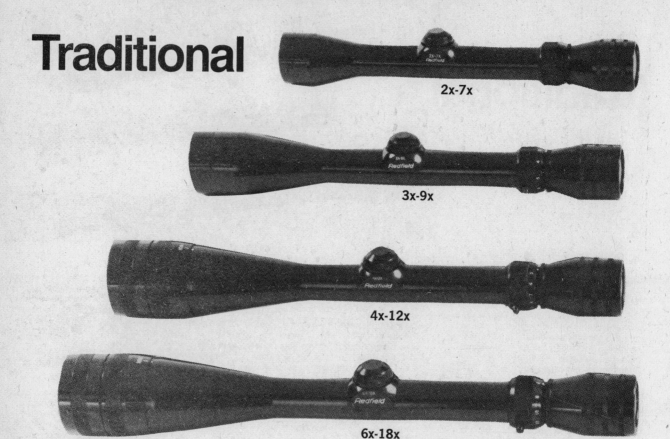

2x-7x

3x-9x

4x-12x

6x-18x

2x-7x Traditional
This model of the Traditional line gives the same advantages of the 4x Traditional, but with the added benefit of a popular variable power range.

2x-7x
1" Tube Diameter

Reticle	Item No.	Price
4-Plex	122106	**$95.30**
PCH	122103	**$95.30**
AR 4-Plex	122116	**$107.80**

Lens Covers	Item No.	Price
Storm Queen	150002	**$3.80**
Storm King	150005	**$4.40**

3x-9x Traditional
Actually works like three scopes in one. At 3x, it's perfect for close-in woods and brush hunting. At 4x-6x, it handles normal open range hunting. And at 9x, it's ideal for long range spotting and shooting.

3x-9x
1" Tube Diameter

Reticle	Item No.	Price
4-Plex	123106	**$111.30**
3x9x Accu-Range Variable		
AR 4-Plex	123116	**$123.80**

PCH	122103	**$95.30**
2x-7x Accu-Range Variable		
AR 4-Plex	122116	**$107.80**

4x-12x
Power to go after everything from varmints to big game. Parallax-Focus (from 50 yards to infinity) on the objective bell is clearly marked and easy to adjust . . . an important feature for varmint and bench-rest shooters to whom the higher power range is vital. Positive stops prevent over-turning of the parallax adjusting sleeve.

4x-12x Variable
1" Tube Diameter

Reticle	Item No.	Price
FCH	119000	**$138.00**
MCH	119001	"
3' to 1' Dot	119002	**$150.50**
4-PCCH	119004	**$138.00**
4-Plex	119006	"
4x-12x Accu-Range Variable		
AR MCH	119011	**$150.50**
AR 4-PCCH	119014	"
AR 4-Plex	119016	"

Lens Covers	Item No.	Price
Storm Queen	150016	**$3.80**
Storm King	150017	**$4.40**

6-18x
A favored scope of higher power for varmint hunting and bench-rest shooting. Excellent field of view at all power settings with Parallax-Focus adjustment from 50 yards to infinity. Stops at either end prevent over-turning of this adjustment.

6x-18x Variable
1" Tube Diameter

Reticle	Item No.	Price
CH	120000	**$149.60**
1½' to ½' Dot	120001	**$162.00**
4-Plex	120003	**$148.60**
6x-18x Accu-Range Variable		
AR CH	120006	**$162.00**
AR 4-Plex	120008	"

Lens Covers	Item No.	Price
Storm Queen	150016	**$3.80**
Storm King	150017	**$4.40**

REDFIELD SCOPES

Widefield

2¾ x

4xLP

4x

6x

4x LP (Low Profile)

Same wide field of view, brilliant optics, hard anodized finish and power flexibility as standard 4x. Sleek, streamlined design at both the objective and eyepiece ends lets this scope be mounted for lowest possible profile.

4x LP
1" Tube Diameter

Reticle	Item No.	Price
4-Plex	144406	**$103.30**

2¾ x

A rugged and efficient lower magnification scope with a 55.5' field of view at 100 yards. For comparatively short range brush and/or slug gun hunting. Even in poor light, dawn or dusk, moving targets are easy to locate.

2¾ x
1" Tube Diameter

Reticle	Item No.	Price
CH	141000	**$78.40**
PCH	141001	"
3' Dot	141002	**$90.80**
4-PCCH	141005	**$78.40**
4-Plex	141007	"

Lens Covers	Item No.	Price
Storm Queen	150020	**$3.80**
Storm King	150023	**$4.40**

4x

The most popular fixed-power member of the Widefield family. Outstanding field of view in an all-purpose, all-around scope with the flexibility to handle close-in shots or those at moderately long range.

4x
1" Tube Diameter

Reticle	Item No.	Price
CH	143000	**$89.00**
PCH	143001	"
3' Dot	143003	**$105.50**
4-PCCH	143004	**$89.00**
4-Plex	143006	"

Lens Covers	Item No.	Price
Storm Queen	150021	**$3.80**
Storm King	150024	**$4.40**

6x

A scope for long ranges in wide open spaces or big mountain country. The combination of 6x magnification and 30% extra field of view has caused many hunters to switch from lower-powered scopes. A proven complement to all-around, flat-shooting sporting rifles for medium to long range varmint hunting.

6x
1" Tube Diameter

Reticle	Item No.	Price
CH	146000	**$99.70**
PCH	146003	"
4-PCCH	146004	"
4-Plex	146006	"
2' Dot	146008	**$112.20**

Lens Covers	Item No.	Price
Storm Queen	150022	**$3.80**
Storm King	150025	**$4.40**

6x LP (Low Profile) All the wanted features of the 6x with the added advantages of the popular low profile. Low mounting on the barrel (it isn't necessary to remove rear sight from most rifles). Fits easily into gun case and saddle scabbard, has sleek, streamlined look. 1" tube diameter. **$115.70**

6x LP (Low Profile)

REDFIELD SCOPES

Widefield

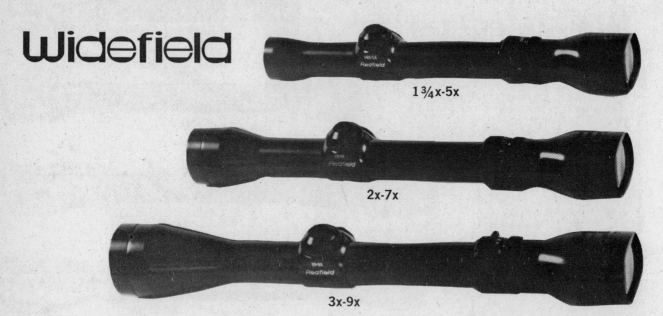

1¾x-5x

2x-7x

3x-9x

1¾x-5x
Ideal for fast, accurate close-in brush and slug shooting . . . the field of view at 100 yards at 1¾x is an outstanding 70 feet. Ample magnification is provided at 5x for longer ranges.

1¾x-5x Variable
1" Tube Diameter

Reticle	Item No.	Price
MCH	113100	**$105.50**
PCH	113103	"
4-PCCH	113104	"
4-Plex	113106	"

1¾x-5x Accu-Range Variable

AR MCH	113110	**$118.90**
AR 4-Plex	113116	"

Lens Covers	Item No.	Price
Storm Queen	150031	**$3.80**
Storm King	150041	**$4.40**

2x-7x
For the all-purpose hunter . . . smaller than the 3x-9x for conventional scabbards, tough enough to handle most any hunting situation or range.

2x-7x Variable
1" Tube Diameter

Reticle	Item No.	Price
MCH	111100	**$123.60**
PCH	111103	"
4-PCCH	111104	"
4-Plex	111106	"
3' to 1' Dot	111109	**$136.00**

2x-7x Accu-Range Variable

AR MCH	111110	**$136.00**
AR 4-Plex	111116	"

Lens Covers	Item No.	Price
Storm Queen	150032	**$3.80**
Storm King	150042	**$4.40**

3x-9x
All the versatility and rugged dependability for big game and varmint hunting are built into this model. It fulfills a variety of purposes from long-range, peak-to-peak spotting and shooting to shorter ranges in wooded situations and poor light conditions.

3x-9x Variable
1" Tube Diameter

Reticle	Item No.	Price
MCH	112100	**$137.80**
PCH	112103	"
4-PCCH	112104	"
4-Plex	112106	"
3' to 1' Dot	112109	**$150.30**

3x-9x Accu-Range Variable

AR MCH	112110	**$150.30**
AR 4-Plex	112116	"

Lens Covers	Item No.	Price
Storm Queen	150032	**$3.80**
Storm King	150042	**$4.40**

3x-9x MS (Metallic Silhouette)

3x-9x MS (Metallic Silhouette)
Instead of "clicking off" distances, the MS scope has a top turret calibrated in meters from 200-500 that lets you change elevation visually. In metallic silhouette shooting, contestants fire at life-sized shapes of animals at various distances. A limited number of Redfield MS scopes are available on special order in the reticle patterns listed for 3x-9x Widefield variables at **$12.50** additional cost above the regular 3x-9x WF price. (without Accu-Range) **$150.30** (with Accu-Range) **$162.80**

REDFIELD SCOPES

The RM 6400 16x, 20x and 24x target scopes are offered with a choice of four reticles. These scopes combine the outstanding optical quality of the 3200 and allow the additional feature of receiver of barrel mounting.

RM target scopes weigh only 18 ounces and are only 17 inches long. The Model RM 6400 offers a 25% wider field of view than the Model 3200. For example, in 16x it's 6.5 feet at 100 yards against 5.2 feet for the Model 3200. Precise ¼ MOA click (accuracy to ± 1/32 MOA) adjustment knobs are provided. This permits immediate adjustment with pinpoint accuracy for serious target and varmint shooters. Packaged in a handsome high-styrene carrying case.

	RETICLES	ITEM NO.	PRICE
16X	FCH	128111	$229.00
	MCH	128110	$229.00
	⅛' Dot	128117	$229.00
	¼' Dot	128112	$229.00
20X	FCH	128121	$229.00
	MCH	128120	$229.00
	⅛' Dot	128127	$229.00
	¼' Dot	128122	$229.00
24X	FCH	128131	$229.00
	MCH	128130	$229.00
	⅛' Dot	128137	$229.00
	¼' Dot	128132	$229.00

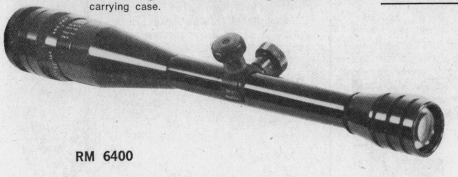

RM 6400

The 3200 Target Scope, available in 2x, 16x, 20x, and 24x powers, is the first sealed target scope with internal adjustments. Precision machining and the use of spring-loaded, hardened steel clicker balls, give the Redfield 3200 crisp consistent ¼-minute adjustments capable of obtaining an accurate ± 1/32 MOA with every positive click.

	RETICLE	ITEM NO.	PRICE
12X	FCH	127000	$199.00
	MCH	127001	$199.00
	¼' Dot	127002	$199.00
	½' Dot	127004	$199.00
16X	FCH	127010	$199.00
	MCH	127011	$199.00
	¼' Dot	127012	$199.00
	½' Dot	127014	$199.00
20X	FCH	127020	$199.00
	MCH	127021	$199.00
	¼' Dot	127022	$199.00
24X	FCH	127030	$199.00
	MCH	127031	$199.00
	¼' Dot	127032	$199.00

⅛' and ⅜' dots are available at additional cost

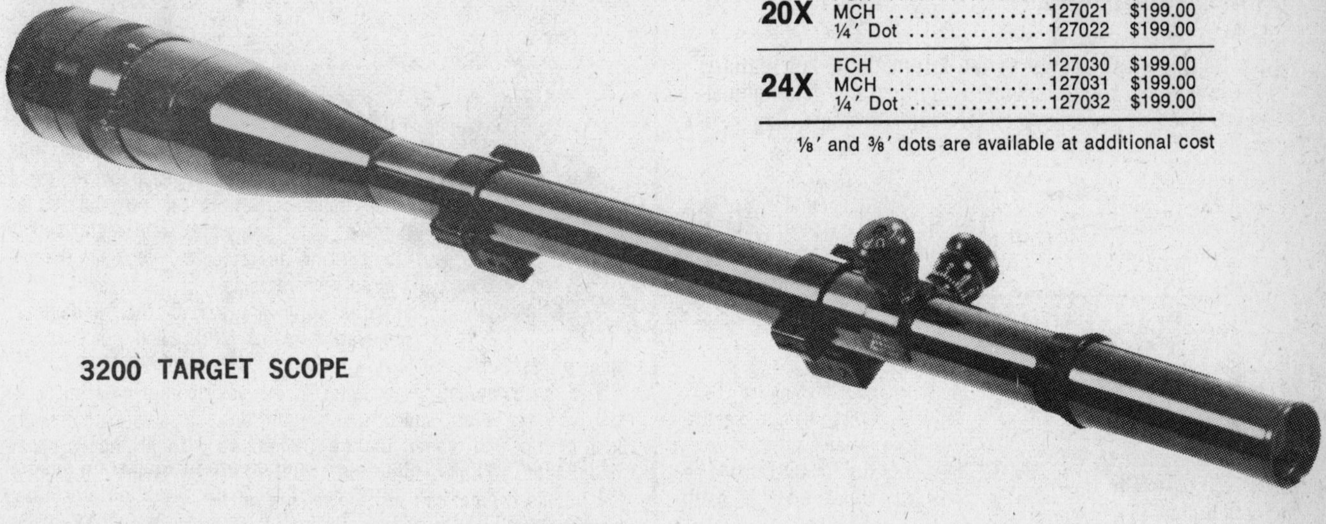

3200 TARGET SCOPE

REDFIELD RECEIVER SIGHTS

International Match

Uniform quarter-minute micrometer click adjustments give the ultimate in precision, accuracy and dependability. The finest steel and quality workmanship go into this sight. Divisions on the elevation staff are 3 minutes of angle or 1 revolution of the knob. One side of the staff is left blank for your own markings for long range matches. Furnished with ⅞" Disc with .046" aperture. Fits the same 0/1 base as the Redfield Olympic.

International Mark 8

with ⅛ Minute Adjustments

Exactly the same quality as the International but features ⅛ minute clicks for shooters wanting the finer adjustment. Used by top shooters for extra precision. Complete w/⅞" Disc.

RECEIVER SIGHT	ITEM NO.	
International Match	.712000	$42.60
International Match Mark 8	.713000	$49.80

REDFIELD SURE-X DISC

Selective Aperture, Match Sighting Disc. Fits any Redfield Target Sight. Selective aperture sizes in increments of .004" from .030" to .058", each size clearly stamped on aperture wheel. Round apertures **$10.00**

Olympic Receiver Sight

Thousands of the world's foremost match riflemen including military teams have insisted on these target receiver sights. Sixty minutes of elevation adjustment and eighteen minutes of windage adjustment from center. Complete w/⅞" Disc.

RECEIVER SIGHT	ITEM NO.	
Olympic	.711000	$32.60

#75 Target Rear Sight

¼" Micrometer click adjustments same as International and Olympic Receiver Sights. All graduations are clearly marked in white. One side of the elevation staff is left blank for shooters' range markings.

NOTE: For new Rem. 540X use item no. 714075 which has special base configuration.

RECEIVER SIGHT	ITEM NO.	
#75 Receiver Sight	.714050	$21.00

MARK 10

The Mark 10 features a mid and long range quick change position by removing one thumb screw. It can be mounted as either a left or right hand sight simply by putting an attaching block on the desired receiver side.

The total adjustment for windage or elevation is 18 MOA. Each click adjustment graduation is ⅛ MOA with accuracy of ± 1/32 MOA.

The base mounting system allows positioning movement of 1-1/16" for short aperture discs up to long diopter units. An adapter block is tapped for the 10mm thread to fit the European model aperture and diopter units with an adapter bushing to accept the standard American discs. Available in limited quantity by special order only.

Mark 10 ......713010 ...$168.00

JR and SR Rings and Bases

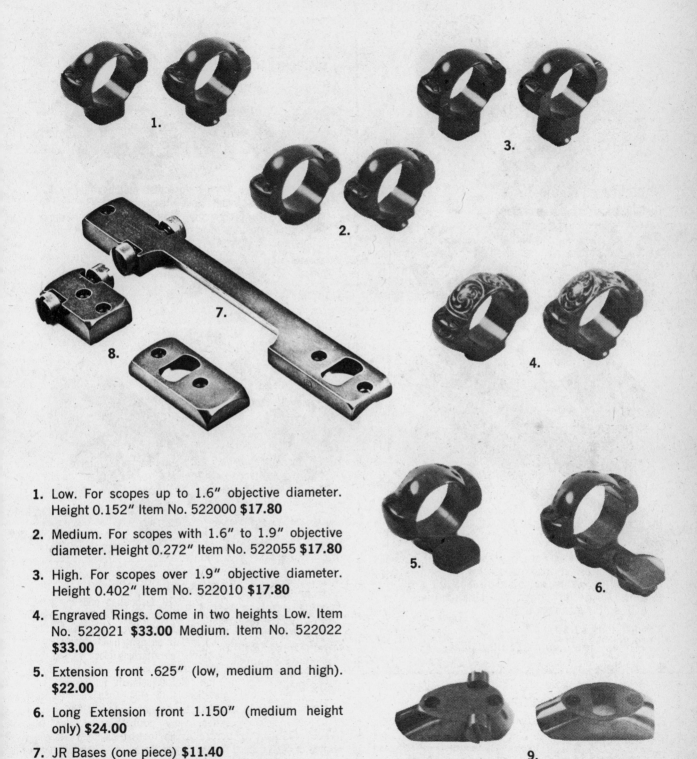

1. **Low.** For scopes up to 1.6" objective diameter. Height 0.152" Item No. 522000 **$17.80**

2. **Medium.** For scopes with 1.6" to 1.9" objective diameter. Height 0.272" Item No. 522055 **$17.80**

3. **High.** For scopes over 1.9" objective diameter. Height 0.402" Item No. 522010 **$17.80**

4. **Engraved Rings.** Come in two heights Low. Item No. 522021 **$33.00** Medium. Item No. 522022 **$33.00**

5. **Extension front** .625" (low, medium and high). **$22.00**

6. **Long Extension** front 1.150" (medium height only) **$24.00**

7. **JR Bases** (one piece) **$11.40**

8. **SR Bases** (two piece) **$11.40** to **$20.00**

9. **Colt Sauer SR Base** (two piece) **$20.00**

FR Rings and Bases

Miscellaneous Rings and Bases

1. **FR Rings. Item No. 551100 $15.00** a pair. (FRontier rings interchangeable with all FRontier mounts.)

2. **FR Bases $3.40**

3. **FR See-Thru Mounts $6.80** a pair.

4. **FR Shotgun Mounts. Item No. 513500 $6.80**

   Uses FRontier rings. Specifically designed for mounting on shotguns for slug hunting. Rugged. Lightweight. Low mounting.

1. **Swing-over Base ($7.20)** and Rings (Item No. 521090 **$14.40** a pair). Swings over to permit iron sight use. Most accurate 2-position on market.

2. **Ring Mounts for Rimfire Rifles** Same as FRontier but fit mounting grooves on most .22's. (¾" Item No. 550000 **$9.80**) (1" Item No. 551000 **$12.00**)

3. **.22 Adapter Bases** For .22 rifles without dovetail receiver.

Rifle	Item No.	Price
Model 39A Marlin	614002	$3.00
Model 57 Marlin	614003	"
Model 10/22 Ruger	614004	"
Browning Auto. .22	614009	$6.00

REDFIELD TARGET SIGHTS

INTERNATIONAL SMALLBORE FRONT

This improved model of an old favorite allows for easy drop-in insertion of eared Skeleton (Polycarbonate) inserts, with inner sleeve which eliminates possibility of light leakage. Round, optically clear, plastic inserts accommodated with speed and ease **$24.60**

GLOBE FRONT SIGHTS

1″ long, ½″ diam. Inserts held firmly by simple locking sleeve, which loosens but doesn't have to be removed when changing inserts.

GLOBE NO.	HEIGHT "A"	BASE	PRICE W/INSERTS
63	.483″	Uses Standard Front Base (Separate $2.95)	**$11.00**
64	.733″	Standard Front Base (separate $2.95)	11.00
65	.421″	Integral male dovetail	8.40
65NB	.421″	base drives into dovetail	8.40
66	.750″	on barrel 66 for Spring	8.40
68	.546″	field dovetail 65, 68 for	8.40
Extra inserts for Globe Front Set			2.20

Target Sight Bases and Accessories

Redfield offers you a complete line of bases and accessories to complement the target sights shown on the previous pages. All are manufactured to the most exacting of specifications in order to provide you with the most professional and dependable sighting equipment available.

Index of Receiver Sight Bases

Receiver Sight Bases

#75

Olympic and International

This base provides a series of threaded attachment holes to permit rear sight mounting locations for any shooting position.

Index of Front Sight Bases

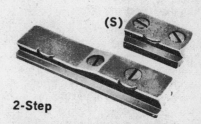

(S)

2-Step

Special base for Small Bore shooting. Height given is for the lower or 100 yard step. 50 yard step is .054″ higher. Fast, convenient, saves wear on your Receiver Sight.

INTERNATIONAL BIG BORE FRONT

For .30 caliber shooting, same as small bore except tube shortened to approximately 2″, eyepiece same size as tube to provide greatest possible rapid fire visibility. **$24.60**
All Big Bore Fronts are within I.S.U. maximum dimension limits.

6 POWER BINOCULAR.

Roof prism optics allow minimum weight of approximately 4 oz. Objective diameter is 16mm. Focus individually adjusted for each eye. Dimensions folded 1¼″ high x 2⅛″ wide x 2¾″ long. **$89.50**

OLYMPIC DETACHABLE FRONT

Admits a greater volume of light, perfectly controlled by shading flanges. Set of 10 easy-change inserts includes five steel apertures, one post, four transparent apertures. Transparent available in clear, green or amber, with or without crosslines. Amber with crosslines will be furnished unless otherwise requested.
Olympic Front w/Inserts
(no base) **$17.00**
Extra Set Olympic Inserts . . . 4.20

REDFIELD SPOTTING SCOPES

Spotting Scopes and Accessories

Redfield's variable spotting scopes and the accessories are designed to make your range shooting time even more enjoyable. The Fifteen-Sixty, (15X-60X) introduced in 1970, is a proven performer on the range and already the choice of champions. The Fifteen-Forty-five, (15X-45X), is designed to give more shooters more quality at an affordable price. These two powerful variable spotting scopes have been designed to exacting Redfield specifications and are subjected to rigid inspection before they leave the factory.

Lenses are anti-reflection coated and of the finest quality available. The large objective lens system is checked for light-gathering quality needed for superior resolution at all powers; eye relief exceeds that of competitive spotting scopes in this power range. Retractable eye shield, and the sliding sunshade on the objective end are extras that enhance the performance of this scope. The handsome red crackletone finish gives it a distinctive, quality appearance.

A mounting boss, tapped 1/4 — 20NS, will adapt either spotting scope to photo or spotting stands. This boss is easily removed for use with saddle-head clamp mounts. Forest rangers, professional guides, bird watchers and many other people with a healthy curiosity have discovered how well these excellent clean-lined, trouble-free instruments perform.

15X-45X

Like the 15X-60X, this scope gives you the same rugged construction, brilliant optical system and features and is finished in the same handsome crackletone "Redfield red" enamel. The only difference is the power range and the price.

15X-60X

This veteran performer features long eye relief, a large objective lens system for gathering the extra light needed for good resolution at high powers, a retractable eye shield and a built-in sunshade.

Specifications

ITEM	15X-45X AT 15X	15X-45X AT 45X	15X-60X AT 15X	15X-60X AT 60X
Actual magnification	14.75X	45.0X	14.75X	59.6X
Clear aperture of object lens	2.365"	45.0X	2.365"	59.6X
Exit pupil	4mm	1.33mm	4mm	1mm
Field of view at 100 yards	15.6'	5.2'	15.6'	3.7'
Eye relief	.80"	80"	.80"	.80"
Overall length focused to infinity	16¾"	16¾"	16¾"	16¾"
Weight	48 oz.	48 oz.	48 oz.	48 oz.

Redfield Tripod stand with saddlehead and screw is the choice of varmint shooters and big game hunters. Wide span tripod legs lock into place and provide a tip-proof base in rough terrain. Folds compactly or is easily carried with scope attached. Also finished in "Redfield red" crackletone to match the scope.

CARRYING CASE

Custom made case with double handle for load balance. Carry your Redfield spotting scopes and tripod or bipod. Made of high impact styrene in red. . . . **$47.00**

ITEM	ITEM NO.
15X-45X Spotting Scope	126045
15X-60X Spotting Scope	126000
Redfield Tripod Stand	126100
Redfield Bipod Stand	126200
Scope/Bipod or Tripod Combination Case	126400

WEATHERBY PREMIER SCOPES

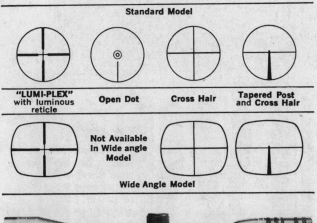

CHOICE OF RETICLES

Standard Model

"LUMI-PLEX" with luminous reticle | Open Dot | Cross Hair | Tapered Post and Cross Hair

Not Available In Wide angle Model

Wide Angle Model

3 TO 9 POWER

The most desirable variable for every kind of shooting from target to long range big game. Outstanding light-gathering power. Fast, convenient focusing adjustment.

4 POWER

This is a fixed power scope for big game and varmint hunting. Bright, clear image. "Never-wear" coated lenses for maximum luminosity under adverse conditions. 31-foot field of view at 100 yards.

2¾ POWER— AVAILABLE IN STANDARD MODEL ONLY

One of the widest fields of view on any scope . . . 45 feet at 100 yards. Ideal for big game because of its clear, bright image. Ruggedly built to withstand even the pounding of our .460 Magnum.

WEATHERBY PREMIER SCOPES

WIDE ANGLE FIELD OF VIEW. Now, a twenty-five per cent wider field! Great for holding running game in full view.

As every hunter knows, one of his most difficult problems is keeping running game in the field of view of his scope.

Once lost, precious seconds fade away trying to find the animal in the scope again. Too much time wasted means the ultimate frustration. No second shot. Or no shot at all.

The Weatherby Wide Angle helps you surmount the problem by increasing your field of view by a full 25%!

FEATURES

OPTICAL EXCELLENCE—NOW PROTECTED WITH NEW "NEVER-WEAR" ANTI-GLARE COATING. • FOG FREE AND WATERPROOF CONSTRUCTION. • CONSTANTLY SELF CENTERED RETICLES. • NON-MAGNIFYING RETICLE. • FINGER TIP ¼" CLICK ADJUSTMENTS. • QUICK VARIABLE POWER CHANGE. • UNIQUE LUMINOUS RETICLE. • LIFETIME NEOPRENE EYEPIECE. • EXCLUSIVE BINOCULAR TYPE SPEED FOCUSING. • RUGGED SCORE TUBE CONSTRUCTION.

SPECIFICATIONS FOR WEATHERBY PREMIER SCOPES

	STANDARD LENS			WIDE ANGLE LENS	
	2¾X40	4X40	3X - 9X40	4X40	3X - 9X40
Field of view	45' 0"	31' 0"	40' - 12'	35' 8"	43' 7" - 14' 8"
Clear aperture of objective lens	40mm	40mm	40mm	40mm	40mm
Diameter of exit pupil	14.56mm	10.0mm	13.3 - 4.4mm	10mm	13.3 - 4.4mm
Relative brightness	211.99	100.0	176.9 - 19.3	100.0	176.9 - 19.3
Eye relief	3.5"	3.5"	3.5"	3.0"	3.4" - 3.0"
Overall length	11.8"	12.7"	12.2"	11.8"	12.1"
Diameter of tube	1"	1"	1"	1"	1"
O.D. of objective end	1.85"	1.85"	1.85"	1.85"	1.85"
O.D. of ocular end	1.53"	1.53"	1.53"	1.71"	1.71"
Weight	12.3 oz.	12.3 oz.	13.7 oz.	14.1 oz.	14.8 oz.
Internal adjustment graduation	¼" clicks 1" calibration marks			¼" clicks 1" calibration marks	
Price and reticle:					
CH or TP&CH	$89.50	$99.50	$109.50	$119.50	$129.50
Lumi-Plex	94.50	104.50	114.50	124.50	134.50
Open Dot	94.50	104.50	114.50	Not Available	

WEAVER "K" MODEL SCOPES

Model	K1.5		K2.5		K3		K4		K6		K8	
Actual Magnification*	1.5	1.5	2.6	2.6	3.1	3.1	4.1	4.1	5.7	5.7	8	8
Field of View* at 100 yds (ft) at 100 m (m)	56.5	18.8	40	13.3	34	11.3	26	8.7	20	6.7	15	5
Eye Distance* (inches) (mm)	5¼	133.4	4½	114.3	4	101.6	4	101.6	3⅞	98.4	3¾	95.3
Tube Diameter (inches) (mm)	1.000	25.4	1.000	25.4	1.000	25.4	1.000	25.4	1.000	25.4	1.000	25.4
Eyepiece Diameter (inches) (mm)	1.485	37.7	1.485	37.7	1.485	37.7	1.485	37.7	1.485	37.7	1.485	37.7
Front End Diameter (inches) (mm)	1.000	25.4	1.000	25.4	1.000	25.4	1.550	39.4	1.725	43.8	1.930	48.6
Length (inches) (mm)	9⅜	238	10⅜	264	10⅝	270	11¾	299	13 7/16	341	14⅝	372
Weight (ounces) (grams)	11¼	319	11½	326	11½	326	13½	383	15¼	432	18	510
Graduated Adjustments (change in inches at 100 yards, or minute of angle)	½	½	½	½	½	½	¼	¼	¼	¼	¼	¼
Reticles** Available**	1,2,3,5	1,2,3,5	1.2.3.5	1,2,3,5	1,2,3,5	1,2,3,5	1,2,3,4,5	1,2;3,4,5	1,2,3,4,5	1,2,3,4,5	1,2,4,5	1,2,4,5

***Weaver-Scopes** offer carefully balanced magnification, field of view, eye relief, and diaphragming to provide hunters with maximum efficiency, safety, and clarity.

****RETICLES** **1** Crosshair **2** Dual X **3** Post and Crosshair **4** Range-Finder **5** Dot
Reticles available as indicated: 1, 2, 3, and 4 at no extra cost. 5 at extra cost.

FOCUS Eyepiece of all scopes adjusts to user's vision.

K MODELS

1. 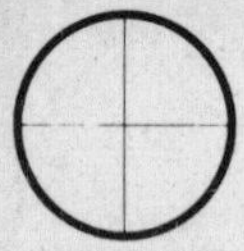

CROSSHAIR

2. 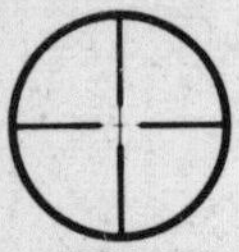

DUAL X®

3. 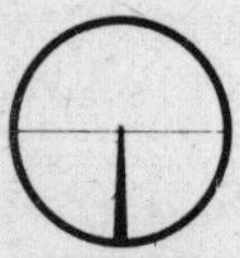

POST AND CROSSHAIR

4. 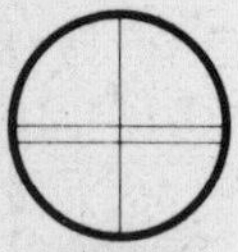

RANGE-FINDER®

5. 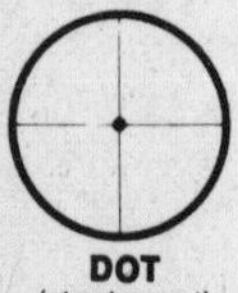

DOT
(at extra cost)

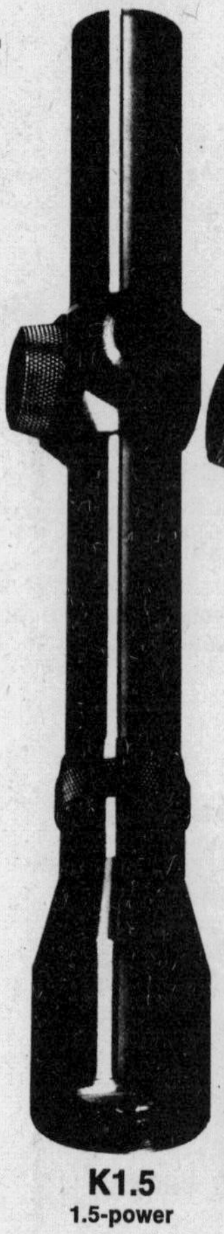

K1.5
1.5-power

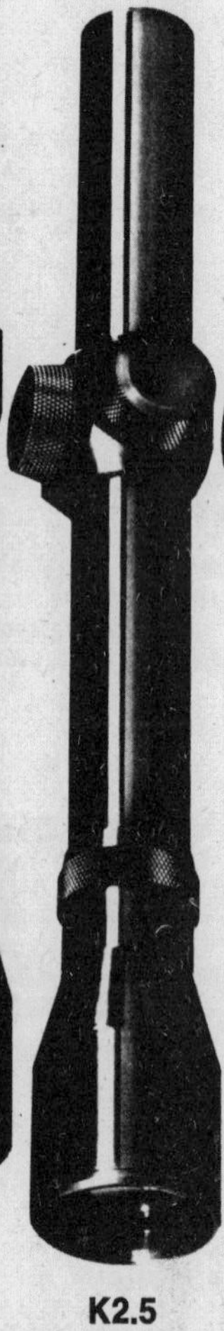

K2.5
2.5-power

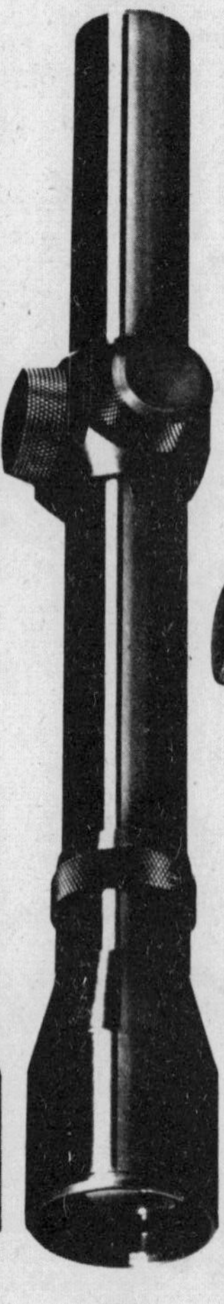

K3
3-power

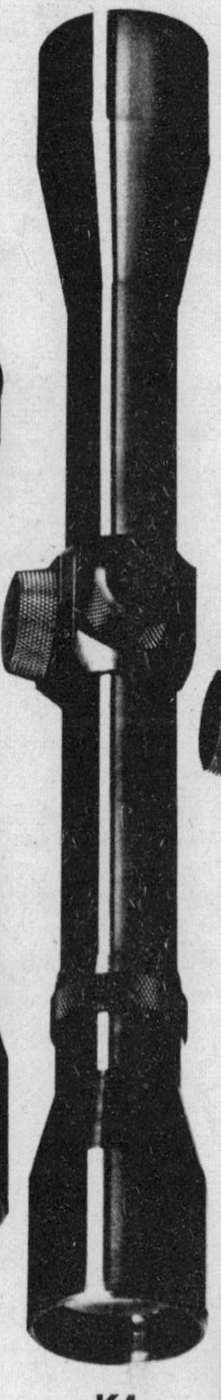

K4
4-power

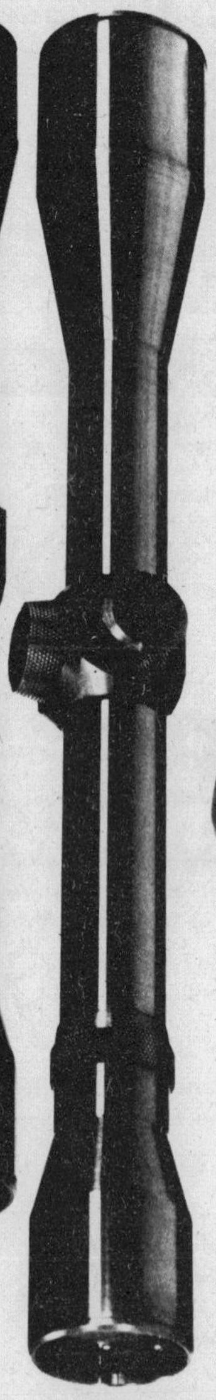

K6
6-power

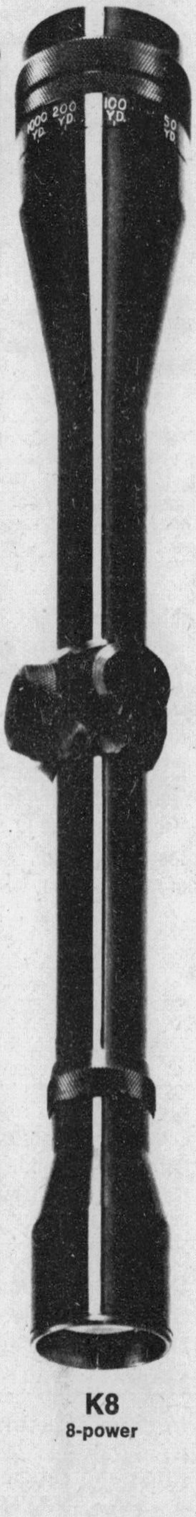

K8
8-power

Model K1.5 . . . . $34.95
Model K2.5 . . . . 44.95
Model K3 . . . . 49.95
Model K4 . . . . 59.95
Model K6 . . . . 69.95
Model K8 . . . . 79.95
Dot Reticle, extra 7.50

ALL STEEL, ALL AMERICAN, ALL WEAVER. EIGHT GREAT K MODELS.

Weaver K Models, pace-setters for almost 30 years, are setting new standards in scope design and scope performance with the All-Steel Scope. Truly the Great American Scope.

Unique one-piece steel tube. The sharp, clean-cut shape is machine-tooled and hand-polished to make it a fine match for the finest of rifles. And highest quality steel provides the best possible protection for the superior optics.

The K Models feature Weaver's micro-adjustable windage and elevation settings for super-accuracy. They're vacuumized, filled with dry nitrogen gas, and super-sealed with a patented process. They're the most dependable, most weatherproof, most fogproof scopes ever designed.

Models K8, K10, and K12 feature compact Weaver Range Focus for precision in long-range shooting.

All five reticle styles are available in most K Models (post and crosshair not offered in K8, K10, K12; Range-Finder not offered in K1.5, K2.5, K3).

WEAVER "K" & "V" MODEL SCOPES

Model	K10		K12		V4.5		V7		V9		V12	
Actual Magnification*	10	10	12	12	1.5-4.2	1.5-4.2	2.4-6.6	2.4-6.6	3-8.3	3-8.3	4-12	4-12
Field of View* at 100 yds (ft) at 100 m (m)	12	4	10	3.3	62-24	20.7-8	40-15	13.3-5	33-12	11-4	24-9	8-3
Eye Distance* (inches) (mm)	3⅝	92	3⅝	92	4½-4	114.3-101.6	4-3⅞	101.6-98.4	3¾-3¾	95.3-95.3	3⅞-4¼	98.4-108
Tube Diameter (inches) (mm)	1.000	25.4	1.000	25.4	1.000	25.4	1.000	25.4	1.000	25.4	1.000	25.4
Eyepiece Diameter (inches) (mm)	1.485	37.7	1.485	37.7	1.485	37.7	1.485	37.7	1.485	37.7	1.485	37.7
Front End Diameter (inches) (mm)	1.930	48.6	1.930	48.6	1.000	25.4	1.550	39.4	1.930	48.6	1.930	48.6
Length (inches) (mm)	15½	394	15¾	400	10⅜	264	12⅜	314	13¾	349	13¾	349
Weight (ounces) (grams)	18¼	517	18½	525	15½	439	18¼	517	22	624	22	624
Graduated Adjustments (change in inches at 100 yards, or minute of angle)	¼	¼	¼	¼	½	½	¼	¼	¼	¼	¼	¼
Reticles** Available	1,2,4,5	1,2,4,5	1,2,4,5	1,2,4,5	1,2,3,4,5	1,2,3,4,5	1,2,3,4,5	1,2,3,4,5	1,2,3,4,5	1,2,3,4,5	1,2,3,4,5	1,2,3,4,5

*Weaver-Scopes offer carefully balanced magnification, field of view, eye relief, and diaphragming to provide hunters with maximum efficiency, safety, and clarity.

**RETICLES 1 Crosshair 2 Dual X 3 Post and Crosshair 4 Range-Finder 5 Dot
Reticles available as indicated: 1, 2, 3, and 4 at no extra cost. 5 at extra cost.
FOCUS Eyepiece of all scopes adjusts to user's vision.

V MODELS

1.
CROSSHAIR

2.
DUAL X®

3.
POST AND CROSSHAIR

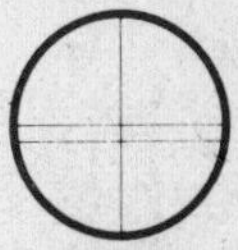

4.
RANGE-FINDER®

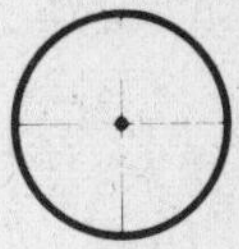

5.
DOT
(at extra cost)

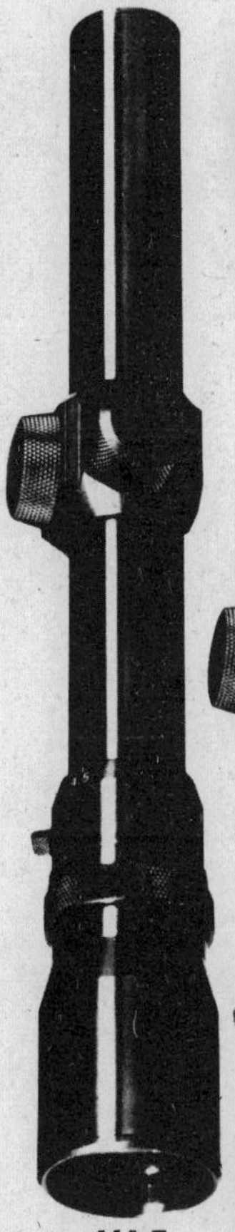

V4.5
1.5- to 4.5-power
$69.95

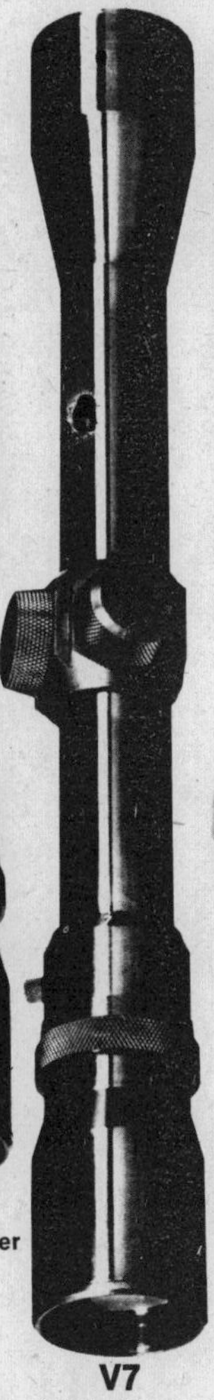

V7
2.5- to 7-power
$79.95

V9
3- to 9-power
$89.95

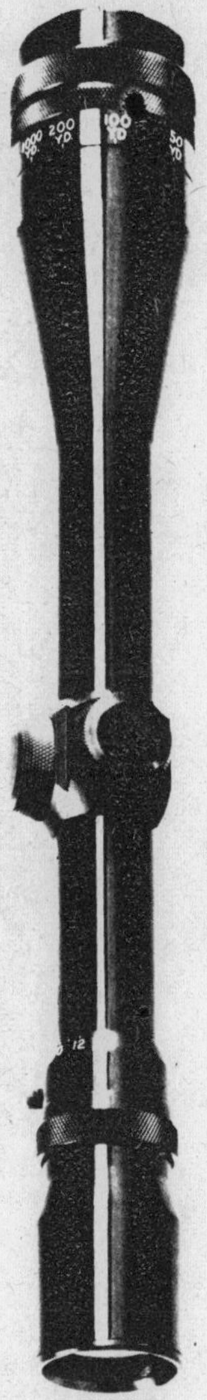

V12
4- to 12-power
$99.95

K10
10-power
$84.95

K12
12-power
$94.95

THE ALL-STEEL VARIABLES. MORE RUGGED, MORE DEPENDABLE THAN EVER.

More and more hunters find that only a Weaver V Model offers all the flexibility and versatility they need — plus the sure year-after-year dependability of the sturdiest fixed-power scopes. An easy turn of the power change ring supplies the magnification that's just right for 'most any hunting situation.

Now Weaver offers important advances in its V Model design: All steel, one-piece tube construction with machine-tooled, handcrafted quality.

Vacuumized, nitrogen processed, and super-sealed with a patented process — to guarantee fogproofing for the life of the scope. Micro-adjustable elevation and windage settings.

Focus and point of impact are the same at all powers. Reticle remains constantly centered.

Precision optics are magnesium fluoride coated. Long eye relief is safe at all magnifications. Models V9 and V12 have Weaver Range Focus. All five reticle styles are offered.

Weaver "K-W" & "V-W" Model Scopes

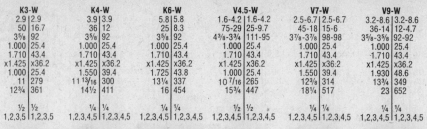

Model	K3-W		K4-W		K6-W		V4.5-W		V7-W		V9-W	
Actual Magnification*	2.9	2.9	3.9	3.9	5.8	5.8	1.6-4.2	1.6-4.2	2.5-6.7	2.5-6.7	3.2-8.6	3.2-8.6
Field of View* at 100 yds (ft) at 100 m (m)	50	16.7	36	12	25	8.3	75-29	25-9.7	45-18	15-6	36-14	12-4.7
Eye Distance* (inches) (mm)	3⅝	92	3⅝	92	3⅝	92	4⅜-3¾	111-95	3⅞-3⅞	98-98	3⅝-3⅝	92-92
Tube Diameter (inches) (mm)	1.000	25.4	1.000	25.4	1.000	25.4	1.000	25.4	1.000	25.4	1.000	25.4
Eyepiece Diameter (inches) (mm)	1.710	43.4	1.710	43.4	1.710	43.4	1.710	43.4	1.710	43.4	1.710	43.4
	x1.425	x36.2	x1.425	x36.2	x1.425	x36.2	x1.425	x36.2	x1.425	x36.2	x1.425	x36.2
Front End Diameter (inches) (mm)	1.000	25.4	1.550	39.4	1.725	43.8	1.000	25.4	1.550	39.4	1.930	48.6
Length (inches) (mm)	11	279	11 ¹³/₁₆	300	13¼	337	10 ⁷/₁₆	265	12⅜	314	13¾	349
Weight (ounces) (grams)	12¾	361	14½	411	16	454	15¾	447	18¼	517	23	652
Graduated Adjustments (change in inches at 100 yards, or minute of angle)	½	½	¼	¼	¼	¼	½	½	¼	¼	¼	¼
Reticles** Available	1,2,3,5	1,2,3,5	1,2,3,4,5	1,2,3,4,5	1,2,3,4,5	1,2,3,4,5	1,2,3,4,5	1,2,3,4,5	1,2,3,4,5	1,2,3,4,5	1,2,3,4,5	1,2,3,4,5

*Weaver-Scopes offer carefully balanced magnification, field of view, eye relief, and diaphragming to provide hunters with maximum efficiency, safety, and clarity.
**RETICLES 1 Crosshair 2 Dual X 3 Post and Crosshair 4 Range-Finder 5 Dot
Reticles available as indicated: 1, 2, 3, and 4 at no extra cost. 5 at extra cost.
FOCUS Eyepiece of all scopes adjusts to user's vision.

K-W & V-W MODELS

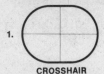

1.

CROSSHAIR

2.

DUAL X®

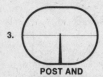

3.

POST AND CROSSHAIR

On Wider-View V-W Models, post does not extend above crosshair.

4.

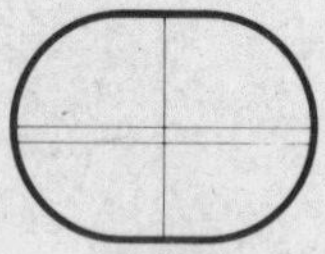

RANGE-FINDER®

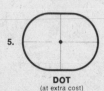

5.

DOT
(at extra cost)

Model K3-W	**$64.95**
Model K4-W	**74.95**
Model K6-W	**84.95**
Model V4.5-W	**84.95**
Model V7-W	**94.95**
Model V9-W	**104.95**
Dot Reticle, extra	**7.50**

K3-W
3-power

K4-W
4-power

K6-W
6-power

V4.5-W
1.5- to 4.5-power

V7-W
2.5- to 7-power

V9-W
3- to 9-power

You see what might be out of the picture with a standard scope.

WEAVER OFFERS THE POPULAR WIDER-VIEW WITH A PICTURE THAT'S UP TO 40% WIDER.

The Great American Scope line features six handsome Wider-View Models. A beautifully-shaped rectangular eyepiece gives a wider view than a standard scope of the same power — as much as 40% wider on the V4.5-W at highest power. And there's no sacrifice in superior quality and outstanding performance.

Wider-View is an All-Steel Scope, designed by Weaver engineers to include all the proven features that have made K and V Models America's leading scopes: one-piece, machine-tooled steel tube. Micro-adjustable windage and elevation settings. Vacuumized, nitrogen-processed, and super-sealed for absolute fogproofing. Bright, crisp, distortion-free optics. Long, safe eye relief.

Range Focus offered on the V9-W. All five reticle styles available (except Range-Finder not offered on K3-W).

WEAVER "22" MODEL SCOPE

Model	D4 (inches)	(mm)	D6 (inches)	(mm)	V22 (inches)	(mm)
Actual Magnification*	4.2	4.2	6.2	6.2	3-5.8	3-5.8
Field of View* at 100 yds (ft) at 100 m (m)	29	9.7	19.75	6.6	31-16.25	10.3-5.4
Eye Distance* (inches) (mm)	2¼	57	2¼	57	1⅝-2¼	41.3-57
Tube Diameter (inches) (mm)	.875	22.2	.875	22.2	.875	22.2
Eyepiece Diameter (inches) (mm)	1.310	33.3	1.310	33.3	1.310	33.3
Front End Diameter (inches) (mm)	.875	22.2	.875	22.2	.875	22.2
Length (inches) (mm)	11⅞	302	12 5/16	313	12⅜	314
Weight (ounces) (grams)	4†	113.4	4†	113.4	4†	113.4
Graduated Adjustments (change in inches at 100 yards, or minute of angle)	1	1	1	1	1	1
Reticles** Available	1 only	1 only	1 only	1 only	1,2	1,2

*Weaver-Scopes offer carefully balanced magnification, field of view, eye relief, and diaphragming to provide hunters with maximum efficiency, safety, and clarity.
**RETICLES 1 Crosshair 2 Dual X Reticles available as indicated: 1 at no extra cost. 2 at extra cost (on V22 only).
†Weight without mount 4 ounces; with mount 5 ounces.
FOCUS Eyepiece of all scopes adjusts to user's vision.

22 MODELS

1.
CROSSHAIR

2.
DUAL X®
(at extra cost, on V22 only)

D4
4-power

D6
6-power

V22
3- to 6-power

Model D4 .... $12.95
Model D6 .... 14.95
Model V22 with Crosshair Reticle 17.95
Model V22 with Dual X Reticle 19.95

AMERICA'S FAVORITE 22 SCOPES. WITH THE BIG SCOPE FEATURES.

Advanced D Models and V22 have outstanding features usually found only in more expensive scopes: large ⅞" tubes, matching turret of modern design, improved optics with larger eyepiece. Lighter and stronger than ever, they are made of finest materials by skilled American craftsmen.

Weaver's constantly-centered reticle permits unusual speed and ease of aim. Use is limited to light recoil rifles only because of relatively short eye relief.

Factory-equipped with Tip-Off or N Mount at no extra cost.

Crosshair reticle is standard in all three scopes; Dual X is optional in the V22 at extra cost.

WEAVER LENS CAPS

Transparent windows allow the scope to be used quickly with the caps in position in emergency. Durable and snug fitting, Weaver Lens Caps provide attractive, inexpensive protection for the scope's optics. Made in eleven sizes:

D4, D6, V22   V9, V12
K1.5   K3-W, V4.5-W
K2.5, K3, V4.5   K4-W, V7-W
K4, V7   K6-W
K6   V9-W
K8, K10, K12

WEAVER PARTS KIT

A handy, comprehensive collection of useful, everyday replacement parts and screws for all Weaver-Scopes and Weaver-Mounts. Includes such often-needed items as turret caps and base screws. Complete set is arranged in a dozen compartments in an attractive, durable plastic box.

WEAVER SIGHTS & MOUNTS

QWIK-POINT®

QUICKEST WAY TO IMPROVE SHOTGUN AND SHORT-RANGE RIFLE SHOOTING.

S-1
for shotguns

S-1100
for Remington 1100 and 870 shotguns

NEW

R-1
for center-fire rifles

R-22
for 22 rifles

Keep your eye on the target. The blaze-orange dot is OUT THERE where your target is.

Dot is bright blaze-orange, even in dim light or heavy cover.

Weaver's amazing Qwik-Point is a completely different sighting concept. It can quickly improve natural shooting skills with shotgun, center-fire rifle, or 22.

With one or both eyes open, simply look at the target, move the blaze-orange dot to the target, and fire. The dot is focused to infinity, so it will automatically appear where eyes are focused.

Dot and target are seen simultaneously in clear, sharp focus. No changing point of focus from sight to target.

On shotguns, Qwik-Point is an effective short-cut to becoming an accomplished wingshot. Makes "swing" and "lead" easy to see, understand, and follow. Helps the expert detect where and why he missed.

Qwik-Point is shockproof, weatherproof, foolproof. Made of lightweight aluminum with durable jet-black anodizing. Easily sighted in like a scope.

Specifications:
Weight:
S-1, 7¾ ounces
S-1100, 7¾ ounces
R-1, 8¾ ounces
R-22, 7½ ounces
Length:
S-1, 6 inches
S-1100, 6 inches
R-1, 6¼ inches
R-22, 6¾ inches
Adjustments:
¼" click at 40 yards
Eye Relief: Infinite
Focus: Universal

Mounting:
Model S-1 for shotguns: Complete with mount and base (8A) for most pumps and automatics.

Model S-1100 for Remington 1100 and 870 shotguns: Complete with side mount and bolts; installed in minutes without special tools.

Model R-1 for center fire rifles: Built-in mount attaches to Weaver Top Mount bases (bases extra). Special bases (77, 78) available for Model 94 Winchester.

Model R-22 for 22's: Complete with mount which fits factory-grooved receivers.

WEAVER TIP-OFF® MOUNTS

Weaver 1" Tip-Off Mount for K Models and other 1" scopes

Weaver ⅞" Tip-Off Mount for D Models, V22, and other ⅞" scopes

Tip-Off Mounts are made for use on 22 rifles with ⅜" dovetail receiver grooves. No bases required. They clamp into the rifle receiver grooves. No tools needed. Clamping screws tighten easily with a coin.

1" Tip-Off Mounts, a pair of split rings, are designed to mount K Models and other 1" scopes.

⅞" Tip-Off Mounts, a pair of solid rings, are designed to mount Weaver D Models, V22, and other ⅞" scopes. Also available in ¾" rings to fit ¾" scopes.

These rifles have ⅜" receiver grooves:
Anschutz 141, 153, Mark 10
Browning T-Bolt, BL-22
CIL 68, 121, 125, 167, 180, 190S, 212, 227, 300, 310, 470
Colt "Colteer"
Cooey 64
Glenfield 10, 20, 60, 70
H&R 422, 750, 751, 755, 760, 800, 865, 866
High Standard 22 Sport-King
Ithaca X5 Lightning
Kodiak 260
Lee-Enfield requires adapter TO-1 at extra cost; must be drilled, tapped
Marlin 49, 56, 57, 80, 81, 88, 89, 98, 99, 101, 122, 780, 781, 782, 783, 980, 989
Mossberg 142, 144, 146, 151, 152, 300 Series, 400, 402, 430, 432, 620, 640
Noble 235, 275, 285, 635, 875, 885
Remington 10, 11, 12, 66, 76, 77, 510, 511, 512, 513S, 521T, 540X, 541, 550, 552, 572, 580, 581, 582, 590M, 591M, 592M
Ruger 10/22 with T9 base
Savage 4, 5, 6, 24, 29, 54, 60, 63, 65, 88, 90, 164, 184, 219
Stevens 34, 46, 73, 84, 85, 86, 87
Weatherby XXII
Winchester 61, 69, 72, 74, 75S, 77, 121, 131, 135, 141, 145, 150, 190, 250, 255, 270, 275, 290, 310, 320, 325, 9422 (T10 adapter base available for 9422)

Model R-1 for rifles 44.95
Model R-22 for 22 rifles .44.95
Model S-1 for shotguns .44.95
Model S-1100 for Remington 1100 and 870 shotguns, and other Remington shotguns and rifles 44.95
Tip-off Mount Solid Rings (pair) in ¾", ⅞" diameters...3.95
Tip-Off Mount Split Rings (pair) in 1" diameter........9.95
Tip-Off Adapter Base TO-1 for Lee Enfield..........2.00

WEAVER-PIVOT MOUNTS

Pivot Mount open

Pivot Mount closed

$12.95

Weaver-Pivot Mounts permit choice of scope or iron sights. Top mounting gives wide spacing of mount rings, rigidity, low scope position, easy installation and removal. Replacement is accurate, alignment exact and fully dependable. Made for ¾" and 1" scopes.

Hi-Style Pivot Mounts are available in 1" diameter only. The high rings position the scope ¼" higher than the standard ring, and provide adequate barrel and iron sight clearance for scopes with objective diameters greater than 1¾". Use Hi-Style Pivot Mounts when installing K6, K6-W, K8, K10, K12, V9, V9-W, and V12 scopes on these rifles: Remington 700, 742, 760, 600, 660; Marlin 336, 444; and Savage 99.

WEAVER N MOUNTS

Type N Mounts (side bracket design) are pressed from tough alloy steel. They are rigid, sturdy, and suitable for use on high-power rifles and 22's. Made in ⅞" diameter for D Models and V22.

The dependability of the inexpensive N Mount has been proved under all conditions and on large caliber rifles. **$2.00**

WEAVER-DETACHABLE MOUNTS

DETACHABLE TOP MOUNT
Made in ¾", ⅞", 1", and 1.023" (26mm) diameters; Hi-Style made in 1" diameter only **$9.95**

EXTENSION TOP MOUNT
Made in 1" diameter only **$11.95**

NEW DETACHABLE LONG SIDE MOUNT
Made in 1" diameter for Winchester 94 and other short-action rifles **$11.95**

Light, compact, and finely finished, Weaver-Detachable Mounts can be used with complete assurance on rifles of heaviest recoil and under roughest hunting use. Installation is easy since most rifle receivers are factory drilled and tapped specifically for Weaver-Mounts.

Hi-Style Top Mounts, made in 1" diameter only, are designed to provide adequate barrel and iron sight clearance for most scopes having objective diameters greater than 1¾". Scopes of this size (1¾") can be mounted on some rifles using regular Top Mounts.

Use Hi-Style Top Mounts when installing K6, K6-W, K8, K10, K12, V9, V9-W, V12 on Remington 600, 660, 788, Marlin 336, 444, Savage 99; K6, K6-W, V9, V9-W, V12, on Remington 740, 742, 760; V9, V9-W, and V12 on Remington 700, 721, 722, 725.

Extension Top Mounts allow the scope to be positioned ¾" further forward for improved eye relief.

Detachable Long Side Mounts are made in 1" diameter with split rings, and are designed for Winchester 94 and other short-action rifles.

WEAVER-RETICLES FOR WEAVER-SCOPES

CROSSHAIR

RANGE-FINDER

POST AND CROSSHAIR

DUAL X

DOT

WILLIAMS SCOPES

Guide-Line Models in 4X, 1.5-4.5X, 2-6X & 3-9X

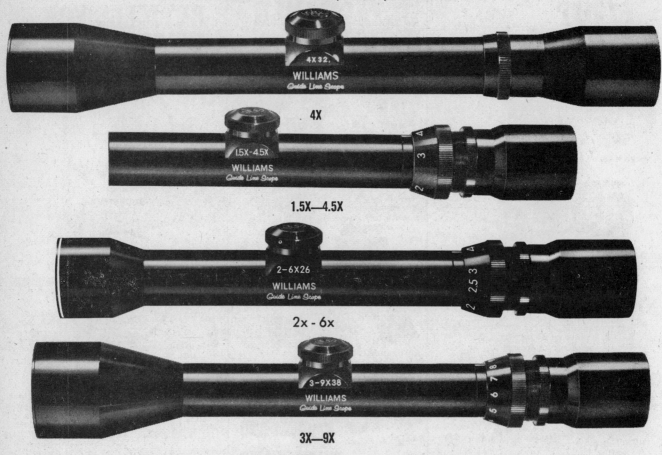

4X

1.5X—4.5X

2x - 6x

3X—9X

Power	Reticle	Price	Power	Reticle	Price	Power	Reticle	Price	Power	Reticle	Price
4X	Crosshair	$93.25	1½X-4½X	Crosshair	$124.75	2X - 6X	Crosshair	$124.75	3X - 9X	Crosshair	$130.00
4X	Dot	$93.25	1½X-4½X	Dot	$124.75	2X - 6X	Dot	$124.75	3X - 9X	Dot	130.00
4X	T-N-T	$93.25	1½X-4½X	T-N-T	$124.75	2X - 6X	T-N-T	$124.75	3X - 9X	T-N-T	130.00
4X	Guide	$93.25	1½X-4½X	Guide	$124.75	2X - 6X	Guide	$124.75	3X - 9X	Guide	130.00

SPECIFICATIONS

	4X	1.5X	4.5X	2 - 6X		3X - 9X	
OPTICAL SPECIFICATIONS		At 1.5X	At 4.5X	At 2X	At 6X	At 3X	At 9X
Clear aperture of objective lens	32mm	20mm	Same	26mm	Same	38mm	Same
Clear aperture of ocular lens	31.7mm	31.7mm	Same	31.7mm	Same	31.7mm	Same
Exit pupil	8mm	14mm	4.7mm	13mm	4.3mm	12.7mm	4.2mm
Relative brightness	64	196	22.1	169	18.5	161	18
Field of view (degree of angle)	5° 40	14° 54	5°	11° 30	3° 50	7° 30	2° 30
Field of view at 100 yards	29.8'	78'	26'	60'	20'	39'	13'
Eye relief	3.75"	4.38"	3.26"	3.3"	3.25"	3.75"	3.25"
Parallax correction	(at) 100 yds.	100 yds.	Same	100 yds.	Same	150 yds.	Same
Lens construction	9	9	Same	11	Same	12	Same
MECHANICAL SPECIFICATIONS							
Outside diameter of objective end	1.558"	1"	Same	1.380"	Same	1.810"	Same
Outside diameter of ocular end	1.420"	1.420"	Same	1.420"	Same	1.420"	Same
Outside diameter of tube	1"	1"	Same	1"	Same	1"	Same
Internal adjustment graduation	½ min.	½ min.	Same	½ min.	Same	½ min.	Same
Minimum internal adjustment	70 min.	70 min.	Same	70 min.	Same	70 min.	Same
Finish			Hard Black Anodized				
Length	11¾"	9½"	Same	10¼"	Same	12.0"	Same
Weight	9.5 oz.	9 oz.	Same	10 oz.	Same	14.5 oz.	Same

WILLIAMS SCOPES

Twilight Models in 2½X, 4X, 2-6X & 3-9X

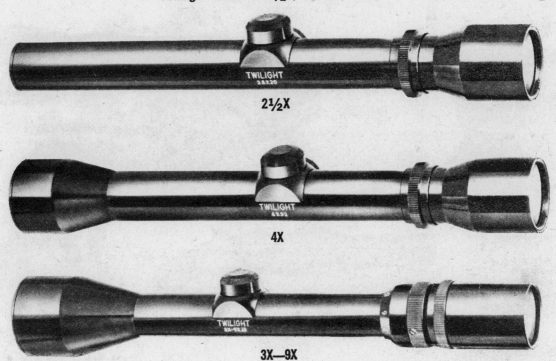

2½X

4X

3X—9X

TWILIGHT SPECIFICATIONS	OPTICAL SPECIFICATIONS	2.5X	4X	2X - 6X At 2X	At 6X	3X - 9X At 3X	At 9X
	Clear aperture of objective lens	20mm	32mm	32mm	Same	38mm	Same
	Clear aperture of ocular lens	32mm	32mm	32mm	Same	32mm	Same
	Exit Pupil	8mm	8mm	16mm	5.3mm	12.7mm	4.2mm
	Relative Brightness	64	64	256	28	161.2	17.6
	Field of view (degree of angle)	12°20'	5°30'	8°30'	3°10'	7°	2°20'
	Field of view at 100 yards	32'	29'	45½'	16¾'	36½'	12¾'
	Eye Relief	3.7"	3.6"	3"	3"	3.1"	2.9"
	Parallax Correction (at)	50 yds.	100 yds.	100 yds.	Same	100 yds.	Same
	Lens Construction	9	9	11	Same	11	Same
	MECHANICAL SPECIFICATIONS						
	Outside diameter of objective end	1.00"	1.525"	1.525"	Same	1.850"	1.850"
	Outside diameter of ocular end	1.455"	1.455"	1.455"	Same	1.455"	Same
	Outside diameter of tube	1"	1"	1"	Same	1"	Same
	Internal adjustment graduation	½ min.	½ min.	½ min.	Same	½ min.	Same
	Minimum internal adjustment	75 min.	75 min.	75 min.	Same	60 min.	Same
	Finish			Glossy Hard Black Anodized			
	Length	11¼"	11¾"	11½"	11½"	12¾"	12¾"
	Weight	8½ oz.	9½ oz.	11½ oz.	Same	13½ oz.	Same

Power	Reticle	Price
2½X	Crosshair	$47.00
2½X	T-N-T	53.50

Power	Reticle	Price
4X	Crosshair	$52.50
4X	T-N-T	58.50

Power	Reticle	Price
2X-6X	Crosshair	$73.50
2X-6X	T-N-T	80.00

Power	Reticle	Price
3X-9X	Crosshair	$81.75
3X-9X	T-N-T	88.25

WILLIAMS 'WIDE GUIDE' FOR THE BIG PANORAMIC VIEW

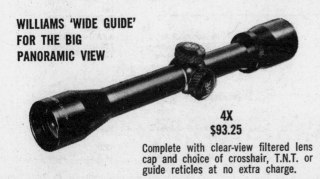

4X
$93.25

Complete with clear-view filtered lens cap and choice of crosshair, T.N.T. or guide reticles at no extra charge.

OPTICAL SPECIFICATIONS	
Clear aperture of objective lens	32 MM
Clear aperture of ocular lens	39 MM
Exit pupil	8 MM
Relative brightness	64
Field of view at 100 yards, vertical	27 ft.
Field of view at 100 yards, horizontal	35 ft.
Eye relief	3¼"
Parallax correction	100 yds.
Lens construction	9

MECHANICAL SPECIFICATIONS	
Outside diameter of objective end	1.610
Outside diameter of ocular end	1.750
Outside diameter of tube	1"
Internal adjustment graduation	½ min.
Minimum internal adjustment	50 min.
Finish	Hard Black Anodized
Length	12¼"
Weight	14 oz.

NEW SIGHT-THRU* MOUNT

INSTANT DUAL SIGHTING — SCOPE ABOVE, IRON SIGHTS BELOW

MODEL 100 WINCHESTER
WITH
Williams 3X — 9X Scope
Sight-Thru Mount
Foolproof Receiver Sight

- One-piece construction
- Large field of view for Iron Sights right under the scope
- Available for a wide assortment of factory drilled rifles
- All parts are precision machined
- Lightweight
- Hard black anodized finish
- Fast accurate sighting under all field conditions

The Williams Sight-Thru Mount provides instant use of scope, above, or iron sights below. Easily installed. Uses existing holes on top of receiver. No drilling or tapping necessary. The Sight-Thru is compact and lightweight — will not alter balance of the rifle. The high tensile strength alloy will never rust. All parts are precision machined. Completely rigid. Shockproof. The attractive streamlined appearance is further enhanced by a beautiful, hard black anodized finish.

Rings are 1" in size

⅞" Sleeves available at $1.00 per set.

Sight-Thru Mount complete (includes front and rear mount, rings, screws **$17.00**

One Ring complete with Sight-Thru base 8.50

Sub Block, when required **$1.70
    *Patent Pending

MODELS

	Front	Rear
Winchester Models 88 and 100, Sako Finnwolf	A	A
Remington Models 760-740-742, Savage Model 170	A	B
Winchester Models 70 Standard, 670 and 770	D	C
Remington Models 700-721-722-725, Weatherby MK-V, Rem .700 LH, BSA. . . .	D	E
Savage Model 110	D	F
Browning High Power Auto and lever action, Mossberg 800	G	G
Late Marlins, Marlin 336, 44 Mag., Rem. 541S	H	H
FN Mauser, Browning High Power, J. C. Higgins 50-51	D	I
Savage 99 New Style	J	K
		w sub Block**
Schultz & Larsen	A	G
1917 Enfield	J	J
Ruger 10-22	L	M
Ruger 44	O	M

SIGHT-THRU MOUNT FOR 22s

These new mounts are precision made. They are designed to fasten on the dovetails of all current 22's. For those 22's not having dovetails, there are mounting plates available to attach to receiver that creates the dovetails. Base of mount can be installed in a very low position with an unobstructed, clear view right down to the top of receiver—yet scope can still be elevated approximately ¼" additional.

These WST-D22 Sight-Thru mounts are recommended for 22's only and are available in ¾", ⅞" and 1" tube diameters. Specify tube diameter when ordering—

WST-D22 ¾"	**$6.00**
WST-D22 ⅞"	**$6.50**
WST-D22 1"	**$7.00**

This Remington model 552 is equipped with a $7.00, WST-D22-1" mount and a $52.50 Williams 4X Twilight scope. This sighting system is much more than just a plinking piece of equipment. It is accurate and dependable for target work and excellent for shooting running game.

WILLIAMS SCOPE MOUNTS

WILLIAMS QC SIDE MOUNTS

HCO Rings place scope overbore.

The Williams QC Side Mounts permit the shooter to have both scope and receiver sight always available for instant use. From the same base, shooter has his choice of rings that place scope directly over the bore or in the offset position.

Williams Side Mounts have positive locks. Using these locks, the mount becomes a "one piece" mount. Used optionally, the mount is quickly detached. Williams QC Mounts are provided with a limited amount of windage in the base to insure you of a good mounting job.

QC Side Mount Base	$11.35
QC Side Mount Complete, with solid, split or extension rings	20.25
QC Side Mount Complete with HCO rings	23.30

Regular Rings place scope offset.

THE QUICK CONVERTIBLE SIDE MOUNT — WITH REGULAR OR HCO RINGS

REMINGTON MODEL 742

Side mount with HCO rings (high central overbore) will position scope to give instant use of iron sights.

Mounting plate for the 30-M1 carbine **$5.95**
(Attach with 8-40 fillister screws). Use the Williams SM-740 side mount base with this mounting plate. Scope can be offset or high overbore.

Mounting plate for SMLE No. 1 .... **$2.95**
(Attach with 8-40 fillister head mounting screws). This mounting plate is supplied with long 8-40 fillister head screws to replace SM-70 short screws. Use the QC SM-70 base. Mount can be installed offset or central overbore.

Mounting plate for the Norwegian Krag **$5.95**
(Attach with 8-40 fillister head screws). Use the Williams QC SM-88 side mount base with the above mounting plate. Scope should not be installed central over-bore because of top ejection of cartridge.

Mounting plate for M1 Garand rifle **$5.95**
The mounting screws for this mounting plate are 8-40 x .475 Fillister head. Use the Williams QC SM-740 (4 holes) side mount with this mounting plate.

SM 70 .... Fits 70, 770, 670, 54 Winchester 600, 660, 700, 721, 722, Remington, Mossberg 800, Weatherby Mauser, Enfield Springfield Jap and 40-45, 322-325, 340-343, Savage, S/W, and Mark X rifles, Stevens, Husqvarna, 7x61 S&H. Round Receivered S.M.L.E.'s. Savage 110 right hand model. Swiss 1911, 7.5, BSA, Mossberg 3000.

SM 71 .... Fits 36, 336, 93, 444, 44 Mag. and 95 Marlins, 71* and 86* Winchesters and Remington 14 and 141, 7.62 Russians, flat receivered S.M.L.E.'s.

SM 81 .... 8-81 *Remington*.

SM 88 .... Fits 88, 100 Winchester, Ruger 44, 10-22, N. Krag with mounting plate, Winchester 150, 190, 250, 270, 290, Weatherby 22 and Browning lever action. Marlin 1894, Sako Finnwolf.

SM-94-36 .... Fits 64, 65, 66 and 94 Winchesters. No drilling or trapping. On 36, 336 Marlins drill and tap just one hole. NOTE: If amount is to be used with FP or 5D receiver sight then use the SM-71 mount equipped with proper 94 screws.

SM 99 .... Fits 99 Savage.

SM 110 LH ...... For the Savage 110, left hand model (fastens on right side of receiver), fits both short or long action and Weatherby Mark 5 left hand.

SM 760-40-42 .... For Remington 760-740-742. Regular mount base with four mounting holes. 30 M1 Garand and Carbine with mounting plate. Browning A.R., Remington 1100, Win. 1200, 1400. Also for flat received shotguns—model 12, 572, 552.

SM MS 52-56 ..... For Mannlicher Schoenauer of the modified version imported by Stoeger in 1952 and altered in 1956. 1903 Greek Mannlicher modified receiver, like the 52-56.

SM Krag .... For Krag*. 788 right and left hand Remington.

Will not accommodate central overbore rings.

QC SIDE MOUNT, BASES ONLY	$11.35
QC SIDE MOUNT, COMPLETE WITH SPLIT, OR EXTENSION RINGS	$20.25
QC SIDE MOUNT, COMPLETE WITH HCO (HIGH CENTRAL OVERBORE) RINGS	$23.30

WILLIAMS DOVETAIL OPEN SIGHT

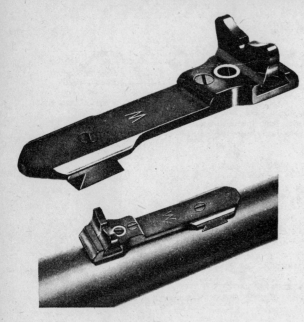

A precision sight made of lightweight high tensile strength alloy. Has steel screws and locks. Fits the standard ⅜" dovetail. Anodized black finish. Rustproof.

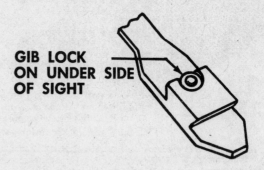

GIB LOCK ON UNDER SIDE OF SIGHT

The revolutionary design of the W.D.O.S. means **no more driving or hammering an open sight into the dovetail** of the rifle. The dovetail of the W.D.O.S. simply slides into the dovetail slot in the rifle barrel with just finger tip pressure as you tighten the locking screw it pulls the steel gib lock up snug against the dovetail on the rifle barrel and locks the sight in place.

Available in four heights with four different styles of blades — the same blades as used in the famous Williams Guide Open Sight — the U, V, SQ, and Britisher type notches.

WINDAGE ADJUSTMENT — Windage Adjustment is obtained by simply loosening the screw to unlock the steel gib lock and then the Williams Open Sight Blade can be moved either to the right or the left. In extreme cases, a double amount of windage can be obtained by getting windage in the dovetail of the barrel as well as with the blade.

ELEVATION — Elevation is obtained simply by an elevation set screw that can be turned in a full 1/16". Since the sight blades are also 1/16" from one model to another, you can get a wide range of adjustment from .281 up to .531. The .281 height is adjustable up to .345 — the .345 height is adjustable up to .406 — the .406 height is adjustable up to .468 — and the .468 height is adjustable up to .531.

Model numbers are:

WDOS—281   WDOS—406
WDOS—345   WDOS—468

TYPES OF BLADES

"SQ"   "U"   "V"   "B"

Sight blades are available in four styles and four heights. The "U", The "V", and "SQ" and the "B" in 3/16", ¼" 5/16" and ⅜".
EXTRA BLADES, each ----------------------------------- $1.75

BLADES

The "U" style is widely used by big game hunters and the "V" has almost as many advocates. The square notch is very popular with target shooters. However, many hunters prefer the square notch blade particularly when using a flat bladed front sight. "B" Britisher blade is exceedingly popular among African big game hunters.

Sight blades are interchangeable and may be quickly removed. Simply loosen the gib lock screw and change to any style or height of blade desired.

Extra sighting blades are just $1.75 each so that an assortment is inexpensive and will provide the shooter with a wide range of heights and styles to suit his taste or requirements.

Price with blade $5.00

WILLIAMS GUIDE OPEN SIGHT

Patent No.
3,199,202

$6.25

The new Guide Open Sight was designed, engineered and field tested by the Williams. It advances a new concept in sighting. It is compact, lightweight, and has a neat streamlined appearance. Both windage and elevation adjustments have positive locks — and various base and blade sizes permit the fitting of most any military or sporting rifle barrel in the greatest range of heights. Also used on rifles when you want iron sights high enough so that sighting plane is above a scope base on the receiver or when you want iron sights close to the height of scope sights.

Fast - the contour of the sighting blade is designed to give the shooter the greatest speed
- Made from high tensile strength metal. Will not rust.
- All parts are milled — no stampings.
- Streamlined and lightweight with tough anodized finish.
- Dovetailed windage and elevation — Adjustments quickly made by loosening one screw.
- Positive locks for windage and elevation.
- Hardened gib locks assure positive retention of zeroing.
- Fits all military and sporting rifles with ramp front sights.

- Easily installed. No dovetailing of barrel necessary. Simply fasten to barrel with two 6-48 screws.
- Interchangeable sighting blades of four different heights and four styles of notches.
- Fits the Drilling and Tapping on the 760, 740, 742, 700, 725 Remington, late 70 Win. etc. (⁹⁄₁₆″ distance center to center on mounting screws.)

SIMPLE WAY TO DESIGNATE SIGHT DESIRED

1) SPECIFY TYPE OF SIGHT —

"WGOS" means Williams Guide Open Sight

2) SPECIFY RADIUS OF BASE DESIRED S-M-L or FLAT
(Small - Medium - Large or Flat)

Small: for barrels .660 to .730
Medium: for barrels .730 to .830
Large: for barrels .830 to .930

SPECIAL high base is available for the Springfield 03, 03A3 and model 70 Winchester with high line of sights.

3) SPECIFY OVERALL HEIGHT DESIRED

HEIGHT

The WGOS with 3/16″ blade is adjustable in height from .369 to .431.
The WGOS with 1/4″ blade is adjustable in height from .431 to .493.
The WGOS with 5/16″ blade is adjustable in height from .493 to .555.
The WGOS with 3/8″ blade is adjustable in height from .555 to .617.
The WGOS with flat base is .050 higher than the above standard models.
The WGOS-Special in extra large radius is .100 higher than any of the above models.
The WGOS flat base with peep sight aperture is adjustable from .481 to .543.

4) SPECIFY STYLE OF BLADE DESIRED

"SQ" - or - "U" - or - "V" or "B"

EXTRA BLADES — $1.55 each

The most popular blade is the 'U' type notch. Because of this, our WGOS are listed by models, all with the 'U' type notch blade fitted in them. You may want the other style notches as extra or as optional equipment. The following are the basic model numbers.

WGOS S 3/16″ 'U'	WGOS M 3/16″ 'U'
WGOS S 1/4″ 'U'	WGOS M 1/4″ 'U'
WGOS S 5/16″ 'U'	WGOS M 5/16″ 'U'
WGOS S 3/8″ 'U'	WGOS M 3/8″ 'U'

WGOS L 3/16″ 'U'
WGOS L 1/4″ 'U'
WGOS L 5/16″ 'U'
WGOS L 3/8″ 'U'

The WGOS can be ordered with other style blades or with the Flat bases instead of the Small (S), Medium (M) or Large (L) radii—or in the WGOS Special.

ALSO USED ON MUZZLE LOADING RIFLES, ETC.

Quite often the Williams Guide Open Sight is used on muzzle loading rifles, falling blocks, etc. using the WGRS aperture rather than the blade. They are interchangeable. This combination can be worked out if care is used in the selection of the proper height front sight. When the Guide Open Sight is installed on the receiver of a rifle it doesn't have as much adjustment as a Guide Receiver Sight would have. The Guide Open Sight flat base with the aperture will give you a height adjustment from approximately .481 to .543.

WILLIAMS SIGHT COMBINATION CHART

Ramp Height	Height from Base to Dovetail	Height of Williams Bead	From Top of Barrel to Top of Bead
1/8"	.035	.250	.285
1/8"	.035	.290	.325
1/8"	.035	.312	.347
3/16"	.0975	.250	.3475
1/8"	.035	.343	.378
3/16"	.0975	.290	.3875
3/16"	.0975	.312	.4095
1/8"	.035	.375	.410
3/16"	.0975	.343	.4405
1/8"	.035	.406	.441
9/32"	.191	.250	.441
9/32"	.191	.290	.481
3/16"	.0975	.375	.4725
5/16"	.2225	.250	.4725
1/8"	.035	.450	.485
9/32"	.191	.312	.503
3/16"	.0975	.406	.5035
5/16"	.2225	.290	.5125
9/32"	.191	.343	.534
5/16"	.2225	.312	.5345
3/8"	.285	.250	.535
3/16"	.0975	.450	.5475
5/16"	.2225	.343	.5655
9/32"	.191	.375	.566
3/8"	.285	.290	.575
9/32"	.191	.406	.597

Ramp Height	Height from Base to Dovetail	Height of Williams Bead	From Top of Barrel to Top of Bead
3/8"	.285	.312	.597
5/16"	.2225	.375	.5975
7/16"	.3475	.250	.5975
3/8"	.285	.343	.628
5/16"	.2225	.406	.6285
7/16"	.3475	.290	.6375
9/32"	.191	.450	.641
7/16"	.3475	.312	.6595
3/8"	.285	.375	.660
5/16"	.2225	.450	.6725
7/16"	.3475	.343	.6905
3/8"	.285	.406	.691
3/8"	.285	.450	.735
7/16"	.3475	.375	.7225
9/16"	.4725	.250	.7225
7/16"	.3475	.406	.7535
9/16"	.4725	.290	.7625
9/16"	.4725	.312	.7845
7/16"	.3475	.450	.7975
9/16"	.4725	.343	.8155
9/16"	.4725	.375	.8475
9/16"	.4725	.406	.8785
9/16"	.4725	.450	.9225

AMOUNT OF ADJUSTMENT NECESSARY TO CORRECT FRONT SIGHT ERROR

DISTANCE BETWEEN FRONT AND REAR SIGHTS		14"	15"	16"	17"	18"	19"	20"	21"	22"	23"	24"	25"	26"	27"	28"	29"	30"	31"	32"	33"	34"
Amount of	1	.0038	.0041	.0044	.0047	.0050	.0053	.0055	.0058	.0061	.0064	.0066	.0069	.0072	.0074	.0077	.0080	.0082	.0085	.0088	.0091	.0093
Error	2	.0078	.0083	.0089	.0094	.0100	.0105	.0111	.0116	.0122	.0127	.0133	.0138	.0144	.0149	.0155	.0160	.0156	.0171	.0177	.0182	.0188
at	3	.0117	.0125	.0133	.0142	.0150	.0159	.0167	.0175	.0184	.0192	.0201	.0209	.0217	.0226	.0234	.0243	.0251	.0259	.0268	.0276	.0285
100 Yards	4	.0155	.0167	.0178	.0189	.0200	.0211	.0222	.0234	.0244	.0255	.0266	.0278	.0289	.0300	.0311	.0322	.0333	.0344	.0355	.0366	.0377
Given in	5	.0194	.0208	.0222	.0236	.0250	.0264	.0278	.0292	.0306	.0319	.0333	.0347	.0361	.0375	.0389	.0403	.0417	.0431	.0445	.0458	.0472
Inches	6	.0233	.0250	.0267	.0283	.0300	.0317	.0333	.0350	.0367	.0384	.0400	.0417	.0434	.0450	.0467	.0484	.0500	.0517	.0534	.0551	.0567

When you replace an open rear sight with a receiver sight, it is usually necessary to install a higher front sight, to compensate for the higher plane of the new receiver sight. The table above shows the increase in front sight height that's required to compensate for a given error at 100 yards. Suppose your rifle has a 19 inch sight radius, and shoots 6 inches high at 100 yards, with the receiver sight adjusted as low as possible. The 19 inch column shows that the correction for a 6 inch error is .0317 inch. This correction is added to the over-all height of the front sight (including dovetail). Use a micrometer or similar accurate device to measure sight height. Thus, if your original sight measured .250 inch, it should be replaced with a sight .290 inch high.

WILLIAMS FRONT SIGHT PUSHER

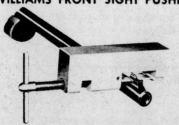

In the past there was only one accepted way to install a front sight in a ramp—pound it in with a hammer from the side. This method frequently marred a beautiful finish and loosened or damaged the ramp.

The Williams Front Sight Pusher provides the easiest and best way to install a front sight in a ramp. By equalizing the pressure on ramp and sight, it permits installation without marring or damaging, and eliminates excessive pressure on the ramp itself. Sight is smoothly and accurately moved into exact position.

The Front Sight Pusher is a precision tool for neat precision work.

WILLIAMS GUIDE RECEIVER SIGHTS

WGRS-100. ON THE 100 WIN.

WGRS-RU22. ON THE RUGER 10/22.

WGRS-742. ON THE 742 REMINGTON.

WGRS-24. ON THE 24 SAVAGE.

WGRS-54. ON THE 141 SAVAGE-ANSCHUTZ.

WGRS.—O3A3. ON THE O3A3 SPRINGFIELD.

- Compact, Low Profile
- Lightweight, Strong, Rustproof
- Positive Windage and Elevation Locks
- Easily Installed
- Quality Made, Neat Appearance
- Price—$8.65

In most cases these sights utilize dovetail or existing screws on top of receiver for installation. They are made from an aluminum alloy that is stronger than many steels. Light. Rustproof.

WGRS-100—For Winchester 88-lever, 100-automatic. Higher front sight needed——.406 high.

WGRS-RU 22 — Fits Ruger 10-22 without drilling or tapping. Normally a higher front sight is required. Usually .468 to .500.

WGRS-44 — For Ruger 44. Similar to but not interchangeable with WGRS-RU22. Usually requires a higher front sight—.468 to .500 will do.

WGRS-742—For 760, 742 Remington. Early models will require a higher front sight. For the BDL's use the Williams FP-740AP.

WGRS-24 — For all late Savage 24s which have upper barrel grooved for sight attachment. Higher front sight required.

WGRS-54 — For Savage - Anschultz 54, 64, 141, 141M, 153, 153S. Also Rem. 552 BDL, 572 BDL. Factory ramp height is sufficient.

WGRS-03A3 — For Springfield army rifles. Sight slides over dovetail.

WGRS-M1-Car. — For the .30 M1 Carbine.

WGRS WITH OPEN SIGHT BLADE

WGRS—37 for Ithaca 37 pump shotgun

WGRS-WR. For late Winchester and Remington slide action and autoloading shotguns. Fits 1200 vent rib and slug barrel. On 1200 plain barrel use Williams Band Ramp, .850 low. Model 1400 vent rib. On 1400 plain barrel use Williams Band Ramp, .850 med. Rem. 11-48 plain barrel and 1100. On 870 plain barrel use Williams large barrel ramp in the low model. Winchester model 12 use Williams Ramp 12-S high.

Quite often shotgun barrels do not align with the receivers as well as they should and have to be adjusted for the point of impact. So some shotguns will require front sights of heights other than those recommended. Sight is easily installed. Just drill and tap two 6-48 mounting screw holes. Screws are furnished.

OPEN SIGHT BLADES FOR THE GUIDE RECEIVER SIGHT

Many shooters wish to make open sights out of receiver sights. This can be done since the blades from our Guide Open Sights are interchangeable with the apertures of the receiver sights. Any Guide Receiver Sight can be ordered special with a Guide Open Sight blade in the SQ, U, V, or the B. Normally the ¼" blade is used since it is the approximate same height as the regular peep sight aperture. WGRS WITH OPEN SIGHT BLADE—$8.00

WGRS-M1-CAR. ON THE M1 CARBINE.

WGRS-WR ON THE 1200 WINCHESTER

WGRS-WR ON THE 1200 WINCHESTER

WGRS-44 ON THE 44 RUGER

WILLIAMS SIGHTS & ACCESSORIES

Patent No. 2578386

WILLIAMS

THE FOOLPROOF

One of the reasons the Foolproof is so popular is that it is free from knobs and other obstructions that impair and blot-out much of the shooter's field of vision.

Internal micrometer adjustments have positive internal locks — there is nothing — no exterior knobs or posts — that could be accidentally jarred or moved to throw the sight out of adjustment.

The Foolproof is strong, rugged, dependable. The alloy used to manufacture this sight has a tensile strength of 85,000 lbs. Yet the Foolproof is light and compact, weighing only 1½ ounces.

$16.25

with Twilight
Aperture—$16.75

These Models Fit More Than 100 Guns

FP 03   for the 03 Springfield.

FP 12, 37   for Win., M-12, 1200, 1400, 150, 190, 250, 255, 270, 275, 290, Ithaca M-37, Remington Spt's 48, 58, '11-'48 1100, 870 models*, and most flat receivered pumps and auto loaders.

FP 14   for the 14 and 141 Remingtons.

FP 17   for the Enfield, Remington Express and British Pattern 14.

FP 30 Car   for Government 30 Carbine.

FP 36   for the 36, 336, 444, 44 Mag. and 93 Marlins, Sears Higgins lever action center fire rifles.

FP 39   for 39A Marlin lever action.

FP 52   for 52 Sporter Winchester or other round receiver 52 models.

FP 70   for 70 and 54 Winchesters and 721, 722, 725 Remingtons Mossberg 800.

FP 70 AP   for the new model 70's, 670's & 770 with high sight line and 700 Remington, 800 Mossberg, BSA, Mossberg 3000.

FP 71   for 71-86-05-07 & 10 Winchesters.

FP 88-100   for the Winchester 88 lever action, Win. 100 Auto., and Marlin 56, 57, 62, 99 auto loading, Sako Finnwolf.

FP 94   for 94-55-64-65-63 Winchesters, Sears, and the 241, Browning center fire lever action.

FP 95   for the 95 Winchester lever action.

FP 98   for military Mauser, Husqvarna, Weatherby Mark V, right and left, and BRNO without dovetailed receiver.

FP 98-AP   for Browning high power bolt with high line of sights. Rem. 700 LH.

FP 99   for the 99 Savage lever action.

FP 99S   for the late Savage 99 with top tang safety.

FP 110   for Savage 110 bolt action, right and left.

FP 121   for Remington M12 and 121.

FP 340   for 322-325-340-342 Stevens-Savage.

FP 600   for the Remington 600, 660 bolt action.

FP 740AP   for all 742 Remingtons and for late 760-740 Remingtons with high comb. (all purpose stock) and high iron sights. Also the higher sight models of the 740 in the 30.06 and 280 calibers above serial numbers, 207, 200 and the .308 above 200,000, 572 BDL, 552 BDL. Savage 170.

FP 760N — 740   for 760 Remington rifles with serial numbers above 154,965 and all later 740 rifles after serial number 65,046 or having ejector in the bolt head not having A.P. Stocks. Also for the 572, 552 and 66 Remingtons. Also Colt Auto., Win. .250, .270, .290.

FP 788   for Remington 788 bolt action.

FP 788 LH   for Remington model 788 lefthand action.

FP A3   for the 03-A3 Springfield.

FP BAR   for Browning auto. loading high power rifle.

FP BR   for the .22 Browning Auto. and 24-241 Remingtons.

FP CGH   for Crown Grade Husqvarna, Smith & Wesson Rifle.

FP FN   for factory drilled and tapped FN and Dumoulin. Mark X, Daisy 99, 299.

FP JAP   for the 25 and 31 caliber Jap rifles.

FP Krag   for American Krag.

FP N. Krag   for Norwegian Krag.

FP RU   for the 44 Magnum Ruger carbine and .22 LR, 10-22 all models.

FP S & L   for the Schultz & Larsen 54J, Model 60 and 65 DL.

FP SMLE   for British Short Magazine Lee Enfields.

FP SSM   for square sterned auto. shotguns. Also fits 8.81 Rem. auto. loaders.

FP SW   for the 1911, Swiss 7.5.

*Special shotgun aperture optional

WILLIAMS SIGHTS & ACCESSORIES

5D-12-37

5D-22-410

5D-94-36

5D-JEMS

The Williams 5D receiver sight is made for big game rifles, shotguns, and .22 Caliber rifles. It is well made of the finest materials with positive windage and elevation adjustments. Standard thread sizes permit use of a wide range of apertures for all sighting conditions. This high-grade alloy is finished with an anodize in a deep blue-black that adds even further to the strength of the sight by creating an extra hard surface $9.00

FOR FOLLOWING MODELS

5D-12-37* — Winchester 1200, 1400, 12-25, 150, 190, 250, 255, 270, 275, 290, Remington 1100, '58, 11-48, Spt's-48, 870 and 31 models, Stevens 620, Ithaca 37 and other shotguns with flat-sided receivers.

5D-22-410 — For the .22-410, 20 (etc.) over and under Savage or Stevens.

5D-39A — Marlin 39A lever action. No drilling or tapping necessary.

5D-43 — For the 43 Winchester bolt action varmint rifle.

5D-46M — Mossberg 46, 26, 42, 44, 50, 51, 151 (factory drilled and tapped), 352's.

5D-49 — For the Ithaca 49 Saddle Gun, .22 cal.

5D-56-989 — For Marlin Levermatic 56, 57, 62, 99 auto; and 88, 100 Winchester. For Marlin 989 and 99's.

5D-61 — Winchester 61 slide action, .22.

5D-63 — Winchester 63 and 03 auto.

5D-70 — For 70 and 54, 670-770 Winchesters and 700, 721, 722 and 725, Remingtons, Mossberg 800.

5D-74 — Winchester Model 74, .22 auto.

5D-76 — Winchester 75, 72 and 69 (some factory drilled and tapped) Marlin 122, Win. 310, 320.

5D-77 — For the Winchester 77, .22 auto.

5D-81 — Marlin 80, 81, and A1 rifles (factory drilled and tapped).

5D-87 — For the Stevens-Savage, .22 autos models 87 and 6 and other Stevens-Savage bolt action and auto-loading rifles having 10-32 mounting screws.

5D-94/36 — For 94, 64, etc., Winchesters and 36-336 Marlin lever actions. Marlin 1894, 44 Mag.

5D-97* — Winchester 97

5D-121 — For the 121 and Model 12 Remington slide action .22's, Browning .22 auto, Rem. 24, 241 autos.

5D-510 — Remington 510, 511, 512 and 513 (some factory drilled and tapped) Nylon 12 tubular loading, Nylon 11 box magazine.

5D-550 — Remington 550 auto (it will also fit some of the Stevens-Savage .22s that are not drilled and tapped).

5D-572 — For Remington 572, 572 BDL, 552 BDL, .22 slide action, Kodiak 260's.

5D-620 — For the Mossberg, 620Ks, 640Ks, 340s, 342s, 346s, 350s, 351s.

5D-760N— —740—742 — For the Remington 760 with serial numbers above 154,965 and 740s above serial number 64,046. Also the Remington nylon 66. For Winchester new series 250, 255, 270, 275 & 290 with ramp. Savage 170.

5D-BDA* — For Browning Double Auto Shotgun.

5D-CR 160 — For the Crosman air rifles model 160.

5D-JEMS — For Jap, Enfield, Mauser and Springfield .03.

5D-Krag — For American Krag.

5D-MBA — Fits Mossberg bolt action shotguns — 185DC, 185K, 190, 85B, 85D, 185D.

5D-N, Krag — For Norwegian Krag.

5D-03-A3 — For the 1903-A3 Springfield.

5D-RU — For the 44 Ruger Carbine and 10-22, All models.

5D—SH — For Sheridan Model "C" Benjamin 340, 342, 347. The Benjamin needs a higher front sight.

5D-SMLE — For the British Short Magazine Lee Enfield, No. 1, 4, 5.

5D-SSM* — Square stern models of Remington, Browning & Savage auto shotguns. Also fits 8.81 Rem. auto. loaders.

*Special shotgun aperture optional. Extra shotgun apertures $2.00
3/8'' OD Aperture with 093 inner hole furnished unless otherwise specified.

Some of the Higgins guns are made by Marlin. Usually if the model number 103 is on a Higgins gun— then it's made by Marlin. Consequently, some of the sights we have designed for Marlin will fit a few models of the Higgins.

AVAILABLE IN IVORY, RED, GOLD

WILLIAMS "GUIDE BEAD" SHOTGUN SIGHTS

Fits all shotguns. Large ⅛" jewel finish bead has exceptional light gathering ability. Gets you on target fast. Easily installed. Screws into existing sight hole. Two thread sizes: 6-48 and 3-56, and two shank lengths, ³⁄₃₂" and ⁵⁄₃₂". $2.00

SWEAT-ON MODEL

SCREW-ON MODEL

STREAMLINED RAMPS

The Williams streamlined ramps are made in sweat-on and screw-on models. It comes with ⅜" dovetail and is blue finished. 6-48 screw furnished, however, the front sight is not included. Available in heights ⁹⁄₁₆", ⁷⁄₁₆", ⅜", ⁵⁄₁₆" and ³⁄₁₆".

Less Hood $5.75
With Hood 6.95
Extra Hoods 1.20

WILLIAMS SCOPE MOUNTS

WILLIAMS QUICK CONVERTIBLE TOP MOUNT

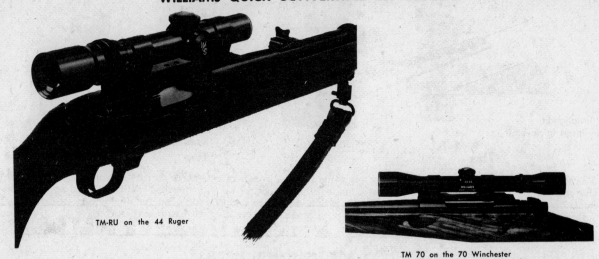

TM-RU on the 44 Ruger

TM 70 on the 70 Winchester

TM-03	For 03 Springfield	**TM-110-L**	For the Savage 110 models, 30-06, .270, 7mm, .264 and .338 Mag. with longer actions.
TM-03/A3	For 03-A3 Springfield	**TM-110-LL**	For the Savage left hand, long action, .270, 30-06, .7mm, .264, .338 Mag.
TM-7x61 (54)	For Sharpe & Hart 7 x 61, 54 bolt action.	**TM-110-LS**	For the Savage left hand, short actions, 243, 308.
TM-7x61 (60)	For Sharpe & Hart 7 x 61, 60 bolt action.	**TM-110-S**	For the Savage 110, 243 and 308 short actions.
TM-14	For Remington Model 14 slide action.	**TM-141**	For Remington 141 slide action.
TM-17	For 1917 Enfield and 30 Express and 720 Remingtons. On the Enfield grind the receiver to the same height and radius in the rear as in the front.	**TM-336N**	Fits late 336 Marlins that are factory drilled and tapped. Mounting screw holes are 8-40. Earlier models must be drilled and tapped. Includes the 444's.
TM-17 Special	For 1917 Enfield. There is enough stock left at the rear of mount base so that the Model 17's not cut to standard specifications may be fitted.	**TM-600**	For Remington 600, 660 bolt action, 40X and XP100 pistol.
TM-22 Auto	Fits numerous .22 Autos including Remington 550, Savage, Stevens, Springfield, Winchester 74, and Mossbergs.	**TM-721-MK5**	Fits the factory drilled and tapped 721, 725, 700 (long action Remingtons and Weatherby Mark 5.
TM-22-RU	For Ruger 10/22 auto rifle.	**TM-722**	Fits the factory drilled and tapped 722, 700 short action Remington.
TM-30	For J. C. Higgins Model 30.	**TM-760**	Fits 760, 740, 742 Remington. Most of these rifles are drilled and tapped on top for this mount. Savage 170.
TM-39N	For late 39A Marlin factory drilled and tapped. Mounting screw holes are 8-40. Earlier model 39 must be drilled and tapped.	**TM-788**	For 788 Remington R & L handed. The .222, 30-30-, 22-250 require no drilling or tapping. The 44 Magnum requires drilling and tapping rear hole
TM-43N	For new Model 43 factory drilled and tapped.	**TM-800**	For the 800 Mossberg.
TM-44M	For the new Marlin lever action 44.	**TM-AR-15**	For the Colt AR15, Military Model M16
TM-50	For early versions of the 50, Sears Roebuck, J. C. Higgins.	**TM-B22-241**	For Browning .22 Auto and Rem. 241 with mount fastening on the barrel and extending back over receiver.
TM-52	Fits late Winchester drilled and tapped 52 Sporter and Target, also undrilled, tapped 52's.	**TM-BAR**	For the Browning High Power Auto rifle and lever action.
TM-56	For 56 Marlin using factory drilled and tapped 8-40 mounting screw holes.	**TM-BRS**	For short action 243 Browning, FN Browning short action.
TM-63/121	For 63 Winchester Auto and Remington 121 slide action.	**TM-CGH**	For Crown Grade Husqvarna. Fits factory drilling and tapping. New Smith Wesson Rifle.
TM-69-75	For 69, 72 & 75 Winchester bolt actions.	**TM-FNA**	For F.N. actions. Fits F.N. actions, Weatherby, and late J. C. Higgins 50's and J. C. Higgins 51's, Browning High Power Rifles. Except the short actions.
TM-70	For all factory drilled 70's and 670's, 770 except 300 H & H and 375 H & H. Rear hole spacing—center to center—.860.	**TM-Jap**	For 6.5 Jap and 7.7 Jap. Bolt alteration is necessary.
TM-77	For Winchester 77 .22 Auto.	**TM-L-46**	For SAKO L46 short action, .222, .222 Mag. Necessary to drill and tap.
TM-88	For Winchester 88 lever action, fitting factory drilling and tapping.	**TM-L57**	For SAKO medium action 243, 308, etc. Necessary to drill and tap.
TM-93/95	For Mexican or Spanish Mausers (Short action). It is necessary to flatten the top of receiver where the five shot clip enters receiver if the gun is not going to be reblued. If it is to be reblued, grind this lobe off entirely. Also for 91 Argentine Mauser, 94 Swedish Mauser.	**TM-MK5-L**	For left hand Weatherby Mark 5.
		TM-RU	For the Ruger .44 Magnum carbine. Fits factory drilling and tapping.
TM-98	For 98 Mauser and standard Husqvarna. It is necessary to flatten the top of receiver where the five shot clip enters receiver if the gun is not going to be reblued. If it is to be reblued, grind this lobe off.	**TM-SHIKAR**	Shikar Rifle
		TM-SW Mauser	for Mauser Mark X
TM-99	For all 99's without tang safety.	**TM-Voere**	For Voere Mauser
TM-99S	For the 99 Savages 99DL and F models with tang type safety.	**TM-WBY-VM**	Varmint Master, WBY-224 & 22-250 calibers.
TM-100	For the model 100 Winchester auto.		

QC Top Mount, Bases only $11.35

QC Top Mount, Complete $20.25

WILLIAMS RAMPS

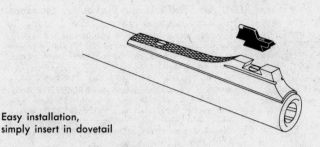

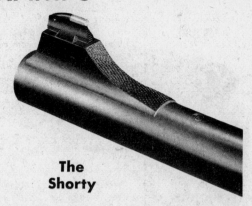

Easy installation, simply insert in dovetail

The Streamlined

The Shorty

WILLIAMS Streamlined RAMPS

SWEAT-ON MODEL   STEEL MODELS

SCREW-ON MODEL

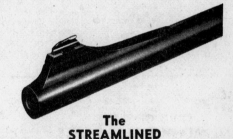

The STREAMLINED

Available in heights of: 9/16″, 7/16″, 3/8″, 5/16″, 3/16″.

WILLIAMS SHORTY RAMP — Steel —

MAY BE SWEATED ON

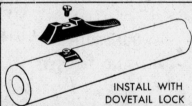

INSTALL WITH DOVETAIL LOCK

SCREW ON IN LOW 1/8″ Model

ATTACH WITH ONE SCREW

A SHORTENED VERSION OF THE POPULAR STREAMLINED RAMP

The new Shorty ramp is the companion to the popular Streamlined ramp. It is much shorter, being designed especially for handguns, .22s and some of the big game rifles. The Shorty is easily installed. It can be sweated on or screwed on a Special locking device that fits the standard 3/8″ dovetail cut and a 6:48 screw is also furnished. The single screw firmly locks ramp snugly to barrel for a neat perfect fit.

Four heights available: 1/8″, 3/16″, 9/32″ and 3/8″.

HOODLESS ONLY

WILLIAMS RIFLE SIGHT ASSORTMENT KIT

Front sights available in eight heights with a 1/16″ bead. Also 3/32″ bead on special order. Half of the sights have a base width of .250 for the Streamlined and Shorty ramp and the other sights have a wide .340 base for the 99 Savage, 94 Winchester, 336 Marlin, etc.

Dovetail open sights available in four heights — from .281 to .468 with a "U" type notch unless otherwise specied.

4 Front Sights .250 high—Gold and White—Two Widths
4 Front Sights .281 high—Gold and White—Two Widths
4 Front Sights .312 high—Gold and White—Two Widths
4 Front Sights .343 high—Gold and White—Two Widths
4 Front Sights .375 high—Gold and White—Two Widths
4 Front Sights .406 high—Gold and White—Two Widths
4 Front Sights .437 high—Gold and White—Two Widths
4 Front Sights .468 high—Gold and White—Two Widths
4 Williams Dovetail Open Sights—Four Heights

WILLIAMS APERTURES & BASES

TWILIGHT APERTURE

REGULAR SERIES

SHOTGUN BIG GAME APERTURE

5D

FP

TWILIGHT APERTURES are designed for shooting under poor light conditions, early morning, late evening and other inclement conditions. They create a sharp contrast that gives quick definition to the aperture hole, and they eliminate the "fuzz" with which many shooters have trouble.

These new apertures are perhaps the greatest development in metallic sights in the last three decades. Positive sighting when the light is poor but the hunting best.

Williams Twilight Apertures will accommodate Redfield, Lyman, Pacific, etc.

TW-⅜—.093	⅜" O.D. with .093 inner hole
TW-⅜—.125	⅜" O.D. with .125 inner hole
TW-½—.093	½" O.D. with .093 inner hole

SHOTGUN BIG GAME APERTURE

All Williams receiver sights can now be equipped with the new shotgun aperture. This new aperture has amazing light gathering ability. Permits clear shooting even when the light is poor. Designed for aerial shooting, slug shooting and for big game rifles. PROVIDES THE FASTEST, MOST ACCURATE SIGHTING YOU CAN HAVE!

REGULAR SERIES Target-Buckbuster Standard

We have always felt that a disc with a small outer diameter and a large inner hole is best for hunting. For this reason, we have made the ⅜" O.D. disc with a .093 inner hole as standard equipment. Other sizes are optional.

For the shooter who wants the FASTEST sighting aperture, we can now supply our BUCKBUSTER model which has a ⅜" O.D. and a large .125 inner hole. Our special target aperture has a ⅝" O.D. with a small .050 inner hole. Williams discs are standard thread size and will accommodate Redfield, Lyman, Pacific, etc.

R-⅜—.050	⅜" O.D. with .050 inner hole
R-⅜—.093	⅜" O.D. with .093 inner hole (STANDARD, unless otherwise specified)
R-⅜—.125	⅜" O.D. with .125 inner hole—BUCKBUSTER
R-½—.093	½" O.D. with .093 inner hole
R-½—.125	½" O.D. with .125 inner hole
R-⅝—.050	⅝" O.D. with .050 inner hole—TARGET
R-⅝—.093	⅝" O.D. with .093 inner hole

GOLD OR SILVER METAL SHOTGUN SIGHTS

Nos. 1 & 2 Front

No. 3 Front

No. 4 Rear

Model	Thread	Bead Dia.	Shank Length
No. 1	6-48	.175	⅛"
No. 2	3-56	.175	⅛"
No. 3	3-56	.130	⅛"
No. 4	3-56	.067	³⁄₃₂"

GARAND CLIP

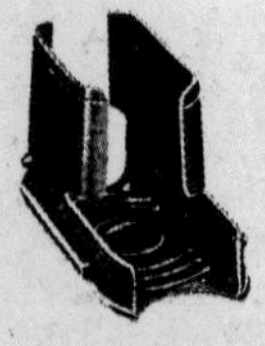

For hunting, most states limit the magazine capacity to five shot.

5 Shot Garand

SMLE EXTRACTOR SPRINGS

New, and specially made from tempered spring steel. Easily fitted. Only a punch is needed.

NUMBER 1   NUMBER 4 & 5

GUNSMITH'S DRILL AND TAP SETS

3-56 Tap (1.35) Carbon

6-48 Tap (1.35) Carbon

8-40 Tap (1.35) Carbon

6-48 H.S. Tap — #31 H.S. Drill

8-40 H.S. Tap — #28 H.S. Drill

10-32 H.S. Tap — #21 H.S. Drill

SLOT BLANK

For appearance sake—use this slot blank after removing iron sight. It will also cover up most burr marks.

Standard ⅜" (left) for Winchester, Stevens, Marlin, Remington, Savage, and other rifles.

OPEN FOLDING SIGHT BASE

See Williams Military Conversion Book for heights and sight combinations.

For Military and Standard Rifles. Will accommodate standard folding sights such as Marble 69, 70, 69H. 70H, Lyman 16A or 16B and Redfield 46, 47 and 48. Base furnished with 6-48 screws. Acts as a riser to give open rear sight necessary height to align properly with ramp front sights or to use with scoped rifles.

760 OPEN SIGHT BASE

for late Remington 760, 740, 725, etc. Also can be used on military rifles. Same hole span as the Guide Open Sight. To fit factory drilling and tapping ⁹⁄₁₆" or .5625 between mounting screws (center to center). Standard 6-48 mounting screws furnished.

TASCO

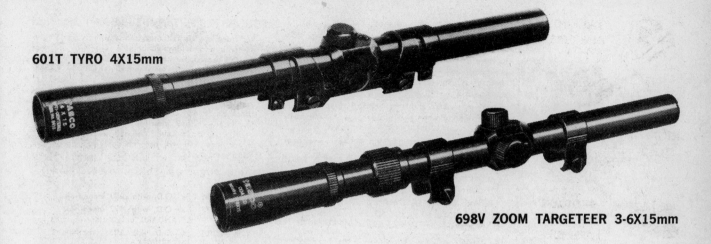

601T TYRO 4X15mm

698V ZOOM TARGETEER 3-6X15mm

601T TYRO
4X15mm — 18' — 2" — 14.06 — ¾" — 11¾" — 7 oz.

Fully coated 5-lens optical system, fogproofed by nitrogen and parallax corrected. ½-minute click stops. Opti-Centered® crosshair reticle. Fits .22 caliber and air rifles with grooved receiver. Haze-filter caps. **$15.95**

698V ZOOM TARGETEER
3-6X15mm — 19.6' — 11.5' — 2⅞" — 25.00 — 6.25 — ¾" — 11⅞" — 6.25 oz.
Coated 7-lens optical system. The per-fect scope for target or small-game shooters. Attached ring mounts fit all .22 rifles with grooved receivers. TV-view, crosshair Opti-Centered® reticle. ½-minute click stops. Fogproofed by nitrogen process. Haze-filter caps.
$27.95

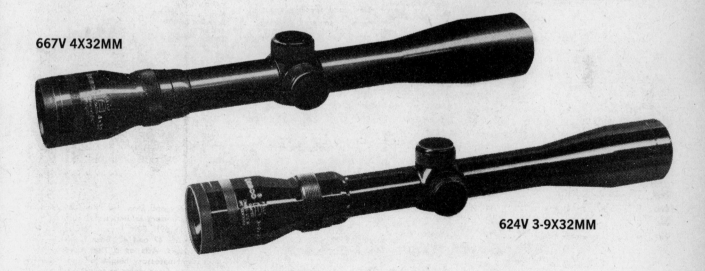

667V 4X32MM

624V 3-9X32MM

667V 4X32mm
36' — 3" — 64.00 — 1" — 11⅞" — 11¼ oz.
Tasco's latest entry in the riflescope field offers a 25% wider (36') field of view than seen through a round image riflescope. The distortion-free range finding 30/30 reticle enables you to determine the distance for a single shot kill. Durable one-piece construction with anodized finish. Waterproof, shockproof, and fogproof. ¼-minute click stops, Opti-Centered® reticle, haze-filter caps. Accurately aligned, fully coated 11-lens optical system. **$79.95**

624V 3-9X32mm
43.5' — 16.5 — 3.5"-3" — 113.64-12.60 — 1" — 12½" — 11½ oz.
Fully coated 10-lens optical system. Opti-Centered® 30/30 range finding reticle. Zooms from 3 to 9 powers while retaining crisp sharp focus. Waterproof, shockproof, and anodized finish. Fogproofed by nitrogen process. ¼-minute click stops. Haze-filter caps. **$119.95**

TASCO

627W SUPER MARKSMAN 3-9X40mm
35'—14'—3.5"—176.89—19.36—1"—12⅜"—14 oz.
A large 40mm objective lens centers your target with edge-to-edge crispness in an Opti-Centered® 30/30 range finding reticle. Fully coated 10-lens optical system is shockproof. Fogproofed by nitrogen. ¼-minute click stops. Haze-filter caps. **$95.95**
620W SUPER MARKSMAN same as 627W with crosshair reticle **$95.95**

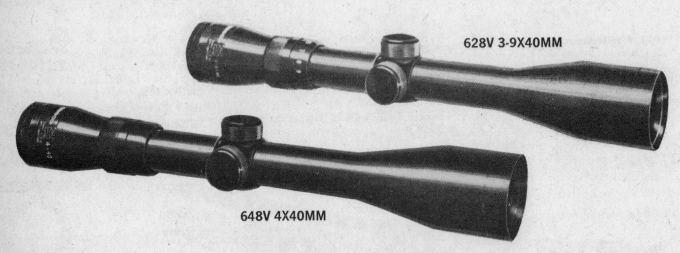

628V 3-9X40MM

648V 4X40MM

648V 4X40mm
36'—3"—100.00—1"—11⅞"—12 oz.
Big 40mm wide angle scope by Tasco. Fully coated 11-lens optical system. Opti-Centered® 30/30 range finding reticle. Crisp, bright images in a broad field of view. Waterproof, shockproof, fogproof, and anodized finish. ¼-minute click stops. Haze-filter caps. **$89.95**

628V 3-9X40mm
42'-15'—3"-3.25"—176.89-19.36—1"—12⅛"—12.25 oz.
Tasco 40mm zoom wide angle. Fully coated 10-lens optical system. Opti-Centered® 30/30 range finding reticle. Zooms from 3 to 9 powers with crisp sharp focus through the full range. Waterproof, fogproof, shockproof, and anodized finish. ¼-minute click stops. Haze-filter caps. **$139.95**

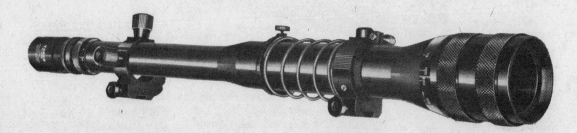

705 TARGET SCOPE 6X-18X40mm
16'-5'—3"—44.35-4.93—28mm—22½"—36.5 oz.
Fully coated 10-lens optical system. Opti-Centered® crosshair reticle. This variable Target Scope has powers of 6, 8, 10, 12, 14, 16 and 18 with clear images at all powers. ¼-minute clicks (when used with a base spacing of 7"). Target-style mounts fit standard available bases. Recoil spring, clamp ring and screw-in dust caps are standard equipment.
$149.95

Ammunition

REMINGTON AND PETERS RIM-FIRE AMMUNITION

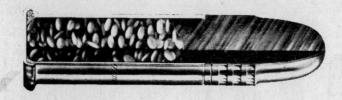

"HIGH VELOCITY" 22s with "golden" bullets

The "golden" bullet is made for perfect mesh with rifling of the barrel. And "High Velocity" 22s are clean because every "golden" bullet is coated with a specially formulated high-temperature lubricant. They shun dirt and grit and lint. "Kleanbore" Priming.

Index No.	Packed 50 per box except where noted	Wt. Grs.	BULLET Style	Price Per Box
REMINGTON "HIGH-VELOCITY"				
1022	22 Short, "High-Velocity"	29	Lead	$1.12
1122	22 Short, "High-Velocity" Hollow Point	27	Lead	1.20
1322	22 Long, "High-Velocity"	29	Lead	1.20
1522	22 Long Rifle, "High-Velocity"	40	Lead	1.27
1500	22 Long Rifle, "High-Velocity" (100 pack)	40	Lead	2.54
1622	22 Long Rifle, "High-Velocity" Hollow Point	36	Lead	1.39
1600	22 Long Rifle, "High-Velocity", Hollow Point (100 pack)	36	Lead	2.78
1822	22 W.R.F. (Remington Special), "High-Velocity"	45	Lead	3.61
1050	5 mm Remington Rim Fire Magnum, "High-Velocity"	38	PLHP	5.08

Index No.	Packed 50 per box except where noted	Wt. Grs.	BULLET Style	Price Per Box
PETERS "HIGH VELOCITY"				
2267	22 Short ....High Velocity	29	Lead	$1.12
2268	22 Short, Hollow Point..High Velocity	27	Lead	1.20
2269	22 Long ....High Velocity	29	Lead	1.20
2283	22 Long Rifle ....High Velocity	40	Lead	1.27
2200	22 Long Rifle (100 pack) High Velocity	40	Lead	2.54
2284	22 Long Rifle, Hollow Point ....High Velocity	36	Lead	1.39
2400	22 Long Rifle, Hollow Point (100 pack) ....High Velocity	36	Lead	2.78

STANDARD VELOCITY 22s

For shorter-range hunting, and for informal target shooting or plinking, Remington or Peters Standard Velocity 22s are an excellent choice. Available in short and long rifle sizes. All Remington and Peters ammunition has "Kleanbore" priming to keep your gun barrel bright and clean.

Index No.	Packed 50 per box except where noted	Wt. Grs.	BULLET Style	Price Per Box
REMINGTON STANDARD VELOCITY				
5522	22 Short	29	Lead	$1.12
5722	22 Short, Gallery Special, Spatter-Less (250 in box)	29	Lead Comp.	4.92
6722	22 Short, New and Improved Spatter-Less (250 in box)	15	Comp. Spec.	4.92
6122	22 Long Rifle	40	Lead	1.27
6100	22 Long Rifle (100 pack)	40	Lead	2.54
7522	22 Win. Automatic	45	Lead	3.71

Index No.	Packed 50 per box except where noted	Wt. Grs.	BULLET Style	Price Per Box
PETERS STANDARD VELOCITY				
2214	22 Short	29	Lead Comp.	$1.12
2224	22 Long Rifle	40	Lead	1.27
2600	22 Long Rifle (100 pack)	40	Lead	2.54

P.L.H.P.—Power-Lokt, Hollow Point

REMINGTON AND PETERS RIM-FIRE AMMUNITION

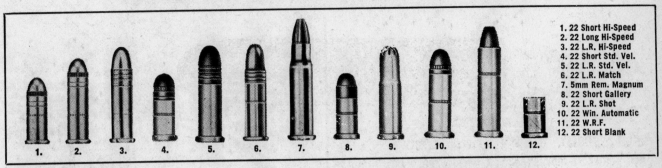

1. 22 Short Hi-Speed
2. 22 Long Hi-Speed
3. 22 L.R. Hi-Speed
4. 22 Short Std. Vel.
5. 22 L.R. Std. Vel.
6. 22 L.R. Match
7. 5mm Rem. Magnum
8. 22 Short Gallery
9. 22 L.R. Shot
10. 22 Win. Automatic
11. 22 W.R.F.
12. 22 Short Blank

MATCH LONG RIFLE 22s

Remington or Peters Match 22s have a bullet shape micro-measured for consistency, with superb wind-bucking qualities—a silicone-base lubricant that makes it unnecessary to clean barrels between stages—a "Kleanbore" priming mixture that insures longer barrel accuracy life—and a close-tolerance brass case with rim shaped for improved ignition.

SHOT AND BLANK RIM FIRE

Index No.	Packed 50 per box except where noted	BULLET Wt. Grs.	Style	Price Per Box
REMINGTON SPECIAL MATCH CARTRIDGES				
6600	22 Long Rifle, Match—for Rifles (100 pack)	40	Lead	$4.21
6800	22 Long Rifle, Match—for Pistols (100 pack)	40	Lead	4.21
REMINGTON SHOT CARTRIDGES				
9322	22 Long Rifle, High-Velocity Rim Fire			2.64

Index No.	Packed 50 per box except where noted	BULLET Wt. Grs.	Style	Price Per Box
REMINGTON BLANK CARTRIDGES				
LOADED WITH SPECIAL POWDER INSURING A LOUD REPORT		Primer No.		
9022	22 Short, Rim Fire	...		$1.21
32BLNK	32 S. & W., Center Fire	5½		5.60
38SWBL	38 S. & W., Center Fire	1½		7.20
38BLNK	38 Special, Center Fire	1½		7.90
5-1BL	5 in 1 Blank, Center Fire (For use in 38/40, 44/40 Rifles and 38/40, 44/40, 45 Colt Revolvers)	2½		16.95

FEDERAL RIM-FIRE AMMUNITION

All Federal rim-fire cartridges have non-corrosive non-mercuric priming. The Hi-Powers are loaded with solid bullets for regular hunting and plinking, and hollow points for predators. The shot cartridges are loaded with no. 12 shot, for small pest control at short range or inexpensive practice on tossed targets.

FEDERAL .22 RIM-FIRE CARTRIDGES

Index No.	Packed 50 per box.	Wt. Grs.	Price
701	22 Short Copper Plated	29	$1.12
703	22 Short, Copper Plated, Hollow Point	29	1.20
706	22 Long, Copper Plated	29	1.20
710	22 Long Rifle, Copper Plated	40	1.27
712	22 Long Rifle, Copper Plated, Hollow Point	38	1.39
716	22 Long Rifle, # 12 Shot	# 12 Shot	2.64
702	22 Short, Lead Lubricated	29	1.12
711	22 Long Rifle, Lead Lubricated	40	1.27

WINCHESTER AND WESTERN RIM-FIRE AMMUNITION

Super-X, High Velocity

No.	Caliber and type bullet	Wt. bullet, grain	No. in box	Per box
WSX22S	22 Short, Kopperklad	29	50	$1.12
WSX22SH	22 Short HP, Kopperklad	27	50	1.20
WSX22LR-1	22 Long Rifle, Kopperklad	40	100	2.54
WSX22LR	22 Long Rifle, Kopperklad	40	50	1.27
WSX22LRH-1	22 Long Rifle, HP, Kopperklad	37	100	2.78
WSX22LRH	22 Long Rifle, HP, Kopperklad	37	50	1.39
WSX22WMR	22 Winchester Magnum, Jacketed HP	40	50	3.45
WSX22MR1	22 Winchester Magnum, Full Metal Case	40	50	3.45

T-22 Standard Velocity

No.	Caliber and type bullet	Wt. bullet, grain	No. in box	Per box
WT22S	22 Short, Lead, Lub.	29	50	$1.12
WT22LR	22 Long Rifle, Lead, Lub.	40	50	1.27

Standard Velocity, Gallery Pack, Disintegrating Bullet

No.	Caliber and type bullet	Wt. bullet, grain	No. in box	Per box
WW226	22 Short, Spatterpruf	27	250	$4.92
WW226S	22 Short, Super Spatterpruf	15	250	4.92

Shot Cartridge

No.	Caliber and type bullet	Wt. bullet, grain	No. in box	Per box
WSX22LRS	22 Long Rifle, No. 12 shot	25	50	2.64

Blank Cartridge

No.	Caliber and type bullet	Wt. bullet, grain	No. in box	Per box
W22BL	22 Short, Black Powder	..	50	1.21

Super-X High Velocity

No.	Caliber and type bullet	Wt. bullet, grain	No. in box	Per box
SX22S	22 Short, Lubaloy	29	50	$1.12
SX22SH	22 Short HP, Lubaloy	27	50	1.20
SX22LR-1	22 Long Rifle, Lubaloy	40	100	2.54
SX22LR	22 Long Rifle, Lubaloy	40	50	1.27
SX22LRH-1	22 Long Rifle HP, Lubaloy	37	100	2.78
SX22LRH	22 Long Rifle HP, Lubaloy	37	50	1.39
SX22WRF	22 WRF (Rem. Spec.), Lubaloy	45	50	3.61
SX22WMR	22 Winchester Magnum, Jacketed HP	40	50	3.45
SX22MR1	22 Winchester Magnum, Full Metal Case	40	50	3.45

Super-Match

No.	Caliber and type bullet	Wt. bullet, grain	No. in box	Per box
SM22LR	22 Long Rifle, Super-Match Mark III, Lead	40	50	2.10
SM22LR4	22 Long Rifle, Super-Match Mark IV Pistol, Lead	40	50	2.10

T-22 Standard Velocity

No.	Caliber and type bullet	Wt. bullet, grain	No. in box	Per box
T-22S	22 Short, Lead	29	50	$1.12
T-22LR	22 Long Rifle, Lead	40	50	1.27

Standard Velocity, Gallery Pack, Disintegrating Bullet

No.	Caliber and type bullet	Wt. bullet, grain	No. in box	Per box
KS22S1	22 Short, Kant-Splash	27	250	$4.92
SKS22S	22 Short Super Kant-Splash	15	250	4.92

Shot Cartridge

No.	Caliber and type bullet	Wt. bullet, grain	No. in box	Per box
SX22LRS	22 Long Rifle, No. 12 Shot	25	50	2.64

Short   Short H.P.   Short Spatterpruf

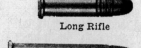

Long Rifle   Long Rifle H.P.

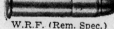

Long Rifle Shot   Long Rifle Match   W.R.F. (Rem. Spec.)

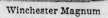

Winchester Magnum

H. P.—Hollow Point   **LUB.—Lubricated**   **L. V.—Low Velocity**

REMINGTON-PETERS
WINCHESTER-WESTERN
CENTER-FIRE
RIFLE AMMUNITION

INTERCHANGEABILITY CHART
Cartridges in groups shown below will interchange

RIM FIRE
22 W.R.F.
22 Remington Special
22 Win. M/1890
in a 22 Win. Magnum Rim Fire
but not conversely

CENTER FIRE
25-20 Remington
25-20 W.C.F.
25-20 Win.
25-20 Win. Hi-Speed
25-20 Marlin
25 W.C.F.

25 Automatic
25 Automatic Cold Pistol (ACP)
25 (6.35 mm) Automatic Pistol
6.35 mm Browning

30-30 Sav.
30-30 Win.
30-30 Marlin
30-30 Win. Hi-Speed
30 W.C.F.

32 Short Colt in
32 Long Colt but not conversely
SEE NOTE A

32 Colt Automatic
32 Automatic Colt Pistol (ACP)
32 (7.65 mm) Automatic Pistol
7.65 mm Automatic Pistol

7.65 mm Browning (not interchangeable with 7.65 mm Luger)

32 S. & W. in
32 S. & W. Long but not conversely

32 S. & W. Long
32 Colt New Police
32 Colt Police Positive

32 W.C.F.★
32 Win.★
32-20 Win. Hi-Speed★
32-20 Colt L.M.R.★
32-20 W.C.F.★
32-20 Win. and Marlin★
SEE NOTE E

38 S. & W.
38 Colt New Police
380 Webley

38 Short Colt in
38 Long Colt but not conversely
Both can be used in 38 Special

38 Colt Special
38 S. & W. Special
38 Targetmaster
38 S. & W. Special Mid-Range
38 Special Hi-Speed (•)
SEE NOTE B
38-44 Special (•)
38 Special
38 Special Flat Point

---

38 Marlin★
38 Win.★
38 Remington★
38-40 Win.★
38 W.C.F.★

38 Automatic in
38 Super but not conversely

380 Automatic
9 mm Browning Short (Corto, Kurz)

9 mm Luger
9 mm Parabellum
SEE NOTE C

44 S. & W. Special but not conversely
SEE NOTE D

44 Marlin
44 Win .
44 Remington
44-40 Win.★
44 W.C.F.

45-70 Government
45-70 Marlin, Win.
45-70-405
Above cartridges can be fired in
45-75 Sharps
45-82 Win.
45-85 Marlin
45-90 Win.
45-100 Sharps

NOTE: ★Hi-Speed Cartridges must not be used in Revolvers. They should be used only in rifles made especially for them.
Exceptions: items marked (•) are designed especially for the 38-44 S. & W. Revolver and the 38 Colt Shooting Master.
Check with the manufacturer of light frame guns prior to use of Hi-Speed ammunition to determine their suitability.
NOTE A: Not for use in revolvers chambered for 32 S. & W. or 32 S. & W. Long.
NOTE B: All 38 Special cartridges can be used in 357 Magnum revolvers but not conversely.
NOTE C: 9mm sub-machine gun cartridge should not be used in hand guns.
NOTE D: 44 Russian and 44 S. & W. Special can be used in 44 Remington Magnum Revolvers but not conversely.
NOTE E: Not to be used in Win. M/66 and M/73.

To identify similar American and European cartridges, the following table is shown. There are no American cartridges made or recommended for the 6.5 mm Italian service rifles, the 25 or 30 caliber (6.5 or 7.7 mm) Japanese rifles, or any Japanese pistol.

● Rifle Cartridges

American	European
22 Savage	5.6 x 52R
25 Remington	6.5 x 52
25-35 Winchester	6.5 x 52R
7 mm Mauser	7 x 57
30-30 Winchester	7.62 x 51R
7.62 Russian	7.62 x 53R
30-06 Springfield	7.62 x 63
303 British	.303 Inch Mark VI or VII
8 mm Mannlicher-Schoenauer (M/1908)	8 x 56
8 mm Mauser	8 x 57

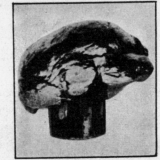

● Pistol Cartridges

American	European
25 Automatic	6.35 Browning
30 Luger	7.65 mm (Parabellum)
30 Mauser	7.63 mm Militaire
32 Automatic	7.65 mm Browning
380 Automatic	9 mm Browning Short
	9 mm Short (Corto, Kurz)
9 mm Luger	9 mm Luger (Parabellum)

CENTER FIRE RIFLE CARTRIDGES

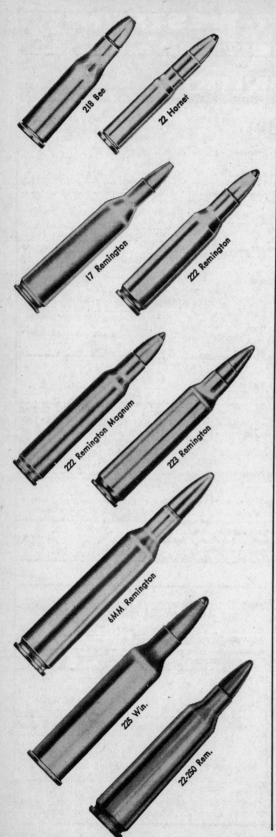

218 Bee

22 Hornet

17 Remington

222 Remington

22 Remington Magnum

223 Remington

6MM Remington

225 Win.

22-250 Rem.

INDEX No.	MAKE	WT. GRS.	STYLE	PRIMER No.	PER BOX OF	
17 REMINGTON (.172″ dia.)						
R17REM	Rem.	25	H.V., Power Lokt	7½	20	\$6.10
P17REM	Peters	25	H.V., Power Lokt	7½	20	
218 BEE: (.224″ dia.)						
R218BE	Rem.	46	Hi-Speed, Hollow Point	6½	50	\$14.95
W218B	Win.	46	Hollow Point, Super-Speed	116	50	\$14.95
218B	West.	46	Open Point Expanding, Super-X	6½	50	
22 HORNET: (.224″ dia.)						
R22HN1	Rem.	45	Hi-Speed, Soft Point	6½	50	\$11.40
R22HN2	Rem.	45	Hi-Speed, Hollow Point	6½	50	
W22H1	Win.	45	Soft Point, Super-Speed	116	50	
W22H2	Win.	46	Hollow Point, Super-Speed	116	50	\$11.40
22H1	West.	45	Soft Point, Super-X	6½	50	
22H2	West.	46	Open Point Expanding, Super-X	6½	50	
222 REMINGTON: (.224″ dia.)						
R222R3	Rem.	50	Hi-Speed, Power-Lokt, H.P.	7½	20	\$5.65
R222R1	Rem.	50	Hi-Speed, Ptd. S.P.	7½	20	
R222R2	Rem.	50	Hi-Speed, Metal Case	7½	20	
2244	Peters	50	High Velocity, Ptd. S.P.	7½	20	\$5.20
W222R	Win.	50	Pointed Soft Point, Super-Speed	116	20	
222R	West.	50	Pointed Soft Point, Super-X	6½	20	
222 REMINGTON MAGNUM: (.224″ dia.)						
R222M1	Rem.	55	Hi-Speed, Ptd. S.P.	7½	20	\$5.70
R222M2	Rem.	55	Hi-Speed, Power-Lokt, H.P.	7½	20	\$6.10
22-250 REMINGTON: (.224″ dia.)						
R22501	Rem.	55	Pointed Soft Point, Hi-Speed	9½	20	\$5.70
P22501	Peters	55	Pointed Soft Point, Hi-Vel.	9½	20	
R22502	Rem.	55	Hi-Speed, Power-Lokt, H.P.	9½	20	\$6.10
W222501	Win.	55	Ptd. S.P., Super-Speed	120	20	\$5.70
222501	West.	55	Ptd. S.P., Super-X	8½	20	
223 REMINGTON (5.56 mm): (.224″ dia.)						
R223R1	Rem.	55	Hi-Speed, Ptd. S.P.	7½	20	\$5.70
P223R1	Peters	55	High Velocity, Ptd. S.P.	7½	20	
R223R2	Rem.	55	Hi-Speed, Power-Lokt, H.P.	7½	20	\$6.10
W223R	Win.	55	Ptd. S.P.	7½	20	\$5.70
223R	West.	55	Ptd. S.P.		20	\$5.70
225 WINCHESTER: (.224″ dia.)						
W2251	Win.	55	Pointed Soft Point, Super-Speed	120	20	\$5.85
2251	West.	55	Pointed Soft Point, Super-X	8½	20	
6MM REMINGTON: (.243″ dia.)						
R6MM1	Rem.	80	Hi-Speed, Ptd. S.P.	9½	20	
R6MM3	Rem.	90	Hi-Speed, Ptd. S.P.	9½	20	
R6MM4	Rem.	100	Hi-Speed, Ptd. S.P., Core-Lokt	9½	20	\$7.05
P6MM4	Peters	100	H.V., Core-Lokt, Ptd. S.P.	9½	20	
P6MM2	Peters	80	H.V., P.L., H.P.	9½	20	\$7.50
R6MM2	Rem.	80	Hi-Speed, Power-Lokt, H.P.	9½	20	\$7.50
6MMR1	West.	80	P.T.S.P.	9½	20	\$7.05
6MMR2	West.	100	P.T.S.P.	9½	20	\$7.05

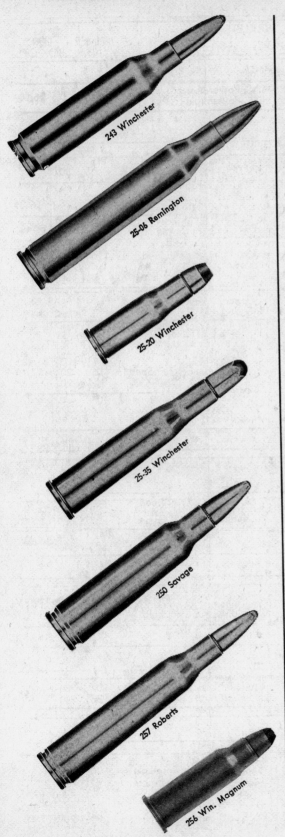

243 Winchester

25-06 Remington

25-20 Winchester

25-35 Winchester

250 Savage

257 Roberts

256 Win. Magnum

INDEX No.	MAKE	WT. GRS.	BULLET STYLE	PRIMER No.	PER BOX OF	
243 WINCHESTER: (.243″ dia.)						
R243W1	Rem.	80	Hi-Speed, Pointed Soft Point	9½	20	
R243W3	Rem.	100	Hi-Speed, Ptd. S.P., Core-Lokt	9½	20	
P243W1	Peters	80	High Velocity, Ptd. S.P.	9½	20	
P243W3	Peters	100	H.V., Core-Lokt Ptd. S.P.	9½	20	**$7.05**
W2431	Win.	80	Pointed Soft Point, Super Speed	120	20	
W2432	Win.	100	Power-Point (S.P.) Super-Speed	120	20	
2431	West.	80	Pointed Soft Point, Super-X	8½	20	
2432	West.	100	Power-Point (S.P.) Super-X	8½	20	
R243W2	Rem.	80	Hi-Speed, Power-Lokt, H.P.	9½	20	**$7.50**
25-06 REMINGTON						
R25061	Rem.	87	Hi-Speed, Hollow Point	9½	20	**$7.70**
R25062	Rem.	100	Hi-Speed, Pt SPCL	9½	20	**$7.70**
R25063	Rem.	120	Hi-Speed, Pointed Soft Point	9½	20	**$7.70**
P25061	Peters	87	H.V., Power-Lokt, H. P.	9½	20	**$7.70**
P25063	Peters	120	H.V., Core-Lokt, Pointed S.P.	9½	20	**$7.70**
P25062	Peters	100	H.V., Core-Lokt, Pointed S.P.	9½	20	**$7.70**
W25061	Win.	90	Positive Expand. Pt.	120	20	
W25062	Win.	120	Positive Expanded Pt.	120	20	**$7.70**
25061	West.	90	Positive Expanded Pt.	8½	20	
25062	West	120	Positive Expanded Pt.	8½	20	
25-20 WINCHESTER: (.257″ dia.)						
R25201	Rem.	86	Lead Bullet Hi-Speed	6½	50	**$10.60**
R25202	Rem.	86	Soft Point Hi-Speed	6½	50	**$11.80**
W25201	Win.	86	Lead Bullet	116	50	**$10.60**
W25202	Win.	86	Soft Point	116	50	**$11.80**
25201	West.	86	Lubaloy	6½	50	**$10.60**
25202	West.	86	Soft Point	6½	50	**$11.80**
25-35 WINCHESTER: (.257″ dia.)						
R2535W	Rem.	117	Soft Point, Core-Lokt	9½	20	
W2535	Win.	117	Soft Point, Super-Speed	120	20	**$8.05**
2535	West.	117	Soft Point, Super-X	8½	20	
250 SAVAGE: (.257″ dia.)						
R250SV	Rem.	100	Hi-Speed, Ptd. S.P.	9½	20	
W2501	Win.	87	Pointed Soft Point, Super-Speed	120	20	
W2503	Win.	100	Silvertip Exp., Super-Speed	120	20	**$6.75**
2501	West.	87	Pointed Soft Point, Super-X	8½	20	
2503	West.	100	Silvertip Expanding, Super-X	8½	20	
256 WINCHESTER MAGNUM: (.257″ dia.)						
2561P	West.	60	Open Point Expanding, Super-X	6½	50	**$12.65**
257 ROBERTS. (.257″ dia.)						
R257	Rem.	117	Express, Soft Point, Core-Lokt	9½	20	
2571	West.	87	Pointed Soft Point, Super-X	8½	20	**$7.45**
2572	West.	100	Silvertip Expanding, Super-X	8½	20	
2573	West.	117	Power-Point (S.P.) Super-X	8½	20	

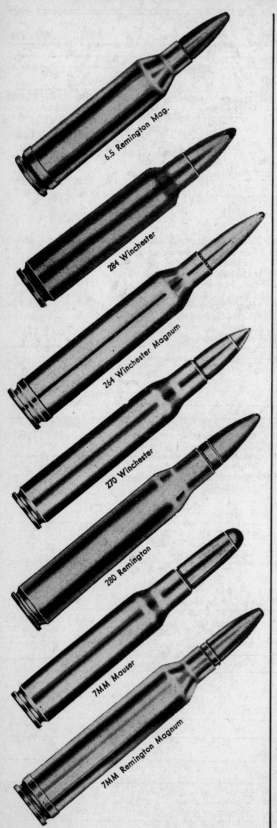

6.5 Remington Mag.

264 Winchester

264 Winchester Magnum

270 Winchester

280 Remington

7MM Mauser

7MM Remington Magnum

INDEX No.	MAKE	BULLET WT. GRS.	BULLET STYLE	PRIMER No.	PER BOX OF
6.5 REMINGTON MAGNUM: (.264" dia.)					
R65MM2	Rem.	120	Hi-Speed, Pointed Soft Point	9½	20 }$12.15
R65MM1	Rem.	100	Hi-Speed, Pointed S.P., Core-Lokt	9½	20
264 WINCHESTER MAGNUM: (.264" dia.)					
R264W1	Rem.	100	Hi-Speed, Ptd. S.P., Core-Lokt	9½M	20
R264W2	Rem.	140	Hi-Speed, Ptd. S.P., Core-Lokt	9½M	20
P264W2	Peters	140	H.V., Pointed S.P., Core-Lokt	9½	20
W2641	Win.	100	Pointed Soft Point, Super-Speed	120	20 } $9.75
W2642	Win.	140	Power-Point (S.P.) Super-Speed	120	20
2641	West.	100	Pointed Soft Point, Super-X	8½	20
2642	West.	140	Power-Point (S.P.) Super-X	8½	20
270 WINCHESTER: (.277" dia.)					
R270W1	Rem.	100	Hi-Speed, Pointed Soft Point	9½	20
R270W2	Rem.	130	Hi-Speed, Ptd. S.P. Core-Lokt	9½	20
R270W3	Rem.	130	Hi-Speed, Bronze Pointed	9½	20
R270W4	Rem.	150	Hi-Speed, Soft Point, Core-Lokt	9½	20
P270W2	Peters	130	H.V., Core-Lokt Ptd. S.P.	9½	20
P270W4	Peters	150	H.V., Core-Lokt Soft Point	9½	20
W2701	Win.	100	Pointed Soft Point, Super-Speed	120	20 } $7.70
W2705	Win.	130	Power-Point (S.P.) Super-Speed	120	20
W2703	Win.	130	Silvertip Exp., Super-Speed	120	20
W2704	Win.	150	Power-Point (S.P.) Super-Speed	120	20
2701	West.	100	Pointed Soft Point, Super-X	8½	20
2705	West.	130	Power-Point (S.P.) Super-X	8½	20
2703	West.	130	Silvertip Expanding, Super-X	8½	20
2704	West.	150	Power-Point (S.P.) Super-X	8½	20
280 REMINGTON: (.284" dia.)					
R280R1	Rem.	150	Hi-Speed, Ptd. S.P., Core-Lokt	9½	20 }$7.85
R280R2	Rem.	165	Hi-Speed, Soft Point, Core-Lokt	9½	20
284 WINCHESTER: (284" dia.)					
W2841	Win.	125	Power-Point (S.P.) Super-Speed	120	20
W2842	Win.	150	Power-Point (S.P.) Super-Speed	120	20 } $7.85
2841	West.	125	Power-Point (S.P.) Super-X	8½	20
2842	West.	150	Power-Point (S.P.) Super-X	8½	20
7MM MAUSER (7x57): (.284" dia.)					
R7MSR	Rem.	175	Express, Soft Point	9½	20
P7MSR	Peters	175	H.V., S.P.	9½	20 } $7.85
W7MM	Win.	175	Soft Point, Super-Speed	120	20
7MM	West.	1.75	Soft Point, Super-X	8½	20
7MM REMINGTON MAGNUM: (.284" dia.)					
R7MM1	Rem.	125	Hi-Speed, Ptd. S.P., Core-Lokt	9½	20
R7MM2	Rem.	150	Hi-Speed. Ptd. S.P., Core-Lokt	9½M	20
R7MM3	Rem.	175	Hi-Speed. Ptd. S.P., Core-Lokt	9½M	20
P7MM2	Peters	150	H.V., Core-Lokt Ptd. S.P.	9½M	20 } $9.55
P7MM3	Peters	175	H.V., Core-Lokt Ptd. S.P.	9½M	20
7MMR1	West.	150	Power-Point, (S.P.) Super-X	8½	20
7MMR2	West.	175	Power-Point, (S.P.) Super-X	8½	20

CENTER FIRE RIFLE CARTRIDGES

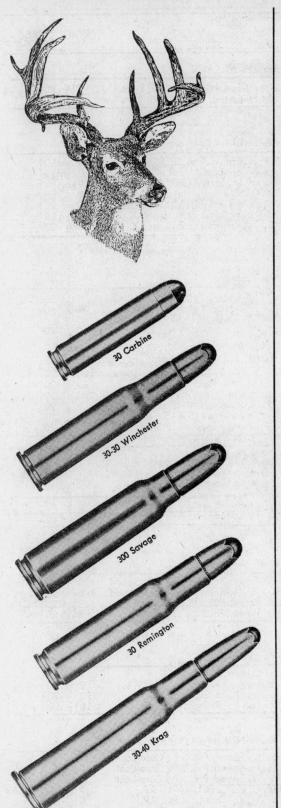

INDEX No.	MAKE	WT. GRS.	BULLET STYLE	PRIMER No.	PER BOX OF	
30 CARBINE: (.308″ dia.)						
R30CAR	Rem.	110	Hi-Speed, Soft Point	6½	50	
P306AR	Peters	110	High Velocity, Soft Point	6½	50	$12.35
W30M1	Win.	110	Hollow Soft Point	116	50	
W30M2	Win.	110	Full Metal Case	116	50	
30-30 WINCHESTER: (.308″ dia.)						
R30301	Rem.	150	Express, Soft Point, Core-Lokt	9½	20	
R30303	Rem.	170	Express, Hollow Point	9½	20	
R30302	Rem.	170	Express, Soft Point, Core-Lokt	9½	20	
P30301	Peters	150	H.V., Core-Lokt Soft Point	9½	20	
P30302	Peters	170	H.V., Core-Lokt, Soft Point	9½	20	
W30301	Win.	150	Super-Speed, Hollow Point	120	20	
W30306	Win.	150	Super-Speed, Power Point (S.P.)	120	20	
W30302	Win.	150	Super-Speed, Silvertip, Exp.	120	20	$6.05
W30303	Win.	170	Super-Speed, Power Point (S.P.)	120	20	
W30304	Win.	170	Super-Speed, Silvertip, Exp.	120	20	
30301	West.	150	Super-X, Open Point Expanding	8½	20	
30306	West.	150	Super-X, Power-Point (S.P.)	8½	20	
30302	West.	150	Super-X, Silvertip Expanding	8½	20	
30303	West.	170	Super-X, Power-Point (S.P.)	8½	20	
30304	West.	170	Super-X, Silvertip Expanding	8½	20	
30 REMINGTON: (.308″ dia.)						
R30REM	Rem.	170	Express, Soft Point, Core-Lokt	9½	20	
W30R2	Win.	170	Super-Speed, Silvertip Exp.	120	20	$8.10
30R2	West.	170	Super-X, Silvertip Expanding	8½	20	
300 SAVAGE: (.308″ dia.)						
R30SV1	Rem.	150	Hi-Speed, Soft Point, Core-Lokt	9½	20	
R30SV2	Rem.	150	Hi-Speed, Ptd. S.P., Core-Lokt	9½	20	
R30SV3	Rem.	180	Express, Soft Point, Core-Lokt	9½	20	
R30SV4	Rem.	180	Express, Ptd. S.P., Core-Lokt	9½	20	
P30SV2	Peters	150	H.V., Core-Lokt Ptd. S.P.	9½	20	
P30SV4	Peters	180	H.V., Core-Lokt Ptd. S.P.	9½	20	
P30SV3	Peters	180	H.V., S.P., Core-Lokt	9½	20	
W3001	Win.	150	Power-Point (S.P.) Super-Speed	120	20	
W3003	Win.	150	Silvertip Exp., Super-Speed	120	20	
W3004	Win.	180	Power-Point (S.P.) Super-Speed	120	20	$7.65
W3005	Win.	180	Silvertip Exp., Super-Speed	120	20	
3001	West.	150	Power-Point (S.P.) Super-X	8½	20	
3003	West.	150	Silvertip Expanding, Super-X	8½	20	
3004	West.	180	Power-Point (S.P.) Super-X	8½	20	
3005	West.	180	Silvertip Expanding, Super-X	8½	20	
30-40 KRAG: (.308″ dia.)						
R30401	Rem.	180	Hi-Speed, Soft Point, Core-Lokt	9½	20	
R30402	Rem.	180	Hi-Speed, Ptd. S.P., Core-Lokt	9½	20	
30401	West.	180	Power-Point (S.P.) Super-X	8½	20	$7.95
30403	West.	180	Silvertip Expanding, Super-X	8½	20	
30404	West.	220	Silvertip Expanding, Super-X	8½	20	

Cartridge illustrations (top to bottom): 30 Carbine, 30-30 Winchester, 300 Savage, 30 Remington, 30-40 Krag

CENTER FIRE RIFLE CARTRIDGES

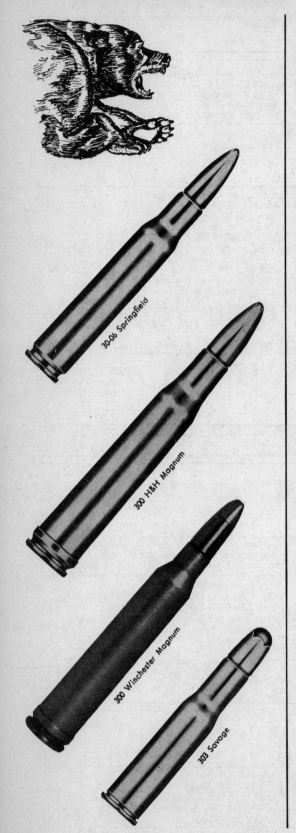

30-06 Springfield

300 H&H Magnum

300 Winchester Magnum

303 Savage

INDEX No.	MAKE	WT. GRS.	BULLET STYLE	PRIMER No.	PER BOX OF	
30-06 SPRINGFIELD: (.308″ dia.)						
R30061	Rem.	125	Hi-Speed, Pointed Soft Point	9½	20	
R30062	Rem.	150	Hi-Speed, Ptd. S.P., Core-Lokt	9½	20	
R30063	Rem.	150	Hi-Speed, Bronze Pointed	9½	20	
R30064	Rem.	180	Hi-Speed, Soft-Point, Core-Lokt	9½	20	
R30065	Rem.	180	Hi-Speed, Ptd. S.P., Core-Lokt	9½	20	
R30066	Rem.	180	Hi-Speed, Bronze Pointed	9½	20	
R30067	Rem.	220	Express, Soft Point, Core-Lokt	9½	20	
P30061	Peters	125	H.V., Pointed S. Ptd.,	9½	20	
P30062	Peters	150	High Velocity, Ptd. Soft Point	9½	20	
P30063	Peters	150	H.V., Bronz Ptd.	9½	20	
P30065	Peters	180	H.V., Core-Lokt Ptd. S.P.	9½	20	
P30064	Peters	180	H.V., Soft Point, Core-Lokt	9½	20	
P30067	Peters	220	H.V., S.P, Core-Lokt	9½	20	
W30060	Win.	110	Pointed Soft Point, Super-Speed	120	20	
W30062	Win.	125	Pointed Soft Point, Super-Speed	120	20	
W30061	Win.	150	Power-Point (S.P.) Super-Speed	120	20	$7.70
W30063	Win.	150	Silvertip Exp., Super-Speed	120	20	
W30064	Win.	180	Power-Point (S.P.) Super-Speed	120	20	
W30066	Win.	180	Silvertip Exp., Super-Speed	120	20	
W30069	Win.	220	Silvertip Exp., Super-Speed	120	20	
30060	West.	110	Pointed Soft Point, Super-X	8½	20	
30062	West.	125	Pointed Soft Point, Super-X	8½	20	
30061	West.	150	Power-Point (S.P.) Super-X	8½	20	
30063	West.	150	Silvertip Expanding, Super-X	8½	20	
30064	West.	180	Power-Point (S.P.) Super-X	8½	20	
30066	West.	180	Silvertip Expanding, Super-X	8½	20	
30068	West.	220	Power-Point (S.P.) Super-X	8½	20	
30069	West.	220	Silvertip Expanding, Super-X	8½	20	
300 H&H MAGNUM: (.308″ dia.)						
R300HH	Rem.	180	Hi-Speed, Ptd. S.P., Core-Lokt	9½M	20	
W300H1	Win.	150	Silvertip Expanding, Super-Speed	120	20	
W300H2	Win.	180	Silvertip Expanding, Super-Speed	120	20	
W300H3	Win.	220	Silvertip Expanding, Super-Speed	120	20	$10.05
300H1	West.	150	Silvertip Expanding, Super-X	8½	20	
300H2	West.	180	Silvertip Expanding, Super-X	8½	20	
300H3	West.	220	Silvertip Expanding, Super-X	8½	20	
300 WINCHESTER MAGNUM: (.308″ dia.)						
R300W1	Rem.	150	Hi-Speed, Ptd. S.P., Core-Lokt	9½M	20	
R300W2	Rem.	180	Hi-Speed, Ptd. S.P., Core-Lokt	9½M	20	
P300W1	Peters	150	H.V., Pointed S.P.	9½	20	
P300W2	Peters	180	H.V., Pointed S.P.	9½	20	
W30WM1	Win.	150	Power-Point (S.P.) Super-Speed	120	20	$10.05
W30WM2	Win.	180	Power-Point (S.P.) Super-Speed	120	20	
W30WM3	Win.	220	Silvertip Exp. Super-Speed	120	20	
30WM1	West.	150	Power-Point (S.P.) Super-X	8½	20	
30WM2	West.	180	Power-Point (S.P.) Super-X	8½	20	
30WM3	West.	220	Silvertip Exp. Super-X	8½	20	
303 SAVAGE: (.308″ dia.)						
R303SV	Rem.	180	Express, Soft Point, Core-Lokt	9½	20	$8.80
W3032	Win.	190	Silvertip Exp., Super-Speed	120	20	$8.05
3032	West.	190	Silvertip Exp., Super-X	8½	20	

CENTER FIRE RIFLE CARTRIDGES

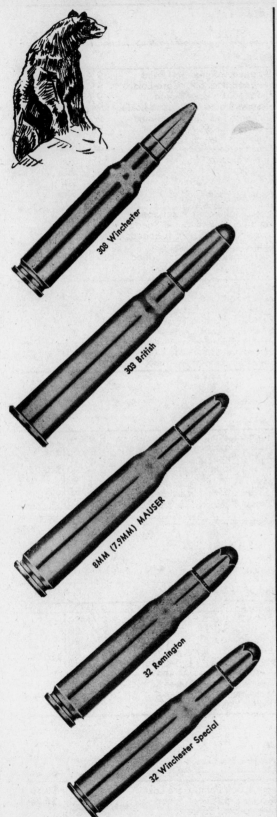

308 Winchester

303 British

8MM (7.9MM) MAUSER

32 Remington

32 Winchester Special

INDEX No.	MAKE	WT. GRS.	BULLET STYLE	PRIMER No.	PER BOX OF	
303 BRITISH: (.311″ dia.)						
R303B1	Rem.	180	Hi-Speed, Soft Point	9½	29	
R303B2	Rem.	215	Express, Soft Point	9½	20	
P303P1	Peters	180	H.V., Core-Lokt Soft Point	9½	20	$7.90
P303P2	Peters	215	H.V., S.P.	9½	20	
W303B1	Win.	180	Power-Point (S.P.) Super-Speed	120	20	
308 WINCHESTER: (.308″ dia.)						
R308W1	Rem.	150	Hi-Speed, Ptd. S.P., Core-Lokt	9½	20	
R308W3	Rem.	180	Hi-Speed, Ptd. S.P., Core-Lokt	9½	20	
R308W2	Rem.	180	Hi-Speed, Soft Point, Core-Lokt	9½	20	
P308W1	Peters	150	H.V., Core-Lokt Ptd. S.P.	9½	20	
P308W3	Peters	180	H.V., Core-Lokt Ptd. S.P.	9½	20	
P308W2	Peters	180	H.V., Core-Lokt Soft Point	9½	20	
W3081	Win.	110	Pointed Soft Point, Super-Sped	120	20	
W3087	Win.	125	Pointed Soft Point, Super-Speed	120	20	
W3085	Win.	150	Power-Point (S.P.) Super-Speed	120	20	
W3082	Win.	150	Silvertip Exp., Super-Speed	120	20	$7.70
W3086	Win.	180	Power-Point (S.P.) Super-Speed	120	20	
W3083	Win.	180	Silvertip Exp., Super-Speed	120	20	
W3084	Win.	200	Silvertip Exp., Super-Speed	120	20	
3081	West.	110	Pointed Soft Point, Super-X	8½	20	
3087	West.	125	Pointed Soft Point, Super-X	8½	20	
3085	West.	150	Power-Point (S.P.) Super-X	8½	20	
3028	West.	150	Silvertip Expanding, Super-X	8½	20	
3086	West.	180	Power-Point (S.P.) Super-X	8½	20	
3083	West.	180	Silvertip Expanding, Super-X	8½	20	
3084	West.	200	Silvertip Expanding, Super-X	8½	20	
8 MM. (7.9 MM.) MAUSER: (.322″ dia.)						
R8MSR	Rem.	170	Hi-Speed, Soft Point, Core-Lokt	9½	20	$7.90
P8MSR	Peters	170	H.V., S.P., Core-Lokt	9½	20	
32-20 WINCHESTER: (.310″ dia.)						
R32201	Rem.	100	Lead, Oil-Proof Hi-Speed	6½	50	$ 9.05
W32201	Win.	100	Lead Bullet, Oil-Proof	116	50	$ 9.05
W32202	Win.	100	Soft Point, Oil-Proof	116	50	$11.25
32201	West.	100	Lubaloy, Oil-Proof	6½	50	$ 9.05
32202	West.	100	Soft Point, Oil-Proof	6½	50	$11.25
32 REMINGTON: (.320″ dia.)						
R32REM	Rem.	170	Express, Soft Point, Core-Lokt	9½	20	$9.10
W32R2	Win.	170	Silvertip Exp., Super-Speed	120	20	$7.65
32R2	West.	170	Silvertip Exp., Super-X	8½	20	

CENTER FIRE RIFLE CARTRIDGES

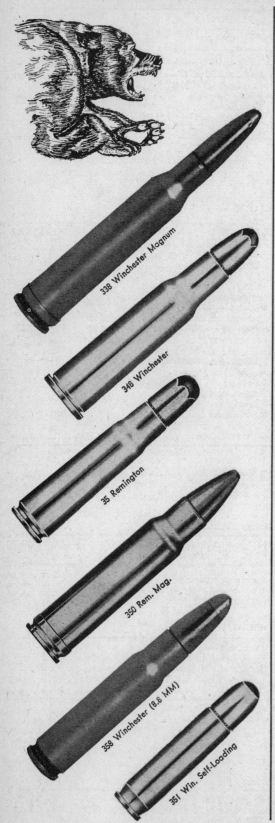

INDEX No.	MAKE	WT. GRS.	BULLET STYLE	PRIMER No.	PER BOX OF	
32 WINCHESTER SPECIAL: (.320″ dia.)						
R32WS1	Rem.	170	Express, Hollow Point, Core-Lokt	9½	20	
R32WS2	Rem.	170	Express, Soft Point, Core-Lokt	9½	20	
P32WS2	Peters	170	H.V., Core-Lokt, Soft Point	9½	20	
W32WS2	Win.	170	Power-Point (S.P.) Super-Speed	120	20	$6.30
W32WS3	Win.	170	Silvertip Exp., Super-Speed	120	20	
32WS2	West.	170	Power-Point (S.P.) Super-X	8½	20	
32WS3	West.	170	Silvertip Exp., Super-X	8½	20	
338 WINCHESTER MAGNUM: (.338″ dia.)						
W3381	Win.	200	Power-Point (S.P.) Super-Speed	120	20	
W3382	Win.	250	Silvertip Exp., Super-Speed	120	20	
W3383	Win.	300	Power-Point (S.P.) Super-Speed	120	20	$10.60
3381	West.	200	Power-Point (S.P.) Super-X	8½	20	
3382	West.	250	Silvertip Exp., Super-X	8½	20	
3383	West.	300	Power-Point (S.P.) Super-X	8½	20	
348 WINCHESTER: (.348″ dia.)						
R348W	Rem.	200	Express, Soft Point, Core-Lokt	9½	20	$13.10
W3482	Win.	200	Silvertip Exp., Super-Speed	120	20	
35 REMINGTON: (.358″ dia.)						
R35R1	Rem.	150	Hi-Speed, Ptd. S.P., Core-Lokt	9½	20	
R35R2	Rem.	200	Express, Soft-Point, Core-Lokt	9½	20	
P35R2	Peters	200	H.V., Core-Lokt Soft Point	9½	20	
P35R1	Peters	150	H.V., Core-Lokt, Ptd. S.P.	9½	20	$7.10
W35R1	Win.	200	Power-Point (S.P.) Super-Speed	120	20	
W35R3	Win.	200	Silvertip Exp., Super-Speed	120	20	
35R1	West.	200	Power-Point (S.P.) Super-X	8½	20	
35R3	West.	200	Silvertip Exp., Super-X	8½	20	
350 REMINGTON MAGNUM: (.358″ dia.)						
R350M1	Rem.	200	Pointed Soft Point, Hi-Speed Core-Lokt	9½M	20	$12.15
R350M2	Rem.	250	Pointed Soft Point, Hi-Speed Core-Lokt	9½M	20	
351 WINCHESTER SELF-LOADING: (.351″ dia.)						
R351SL	Rem.	180	Soft Point	6½	50	
W351SL2	Win.	180	Soft Point, Oil-Proof	116	50	$18.60
351SL2	West.	180	Soft-Point, Oil-Proof	6½	50	
358 WINCHESTER (8.8 MM): (.358″ dia.)						
W3581	Win.	200	Silvertip Exp., Super-Speed	120	20	
W3582	Win.	250	Silvertip Exp., Super-Speed	120	20	$9.75
3581	West.	200	Silvertip Exp., Super-X	8½	20	
3582	West.	250	Silvertip Exp., Super-X	8½	20	

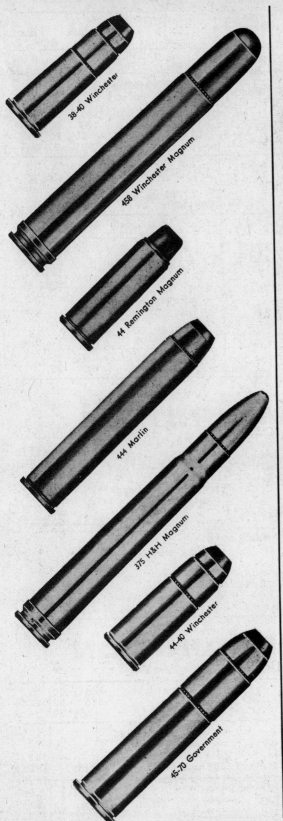

38-40 Winchester

458 Winchester Magnum

44 Remington Magnum

44 Marlin

375 H&H Magnum

44-40 Winchester

45-70 Government

INDEX No.	MAKE	BULLET WT. GRS.	STYLE	PRIMER No.	PER BOX OF	
375 H&H MAGNUM: (.375" dia.)						
R375M1	Rem.	270	Soft Point Hi-Speed	9½M	20	
R375M2	Rem.	300	Metal Case Hi-Speed	9½M	20	
W375H1	Win.	270	Power-Point (S.P.) Super-Speed	120	20	$12.50
W375H2	Win.	300	Silvertip Exp., Super-Speed	120	20	
W375H3	Win.	300	Full Metal Case, Super-Speed	120	20	
375H1	West.	270	Power-Point (S.P.) Super-X	8½	20	
375H2	West.	300	Silvertip Exp., Super-X	8½	20	
38-40 WINCHESTER: (400" dia.)						
R3840W	Rem.	180	Soft-Point, Oil-Proof	2½	50	
W3840	Win.	180	Soft-Point, Oil-Proof	111	50	$13.65
3840	West.	180	Soft-Point, Oil-Proof	7	50	
44-40 WINCHESTER: (.425" dia.)						
R4440W	Rem.	200	Soft Point, Oil-Proof	2½	50	
W4440	Win.	200	Soft Point, Oil-Proof	111	50	$16.10
4440	West.	200	Soft Point, Oil-Proof	7	50	
444 MARLIN: (.430" dia.)						
R444M	Rem.	240	Soft Point Hi-Speed	9½	20	$7.95
P444M	Peters	240	H.V., S.P.,	9½	20	
44 REMINGTON MAGNUM: (.430" dia.)						
R44MG2	Rem.	240	Soft Point, Oil-Proof	2½	20	$5.70
R44MG3	Rem.	240	Semi-Jacketed H.P.	2½	20	$5.70
P44MG1	Peters	240	Lead, Gas-Check, Oil-Tite	2½	50	$14.20
P44MG2	Peters	240	Soft Point, Oil-Tite	2½	20	$5.70
44MP	West.	240	Lubaloy, Gas-Check, Super-X	7	50	$14.20
44MHSP	West.	240	Hollow Soft Point, Super-X	7	20	$5.70
45-70 GOVERNMENT: (.457" dia.)						
R4570G	Rem.	405	Soft Point	9½	20	$8.50
P4570G	Peters	405	H.V., S.P.	9½	20	
W4570	Win.	405	Soft Point	120	20	$8.50
458 WINCHESTER MAGNUM: (.458" dia.)						
R458W1	Rem.	500	Metal Case	9½M	20	$25.40
R458W2	Rem.	510	Soft Point	9½M	20	$16.70
W4580	Win.	500	Full Metal Case, Super-Speed	120	20	$25.40
W4581	Win.	510	Soft Point, Super-Speed	120	20	$16.70

NORMA RIFLE AMMUNITION

Cartridges	Price Box/20
.220 Swift	
50 gr. SPP	$8.45
.222 Remington	
50 gr. SPP	5.20
.243 Winchester	
100 gr. SPP	7.05
6.5 Jap	
139 gr. SPPBT	9.95
156 gr. SPR	9.95
6.5 Carcano	
156 gr. SPP	9.95
6.5 Norma (6.5 x 55)	
139 gr. PPSP	9.95
156 gr. SPR	9.95
.270 Winchester	
110 gr. SPP	7.70
130 gr. SPPBT	7.70
150 gr. SPPBT	7.70
7 MM Mauser	
110 gr. SPP	7.85
150 gr. SPPBT	7.85
7x57R	
150 gr. SPSPBT	10.85

Cartridges	Price Box/20
7 x 61	
160 gr. SPPBT	11.00
7x64	
150 gr. SPSBT	11.45
7 M/M Rem. Mag.	
150 gr. SPF	9.55
.308 Winchester	
130 gr. SPPBT	7.70
150 gr. SPPBT	7.70
.308 Winchester w/Dual-Core	
180 gr. SP Dual-Core	8.30
.30-06	
130 gr. SPPBT	7.70
150 gr. SPPBT	7.70
180 gr. SPPBT	7.70
.30-06 w/Dual-Core	
180 gr. SP Dual-core	8.30
8x57J .319 DIA.	
196 gr. SPRN	9.10
.30 US Carbine	
110 gr. SP	4.95

Cartridges	Price Box/20
.303 British	
150 gr. SPP	$7.90
180 gr. SPPBT	7.90
.308 Norma Belted Mag.	
180 gr. Dual-Core	12.75
7.5 x 55	
180 gr. SP	10.15
7.62 Russian	
180 gr. SPPBT	10.15
7.65 Argentine Mauser	
150 gr. SPP	10.15
7.7 MM Jap	
130 gr. SPP	10.15
180 gr. SPPBT	10.15
8 MM Mauser .323 DIA.	
196 gr. SPP	6.60
.358 Norma Belted Mag.	
250 gr. SP	7.90
358 Winchester	
250 gr. SP	12.85
9.3x57 Dual-Core	
286 gr. PPRN	12.85
9.3x62 Dual-Core	
286 gr. PPRN	12.85

NORMA PISTOL AMMUNITION

Cartridges		Price
.25 A.C.P.		
50 gr. FJRN	Box 50	$7.40
.32 A.C.P.		
77 gr. FJ	Box 50	$8.45
.32 S & W		
85 gr. Lead	Box 50	$6.45
9 MM Luger		
116 gr. FJ	Box 50	$10.55
115 gr. HP	Box 50	$10.55
116 gr. SPRN	Box 50	$10.55
357 Magnum		
158 gr. HP	Box 50	$11.15
158 gr. SPRN	Box 50	$11.15

Cartridges		Price
.38 Special		
158 gr. RN	Box 50	$8.20
158 gr. HP	Box 50	$9.95
110 gr. HP	Box 50	$9.95
158 gr SPRN	Box 50	$9.95
.30 Luger		
93 gr. FJ	Box 50	$13.75
.38 Special MATCH AMMO		
148 gr. WC (Sharp shoulder—mid-range)	Box 50	$8.35
.38 S&W		
146 gr. Lead RN	Box 50	$7.95
.44 Magnum		
236 gr. HP	Box 50	$14.20

FEDERAL PISTOL AMMUNITION

25AP	25 Automatic Pistol, Metal Case	50	$7.40
32AP	32 Automatic Pistol, Metal Case	71	$8.45
9AP	9mm Luger, Metal Case	123	$10.55
9BP	9mm Luger, Auto. Pistol, Jktd. Hol. Pt. Bullet	115	$10.55
380AP	380 Automatic Pistol, Metal Case	95	$8.65
357A	357 Mag., Ni. Pl. Case. Jacketed Soft Point Bullet	158	$11.15
357B	357 Mag., Jacket Hollow Point Bullet	125	$11.15
38A	38 Special Match, Mid-Range Wadcutter	148	$8.35
38B	38 Special, Nickel Plated Case, Lead Bullet	158	$8.00
38C	38 Special N. C. Pl. CS., lead Semi-Wadcutter Bullet	158	$8.20
38D	38 Special High Vel, Lead Bullet	158	$8.90
38E	38 Special High Vel., Jacketed Hollow Point	125	$9.95
45A	45 Automatic Match, Metal Case Bullet	230	$11.35
45B	45 Automatic Match, Jacketed Wadcutter	185	$12.00

FEDERAL RIFLE AMMUNITION

CENTER FIRE RIFLE CARTRIDGES

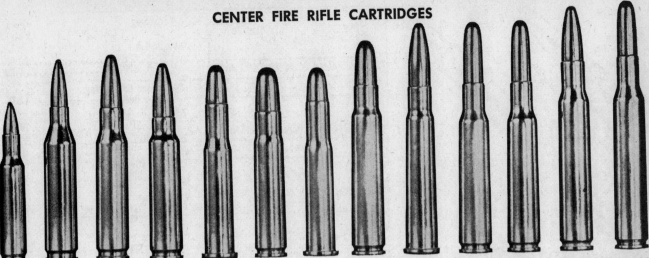

Federal rifle cartridges: Left to Right, .222 Rem. 50 gr., .223A Rem. 55 gr., .243 Win. 100 gr., .308 Win. 180 gr., .300 Sav. 180 gr., 30-30 Win. 170 gr., .35 Rem. 200 gr., .32 Win. Spl. 170 gr., 8mm Mauser 170 gr., .303 Brit. 180 gr., 7mm Mauser 175 gr., 270 Win. 150 gr., .30-06 Springfield 150 gr., and .30-06 Springfield 180 gr.

Load No.	Cartridges	Bullet Weight Grains	Per 20
222A	222 Remington, *Soft Point Bullet*	50	$5.20
22250A	22-250 Rem. Soft Point	55	5.70
223A	223 Remington, (5.56mm)	55	5.70
243A	243 Winchester, *Soft Point Bullet*	80	7.05
243 B	243 Winchester, *Soft Point Bullet*	100	7.05
2506A	2506 Remington, Hollow Point Bullet	90	7.70
2506B	2506 Remington, Soft Point Hi-Shok Bullet	117	7.70
270A	270 Winchester, *Soft Point Bullet*	130	7.70
270 B	270 Winchester, *Soft Point Bullet*	150	7.70
7A	7 mm Mauser, *Soft Point Bullet*	175	7.85
7B	7mm Mauser	139	7.85
7RA	7mm Remington Magnum	150	9.55
7RB	7mm Remington Magnum	175	9.55
30CA	30 Carbine *Soft Point Bullet*	110	4.95
3030A	30-30 Winchester, *Soft Point Bullet*	150	6.05
3030 B	30-30 Winchester, *Soft Point Bullet*	170	6.05

Load No.	Cartridges	Bullet Weight Grains	Per 20
300WA	300 Win. Magnum *Soft Point Bullet*	150	$10.05
300WB	300 Win. Magnum *Soft Point Bullet*	180	10.05
3006A	30-06 Springfield, *Soft Point Bullet*	150	7.70
3006 B	30-06 Springfield, *Soft Point Bullet*	180	8.20
3006C	30-06 Springfield, *Soft Point Bullet*	125	7.70
3006D	Springfield, *Boat Tail Soft Point*	165	8.20
300A	300 Savage, *Soft Point Bullet*	150	7.70
300 B	300 Savage, *Soft Point Bullet*	180	7.65
303A	303 British, *Soft Point Bullet*	180	7.65
308A	308 Winchester, *Soft Point Bullet*	150	7.70
308 B	308 Winchester, *Soft Point Bullet*	180	7.70
8A	8 mm Mauser, *Soft Point Bullet*	170	7.90
32A	32 Win. Special, *Soft Point Bullet*	170	6.30
35A	35 Remington, *Soft Point Bullet*	200	7.10
44A	44 Rem. Magnum Hollow *soft point*	240	5.70

WEATHERBY RIFLE AMMUNITION

CENTER FIRE RIFLE CARTRIDGES

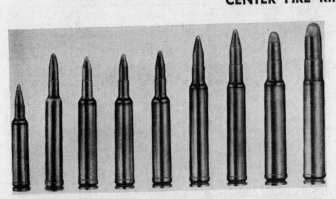

Weatherby Magnum Cartridges: Left to Right—.224 W.M., .240 W.M., .257 W.M., .270 W.M., 7mm W.M., .300 W.M., .340 W.M., .378 W.M., and .460 W.M.

Cartridge	Ammunition 20 per box	Unprimed Cases 20 per box
.224—50 or 55 gr.	$ 7.95	$ 5.50
.240—70, 87 or 100 gr.	10.95	6.50
—85 or 100 gr. Nosler	13.95	
.257—87, 100 or 117 gr.	11.95	6.50
—100 or 117 gr. Nosler	14.95	
.270—100, 130 or 150 gr.	11.95	6.50
—130 or 150 gr. Nosler	14.95	
7mm—139, 154 or 175 gr.	11.95	6.50
—140, 160 or 175 gr. Nosler	14.95	
.300—110, 150, 180 or 220 gr.	12.95	7.20
—150, 180 or 200 gr. Nosler	15.95	
.340—200 or 250 gr.	12.95	7.20
—210 or 250 gr. Nosler	15.95	
.375—270, 300 RN or 300 FMJ	14.95	7.75
—270 or 300 gr. Nosler	17.95	
.378—270, 300 RN or 300 FMJ	22.95	12.95
—300 gr. FMJ	24.95	
—270 or 300 gr. Nosler	25.95	
.460—500 RN	23.95	12.95
—500 RMJ	25.95	

PISTOL & REVOLVER CARTRIDGES

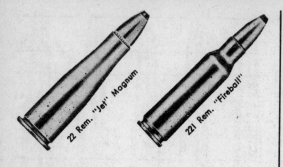

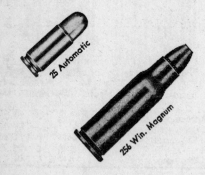

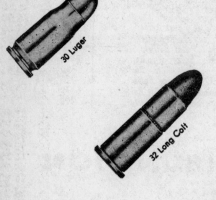

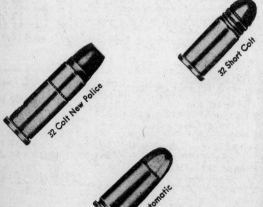

INDEX No.	MAKE	WT. GRS.	BULLET STYLE	PRIMER No.	PER BOX OF	

22 REMINGTON "JET" MAGNUM: (Adapted to Smith & Wesson revolvers)

INDEX No.	MAKE	WT. GRS.	STYLE	PRIMER No.	PER BOX OF	
R22JET	Rem.	40	Hi-Speed, Soft-Point	6½	40	$13.35

221 REMINGTON "FIREBALL": (Adapted to Remington XP-100 pistol)

R221F	Rem.	50	Hi-Speed, Soft Point	7½	20	$6.15

25 (6.35 MM.) AUTOMATIC PISTOL:
(Adapted to Colt, Browning, Mauser, Llama, other automatic pistols.)

R25AP	Rem.	50	Metal Case, Oil-proof	1½	50	
P25AP	Peters	50	Metal Case, Oil-Tite	1½	50	
W25AP	Win.	50	Full Metal Case, Oil-proof	108	50	$7.40
25AP	West.	50	Full Metal Case, Oil-proof	1½	50	

256 WINCHESTER MAGNUM: (Adapted to Ruger Hawkeye revolver.)

2561P	West.	60	Open Point Exp., Super-X	6½	50	$12.65

30 (7.65 MM.) LUGER AUTOMATIC PISTOL:
(Adapted to Luger automatic pistol; cannot be used in Luger Carbine.)

R30LUG	Rem.	93	Metal Case, Oil-proof	1½	50	
W30LP	Win.	93	Full Metal Case, Oil-proof	108	50	$11.80
30LP	West.	93	Full Metal Case, Oil-proof	1½	50	

32 SHORT COLT: (Adapted to Colt, Webley, other revolvers; Marlin 1892 repeating rifles; not adapted to revolvers chambered for 32 Smith & Wesson cartridge.)

R32SC	Rem.	80	Lead, Oil-proof	1½	50	
32SCP	West.	80	Lubaloy, Oil-proof	1½	50	$6.45

32 LONG COLT: (Adapted to Colt, Webley, other revolvers; Marlin 1892 repeating rifles; not adapted to revolvers chambered for 32 Smith & Wesson Long cartridges.)

R32LC	Rem.	82	Lead, Oil-proof	1½	50	
32LCP	West.	82	Lubaloy, Oil-proof	1½	50	$6.75

32 COLT NEW POLICE: (Adapted to Colt, Smith & Wesson, other revolvers not adapted to revolvers chambered for 32 Long Colt cartridge.

R32NP	Rem.	100	Lead, Oil-proof	1½	50	
W32CNP	Win.	98	Lead Bullet, Oil-proof	108	50	$8.60

32 (7.65 MM.) AUTOMATIC PISTOL: (Adapted to Browning, Colt, Mauser; Remington, Savage, Llama, Smith & Wesson, other automatic pistols.)

32AP	Rem.	71	Metal Case, Oil-proof	1½	50	
P32AP	Peters	71	Metal Case, Oil-tite	1½	50	
W32AP	Win.	71	Full Metal Case, Oil-proof	108	50	$8.45
32AP	West.	71	Full Metal Case, Oil-proof	1½	50	

PISTOL & REVOLVER CARTRIDGES

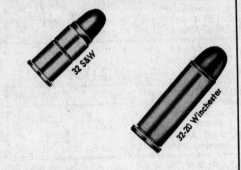

32 S&W

32-20 Winchester

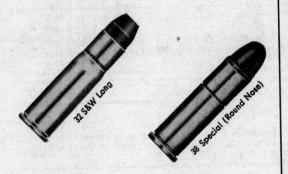

32 S&W Long

38 Special (Round Nose)

38 Short Colt

INDEX No.	MAKE	WT. GRS.	STYLE	PRIMER No.	PER BOX OF	
32 SMITH & WESSON:						
R32SW	Rem.	88	Lead, Oil-proof	5½	50	
P32SW	Peters	88	Lead, Oil-tite	5½	50	$6.45
W32SWP	Win.	85	Lead Bullet, Oil-proof	108	50	
32SWP	West.	85	Lubaloy, Oil-proof	1½	50	
32 SMITH & WESSON LONG:						
R32SWL	Rem.	98	Lead, Oil-proof	1½	50	
P32SWL	Peters	98	Lead, Oil-tite	1½	50	$6.75
W32SWLP	Win.	98	Lead Bullet, Oil-proof	108	50	
32SWLP	West.	98	Lubaloy, Oil-proof	1½	50	

32-20 WINCHESTER: (Adapted to Colt, Smith & Wesson revolvers; use cartridge with 100 grain all lead bullet only.) Note: 32-20 Winchester "Hi-Speed" cartridge is for use in rifles only and should not be used in revolvers. See Center Fire Rifle section.

INDEX No.	MAKE	WT. GRS.	STYLE	PRIMER No.	PER BOX OF	
R32201	Rem.	100	Lead, Oil-proof, Hi-Speed	6½	50	$9.05
W32201	Win.	100	Lead Bullet, Oil-proof	116	50	$9.05
W32202	Win.	100	Soft Point, Oil-proof	116	50	$11.25
32201	West.	100	Lubaloy, Oil-proof	6½	50	$9.05
32202	West.	100	Soft Point, Oil-proof	6½	50	$11.25

INDEX No.	MAKE	WT. GRS.	STYLE	PRIMER No.	PER BOX OF	
38 SPECIAL:						
R38S2	Rem.	125	Semi-jacketed, Hollow Point	1½	50	$9.95
R38S6	Rem.	158	Lead, Semi Wadcutter	1½	50	$8.20
R38S5	Rem.	158	Lead, Oil-Proof	1½	50	$8.00
R38S9	Rem.	200	Lead, Oil-Proof	1½	50	$8.35
R38S7	Rem.	158	Metal Point, Oil-Proof	1½	50	$9.95
R38S8	Rem.	158	Hi-Speed, Lead (38-44)	1½	50	$8.90
R38S1	Rem.	95	Semi-jacketed, Hallow Point, Hi-Speed	1½	50	$9.95
P38S2	Peters	125	Semi-jacketed, Hollow Point	1½	50	$8.65
P38S7	Peters	158	Metal Point	1½	50	
P38S4	Peters	158	Targetmaster, Round Nose Bullet, Lead	1½	50	$7.10
P38S5	Peters	158	Lead, Oil-Tite	1½	50	$6.95
W38S1P	Win.	158	Lead, Oil-Proof	108	50	$8.00
W38S2P	Win.	158	Metal Point, Oil-Proof	108	50	$9.95
W38S3P	Win.	200	Lead, Oil-Proof	108	50	$8.35
W38SPD	Win.	158	Hollow Point, Oil-Proof	108	50	$9.95
W38WCP	Win.	158	Semi-Wadcutter	108	50	$8.20
38S1P	West.	158	Lubaloy, Oil-Proof	1½	50	$8.00
38S2P	West.	158	Metal Point, Oil-Proof	1½	50	$9.95
38S3P	West.	200	Lubaloy Super Police, Oil-Proof	1½	50	$8.35
38S4P	West.	150	Super-X, Lubaloy, Oil-Proof	1½	50	$8.70
38S5P	West.	150	Super-X, Metal Piercing, Oil-Proof	1½	50	$10.35

INDEX No.	MAKE	WT. GRS.	STYLE	PRIMER No.	PER BOX OF	
38 SPECIAL MATCH AMMUNITION:						
R38S6	Rem.	148	Targetmaster, Lead, Wadcutter. Bullet, Oil-Proof	1½	50	$8.20
R38S4	Rem.	158	Targetmaster, Lead, Round-Nose Bullet, Oil-Proof	1½	50	$8.20
P38S3	Peters	148	Police Match, Wadcutter	1½	50	$8.35
W38SMRP	Win.	148	Mid-Range (Sharp Corner) Match	108	50	$8.35
38SMRP	West.	148	Lead, Mid-Range (Clean Cutting)	1½	50	$8.35
38SMP	West.	158	Lead, Round-Nose Bullet, Super Match	1½	50	$8.20

38 SHORT COLT: (Adapted to Colt revolvers.)

INDEX No.	MAKE	WT. GRS.	STYLE	PRIMER No.	PER BOX OF	
R38SC	Rem.	125	Lead, Oil-Proof	1½	50	$7.25
38SCP	West.	130	Lubaloy, Oil-Proof	1½	50	

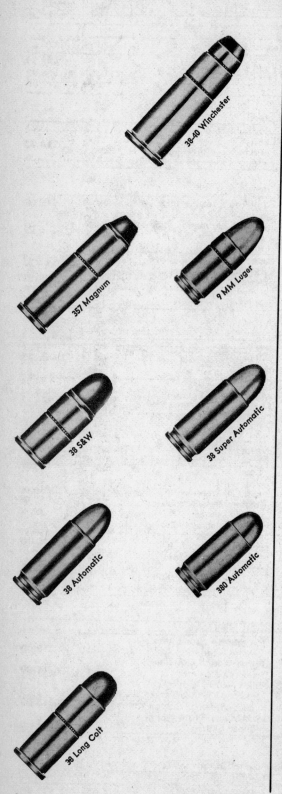

INDEX No.	MAKE	BULLET WT. GRS.	BULLET STYLE	PRIMER No.	PER BOX OF	

38 LONG COLT: (Adapted to Colt, Smith & Wesson revolvers.)

INDEX No.	MAKE	WT. GRS.	STYLE	PRIMER No.	PER BOX OF	Price
R38LC	Rem.	150	Lead, Oil-Proof	1½	50	$10.00
38LCP	West.	150	Lubaloy, Oil-Proof	1½	50	

38-40 WINCHESTER: (Adapted to Colt revolvers—"Hi-Speed" cartridges are for use in rifles only and should not be used in revolvers.)

R3840W	Rem.	180	Soft Point, Oil-Proof	2½	50	$13.65
W3840	Win.	180	Soft Point, Oil-Proof	111	50	
3840	West.	180	Soft Point, Oil-Proof	7	50	

357 MAGNUM HI-SPEED: (Adapted to Smith & Wesson and other revolvers originally chambered for this cartridge.)

R357M5	Rem.	158	Hi-Speed, Lead, Oil-Proof	5½	50	$ 9.45
R357M4	Rem.	158	Hi-Speed, Metal Point	5½	50	$10.75
R357M3	Rem.	158	Hi-Speed, Soft Point	5½	50	$11.15
R357M2	Rem.	158	Semi-jacketed, Hollow Point	5½	50	$11.15
R357M1	Rem.	125	Semi-jacketed, Hollow Point,	5½	50	$11.15
P357M2	Peters	158	Semi-jacketed, Hollow Point, High Velocity	5½	50	$11.15
P357M5	Peters	158	High-Velocity, Lead, Oil-Tite	5½	50	$ 8.20
P357M3	Peters	158	Soft Point, H. Y.	5½	50	$ 9.65
3571P	West.	158	Lubaloy, Super-X, Oil-Proof	1½	50	$ 9.95
3572P	West.	158	Metal Piercing, Super-X	1½	50	$10.75
3573P	West.	110	Jacketed H. Pt.	1½	50	$11.15
3574P	West.	158	Jacketed Hollow Point	1½	50	$11.15
3575P	West.	158	Jacketed Hollow Point	1½	50	$11.15

9 MM. LUGER AUTOMATIC PISTOL: (Adapted to Smith & Wesson, Col **(PARABELLUM)** and other semi-automatic pistols.)

R9MM2	Rem.	124	Metal Case, Oil-Proof	1½	50	
R9MM1	Rem.	115	Jacketed Hollow Point	1½	50	
P9MM1	Peters	115	Jacketed Hollow Point	1½	50	
P9MM2	Peters	124	Metal Case, Oil-Tite	1½	50	$10.55
W9LP	Win.	115	Full Metal Case, Oil-Proof	108	50	
W9MMPP	Win.	100	Power Point	108	50	
W9MMJHP	Win.	100	Jacketed H. Ptd.	108	50	

38 SMITH & WESSON: (Adapted to Smith & Wesson, Colt, other revolvers.)

R38SW	Rem.	146	Lead, Oil-Proof	1½	50	
P38SW	Peters	146	Lead, Oil-Tite	1½	50	$7.95
W38SWP	Win.	145	Lead, Oil-Proof	108	50	
38SWP	West.	145	Lubaloy, Oil-Proof	1½	50	

38 SUPER AUTOMATIC COLT PISTOL: (Adapted to Colt Super 38 Automatic, Colt Commander and Llama automatic pistols only.)

R38SUP	Rem.	130	Metal Case, Oil-Proof	1½	50	
P38SUP	Peters	130	Metal Case	1½	50	$8.95
W38A1P	Win.	130	Super-Speed, Full Metal Case	108	50	
38A1P	West.	130	Super-X, Full Metal Case	1½	50	

38 AUTOMATIC COLT PISTOL: (Adapted only for 38 Colt Sporting, Military and Pocket Model Automatic pistols. These pistols were discontinued after 1928.)

R38ACP	Rem.	130	Metal Case, Oil-Proof	1½	50	
W38A2P	Win.	130	Full Metal Case, Oil-Proof	108	50	$8.95
38A2P	West.	130	Full Metal Case, Oil-Proof	1½	50	

380 AUTOMATIC PISTOL: (Adapted to Browning, Colt, Remington, Llama, Savage, Walther, other automatic pistols.)

R38OAP	Rem.	95	Metal Case, Oil-Proof	1½	50	
P38ACP	Peters	95	Metal Case, Oil-Tite	1½	50	$8.65
W380AP	Win.	95	Full Metal Case, Oil-Proof	108	50	
380AP	West.	95	Full Metal Case, Oil-Proof	1½	50	

PISTOL & REVOLVER CARTRIDGES

41 Magnum

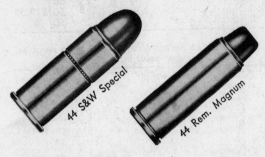
44 S&W Special

44 Rem. Magnum

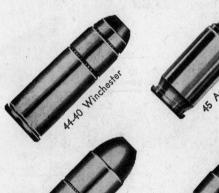
44-40 Winchester

45 Automatic

45 Colt

45 Automatic Rim

INDEX No.	MAKE	WT. GRS.	STYLE	PRIMER No.	PER BOX OF	
41 MAGNUM: (Adapted to Smith & Wesson 41 Magnum revolver.)						
R41MG2	Rem.	210	Lead	2½	50	**$12.30**
R41MG1	Rem.	210	Soft Point	2½	50	**$14.05**
P41MG1	Peters	210	S. P.	2½	50	**$14.05**
44 SMITH & WESSON SPECIAL: (Adapted to Smith & Wesson, Colt revolvers.)						
R44SW	Rem.	246	Lead, Oil-Proof	2½	50	**$10.90**
W44SP	Win.	246	Lead Bullet, Oil-Proof	111	50	
44 REMINGTON MAGNUM:						
R44MG1	Rem.	240	Lead, Gas-Check, Oil-Proof	2½	50	**$14.20**
R44MG2	Rem.	240	Soft Point	2½	20	
R44MG3	Rem.	240	Semi-jacketed Hollow Point	2½	20	**$ 5.70**
P44MG2	Peters	240	Soft Point	2½	20	
P44MG3	Peters	240	Semi-jacketed Hollow Point	2½	20	
P44MG1	Peters	240	Lead, Gas-Check, Oil-Tite	2½	50	**$14.20**
44MP	West.	240	Lubaloy, Gas-Check	7	50	
44MHSP	West.	240	Hollow Soft Point	7	20	**$ 5.70**
44-40 WINCHESTER: (Adapted to Colt revolvers—Hi-Speed cartridges are for use in rifles only and should not be used in revolvers.)						
R4440W	Rem.	200	Soft Point, Oil-Proof	2½	50	
W4440	Win.	200	Soft Point, Oil-Proof	111	50	**$16.10**
4440	West.	200	Soft Point, Oil-Proof	7	50	
45 COLT:						
R45C	Rem.	250	Lead, Oil-Proof	2½	50	
P45C	Peters	250	Lead	2½	50	**$10.95**
W45CP	Win.	255	Lead Bullet, Oil-Proof	111	50	
45CP	West.	255	Lubaloy, Oil-Proof	7	50	
45 AUTOMATIC: (Adapted to Colt Automatic Pistol, Llama 45 Automatic Pistol, Thompson Sub-Machine-gun, Colt 1917 revolver with clips; Smith & Wesson 1917 revolver with clips; Smith & Wesson 1950 & 1955 revolvers.)						
R45AP2	Rem.	185	Jacket A.P	2½	50	**$12.00**
R45AP4	Rem.	230	Metal Case, Oil-Proof	2½	50	
P45AP4	Peters	230	Metal Case, Oil-Tite	2½	50	**$11.35**
W45A1P	Win.	230	Full Metal Case, Oil-Proof	111	50	
45A1P	West.	230	Full Metal Case, Oil-Proof	7	50	
45 AUTOMATIC MATCH AMMUNITION:						
R45AP1	Rem.	185	Targetmaster, Wad-Cutter, Oil-Proof, Metal Case	2½	50	**$12.00**
R45AP3	Rem.	230	Targetmaster, Metal Case, Oil-Proof	2½	50	**$12.00**
P45AP1	Peters	185	Targetmaster, Metal Case, Jacketed H.P. Wad-Cutter	2½	50	**$12.00**
45AWCP	West.	185	Super-Match, Full Metal Case, (Clean Cutting)	7	50	**$12.00**
45 AUTOMATIC RIM: (Adapted to Colt 1917 revolver, Smith & Wesson 1917 revolver; Smith & Wesson 1950 & 1955 revolvers.)						
R45AR	Rem.	230	Lead, Oil-Proof	2½	50	**$11.90**

Illustrated at right is a full length cutaway view of a center-fire pistol cartridge.

Illustrated below are cutaway views of some of the available pistol bullet styles.

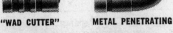

"WAD CUTTER"   METAL PENETRATING

METAL POINT   LEAD

LEAD GAS-CHECK

S & W Center Fire Rifle Cartridges

Symbol Number	Caliber	Bullet Grain Weight	Bullet Style	Primer Size	†Avg. Case Wt. Lbs.	Number In Package	Retail Price Per M	Per Box
S243-80PSP	243 Win.	80	PTD S.P.		25	10	$350.00	$3.50
S243-10PSP	243 Win.	100	PTD S.P.		25	10	350.00	3.50
S270-13PSP	270 Win.	130	PTD S.P.		32	10	385.00	3.85
S270-15SP	270 Win.	150	S.P.		32	10	385.00	3.85
S30/30-15SP	30/30 Win.	150	S.P.	Large Rifle	27	10	300.00	3.00
S30/30-17SP	30/30 Win.	170	S.P.		27	10	300.00	3.00
S30/06-15PSP	30/06 Spgfld.	150	PTD S.P.		35	10	385.00	3.85
S30/06-18SP	30/06 Spgfld.	180	S.P.		35	10	385.00	3.85
S308-15PSP	308 Win.	150	PTD S.P.		30	10	385.00	3.85
S308-18SP	308 Win.	180	S.P.		30	10	385.00	3.85

† Case Quantity 500 Rounds

S & W Center Fire Pistol and Revolver Cartridges

Symbol Number	Caliber	Bullet Grain Weight	Bullet Style	Primer Size	†Avg. Case Wt. Lbs.	Number In Package	Retail Price Per M	Per Box
●S357-90JSP	357 Magnum	90	J.S.P.		28	50		
●S357-110JHP	357 Magnum	110	J.H.P.		33	50		
●S357-125JSP	357 Magnum	125	J.S.P.		34	50	223.00	11.15
●S357-125JHP	357 Magnum	125	J.H.P.		34	50		
●S357-158JHP	357 Magnum	158	J.H.P.		39	50		
●S357-158JSP	357 Magnum	158	J.S.P.		39	50		
●S38-158RN	38 Special	158	R.N.		35	50	160.00	8.00
●S38-90JSP	38 Special	90	J.S.P.		26	50		
●S38-110JHP	38 Sp. +P	110	J.H.P.		28	50		
●S38-125JHP	38 Sp. +P	125	J.H.P.		32	50	199.00	9.95
●S38-125JSP	38 Sp. +P	125	J.S.P.		32	50		
●S38-158JHP	38 Sp. +P	158	J.H.P.		35	50		
●S38-158JSP	38 Sp. +P	158	J.S.P.		35	50		
●S38-148WC	38 Special	148	W.C.		33	50	167.00	8.35
●S38-158SWC	38 Special	158	S.W.C.		35	50	164.00	8.20
●S38-158SWCHP	38 Sp. +P	158	S.W.C.H.P.	Small Pistol	35	50	178.00	8.90
●S9-90JHP	9 mm	90	J.H.P.		23	50		
●S9-90JSP	9 mm	90	J.S.P.		23	50		
●S9-100FMC	9 mm	100	F.M.C.		25	50	211.00	10.55
●S9-115FMC	9 mm	115	F.M.C.		27	50		
●S9-115JHP	9 mm	115	J.H.P.		27	50		
●S9-115MCSWC	9 mm	115	M.C.S.W.C.		27	50		
●S25ACP-50MC	25 Auto	50	M.C.		13	50	148.00	7.40
●S32S&W-88RN	32 S&W	88	R.N.		22	50	129.00	6.45
●S32ACP-71MC	32 Auto	71	M.C.		18	50	169.00	8.45
●S380-84JHP	380 Auto	84	J.H.P.		21	50	173.00	8.65

† Case Quantity 1000 Rounds

S & W Rim Fire Cartridges

"MAX-VELOCITY"-LONG RANGE

Symbol Number	Caliber	Grain Weight	Style	Number Rounds Per Case	Avg. Case Wt. Lbs.	Number In Package	Retail Price Per M	Per Box
●S22LR-MV	22 Long Rifle	40	LEAD	5,000	40	50	25.40	1.27
●S22S-MV	22 Short	29	LEAD	5,000	29	50	22.40	1.12

STANDARD VELOCITY-TARGET

Symbol Number	Caliber	Grain Weight	Style	Number Rounds Per Case	Avg. Case Wt. Lbs.	Number In Package	Retail Price Per M	Per Box
●S22LR-SV	22 Long Rifle	40	LEAD	5,000	40	50	25.40	1.27

BLANKS (CRIMPED)

Symbol Number	Caliber		Style	Number Rounds Per Case	Avg. Case Wt. Lbs.	Number In Package	Retail Price Per M	Per Box
●SW22BID	22 Short In.	Med. Rep.		10,000	16	100	24.20	1.21
●SW22BOD	22 Short Out.	Loud Rep.		10,000	16	100	24.20	1.21

PTDSP — Pointed Soft Point
SP — Soft Point
JHP — Jacketed Hollow Point
JSP — Jacketed Soft Point
MC — Metal Case

RN — Round Nose-Lead
WC — Wad Cutter-Lead
SWC — Semi-Wad Cutter-Lead
SWCHP — Semi-Wad Cutter-Lead Hollow Point
MCSWC — Metal Case Semi-Wad Cutter

LOADS AND SHOT SIZES

SUGGESTED SHOT SIZES FOR GAME

GAME	SHELL	SHOT SIZE	SUGGESTED CHOKES
DUCKS	High Base	4, 5, 6	FULL—For Pass Shooting MODIFIED—Oxer Decoys
GEESE	High Base	BB, 2, 4	FULL
PHEASANTS	High Base	5, 6	MODIFIED FULL—For Long Cornfield Shots
GROUSE, PARTRIDGE	High Base or Low Base	5, 6 7½, 8	IMPROVED CYLINDER—OR MODIFIED— For Brush Work. FULL—For Open Ranges
QUAIL	Low Base	7½, 8, 9	IMPROVED CYLINDER OR MODIFIED
DOVES, PIGEONS	Low Base or High Base	6, 7½, 8	MODIFIED
WOODCOCK	Low Base	7½, 8, 9	IMPROVED CYLINDER OR MODIFIED
RABBITS	Low Base or High Base	4, 5, 6	IMPROVED CYLINDER OR MODIFIED—For Brush FULL—For Long Open Shots
SQUIRRELS	High Base	5, 6	MODIFIED
RAIL	Low Base	7½, 8, 9	IMPROVED CYLINDER
TURKEY	High Base	BB, 2, 4	FULL
FOX	High Base	BB, 2	FULL
DEER, BLACK BEAR, WOLF	High Base	Rifled Slug and Buck Shot	For rifled slugs . . . any choke For buckshot loads . . . full choke

SHOT AND ITS MANUFACTURE

The forerunner of modern shot is the old grape shot of the middle ages which is mentioned as far back as 1420. By the year 1510 this was employed in the earliest handguns. Actual manufacture in the form of balls dates back to the British Patent No. 725 of the year 1758 whereby the shot was poured and then polished in drums. Manufacture of shot is based on the British Patent 1347 of the year 1782. The first shot tower was constructed in Austria in 1818. The exact composition of shot varies but is principally of lead with some arsenic added which has the property of not only making the lead harder but to make it flow more readily. The arsenic content in the small size shot may run approximately .2% and in larger shot sizes nearly twice that amount. This alloy is made up into blocks which are then used for shot manufacture which is usually carried out in one of two manners.

No. 1—The melted alloy is poured through a sieve-like container from which the ball shape drops fall from a considerable height into a tank of cold water. In the course of the fall the shot becomes rounded and the size depends upon the sieve. For very small sizes the drop is usually 100 ft. and for larger sizes as much as 100 yards.

No. 2—The melted alloy falls upon a quickly rotating metal disc from which the pellets are thrown by centrifugal force against an apron and then dropped into water. The size of the shot depends upon the speed of the revolving disc. The sorting of the shot for sizes is accomplished by rolling them down a surface with various size openings. The shot which have thus been sorted are mixed with very finely ground graphite and placed in revolving drums. This completely rounds the shot and covers them with a coat of graphite which protects them from oxidation. Hard shot contains in addition to the arsenic about 2% antimony. Such shot retain their form better than soft shot and consequently are less apt to stray away from the central shot mass and thus give better pattern with greater penetration. The most essential point is that the shot be round which is much more important than exact sizes. The characteristic of hard shot is enhanced by copper plating but this adds considerably to the cost and relatively little to performance.

Above: Remington "Power Piston" plastic shotshell.

SHOT			BUCKSHOT		
NUMBER	DIAM. IN INCHES	APPROX. PELLETS IN 1 OZ.	NUMBER	DIAM. IN INCHES	APPROX. PELLETS IN 1 LB.
12	.05	2385	4	.24	340
9	.08	585			
8	.09	410	3	.25	300
7½	.09½	350			
6	.11	225	1	.30	175
5	.12	170			
4	.13	135	0	.32	145
2	.15	90			
BB	.18	50	00	.33	130

REMINGTON PLASTIC SHOTSHELLS

REMINGTON "EXPRESS" SHOTGUN SHELLS WITH "POWER PISTON" WAD

Load No.	Gauge	Length Shell Inches	Powder Equiv. Drams	Shot Ozs.	Size Shot	(25) Per Box
SP10	10	2⅞	4¾	1⅝	4	$7.65
SP12	12	2¾	3¾	1¼	BB,2,4,5,6,7½,9	5.65
SP16	16	2¾	3¼	1⅛	4, 5, 6, 7½, 9	5.20
SP20	20	2¾	2¾	1	4, 5, 6, 7½, 9	4.95
SP28	28	2¾	2¼	¾	6, 7½, 9	4.95
SP410	410	2½	Max.	½	4, 6, 7½, 9	3.90
SP4103	410	3	Max.	11/16	4, 5, 6, 7½, 9	4.60

† 28 Ga. and 410 Ga. 9 Shot marked "Skeet Load."
• Standard wad column.

REMINGTON "EXPRESS" MAGNUM LOADS WITH "POWER PISTON" WAD

Load No.	Gauge	Length Shell Inches	Powder Equiv. Drams	Shot Ozs.	Size Shot	(25) Per Box
SP10 Mag.•	10	3½	Max.	2	2 (Mag.)	$12.90
SP12S Mag.	12	2¾	Max.	1½	2, 4, 5, 6 (Mag.)	7.20
SP12 Mag.	12	3	4	1⅝	2, 4, 6 (Mag.)	7.85
SP12H Mag.	12	3	Max.	1⅞	BB, 2, 4 (Mag.)	8.45
SP16C Mag.	16	2¾	Max.	1¼	2, 4, 6 (Mag.)	6.25
SP20S Mag.	20	2¾	Max.	1⅛	4,6,7½(Mag.)	5.65
SP20H Mag.	20	3	Max.	1¼	4,6,7½(Mag.)	6.40

REMINGTON "EXPRESS" BUCKSHOT "POWER-PAKT"

Load No.	Gauge	Length Shell Inches	Powder Equiv. Drams	Shot Ozs.	Size Shot	(25) Per Box
SP12BK	12	2¾	3¾	...	00 Buck–9 Pellets	$7.85
†SP12BK-5PK	12	2¾	3¾	...	00 Buck-9 Pellets	1.57
SP12BK	12	2¾	3¾	...	0 Buck–12 Pellets	7.85
†SP12BK-5PK	12	2¾	3¾	...	0 Buck-12 Pellets	1.57
SP12BK	12	2¾	3¾	...	1 Buck–16 Pellets	7.85
†SP12BK-5PK	12	2¾	3¾	...	1 Buck-16 Pellets	1.57
SP12BK	12	2¾	3¾	...	4 Buck–27 Pellets	7.85
†SP12BK-5PK	12	2¾	3¾	...	4 Buck 27 Pellets	1.57
†SP16BK-5PK	16	2¾	3	...	1 Buck-12 Pellets	1.55
SP20BK	20	2¾	2¾	...	3 Buck–20 Pellets	7.75
†SP20BK-5PK	20	2¾	2¾	...	3 Buck-20 Pellets	1.55

REMINGTON "EXPRESS" MAGNUM BUCKSHOT "POWER-PAKT"

Load No.	Gauge	Length Shell Inches	Powder Equiv. Drams	Shot Ozs.	Size Shot	(25) Per Box
SP12S Mag. BK	12	2¾	4	...	00Buck-12Pellets	$8.85
†SP12SMag. BK-5PK	12	2¾	4	...	00 Buck-12Pellets	1.77
SP12S Mag. BK	12	3	4	...	1 Buck-20 Pellets	8.85
†SP12SMag. BK-5PK	12	2¾	4	...	1 Buck-20 Pellets	1.77
SP12H Mag. BK	12	3	4½	...	00Buck-15Pellets	10.05
†SP12HMag. BK-5PK	12	3	4½	...	00Buck-15Pellets	2.01
SP12HMag. BK	12	3	4½	...	1Buck-24 Pellets	10.05
†SP12HMag. BK 5PK.	12	3	4½	...	1Buck-24 Pellets	2.01
SP12H Mag. BK	12	3	4½	...	4 Buck-41Pellets	10.05
†SP12HMag. BK-5PK	12	3	4½	...	4 Buck-41Pellets	2.01

REMINGTON "EXPRESS" RIFLED SLUG

Load No.	Gauge	Length Shell Inches	Powder Equiv. Drams	Shot Ozs.	Size Shot	(25) Per Box
SP12RS	12	2¾	3¾	⅞	Rifled Slug	$9.05
†SP12RS-5PK	12	2¾	3¾	⅞	Rifled Slug	1.81
SP16RS-5PK	16	2¾	3	⅘	Rifled Slug	1.73
SP20RS	20	2¾	2¾	⅝	Rifled Slug	8.25
†SP20RS-5PK	20	2¾	2¾	⅝	Rifled Slug	1.65
SP410RS-5PK	410	2½	Max.	⅕	Rifled Slug	1.57

"SHUR SHOT" PLASTIC FIELD LOADS WITH "POWER PISTON" WAD

Load No.	Gauge	Length Shell Inches	Powder Equiv. Drams	Shot Ozs.	Size Shot	(25) Per Box
R12L	12	2¾	3¼	1	4, 5, 6, 8	$4.45
R12H	12	2¾	3¼	1⅛	4, 5, 6, 7½, 8, 9	4.80
RP12H	12	2¾	3¼	1¼	7½, 8	5.00
R16	16	2¾	2½	1	6, 8	4.30
R16H	16	2¾	2¾	1⅛	4, 5, 6, 7½, 8, 9	4.45
R20	20	2¾	2½	⅞	6, 8	4.00
R20M	20	2¾	2½	1	4, 5, 6, 7½, 8, 9	4.35

"SHUR SHOT" PLASTIC SCATTER LOADS

Load No.	Gauge	Length Shell Inches	Powder Equiv. Drams	Shot Ozs.	Size Shot	(25) Per Box
RSL12	12	2¾	3	1⅛	8	$5.10

"RXP" TRAP AND SKEET LOADS WITH "POWER PISTON" WAD

Load No.	Gauge	Length Shell Inches	Powder Equiv. Drams	Shot Ozs.	Size Shot	(25) Per Box
XR12L	12	2¾	3	1⅛	7½, 8½, 9	$4.70
XR12M	12	2¾	2¾	1⅛	7½, 8½, 9	4.70

REMINGTON TARGET LOADS "POWER PISTON" WAD

Load No.	Gauge	Length Shell Inches	Powder Equiv. Drams	Shot Ozs.	Size Shot	(25) Per Box
R16H	16 Ga.	2¾	2¾	1⅛	9	$4.45
SP28	28 Ga.	2¾	2	¾	9	4.95
SP410	410 Ga.	2½	Max.	½	9	3.90
SP4103	410 Ga.	3	Max.	11/16	9	4.60

"EXPRESS" PLASTIC INTERNATIONAL TARGET LOADS WITH "POWER PISTON" WAD

Load No.	Gauge	Length Shell Inches	Powder Equiv. Drams	Shot Ozs.	Size Shot	(25) Per Box
SP12L	12	2¾	3¼	1¼	7½, 8	$5.00
NSP12L	12	2¾	3¼	1¼	7¾, 8 (Nickel)	5.75
SP12H	12	2¾	3¼	1½	7½, 8	5.00

REMINGTON-PETERS SHOTGUN SHELLS WITH "POWER PISTON" ONE-PIECE WADS

The "Power Piston" shot cup is designed to keep the shot from touching the inside of the barrel. This means rounder truer shot that flies straighter and improves patterns without leading your barrel.

PETERS PLASTIC SHOTSHELLS

Load Number	Gauge	Length Shell Inches	Powder Equiv. Drams	Ozs. Shot	Size Shot	Avg. Wgt. Per Case		Price Per M	Price Per Box
"HIGH VELOCITY" EXTRA LONG RANGE SHOTGUN SHELLS — "POWER PISTON" WAD									
PS 12	12 Ga.	2¾	3¾	1¼	BB, 2, 4, 5, 6, 7½, 9	58		$226.00	$5.65
PS 16	16 Ga.	2¾	3¼	1⅛	4, 5, 6, 7½, 9	52		208.00	5.20
PS 20	20 Ga.	2¾	2¾	1	4, 5, 6, 7½, 9	46		198.00	4.95
PS 28	28 Ga.	2¾	2¼	¾	6, 7½, 9■	37		198.00	4.95
PS 410	410 Ga.	2½	Max.	½	4, 6, 7½, 9■	22		156.00	3.90
PS 4103	410 Ga.	3	Max.	11⁄16	4, 5, 6, 7½, 9■	31		184.00	4.60

■ 28 Ga. 9 shot marked target — 410 Ga. 9 shot marked skeet.

Load Number	Gauge	Length Shell Inches	Powder Equiv. Drams	Ozs. Shot	Size Shot	Avg. Wgt. Per Case		Price Per M	Price Per Box
"HIGH VELOCITY" MAGNUM LOADS — "POWER PISTON" WAD									
PS 12S Mag.	12 Ga.	2¾	Max.	1½	2, 4, 5, 6	66		288.00	7.20
PS 12 Mag.	12 Ga.	3	4	1⅝	2, 4, 6	70		314.00	7.85
PS 12H Mag.	12 Ga.	3	Max.	1⅞	BB, 2, 4	77		338.00	8.45
PS 16C Mag.	16 Ga.	2¾	Max.	1¼	2, 4, 6	56		250.00	6.25
PS 20S Mag.	20 Ga.	2¾	Max.	1⅛	4, 6, 7½	50		226.00	5.65
PS 20H Mag.	20 Ga.	3	Max.	1¼	4, 6, 7½	55		256.00	6.40

Load Number	Gauge	Length Shell Inches	Powder Equiv. Drams	Ozs. Shot	Size Shot	Avg. Wgt. Per Case		Price Per M	Price Per Box
"HIGH VELOCITY" BUCKSHOT LOADS — "POWER-PAKT"									
PS 12BK	12 Ga.	2¾	3¾	......	00 Buck - 9 Pellets	55		314.00	7.85
PS 12BK	12 Ga.	2¾	3¾	......	0 Buck - 12 Pellets	63)			
PS 12BK	12 Ga.	2¾	3¾	......	1 Buck - 16 Pellets	63 }		314.00	7.85
PS 12BK	12 Ga.	2¾	3¾	......	4 Buck - 27 Pellets	60)			
PS 16BK-5PK	16 Ga.	2¾	3	......	1 Buck - 12 Pellets	50)		310.00	1.55
PS 20BK	20 Ga.	2¾	2¾	......	3 Buck - 20 Pellets	47 }		310.00	7.75

Load Number	Gauge	Length Shell Inches	Powder Equiv. Drams	Ozs. Shot	Size Shot	Avg. Wgt. Per Case		Price Per M	Price Per Box
"HIGH VELOCITY" MAGNUM BUCKSHOT LOADS — "POWER-PAKT"									
PS 12S Mag. BK	12 Ga.	2¾	4	......	00 Buck - 12 Pellets	67)		354.00	8.85
PS 12S Mag. BK	12 Ga.	2¾	4	......	1 Buck - 20 Pellets	67 }			
PS 12H Mag. BK	12 Ga.	3	4½	......	00 Buck - 15 Pellets	79 }		402.00	10.05
PS 12H Mag. BK	12 Ga.	3	4½	......	4 Buck - 41 Pellets	81)			

Load Number	Gauge	Length Shell Inches	Powder Equiv. Drams	Ozs. Shot	Size Shot	Avg. Wgt. Per Case		Price Per M	Price Per Box
"HIGH VELOCITY" RIFLED SLUG									
PS12RS-25PK	12 Ga.	2¾	3¾	⅞	Rifled Slug	51		362.00	9.05
†PS12RS-5PK	12 Ga.	2¾	3¾	⅞	Rifled Slug	51		362.00	1.81
†PS16RS-5PK	16 Ga.	2¾	3	⅘	Rifled Slug	47		346.00	1.73
PS20RS-25PK	20 Ga.	2¾	2¾	⅝	Rifled Slug	37		330.00	8.25
†PS20RS-5PK	20 Ga.	2¾	2¾	⅝	Rifled Slug	37		330.00	1.65
†PS410RS-5PK	410 Ga.	2½	Max.	⅕	Rifled Slug	14		314.00	1.57

Load Number	Gauge	Length Shell Inches	Powder Equiv. Drams	Ozs. Shot	Size Shot	Avg. Wgt. Per Case		Price Per M	Price Per Box
HEAVY FIELD SHOTGUN LOADS—"POWER PISTON" WAD									
PV 12L	12 Ga.	2¾	3¼	1	4, 6, 8	48		178.00	4.45
PV 12H	12 Ga.	2¾	3¼	1⅛	4, 6, 7½, 8, 9	51		192.00	4.80
PP 12H	12 Ga.	2¾	3¼	1¼	7½, 8	58		200.00	5.00
PV 16	16 Ga.	2¾	2½	1	6, 8	47		172.00	4.30
PV 16H	16 Ga.	2¾	2¾	1⅛	4, 6, 7½, 8, 9.	51		178.00	4.45
PV 20	20 Ga.	2¾	2½	⅞	6, 8	41		160.00	4.00
PV 20M	20 Ga.	2¾	2½	1	4, 6, 7½, 8, 9	45		174.00	4.35

Load Number	Gauge	Length Shell Inches	Powder Equiv. Drams	Ozs. Shot	Size Shot	Avg. Wgt. Per Case		Price Per M	Price Per Box
PETERS "RXP" TRAP AND SKEET LOADS — "POWER PISTON" WAD									
XP 12M	12 Ga.	2¾	3	1⅛	7½, 8, 8½, 9	54)		188.00	4.70
XP 12L	12 Ga.	2¾	2¾	1⅛	7½, 8, 8½, 9	54 }		160.00	
XP 20	20 Ga.	2¾	⅞	9		41			

Load Number	Gauge	Length Shell Inches	Powder Equiv. Drams	Ozs. Shot	Size Shot	Avg. Wgt. Per Case		Price Per M	Price Per Box
PETERS INTERNATIONAL TARGET LOADS — "POWER PISTON" WAD									
PS 12L	12 Ga.	2¾	3¼	1¼	7½, 8	58		200.00	5.00
NPS 12L	12 Ga.	2¾	3¼	1¼	7½, 8 (Nickeled)	58		230.00	5.75

Load Number	Gauge	Length Shell Inches	Powder Equiv. Drams	Ozs. Shot	Size Shot	Avg. Wgt. Per Case		Price Per M	Price Per Box
PETERS PLASTIC TARGET LOADS — "POWER PISTON" WAD									
PV 16H	16 Ga.	2¾	2¾	1⅛	9	51		178.00	4.45
PS 28	28 Ga.	2¾	2¼	¾	9	37		198.00	4.95
PS 410	410 Ga.	2¾	Max.	½	9	22		156.00	3.90
PS 4103	410 Ga.	2½ 3	Max.	11⁄16	9	31		184.00	4.60

All loaded shells packed 25 per box — 500 per case except where noted.   †Packed 5 per box — 500 per case.

WINCHESTER SHOTSHELLS

SUPER-X LONG RANGE LOADS

Symbol No.	Gauge	Length of Shell Inches	Powder Dram Equiv.	Oz. Shot	Shot Sizes	Suggested Retail Price Per Box
•WSX10	10	2⅞	Max.	1⅝	4	7.65
WSX12P	12	2¾	Max.	1¼	BB, 2, 4, 5, 6, 7½, 9	5.65
WSX16PH	16	2¾	3¼	1⅛	4, 5, 6, 7½, 9	5.20
WSX20P	20	2¾	Max.	1	4, 5, 6, 7½, 9	4.95
WSX28	28	2¾	Max.	¾	6, 7½	4.95
WSX41	410	2½	Max.	½	4, 6, 7½	3.90
WSX413	410	3	Max.	11/16	4, 5, 6, 7½, 9	4.60

SUPER-X LONG RANGE MAGNUM LOADS

Symbol No.	Gauge	Length of Shell Inches	Powder Dram Equiv.	Oz. Shot	Shot Sizes	Suggested Retail Price Per Box
†•SX10M	10	3½ Mag.	Max.	2	2	12.90
WSX12PH	12	2¾ Mag.	Max.	1½	2, 4, 5, 6	7.20
WSX12X	12	2¾ Mag.	Max.	1½	2, 4	7.65
WSX12PJ	12	3 Mag.	Max.	1⅜	2, 4, 6	7.20
WSX12PM	12	3 Mag.	Max.	1⅝	2, 4, 6	7.85
WSX123P	12	3 Mag.	Max.	1⅞	BB, 2, 4	8.45
WSX123X	12	3 Mag.	Max.	1⅞	2, 4	8.95
WSX16PM	16	2¾ Mag.	Max.	1¼	2, 4, 6	6.25
WSX20PH	20	2¾ Mag.	Max.	1⅛	4, 6, 7½	5.65
WSX20PM	20	3 Mag.	Max.	1¼	4, 6, 7½	6.40

SUPER-X WITH LUBALOY (COPPERIZED) SHOT

Symbol No.	Gauge	Length of Shell Inches	Powder Dram Equiv.	Oz. Shot	Shot Sizes	Suggested Retail Price Per Box
†L12P	12	2¾	Max.	1¼	2, 4, 5, 6, 7½	6.70
†L20P	20	2¾	Max.	1	4, 5, 6, 7½	5.80

SUPER-X WITH LUBALOY (COPPERIZED) SHOT MAGNUM LOADS

Symbol No.	Gauge	Length of Shell Inches	Powder Dram Equiv.	Oz. Shot	Shot Sizes	Suggested Retail Price Per Box
†L12PH	12	2¾ Mag.	Max.	1½	2, 4	8.25
†L12PJ	12	3 Mag.	Max.	1⅜	2, 4, 6	8.25
†L12PM	12	3 Mag.	Max.	1⅝	2, 4, 6	9.45
†L20PM	20	3 Mag.	Max.	1⅛	6	8.60
†L20PMH	20	3 Mag.	Max.	1 3/16	4	9.05

SUPER-X MARK 5 SUPER BUCKSHOT LOADS

Symbol No.	Gauge	Length of Shell Inches	Powder Dram Equiv.	Oz. Shot	Shot Sizes	Suggested Retail Price Per Box
WSX12PRB	12	2¾	—	—	00 Buck— 9 Pellets	7.85
WSX12P0B	12	2¾	—	—	0 Buck—12 Pellets	7.85
•WSX12P1B	12	2¾	—	—	1 Buck—16 Pellets	7.85
WSX12P4B	12	2¾	—	—	4 Buck—27 Pellets	7.85
WSX16PB	16	2¾	—	—	1 Buck—12 Pellets	7.75
•WSX20PB	20	2¾	—	—	3 Buck—20 Pellets	7.75

SUPER-X MARK 5 SUPER BUCKSHOT LOADS—5 ROUND PACK

Symbol No.	Gauge	Length of Shell Inches	Powder Dram Equiv.	Oz. Shot	Shot Sizes	Suggested Retail Price Per Box
WSX12RB5PK	12	2¾	—	—	00 Buck— 9 Pellets	1.57
WSX120B5PK	12	2¾	—	—	0 Buck—12 Pellets	1.57
†•SX121B5PK	12	2¾	—	—	1 Buck—16 Pellets	1.57
WSX124B5PK	12	2¾	—	—	4 Buck—27 Pellets	1.57
WSX16B5PK	16	2¾	—	—	1 Buck—12 Pellets	1.55
•WSX20B5PK	20	2¾	—	—	3 Buck—20 Pellets	1.55

SUPER-X MAGNUM MARK 5 SUPER BUCKSHOT LOADS

Symbol No.	Gauge	Length of Shell Inches	Powder Dram Equiv.	Oz. Shot	Shot Sizes	Suggested Retail Price Per Box
WSX12PB	12	2¾ Mag.	—	—	00 Buck—12 Pellets	8.85
WSX123PB	12	3 Mag.	—	—	00 Buck—15 Pellets	10.05
†•SX12MB	12	2¾ Mag.	—	—	1 Buck—20 Pellets	8.85
†•SX1231B	12	3 Mag.	—	—	1 Buck—24 Pellets	10.05
WSX12PMB	12	3 Mag.	—	—	4 Buck—41 Pellets	10.05

•No Shot Collar Paper symbols are in red.
*U16H. 16 Ga. and U20H, 20 Ga. with 7½ or 8 shot, recommended for trapshooting.
‡9 Shot recommended for Skeet £ Black Powder
†Supplied in WESTERN brand only.

SUPER-X MAGNUM MARK 5 SUPER BUCKSHOT LOADS—5 ROUND PACK

Symbol No.	Gauge	Length of Shell Inches	Powder Dram Equiv.	Oz. Shot	Shot Sizes	Suggested Retail Price Per Box
WSX12B5PK	12	2¾ Mag.	—	—	00 Buck—12 Pellets	1.77
WSX123B5PK	12	3 Mag.	—	—	00 Buck—15 Pellets	2.02
†•SX12M1B5PK	12	2¾ Mag.	—	—	1 Buck—20 Pellets	1.77
† SX1231B5PK	12	3 Mag.	—	—	1 Buck—24 Pellets	2.02
WSX12MB5PK	12	3 Mag.	—	—	4 Buck—41 Pellets	2.02

SUPER-X RIFLED SLUG LOADS

Symbol No.	Gauge	Length of Shell Inches	Powder Dram Equiv.	Oz. Shot	Shot Sizes	Suggested Retail Price Per Box
WSX12PRS	12	2¾	Max.	⅞	Rifled Slug	9.10
WSX16PRS	16	2¾	Max.	⅘	Rifled Slug	8.65
WSX20PRS	20	2¾	Max.	⅝	Rifled Slug	8.25
WSX41RS	410	2½	Max.	⅕	Rifled Slug	7.85

SUPER-X RIFLED SLUG LOADS—5 ROUND PACK

Symbol No.	Gauge	Length of Shell Inches	Powder Dram Equiv.	Oz. Shot	Shot Sizes	Suggested Retail Price Per Box
WSX12RS5PK	12	2¾	Max.	⅞	Rifled Slug	1.82
WSX16RS5PK	16	2¾	Max.	⅘	Rifled Slug	1.73
WSX20RS5PK	20	2¾	Max.	⅝	Rifled Slug	1.65
WSX41RS5PK	410	2½	Max.	⅕	Rifled Slug	1.57

UPLAND FIELD LOADS

Symbol No.	Gauge	Length of Shell Inches	Powder Dram Equiv.	Oz. Shot	Shot Sizes	Suggested Retail Price Per Box
WU10BL	10	2⅞	8	—	Blank £	8.75
WU12	12	2¾	3	1	4, 5, 6, 8	4.45
WU12H	12	2¾	3¼	1⅛	4, 5, 6, 7½, 8, 9	4.80
WU12P	12	2¾	3¼	1¼	6, 7½, 8	5.00
WU12BL	12	2¾	6	—	Blank £	5.85
WU16	16	2¾	2½	1	6, 8	4.30
‡*WU16H	16	2¾	2¾	1⅛	4, 5, 6, 7½, 8, 9	4.45
WU20	20	2¾	2¼	⅞	6, 8	4.00
*WU20H	20	2¾	2½	1	4, 5, 6, 7½, 8, 9	4.30

WESTERN FIELD TRIAL POPPER LOAD

Symbol No.	Gauge	Length of Shell Inches	Powder Dram Equiv.	Oz. Shot	Shot Sizes	Suggested Retail Price Per Box
†•XP12FBL	12	2¾	—	—	Blank £	3.35

UPLAND BRUSH LOAD

Symbol No.	Gauge	Length of Shell Inches	Powder Dram Equiv.	Oz. Shot	Shot Sizes	Suggested Retail Price Per Box
•WU12BR	12	2¾	3	1⅛	8	5.10

DOUBLE A TRAP LOADS

Symbol No.	Gauge	Length of Shell Inches	Powder Dram Equiv.	Oz. Shot	Shot Sizes	Suggested Retail Price Per Box
WW12AA	12	2¾	2¾	1⅛	7½, 8, 8½	4.70
WW12MAA	12	2¾	3	1⅛	7½, 8, 8½	4.70

DOUBLE A INTERNATIONAL TRAP LOAD

Symbol No.	Gauge	Length of Shell Inches	Powder Dram Equiv.	Oz. Shot	Shot Sizes	Suggested Retail Price Per Box
WWIN12AH	12	2¾	3¼	1⅛	7½, 8 (Nic. Pl. Shot.)	5.75
WWIN12A	12	2¾	3¼	1⅛	7½, 8	5.00

DOUBLE A HANDICAP TRAP LOADS

Symbol No.	Gauge	Length of Shell Inches	Powder Dram Equiv.	Oz. Shot	Shot Sizes	Suggested Retail Price Per Box
WW12AAX	12	2¾	3	1⅛	7½, 8	4.70

DOUBLE A SKEET LOADS

Symbol No.	Gauge	Length of Shell Inches	Powder Dram Equiv.	Oz. Shot	Shot Sizes	Suggested Retail Price Per Box
WW12AA	12	2¾	2¾	1⅛	9	4.70
WW12MAA	12	2¾	3	1⅛	9	4.70
WW20AA	20	2¾	2½	⅞	9	4.00
WW28AA	28	2¾	2	¾	9	4.95
WW41AA	410	2½	Max.	½	9	3.90

SUPER TARGET LOADS

Symbol No.	Gauge	Length of Shell Inches	Powder Dram Equiv.	Oz. Shot	Shot Sizes	Suggested Retail Price Per Box
WW12	12	2¾	2¾	1⅛	8, 9	4.40
WW12M	12	2¾	3	1⅛	7½, 8, 9	4.40

WESTERN SHOTSHELLS

SUPER-X LONG RANGE LOADS

Symbol No.	Gauge	Length of Shell Inches	Powder Dram Equiv.	Oz. Shot	Shot Sizes	Suggested Retail Price Per Box
•SX10	10	2⅞	Max.	1⅝	4	7.65
SX12P	12	2¾	Max.	1¼	BB, 2, 4, 5, 6, 7½, 9	5.65
SX16PH	16	2¾	3¼	1⅛	4, 5, 6, 7½, 9	5.20
SX20P	20	2¾	Max.	1	4, 5, 6, 7½, 9	4.95
SX28	28	2¾	Max.	¾	6, 7½	4.95
SX41	410	2½	Max.	½	4, 6, 7½	3.90
SX413	410	3	Max.	11/16	4, 5, 6, 7½, 9	4.60

SUPER-X LONG RANGE MAGNUM LOADS

•SX10M	10	3½ Mag.	Max.	2	2	12.90
SX12PH	12	2¾ Mag.	Max.	1½	2, 4, 5, 6	7.20
SX12X	12	2¾ Mag.	Max.	1½	2, 4	7.65
SX12PJ	12	3 Mag.	Max.	1⅜	2, 4, 6	7.20
SX12PM	12	3 Mag.	Max.	1⅝	2, 4, 6	7.85
SX123P	12	3 Mag.	Max.	1⅞	BB, 2, 4	8.45
SX123X	12	3 Mag.	Max.	1⅞	2, 4	8.95
SX16PM	16	2¾ Mag.	Max.	1¼	2, 4, 6	6.25
SX20PH	20	2¾ Mag.	Max.	1⅛	4, 6, 7½	5.65
SX20PM	20	3 Mag.	Max.	1¼	4, 6, 7½	6.40

SUPER-X WITH LUBALOY (COPPERIZED) SHOT

L12P	12	2¾	Max.	1¼	2, 4, 5, 6, 7½	6.70
L20P	20	2¾	Max.	1	4, 5, 6, 7½	5.80

SUPER-X WITH LUBALOY (COPPERIZED) SHOT MAGNUM LOADS

L12PH	12	2¾ Mag.	Max.	1½	2, 4	8.25
L12PJ	12	3 Mag.	Max.	1⅜	2, 4, 6	8.25
L12PM	12	3 Mag.	Max.	1⅝	2, 4, 6	9.45
L20PM	20	3 Mag.	Max.	1⅛	6	8.60
L20PMH	20	3 Mag.	Max.	1 3/16	4	9.05

SUPER-X MARK 5 SUPER BUCKSHOT LOADS

SX12PRB	12	2¾	—	—	00 Buck— 9 Pellets	7.85
SX12POB	12	2¾	—	—	0 Buck—12 Pellets	7.85
•SX12P1B	12	2¾	—	—	1 Buck—16 Pellets	7.85
SX12P4B	12	2¾	—	—	4 Buck—27 Pellets	7.85
SX16PB	16	2¾	—	—	1 Buck—12 Pellets	7.75
•SX20PB	20	2¾	—	—	3 Buck—20 Pellets	7.75

SUPER-X MARK 5 SUPER BUCKSHOT LOADS—5 ROUND PACK

SX12RB5PK	12	2¾	—	—	00 Buck— 9 Pellets	1.57
SX120B5PK	12	2¾	—	—	0 Buck—12 Pellets	1.57
•SX121B5PK	12	2¾	—	—	1 Buck—16 Pellets	1:57
SX124B5PK	12	2¾	—	—	4 Buck—27 Pellets	1.57
SX16B5PK	16	2¾	—	—	1 Buck—12 Pellets	1.55
•SX20B5PK	20	2¾	—	—	3 Buck—20 Pellets	1.55

SUPER-X MAGNUM MARK 5 SUPER BUCKSHOT LOADS

SX12PB	12	2¾ Mag.	—	—	00 Buck—12 Pellets	8.85
SX123PB	12	3 Mag.	—	—	00 Buck—15 Pellets	10.05
•SX12MB	12	2¾ Mag.	—	—	1 Buck—20 Pellets	8.85
•SX1231B	12	3 Mag.	—	—	1 Buck—24 Pellets	10.05
SX12PMB	12	3 Mag.	—	—	4 Buck—41 Pellets	10.05

•No Shot Collar Paper symbols are in red.
*U16H, 16Ga. and U20H, 20 Ga. with 7½ or 8 shot, recommended for trapshooting.
†Supplied in WINCHESTER brand only. £ Black Powder
‡ 9 Shot recommended for Skeet.

SUPER-X MAGNUM MARK 5 SUPER BUCKSHOT LOADS—5 ROUND PACK

SX12B5PK	12	2¾ Mag.	—	—	00 Buck—12 Pellets	1.77
SX123B5PK	12	3 Mag.	—	—	00 Buck—15 Pellets	2.02
•SX12M1B5PK	12	2¾ Mag.	—	—	1 Buck—20 Pellets	1.77
SX1231B5PK	12	3 Mag.	—	—	1 Buck—24 Pellets	2.02
SX12MB5PK	12	3 Mag.	—	—	4 Buck—41 Pellets	2.02

UPLAND FIELD LOADS

Symbol No.	Gauge	Length of Shell Inches	Powder Dram Equiv.	Oz. Shot	Shot Sizes	Suggested Retail Price Per Box
† WU10BL	10	2⅞	8	—	Blank £	8.75
U12	12	2¾	3	1	4, 5, 6, 8	4.45
U12H	12	2¾	3¼	1⅛	4, 5, 6, 7½, 8, 9	4.80
U12P	12	2¾	3¼	1¼	6, 7½, 8	5.00
† WU12BL	12	2¾	6	—	Blank £	5.85
U16	16	2¾	2½	1	6, 8	4.30
‡*U16H	16	2¾	2¾	1⅛	4, 5, 6, 7½, 8, 9	4.45
U20	20	2¾	2¼	⅞	6, 8	4.00
*U20H	20	2¾	2½	1	4, 5, 6, 7½, 8, 9	4.30

WESTERN FIELD TRIAL POPPER LOAD

•XP12FBL	12	2¾	—	—	Blank £	3.35

UPLAND BRUSH LOAD

•U12BR	.12	2¾	3	1⅛	8	5.10

DOUBLE A TRAP LOADS

WW12AA	12	2¾	2¾	1⅛	7½, 8, 8½	4.70
WW12MAA	12	2¾	3	1⅛	7½, 8, 8½	4.70

DOUBLE A INTERNATIONAL TRAP LOAD

WWIN12AH	12	2¾	3¼	1⅛	7½, 8 (Nic. Pl. Shot)	5.75
WWIN12A	12	2¾	3¼	1⅛	7½, 8	5.00

DOUBLE A SKEET LOADS

WW12AA	12	2¾	2¾	1⅛	9	4.70
WW12MAA	12	2¾	3	1⅛	9	4.70
WW20AA	20	2¾	2½	⅞	9	4.00
WW28AA	28	2¾	2	¾	9	4.95
WW41AA	410	2½	Max.	½	9	3.90

DOUBLE A HANDICAP TRAP LOADS

WW12AAX	12	2¾	3	1⅛	7½, 8	4.70

SUPER TARGET LOADS

WW12	12	2¾	2¾	1⅛	8, 9	4.40
WW12M	12	2¾	3	1⅛	7½, 8, 9	4.40

SUPER-X RIFLED SLUG LOADS

SX12PRS	12	2¾	Max.	⅞	Rifled Slug	9.10
SX16PRS	16	2¾	Max.	⅘	Rifled Slug	8.65
SX20PRS	20	2¾	Max.	⅝	Rifled Slug	8.25
SX41RS	410	2½	Max.	⅕	Rifled Slug	7.85

SUPER-X RIFLED SLUG LOADS—5 ROUND PACK

SX12RS5PK	12	2¾	Max.	⅞	Rifled Slug	1.82
SX16RS5PK	16	2¾	Max.	⅘	Rifled Slug	1.73
SX20RS5PK	20	2¾	Max.	⅝	Rifled Slug	1.65
SX41RS5PK	410	2½	Max.	⅕	Rifled Slug	1.57

FEDERAL SHOTSHELLS

FEDERAL FIELD LOADS

GAUGE	LOAD NO.	SHELL LENGTH INCHES	POWDER DRAMS EQUIV.	OUNCES SHOT	SHOT SIZES		PER BOX
12	F123	2¾	3¼	1⅛	4 5 6 7½ 8 9		$4.80
12	F124	2¾	3¼	1¼	7½ 8 9		5.00
16	F162	2¾	2¾	1⅛	4 5 6 7½ 8 9		4.45
20	F202	2¾	2½	1	4 5 6 7½ 8 9		4.35

FEDERAL GAME LOADS

12	F121	2¾	3¼	1	6, 8	$4.45
16	F160	2¾	2½	1	8	4.30
20	F200	2¾	2½	⅞	8	4.00

TARGET LOADS WITH EXTRA HARD SHOT

GAUGE	LOAD NO.	SHELL LENGTH INCHES	POWDER DRAMS EQUIV.	OUNCES SHOT	SHOT SIZES	PER BOX
12	K117	2¾	2¾	1⅛	7½ 8 8½ 9	$4.70
12	K118	2¾	3	1⅛	7½ 8 8½ 9	4.70
12	C117	2¾	2¾	1⅛	7½ 8 8½ 9	4.40
12	C118	2¾	3	1⅛	7½ 8 8½ 9	4.40
12	K125	2¾	3¼	1⅛	7⅛ 8 9	5.00
16	F167	2¾	2¾	1⅛	7½ 8 9	4.45
20	F206	2¾	2½	⅞	8 9	4.00
20	S206	2¾	2½	⅞	8 9	4.00
28	F280	2¾	2	¾	9	4.95
410	F412	2½	Max.	½	9	3.90

FEDERAL HI-POWER LOADS

HI-POWER SHOT SHELLS Maximum Loads Packed 25 per box 500 per case	GAUGE	LOAD NO.	SHELL LENGTH INCHES	POWDER DRAMS EQUIV.	OUNCES SHOT	SHOT SIZES		PER BOX
	12	F127	2¾	3¾	1¼	BB 2 4 5 6 7½ 9		$5.65
	16	F164	2¾	3¼	1⅛	4 5 6 7½ 9		5.20
	20	F203	2¾	2¾	1	4 5 6 7½ 9		4.95
	28	F283	2¾	2¼	⅞	6 7½ 8		4.95
	410	F412	2½	Max.	½	6 7½		3.90
	410	F413	3	Max.	11/16	4 5 6 7½ 9		4.60

FEDERAL MAGNUM LOADS

MAGNUM LOADS Packed 25 per box 500 per case	GAUGE	LOAD NO.	SHELL LENGTH INCHES	POWDER DRAMS EQUIV.	OUNCES SHOT	SHOT SIZES	PER BOX
	12	F131	3	4	1⅞	BB 2 4	$8.45
	12	F129	3	4	1⅝	BB 2 4 6	7.85
	12	F130	2¾	3¾	1½	2 4 5 6	7.20
	16	F165	2¾	3¼	1¼	2 4 6	6.25
	20	F205	2¾	2¾	1⅛	4 6 7½	5.65
	20	F207	3	3	1¼	2 4 6 7½	6.40

HI-POWER BUCKSHOT AND RIFLED SLUG LOADS

BUCKSHOT and RIFLED SLUG LOADS Packed 5 per box 250 per case	GAUGE	LOAD NO.	SHELL LENGTH INCHES	POWDER DRAMS EQUIV.		SHOT SIZES		PER BOX
	12	F131	3	Sup. Mag.		00 Buck, 15 Pellets		$2.01
	12	F131	3	Sup. Mag.		No. 4 Buck, 41 Pellets		2.01
	12	F131	3	Sup. Mag.		No. 1 Buck, 24 Pellets		2.01
	12	F130	2¾	Mag.		No. 1 Buck, 20 Pellets		1.77
	12	F130	2¾	Mag.		No. 4 Buck, 20 Pellets		1.77
	12	F130	2¾	Mag.		00 Buck, 12 Pellets		1.77
	12	F127	2¾	Max.		00 Buck, 9 Pellets		1.57
	12	F127	2¾	Max.		0 Buck, 12 Pellets		1.57
	12	F127	2¾	Max.		No. 1 Buck, 16 Pellets		1.57
	12	F127	2¾	Max.		No. 4 Buck, 27 Pellets		1.55
	20	F207	3	Mag.		No. 2 Buck, 18 Pellets		1.77
	20	F203	2¾	Max.		No. 3 Buck, 20 Pellets		1.55
	12	F127	2¾	Max.		⅞ oz. Rifled Slug		1.81
	16	F164	2¾	Max.		⅘ oz. Rifled Slug		1.73
	20	F203	2¾	Max.		⅝ oz. Rifled Slug		1.65
	410	F412	2½	Max.		⅕ oz. Rifled Slug		1.57

Reloading

DUPONT SMOKELESS POWDERS

SHOTSHELL POWDER

Hi-Skor 700-X Double-Base Shotshell Powder. Specifically designed for today's 12-gauge components. Developed to give optimum ballistics at minimum charge weight (means more reloads per pound of powder). 700-X is dense, easy to load, clean to handle, and loads uniformly. Wad pressures are not critical.

PB Shotshell Powder. Replace old Du Pont MX. For use in low-base shells. Produces exceptional 20- and 28-gauge skeet reloads; preferred by many in 12-gauge target loads,

it gives 3-dram equivalent velocity at relatively low chamber pressures.

SR-4756 Powder. Great all-around powder for target and field loads.

SR-7625 Powder. A fast growing "favorite" for reloading target as well as light and heavy field loads in 4 gauges. Excellent velocity-chamber pressure.

IMR-4227 Powder. Can be used effectively for reloading .410-gauge shotshell ammunition.

RIFLE POWDER

IMR-3031 Rifle Powder. Specifically recommended for medium-capacity cartridges.

IMR-4064 Rifle Powder. Has exceptionally uniform burning qualities when used in medium- and large-capacity cartridges.

IMR-4198. Made the Remington 222 cartridge famous. Developed for small- and medium-capacity cartridges.

IMR-4227 Rifle Powder. Fastest burning of the IMR Series. Specifically designed for the 22 Hornet class of cartridges.

IMR-4320. Recommended for high-velocity cartridges.

IMR-4350 Rifle Powder. Gives unusually uniform results when loaded in magnum cartridges. Slowest burning powder of the IMR series.

IMR-4831. Produced as a canister-grade handloading powder. Packaged in 1 lb. canister, 8 lb. caddy and 20 lb. kegs.

IMR-4895 Rifle Powder. The time-tested standard for caliber 30 military ammunition is now being manufactured again. Slightly faster than IMR-4320. Loads uniformly in all powder measures. One of the country's favorite powders.

PISTOL POWDER

PB Powder. Another powder for reloading a wide variety of center-fire handgun ammunition.

IMR-4227 Powder. Can be used effectively for reloading "magnum" handgun ammunition.

"Hi-Skor" 700-X Powder. The same qualities that make it a superior shotshell powder contribute to its excellent

performance in all the popular handguns.

SR-7625 Powder. For reloading a wide variety of center-fire handgun ammunition.

SR-4756, IMR-3031 and IMR-4198. Three more powders in a good selection—all clean burning and with uniform performance.

SMOKELESS SPORTING POWDERS

HERCULES

FOR RELOADING

Seven types of Hercules smokeless sporting powders are available to the handloader. These have been selected from the wide range of powders produced for factory loading to provide at least one type that can be used efficiently and economically for each type of ammunition. These include:

RED DOT®

The preferred powder for light-to-medium shotshell use; specifically designed for 12-gauge target loads. Available in 1-, 4-, 8-, and 15-pound containers.

HERCO®

A coarse-grained shotshell powder for use in heavy 12-gauge shotshells and medium-small-gauge shotshell loads. Available in 1-, 4-, 8-, and 15-pound containers.

GREEN DOT®

Designed for use in 12-gauge medium shotshell loads. Outstanding in 20-gauge skeet loads. Available in 1-, 4-, 8-, and 15-pound containers.

BULLSEYE®

A high-energy, quick-burning powder designed for pistol and revolver use. Available in 1-, 4-, 8-, and 15-pound containers.

UNIQUE®

The all-around powder. Performs well in pistol and revolver, shotshell, and rifle gallery loads. Available in 1-, 4-, 8-, and 15-pound containers.

BLUE DOT®

The most recent addition to the Hercules line, Blue Dot is specifically designed for magnum waterfowl shotshells. Available in 1-pound containers.

HERCULES 2400®

A fine-grained powder intended for small-capacity rifle cartridges and/or reduced loads in larger capacity rifle cartridges. Outstanding with cast bullets. Available in 1-, 4-, 8-, and 15-pound containers.

HODGDON SMOKELESS POWDER

RIFLE POWDER

In Order of Approximate Burning Rates

H4227 and H4198

H4227 is the fastest burning of the IMR series. Well adapted to Hornet, light bullets in 222 and all bullets in 357 and 44 magnum pistols. Cuts leading with lead bullets. H4198 was developed especially for small and medium capacity cartridges.

1 lb. Can $4.95 • 8 lb. Keg $35.75 • 20 lb. Keg $81.00

SPHERICAL BL-C, ® Lot No. 2

A highly popular favorite of the Bench-rest shooters. Best performance is in the .222, and in other cases smaller than 30/06.

1 lb. Can $4.95 • 8 lb. Keg $35.75 • 20 lb. Keg $81.00

SPHERICAL H335®

Similar to BL-C(2), H335 is becoming popular for its performance in medium capacity cases, especially in 222 and 308 Winchester.

1 lb. Can $2.75 • 8 lb. Keg $18.50 • 20 lb. Keg $41.25

HODGDON BLACK POWDER —FG, FFG, FFFG

Made in Scotland by Curtis and Harvey, Hodgdon's Black Powder is cleaner burning, uniform in grain size and is perfect for cap and ball pistols, muzzle loading rifles, shotguns and cannons.

4895®

4895 may well be considered the most versatile of all propellants. It gives desirable performance in almost all cases from 222 Rem. to 458 Win. Reduced loads, to as low as 3/5 of maximum, still give target accuracy.

1 lb. Can $4.95 • 8 lb. Keg $35.75 • 20 lb. Keg $81.00

SPHERICAL H380®

This number fills a gap between 4320 and 4350. It is excellent in 22/250, 220 Swift, the 6mm's, 257 and 30/06.

1 lb. Can $4.95 • 8 lb. Keg $35.75 • 20 lb. Keg $81.00

SPHERICAL H414®

A new development in spherical powder. In many popular medium to medium-large calibers, pressure velocity relationship is better.

1 lb. Can $4.95 • 8 lb. Keg $35.75 • 20 lb. Keg $81.00

4831®—NEWLY MANUFACTURED

Here is a new batch of the original 4831. Use same loading data as our original surplus powder. Outstanding performance with medium and heavy bullets in the 6mm's, 25/06, 270 and Magnum calibers.

1 lb. Can $4.95 • 8 lb. Keg $33.75 • 20 lb. Keg $81.00

SPHERICAL H450®

A powder well adapted to maximum loads in most cartridges. Gives excellent performance in 30/06.

1 lb. Can $4.95 • 8 lb. Keg $35.75 • 20 lb. Keg $81.00

SPHERICAL H870®

H870 is our slowest propellant, best adapted to the so-called overbore capacity magnums. Use is 257, 264, 270, and 300 mags with heavy bullets.

1 lb. Can $2.75 • 8 lb. Keg $18.50 • 20 lb. Keg $41.25

Left to Right Shows Order of Approximate Burning Rates

SHOTGUN AND PISTOL POWDER

HP38

A fast pistol powder for most pistol loading. Especially recommended for in a range. 38 special.

12 oz. Can $4.05 •   12 lb. Keg $51.95

TRAP 100

Trap 100 is a spherical trap and light field load powder, also excellent for target loads in centerfire pistol.

8 oz. Can $2.70   12 lb. Keg $48.50

HS-5, HS-6 AND HS-7

HS-5 for heavy field and HS-6 and HS-7 for magnum field loads are unsurpassed since they do not pack in the measure. They deliver uniform charges and are dense so allow sufficient wad column for best patterns.

1 lb. Can $4.95   12 lb. Keg $48.50

H110

A spherical powder made especially for the 30 MI carbine. H110 also does very well in 357, 44 Spec., 44 Mag. or 410 ga. Shotshell. Magnum primers are recommended for consistent ignition.

1 lb. Can $4.95 •   20 lb. Keg $81.00

NORMA SMOKELESS POWDER

(Prices vary in different areas)

RIFLE POWDERS

NORMA 200

A fast-burning powder, for small capacity cartridge cases as the 222, but also for use with light bullets and/or light loads in larger calibers.

NORMA 201

Slower than the 200, used with lighter bullets in medium-size cases, or with big-caliber cartridges where a large bore volume is to be filled up quickly by expanding gases.

NORMA 203

Adjusted to fit the medium-sized cartridge types such as: 30-06; 303 British; European 7, 8 MM's etc. unless light bullets necessitate a faster powder.

NORMA 204

A slow-burning powder, adapted for cartridges with a large case capacity and/or using heavy bullets in relation to the caliber.

NORMA 205

Exceptionally slow-burning, high-energy powder for highest velocity with large capacity cases. A must for Magnums.

HANDGUN POWDERS

THE NORMA 1010

Is a fast burning, easily ignited powder for revolver and pistol ammunition. Produced from a double base composition and consequently is virtually non-hygroscopic. As a result velocities and pressures show little change if the powder is exposed to very dry or damp conditions.

THE NORMA 1020

Is a slower burning powder especially designed for high velocity loads at economical charge weights in Magnum handgun calibers. Produced from a double base composition and thus is virtually non-hygroscopic.

SHOTGUN POWDERS

THE NORMA 2010

Has been designed for light and standard shotshell loads and is especially suited for skeet and trap cartridges. A double base powder and is virtually non-hygroscopic. Contains ingredients which reduce the gas temperature and consequently the barrel temperature. The special method of manufacture employed gives granules with excellent flow properties, the thickness being such that they will not bind in the powder measure.

THE NORMA 2020

Is a slower burning powder specially designed for Magnum and hunting loads with a heavier shot charge. It is similar in composition and granule form to Norma 2010. Both powders are suitable for use in all climatic conditions.

DOMESTIC PRIMERS

MAKE	PRIMER NUMBER	TYPE	DIA.	DESCRIPTION	CALIBERS		Per 1,000
For Small Pistol Cartridges							
Remington	1½	Small Pistol	.175″	Brass. Nickel-plated. For center-fire Pistol and Revolver cartridges.	25 Automatic 30 Mauser 30 Luger 32 Automatic 32 S&W 32 S&W Long 32 Short Colt 32 Long Colt 32 Colt New Police 357 Magnum	9m/m Luger 38 S&W 38 Special 38 Short Colt 38 Long Colt 38 Colt New Police 38 Auto-Super 38 Automatic 380 Automatic 41 Long Colt	$9.35
Peters	1½	Small Pistol	.175″				
Winchester	1½-108	Small Pistol	.175″				
Western	1½-108	Small Pistol	.175″				
Cascade	500	Small Pistol	.175″				
Alcan	Max.-Fire	Small Pistol	.175″				
RWS	4031	Small Pistol	.175″				
Remington	5½	Small Rifle	.175″	Brass. Nickel-plated. For center-fire Revolver cartridges.	32 S&W 357 Magnum		$9.35
For Large Pistol Cartridges							
Remington	2½	Large Pistol	.210″	Brass. Nickel-plated. For center-fire Rifle, Pistol and Revolver cartridges, also Brass Shot Shells except .410 gauge.	38-40 Winchester 44 S&W Special 44 Magnum 44-40 Winchester 45 Colt	45 Auto Rim 45 Automatic	$9.35
Peters	2½	Large Pistol	.210″				
Winchester	7-111	Large Pistol	.210″				
Western	7-111	Large Pistol	.210″				
Cascade	300	Large Pistol	.210″				
Alcan	Max.-Fire	Large Pistol	.210″				
RWS	5337	Large Pistol	.210″				
For Small Rifle Cartridges							
Remington	6½	Small Rifle	.175″	Brass. Nickel-plated. For center-fire Rifle and Revolver cartridges.	22 Remington "Jet" Magnum 218 Bee 22 Hornet 25-20 Winchester 25-20 Winchester H.V.	256 Winchester Magnum 30 Carbine 32-20 Winchester 32-20 Winchester H.V.	$9.60
Peters	6½	Small Rifle	.175″				
Remington	6½-116	Small Rifle	.175″				
Western	6½-116	Small Rifle	.175″				
Cascade	400	Small Rifle	.175″				
RWS	4033	Small Rifle	.175″				
Remington	7½	Small Rifle	.175″	Brass. Nickel-plated. For center-fire Rifle and XP-100 Pistol cartridges.	221 Remington "Fireball" 222 Remington	222 Remington Mag. 223 Remington (5.56 mm)	$8.50
Alcan	Max.-Fire	Small Rifle	.175″				
For Large Rifle Cartridges							
Remington	9½	Large Rifle	.210″	219 Zipper 220 Swift 22-250 Remington 243 Winchester 6mm Remington 244 Remington 25-35 Winchester 250 Savage 257 Roberts 264 Winchester Magnum 270 Winchester 280 Remington 284 Winchester 7mm Mauser	7mm Remington Magnum 30-30 Winchester 30 Remington 30-06 Springfield 30-40 Krag 300 Winchester Magnum 300 H&H Magnum 300 Savage 303 Savage 303 British 308 Winchester 32 Winchester Special	32 Remington 32-40 Winchester 8mm Mauser 338 Winchester Magnum 348 Winchester 35 Remington 358 Winchester 375 H&H Magnum 38-55 Winchester 444 Marlin 45-70 Government 458 Winchester Magnum	$9.60
Peters	9½	Large Rifle	.210″				
Winchester	8½-120	Large Rifle	.210″				
Western	8½-120	Large Rifle	.210″				
Cascade	200	Large Rifle	.210″				
Alcan	Max.-Fire	Large Rifle	.210″				
RWS	1973	Large Rifle	.210″				
Remington	9½M	Large Rifle	.210″	Brass. Nickel-plated. For center-fire belted Magnum Rifle.	264 Winchester Magnum 7mm Remington Magnum 300 H&H Magnum 300 Winchester Magnum	350 Remington Magnum 375 H&H Magnum 458 Winchester Magnum	$11.05

For Shotgun Shells (Battery Cup Type)

MAKE	No.	DESCRIPTION	Per 1,000
Remington	97 (209 Size)	Battery Cup. Used in Remington and Peters 12- and 20-gauge target loads and all 28-gauge loads with plastic base wad.	$16.95
Remington	209 Target	Battery Cup. With integral and covered flash hole.	$16.95
Remington	57	Battery Cup. Used in all Remington and Peters 10-, 12-, 16-, 20- and 28-gauge shells (except 12 and 20 plastic target loads and all 28-gauge shells with plastic base wad.)	$16.95
Remington	97-4	Battery Cup. Used in 410 Gauge, 2½ and 3″ plastic shotshells with solid plastic base wad.	$16.95

MAKE	No.	DESCRIPTION	Per 1,000
Winchester Western	209	Battery Cup. Used in 10, 12, 16, 20, 28 and .410 gauge.	$15.40
Cascade	109	Battery Cup. (Winchester Size).	$15.40
Cascade	157	Battery Cup. (Remington Size).	$15.40
Alcan	220	Battery Cup. (All plastic cases)	$15.40
RWS	209S	Battery Cup. (Win. Size—all gauges)	$15.40

UNPRIMED CASES FOR RELOADERS

WINCHESTER CENTER FIRE RIFLE CARTRIDGE CASES
(Packed 20 per Box)

Cartridge Case Caliber & Symbol	Per 100
*218 Bee	
U218B Unprimed	$10.47
*22 Hornet	
U22H Unprimed	10.47
22-250 U22250 Unprimed	17.16
220 Swift	
U220S Unprimed	16.83
222 Remington	
U222R Unprimed	11.99
225 Winchester	
U225 Unprimed	13.64
243 Winchester	
U243 Unprimed	17.16
*25-20 Winchester	
U2520 Unprimed	11.16
25-35 Winchester	
U2535 Unprimed	17.14
250 Savage	
U250 Unprimed	17.16
25-06 U2506 Unprimed	18.15
257 Roberts	
U257 Unprimed	17.16
264 Winchester Magnum	
U264 Unprimed	22.22

*Packed 50 to the box—all others 20 per box.

Cartridge Case Caliber & Symbol	Per 100
270 Winchester	
U270 Unprimed	$18.15
284 Winchester	
U284 Unprimed	19.32
7 mm Mauser	
U7MM Unprimed	18.15
7 mm Remington Magnum	
U7MMR Unprimed	22.22
*30 Carbine	
UW30M1 Unprimed	10.45
30-30 Winchester	
U3030 Unprimed	15.57
Remington	
U30R Unprimed	16.27
30-06 Springfield	
U3006 Unprimed	18.15
30-40 Krag	
U3040 Unprimed	18.15
300 Winchester Magnum	
U30WM Unprimed	22.55
300 H & H Magnum	
U300H Unprimed	23.10
300 Savage	
U300 Unprimed	17.16
303 Savage	
U303 Unprimed	16.27
303 British	
UW303B Unprimed	18.15

Cartridge Case Caliber & Symbol	Per 100
308 Winchester	
U308 Unprimed	$17.16
32 Winchester Special	
U32WS Unprimed	15.57
32 Remington	
U32R Unprimed	16.27
*32-20 Winchester	
U3220 Unprimed	11.16
8 mm Mauser	
UW8MM Unprimed	18.15
338 Winchester Magnum	
U338 Unprimed	23.54
348 Winchester	
UW348 Unprimed	22.66
35 Remington	
U35R Unprimed	17.16
358 Winchester	
U358 Unprimed	17.49
375 H & H Magnum	
U375H Unprimed	24.64
*38-40 Winchester	
U3840 Unprimed	10.67
*44-40 Winchester	
U4440 Unprimed	10.67
45-70 Government	
UW4570 Unprimed	15.57
458 Winchester Magnum	
UW458 Unprimed	24.20

WINCHESTER PISTOL & REVOLVER CARTRIDGE CASES
(Packed 50 per Box)

Cartridge Case Caliber & Symbol	Per 100
25 Automatic	
U25AP Unprimed	$6.49
256 Winchester Magnum	
U256P Unprimed	11.39
30 Luger	
U30LP Unprimed	10.01
32 Automatic	
U32AP Unprimed	6.38
32 S & W	
U32SWP Unprimed	5.61
32 S & W Long	
U32SWLP Unprimed	5.61
32 Short Colt	
U32SCP Unprimed	5.61

Cartridge Case Caliber & Symbol	Per 100
32 Long Colt	
U32LCP Unprimed	$5.61
32 Colt New Police	
UW32CNP Unprimed	5.61
357 Magnum	
U357P Unprimed	7.59
9 mm Luger	
UW9LP Unprimed	10.01
38 S & W	
U38SWP Unprimed	6.38
38 Special	
U38SP Unprimed	6.93
38 Short Colt	
U38SCP Unprimed	6.38

Cartridge Case Caliber & Symbol	Per 100
38 Long Colt	
U38LCP Unprimed	$6.93
38 Automatic	
U38AP Unprimed	7.59
380 Automatic	
U380AP Unprimed	6.38
44 S & W	
UW44SP Unprimed	8.25
44 Magnum	
U44MP Unprimed	10.67
45 Colt	
U45CP Unprimed	10.67
45 Automatic	
U45AP Unprimed	10.01

NORMA EMPTY UNPRIMED RIFLE CASES

Stock Number	Caliber	Box 20
751	.220 Swift	$4.04
752	.222 Remington	2.90
753	.243 Winchester	3.78
757	6.5 MM Jap	4.30
829	6.5 Carcano	4.30
759	6.5 Norma (6.5 x 55)	4.30
760	.270 Winchester	3.99
761	7 MM Mauser	3.99
847	Super 7 x 61	5.68
796	.358 Norma Belted Magnum	5.73
855	7x57R	5.40
775	9.3x57	5.73
786	8x57J .319 Dia.	4.30

Stock Number	Caliber	Box 20
826	7 MM Remington Magnum	$5.40
763	.30 U. S. Carbine	2.30
765	.308 Winchester	3.99
811	.308 Norma Belted Magnum	5.68
766	.30-06 Springfield	3.99
768	.303 British	3.99
854	7.5 x 55 (7.5 Swiss)	4.58
819	7.62 Russian	4.58
815	7.65 Argentine Mauser	4.58
769	7.7 MM Jap	4.58
772	8 MM Mauser .322 Diam.	3.99

NORMA EMPTY UNPRIMED PISTOL CASES

Stock Number	Caliber	Box 50
808	.44 Magnum	$6.41
820	.38 S&W	6.88

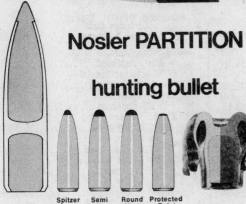

≈NOSLER *High Performance Bullets*

Nosler PARTITION

hunting bullet

Spitzer Semi Spitzer Round Nose Protected Point

While Nosler bullets resemble traditional bullet styles outwardly, important design differences, shown in the cutaway drawing, give these bullets exceptional performance characteristics.

The Partition bullet, easily recognized by the visible base lead core, is a unique concept that retains about two-thirds of the bullet weight after impact. Consistent, controlled expansion and deeper penetration make it an ideal big-game hunting bullet.

An unusual design, plus impact-extrusion forming which allows unique control over weight distribution, make the Solid Base superbly accurate. It is an exceptional bullet for varmint hunting or target shooting.

CAL.	DIA.	BULLET WEIGHT AND STYLE	50 PER BOX
6MM	.243	85 Gr. Semi Spitzer	$7.75
	.243	95 Gr. Spitzer	7.85
	.243	100 Gr. Semi Spitzer	8.00
.25	.257	100 Gr. Spitzer	8.00
	.257	115 Gr. Spitzer	8.40
	.257	117 Gr. Semi Spitzer	8.45
6.5MM	.264	125 Gr. Spitzer	8.70
	.264	140 Gr. Spitzer	9.15
.270	.277	130 Gr. Spitzer	8.80
	.277	150 Gr. Spitzer	9.25
	.277	160 Gr. Semi Spitzer	9.70
7MM	.284	140 Gr. Spitzer	9.35
	.284	150 Gr. Spitzer	9.50
	.284	160 Gr. Spitzer	9.70
	.284	175 Gr. Semi Spitzer	9.95
.30	.308	150 Gr. Spitzer	9.35
	.308	150 Gr. Protected Point	10.00
	.308	165 Gr. Spitzer	9.50
	.308	165 Gr. Protected Point	10.25
	.308	180 Gr. Spitzer	9.70
	.308	180 Gr. Protected Point	10.45
	.308	200 Gr. Round Nose	9.95
.338	.338	210 Gr. Spitzer	13.45
	.338	250 Gr. Round Nose	14.30
.375	.375	270 Gr. Round Nose	19.20
	.375	300 Gr. Round Nose	20.00

Nosler SOLID-BASE

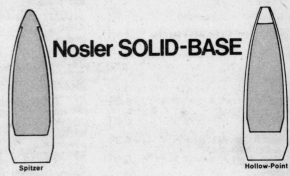

Spitzer Hollow-Point

CAL.	DIA.	BULLET WEIGHT AND STYLE	100 PER BOX
.22	.224	50 Gr. Spitzer	$5.15
	.224	50 Gr. Hollow-Point	5.15
	.224	50 Gr. Hollow-Point, Match	7.55
	.224	52 Gr. Hollow-Point	5.60
	.224	52 Gr. Hollow-Point, Match	7.00
	.224	55 Gr. Spitzer	5.20
6MM	.243	70 Gr. Hollow-Point	6.70
	.243	70 Gr. Hollow-Point, Match	9.50
	.243	85 Gr. Spitzer	7.10
.30	.308	150 Gr. Hollow-Point	9.25
	.308	150 Gr. Hollow-Point, Match	11.50
	.308	168 Gr. Hollow-Point	9.75
	.308	168 Gr. Hollow-Point, Match	12.00

SIERRA BULLETS

JACKETED RIFLE BULLETS

.22 CALIBER .223 Diameter Hornet

	40 gr. Hornet	4.35
	45 gr. Hornet	4.35

.22 CALIBER .224 Diameter Hornet

	40 gr. Hornet	4.35
	45 gr. Hornet	4.35

.22 CALIBER .224 Diameter High Velocity

	45 gr. Semi-pointed	4.45
	45 gr. Spitzer	4.45
	50 gr. Semi-pointed	4.60
	50 gr. Spitzer	4.60
	50 gr. Blitz	4.60
	55 gr. Semi-pointed	4.65
	55 gr. Spitzer	4.65
	63 gr. Semi-pointed	4.70

.22 CALIBER .224 Diameter Bench Rest

	53 gr. Hollow Point	5.70
	52 gr. Hollow Point B.T.	5.70

6MM .243 Diameter

	60 gr. Hollow Point	5.65
	75 gr. Hollow Point	6.05
	85 gr. Spitzer	6.30
	85 gr. Hollow Point B.T.	6.30
	100 gr. Spitzer	6.75
	100 gr. Semi-pointed	6.75

.25 CALIBER .257 Diameter

	75 gr. Hollow Point	6.15
	87 gr. Spitzer	6.40
	90 gr. Hollow Point B.T.	6.45
	100 gr. Spitzer	6.70
	117 gr. Spitzer Boat Tail	7.10
	117 gr. Spitzer Flat Base	7.10
	120 gr. Hollow Point B.T.	7.10

6.5MM .264 Diameter

	85 gr. Hollow Point	6.30
	100 gr. Hollow Point	6.75
	120 gr. Spitzer	7.10
	140 gr. Spitzer Boat Tail	7.55
	140 gr. Matchking H.P.	8.20

.270 CALIBER .277 Diameter

	90 gr. Hollow Point	6.85
	110 gr. Spitzer	7.00
	130 gr. Spitzer Boat Tail	7.65
	130 gr. Spitzer Flat Base	7.65
	150 gr. Spitzer Boat Tail	7.95

7MM .284 Diameter

	120 gr. Spitzer	6.95
	140 gr. Spitzer	7.45
	160 gr. Spitzer Boat Tail	8.05
	168 gr. Matchking H.P.	8.30

.30 CALIBER .307 Diameter

	150 gr. Flat Nose 30-30	7.55
	170 gr. Flat Nose 30-30	7.85

.30 CALIBER .308 Diameter

	110 gr. Rd. Nose Carbine	5.65
	110 gr. Hollow Point	6.75
	125 gr. Spitzer	7.15
	150 gr. Spitzer	7.60
	150 gr. Round Nose	7.60
	165 gr. Hollow Point B.T.	7.95
	180 gr. Spitzer Flat Base	7.95
	180 gr. Spitzer Boat Tail	8.05
	180 gr. Round Nose	7.95
	220 gr. Round Nose	8.65

.30 CALIBER Competition

	168 gr. International H.P.	9.40
	190 gr. Matchking H.P.	9.70
	180 gr. Matchking H.P.	9.70
	200 gr. Matchking H.P.	9.80

.303 CALIBER .311 Diameter

	150 gr. Spitzer	7.70
	180 gr. Spitzer	8.00

8MM .323 Diameter

	150 gr. Spitzer	7.80
	175 gr. Spitzer	8.05

JACKETED PISTOL BULLETS

.38 CALIBER .357 Diameter

	110 gr. Jacketed Hollow Cavity	5.50
	125 gr. Jacketed Soft Point	5.60
	125 gr. Jacketed Hollow Cavity	5.60
	150 gr. Jacketed Hollow Cavity	5.70
	158 gr. Jacketed Soft Point	5.70

9MM .355 Diameter

	90 gr. Jacketed Hollow Cavity	5.50
	115 gr. Jacketed Hollow Cavity	5.60

.41 CALIBER .410 Diameter

	170 gr. Jacketed Hollow Cavity	6.95
	210 gr. Jacketed Hollow Cavity	7.10

44 MAGNUM .4295 Diameter

	180 gr. Jacketed Hollow Cavity	7.00
	240 gr. Jacketed Hollow Cavity	7.10

.45 CALIBER .4515 Diameter

	185 gr. ACP Jacketed Hollow Cavity	7.05
	.308 165 gr. Spitzer Boat Tail	7.95
	.45-70 Gov't 300 gr. Flat Nose *	4.65
	6mm .243 70 gr. Hollow Point B.T. Bench Rest	6.30
	7mm .284 dia 175 gr. Spitzer Boat Tail	8.45
	.35 200 gr. Round Nose *	4.30
	.338 250 gr. Spitzer Boat Tail *	5.55

*Priced and packaged per 50

SPEER HANDGUN AMMO & BULLETS

Jacketed Pistol Bullets
(Packed 100 Per Box)

9mm CALIBER (.355)

100 grain Hollow Point, #3983 .... $5.10

125 grain Soft Point, #4005 .... 5.20

38 CALIBER (.357)

110 grain Hollow Point, #4007 .... $5.10

125 grain Hollow Point, #4013 .... 5.20

125 grain Soft Point, #4011 .... 5.20

140 grain Hollow Point, #4203 .... 5.50

146 grain Hollow Point, #4205 .... 5.10

158 grain JHP, #4211 .... 5.40

158 grain Soft Point, #4217 .... 5.40

160 grain Soft Point, #4223 .... 5.10

41 CALIBER (.410)

200 grain Hollow Point, #4405 .... $6.20

220 grain Soft Point, #4417 .... 6.35

44 CALIBER (.429)

200 grain Magnum HP, #4425 .... $6.50

Bullets priced per 100

---

225 grain Hollow Point, #4435 ..... 6.25

240 grain Soft Point, #4447 ..... 6.45

240 grain Magnum HP, #4453 ..... 6.75

240 grain Magnum SP, #4457 ..... 6.75

45 CALIBER (.451)

200 grain HP, #4477 .... $6.70

225 grain Magnum HP, #4479 ..... 6.75

Lead Pistol Bullets
(Packed 100 Per Box)

9mm CALIBER (.356)

125 grain RN, #4601 .... $4.05

38 CALIBER (.358)

148 grain BBWC, #4605 .... $3.70

148 grain HBWC, #4617 .... 3.80

158 grain Semi-Wadcutter, #4623 .... 4.05

158 grain Round Nose, #4647 .... 4.05

44 CALIBER (.430)

240 grain SWC, #4660 .... $5.75

---

45 CALIBER (.452)

200 grain SWC, #4677 .... $4.80

230 grain Round Nose, #4690 .... 5.65

250 grain SWC, #4683 .... 5.75

22 CALIBER (.223)

40 grain Spire Point #1005 ..... $4.25 | 45 grain Spitzer #1011 ..... 4.25

22 CALIBER (.224)

40 grain Spire Point #1017 ..... $4.25 | 45 grain Spitzer #1023 ..... 4.25

50 grain Spitzer, #1029 .... 4.40

52 grain Hollow Point, #1035 .... 5.10

52 grain GOLD MATCH, #1039 .... 7.30

55 grain Full Metal Jacket, #1045 .... 4.80

55 grain Spitzer, #1047 .... 4.45

70 grain Semi-Spitzer, #1053 ..... 5.40

22 CALIBER (.228)

70 grain Semi-Spitzer, #1057 ..... $5.40

6mm CALIBER (.243)

75 grain Hollow Point, #1205 .... $5.60

80 grain Spitzer, #1211 .... 5.65

90 grain Full Metal Jacket, #1215 ...... 6.25

90 grain Spitzer, #1217 .... 5.90

HOT-COR BULLETS

SPEER HANDGUN AMMO & BULLETS

105 grain Round Nose, #1223 6.25

105 grain Spitzer, #1229 6.25

25 CALIBER (.257)

60 grain Spire Point, #1235 $5.40

87 grain Spitzer, #1241 5.90

100 grain Hollow Point, #1407 6.25

100 grain Spitzer, #1405 6.25

120 grain Spitzer, #1411 6.50

6.5mm CALIBER (.263)

87 grain Hollow Point, #1417 $5.90

87 grain Spitzer, #1423 5.90

100 grain Hollow Point, #1429 6.25

120 grain Spitzer, #1435 6.55

140 grain Spitzer, #1441 7.10

270 CALIBER (.277)

100 grain Hollow Point, #1447 $6.50

100 grain Spitzer, #1453 6.50

130 grain Spitzer, #1459 7.10

150 grain Spitzer, #1605 7.35

---

170 grain Round Nose, #1611 7.95

7mm CALIBER (.284)

115 grain Hollow Point, #1617 $6.50

130 grain Spitzer, #1623 6.75

145 grain Spitzer, #1629 7.10

160 grain Spitzer, #1635 7.60

160 grain Magnum MAG-TIP, #1637 8.45

175 grain Magnum MAG-TIP, #1641 8.80

30 CALIBER (.308)

100 grain PLINKER, #1805 $4.20

110 grain HP VARMINTER, #1835 4.80

110 grain Round Nose, #1845 5.40

110 grain Spire Point, #1855 6.25

130 grain Hollow Point, #2005 6.75

150 grain Flat Nose, #2011 7.20

150 grain Round Nose, #2017 7.20

---

150 grain Spitzer, #2023 7.20

150 grain Magnum MAG-TIP, #2025 7.95

165 grain Round Nose, #2029 7.25

165 grain Spitzer, #2035 7.25

170 grain Flat Nose, #2041 7.35

170 grain

180 grain Round Nose, #2047 7.45

180 grain Spitzer, #2053 7.45

180 grain Magnum MAG-TIP, #2059 8.95

185 grain
Step-Boattail Match, #2055 14.15

200 grain Round Nose, #2205 7.95

200 grain Spitzer, #2211 7.95

30 CALIBER (.309)

170 grain
Step-Boattail Match, #2049 $14.15

185 grain
Step-Boattail Match, #2061 14.15

SPEER RIFLE BULLETS

303 CALIBER (.311)

150 grain Spitzer, #2217 $7.20

180 grain Round Nose, #2223   7.45

7.65mm CALIBER (.313)

175 grain Round Nose, #2241 $7.60

32 CALIBER (.321)

170 grain Flat Nose, #2259 $7.35

8mm CALIBER (.323)

125 grain Spire Point, #2271 $6.75

150 grain Spitzer, #2277   7.25

170 grain Semi-Spitzer, #2283   7.35

225 grain Round Nose, #2287   9.60

338 CALIBER (.338)

200 grain Spitzer, #2405 $8.20

275 grain Semi-Spitzer, #2411   10.20

35 CALIBER (.358)

180 grain Flat Nose, #2435 $8.05

---

220 grain Flat Nose, #2441   8.80

250 grain Round Nose, #2447   9.30

250 grain Spitzer, #2453   9.30

9.3mm CALIBER (.366)

250 grain Spitzer, #2460 $9.90

375 CALIBER (.375)

235 grain Semi-Spitzer, #2471 $9.30

45 CALIBER (.458)

400 grain Flat Nose, #2479 $11.20

LAWMAN SERIES

Marshal
9mm Luger, 100 JHP, Brass #3610 $10.55
MV*-1315 Ft/Sec., ME-384   Ft. Lbs.

M-P
9mm Luger, 125 JSP, Brass #3620   10.55
MV*-1120 Ft/Sec., ME-348   Ft. Lbs.

Special Agent
38 Special, 110 JHP, Nickel #3710   9.95
MV*-1245 Ft/Sec., ME-378   Ft. Lbs.

Detective
38 Special, 125 JHP, Nickel +P #3720   9.95
MV*-1425 Ft/Sec., ME-563   Ft. Lbs.

Patrolman
38 Special, 125 JSP, Nickel +P #3725   9.95
MV*-1425 Ft/Sec., ME-563   Ft. Lbs.

Deputy
38 Special, 140 JHP, Nickel +P #3740   9.95
MV*-1200 Ft/Sec., ME-447   Ft. Lbs.

Match
38 Special, 148 HBWC, Brass #3748   8.35
MV*-825   Ft/Sec., ME-223   Ft. Lbs.

Service
38 Special, 158 SWC, Nickel #3752   8.25
MV*-975   Ft/Sec., ME-333   Ft. Lbs.

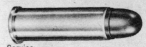

Service
38 Special, 158 RN, Nickel #3758   8.25
MV*-975   Ft/Sec., ME-333   Ft. Lbs.

Trooper
38 Special, 158 JSP, Nickel +P #3759   9.95
MV*-1025 Ft/Sec., ME-368   Ft. Lbs.

Service
38 Special, 200 RN, Nickel #3790   8.65
MV*-850   Ft/Sec., ME-320   Ft. Lbs.

38/357 Shotshell, Nickel #3708
#9 shot (box of 50)   11.80
38/357 Shotshell, Nickel #3709
#9 shot (box of 6)   1.80
MV*-1150 Ft/Sec., ME-308 Ft. Lbs. (total)

Special Agent
357 Magnum, 110 JHP, Nickel #3910   11.15
MV*-1700 Ft/Sec., ME-705   Ft. Lbs.

Detective
357 Magnum, 125 JHP, Nickel #3920   11.15
MV*-1900 Ft/Sec., ME-1001 Ft. Lbs.

SPEER RIFLE BULLETS

Patrolman
357 Magnum, 125 JSP, Nickel #3925   11.15
MV*-1900 Ft/Sec., ME-1001 Ft. Lbs.

Deputy
357 Magnum, 140 JHP, Nickel #3940   11.15
MV*-1780 Ft/Sec., ME-984 Ft. Lbs.

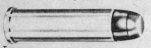

Trooper
357 Magnum, 158 JSP, Nickel #3959   11.15
MV*-1625 Ft/Sec., ME-926 Ft. Lbs.

Sheriff
44 Magnum, 200 JHP, Brass, #3972 box of 25 7.15
MV*-1675 Ft/Sec., ME-1246 Ft. Lbs.

Sheriff
44 Magnum, 240 JSP, Brass, #3974 box of 25 7.15
MV*-1650 Ft/Sec., ME-1450 Ft. Lbs.

44 Magnum Shotshell, Brass, #3978
#9 shot (box of 25) $8.75
44 Magnum Shotshell, Brass, #3979
#9 shot (box of 6) $2.35
MV*-1200 Ft/Sec., ME-494 Ft. Lbs. (total)

Inspector 45 Auto, 200 JHP, Brass #3965
MV*-1025 Ft/Sec., ME-466 Ft. Lbs.   6.00

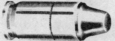

Match 45 Auto, 200 SWC, Brass #3969   5.65
MV*-750 Ft/Sec., ME-248 Ft. Lbs.

Above packed 50 per box except where noted.

BICENTENNIAL BULLET BOARD

The United States' Bicentennial (1975-1976) is celebrated on the current Speer bullet display board with a painting by artist Jack Woodson. Since the Colonial Army's marksmanship had a certain bearing on this country's independence, the theme is not only appropriate but it makes the board a valid collector's piece, suitable for hanging in the home. **$16.75**

NEW SPEER SHOTSHELL
. . . for 38 Special, 357 and 44 magnum

The new Speer 38/357 or 44 Shotshell produces a consistent, even shot pattern...deadly on snakes . . . outstanding for controlling rodents, pests and small varmints. A special-formula plastic capsule holds the #9 shot and protects the barrel. Add a new dimension to your handgun on your next hunting, fishing, hiking or camping trip! (Great for home protection.)

SPEER

Plastic Boxes

All SPEER handgun ammunition and bullets are packed in durable, moisture-proof reusable boxes, to prevent tarnishing. Ideal for hunting and back-packing.

SPEER-LAPUA

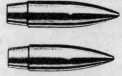

a unique concept in 30 caliber match bullet design

World match winner. Superior external ballistics at ranges from 100 to 1,000 yards. Available in .308" or .309" diameters in 170 and 185 grain weights. .309 preferred for best accuracy in most rifles.

Shot Capsules

Plastic shot capsules (2-piece) for 38 Special, 357 and 44 Magnum reloading. #9 shot recommended. Packed 50 sets to a box.

Box 38 Special
. . . . $2.22
Box 44 Magnum
. . . . $2.75

Sub-velocity Ammunition
with *reusable* plastic case and bullet

Originally developed for the Air Force . . . extensively used by law enforcement agencies . . . enjoyed by thousands of handgun shooters for inexpensive training and fun. No powder required (primer does the job—we recommend CCI 350 Mag. primer). No tools needed for reloading. Use over and over!

	50 Bullets	50 Cases
Target 38®	$2.00	$2.00
Target 44®	2.25	2.25
Target 45®	2.25*	—

*(for use in standard ACP metal cases)

BALLISTIC CALCULATOR

Now you can compute bullet drop and remaining velocity, from 100 to 1,000 yards. Combine this calculator with the Speer Manual and you'll have all you need for top performing reloads. Easy to use, and only **$2.95**

BULLET JACKETS:

30 & 38 Cal., ½-jackets $20.35/M
44 & 45 Cal., ½-jackets 23.80/M
38 Cal., ¾-jackets 27.20/M
41 & 44 Cal., ¾-jackets 32.85/M

LEAD WIRE
10 lb Box*
.250 (30 Cal.) $8.35
.300 (38 Cal.) 8.35
.365 (44 & 45 Cal.) 8.35
*Packed in 12-inch lengths

BAIR RELOADING TOOLS

HONEY BAIR

The Honey Bair is the newest addition to the Bair line of shotshell reloaders. The Honey Bair features compact large capacity hoppers with built in shut off, crimp-easy crimp die requiring 30% less crimping pressure, built in primer catcher, maximum leverage for ease of operation and precision alignment. Interchangeable charge bar bushings, die sets and powder and shot hoppers make changing gauges or loads quick and easy. Paper or plastic cases may be loaded without die change.

405-110 Honey Bair Loader Complete—
For 12M, 12, 20M or 20 gauge **$100.00**
For 16, 28, 410M or 410 gauge **$105.00**

405-2 Conversion kit—12M, 12, 20M or 20 gauge. **$30.00**
16, 28, 410M or 410 gauge **$35.00**

HONEY BAIR WITH AUTOMATIC PRIMER FEED

All New Automatic Priming System. Primer is transferred from tubular magazine to primer seating base automatically. No handling of primer or extra movements required. Includes 308-000 primer tube filler as standard equipment.

405-210 Honey Bair Reloader as described above with Automatic Primer Feed and primer tube filler. 12M, 12, 20M, or 20 gauge . **$113.00**
16, 28, 410M or 410 gauge **$118.00**

405-200 Kit to convert 405-110 to Automatic Primer Feed **$19.50**

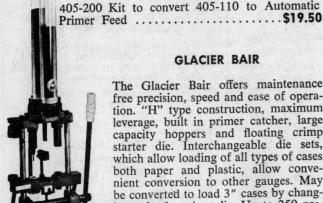

GLACIER BAIR

The Glacier Bair offers maintenance free precision, speed and ease of operation. "H" type construction, maximum leverage, built in primer catcher, large capacity hoppers and floating crimp starter die. Interchangeable die sets, which allow loading of all types of cases both paper and plastic, allow convenient conversion to other gauges. May be converted to load 3" cases by changing only the crimp die. Up to 250 precision reloads per hour.

500-110 Glacier Bair Loader Complete—
12M, 12, 20M, or 20 gauge **$139.50**
6, 28, 410M or 410 gauge **$144.90**

500-1 Conversion kit for
12M, 12, 20M or 20 gauge **$32.00**
16, 28, 410M or 410 gauge **$37.00**

BROWN BAIR III

The Brown Bair III "H" type press offers speed and convenience. Three station design allows loading of either pistol or rifle cartridges without die change. Special built in automatic priming system which includes both large and small tubes, feeds primers and operates primer arm without additional effort or attention of operator. Primer seating depth is completely adjustable. Exceptional leverage and strength allow for swift, easy performance of all reloading operations.

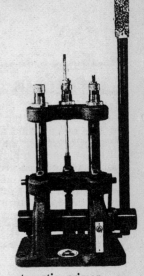

#160-100 Brown Bair III, with automatic primer feeding system **$139.90**
#160-110 Brown Bair III, with automatic primer feeding system, set of Bair Cub precision engineered dies and shell holders **$169.90**

POLAR BAIR

The Polar Bair features reloading at a popular price. Compare the features offered by the Polar Bair. Each pull of the lever produces a completed, factory like reload, up to 600 per hour. Built in provision for complete case resizing including head and rim. New "Crimp-easy" crimp die that requires 30% less effort for crimping. New swing away wad guide greatly speeds operation. Floating, self aligning crimp starter die. Positive cam actuated charge bar. Interchangeable charge bar bushings and die sets for all popular gauges except .410. Includes automatic primer feed and primer tube filler.

600-210 Polar Bair Loader Complete—
For 12 or 20 gauge **$224.90**
For 16 or 28 gauge **$229.90**
600-2 Conversion kit for 12 or 20 gauge **$48.90**
For 16 or 28 gauge **$53.90**
Kits do not include brushings.

BLACK BAIR

This Bair has found a home on many reloading benches across the country by introducing sportsmen to the economy and enjoyment of Metallic Shell Reloading.
Reduces shooting costs 60 per cent.
• Heavy annealed cast-iron frame. •
Accepts standard dies—7 x 14 thread and interchangeable shell-holder heads.
• Fully automatic primer feed optional.
Black Bair **$44.90**

BAIR RELOADING TOOLS

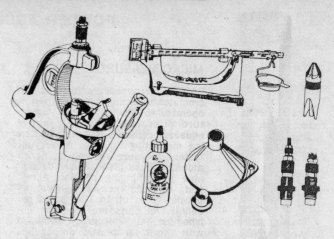

GRIZZLY BAIR

The Grizzly Bair "C" Press combines strength, quality and ease of operation for all reloading operations including bullet swaging. Precision alignment, hardened and ground pins, universal primer arm and ram that is designed to accept interchangeable shell holder heads assure you of the very most for your money. Standard ⅞ x 14 thread accepts Bair cub and similar size die sets.

130-100 Grizzly Bair C Press with ram and primer arm $49.90
322-000 Primer catcher .... $ 3.00
130-110 Grizzly Bair C Press, removable shell holder head, primer arm and one set of precision dies. Everything to load one caliber $69.90
130-013 Universal C-Press Ram, for removable shell holder head. .... $ 7.00
310-000 Removable shell holder head. .... $ 3.00

SPORTSMAN SPECIAL

A complete kit of matched precision tools and accessories. Obtain additional savings by purchasing the complete kit. Consists of: Grizzly Bair "C" Micro Measure, Magna Damp Scale, Primer Catcher, Case Lubricant, Shell Holder Head, Chamfer and Deburring Tool, Set of Bair Cub Dies.

130-200 Sportsman Special $144.90

BAIR CUB DIE SETS
(3 Die Pistol Set, 2 Die Rifle Set)

Bair Cub metallic cartridge reloading dies are made in over 80 popular rifle and pistol calibers. All Bair Cub dies are reamed and honed to minimum SAAMI standards, hardened by a special carbon nitrate process then polished to ultra smooth finish. Die bodies receive a special chrome plating to eliminate rust and corrosion, other parts are finished using Bair Company's special gun blue finish. All rifle caliber seating dies have adjustable crimper, pistol caliber seating dies have built in crimper. Every Bair Cub Set is packaged in a durable plastic storage box.

223-000 2 Die Rifle Set .... $ 18.00
224-000 3 Die Rifle Set .... $ 28.50
    Includes Neck Sizes. Full Length Size and Seater Dies
210-000 Full Length Size Die Only .. $ 9.00
230-00 Neck Size Die Only .... $ 10.50
220-000 Seating Die Only .... $ 8.00
240-000 File Type Trim Die .... $ 9.50
256-000 3 Die Pistol Set .... $ 18.00
250-000 Pistol Size Die Only ...... $ 7.00
260-000 Pistol Expander Die Only .. $ 7.00
270-000 Pistol Seating Die Only ... $ 7.00
210-101 Plastic Die Box
    (for 2 or 3 Die Set) Only .... $ 1.00

HUNTER'S SPECIAL

Save money with this economical Kit of Bair essentials with everything needed for you to start reloading your favorite rifle or pistol ammunition. Included is the Black Bair "C" Press and primer arm, set of Bair Cub dies, magna Damp Powder Scale, Shell holder head, camfer and deburring tool, case lubricant, Speer reloading manual and powder funnel. $97.90

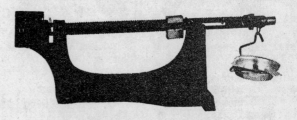

MAGNA DAMP SCALE

The Bair Magna Damp Scale is designed to quickly bring under control unwanted oscillation of scale beam. Magnetic dampening cannot impair the accuracy of the scale. Precision ground and hardened knife bearings, 500 grain capacity, three counterpoise adjustment, tenth grain over and under scale, adjustable leveling screw and clearly marked anodized scale beam.

#317-100
Magna Damp Scale $24.90

BULLET PULLER

Here is a chrome plated bullet puller to fit all basic tools. A new collet design maintains an even pressure on the bullet. It will not mar or scratch. The fast action of the collet promptly releases the bullet when tension is off. Puller comes equipped with standard ⅞ x 14 thread.

Order #320-000 Bullet Puller and Collet $12.50

BAIR RELOADING TOOLS

POWDER ACCESSORY TOOLS

MICRO-MEASURE

BAIR'S micro-measure features micrometer adjusting screw to permit operator to record settings for future reference. A built-in baffle equalizes pressure of powder entering measuring housing. A wing-nut fastens measure securely to bench mounted base plate. Easily detachable for emptying powder. Allows fast, accurate measurement of all powder types up to 100 grains per charge. All parts are precision finished for lifetime accuracy. Equipped with two clear plastic drop tubes (.22 - .30 caliber and .30 - .45 caliber).

#316-000 Micro-Measure   **$34.90**

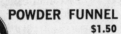

POWDER FUNNEL
$1.50

PISTOL POWDER MEASURE

The measure is fitted with a visible powder tube. Its cone shaped nozzle will accommodate all case sizes. Wing nut fastens the measure securely to bench mounted base plate. Detached easily for removing powder. Equipped with fixed charge rotor.

#315-000 Pistol Measure
(With rotor, state charge)

$17.90

#315-200 Extra Rotor (state powder drop desired)   **$4.00**

Bair Pistol Powder Measure Rotors are available in the following charges: Bullseye: 2, 2.5, 2.7, 3, 3.5, 4, 4.5, and 5 grain

Unique: 6, 8, and 10 grain   2400: 12, 14 and 16 grain.

Blank rotors are available for those who wish to make up rotors for other charges.

CASE TRIMMER

Completely adjustable for all cartridge lengths, the BAIR case trimmer uses a regular shell holder head instead of collets to provide added versatility for removable shell head holder users. Shells are clamped firmly in place and perfectly aligned for safe precision trimming. It may be easily mounted on work bench, or clamped in a vise. The fastest hand trimmer available, this BAIR can easily be converted to power trimming simply by loosening one set screw. The handle may be removed and any ¼" drill quickly attached. The drill requires no special stand or attachment. There is no added cost for the versatility of trimming large quantities of shells.

#313-000 BAIR case trimmer with pilot.   **$29.90**
#313-100 Extra case trimmer pilots   **$1.30**

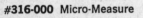

CHAMFERING & DEBURRING TOOL

This BAIR tool will chamfer and deburr the mouth of new or trimmed cartridge cases without chattering. It leaves a smooth, even edge when used by hand.

#311-000 Chamfering and Deburring Tool.   **$5.50**

FILE TYPE TRIMMER & CASE FORMER

Made of hardened steel, this BAIR trimmer uses a fine grade file for fast, accurate trimming. (Refer to page 6 for caliber listings.)

#240-000 File Type Trimmer and Case Former.   **$9.50**

PRIMER POCKET REAMER

Reamer may be used by hand to quickly remove crimp from primer pocket to accommodate seating of new primer. Available for large or small primer pockets.

#312-000 Primer Pocket Reamer (small).   **$4.50**
#312-100 Primer Pocket Reamer (large).   **$4.50**

BONANZA RELOADING TOOLS

CO-AX PRESS

MODEL 68 PRESS

CO-AX PRESS
Snap-in and snap-out die change, positive spent primer catcher, automatic self-acting shell holder, floating guide rods, perfect alignment of die and case is assured, good for right- or left-handed operators, uses standard 7⁄8 x 14 dies.

MODEL 68 PRESS
No obstructions to visibility of operator, open working space, upright mounting, equal thrust distribution, simple in construction, heavy duty, constructed of automotive-type casting, ram is machined and fitted.

BONANZA MODEL 68 PRESS $37.50
BONANZA CO-AX PRESS (B-1) less dies 74.95
BONANZA CO-AX PRESS & Co-Ax dies 85.45
BONANZA CO-AX PRESS BENCH REST dies . . 86.45
EXTRA SET JAWS for Co-Ax . . . . set 10.00

PISTOL DIES

CO-AX RIFLE DIES

BONANZA PISTOL DIES are three-die sets. **The .38 Spl. & .357 Mag., and the .44 Spl. & .44 Mag. are so designed that each set may be used to load the two calibers.** You need not buy extra dies to load the magnums. The Bonanza Cross Bolt Lock Ring is standard on all Bonanza Dies. A special taper crimp die is available for .45 ACP and 38-357.
Bonanza Three-Die Pistol Set $16.50
Bonanza Taper Crimp Die 8.25
All Bonanza Dies are made with 7⁄8 x 14 threads and

can be used on various other makes of presses. The CO-AX SEATER can be adjusted to crimp or not to crimp. All calibers crimp except .22 caliber. The Sizer, with **elevated expander button,** is the same as is supplied with the Bench Rest Dies. This "E-Z" OUT expander button is drawn through the case neck while the operator uses the full mechanical advantage of the press.
Bonanza CO-AX Die Set $16.50
Bonanza CO-AX Seating Dies only 7.25
Bonanza CO-AX Sizing Die only 10.50

BONANZA RELOADING TOOLS

CO-AX INDICATOR

Gives a reading of how closely the axis of the bullet corresponds with the axis of the cartridge case. Spring-loaded plunger holds against cartridges **a recessed, adjustable rod** supported in a "V" block.

BONANZA CO-AX INDICATOR, less Indicator Dial $11.95

Indicator Dial only $19.50

CASE TRIMMER

Neck case pilot eliminates the need for a collet and shell holder. Reversible mandrell and four-blade case-mouth trimmer. Dull cutter is exchanged for a sharpened cutter.

BONANZA CASE TRIMMER, complete with Pilot
(state caliber) $14.00
extra Pilots (state caliber) .... .50
extra Cutter 2.50
Cutter Sharpening "Exchange" 1.00

BONANZA POWDER MEASURES

PISTOL POWDER MEASURE

BENCH REST POWDER MEASURE

BONANZA BULLS-EYE PISTOL POWDER MEASURE

Powder is metered from the charge arm.
Measure will throw uniform charges from 2½-grains bullseye to 95-grains 4320.
Measure empties by removing charge bar from charge arm, letting contents flow through charge arm into powder container.
Bonanza Pistol Powder Measure and One Rotor . . **$17.50**
Extra Rotor or Blank Rotor 3.25

BONANZA BENCH REST POWDER MEASURE

Measure has fixed-charge rotor. Supplied with a quick detachable bracket for use on a bench, or it can be held by hand.
BBRPM BONANZA BENCH REST POWDER MEASURE $25.50

BONANZA RELOADING TOOLS

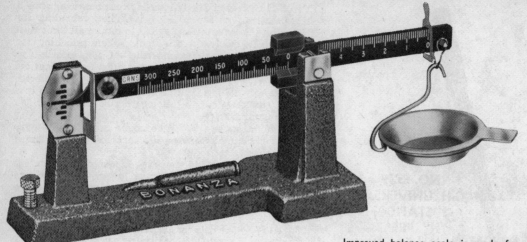

BONANZA POWDER AND BULLET SCALE MODEL "C"

Improved balance scale is made from "Marlon-Lexon," an inert, non-magnetic material. Allows greater sensitivity, precision alignment and bearing, eliminates static electricity, accuracy guaranteed to 1/10 grain.

Bonanza Powder and Bullet Scale Model "C" **$15.95**

BONANZA "M" MAGNETIC DAMPENED SCALE

505 grain capacity, tempered stainless steel right hand poise, diamond polished agate "V" bearings, non-glare white markings, three point suspension base, strengthened beam at pivot points, powder pan for right or left pouring, guaranteed accurate to 1/10 grain.

Bonanza "M" Magnetic Dampened Scale **$21.50**

BONANZA CO-AX PRIMER SEATER

The Bonanza Primer Seater is designed so that primers are seated Co-Axially (primer in line with primer pocket). Mechanical leverage allows primers to be seated fully without crushing. With the addition of one extra set of Disc Shell Holders and one extra Primer Unit, all modern cases, rim or rimless, from .222 up to .458 Magnum can be primed. Shell Holders are easily adjusted to any case by rotating to contact rim or cannelure of the case.

Bonanza Primer Seater **$22.95**
Primer Tube . . . .**$ 1.75**

C-H RELOADING TOOLS

**NO. 333
C-H UNIVERSAL
3 STATION
"H" PRESS**

The C-H Universal is a unique H press because it has **3** stations, instead of the usual two. When reloading for pistol, using a 3-die set it is possible to mount all three dies simultaneously easily, in this tool. When reloading for rifle, with conventional two-die rifle set, it is possible to mount the C-H powder measure in the third (open) station.

This is a heavy duty production press designed for speedy, easy reloading. The manufacturer claims that it is possible, with this tool to full length size three cartridge cases simultaneously.

All components are precision made from heavy duty tool steel. Except for the bearing surfaces, exterior finish is black crinkle.

The main drive bar—to which is connected the operating lever—is equipped with two power levers which activate the moving shell holder base. More than adequate leverage and power is provided by this system.

No. 333 PRESS—Complete for one caliber (rifle).
No. 333 Press w/3 Rams and 3 shell holders and one
   Primer Arm $69.50
No. 408 Shell Holder Head (2 @ 2.50).................. 5.00
No. 407 Shell Holder Ram (2 @ 2.50).................. 5.00
No. 413 Primer Arm. Large or Small 2.00
No. 333 Press complete for one caliber (pistol) 81.50

ACCESSORIES FOR C-H UNIVERSAL 3-STATION "H" PRESS:
No. 501-1 C-H Powder (Stand only) $3.50
No. 501-2 C-H Powder Insert (for mounting on No. 333 Press) 2.50
No. 402 C-H Bullet Puller complete w/one collet.......... 4.95

**NO. 204
C-H CAST IRON
"C" PRESS**
Up and Down Stroke

**FITS ALL STANDARD
AND UNIVERSAL SHELL
HOLDERS, SHELL HOLDER
RAMS AND PRIMING ARMS**

Press, with handle, toggle, Universal shell holder ram, one shell holder, Universal priming arm and full sized bottle of C-H lube $37.50
Complete with one set of dies (⅞"x14) $49.50

**AUTO-
CHAMPION**

PRESENTLY AVAILABLE FOR 38 SPECIAL AND 357 MAGNUM (ACCESSORY PARTS FOR 9MM AND 45 ACP IN THE NEAR FUTURE).

PRICE COMPLETE

$429.50

Includes 38 Special and 357 Magnum die set, 1 primer tube, 2 case tubes.)

• Truly progressive Loading • Complete! No extras to buy • One completed round with each pull of the handle. Our timed tests show we can load a box of 50 in less than 3 minutes • Case feeder and Automatic Positive Indexing at no extra cost • Uses Standard ⅞" sizing and seating Dies (Bell-Expanding Die altered to allow powder to drop) • Tungsten Carbide Sizing die at no extra cost! • Fixed powder bars. Absolutely no mistakes! • Automatic indexing makes double powder charge impossible • Seating stems for any type of bullet • Exclusive "Speed Seater" die included!

C-H RELOADING TOOLS

C-H TRIM DIES

By using these C-H Trim Dies you can shorten the neck of your cases with a file or a fine-tooth hacksaw. Dies are hardened and will not be effected by the filing. Available in the following calibers: 222 Rem., 22-250, 225 Win., 243 Win., 6mm R, 257 Robts., 25-06, 257 Wea., 6.5x55, 270 Win., 7x57 Mauser, 7mm Rem. Mag., 7mm Wea., 308 Win., 30-06, 300 Win. Mag., 300 Wea., 8x57.

File Trim Die **$7.50**

3-Die Sets

SIZE - NECK - SEAT

For the reloader who wants to both full-length size and neck size his brass, the C-H 3-die set contains a full-length sizer, neck sizer (body and ring) and seater. Dies are the regular high-quality mirror finish inside and specially treated outside.

Available in the following calibers: 222 Rem., 22-250 Rem., 6mm Rem., 243 Win., 25-06 Rem., 270 Win., 7mm Rem. Mag., 30-06, 303 Win., 300 Win. Mag., 300 Wea. Mag.

C-H 3-piece Rifle Die Set,
   complete **$19.95**

C-H TUNGSTEN CARBIDE EXPANDER BALLS

Now available as an accessory, the C-H Tungsten Carbide Expander Ball eliminates the need for lubricating the inside of the case neck.

Available in the following calibers: 22, 243, 25, 270, 7mm, 30, 320, 322. Calibers 7mm and larger have 10-32 inside threads, 243 to 270 have 8-32 inside threads, and 22 has 6-32 inside threads.

C-H Carbide Expander Ball . . **$5.50**
For the RCBS 22 expander unit we can provide a complete rod with carbide expander that will fit their die body.

C-H Carbide Expander Ball to fit . . . .
   22 cal. RCBS die **$6.50**

C-H HEAVYWEIGHT C-HAMPION PRESS

Compound leverage press for all phases of re-loading. Heavyweight (26#) C-Hampion comes complete with primer arm, ⅞x14 bushing for use with all reloading dies. Spent primers fall through back of press into waste basket. 'O' frame design will not spring under any conditions. Ideal press for swaging bullets. Top of frame bored 1¼x18 for use with special dies and shot-shell dies.

$89.50

C-H RELOADING DIES

Each die is precision honed and lapped and polished to a mirror finish inside. Outside has a satin finish. Standard ⅞ x 14 fits all standard loading tools.

2 pc. Rifle Die sets $15.00
3 pc. Pistol Die sets $15.00

Decapping Pins, specify caliber
   (std. or heavy duty) . . . . pkg. of 5 50
Quick-Loc Die Rings . . . . . . per set 95
Plastic Die Boxes 75

PISTOL CHAMP

333-X PISTOL CHAMP with all accessories and one steel sizing die—your choice from calibers shown above **$114.00**
333-X PISTOL CHAMP with all accessories as above, but with carbide sizing die (38 and 357) **123.00**
Extra Powder Bushing **$2.40**
Extra Priming Arm **2.00**
Conversion set of dies (with steel sizing die) **35.90**
Conversion set of dies (with carbide sizing die) 38 Spl. **47.40**

Conversion kit includes priming post, sizing die, powder bushing, expander die, speed seater die, and 3 shell holders.

C-H RELOADING TOOLS

CHAMPION Jr. RELOADING PRESS

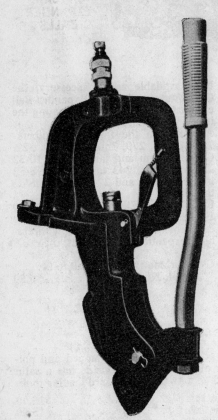

CHAMPION Jr. Heavy Duty Reloading Press—semi steel (cast iron) "0" press offset so the opening is 210 degrees for better access. Solid steel handle is offset to match opening.

Positioning of toggle pin provides maximum leverage—so powerful that a 30/06 case can be forced into a 250 full length resizing die. In addition to usual 2 bolt fastening we put a 3rd bolt so the "big" jobs using maximum power won't break off your bench.

Weight 13½ lbs.

Uses standard detachable shell holders.

Price complete w/primer arm and 1 shell holder $44.50

Price complete with 1 die set $56.50

C-H DIE BOX

Protect your dies from dust and damage with a C-H 3-compartment plastic Die Box. High-impact plastic—will not break. Easy to label and stack.
No. 700 C-H Die Box ....75¢

BULLET SWAGING DIE EJECTOR

A useful accessory for use with the new C-H jacketed bullet swaging dies.

The ejector attaches easily to the swaging die body with one screw. Can be used with either the core seating die or the swage die. Ejects the seated core or finished bullet with ease. No more tapping the top of the die.

Price $9.95

FROM C-H 3/4 JACKETED PISTOL BULLET SWAGING DIES

- Any bullet weight from 110 gr. to 250 gr. with same set of dies
- Can be used in any good ⅞ x 14 loading tool
- Absolutely no leading
- Complete — no extras to buy
- Increased velocity
- Solid Nose or hollow point (hollow point $2.50 extra)
- Available in 38/357, 41 S & W 44 Mag. and 45 colt calibers

PRICE
$29.95

FROM C-H NEW - SOLID STEEL CANNELURE TOOL

PRICE
$16.95

- Will work on all sizes of bullets, from .17 to .45
- Completely adjustable for depth and height
- One set will process thousands of bullets
- Necessary for rolling in grooves on bullets prior to crimping
- Hardened cutting wheel, precision machined throughout. A top line product.

C-H RELOADING ACCESSORIES

NO. 725 POWDER and BULLET SCALE

Chrome plated, brass beam. Graduated in 10 gr., 1 gr., and 1/10th gr. increments. Convenient pouring spout on pan. Leveling screw on base. All metal construction. 360 gr. capacity.

Price $15.95

C-H PRIMER CATCHER FOR C-H "C" PRESSES

Features wide rim with deep cavity for holding primers. Attaches easily.

No. 201-1 C-H Universal Primer Catcher for Universal "C" Press **$3.00**
No. 202-1 Catcher for Standard "C" Press **3.00**
No. 204-1 Catcher for cast iron press **3.00**
No. 206-1 Catcher for "T.O." press **3.50**

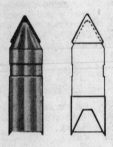

C-H INSIDE-OUTSIDE TUNGSTEN CARBIDE DEBURRING TOOL

Lifetime use on any material and for any purpose. Quickly and easily removes sharp edges and burrs after trimming metallic 22 to 45 caliber cases.

No. 425-TC **$4.95**

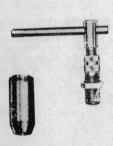

C-H BULLET PULLER

C-H Bullet Puller features positive die-locking action, removes the bullet easily without any damage to housing or bullet. The detachable handle is constructed of 3/8" stock and adjusts to any position. The hex nut for crescent wrench adjustment locks the die into firm position. Extra long internal thread for extra locking leeway.

No. 402 with Collet . .**$4.95**
No. 402-1 Extra Collet **1.50**
No. 402-2 Puller less collet **3.45**

C-H CARTRIDGE RACK TRAY

Holds 60 cartridges. Comes in black, white or red. It is handy for the reloader who works up cases for different loads, etc. Holes are 15/16" deep which is too deep for 38 Spl. Holes are not large enough for 45/70 or 348 but hold all sizes up to 375 H&H.

No. 403 Cartridge Rack Tray . . . . .95¢

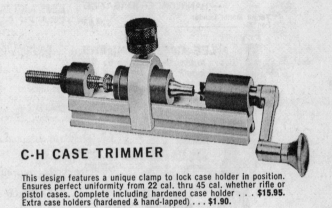

C-H CASE TRIMMER

This design features a unique clamp to lock case holder in position. Ensures perfect uniformity from 22 cal. thru 45 cal. whether rifle or pistol cases. Complete including hardened case holder . . . **$15.95**
Extra case holders (hardened & hand-lapped) . . . **$1.90**

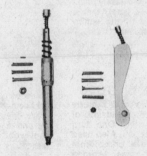

C-H UNIVERSAL PRIMING ARMS

Accommodates all standard rifle and pistol primers. Made of fine metal—not a stamping, for extra strength and dimensional stability. Packaged in clear acetate tube.

No. 413 C-H Universal "H" Priming Arm . .**$4.00**
No. 414 C-H Universal "C" Priming Arm . . **3.00**

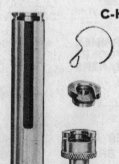

C-H UNIVERSAL SHELL HOLDERS

Up to now, shell holders came in one piece and you had to have as many shell holders as the calibers you wished to reload. However, with the C-H Universal Shell Holder all the reloader needs is the Shell Holder ram and then get the heads for the calibers desired.

No. 408 C-H Universal "C" or "H" Shell Holder Head **$2.50**
No. 407 C-H Universal "H" Shell Holder Ram **2.50**
No. 412 C-H Universal "C" Shell Holder Ram **3.50**

LEE TARGET MODEL LOADER

"The features employed in the Lee Target Model Loader reflect, and are consistent with, the best and most current thinking and practice in the field of loading ultra-fine ammo."

— HANDLOADER MAGAZINE

Target Model Loader
Per Kit $28.98

LEE CASE TRIMMERS

Automatically squares the mouth while trimming the case to the proper length. A couple of light turns is all it takes. Eliminates danger of excessively long cases.

Cutter & Lock Stud — Fits all calibers $1.48
Pilot and Holder — Order pilot by caliber and proper holder is included $1.98

LEE PRIMING TOOL

All metal construction, designed for a lifetime of service. This handsome tool accurately and safely seats primer with a "feel" that is appreciated by the experienced reloader.

Priming Tool, each $2.98
Shell Holder, each $1.80

LEE CHAMFER TOOL

Chamfers and deburrs inside and outside of case necks. One turn does the job. Also used to remove crimp from primer pockets of G.I. brass. Nitrided steel stays sharp. Self-protected safety edges won't chip. Fits all calibers.

Each $1.48

LEE PRIMER POCKET CLEANERS

Just a light twist does the job.

Each .... $ .49*

LEE DECAPPER AND BASE FOR G.I. BRASS

Easily removes crimped-in primers. Guaranteed unbreakable. Free replacement if it breaks — simply return to factory.

Each $2.45*

LEE LOADER FOR RIFLE & PISTOL

Complete, ready to use, nothing more to buy. Powder measure is preset to give the correct charge without expensive scales. Unbreakable decapping pin, accurate neck resizer, primer is totally enclosed when seated for safety, top bullet loading.
Per Kit $10.98

LEE AUTOMATIC PRIMER POCKET CLEANER

The fastest and easiest way to scrape the residue from primer pocket without damaging pocket or flash hole. One quick push does the job — works like a Yankee Screw Driver.

Only $1.98

LEE POWDER MEASURE KIT

13 powder measures, slide chart in a neat box. 69 different powders are listed; over 897 loads.
Per Kit $3.98

LEE CASE SPINNER

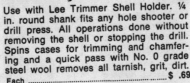

Use with Lee Trimmer Shell Holder. ¼ in. round shank fits any hole shooter or drill press. All operations done without removing the shell or stopping the drill. Spins cases for trimming and chamfering and a quick pass with No. 0 grade steel wool removes all tarnish, grit, dirt.
Each .... $ .69

LEE CASE SPINNER KIT

Includes Spinner, above, and six shell holders for over 79 different calibers. Packed in a slide top storage box.
Case Spinner Kit $2.98

LEE PISTOL MACHINE REST

Test the accuracy of your handgun and its ammunition. Does not require heavy base for mounting.
Machine Rest and Carrier $25.00
Gun Holder $14.98

*Included with the Lee Target Model Loader at no extra cost.

LEE LOADER FOR SHOT SHELLS

Permits reloading shells anywhere — trap, field or magnum loads. Patented loader makes it possible to produce such a successful tool at a low price without sacrificing quality.

10 ga. $11.98
12, 16, 20, 28 and .410 ga. $9.98

LEE LOADER DELUXE MODEL

Includes the same fine Lee Loader that's been proven for the past 14 years. Also contains the time proven nylon crimp starter for 6 & 8 segments, a new full length wad starter and 3 shot measures. Completely ready to load plastic or paper shotshells with trap, field or magnum loads.
12-16-20 Gauge, Standard or 3" Mag. $11.98

LEE STAR CRIMPERS

For plastic shells or unfired paper tubes. Unbreakable nylon. 6 or 8 Segm'ts. 12, 16, 20 Ga.
Each .... $ .98

LEE WAD GUIDES

Easy to start wads in all types of shells. 12, 16, 20 Ga.
Each .... $ .98

LEE DELUXE WAD GUIDE

Full length wad guide with the famous Lee Wad Fingers is now available for all shotshells except 10 gauge.

Each $1.98

LEE WAD FINGERS

Replacement fingers for the Lee Deluxe Wad Guide and all presses using MEC style fingers. 12, 16, 20, 28, 410 gauge.

Per pkg. of 2 .. $ .75

LYMAN RELOADING TOOLS

FOR RIFLE OR PISTOL CARTRIDGES

The 310 Tool is a compact, portable reloading kit that can be used anywhere—home, hunting camp, in the field, on the range. Using the 310 Tool, the novice can start reloading with a small investment. The 310 Tool performs all the operations required for reloading metallic cartridges for handguns and rifles. It removes the old primer, resizes the cartridge neck, it inserts a new primer, and seats the new bullet. A practiced reloader can load, fire, adjust and reload his charge right on the range, test firing until he determines his best load.

310 Tool Complete with one set of dies **$26.00**
310 Tool Handles Only (large or small) **$11.00**
     See caliber list (page 286) for handle size.
310 Dies (rifle or handgun)—Set consists of five pieces: Neck Resizing and Decapping Die, Priming Chamber, Neck Expanding Chamber, Bullet Seating Chamber and an Adapter Die **$15.00**

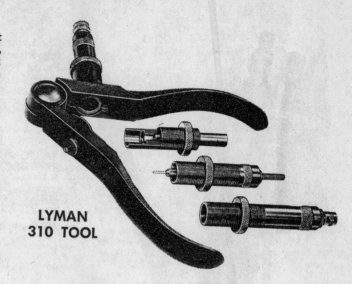

**LYMAN
310 TOOL**

LYMAN ALL-AMERICAN TURRET PRESS

The All-American Turret Press (uses standard 7⁄8" x 14 dies or Lyman Ideal Dies with 7⁄8" x 14 adapter) makes it possible to completely reload any cartridge without removing it from the shell holder. The four-station turret mounts three dies and a powder measure in reloading operation sequence. As the turret is revolved, dies remain in place, and positioned directly over the shell holder with a positive-locking, audible-click action at each of the four turret stations. The Lyman 55 Powder Measure and the push-button primer feed are optional. The press can be used in either up or down-stroke (left or right-hand) operation.

All-American Turret Press only **$84.50**
Push-Button Primer Feed (rifle & pistol only) 18.00
Shell Holder (J-type) 4.00
Priming Punch (T-type) 2.50
Shell Holder Adapter (use w/spec. T.) 3.00
"Special" Priming Punch 4.00

The first edition of the Lyman Shotshell Handgun features an authoritative study devoted exclusively to shotshell reloading—a reloading handbook which covers every aspect of modern shotshell reloading. Dealing with the latest components it is an indispensable reference book which belongs on every reloading bench. Complete "How To Reload" section on choosing a load, factory velocities, assembling shotshells, etc. Reference section covers up-to-date pressure information, four color case identification chapter, plus chapters on wads, patterns, powder and primers. Over 1000 tested loads covering all gauges 10, 12, 16, 20, 28 and 410. Contains suggested reloads using modern components from all of the major manufacturers **$4.00**

LYMAN RELOADING TOOLS
FOR RIFLE OR PISTOL CARTRIDGES

LYMAN SPAR-T TURRET PRESS

The Lyman Spar-T Press combines the maximum speed of turret loading with the operating ease, and strength of the ever popular C Frame Press. It's massive frame, and 6 station Turret, are ruggedly constructed of high-silicone, iron-steel castings (not aluminum alloy). It's Verti-Lock Turret is firmly secured to the frame by a heavy duty 3/4" steel stud. Positive stop, audible click action insures foolproof cartridge to die alignment and rapid operation. Uses standard 7/8 x 14 dies.

Features: • Lock nut rigidly locks turret in one position for swaging. • Powerful toggle-link leverage (25 to 1) • UP or DOWN STROKE operation. • Alignment ramp positions Shell Holder at top of stroke. • Uses standard Spartan accessories.

Spar-T Press only **$49.50**
Spar-T Auto Primer Feed (as shown).................**$10.00**

SPAR-T SET: Consists of Spar-T Press, Spar-T Auto-Primer Feed, Spartan Primer Arm, Spartan Shell Holder Head, Complete set of All-American Dies. **$61.50**

SPARTAN SET: Consists of Spartan Press, Spartan Ram, Spartan Shell Holder Head, Spartan Primer Arm, Complete set of All American Dies (standard 7/8" by 14). **$46.50**

LYMAN SPARTAN RELOADING PRESS

The Lyman Spartan Press is a massive, 11 lb. heavy-duty iron frame press which reloads all rifle and pistol cases quickly, accurately and easily. Its powerful toggle-link mechanism multiplies the force applied to the handle 25 times and takes the hard work out of full-length resizing and case forming, and is even rugged enough for bullet swaging.
• Uses Lyman All-American (standard 7/8" x 14) dies • Simple changeover to either up- or down-stroke • Alignment ramp positions shell holder at top of each stroke • Precision bored frame ensures perfect alignment • Maximum serviceability at extremely low cost.
Spartan Press only **$29.50**

ACCESSORIES

SPARTAN RAM: Designed for perfect alignment. Fits Lyman Spartan press. Pacific Standard, RCBS, Jr., C & H Super C. **$4.00**

SPARTAN DETACHABLE SHELL HOLDER: Precision cut and hardened to ensure perfect case fit. Used with the Spartan Ram on the Spartan Press and on many other presses. **$2.50**

SPARTAN UNIVERSAL PRIMING ARM: Seats all sizes and types of primers. Supplied with two priming sleeves (large and small) two flat priming punches (large and small), and two round priming punches (large and small). **$4.00**

SPARTAN AUTO-PRIMER FEED: Eliminates handling of primer with oily fingers, speeds loading. Supplied with two tubes (large and small). **$8.50**

No. 67, 1976 EDITION

543

LYMAN RELOADING DIES

The All-American Dies shown on this page are designed for use with the Lyman Spartan, Spar-T, AA Turret, and all other reloading presses having ⅞″ x 14″ thread die stations. AA die sets are offered in either 2 or 3 die combinations, depending on shape of cartridge case, and type of bullet to be loaded.

Outer surfaces of all dies are chrome-plated. All bullet seating dies are adjustable to crimp or not crimp the bullet. Sizing dies for bottleneck cartridges are vented to prevent air traps.

TWO-DIE RIFLE SET

These sets consist of two dies. The first die full-length resizes, decaps, and expands, while the second die seats the bullet and crimps when desired. Two die sets are specifically designed for loading bottleneck shape cartridge cases using jacketed bullets. These sets are not offered for straight-taper shape cases. They should not be used with cast bullets unless in conjunction with an "M" die (see below).

Two-die rifle set (complete with wrench) $15.00

THREE-DIE RIFLE SET

Required to load straight-taper cartridge cases, and all other cartridges when using cast bullets.

This set consists of: full-length resizing and decapping die, a 2-step neck expanding die, and a bullet seating and crimping die. The added advantage of the three-die set is in the use of the 2-step neck expanding die which allows the bullet to enter the case freely, without cutting or marring lead. This method of neck-expanding insures precise case neck tension on seated bullet.

Standard Three-die rifle set
(complete with wrench) $15.00

DELUXE SETS

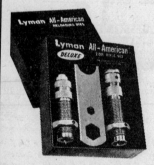

TWO-DIE RIFLE SET

For use with Bottleneck Rifle Cartridges using Jacketed Bullets.

This set consists of a Full-Length Resizing, Decapping and Expanding Die, plus the Lyman P-A (precision alignment) Die for Bullet Seating and Crimping.

Deluxe Two-Die Rifle Set (complete with wrench) $17.00
Deluxe Three-Die Rifle Set (complete with wrench) ...$18.00

THREE-DIE PISTOL SET

Available for pistol calibers 38 S & W, 38ACP, 38 Super, 38 Special, 357 Magnum, 41 Magnum, 44 Special, 44 Magnum, 45 ACP, 45 Colt. Set consists of a Lyman T-C (Tungsten Carbide) Full-Length Resizing and Decapping Die, plus a 2-Step Neck Expanding Die and a Bullet Seating and Crimping Die.

Deluxe Three-Die Pistol Set (complete with wrench) .. $29.00

THREE-DIE PISTOL SETS

Available for all pistol calibers this set can be used with either cast of jacketed bullets.

Set consists of: full-length resizing and decapping die, a 2-step neck expanding die, and a bullet seating and crimping die. Available for various bullet styles.

Standard Three-die pistol set
(complete with wrench) $15.00

TWO-STEP "M" NECK-EXPANDING DIE FOR CAST RIFLE BULLETS

Available for all rifle cases this die is required when loading cast bullets, and will also improve the accuracy of jacketed bullet reloads. The first step expands the neck of the cartridge to slightly under bullet diameter. The second step expands the first 1/16″ of the neck to slightly over bullet diameter, allowing the bullet to enter the case freely, without cutting lead. This die insures precise case neck tension on seated bullet. **$5.00**

LYMAN RELOADING DIES

T-C* PISTOL DIE

*Tungsten Carbide Resizing
& Decapping Die for handgun cartridges.

A lifetime of reloads, some 200,000 rounds can be pushed through this Full-Length Sizing and Decapping Die without a sign of wear. Its diamond-like sizing surface of polished tungsten carbide creates far less friction (75% less) than steel dies. With the Lyman T-C Die, cases need not be lubricated and even dirty cases come out of the die with a polished burnished appearance. T-C Dies are available for the following pistol cartridges.

38 S & W (also fits 38 ACP & 38 Super)	44 Special (also fits 44 Magnum)
38 Special (also fits 357 Magnum)	45 ACP
	45 Colt
41 Magnum	

T-C Pistol Die **$20.00**

P-A* RIFLE DIE

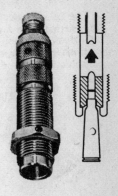

*Precision Alignment seating die for bottleneck rifle cartridges.

This bullet seating and crimping die is uniquely designed to give maximum alignment to bullets when seating them in bottleneck cases. The illustration shows how the cartridge neck and bullet are immediately centered by the sliding inner sleeve. As the case is pushed further into the die, the sleeve moves upwards, holding the bullet and case neck in alignment. These dies can also be adjusted to crimp the bullet in place, if desired. P-A Dies are available for all bottleneck rifle cartridges. **$9.50**

Both the bullet, and case neck, are trapped and aligned by the sliding inner sleeve. As the case is pushed into the die, the sleeve moves upwards holding the bullet and neck in alignment throughout the seating operation. The base of the cartridge case is centered by the lower portion of the die body. This die insures alignment of base, neck and bullet.

AA DIE ACCESSORIES

HEX NUTS (7/8 x 14 Thread)
These heavy duty steel check nuts are supplied as standard equipment with All-American Dies. They must be used on other brands of 7/8" x 14 thread dies when used on the Spar-T Press.
Price (each) .50

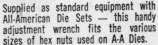

DIE WRENCH
Supplied as standard equipment with All-American Die Sets — this handy adjustment wrench fits the various sizes of hex nuts used on A-A Dies.
Price: .50

EXTRA DECAPPING PINS
(package of ten)
$1.00

TRU-LINE JR. DIES

Designed for use with the Lyman Tru-Line Jr. Press, these dies may be used (with 7/8" x 14 adapters) on other presses.

T-L Die Sets are offered in either 2 or 3 die combinations, depending on shape of cartridge case, and type of bullet to be loaded. Sizing Dies for ALL HANDGUN CARTRIDGES, plus the following rifle cartridges do full-length resizing.

.221 Fire Ball	25/20	38/40
22 Hornet	.223 Rem.	44/40
.218 Bee	.256 Win.	
.222 Rem.	.30M1	
.222 Rem. Mag.	32/20	

Dies for other rifle calibers do neck resizing only. All Die Sets are priced less Priming Punch and Shell Holder. For Tru-Line Jr. Presses use "J" Shell Holder with "T" Priming Punch.

TRU-LINE JR. TWO-DIE SET

To reload bottleneck cartridges using jacketed bullets.
These sets are supplied with a resizing, decapping and expanding die, plus a bullet seating and crimping die. Two-Die Sets are designed for use with bottleneck shape cases using jacketed bullets. For straight-taper shape cases, or cast bullets, the Three-Die Set is required.
$13.00

TRU-LINE JR. THREE-DIE SET

Required to load handgun cartridges, straight-taper shape rifle cartridges and all other cartridges when using cast bullets.
This set consists of: a Resizing and Decapping Die, a 2-Step Neck Expanding Die, and a Bullet Seating and Crimping Die. The added advantage of the Three-Die Set is in the use of the 2-Step Expanding Die which allows the bullet to enter the case freely without cutting or marring lead.
Available for various bullet styles. . . . **$13.00**

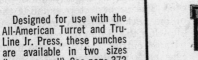

"T" PRIMING PUNCH
Designed for use with the All-American Turret and Tru-Line Jr. Press, these punches are available in two sizes (large or small). See page 372 for correct size. **Price: $2.50**

"J" SHELL HOLDER
Designed for use with the All-American Turret and Tru-Line Jr. Press, see complete listing of Shell Holders on page 372. **Price: $4.00**

7/8 x 14 ADAPTERS
These dies are used to adapt the smaller diameter True-Line Die to 7/8 x 14 thread. One Adapter is required for each reloading die.
Price (each) $1.00

LYMAN RELOADING DIES CHART

The listing below shows the popular calibers available in either All-American, Tru-Line or 310 Dies. Asterisk preceding the caliber indicates that reloading dies for this cartridge are available in 3-Die Sets only. (*) Available in 3-Die sets only (S) Small (L) Large

Rifle Cartridges	Shell Holders "J" type	Spartan	Priming Punch "T" (Spartan & Spar-T Use universal type)	310 Handle Size	Rifle Cartridges	Shell Holders "J" type	Spartan	Priming Punch "T" (Spartan & Spar-T Use universal type)	310 Handle Size	Rifle Cartridges	Shell Holders "J" type	Spartan	Priming Punch "T" (Spartan & Spar-T Use universal type)	310 Handle Size
.221 Fire Ball	J26	X26	S	S	7.65 Argentine	J8	X8	L	L	*38/55	J6	X6	L	L
.256 Win.	J1	X1	S	S	7.7 Jap	J2	X2	L	L	*.401 Win. S.L.	J2	X2	L	L
.218 Bee	J10	X10	S	S	.280 Rem.	J2	X2	L	L	.405 Win.	J7	X7	L	L
.219 Zipper	J6	X6	S	S	.284 Win.	J2	X2	L	L	11 M/M Mauser	J20	X20	L	L
.22 Hornet	J4	X4	S	S	*30M1 Carbine	J19	X19	S	S	43 Spanish	J20	X20	L	L
22/250 Varminter	J2	X2	L	L	30/30 Win.	J6	X6	L	L	44/40 Win.	J14B	X14B	L	S
22 Sav. Hi-Power	J6	X6	L	L	30 Rem.	J15	X15	L	L	*444 Marlin	J14B	X14B	L	L
.220 Swift	J5	X5	L	L	.300 Sav.	J2	X2	L	L	*45/70	J17	X17	L	L
.222 Rem.	J26	X26	S	S	.300 Weatherby	J13	X13	L	L	*.458 Win.	J13	X13	L	L
.222 Rem. Mag.	J26	X26	S	S	.300 H & H	J13	X13	L	L					
.223 (AR-15)	J26	X26	S	S	.300 Win. Mag.	J13	X13	L	L	**Pistol Cartridges**				
.224 Weatherby	J3	X3	L	S	.308 Win. (7.62 Nato)	J2	X2	L	L	*22 Rem. Jet	J1	X1	S	S
.225 Win.	J5	X5	L	S	.308 Norma Mag.	J13	X13	L	L	*30 Luger	J12	X12	S	S
.243 Win.	J2	X2	L	S	30/06	J2	X2	L	L	*30 Mauser	J12	X12	S	S
6 M/M Rem.	J2	X2	L	L	30/40 Krag	J7	X7	L	L	*32 S & W Long	J9	X9	S	S
.244 Rem.	J2	X2	L	L	.303 Sav.	J2	X2	L	L	*32 Colt N.P.	J9	X9	S	S
25/20 Repeater	J10	X10	S	S	.303 British	J7	X7	L	L	*32 Auto	J23	X23	S	S
25/20 Single Shot	J23	X23	S	S	*32/20	J10	X10	L	S	*32/20	J10	X10	S	S
25/35 Win.	J6	X6	L	L	32/40	J6	X6	L	L	*.357 Mag.	J1	X1	S	S
250/3000 Sav.	J2	X2	L	L	32 Win. Spec.	J6	X6	L	L	*9 M/M Luger	J12	X12	S	S
25 Rem.	J15	X15	L	L	32 Rem. Auto	J15	X15	L	L	*38 S & W	J21	X21	S	S
.256 Win.	J1	X1	S	S	8 M/M Mauser	J2	X2	L	L	*38 Colt Auto	J12	X12	S	S
.257 Weatherby	J13	X13	L	L	8 M/M Lebel	J18S	X18S	L	L	*38 Spec.	J1	X1	S	S
.257 Roberts	J8	X8	L	L	33 Win.	J17	X17	L	L	*.380 Colt Auto.	J26	X26	Spec.	S
6.5 M/M Carcano	J28	X28	L	L	.338 Win.	J13	X13	L	L	*38/40 (revolver)	J14B	X14B	L	S
6.5 M/M Jap	J6	X6	L	L	.348 Win.	J18	X18	L	L	*41 Colt	J14LC	X14LC	L	S
6.5 M/M Mann. Schoe.	J28	X28	L	L	35 Rem.	J27	X27	L	L	*41 S & W Mag.	J30	X30	L	S
6.5 M/M Swed.	J27	X27	L	L	35 Win.	J7	X7	L	L	*44 S & W Russian	J7	X7	L	S
.264 Win.	J13	X13	L	L	35 Whelan	J2	X2	L	L	*44 Spec.	J7	X7	L	S
.270 Win.	J2	X2	L	L	*35 Win. S.L.	J15	X15	L	L	*44 Mag.	J7	X7	L	S
.270 Weatherby	J13	X13	L	L	*.351 Win. S.L.	J15	X15	L	S	*44/40	J14B	X14B	L	S
7 x 61 Sharp & Hart	J13	X13	L	L	9 M/M Mann. Schoe.	J2	X2	S	S	*45 Auto Rim	J14A	X14A	L	S
7 M/M Mauser	J2	X2	L	L	.358 Win.	J2	X2	L	L	*45 Colt Auto	J2	X2	L	S
7 M/M Rem. Mag.	J13	X13	L	L	.358 Norma Mag.	J13	X13	L	L	*45 Colt	J11	X11	L	S
7 M/M Weatherby	J13	X13	L	L	.375 H & H Mag.	J13	X13	L	L	*455 Webley	J13	X13	L	S
7.35 M/M Carcano	J28	X28	L	L	.375 Weatherby	J13	X13	L	L					
7.62 M/M Russian	J16	X16	L	L	*38/40 Win.	J14B	X14B	L	S					

#310 DIES

SEPARATE DIES COMPLETE

A. ADAPTER DIE		$2.50
C. PRIMING CHAMBER		4.00
O. NECK RESIZING & DECAPPING DIE		4.50
F. NECK EXPANDING CHAMBER & PLUG		3.00
E. BULLET SEATING CHAMBER & SCREW		4.50

Separate Die Parts:

(O)	Die Body only	4.00
(O)	Decapping Rod only	2.00
(F)	Chamber only	2.00
(F)	Expanding Plug only	2.00
(E)	Chamber only	4.00
(E)	Bullet Seating Screw only	2.00

TRU-LINE JR. DIES & PARTS

SEPARATE DIES COMPLETE (For 2-Die Sets)

S. NECK RESIZING, DECAPPING & EXPANDING DIE		9.00
*K. FULL LENGTH RESIZING, DECAPPING & EXPANDING DIE		9.00
E. BULLET SEATING CHAMBER & SCREW		4.50

Separate Die Parts:

(S)	Die Body only	7.00
*(K)	Die Body only	7.00
(S) or (K)	Decapping Rod only	2.00
(S) or (K)	Expanding Button only	1.00
(E)	Chamber only	4.00
(E)	Bullet Seating Screw only	1.75

*Die K is available for bottleneck cases only and for limited calibers

SEPARATE DIES COMPLETE (For 3-Die Sets)

*R. FULL LENGTH RESIZING & DECAPPING DIE		8.00
**K-3 FULL LENGTH RESIZING & DECAPPING DIE		8.00
***O. NECK RESIZING & DECAPPING DIE		4.50
F. NECK EXPANDING CHAMBER & PLUG		3.00
E. BULLET SEATING CHAMBER & SCREW		4.50

Separate Die Parts:

*(R)	Die Body only	5.00
**(K-3)	Die Body only	7.00
***(O)	Die Body only	4.00
(R) (K-3), (O)	Decapping Rod only	2.00

(F) Chamber only		2.00
(F) Expanding Plug only		2.00
(E) Chamber only		4.00
(E) Bullet Seating Screw only		2.00

*Die R is available for all handgun calibers and caliber 30M1.

**Die K-3 is available for bottleneck cases only and for limited calibers

***Die O is available for all rifle calibers.

ALL-AMERICAN DIES & PARTS

SEPARATE DIES COMPLETE (For 2-Die Rifle Sets)

W. FULL LENGTH RESIZING, DECAPPING & EXPANDING DIE		$7.00
U. BULLET SEATING CHAMBER & SCREW		4.75

Separate Die Parts:

(W)	Die Body only	5.00
(W)	Decapping Rod only	2.00
(W)	Expanding Button only	1.25
(U)	Chamber only	3.75
(U)	Bullet Seating Screw only	1.50

SEPARATE DIES COMPLETE (For 3-Die Rifle Sets)

W-1. FULL LENGTH RESIZING & DECAPPING DIE		6.00
M. TWO-STEP NECK EXPANDING DIE		5.00
U. BULLET SEATING CHAMBER & SCREW		4.75

Separate Die Parts:

(W-1)	Die Body only	5.00
(W-1)	Decapping Rod only	2.00
(M)	Die Body only	3.00
(M)	Expanding Plug only	2.50
(U)	Chamber only	5.50
(U)	Bullet Seating Screw only	1.50

SEPARATE DIES COMPLETE (For 3-Die Pistol Sets)

YD. FULL LENGTH RESIZING & DECAPPING DIE		5.50
M. TWO-STEP NECK EXPANDING DIE		5.00
U. BULLET SEATING CHAMBER & SCREW		4.75

Separate Die Parts:

(YD)	Die Body only	4.50
(YD)	Decapping Rod only	2.00
(M)	Die Body only	3.00
(M)	Expanding Plug only	2.50
(U)	Chamber only	3.75
(U)	Bullet Seating Screw only	1.50

LYMAN RELOADING ACCESSORIES

PRIMER POCKET REAMER

Cleans and removes rough metal edges from a primer pocket. This tool is a must for military type primers. Available in large or small—see priming punch size in cartridge table.

Price **$4.00**

SHELL CHAMFERING REAMER

Tapers case mouth for easier bullet seating. One size adapts to all cartridges.

Price **$4.50**

POWDER FUNNEL

This plastic powder funnel is designed to fill cases from .22 Hornet through 45-70 without inserts or adjustments.

Price: **$1.25**

Powder Dribbler **$4.00**

THE NO. 55 POWDER MEASURE

This Powder Measure and dispensing device charges any number of cases with black, or smokeless, powder loads that are consistent within a fraction of a grain. Its three-slide micrometer adjustable cavity adjusts the load accurately, and locks in place to provide accurate charging. The 2400 grain capacity plastic reservoir gives a clear view of the powder level. The reservoir is fabricated from blue-tinted polyvinylchloride plastic that resists chemical action of double base powders, and filters out light rays that would damage powders. An optional 7000 grain reservoir is available. The measure clamps securely to the loading bench, or mounts directly to any turret press by means of threaded drop tubes (supplied with measure). A knocker mounted on the side of the measure insures complete discharge of powder directly into the cartridge case. No funnel is required.

No. 55 POWDER MEASURE **$29.50**
Optional 7000 grain capacity reservoir .. **$4.00**
⅞" x 14 Adapter for Turret Mounting **$1.00**

The unique three-slide micrometer adjustable cavity is the key to the unfailing accuracy of the 55 Powder Measure. Micrometer adjustments for both width and depth provide a dependable, consistent measure that minimizes cutting of coarse powder.

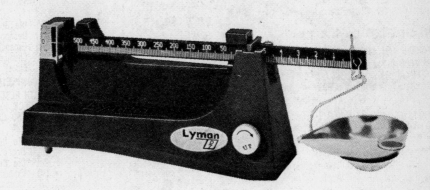

LYMAN D-7 SCALE

Dial markings are white on jet black for easy reading. The pointer, and dial, are placed on the same plane to eliminate parallax error. Its high capacity of up to 505 grains, permits the heaviest charges and even bullets to be weighed. Features magnetic damping. Genuine agate bearings guarantee one tenth of a grain of sensitivity. **Lyman D-7 Scale** **$27.00**

LYMAN BULLET MOULDS

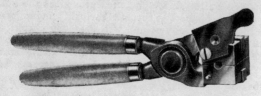

LYMAN SINGLE CAVITY MOULD

Blocks are interchangeable with handles. Permits use of blocks for casting different bullets with the same set of handles. Attaching screws are concealed and handles gie a cool comfortable grip. Group A—$14.00; Hollow Base or Hollow Point—$20.00; Group B—$16.00; Hollow Base or Hollow Point—$22.00; Group C—$22.00; Hollow Base or Hollow Point—Not Available; Handles—$6.00.

LYMAN DOUBLE CAVITY MOULD

The Ideal Double Cavity Mould has blocks which are interchangeable in handles adapted for large size blocks. Double-Cavity Mold Block only Group A—$18.00; Group B—$20.50; Handles—$6.00.

LYMAN FOUR CAVITY MOULD

Mould blocks and handles can be supplied as separate units. If you already have a pair of handles you need only order a set of blocks as these can be used on the same handles. Group A—$34.00; Handles—$9.00.

INERTIA BULLET PULLER

Quickly and easily removes bullets from cartridges.
Price: $10.50

MOULD MASTER FURNACE

MOULD MASTER BULLET CASTING FURNACE—

Heavy-duty, 11 lb. capacity furnace. Operates on standard household power—115 volts, A.C. or D.C., 1000 Watts. Calibrated dial control heats from 450° to 850° F. within 20°. Discharge spout is controlled by a lever operated valve.
Mould Master Furnace complete with Ingot
Mould and Mould Guide $81.95
Extra Ingot Mould .... 4.00 each
Mould Guide 10.00

LEAD POT

Cast iron pot and holder for melting lead alloy using any source of heat. Pot capacity is 10 pounds of alloy. Holder keeps pot secure and level, prevents lead from splashing on stove or burner.
Lead Pot $4.50

GAS CHECKS—Gas checks are gilding metal caps which fit to the base of cast bullets. These caps protect the bullet base from the burning effect of hot powder gases and permit higher velocities. Easily seated during the bullet sizing operation, only Lyman gas checks should be used with Lyman cast bullets. .22 through .45 caliber (per 1000) $8.50
Note: .38 Special same as .35 caliber.

LEAD DIPPER—Dipper with cast iron head. Spout is shaped for easy, accurate pouring that prevents air pockets in the finished bullet. $4.50

LYMAN BULLET SIZING EQUIPMENT

450 BULLET SIZER

The 450 Bullet Sizer and Lubricator sizes the bullet to the correct diameter, forces lubricant under pressure into the bullet grooves, and will seat gas checks, if required—all in one rapid, accurate operation. Adaptable to all bullets by changing "G" and bullet sizing assembly "H & I". Use with Ideal Bullet Lubricant......**$42.00**

G, H & I DIES "WITH SWAGING ACTION":

Cast bullets as much as ten thousandths oversize can be easily formed to size by the use of these dies. Lyman bullet sizing dies have been newly designed to supply a swaging rather than shearing action in reducing bullet diameters. The mouth of the "H" die contains a gentle taper which allows the gas check and bullet to start into the die easily. This tapering of the mouth combined with the exact tolerance and ultra-smoothness of the hardened inner chamber, completely eliminates shearing of lead and produces a perfectly cylindrical bullet. As this swaging action compresses and work hardens the alloy, a tougher, smoother, and more accurate bullet results.

"G" TOP PUNCH: Top Punches are designed to fit the contour of the bullet point. See following pages for "G" punch numbers **$2.50**

"H & I" SIZING DIE ASSEMBLY: H & I Dies should be supplied as one unit. Their diameter should correspond to the groove diameter of your rifle, or pistol. The listing below shows the basic groove diameter for many popular calibers. A complete listing of all available sizes is also shown for the shooter who wishes to experiment with different bullet diameters or for those who have rifles with worn or non-standard bores **$7.50**

"G"

"H"

"I"

$34.50

IDEAL BULLET LUBRICANT . . .
Special grease developed especially for use as a cast bullet lubricant. One stick lubricates 2500 small of 500 large bullets.

Ideal Bullet Lubricant **$1.00**
Highest Quality Graphite
Lubricant **$1.50**

BULLET SIZING CHAMBER AND PLUG . . .
For use with the 310 reloading tool. Reduces cast bullet diameter as required for use. Available in the following bullet diameters:

.223, .224, .225, .226, .228, .244, .245, .257, .258, .263, .266, .278, .280, .285, .287, .299, .301, .308, .309, .311, .312, .313, .315, .320, .321, .322, .323, .338, .350, .356, .357, .358, .359, .360, .366, .386, .400, .401, .403, .410, .412, .424, .427, .428, .429, .430, .431, .448, .450, .451, .452, .454, .456, .457, .509, .512, .515.

Bullet Sizing Chamber and Plug **$9.00**

BASIC GROOVE DIAMETER FOR RIFLES

Caliber	Groove Dia.	Caliber	Groove Dia.
All 22 cal. (except 22 Hi-power)	.224	338 Win. & 33 Win.	.338
.22 Hi-Power	.226	348 Win.	.348
.243, .244, 6 M/M	.243	35 Win. S.L. & 351 S.L.	.352
.256 Win. & All 25 cals.	.257	9 x 56 M/M & 9 x 57 M/M	.354
.264 Win., 6.5 M/M	.264	35 cal.	.358
.270 Win.	.277	375 H & H Mag.	.375
7 M/M, .280 Rem., .284 Win.	.284	38/55	.379
7.35 Carcano	.299	38/40	.400
30 cals.	.308	401 S.L.	.406
7.62 Russian	.310	405 Win.	.412
32/20 Win.	.311	44/40 Win. Rifles	.428
7.65 Mauser	.311	44/40 Rem. Rifles	.425
.303 British, 7.7 M/M Jap.	.313	444 Marlin	.430
8 M/M Mauser (J.Bore)	.318	11 Mauser	.439
8 M/M Mauser (S Bore)	.323	45/70 & 458 Win.	.457
32 Win. Spec. 32 S.L. & 32 Rem.	.321		

BASIC GROOVE DIAMETER FOR PISTOLS

Caliber	Groove Dia.	Caliber	Groove Dia.
22 Jet	.222	38/40	.400
30 Mauser	.309	41 Colt	.406
30 Luger	.310	41 S & W Mag.	.410
32 Auto	.311	44/40 (revolver)	.425
32/20	.312	44 S & W Spec. & 44 Russian	.429
32 S & W & 32 Colt N.P.	.314	44 Mag. (S & W & Ruger)	.430
9 M/M Luger	.354	45 A.C.P.	.450
38 Special & 357 Mag. (Colt),		45 Auto Rim	.451
38 A.C.P. & 380 Auto	.355	45 Colt (post-war)	.451
38 Special & 357 Mag. (S & W)	.357	45 Colt (pre-war)	.454
38 S & W	.360	.455 Webley	.457

COMPLETE LIST OF H & I DIAMETERS

.222	.223	.224	.225	.228	.243	.244	.245	.257	.258	.259	.263	.264
.266	.277	.278	.280	.284	.285	.287	.299	.301	.308	.309	.310	.311
.312	.313	.314	.315	.316	.318	.319	.320	.321	.322	.323	.325	.338
.340	.348	.350	.352	.354	.355	.356	.357	.358	.359	.360	.366	.375
.377	.378	.379	.380	.386	.400	.401	.403	.406	.410	.412	.414	.419
.424	.425	.427	.428	.429	.430	.431	.434	.439	.446	.450	.451	.452
.454	.456	.457	.459	.509	.512	.515	.580 (lub. only)					

LYMAN SHOTSHELL PRESS

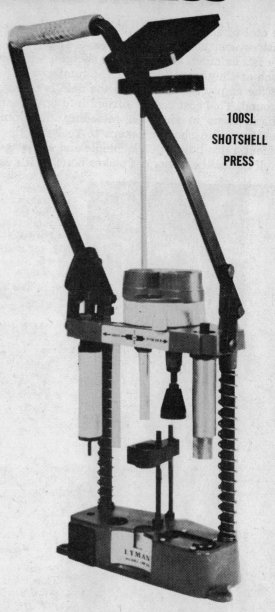

100SL

SHOTSHELL

PRESS

ADJUSTABLE POWDER AND SHOT DIPPER . . .

Measures bulk smokeless or black powder in drams, and measures lead and copperized shot in ounces. Note—Not for use with progressive burning smokeless powders. **$4.00**

EXTRA SPRING FINGERS

Replacement spring fingers to fit the wad chamber of the Easy Shotshell Reloader are available in all gauges. Specify gauge required when ordering.
Price: . . . . **$ .75**

ROLL CRIMPER HEAD . . . with drill

press adapter. For roll crimping shotshells. This head also works on rifled slugs; mounts in any drill press. Specify .12 or 20 gauge. **$7.50**

SELF ALIGNING ARM

EASY CRIMP STARTER ASSEMBLY

The Easy Crimp Starter is designed with a unique self-aligning feature. Plastic cases can be rapidly processed without the usual bother of manually aligning each case. You simply place your case under the starter head and pull down the handle. The aligning arm will pivot the starter head so that it meshes to the existing fold creases in the case mouth.

The Easy Crimp Starter works equally well on new paper cases. It's extremely easy to install and simple to operate.

EASY CRIMP STARTER ASSEMBLY 12, 16, 20 ga. with Starter Heads, six fold or eight fold **$5.00**

100SL SHOTSHELL PRESS

One of the fastest single-station presses available to the shotshell reloader, the 100SL offers all the most wanted features:
● Full length sizing, hi or low brass, 2¾ or 3″ shell smooth cam ejection of all sizes without adjustment. ● Auto Primer Feed—the Primer is automatically placed each complete cycle of the press. ● Optional Primer Reservoir holds 100 primers and automatically feeds primers to the Primer drop tube. ● Floating wad guide automatically positions itself on the case mouth during wad insertion. ● Clear view wad pressure indicator clearly indicates wad pressure at a glance. ● Floating crimp starter aligns itself on case mouth folds and applies the exact amount of fold required for a uniformly tight crimp. ● Crimping die applies a uniformly tight crimp to each shell assuring durability in the field and smooth functioning through the gun action. ● Quick-dump reservoirs are emptied by activating a dump valve. The 100SL
Available in either 12 or 20 gauge $84.50
Conversion kits:
12 to 20 gauge $19.50
20 to 12 gauge 19.50

LYMAN SHOTSHELL PRESS

The cost of shotgun shells, like other costs, has been rising rapidly over the last several years. When a box of shells that you could once buy for $1.25, costs as much as $3.75, most shotgun enthusiasts can't afford to shoot as much as they would like to. The hunter who fires a shell, ejects it, and leaves the empty case behind in the field is throwing away half the cost of each round. This cost can be turned into an investment by reloading.

The basic steps in shotshell reloading, decapping, priming, loading the powder, wad and shot, are steps to real shooting economy. With Lyman equipment, reloading is quick, simple and safe—and the equipment will pay for itself out of the savings it makes possible in just one season of shooting.

LYMAN "EASY" SHOTSHELL RELOADER

Complete with dies to load and fold crimp plastic or paper cases. Also handles all brass, zinc and Winchester AA cases.

12, 16, 20 and 28 gauge **$59.50**

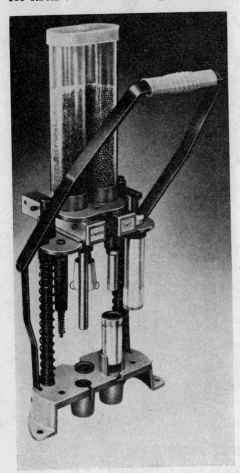

- Adaptable to all gauges 10, 12, 16, 20, 28.
- Loads all shell lengths 2½" to 3½".
- Adaptable to all case styles, high-brass, low brass, all brass, zinc, paper and all types of plastic.
- Adaptable to all crimp styles—fold, roll or bevel.
- Adaptable to all loads—10 gauge magnum to 410 skeet, rifle slugs, or buckshot.
- High production rate—15 seconds a shell, average 240 per hour.
- Large capacity reservoirs. 1 pound of powder and 5 pounds of shot.
- Quick change powder and shot bushings, change loads in seconds.
- Foolproof operations—each function completed with a positive stop.
- Comes completely assembled and adjusted ready to use.

New Adjustable Powder Bar

This replaces the standard shotshell powder slide and allow you to adjust your loader for any shotshell charge. No extra powder bushings to buy **$13.00**

EASY STANDARD FOLD CRIMP CONVERSION KIT

A complete conversion kit which contains everything necessary to convert your standard loader to fold crimp in another gauge. This complete kit is made up of units A and B (as described below) plus a crimp starter with one starter head.

Easy Standard Fold Crimp Conversion Kits are available for 12, 16, 20 . . . . **$19.50**

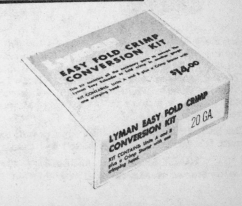

mec
600 jr.
the plastic master

Choice of 10, 12, 16, 20, 28 or .410 gauges — fitted in beautiful lifetime chrome

price complete

$79.20

Any MEC reloader can be used for reloading plastic shells, but the "600 jr." positively masters the process. The PLASTIC MASTER is a single stage tool, but is designed to permit rapid, progressive operation. Every step from fired shell to the fresh-crimped product is performed with a minimum of motion. An exclusive shell holder positions and holds the shell at each station. No transfer die is required . . . resizing dies at reconditioning and crimping stations give your shell its proper form.

- CAM-ACTUATED RECONDITIONING STATION
- SPINDEX STAR CRIMP HEAD
- ADJUSTA-GUIDE WAD FEED
- CAM-LOCK CRIMP
- HARDENED CHARGING BAR
- TOGGLE LINKAGE
- FLIP-TYPE MEASURE
- ALL STEEL CONSTRUCTION
- PRIMER CATCHER

- CAM-ACTUATED RECONDITIONING STATION
- PRO-CHECK
- SPINDEX STAR CRIMP HEAD
- ADJUSTA-GUIDE WAD FEED
- CAM LOCK CRIMP
- HARDENED CHARGING BAR
- TOGGLE LINKAGE
- FLIP TYPE MEASURE
- PRIMER CATCHER
- ALL STEEL CONSTRUCTION

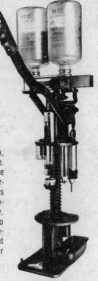

The exclusive Platform Cam which provides the longer ejection stroke necessary to eject existing field shells at the resize station. No adjustments or part changes are required, regardless of brass length. The Pro-Check, which programs the charge bar and wad guide. This ingenious device programs the measure assembly to position the charge bar in the correct sequence. Even the hunter who reloads once or twice a year cannot err . . . the Pro-Check eliminates mistakes . . . automatically. The paper crimp starter which assembles into the Spindex Crimper. Only seconds are required to change from the 6 or 8 point plastic crimp spinner to the smooth cone for fired paper shells.

mec
700
versamec
the single stage ultimate

Choice of 12, 16, 20, 28 or .410 gauges — fitted in beautiful lifetime chrome.

price complete

$90.75

---

mec
650
the reloader
with a memory
and
super 600

Choice of 12, 16, 20, 28 or .410 gauges — fitted in beautiful lifetime chrome

price complete

$167.30

SUPER 600 — $155.20

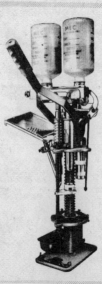

Up to 12 operations on 6 individual shells are performed simultaneously with one stroke of the press handle. Outstanding features of the 650 include a revolutionary Star Crimp Head, Automatic Primer feeding, exclusive Resize-Deprime apparatus, Toggle linkage, cam operated crimping die and Auto-Cycle charging sequence. The Auto-Cycle charging sequence automatically maintains the correct operating sequence of the charge bar. The charge bar can be actuated only when a shell is properly located to receive the powder. The MEC 650 can even handle the 3 inch shells . . . high-base, low base and light or heavy plastics. It's all steel with an extra heavy base-column. Tool comes completely assembled, tested and ready to use . . . without adjustment. The MEC 650 is the finest reloader on the market . . . bar none!

The Super 600 is the same as the 650 except it does not have Auto-Cycle.

- AUTOMATIC PRIMER FEED.
- AUTOMATIC POWDER AND SHOT CHARGING
- FLIP-TYPE MEASURE
- HARDENED CHARGING BAR
- OPEN BASE
- PRIMER CATCHER
- EXCLUSIVE CAM-OPERATED CRIMP
- EXCLUSIVE RESIZE-DEPRIME APPARATUS
- 12 OPERATIONS WITH 1 STROKE
- SPINDEX STAR CRIMP HEAD
- AUTO-CYCLE

mec
650
and super 600
hydramec

the miniature reloading factory

Take the 650 or the Super 600 reloader and marry it to a hydraulic system . . . the result is the hydraMEC, today's most advanced concept in high-volume reloaders. The hydraulic system is compact, lightweight and designed for long, trouble-free service. The motor operates on regular 110 volt household current and the pump supplies instant, constant pressure . . . no slowdown, no misses. The entire downstroke and upstroke functions are utilized and synchronized to allow continuous action. Every stroke of the cylinder piston is positive and performs up to 12 operations on six reloading stations. Every downstroke of the reloader produces one finished shell. The operator inserts empty shells and wads . . . the hydraMEC does the rest . . . automatically.

Tool linked for hydraulic operation to include base and cylinder.
hydraMEC 650 . . . . $210.20
hydraMEC 600 . . . . $197.83

HYDRAULIC UNIT ONLY—Hydraulic unit to include pump, motor, cylinder, controls, base, links and bolts required to attach to reloader with instructions. $292.82

- AUTOMATIC PRIMER FEED
- AUTOMATIC POWDER & SHOT CHARGING
- FLIP-TYPE MEASURE
- HARDENED CHARGING BAR
- PRIMER CATCHER
- EXCLUSIVE CAM-OPERATED CRIMP
- EXCLUSIVE RESIZE-DEPRIME APPARATUS
- TOGGLE LINKAGE
- FOOL PROOF HYDRAULIC SYSTEM
- 12 OPERATIONS WITH 1 STROKE

$445.60
SUPER 600 — $433.50

Choice of 12, 16, 20, 28 or .410 gauges — fitted in beautiful lifetime chrome

---

ACCESSORY EQUIPMENT
MEC E-Z PRIME "V" & "S"

COMPLETELY AUTOMATIC PRIMER FEED

SPINDEX STAR CRIMP HEAD

The SPINDEX STAR CRIMP HEAD is a revolutionary crimp starter that prepares plastic shells for a perfect crimp . . . everytime. The SPINDEX automatically engages the original folds of each shell. No prior indexing of the shell is required . . . even on some of the earlier, unskived plastics that show no impressions of the original crimp folds. Because it employs a pressed metal part that spins into alignment with the original folds, the SPINDEX starts every crimp perfectly. And even, better . . . you have a choice of an 8-segment, 6-segment, or smooth crimp starter, depending on the shells you are reloading.

E-Z PRIME "V"
For 600 Jr. & 700 Versamec
$20.00

FROM CARTON TO SHELL WITH SECURITY, IT PROVIDES SAFE, CONVENIENT PRIMER POSITIONING AND INCREASES RATE OF PRODUCTION. REDUCES BENCH CLUTTER, ALLOWING MORE FREE AREA FOR WADS AND SHELLS.

- PRIMERS TRANSFER DIRECTLY FROM CARTON TO RELOADER — ELIMINATING TUBES AND TUBE FILLERS.
- POSITIVE MECHANICAL FEED (NOT DEPENDENT UPON AGITATION OF PRESS)
- VISIBLE SUPPLY
- AUTOMATIC — ELIMINATES HAND MOTION
- LESS SUSCEPTIBLE TO DAMAGE
- ADAPTS TO ALL DOMESTIC AND MOST FOREIGN PRIMERS WITH ADJUSTMENT OF THE COVER
- MAY BE PURCHASED SEPARATELY TO REPLACE TUBE TYPE PRIMER FEED OR TO UPDATE YOUR PRESENT RELOADER.

E-Z PRIME "S"
For Super 600 & 650
$20.00

MEC E-Z PAK   IT'S ALL STEEL! IT'S TILTED!

Here's how to pack shot shell reloads the easy way. As each shell is reloaded, they're placed in E-Z PAK, exactly as if they were being placed in the box. After each 25 shells, original box is slipped over E-Z PAK, which is then inverted, and removed. Nothing easier — nothing neater. Available in all gauges.

$2.42

MEC E-Z WAD DISPENSER

Makes Wad handling as easy as 1-2-3: The MEC Wad Dispenser is "Reloader-high", making your wadding operation faster . . . neater . . . more convenient.

$12.10

MEC CASE CONDITIONER

Companion to the loading tool that does not resize the brass, or one that does not resize sufficiently. The MEC Case Conditioner completely and truly resizes case head, restores head space and irons out case mouth, making it possible to reload any case, including the plastics. All gauges.

PRICE $36.30

Separate dies for converting to other gauges - - - - - $ 9.02

FOR THE MEC 600 JR.

MEC DIE SETS—(12-16-20-28-.410) $27.50
(10 gauge) $30.80
PRO-CHECK . . . . $ 2.42

FOR THE VERSAMEC 700

741V DIE SET—(10-12-16-20-28-.410) specify gauge $30.80

MEC CHARGING BARS—A complete assortment of "quick change" charging bars is available for any load or gauge. (Request charging bar guide from your dealer.) Please specify gauge and bar no., along with Part No. 502 which denotes progressive tools or Part 302 for all others. 302 and 502 charge bars, fixed shot, powder side bored to accept MEC bushing.
Specify weight of shot charge, price per bar . . . . $ 4.40
MEC powder bushings, (select from chart) . . . . $ 1.10
302 or 502 charge bars, standard as listed on chart . . . . $ 3.85

SPINDEX STAR CRIMP HEAD
SPINDEX STAR CRIMP HEAD 234-434-534 (specify gauge and model) . . . . $ 4.95
* 634P INSERT FOR PRE—CRIMPING (CONING) PAPER SHELLS . . . . $ 2.42
453 FINGERS (specify gauges) . . . . $ .66 ea.
30IL—13x CONTAINER . . . . $ .99 ea.

DU-O-MEASURE™

PRICE $40.00

The new Du-O-Measure represents a strikingly different approach to the age old concept of volume metering. Fundamental to its modern design are the requisites essential for trouble free reloading. One, the Du-O-Measure is remarkably easy to understand, to adjust and to operate. Two, it is completely dependable.

The Du-O-Measure may be used for all metallic cartridges, rifle or pistol, and a full range of reloading powders. Its single precision fitted drum contains **two separate metering cavities** which respond to micrometer type adjustment. The low profile, one pound capacity reservoir has a **built in quick dump feature** which allows for instant drainage when changing powders. Two transparent drop tubes (supplied with the measure) are uniquely funneled to accommodate all of the various mouth sizes of metallic cartridges.

- Single precision fitted drum contains two separate metering cavities.
- Knife-like cavity edges cleave through coarser powders to produce uniformity, charge after charge.
- Micrometer type adjustments for both rifle and pistol cavities.
- Reference points relating to the volume of each cavity are clearly marked.
- Measure has quick dump feature plus a pitcher-type pouring spout built into the reservoir.
- Supplied with 11" x 17" graph type wall chart covering approximate settings for all rifle and pistol powders.

MODEL NO. 7200

WHAT COULD BE EASIER

FOR PISTOL CHARGES? To make use of the smaller cavity and to ready the measure for pistol charges, you simply insert the stopscrew in the hole marked "S". The micrometer type wheel adjustment on the left side of the drum moves the smaller cavity through a range of adjustment from 1/2 to 15 grains and locks securely.

FOR RIFLE CHARGES? To make use of the larger cavity and to ready the measure for rifle charges, you simply insert the stopscrew in the hole marked "L". The micrometer adjustment located on the tool handle provides a range of adjustment from 15 to 100 grains and locks securely.

A RELIABLE RELOADING SCALE MUST BE USED IN THE FINAL ADJUSTMENT OF ALL POWDER MEASURES.

DELUXE POWDER MEASURE STAND

$9.75
MODEL NO. 7250

A tough aluminum casting which mounts solidly to the bench top, this stand is a highly practical accessory. Equipped with a 7/8" x 14 thread it may be used with the Du-O-Measure or competitive brands.

CASE LENGTH GAUGE

$3.50
MODEL NO. 1350

A tough plastic vernier caliper for accurate measurement of overall case length. Supplied with instructions and wall chart that lists maximum and trim-to-length for 120 popular cartridges.

TRIGGER PULL GAUGE

A necessary accessory for the serious shooter, this gauge features a high strength housing and aluminum face. Contrasting black calibrations give accurate readings in both ounces and grams.

MODEL NO. 8004-T
$6.00

RELOADING SCALES

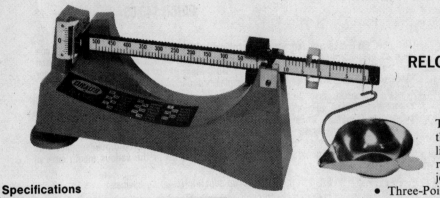

RELOADING SCALE MODEL 5-0-5

Specifications

Capacity	511 grain
Sensitivity	0.1 grain

Calibrations	
Beam, left end	500 x 10 grain
Beam, center	10 x 1 grain
Beam, right end	1 x 0.1 grain

The Ohaus Reloading Scale features a three-poise beam system. This rugged little measurement device delivers accuracy and precision for a lifetime of enjoyable reloading.
• Three-Poise System simplifies settings and readings.
• Magnetic-Damping System speeds weighing. The 5-0-5 was the first reloading scale to use magnetic damping.
• Tip-proof, gold-anodized aluminum pan prevents spilling and sticking of powder. Features pouring spout and handle.
• Precision-hardened knives and agate bearings provide long life and permanent sensitivity.
• Oversized foot makes scale tip-proof.
• An ounces-(½ to 2½) to-grain conversion chart, helpful to shotshell reloaders, is mounted on base of scale.
Price **$26.00**

DIAL-O-GRAIN MODEL 304

Specifications

Capacity	1,110 grain
Sensitivity	0.1 grain

Calibrations	
Beams	1,000 x 100 grain 100 x 10 grain
Dial	10 x 0.1 grain

The Ohaus Dial-O-Grain (like all Ohaus Reloading Scales) offers laboratory quality to the reloader. Direct reading, precision-engraved in values from 0.1 to 10 grains, affords sensitivity and accuracy found only in the laboratory. Two-tiered beams feature widely spaced, deep notches and center-reading poises. Hardened-steel knives and polished-agate bearings ensure long life and precision. Supplied with Model 7150 Powder Trickler and adjustable built-in stand. Oversized pan with pouring spout makes weighing easier. An ounce-to-grain conversion chart is mounted on the extra-stable die-cast base. Standard equipment in most ballistic labs, the Ohaus Dial-O-Grain has won popularity with many reloaders.
Price **$88.50**

RELOADING SCALES

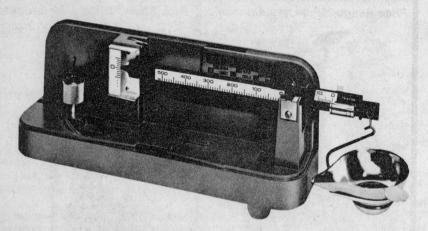

PRICE $37.50

(Capacity 1,010 grains)

Offering a full spectrum of Ohaus features including the **Micrometer Poise** and **Approach to Weight Systems.**

Employing magnetic damping and utilizing self-aligning agate bearings to support its hardened steel beam pivots, the 10·10 Model has a guaranteed sensitivity of 0.1 grain. The left side of the beam is graduated in full 10 grain increments affording **widely spaced deep beam notches.** The right side of the beam makes use of a **dependable micrometer poise.** You adjust for any setting from 0.1 grain to 10 grains by simply rotating the micrometer drum. A positive lock holds this poise in adjustment.

The new **Approach to Weight** system alerts the user to beam movement before the pointer reaches the zero scale. As pictured, the scale capacity is 510 grains. When the attachment weight is added, this **capacity increases to 1,010 grains.** When the scale is not in use, the precision die cast base holds the scale components and converts into a dust proof carrying case.
★ Pat. Pending

Micrometer poise for any setting of 0.1 to 10 grains.

Approach to weight alerts user to beam movement.

Anti-tip pan insures against tipping when weight is off center.

Attachment weight increases capacity without loss of sensitivity.

Tough molded cover forms convenient carrying case.

POWDER FUNNEL

$1.25
MODEL NO. 7170

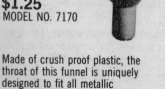

Made of crush proof plastic, the throat of this funnel is uniquely designed to fit all metallic cartridge cases.

LOADING BLOCK

$2.00
MODEL NO. 7160

"Flips over Fits all cases"

Made of unbreakable molded plastic, this "one size" loading block fits all metallic cartridge cases. Its unique flip over design allows for a full range of hole variations. There are 80 cavities on one side, 40 on the other, of 3 different depths, and diameters to accommodate all cartridge cases.

POWDER TRICKLER

$6.00
MODEL NO. 7150

Featuring a large aluminum reservoir and heavy steel tip-resistant base, the Ohaus Trickler provides the finger tip control necessary when adding small quantities of powder to the scale pan.

PACIFIC SHOTSHELL LOADERS

DL-155

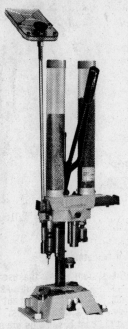

PACIFIC'S DL-266®

Most Advanced Reloader in its Price Range...Patented Automatic Primer Feed.

PACIFIC'S DL-366®

Turns out a Perfect Reload with Each Lever Stroke...All Gauges, Paper or Plastic.

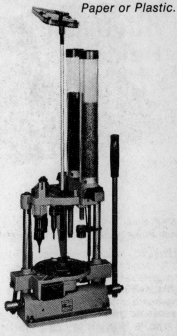

The DL-155 Automatic Primer Feed teams with Pacific primer tube filler to give you safe, sure, error-free priming at increased speed. Large capacity tube holds 50 primers, refills instantly with a turn of the tube filler dial. The functional base design of this loader makes the Pacific DL-155 APF a reloading machine any beginner can master in a few rounds. Detachable hoppers make powder and shot changing fast, easy. Full view wad pressure indicator guarantees shell uniformity. Special wad guide with strong, tightly-spaced spring fingers eliminates "tipped" wads.

FAST—Can produce 8 boxes (200 rounds) per hour.

The most advanced loader in its price range. Right or left-hand operation to suit the operator. New wad guide with unbreakable spring fingers prevents wad tipping. Two-way adjustable crimper assures precise crimp depth and taper. Automatic primer feed automatically drops primer when preceding shell is powder charged.

SAFE AND CONVENIENT—Charging assembly constructed for no-spark safety. Shot and powder assembly removes completely for fast, easy load change.

Progressive operation with improved semi-automatic design. Turns out a perfect reload with each stroke of the lever. Right- or left-hand operation. Takes only 30 seconds to interchange operating lever. Automatic primer feed gives fast, error-free priming. Standard primer tube filler speeds up insertion of primers into feed tube. Loads all gauges, paper or plastic.

EXTRA CONVENIENCE—Three-step operation—insert shell case, wads and pull lever. Produces a perfect round every time—even for beginners.

DL-155-10 Shotshell Reloader
10 gauge
$99.50
DL-155 APF SHOTSHELL RELOADER
Complete with charge bushings.
12 & 20 ga. **$99.50**; 16, 28 & 410 ga. **$104.50**.
DL-155/DL-155 APF DIE SET
For quick-change conversion to different gauge.
12 & 20 ga. **$27.50**; 16, 28 & 410 ga. **$29.50**.
DL-155/DL-155 APF
   MAGNUM CONVERSION SET **$10.50**
Converts 2¾" dies to load 3" shells of same gauge, or vice versa.
AUTOMATIC PRIMER FEED
   CONVERSION UNIT **$25.50**
EXTRA CRIMP STARTER ..**$ 1.50**
EXTRA CHARGE BUSHINGS .. ...**$ 2.00**

DL-266 SHOTSHELL RELOADER
Complete with charge bushings.
12 & 20 ga. **$139.50**; 16, 28 & 410 ga. **$144.00**.
DL-266 DIE SET
For conversion to different gauge.
12 & 20 ga. **$29.50**; 16, 28 & 410 ga. **$32.00**.
DL-266 MAGNUM CONVERSION SET $ 9.50
Converts 2¾" dies to load 3" shells of same gauge, or vise versa.
EXTRA CRIMP STARTER   **$ 1.50**
EXTRA CHARGE BUSHINGS ......**$ 2.00**

DL-366 SHOTSHELL RELOADER
Complete with charge bushings.
12 & 20 ga. **$234.50**; 16, 28 & 410 ga. **$239.50**.
DL-366 DIE SET
For conversion to different gauge.
12 & 20 ga. **$48.50**; 16, 28 & 410 ga. **$52.50**.
DL-366 MAGNUM CONVERSION SET $ 9.50
Converts 2¾" dies to load 3" shells of same gauge, or vice versa.
EXTRA CRIMP STARTER   ..**$ 1.50**
EXTRA CHARGE BUSHINGS ......**$ 2.00**

Pacific DL-105

Shotshell Reloader

- All the features of expensive reloaders . . . without sacrificing quality.
- Crimps shells perfectly. Floating crimp starter automatically aligns with original crimp folds. Final crimp die is fully adjustable.
- Seats wads easily with built-in wad guide.
- Eliminates guesswork . . . all operations end on positive stop.

DL-105 SHOTSHELL RELOADER $54.50
Complete with charge bushings.

DL-105 DIE SET $16.50
For quick-change conversion to different gauge.

DL-105 MAGNUM CONVERSION SET . . $ 8.00
Converts 2¾" dies to load 3" shells of same gauge, or vice versa.

DL-105 CRIMP STARTER . . . . $ 1.50
(8-point crimp starter standard equipment with loader and with Die Sets).

EXTRA CHARGE BUSHINGS . . . .$ 2.00

PACIFIC'S POWER 'C'®

"C" Type Metallic Cartridge Reloading Tool

- Pacific's patented primer system for convenient and positive primer seating.
- Pacific's patented automatic primer feed easily attached.
- Convenient offset handle for maximum leverage. Handle locks out of the way in "up" position when not in use.
- All bearing surfaces hardened and precision ground.

$39.90

POWER-C RELOADING PRESS . . .
(frame, toggle, handle, removable-head shell holder ram and universal primer arm)

POWER-C RELOADING ACCESSORIES

Shell Holder Head Only	$ 3.00
Primer Catcher	$ 3.00
Durachrome Dies	$15.00
Pacific Rifle and Pistol Manual	$ 4.00
Automatic Primer Feed with 1 tube	$ 7.00

COMPLETE POWER-C RELOADING SET
Includes: Power-C Press • Primer Catcher • Set of Pacific Durachrome Dies • Shell Holder Head. A $53.00 value.

$54.90

PACIFIC'S MULTI-POWER 'C'®

Smooth, precise operation. More power with minimum effort for all reloading jobs . . . including bullet swaging.

- Pacific's patented primer system for convenient and positive primer seating.
- Pacific's patented automatic primer feed easily attached.
- "O" frame of high-density annealed cast iron insures perfect alignment of die and shell holder. Impossible for frame to spring even when swaging large caliber bullets.
- Swinging toggle multiplies leverage for easy operation when resizing and case forming.
- Steel links for maximum strength.
- All bearing surfaces hardened and precision ground.

$55.90

MULTI-POWER PRESS . . . .
(frame, handle, toggle and ram designed for removable-head shell holders and universal primer arm.)

MULTI-POWER TOOL ACCESSORIES

Shell holder head only	$ 3.00
Durachrome dies	$15.00
Automatic Primer Feed with 1 tube	$ 7.00
Primer catcher	$ 3.00
Pacific Rifle & Pistol Manual	$ 4.00

COMPLETE MULTI-POWER RELOADING SET
Includes: Multi-Power Press • Primer Catcher • Set of Pacific Durachrome Dies • Shell Holder Head. A $71.00 value.

$69.90

2 DIE SETS
(for bottleneck cases)

DURACHROME

2 DIE SET SERIES 1	.....$15.00
Full length size die only	10.00
Seating die only	7.00
Neck size die only	10.00
SERIES III	18.00

DELUXE FILE TYPE TRIM DIE

Uses a fine grade file to insure precision case length. The most inexpensive and practical way to trim and form rifle cases.

- Made of finest steel with lifetime Durachrome finish.
- Available in most rifle calibers.

Deluxe FILE TYPE TRIM DIE .....$ 8.00

3 DIE SETS
(for straight sided cases)

DURACHROME

3 DIE SET SERIES II	.....$15.00
Size die only	5.00
Expander die only	6.50
Seating die only	6.00
Extra die box	1.00
SERIES IV	18.00

#1 CARBIDE SIZE DIES
For 3 Die Sets

The ideal answer for large volume reloading. Diamond-hard finish won't scratch cases, no lubrication needed. Cases need not be cleaned.

3 Die set with Carbide size die SERIES II	$37.50
Carbide size die only	27.50

AVAILABLE IN:

38 Special & 357 Mag.; 44 Special & 44 Mag.; 45 ACP & 45 AR; 9 MM. Luger.

PACIFIC'S
DURACHROME® DIES
GUARANTEED FOR LIFE
For All Popular Rifle & Pistol Calibers

- **LIFETIME DURACHROME FINISH**—satin-hard chrome protection that keeps dies looking and working like new. Guaranteed never to chip, crack or peel.

- **HEXAGON SPINDLE HEADS**—for easy removal of stuck cases and more positive adjustment.

- **PRECISION-ROLLED** ⅞ x 14 threads held to perfect size and pitch. Fits most other tools because this pioneer Pacific development has been widely copied.

- **FAST CONVENIENT ADJUSTMENT** is made possible by Pacific's all-steel lock rings.

- **BUILT IN PROVISION FOR CRIMPING** provided on all bullet seating dies.

- **ALL STEEL CONSTRUCTION**—no inexpensive substitute metals.

- **PRECISE DIMENSIONS**—minimum tolerances maintained throughout. After chambering, dies are hardened for lifetime wear, then polished to insure perfect dimensions and smooth interior surfaces.

- **HEAVY DUTY STORAGE BOX,** sample of Pacific Die Lube and spare decap pin are included with each set.

Removable Head SHELL HOLDER

Precision machined from hardened steel then heat treated to prevent wear and give lifetime operation. Each Shell Holder is specifically designed for case to assure accurate alignment and eliminate tipping and side movement. Fits all tools using Pacific "C" design. $3.00

PACIFIC'S CALIBER LIST

Caliber	Number Of Dies	Neck Dies	File Trim Dies	Shell Holder
218 Bee	2	no	no	7
219 Zipper	2	no	yes	2
22 Hornet	2	no	no	3
22K Hornet	2	no	no	3
22 RCFM (Jet)	2	no	no	6
17-222	2	yes	yes	16
17-223	2	yes	no	16
221 Remington-(Fireball)	2	no	no	16
222 Remington	2	yes	yes	16
222 Remington Magnum	2	yes	yes	16
223 Remington	2	yes	yes	16
224 Weatherby	2	yes	yes	17
225 Winchester	2	yes	yes	18
22-250	2	yes	yes	1
220 Swift	2	yes	yes	4
22 Savage H. P.	2	no	no	2
243 Winchester	2	yes	yes	1
244-6mm Remington	2	yes	yes	1
6mm Internationl	2	yes	yes	1
6mm-284	2	yes	yes	1
6 x 47 Remington	2	yes	no	16
25-20 Winchester	2	no	no	7
250 Savage	2	yes	yes	1
25 Remington	2	no	no	12
25-35 Winchester	2	yes	yes	2
25-06	2	yes	yes	1
256 Winchester	2	no	no	6
257 Roberts	2	yes	yes	1
257 Weatherby	2	yes	yes	5
25-284	2	yes	yes	1
6.5 x 55	2	no	yes	19
6.5-06	2	yes	yes	1

Caliber	Number Of Dies	Neck Dies	File Trim Dies	Shell Holder
6.5 Remington Magnum	2	yes	yes	5
6.5 Mannlicher	2	no	yes	20
6.5 Carcano	2	no	yes	21
6.5 Jap	2	no	yes	34
264 Winchester Magnum	2	yes	yes	5
270 Winchester	2	yes	yes	1
270 Weatherby	2	yes	yes	5
7mm Mauser	2	yes	yes	1
7x61 Sharpe & Hart	2	yes	yes	35
7mm Remington Magnum	2	yes	yes	5
7mm Weatherby	2	yes	yes	5
7x57 Rim	2	no	yes	13
280 Remington	2	yes	yes	1
284 Winchester	2	yes	yes	1
30 M1	3	no	no	22
30-30 Winchester	2	yes	yes	2
300 Savage	2	yes	yes	1
303 Savage	2	no	no	33
303 British	2	yes	yes	11
308 Winchester	2	yes	yes	1
30-40	2	no	yes	11
308 Norma Magnum	2	yes	yes	5
7.35 Carcano	2	no	no	21
7.62 Russian	2	no	no	23
7.65 Belgium	2	no	no	24
7.7 Jap	2	no	no	1
30-06	2	yes	yes	1
300 H&H Magnum	2	yes	yes	5
300 Weatherby	2	yes	yes	5
300 Winchester Magnum	2	yes	yes	5
30 Luger	2	no	no	8

Caliber	Number Of Dies	Neck Dies	File Trim Dies	Shell Holder
32-20	2	no	no	7
32-40	2	no	no	2
32 Winchester Special	2	no	yes	2
32 Remington	2	no	no	12
33 Winchester	2	no	no	14
8mm Mauser	2	yes	yes	1
8x57 Rim	2	yes	yes	13
8mm-06	2	yes	yes	1
8mm-06 Improved	2	no	no	1
30-338	2	yes	yes	5
338 Winchester	2	yes	yes	5
348 Winchester	2	no	no	25
35 Remington	2	yes	yes	26
350 Remington Magnum	2	yes	yes	5
358 Norma Magnum	2	yes	no	5
375 H&H Magnum	2	yes	yes	5
358 Winchester	2	no	no	1
9mm Luger	3	no	no	8
38 Super Auto	3	no	no	8
38 S & W	3	no	no	28
38 Special	3	no	no	6
38-40	3	no	no	9
357 Magnum	3	no	no	6
41 Magnum	3	no	no	29
44 Special	3	no	no	30
44 Magnum	3	no	no	30
444 Marlin	3	no	no	27
44-40	3	no	no	9
45 ACP	3	no	no	1
45 Colt	3	no	no	32
45-70	3	no	no	14
458 Winchester	3	no	no	5

PACIFIC ACCESSORIES

BULLET PULLER

Heavy-duty Bullet Puller has improved collet lockup. Hardened steel handle pushes precision collet down over bullet to grab even the shortest bullets. (Collets are hardened to last a lifetime.) **$4.00** without collet.

FIRING PIN PROTECTOR

Slip Pacific's Firing Pin Protector into the chamber of your shotgun and you can dry-fire without damaging the firing pin. Firing pin falls on spring-loaded nylon button. Body is machined from solid aluminum, and cannot scratch your gun's chamber. Neoprene gasket prevents full ejection. Available in all gauges. **$3.00**

Primer Pocket Reamer

Makes GI brass reloadable by cutting away the primer pocket crimp. Available for large or small primer pockets. Made of solid steel with blued, knurled finish.

$4.00

Chamfering-Deburring Tool

Prepares inside and outside of case mouth for reloading. Removes burrs after trimming and bevels case mouth for easy bullet seating. Does not "chatter." Made of hardened solid steel with deep-blued finish. Handles all cases from 17 cal. to 45 cal.

$4.00

Carbide Expander Spindle Assembly

If you reload bottleneck cartridges, you can increase the ease and convenience of resizing by replacing your present spindle assembly with Pacific's Carbide Expander Spindle Assembly. The carbide expander provides effortless, chatter-free neck expanding, while eliminating the need for inside-neck lubrication. It also reduces neck stretching and leaves inside of neck extra smooth.

Available for both Pacific Durachrome and RCBS dies, in rifle calibers 22-30.

$8.20

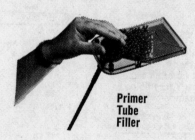

Primer Tube Filler

The Pacific Primer Tube Filler ends the time-consuming job of inserting primers one-by-one into the feed tubes of reloaders that have automatic priming systems. It holds a full box of primers and dispenses them as you turn the dial. For extra safety, it will not drop upside-down primers into the feed tube. Standard equipment on Pacific DL-155APF, DL-266, and DL-366. May also be used with other automatic priming systems that use primer tubes of size similar to Pacific's.

$9.50

Versalite Wad   Verelite Wads

One-piece plastic Verelite Wads are designed specifically for reloading. The unique post section prevents tilting or collapsing during the wad seating operation, yet it "gives" when the shotshell is fired to cushion the shot. Verelites provide maximum gas sealing and shot protection for top ballistic performance and uniform patterns.

$13.00 per thousand.

Versalite Wad

Versalite Wads are specially designed for home reloaders. The self-adjusting center acts as a shock absorber, giving top velocities with less powder. The center is engineered to avoid tipping during seating. Flared shot cup lets you slip wad over wad-seating punch.

Available in 12 and 20 gauge.

$13.00 per thousand.

Pacific Deluxe Trimmer

The Deluxe Trimmer is completely adjustable for all sizes of cartridge cases. Using the same removable head shell holder you use in your press, the Deluxe Trimmer holds shells in perfect alignment while its high-speed cutters trim the case to an exact pre-set length.

Can be mounted on your bench or clamped in a vise, and can be used with electric drill for power trimming.

$22.00 Does not include shell holder or pilot.

PACIFIC'S
MESUR-KIT™

An accurate, inexpensive portable measure at home, in the field or on the bench. Simple to use. Precise graduations make adjustable tube easy to set. Shearing action of Mesur-Kit arm gives precise charge leveling. Complete with chart for more than 1,000 load settings. Includes universal powder can.

$10.00

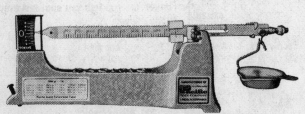

Now, Magnetic or Oil Dampened PACIFIC DELUXE SCALE

Single balance beam teams with three counterpoises to give you added speed and accuracy. Graduated over/under scale lets you check powder charge or bullet weight variation without adjustments. Accepts weights up to 500 grains. Your choice of either oil dampened (Model "O") or magnetic dampened (Model "M") models.

$22.00

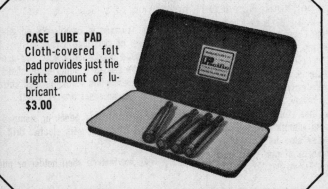

CASE LUBE PAD Cloth-covered felt pad provides just the right amount of lubricant.
$3.00

ALUMINUM POWDER FUNNEL

All-aluminum construction of Pacific's powder funnel eliminates the static electricity and powder clinging that occurs with plastic funnels. Available in three sizes.

$1.50

DELUXE POWDER MEASURE

Fast, accurate measurement of all powder types. Threaded ⅞ x 14 for use with standard measure stand or tool die head. Includes 22-30 cal. and 30-45 cal. drop tubes. Mounts easily to tool bench or shelf. Choice of rifle or pistol drum.

Measure with stand	**$28.00**
Extra measure drum	**$ 9.00**

NEW PACIFIC PISTOL POWDER MEASURE

Unique charge bar operation gives extra measurement for all pistol powders. Machined interchangeable brass bushings available for charges from 2.5 grains bullseye to 15.5 grains of 2400. Large capacity powder hopper. Uses same stand as Deluxe Measure.

Pistol Powder Measure
Complete with stand (less bushing) $15.00
Bushings (see complete list) ....$ 1.50

PISTOL POWDER MEASURE BUSHING CHART

Stock No.	Size No.	Hercules Bullseye	Hercules Unique	Winchester 230P	Alcan AL5	Alcan AL7	Hercules Herco	Hercules 2400	Dupont 4227
290006	1	2.6	NR	2.9	NR	NR	NR	NR	NR
290007	2	2.8	NR	3.2	NR	NR	NR	NR	NR
290008	3	3.0	NR	3.4	NR	NR	NR	NR	NR
290009	4	3.4	3.4	3.9	4.1	NR	NR	NR	NR
290010	5	3.7	3.6	4.3	4.4	NR	NR	NR	NR
290011	6	3.9	3.9	4.5	4.7	NR	NR	NR	NR
290012	7	4.1	4.3	4.8	5.0	NR	3.6	NR	NR
290013	8	4.4	4.5	5.0	5.4	NR	3.8	NR	NR
290014	9	4.5	4.6	5.2	5.5	NR	3.9	NR	NR
290015	10	5.1	5.3	6.0	6.3	NR	4.3	NR	7.3
290016	11	5.2	5.4	6.2	6.4	6.3	4.5	7.3	7.5
290017	12	NR	5.8	NR	6.9	6.7	4.8	7.9	8.0
290018	13	NR	6.5	NR	7.5	7.3	5.3	8.7	8.8
290019	14	NR	6.8	NR	7.9	7.7	5.7	9.3	9.4
290020	15	NR	7.2	NR	8.4	8.2	5.9	9.8	9.9
290021	16	NR	7.5	NR	8.8	8.6	6.2	10.3	10.3
290022	17	NR	8.4	NR	10.0	9.8	6.8	11.4	11.5
290023	18	NR	8.7	NR	10.4	10.2	7.3	12.0	12.1
290024	19	NR	9.2	NR	11.1	10.7	7.7	12.7	12.3
290025	20	NR	9.7	NR	11.7	11.2	8.1	13.4	13.4
290026	21	NR	10.6	NR	12.6	12.2	8.7	14.7	14.7
290027	22	NR	11.4	NR	13.4	13.2	9.5	15.5	15.7

NR = Not Recommended   **Note:** All Powder designated in Grains

PONSNESS-WARREN
SHOTSHELL RELOADING TOOLS

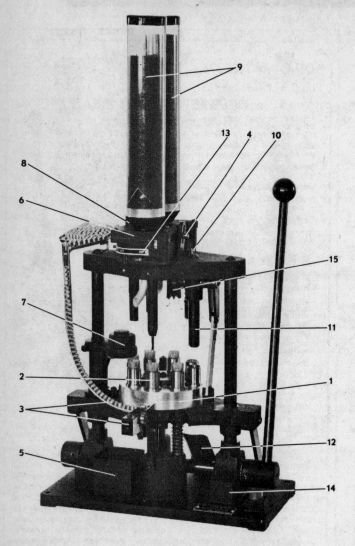

SIZE-O-MATIC 800B

THE ULTIMATE IN SHOTSHELL RELOADING

OUTSTANDING QUALITY FEATURES

1. Cylinder rotates automatically to next station.
2. Absolute resizing, eight precision ground and polished full-length sizing dies completely resize case including brass and rim. (Shell stays in sizing die through entire operation.)
3. Primer feed is ingeniously easy loading, dedendable and safe. (See illustration on right.)
4. Automatically charges shot and powder with complete safety.
5. Spent primers collect in handy metal container.
6. Desired loads obtained by changing shot and powder bushings—takes but a few minutes!
7. Cam-operated wad carrier automatically swings out to receive all types of wads.
8. Wad pressure is adjustable from 10 to 130 lbs.
9. Extra-large shot and powder reservoirs.
10. Crimp may be set to any desired depth instantly, with the turn of one screw.
11. Shell knockout rod ejects finished or unfinished shells.
12. Ejected shells drop by gravity down convenient shell chute.
13. Shutoff valves enable operator to stop flow of powder or shot at any time during cycle. Shutoff valves include a drain feature which permits complete draining of reservoirs.
14. Rugged castings are beautifully finished in baked-on black wrinkle varnish.
15. Eight and six point crimp starters are ball bearing lined to give perfect alignment every time.

All tooling in this shotshell reloader is grounded to exacting specifications, then polished or richly blued. Nylon bushings virtually eliminate wear. Each shell is held in an individual sizing die through the entire operation, affording consistently perfect, reloaded shotshells with ease and speed. The number of shells reloaded per hour is entirely dependent upon the dexterity of the operator or operators. Tests prove that one reasonably adept operator can reload paper or plastic shells, new or used, at a rate of 700 rounds per hour; two people, 1200 rounds; three people, 1800 rounds per hour. Remember, no ironing of cases is necessary with Size-O-Matic.

MODEL 800B PRICE DATA

Size-O-Matic 800B, complete in 12, 20, 28 or 410 Gauge (with 6 point crimp starter)	**$545.00**
The 28 and 410 gauge 800B's are designed primarily to load plastic casings using one piece plastic wads.	
800B Crimp Starter, Complete (8 or 6 point) each	12.00
800B Crimp Starter, Head Only (8 or 6 point) each	6.00
800B Special Paper Crimp Assembly (12 and 20 gauge only)	8.50
800B Additional Shot or Powder Bushings	1.50
800B Additional Wad Guide Fingers	1.00

PONSNESS-WARREN
SHOTSHELL RELOADING TOOLS

MULT-O-MATIC 600
THE PRO'S CHOICE

OUTSTANDING QUALITY FEATURES

1. Cylinder rotates automatically to next station.
2. Absolute resizing, precision ground and polished full-length sizing dies completely resize case including brass and rim. (Shell stays in sizing die through entire operation.)
3. Double post construction for greater leverage and wear.
4. Cam-operated wad carrier automatically tips-out to receive all types of wads.
5. Adjustable wad pressure.
6. Extra-large shot and powder reservoirs.
7. Crimp may be set to any desired depth.
8. Desired loads obtained by changing shot and powder bushings—takes but a few minutes!
9. Shot and powder may be drained out completely through shot and powder drop tube.
10. Shutoff valves enable operator to stop flow of powder or shot at any time during cycle.
11. Ejected shells drop by gravity down convenient shell chute.
12. Spent primers collect in handy metal container.
13. Rugged castings are beautifully finished in baked-on black wrinkle varnish.
14. Eight and six point crimp starters are ball bearing lined to give perfect alignment every time. (See illustration on ACCESSORIES page.)

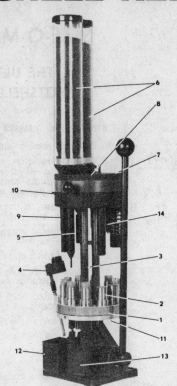

DU-O-MATIC 375
FIELD • TRAP • SKEET

OUTSTANDING QUALITY FEATURES

1. Absolute resizing, shell stays in full-length sizing die through entire operation.
2. Sizing-die arm is centered at each station by sring-loaded ball check.
3. Handy, removeable spent-primer box.
4. Large shot and powder reservoirs.
5. Powder baffle assures even flow of powder.
6. Trouble-free tip-out wad guide.
7. Double post construction for greater leverage and wear.
8. Charging ring has positive lock to prevent accidental flow of powder.
9. Shot and powder may be drained out completely through shot and powder drop tube.
10. Eight and six point crimp starters are ball bearing lined to give perfect crimp alignment everytime. (See illustration on Accessories Page.)
11. Headplate can hold two gauges simultaneously.

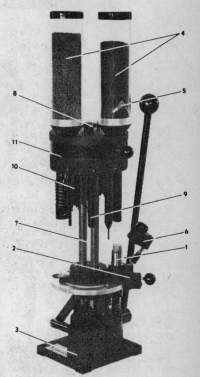

The Mult-O-Matic 600 was designed with today's serious trap and skeet shooter in mind. A precision unit, carefully machined, built to provide a high production rate for the trap shooter and complete versatility for the skeet shooter. Each shell is contained in its own full length sizing die through the entire reloading operation, affording you perfectly sized and top quality reloads in every gauge from 12 to 410. One operator can readily load at a rate of 500 rounds per hour. Additional tooling sets are easily installed in 5 to 10 minutes, and are available in all standard gauges. All tooling and dies are precision ground, then polished or richly blued. Castings are of the finest grade aluminum, precision machined, and like our other tools, beautifully finished in baked-on, black wrinkle varnish.

The most versatile reloader made. Holds tooling for one or two gauges simultaneously. Can be converted from one gauge to the other in less than five minutes. Three inch conversion kits easily installed in even less time. Factory looking reloads are made consistently by moving shell, incased in a full length sizing die, around the five station loading plate. There is no compromise on quality here! Castings are of high grade materials, precision machined, beautifully finished in baked-on, black wrinkle varnish. Full-length sizing dies and tooling are precision ground, then polished or richly blued. Under normal conditions, a single operator can load more than 250 rounds in an hour's time, paper or plastic shells—new or used.

MODEL 600 PRICE DATA

Mult-O-Matic 600 Complete in 12, 16 or 20 gauge (with 8 or 6 point crimp starter—specify) **$289.50**
Mult-O-Matic 600 Complete in 28 or 410 gauge (with 6 point crimp starter) **$319.50**
   The 28 and 410 gauge 600's are designed primarily to load plastic casings using one piece plastic wads.
600 Additional Tooling Sets, 12, 16 or 20 gauge, Complete (with 8 or 6 point crimp starter—specify) each **$109.50**
600 Additional Tooling Sets, 28 or 410 gauge, Complete (with 6 point crimp starter) each **$129.50**
   The 28 and 410 gauge tooling is designed primarily to load plastic casings using one piece plastic wads.
600 Crimp Starter, Complete (8 or 6 point) each . . . . **$ 12.00**
600 Crimp Starter Head Only (8 or 6 point) each . . . . **$ 6.00**
600 Special Paper Crimp Assembly (12 and 20 gauge only) . . . **$ 8.50**
600 Additional Shot or Powder Bushings . . . . **$ 2.00**
600 Additional Wad Guide Fingers . . . . **$ 1.00**

MODEL 375 PRICE DATA

Du-O-Matic 375, Complete in One Gauge (with 8 or 6 point crimp starter—specify) **$139.50**
375 Additional Tooling Sets—12, 16, 20, 28, 410 gauges, each . . . **$ 44.50**
375 Crimp Starter Complete (8 or 6 Point) each . . . . **$ 12.00**
375 Crimp Starter, Head Only (8 or 6 Point) each . . . . . . **$ 6.00**
375 3" Conversion Kit (12, 20 or 410 gauges) . . . . **$ 8.50**
   When you desire to go from standard length shells to 3" shells you need only to order a 3" conversion kit, but because of the differences in 3" shells lengths:
     With 20 gauge 3" dies, specify the brand of ammunition you will be using. With 410 gauge 3" dies, specify whether you will be loading paper or plastic hulls.
375 Additional Sizing Dies . . . . **$ 7.50**
375 Special Paper Crimp Assembly . . . . **$ 8.50**
375 Additional Shot or Powder Bushings . . . . **$ 2.00**
375 Additional Wad Guide Fingers . . . . **$ 1.00**
375 Headplates (no tooling included) . . . . **$ 19.95**

PONSNESS-WARREN

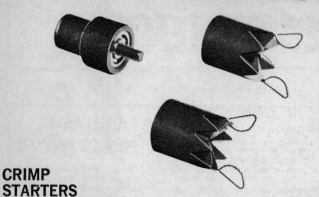

CRIMP STARTERS

Six and eight point crimp starters are ball bearing lined and have automatic pick-up to assure perfect crimp alignment every time.

Crimp Starter Complete (8 or 6 Point) .....$12.00 ea.
Crimp Starter Head Only (8 to 6 Point) ....$ 6.00 ea.

SPECIAL PAPER CRIMP ASSEMBLY

This paper crimp conversion kit is intended for shooters who reload paper shells predominately. The crimp assembly which is standard on all Ponsness-Warren tools is designed primarily for plastic shells, and while paper shells can be loaded adequately, this special paper crimp assembly provides the same optimum appearance for paper shells. Installation can be accomplished easily in just a few minutes.

Special Paper Crimp Assembly $8.50

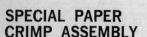

S.T.O.S. LUBRICANT

Special reloading machine and case sizing lubricant, with self-coating action. The most amazing lubricant you will ever use.

S.T.O.S. 4 oz. jar $2.95

SHOT BAFFLE

Shot baffle assures a constant weight of one inch of shot over the shot bushing at all times. This affords even greater accuracy and a reduction in cut shot.

Shot Baffle $1.50

SHOT AND POWDER BUSHINGS

These bushings are manufactured with extreme care to assure absolute accuracy and consistent performance. Shot and powder bushings are of different diameters to eliminate any possibility of their being reversed. Aluminum powder bushings absolutely eliminate sparking. All bushings are clearly and permanently marked.

Shot and Powder Bushing ....$2.00 ea.

WAD GUIDE FINGERS

This special plastic wad guide fingers give longer life, with more spring action. They assure exact wad seating, accommodating all wads. (Adaptable to most reloading machines).

WAD GUIDE FINGER ....1.00 ea.

RCBS
RELOADING EQUIPMENT

RCBS PRIMING TOOL

Precision-engineered to provide fast, accurate, and uniform seating of primers in one simple step. Single-stage leverage system is so sensitive it enables you to actually "feel" the primer being seated to the bottom of the primer pocket. This priming tool permits you to visually check each primer pocket before seating the primer; thus eliminating wasted motion or slowing down the reloading process.

Primers are released one at a time through the RCBS automatic primer feed, eliminating contamination caused by handling primers with oily fingers.

Both primer rod assemblies furnished with this tool will handle all large and small American-made Boxer-type rifle and pistol primers.

ECONOMY FEATURES: If you already have RCBS automatic primer feed tubes, and RCBS shell holders, they will fit this RCBS Priming Tool—thus eliminating the need to buy extras.

BERDAN PRIMER ROD ASSEMBLIES

Optional Berdan Primer Rod Assemblies are available in the three sizes shown below, and are interchangeable with the American Boxer-type Primer Rod Assemblies, furnished with the Priming Tool.

PART NO.	DESCRIPTION	PRICE
09460	Priming Tool (less Shell Holder)	$25.50
09461	Priming Tool (less Shell Holder and Automatic Primer Feed Tubes)	22.50
09469	Primer Rod Assembly, large	3.00
09470	Primer Rod Assembly, small	3.00
09457	Primer Rod Assembly, .255" Berdan	3.00
09458	Primer Rod Assembly, .240" Berdan	3.00
09459	Primer Rod Assembly, .217" Berdan	3.00

RCBS AUTOMATIC PRIMER FEED

Stop misfires — greasy hands never need to touch primers. Automatically drops primers one at a time into the Primer Plug and Sleeve of the Primer Arm. Adjustable Primer Stop Pin eliminates jamming found in other Automatic Primer Feeds. Easily mounted on RCBS and most "C" type Presses. The Primer Tubes for large and small primers are completely interchangeable with the Body.

PART NO.	AUTO. PRIMER FEED	PRICE
09589	Combo for large and small primers	$7.50
09590	For large primers	6.00
09591	For small primers	6.00
09592	Tube for large primers	2.10
09593	Tube for small primers	2.10
09594	Body only	4.50

RCBS PRIMER POCKET SWAGER

For fast, precision removal of primer pocket crimp from military cases. Leaves primer pocket perfectly rounded and with correct dimensions for seating of American Boxer-type primers. Will not leave oval-shaped primer pocket that reaming produces. Swager Head Assemblies furnished for large and small primer pockets — no need to buy a complete unit for each primer size. For use with all presses with standard $\frac{7}{8}$"-14 top thread, except RCBS "A-3" Press. The RCBS "A-2" Press requires the optional Case Stripper Washer.

PART NO.	POCKET SWAGER	PRICE
09495	Combo for large and small primers	$8.50
09480	For large primers	6.00
09481	For small primers	6.00
09483	Head for large primers	3.00
09484	Head for small primers	3.00
09486	Rod	.60
09498	Rod, .223 Rem*	.60
09488	Case Stripper Washer for use with RCBS "A-2" Press	.30

*Converts Part No. 09481 for use with .223 Remington cases.

RCBS UNIVERSAL PRIMER ARM

ONE PRIMER ARM HANDLES ALL PRIMERS

RCBS Primer Arms are designed for fast, accurate seating of primers. Interchangeable Primer Plugs and Sleeves eliminate necessity of having to buy a complete new Primer Arm for each primer size. Primer Plugs and Sleeves furnished for large and small primers. Body cast of rust-resistant zinc alloy. The Universal Primer Arm is designed for use with RCBS Rock Chucker and J.R. as well as most "C" type Presses.

PART NO.	UNIVERSAL PRIMER ARM	PRICE
09500	For large and small primers	$3.60
09502	Plug and Sleeve for large primers	1.20
09503	Plug and Sleeve for small primers	1.20
09504	Plug for large primers	.60
09505	Plug for small primers	.60
09506	Sleeve for large primers	.60
09507	Sleeve for small primers	.60
09508	Plug Spring (Coil)	.60
09112	Plug Setscrew	.30

RCBS PRIMER TRAY

For fast, easy handling of primers and loading Automatic Primer Feed Tubes, place primers in this tray, shake tray horizontally, and primers will automatically position themselves anvil side up. Sturdy plastic case.

PART NO.	PRIMER TRAY	PRICE
09475	Single Tray	$ 1.00

RCBS PRIMER POCKET BRUSH

A slight twist of this tool thoroughly cleans residue out of primer pockets. Interchangeable stainless steel brushes, for large and small primer pockets, attaches easily to Accessory Handle.

PART NO.	PRIMER POCKET BRUSH	PRICE
09574	Complete, Combo	$5.00
09575	Complete, Large	3.00
09576	Complete, Small	3.00
09577	Brush Only, Large	2.40
09578	Brush Only, Small	2.40

RCBS RELOADING TOOLS

RCBS CASE LUBE KIT

Everything you need for proper case lubrication! Kit contains RCBS Case Lube Pad, 2 ounce tube RCBS Resizing Lubricant and RCBS Accessory Handle with .22 and .30 caliber Case Neck Brushes. See descriptions of items below.

PART NO.	DESCRIPTION	PRICE
09335	Case Lube Kit	$5.70

RCBS RESIZING LUBRICANT

A must for proper lubrication of cases before sizing or forming. Easily applied to cases with an RCBS Case Lube Pad. Packaged in convenient 2 ounce tube.

PART NO.	RESIZING LUBRICANT	PRICE
09300	Single Tube	$ .75

RCBS CASE NECK BRUSH

A handy tool for removing dirt and powder residue, and for lightly lubricating the insides of case necks to ease neck expanding operation. Accessory Handle accepts interchangeable nylon bristle Case Neck Brushes in the calibers shown below. Order Accessory Handle, and Brush in caliber of your choice.

PART NO.	DESCRIPTION	PRICE
09330	Accessory Handle*	$1.00
	CASE NECK BRUSHES	
09319	.17 caliber	.60
09320	.22 caliber	.60
09321	6mm caliber	.60
09322	.25 caliber	.60
09323	.270 caliber	.60
09324	.30 caliber	.60
09325	.35 caliber	.60
09326	.45 caliber	.60

*May be used with the RCBS Primer Pocket Brush.

RCBS CASE LUBE PAD

This companion to RCBS Resizing Lubricant is ideal for lubricating cases before sizing or forming. Cases rolled lightly across Pad pick up just the right amount of lubricant. Plastic cover to protect pad.

PART NO	CASE LUBE PAD	PRICE
09305	1 Pad	$ 3.00

RCBS RELOADING SCALE

A major improvement in reloading scales. Gives fast, accurate weighings of powder charges and cartridge components, from 1/10th to 510 grains. **NEW Micrometer Poise** permits fast precision adjustments from 1/10th to 10 grains by merely rotating micrometer-type cylinder. **NEW Approach-to-Weight** Feature visually tells reloader when he is approaching the pre-set weight. **Easy-to-read scale beam** is graduated in 1/10th grain increments; has conventional large poise and extra-deep notches. **Magnetic Damper** eliminates beam oscillation. All-metal base and extra-large leveling foot reduce tipping. Weighted, anti-tip pan hanger, and pan platform accommodate long cartridges and components. **$29⁹⁵**

PART NO.	DESCRIPTION	PRICE
09070	Reloading Scale	$29.95

RCBS POWDER TRICKLER

For fast, easy balancing of scales with precision powder charges. Merely twist knob and powder trickles into the scale pan a kernel at a time. Has large capacity powder reservoir. Extra large base minimizes tipping.

PART NO.	DESCRIPTION	PRICE
09094	Powder Trickler	$4.50

RCBS POWDER MEASURE STAND

NEW IMPROVED

Now more height — a full seven inches from the reloading bench to the bottom of the threads! The ideal accessory for raising Powder Measure to proper working height. Permits placing of Reloading Scale or cases in loading block under Powder Measure Drop Tube. Easily bolts to loading bench. For all Powder Measures with standard ⅞" - 14 thread.

PART NO.	DESCRIPTION	PRICE
09030	Powder Measure Stand	$8.95

RCBS UNIFLOW POWDER MEASURE

This tool saves the time of having to weigh every powder charge when reloading a quantity of cases. With it you will be able to throw consistently accurate and uniform powder charges directly into cases. RCBS Precisioneered Measuring Cylinder pours powder into case to eliminate clogging that occurs in powder measures that "dump" charges. Adjusts quickly and easily from one charge to another without emptying powder hopper. Powder level visible at all times. Includes stand plate for mounting on press or bench, and two drop tubes to fit from .22 to .45 caliber cases. Optional .17 caliber drop tube also available. Choice of large measuring cylinder for rifle cases, or small measuring cylinder for bench rest or pistol cases. **$25⁵⁰**

PART NO.	POWDER MEASURE	PRICE
09001	With Large Measuring Cylinder	$25.50
09002	With Small Measuring Cylinder	25.50
09000	Combo with Large & Small Measuring Cylinders	31.50
09003	Large Measuring Cylinder Assembly*	7.50
09004	Small Measuring Cylinder Assembly*	7.50
09028	Drop Tube .17 caliber	3.00

*Consists of Measuring Cylinder and Measuring Screw.

RCBS POWDER FUNNEL

For powder charging just a few cases at a time! Large, easy-to-use, plastic Powder Funnel in two sizes: .22 to .45 calibers, and .17 caliber. Specially designed drop tube prevents powder spills around case mouths. Antistatic treatment prevents powder from sticking. Square lip stops Funnel from rolling.

PART NO.	POWDER FUNNEL	PRICE
09090	.22-.45 calibers	$1.20
09088	.17 caliber	2.40

RCBS RELOADING TOOLS

RELOADER SPECIAL
RCBS J.R. PRESS COMBINATION OFFER

Costs less than 9 boxes of .30-06 cartridges

This RCBS J.R. Press is the Ideal setup to get started reloading your own rifle and pistol ammo — from the largest Magnums down to .22 Hornets. This Press develops ample leverage and pressure to perform all reloading tasks including (1) resizing cases their full length, (2) forming cases from one caliber into another, (3) making bullets. Rugged Block "O" Frame, designed by RCBS, prevents Press from springing out of alignment — even under tons of pressure. Extra-long ram-bearing surface minimizes wobble and side play. Comfort grip handle. Converts to up or down stroke in minutes. Standard 7/8"-14 thread accepts all popular dies and reloading accessories. Price includes: PRIMER CATCHER, to collect ejected primers; RCBS UNIVERSAL PRIMER ARM with large and small primer plugs and sleeves; RCBS SHELL HOLDER; one set of RCBS DIES in choice of calibers shown below.

PART NO.	J.R. PRESS, LESS DIES	PRICE
09351	With #3 Shell Holder	$40.50
09356	Less Shell Holder	39.00
09357	Less Primer Arm & Shell Holder	37.50

$46⁵⁰ → $46.50

ROCK CHUCKER "COMBO"
RCBS R.C. PRESS COMBINATION OFFER

For Heavy-Duty Reloading

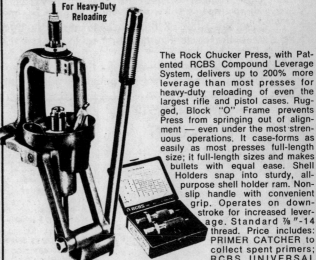

U.S. Pat. No. 2,847,895

The Rock Chucker Press, with Patented RCBS Compound Leverage System, delivers up to 200% more leverage than most presses for heavy-duty reloading of even the largest rifle and pistol cases. Rugged, Block "O" Frame prevents Press from springing out of alignment — even under the most strenuous operations. It case-forms as easily as most presses full-length size; it full-length sizes and makes bullets with equal ease. Shell Holders snap into sturdy, all-purpose shell holder ram. Non-slip handle with convenient grip. Operates on down-stroke for increased leverage. Standard 7/8"-14 thread. Price includes: PRIMER CATCHER to collect spent primers; RCBS UNIVERSAL PRIMER ARM with large and small primer plugs and sleeves; one RCBS SHELL HOLDER; one set of RCBS DIES in choice of calibers shown below.

PART NO.	ROCK CHUCKER PRESS, LESS DIES	PRICE
09361	With #3 Shell Holder	$61.50
09366	Less Shell Holder	60.00
09367	Less Primer Arm and Shell Holder	58.50

$67⁵⁰ → $67.50

RCBS DIE CHART

RELOADER SPECIAL PART NO.	ROCK CHUCKER COMBO PART NO.	RIFLE CALIBERS	RELOADER SPECIAL PART NO.	ROCK CHUCKER COMBO PART NO.	RIFLE CALIBERS	RELOADER SPECIAL PART NO.	ROCK CHUCKER COMBO PART NO.	PISTOL CALIBERS
10071	10081	.218 Bee	14171	14181	.284 Winchester	10471	10481	.22 Remington Jet
10271	10281	.22 Hornet	17171	17181	7.5mm Schmidt-Rubin	10871	10881	.221 Remington Fire Ball
10471	10481	.22 Remington Jet	14371	14381	7.65x53mm Mauser (Belgian)	21074	21084	.25 ACP (.25 Automatic)
10571	10581	.22 Savage High Power	14471	14481	7.7mmx58 Japanese Arisaka	20074	20084	.32 ACP (7.65mm Auto)
10671	10681	.22-250 (.22 Varminter)	18071	18081	.30 M1 Carbine	20174	20184	.32 Smith & Wesson Long
10771	10781	.220 Swift	14671	14681	.30-30 Winchester	18171	18181	.32-20 Winchester
10871	10881	.221 Remington Fire Ball	14771	14781	.30-40 Krag	18275	18285	.357 Magnum (RN)
10971	10981	.222 Remington	14871	14881	.30-06 Springfield	18276	18286	.357 Magnum (SWC)
11071	11081	.222 Remington Magnum	15071	15081	.300 H&H Magnum	18277	18287	.357 Magnum (WC)
11171	11181	.223 Remington (5.56mm)	15171	15181	.300 Savage	20274	20284	.38 Colt Super Automatic
11371	11381	.225 Winchester	15271	15281	.300 Weatherby Magnum	20374	20384	.38 Smith & Wesson
17071	17081	.240 Weatherby Magnum	15371	15381	.300 Winchester Magnum	18375	18385	.38 Special (RN)
11471	11481	.243 Winchester	15471	15481	.303 British	18376	18386	.38 Special (SWC)
11571	11581	6mm Remington (.244 Rem.)	15571	15581	.308 Winchester	18377	18387	.38 Special (WC)
11871	11881	.25-20 Winchester	15671	15681	.308 Norma Magnum	20474	20484	.380 Auto Pistol
12071	12081	.25-06	15771	15781	.32 Winchester Special	18475	18485	.38-40 Winchester (RN)
12171	12181	.25-35 Winchester	15971	15981	8x57 Mauser (8mm Mauser)	20574	20584	9mm Luger
12271	12281	.250 Savage (.250-3000 Sav.)	16371	16381	.338 Winchester Magnum	18575	18585	.41 Magnum (RN)
12371	12381	.256 Winchester Magnum	16471	16481	.348 Winchester	18576	18586	.41 Magnum (SWC)
12571	12581	.257 Roberts	16571	16581	.35 Remington	18577	18587	.41 Magnum (WC)
12671	12681	.257 Weatherby Magnum	16671	16681	.350 Remington Magnum	18675	18685	.44 Magnum (RN)
12771	12781	.264 Winchester Magnum	16971	16981	.375 H&H Magnum	18676	18686	.44 Magnum (SWC)
13171	13181	6.5mm Remington Magnum	20674	20684	.38-55 Winchester-Ballard	18677	18687	.44 Magnum (WC)
13271	13281	6.5mmx55 Swedish Mauser	20774	20784	.444 Marlin	18776	18786	.44 Special (SWC)
13471	13481	.270 Weatherby Magnum	20874	20884	.458 Winchester Magnum	18875	18885	.44-40 Win. (.44 Win.) (RN)
13571	13581	.270 Winchester	20974	20984	.45-70 U.S. Government	18975	18985	.45 Auto (.45 ACP) (RN)
13671	13681	7mm Remington Magnum				18976	18986	.45 Auto (.45 ACP) (SWC)
13771	13781	7mm Weatherby Magnum				18977	18987	.45 Auto (.45 ACP) (WC)
13871	13881	7x57 Mauser (7mm Mauser)				19075	19085	.45 Auto Rim (RN)
14071	14081	.280 Remington				19175	19185	.45 Colt (RN)
						19176	19186	.45 Colt (SWC)

NOTE: The following abbreviations are used to indicate bullet seater plug types: (RN) Round Nose, (SWC) Semi-Wadcutter, (WC) Wadcutter.

RCBS RELOADING TOOLS

A common mistake to avoid in buying reloading Dies is to judge Die performance and quality by outside looks. It's what's *inside* a Die that counts *inside* your gun chamber.

Each Die chamber is precision machined to resize cases down to the critical requirements of each caliber of gun chamber. After sizing, the case mouth is then expanded to the correct circumference to accept the new bullet.

RCBS Dies are machined—one at a time, from scientifically heat-hardened steels—to outlast a dozen gun

barrels. Instead of decorative or other chrome-plating, the natural steel finish of each RCBS Die is hand-polished.

The final test of a Die's performance and quality is the reloaded cartridge you put into your gun chamber.

All RCBS Seater Dies for 2 and 3 Die Sets have built-in crimpers for fast, precise crimping to bullet cannelure. Bullets can be seated without crimping by unscrewing Die one full turn. All RCBS Dies come packed in heavy-duty plastic storage boxes.

RCBS 2-Die Set for bottle neck type Rifle and Pistol cases.

GROUP A CALIBER	FULL LENGTH DIE SET 1½ lbs. $16.50 PART NO.	TRIM DIE ½ lb. $8.10 PART NO.
.218 Bee	10001	10065†
.22 Hornet	10201	10265†
.22 Remington Jet	10401	10465†
.22 Savage High-Power	10501	10565
.22-250 (.22 Varminter)	10601	10665
.220 Swift	10701	10765
.221 Remington Fire Ball	10801	10865†
.222 Remington	10901	10965
.222 Remington Magnum	11001	11065
.223 Remington (5.56mm)	11101	11165
.224 Weatherby Magnum	11201	11265
.225 Winchester	11301	11365
.240 Weatherby Magnum	17001	17065
.243 Winchester	11401	11465
6mm Remington (.244 Rem.)	11501	11565
.25-20 Winchester	11801	11865
.25-06	12001	12065
.25-35 Winchester	12101	12165
.250 Savage (.250-3000 Savage)	12201	12265†
.256 Winchester Magnum	12301	12365
.257 Roberts	12501	12565
.257 Weatherby Magnum	12601	12665
.264 Winchester Magnum	12701	12765
6.5mmx50 Japanese Arisaka	13001	13065
6.5mm Remington Magnum	13101	13165
6.5mmx55 Swedish Mauser	13201	13265
.270 Weatherby Magnum	13401	13465
.270 Winchester	13501	13565
7mm Remington Magnum	13601	13665
7mm Weatherby Magnum	13701	13765
7x57 Mauser (7mm Mauser)	13801	13865
.280 Remington	14001	14065
.284 Winchester	14101	14165
7.5mm Schmidt-Rubin	17101	17165
7.65x53mm Mauser (Belgian)	14301	14365

GROUP A Continued CALIBER	FULL LENGTH DIE SET 1½ lbs. $16.50 PART NO.	TRIM DIE ½ lb. $8.10 PART NO.
7.7mmx58 Japanese Arisaka	14401	14465
.30-30 Winchester	14601	14665
.30-40 Krag	14701	14765
.30-06 Springfield	14801	14865
.300 Holland & Holland Magnum	15001	15065
.300 Savage	15101	15165
.300 Weatherby Magnum	15201	15265
.300 Winchester Magnum	15301	15365
.303 British	15401	15465
.308 Winchester	15501	15565
.308 Norma Magnum	15601	15665
.32 Winchester Special	15701	15765
.32-40 Winchester	15801	15865
8x57 Mauser (8mm Mauser)	15901	15965
8mm-06	16001	16065
.338 Winchester Magnum	16301	16365
.348 Winchester	16401	16465
.35 Remington	16501	16565
.350 Remington Magnum	16601	16665
.358 Winchester	16701	16765
.375 Holland & Holland Magnum	16901	16965

GROUP D CALIBER	FULL LENGTH DIE SET 1½ lbs. $19.50	TRIM DIE ½ lb. $9.60
.30 Luger (7.65mm Luger)	25001	— —
.30 Mauser (7.63mm Mauser)	25101	— —
.17 Remington	32001	32065
.17-222 Remington	25501	25565
.17-223 Remington	25701	25765
.219 Zipper	26001	26065
.22 K-Hornet	26201	26265†
6mmx47 Remington	26801	26865
6mm-284 Winchester	32101	32165
.25 Remington	27101	27165
.25-06 Improved (40°)	27401	27465
.257 Improved (40°)	32201	32265
6.5mmx52 Carcano	27601	27665
6.5mmx54 Mann.-Schoenauer	27701	27765
6.5mm-06	27801	27865
7mmx57 Improved (40°)	28301	28365
7mmx64 Brenneke	28501	28565
7.62mm Russian	29001	29065
.30 Remington	29201	29265
.30-338 Winchester Magnum	29401	29465
.30-06 Improved (40°)	29501	29565
.303 Savage	29601	29665
8x57 JR./.318"	30101	30165
8.15x46 Rim	30401	30465
.33 Winchester	30501	30565
.340 Weatherby Magnum	30601	30665
.35 Whelen	30701	30765
.358 Norma Magnum	31001	31065
.378 Weatherby Magnum	31601	31665

†Extended Shell Holder required for trimming or forming.

RCBS 3-Die Set for straight wall type Rifle and Pistol cases.

GROUP B CALIBER	3-DIE SET 1½ lbs. $16.50	TRIM DIE ½ lb. $8.10
.30 M-1 Carbine (RN)	18005	18065†
.32-20 Winchester (RN)	18105	18165†
.357 Magnum (RN)	18205	
.357 Magnum (SWC)	18206	18265†
.357 Magnum (WC)	18207	
.38 Special (RN)	18305	
.38 Special (SWC)	18306	18365†
.38 Special (WC)	18307	
.38-40 Winchester (RN)*	18405	18465†
.41 Magnum (RN)	18505	
.41 Magnum (SWC)	18506	18565†
.41 Magnum (WC)	18507	
.44 Magnum (RN)	18605	
.44 Magnum (SWC)	18606	18665†
.44 Magnum (WC)	18607	
.44 Special (SWC)	18706	18765†
.44-40 Win. (.44 Win.) (RN)*	18805	18865†
.45 Automatic (.45 ACP) (RN)	18905	
.45 Automatic (.45 ACP) (SWC)	18906	18965†
.45 Automatic (.45 ACP) (WC)	18907	
.45 Auto Rim (RN)	19005	19065†
.45 Colt (RN)	19105	19165†
.45 Colt (SWC)	19106	

GROUP E CALIBER	3-DIE SET 1½ lbs. $19.50	TRIM DIE ½ lb. $9.60
.41 Long Colt (RN)	35305	35365†

*Jacketed Bullets only

†Extended Shell Holder required for trimming or forming.
NOTE: The following abbreviations are used to indicate Bullet Seater Plug types: (RN) Roundnose, (SWC) Semi-Wadcutter, (WC) Wadcutter.

IMPORTANT

To Convert the .38 Special Die Set for use with .357 Magnum cases, order a #09623 Medium Decapping Assembly at $2.70 for installation in the Sizer Die. The Decapping Pin furnished in the Expander Die is too short for the magnum cases. The Dies must then be backed away from the Shell Holder to allow for the difference in case length.

The .44 Special Dies may be used with .44 Magnum cases by backing away the Dies from the Shell Holder to allow for the difference in case length.

RCBS RELOADING TOOLS

Die Groups:

Dies are divided into groups for easy identification and pricing. Group A, B, and C Dies ar the most popular, and therefore are our lowest priced. Group D, E, and F Dies cost slightly more because they ar made in smaller quantities, spreading machining costs over fewer Dies.

RCBS 3-Die Set for straight wall type Rifle and Pistol cases.

GROUP C

CALIBER	3-DIE SET 1½ lbs. $16.50	TRIM DIE ½ lb. $9.60
.25 Automatic (.25 ACP)	21004	— —
.32 ACP (7.65mm Automatic)	20004	— —
.32 Smith & Wesson Long	20104	— —
.38 Colt Super Automatic	20204	— —
.38 Smith & Wesson	20304	— —
.380 Auto Pistol	20404	— —
9mm Luger	20504	— —
.38-55 Winchester & Ballard	20604	20665
.444 Marlin	20704	20765
.458 Winchester Magnum	20804	20865
.45-70 U.S. Government	20904	20965

GROUP F

CALIBER	3-DIE SET 1½ lbs. $19.50	TRIM DIE ½ lb. $9.60
8mm Nambu	36404	— —
.50-70 U.S. Government	38704	38765

RCBS TRIM DIE

A specially hardened Die for trimming cases to the correct overall length with a file. Doubles as a visual case gauge — if any portion of the case mouth is above the face of the Die, it is too long! Standard ⅞"-14 thread. Available for most calibers as shown in tables on these pages.

Some calibers of cases, such as those mentioned below, require special handling to ensure proper chambering, and a minimum of resizing to extend case life. Because Standard Dies cannot efficiently meet these requirements, we have designed the Specialized Dies listed below. NOTE: Cases reloaded with Specialized Dies must be used **only** in those rifles and pistols mentioned.

SMALL BASE DIES

For reloading cases to be used **only** in automatic, pump, slide, and some lever-action rifles including the Browning lever-action rifles in .243 Winchester and .308 Winchester calibers.

GROUP A

CALIBER	SMALL BASE DIE SET 1½ lbs. $16.50	SMALL BASE SIZER DIE ¾ lb. $10.80
.223 Remington (5.56mm) (SB)	11103	11131
.243 Winchester (SB)	11403	11431
6mm Rem. (.244 Rem.) (SB)	11503	11531
.270 Winchester (SB)	13503	13531
.280 Remington (SB)	14003	14031
.284 Winchester (SB)	14103	14131
.30-06 Springfield (SB)	14803	14831
.300 Savage (SB)	15103	15131
.308 Winchester (SB)	15503	15531

ULTRA SMALL BASE DIES

For reloading **only** .243 and .308 Winchester cases to be used in Savage Models 99 and 110 rifles. **Not** recommended for cases to be used in any other rifles.

GROUP A

CALIBER	ULTRA SMALL BASE DIE SET 1½ lbs. $16.50	ULTRA SMALL BASE SIZER DIE ¾ lb. $10.80
.243 Winchester (USB)	11404	11433
.308 Winchester (USB)	15504	15533

BROWNING AUTOMATIC RIFLE DIES

For reloading **only** 7mm Remington Magnum and .300 Winchester Magnum cases to be used in Browning Automatic Rifles. **Not** recommended for cases to be used in any other rifles.

NOTE: Browning Automatic Rifles in .243 Winchester, .270 Winchester, .30-06 and .308 Winchester calibers require **Small Base Dies** shown above. The .338 caliber Rifle requires standard **Group A Dies** shown on preceding page.

GROUP A

CALIBER	B.A.R. DIE SET 1½ lbs. $16.50	B.A.R. SIZER DIE ¾ lb. $10.80
7mm Remington Magnum (BAR)	13605	13640
.300 Winchester Magnum (BAR)	15305	15340

NECK DIES

For use with bottleneck type cases only. Sizer Die sizes the neck of the case (not shoulder or body) only enough to hold the bullet. Available in calibers listed below — other calibers on Special Order at extra cost.

GROUP A

CALIBER	NECK DIE SET 1½ lbs. $16.50	NECK SIZER DIE ¾ lb. $10.80
.22-250 (.22 Varminter)	10602	10630
.222 Remington	10902	10930
.222 Remington Magnum	11002	11030
.223 Remington (5.56mm)	11102	11130
.243 Winchester	11402	11430
6mm Remington (.244 Rem.)	11502	11530
.25-06	12002	12030
.270 Winchester	13502	13530
7mm Remington Magnum	13602	13630
7x57 Mauser (7mm Mauser)	13802	13830
.30-06 Springfield	14802	14830
.300 Winchester Magnum	15302	15330
.308 Winchester	15502	15530

CARBIDE DIES

No case lubrication necessary, because Tungsten Carbide insert pushes residue and dirt ahead of case instead of into Die wall.* Tapered insert eliminates belt or shoulder left on case by ordinary Tungsten Carbide Sizer Dies.

*NOTE: .30 M-1 Carbine cases must be lightly lubricated because of case design. The .30 M-1 Carbine Carbide Sizer Die is for use with American factory cases only — not foreign or military cases.

GROUP B

CALIBER	3-DIE CARBIDE SET 1½ lbs. $31.50	CARBIDE SIZER DIE ½ lb. $21.00
.30 M-1 Carbine (RN)	18009*	18037**
.357 Magnum (RN)	18209	
.357 Magnum (SWC)	18210	
.357 Magnum (WC)	18211	18237
.38 Special (RN)	18309	
.38 Special (SWC)	18310	
.38 Special (WC)	18311	
.41 Magnum (RN)	18509	
.41 Magnum (SWC)	18510	18537
.41 Magnum (WC)	18511	
.44 Magnum (RN)	18609	
.44 Magnum (SWC)	18610	18637
.44 Magnum (WC)	18611	
.44 Special (SWC)	18710	
.45 Auto (.45 ACP) (RN)	18909	
.45 Auto (.45 ACP) (SWC)	18910	18937
.45 Auto (.45 ACP) (WC)	18911	
.45 Auto Rim (RN)	19009	
.45 Colt (RN)	19109	19137
.45 Colt (SWC)	19110	
	*$45.00	**$34.50

GROUP C

CALIBER	3-DIE CARBIDE SET 1½ lbs. $33.00	CARBIDE SIZER DIE ½ lb. $22.50
.38 Colt Super Automatic	20209	20237
.380 Auto Pistol	20409	20437
9mm Luger	20509*	20537**
	*$39.00	**$28.50

RCBS RELOADING TOOLS

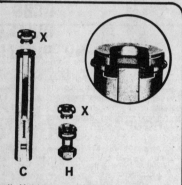

Shell Holders are Precisioneered to the most exacting tolerances to hold the case securely and to eliminate any problems with headspace or improper sizing. Interchangeable Shell Holders available to fit practically every caliber. For all RCBS, as well as most "C" and "H" type Presses. Precision machined Shell Holder Rams for use with the presses indicated. Holds Shell Holder firmly in place — free from side movement and wobble. "Snap Action" Clip Spring allows Shell Holder to be rotated to any convenient angle without loss of alignment for perfect primer seating.

SHELL HOLDERS

PART NO.	GROUP NO.	PART NO.	GROUP NO.
09201	1	09216	16
09202	2	09217	17
09203	3	09218	18
09204	4	09219	19
09205	5	09220	20
09206	6	09221	21
09207	7	09222	22
09208	8	09223	23
09209	9	09225	25
09210	10	09226	26
09211	11	09227	27
09212	12	09228	28
09213	13	09229	29
09214	14	09230	30
09215	15	09231	31

KEY	PART NO.	SHELL HOLDER RAMS	PRICE
C	09109	For RCBS J.R. and most "C" Presses	3.90
H	09180	For "H" Presses	3.90
X	*	Shell Holder	3.00

*Order from chart above.

RCBS DIE BOX

Heavy-duty plastic storage box — with "T" lock — protects and holds Dies firmly in place. Includes label for recording loads on inside lid. Label on end of box identifies caliber. Holds from one to four Dies.

PART NO.	DIE BOX	PRICE
09890	Each	$ .90
09894	4-Pack Carton	3.00

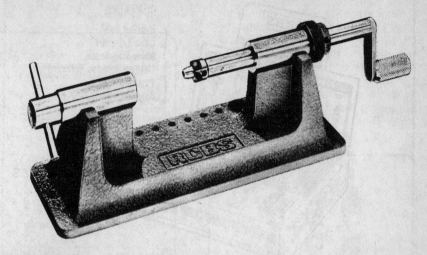

RCBS ROTARY CASE TRIMMER
PRECISIONEERED®

This tool is used to (1) trim to standard length those cases which have stretched after repeated firings; (2) to trim a quantity of cases to the same length for uniform bullet seating; (3) to correct uneven case mouths.

The RCBS Rotary Case Trimmer works just like a lathe. To trim a brass case to the desired length — quickly, easily, and accurately — you lock the case into the trimmer collet. Then adjust the cutting blade to the length you wish case trimmed . . . turn the handle a few times . . . and your case is trimmed. Neatly and accurately. Bevel and deburr the trimmed case mouth with an RCBS Burring Tool and you're ready to reload it!

Interchangeable quick-release collets, available for all popular calibers (.17 to .45), lock cases securely into place for trimming. Trimmer Pilots are Precisioneered to the exact dimension of the case mouth, and lock into the cutter with a setscrew. This eliminates wobbling and ensures perfect vertical and horizontal alignment of case. Pilots are interchangeable and available in twenty sizes to fit from .17 to .45 caliber cases.

Double lock rings on the cutting assembly permit any quantity of cases to be trimmed to the same length with a single adjustment. Cutter blades are made of hardened mill-type steel for extended service life, and removable for sharpening.

The RCBS Case Trimmer is 100 percent metal — no wood or plastic. Has slots for holding extra collets and pilots. Base can be secured to bench with screws.

09368   CASE TRIMMER WITH NO. 1 COLLET AND .30 CALIBER PILOT

Price
$25.00

CASE TRIMMER COLLET
Price $3.25

PART NO.	COLLET NO.	PART NO.	COLLET NO.
09371	1	09373	3
09372	2	09374	4

CASE TRIMMER PILOT
Price $1.00

PART NO.	PILOT CAL.	PART NO.	PILOT CAL.
09377	.17	09387	.33
09378	.22	09388	.34
09379	.24	09390	.36
09380	.25	09391	.37
09381	.26	09392	.40
09382	.27	09393	.41
09383	.28	09394	.44
09384	.30	09395	.45
09385	.31	09396	.45-R
09386	.32		

RCBS RELOADING TOOLS

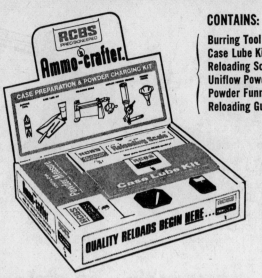

CONTAINS:

Burring Tool
Case Lube Kit
Reloading Scale
Uniflow Powder Measure
Powder Funnel
Reloading Guide

Contains everything you'll need to prepare cases for reloading, and handling powder charges. No more running around for bits and pieces — no more settling for second best. It's all **here!** It's all Precisioneered by RCBS. And, it's all available in one time-saving, money-saving visit to your favorite gun shop.

BURRING TOOL: For beveling and smoothing .17 to .45 caliber case mouths for ease of precision bullet seating. **CASE LUBE KIT:** Case Lube Pad; 2-oz. tube of Resizing Lubricant; Accessory Handle with interchangeable .22 and .30 caliber Case Neck Brushes. **RELOADING SCALE** with Micrometer Poise gives fast, accurate weighings of powder charges for setting your Uniflow Powder Measure. Weighs from 1/10th to 510 grains — powder or bullets. **UNIFLOW POWDER MEASURE:** Saves time of weighing each charge when charging a quantity of cases. Accurately measures and pours powder directly into each case with a flip of the handle.

POWDER FUNNEL: When powder charging just a few cases, powder can be poured from powder scale pan through plastic funnel and into cases without spilling. Fits .22 to .45 caliber cases.

$64.95

PART NO.	DESCRIPTION	PRICE
09050	Ammo-crafter Kit	$64.95

RCBS BULLET PULLER

A valuable tool for pulling bullets from cases that have wrong powder charges, or for salvaging bullets from old ammo. Pulls bullets of any length or shape without damaging or marking them. Soft lead bullets may distort. Interchangeable Bullet Puller Collets work like a draw collet on a lathe, securely holding the bullet as the case is pulled away. Each Collet is precision-machined internally to the exact bullet diameter. Fits all reloading presses with standard ⅞"-14 thread. Order Bullet Puller plus one Collet in caliber of your choice from chart below.

PART NO.	DESCRIPTION		PRICE
09440	BULLET PULLER (less Collet)		$3.75
	BULLET PULLER COLLETS		3.25

PART NO.	CALIBER	PART NO.	CALIBER
09419	.17	09428	.32/8mm
09420	.22	09429	.348
09421	6mm	09430	.35/.38 Spec.
09422	.25	09431	.375
09423	6.5mm	09432	.40
09424	.270	09433	.41
09425	7mm	09435	.44/11mm
09426	.30/7.35 Carc	09436	.45
09427	.338		

RCBS STUCK CASE REMOVER

Removes stuck cases from Sizer Dies quickly and efficiently. To use, back Die Expander-Decapping unit away from case head, drill case head and tap. Then place RCBS Stuck Case Remover on top of case head and turn hexhead screw until stuck case pulls free!

PART NO.	DESCRIPTION	PRICE
09340	STUCK CASE REMOVER	$4.50

RCBS BURRING TOOL

For beveling and removing burrs from case mouths of new factory cases, newly formed and trimmed cases. To bevel, insert pointed end of tool into case mouth and twist slightly. To remove burrs, place other end of tool over case mouth and twist. Centering pin keeps case aligned during deburring. Precision-machined and hardened for years of usage. Knurled for use by hand or in lathe. For .17 to .45 calibers.

PART NO.	DESCRIPTION	PRICE
09349	Burring Tool	$4.50

RCBS SETSCREW WRENCH

Here's a handy item for every reloading bench. The convenient hexagonal plastic handle will not roll off bench. Size is stamped in large easy-to-read numbers for quick identification. Available in two sizes to fit all popular RCBS products as shown below:

3/32" Dies/Trim Dies/Case Forming Dies/Automatic Primer Feed attaching screws, bullet molds.

5/64" Universal Primer Arm (new)•Case Trimmer

PART NO.	SETSCREW WRENCH	PRICE
09646	Combo	$2.25
09647	3/32"	1.20
09648	5/64"	1.20

RCBS RELOADING GUIDE

Discover how safe and easy reloading actually is. Shows step by step with illustrations how to reload rifle and pistol ammunition. Contains articles by famous gun writers and instructions by renowned experts and manufacturers. Lists tools you need to start reloading and a beginner's table of powder loads.

PART NO.	RELOADING GUIDE	PRICE
09298	Each	$ 2.00

REDDING RELOADING TOOLS

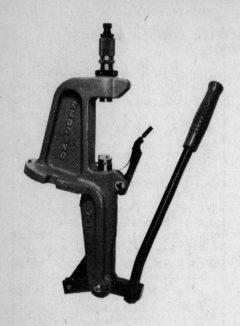

IMPROVED "C" PRESS
MODEL No. 7

New improvements include: Stronger frame (ASTM 30 alloy) for the heaviest reloading task; extremely shallow throat eliminates deflection; stronger (alloy steel) lower linkage; added rear mounting lug—prevents springing and "bench splitting;" snap-in shell holder may be rotated to any position; accepts all standard ⅞-14 threaded dies and all universal shell holders. Press includes primer arm for seating both large and small primers.
No. 7 "C" Press, complete $34.00
No. 7K Kit includes press, shell holder, case lube and one set of dies . $51.00

SUPER 32
SHOTSHELL RELOADER

This is a turret-type shotshell press capable of producing in excess of 300 reloads per hour. All reloading operations performed at one station eliminates shell handling. Resizes cases of any brass length without adjustments. Other features include a foolproof charge bar, fully adjustable wad pressure and a tilt top which allows easy change of powder and shot. The most unique feature of this press is a quick-release die head assembly which allows a complete gauge change in seconds. Press comes complete with all necessary bushings, dies, shell holder and crimp starter.
Super 32, complete, 12 or 20 ga. $89.50
16, 28 or .410 ga. $93.50

TURRET RELOADING PRESS
MODEL 25:

Extremely rugged, ideal for production reloading. Choice of four or six Station Turrets. No need to move shell, just rotate turret head to positive alignment. Ram accepts any standard snap-in shell holder. Includes primer arm for seating both small and large primers.
No. 25 Press, complete $81.00
No. 25K Kit, includes press, shell holder, case lube and one set of dies.
.... $98.00
No. 25T Extra Turret (4 or 6 Station) $18.00

REDDING RELOADING TOOLS

MASTER CASE TRIMMER, MODEL 14

A unique spindle design permits all operations to be done with the handle of the tool: After insertion of case, a one-quarter turn clockwise of handle locks the case; handle is then advanced toward cutter and rotated clockwise to cut; handle is withdrawn to remove case neck from pilot; handle is turned about one-quarter turn counter-clockwise to release case. The handle is provided with a large knurled and rounded knob that rotates freely under pressure.

Supplied with two cutting blades.

Retail, Less Pilot $18.50
Extra Pilots ....$1.25 each.

MASTER CASE TRIMMER MODEL No. 14K

This unit features a universal collet that accepts all rifle and pistol cases. This trimmer is also unique in that it chamfers and deburrs the case neck at the same time it is trimmed to length. The frame is solid cast iron with storage holes in the base for extra pilots. Both coarse and fine adjustments are provided for case length.

The case-neck cleaning brush and primer pocket cleaners attached to the frame of this tool make it a very handy addition to the reloading bench.

Trimmer comes complete with the following:

* Two cutting blades (one cuts straight, one chamfers while cutting)
* Two pilots (.22 cal. and .30 cal.)
* Universal collet
* Two neck cleaning brushes (.22 thru .30 cal.)
* Two primer pocket cleaners (Large and Small)

No. 14K Master Case Trimmer complete. $24.00
No. 15 Pilots. ....$ 1.25

MASTER POWDER MEASURE MODEL 3

Universal- or pistol-metering chambers interchange in seconds. Measures charges from ½ to 100 grains. Unit fitted with lock ring for fast dump with large "clear" plastic reservoir. "See-thru" Drop Tube accepts all calibers from .22 to .600. Precision-fitted rotating drum, critically honed to prevent powder escape. Knife-edged powder chamber shears coarse-grained powders with ease, ensuring accurate charges.

No. 3 Master Powder Measure, (Specify Universal- or Pistol-Metering chamber) $26.50
No. 3K Kit Form, includes both Universal and Pistol chambers. ..$33.00
No. 3-12 Universal or Pistol chamber. ....$ 8.00

POWDER TRICKLER MODEL No. 5

Brings underweight charges up to accurate reading, adding powder to scale pan a granule or two at a time by rotating knob. Speeds weighing of each charge. Solid steel, low center of gravity. "Companion" height to Redding scales.

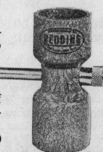

No. 5 Powder Trickler. $4.50

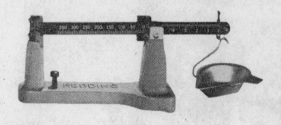

STANDARD POWDER AND BULLET SCALE
Model No. 1

For the beginner or veteran reloader. Only two counterpoises need to be moved to obtain the full capacity range of 1/10 grain to 380 grains. Clearly graduated with white numerals and lines on a black background. Total capacity of this scale is 380 grains. An over and under plate graduate in 10th grains allows checking of variations in powder charges or bullets without further adjustments.

Model No. 1 ....$17.50

REDDING RELOADING TOOLS

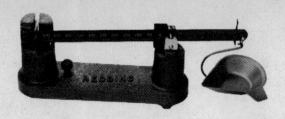

MASTER POWDER AND BULLET SCALE
MODEL No. 2

Guaranteed accurate to less than 1/10 grain. Master model has magnetic dampening for fast readings. 1/10 grain graduated over/under plate permits checking powder charge variations without moving counterpoises. Features also include: 505-grain capacity; high-visibility graduated beam; pour-spout pan; stable cast base; large convenient leveling screw; hardened and honed, self-aligning beam bearings for lifetime accuracy.

No. 2 Scale **$22.50**

"SUPERCHARGER"
POWDER MEASURE KITS
MODEL No. 101 AND 102

Supercharger Kit No. 101
Contains: Model No. 1 Standard Powder and Bullet Scale, Model No. 3 Master Powder Measure, Model No. 5 Powder Trickler and Model No. 6 Bench Stand.

No. 101 ....**$51.00**

Supercharger Kit No. 102
Contains: Model No. 2 Master Powder and Bullet Scale, Model No. 3 Powder Measure, Model No. 5 Powder Trickler and Model No. 6 Bench Stand.

No. 102 ....**$56.00**

RELOADING DIES
MODEL No. 10

Top quality, made from the best alloy steels available. Manufactured to exacting tolerances, properly heat-treated and hand-polished. No aluminum or chrome-plating used. Available in usual calibers, singly, in two-die rifle and three-die pistol sets. Standard ⅞-14 thread.

No. 10 Reloading Dies **$16.50**

SELF-INDEXING STAR
CRIMP STARTER
MODEL 23

In reloading some plastic and new paper cases, a good folded crimp can only be obtained by use of a Star Crimp Starter. The Redding Self-indexing Star Crimp Starter attaches to the No. 32 Shotshell Reloader and is available in 6 or 8 point star. Fired cases must be recrimped with the same number of folds as in the original for best results. Available in 12, 16, 20 Ga., 6 & 8 point—28 & .410 Ga., 6 point only.

Model No. 23 Crimp Starter, 6 or 8 point.......... **$4.50**

CASE LUBE KIT
MODEL No. 12
New Case Lube Tongs simplify and increase speed of case lubrication.

Conforms to all cartridge cases, especially useful to ensure proper case neck lubrication. Eliminates stuck cases and pulled rims. Prolongs life of dies and simplifies case reforming. Includes 2 oz. plastic bottle of Redding case lube.

No. 12 Case Lube Kit **$3.50**
No. 21 Case Lube only, 2 oz. Bottle **$1.00**

STANDARD POWDER
MEASURE
MODEL No. 4

Capacity from 0 to 100 grains. Powder pours directly from metering chamber into cartridge case. Metering chamber is chrome-plated, adjustable and easily removed. Includes mounting bracket. Extra metering chambers available.

No. 4 Standard Powder Measure, complete ...**$14.00**

Index